D1171626

BIOCHEMISTRY

ABRAHAM CANTAROW, M.D.
EMERITUS PROFESSOR OF BIOCHEMISTRY,
JEFFERSON MEDICAL COLLEGE

BERNARD SCHEPARTZ, Ph.D.
PROFESSOR OF BIOCHEMISTRY,
JEFFERSON MEDICAL COLLEGE

FOURTH EDITION • 1967

W. B. Saunders Company • Philadelphia & London

W. B. Saunders Company: West Washington Square
Philadelphia, Pa. 19105

12 Dyott Street
London W.C.1

Biochemistry

 Made in the United States of America. Press of W. B. Saunders Company. Library of Congress catalog card number 67-10134.

PREFACE TO THE FOURTH EDITION

THE CENTRAL purpose of this, as of previous editions, is to present an adequate portrayal of knowledge in the field of biochemistry in a manner most helpful to the first-year medical student. All chapters have been extensively revised and many sections entirely rewritten. These include: the chemistry of glycolipids; levels of structural organization of proteins; structures and macromolecular properties of nucleic acids; metabolism and mechanisms of action of hormones; coagulation of blood.

The chapters on Enzymes and on Biological Oxidations have been revised to conform to present nomenclature of coenzymes and recommendations of the Enzyme Commission of the International Union of Biochemistry with respect to classification and trivial names of enzymes. Generally, but particularly in sections on metabolism, the current practice has been followed of naming acidic metabolites as anions, although the un-ionized forms are used at times in figures and formulas, for typographic convenience.

A few changes have been made in the organization of the text. An introductory chapter is designed to provide a broad view of the field of biochemistry, so that the student may approach the subsequent detailed considerations of individual areas with better appreciation of their overall relevance. The chapter on metabolism of nucleic acids has been placed before that on metabolism of proteins in order to establish the foundation for understanding of the role of the former in the mechanism of biosynthesis of the latter. Discussions of regulatory influences on individual metabolic processes have been inserted where relevant. In addition, the entire subject of regulation of metabolism is reviewed in a separate chapter, which includes a discussion of biochemical genetics. In figures, regulatory influences are indicated by broad arrows: gray, pointing in the direction of the reaction, for generally enhancing influences; striated, at right angles to the direction of the reaction, for generally repressing influences.

Physicochemical concepts are considered in their direct relation to biological phenomena, mainly in chapters on Water Balance, Neutrality Regulation and Chemistry of Proteins. Reading assignments may be made in these sections conveniently for introductory reviews of relevant aspects of physical chemistry.

We continue to be indebted to many colleagues, students and other friends for helpful suggestions and criticism, and to those who have generously permitted reproduction of illustrations from their original publications. We must also acknowledge, with gratitude, the unfailing cooperation of the publishers at every stage of the production of this volume.

A. Cantarow
B. Schepartz

PREFACE TO THE FIRST EDITION

THIS BOOK is designed primarily to meet the needs of the first-year medical student. We feel that this aim requires no apology. However, the addition of another textbook of biochemistry to the several already available does require some explanation.

Long experience with students at every stage of their medical education, both undergraduate and postgraduate, has impressed us with the fact that their comprehension of biochemistry is generally poorer than that of the other medical sciences. Although biochemistry currently occupies a focal position in all of the medical sciences, as well as in clinical medicine, this is the one subject in the medical curriculum that the average student is not adequately equipped to grasp readily in the form in which it is usually presented.

The difficulty in this connection stems mainly from the fact that the enormous progress in this field in recent years has been in highly specialized areas, comprehension of which is impeded by barriers of technical nomenclature and inadequate grounding in such basic disciplines as organic and physical chemistry. The student often becomes discouraged, and acquires a feeling of inadequacy which interferes seriously with his desire and ability to comprehend those phases of the subject which he is really in a position to understand.

Attempts to supply these deficiencies in a textbook of biochemistry for medical students often lead to more confusion than enlightenment, for they can usually be considered only superficially. Moreover, if isolated aspects of fundamental chemistry are discussed in detail, they assume an importance that is out of proportion to the place they occupy in the over-all picture of biochemistry, and the student has difficulty in appreciating their true significance for biochemical phenomena. We feel that elucidation of such matters should be left to textbooks on these subjects and to the classroom.

Emphasis has been placed here on dynamic aspects of biochemistry, rather than on fundamental considerations of structure, reactions, and basic chemical principles, except insofar as these have a direct bearing on the role of the substances in question in mammalian physiology. Admittedly, these distinctions are not always well defined, for many of these relationships are as yet imperfectly understood. We have attempted to provide an adequate description of substances of major biological importance. However, insofar as is feasible, isolated considerations of abstract chemical and physiochemical topics are avoided, and these are introduced into the text and discussed mainly in direct relation to their pertinence to biological phenomena.

The major emphasis throughout is on the integration of biochemical processes and on the mechanisms involved in the regulation and coordination of various aspects of metabolism. The aim is to enable the student to perceive the nature of metabolic interrelations and homeostasis, and thus to place biochemistry in its proper relation to physiology, normal and pathological. It has been our experience that this approach best serves to arouse the student's interest and imagination and to stimulate his desire to grasp the essential features of this subject.

There has been a growing tendency to include in textbooks of biochemistry an increasing volume of material on biochemical abnormalities in disease. Much of this is irrelevant to a consideration of physiological chemistry, and is inadequate for any other purpose. We believe that, whereas every attempt should be made to indicate the possible applications of biochemical facts and principles in his future studies of disease processes, the first-year student is not in a position to appreciate the significance of clinical or pathological biochemistry, except in a very general way. He knows nothing of the causes, nature, or effects of diseases, which, to him, are merely names, without real meaning. Emphasis in this connection should be placed on aberrations of normal mechanisms, rather than on isolated details, appreciation of which requires a background of information concerning disease processes and special organ pathology which he has not yet acquired.

These two major questions, namely, how little material should be included on fundamental aspects of organic and physical chemistry, and how much on biochemical abnormalities in disease, have been answered here rather arbitrarily. The manner in which the former is dealt with has been indicated. The view has been taken that disease states should be introduced into the discussion whenever an understanding of the incident biochemical aberrations aids in an understanding of normal reactions and mechanisms. Diabetes mellitus and disturbances of "acid-base" balance are excellent examples of such conditions.

With few exceptions, the main subject headings are those employed in the majority of current textbooks on this subject. Because we feel that a detailed consideration of dietetics does not fall within the province of biochemistry, data on the composition of foods are not presented in detail, and foodstuffs are discussed only with reference to the general nutritional significance of proteins, carbohydrates, and fats.

Each topic is discussed as an entity, with extensive cross references to more detailed discussions of various aspects in other sections. This permits a logical, comprehensive presentation of each subject, and consecutive reading of any section without the necessity of referring frequently to others, which disrupts the continuity of thought.

It is our belief that numerous literature references in the text are superfluous, if not indeed undesirable in a book of this nature. We feel that at this educational level the student derives more benefit, and less confusion, from critical reviews than from original contributions in highly specialized fields, which he may not be able to understand fully, and which he is seldom able to evaluate adequately. In the interests of reading continuity, we have omitted virtually all direct references from the text. There is a brief list of selected reading references at the end of each chapter, mainly to monographic discussions and reviews.

The first-year medical student must do a truly enormous amount of reading. He must, therefore, be able to get desired information with a minimum expenditure of time. To this end, no feature of a textbook is more important than its index. We have attempted to index each important item in the text according to the various points of view from which it may be approached in the mind of the student.

A textbook, in which the current status of a subject is surveyed, represents a synthesis of the contributions of all workers in the field. We are particularly indebted to those who have generously permitted reproduction of figures and tabulated data from their original publications. We wish to express our thanks also to the publishers, for their unfailing cooperation at every stage of the preparation of this book.

A. C.
B. S.

Philadelphia, Pa.

CONTENTS

CHAPTER 1

THE NATURE AND AIMS OF BIOCHEMISTRY

THE American Society of Biological Chemists has recently adopted the working definition: "A biochemist is an investigator who utilizes chemical, physical, or biological techniques to study the chemical nature and behavior of living matter." In contrast to investigators in related fields who may employ similar methods on similar problems, it may be added that the biochemist usually approaches these problems on the molecular level.

Since study of the *chemical nature* of living matter utilizes the tools, methods, and indeed the services of organic and physical chemists, there is necessarily much overlap and cross-fertilization between biochemistry and its parent disciplines on the "chemical" side of the family tree. Study of the *behavior* of living matter, on the other hand, employs techniques borrowed from the biologist and physiologist, and again, much overlap and cross-fertilization exist.

In its youth, animal biochemistry derived much of its impetus from problems of clinical medicine; although the latter area remains a fruitful source of problems, in recent times the equilibrium appears to have shifted. With the tremendous expansion of biochemistry as a basic science, and with its increased and increasing ability to attack virtually all biological problems on a molecular level, biochemistry itself is now a significant stimulus to medicine, as any study of recent Nobel prize awards in medicine will confirm.

What should the student of medicine and allied fields expect of biochemistry? The answer, of course, is provided *in extenso* in the rather ponderous remainder of this text. In brief, biochemistry should provide the student with an understanding of: (1) the structures and properties of substances comprising the framework of cells and tissues; (2) the structures and properties of substances entering the cell as useful working materials or sources of energy or leaving the cell as waste products; (3) the chemical changes undergone by substances within the cell, the process termed "metabolism;" (4) the molecular basis for the performance of various forms of work by the cell; (5) the energy exchanges occurring in connection with items (3) and (4); and (6) the coordination of all of these phenomena into a normally functioning biological machine by appropriate regulatory (homeostatic) mechanisms.

A brief sketch of some of these matters, by way of preview, is presented in Figure 1–1.

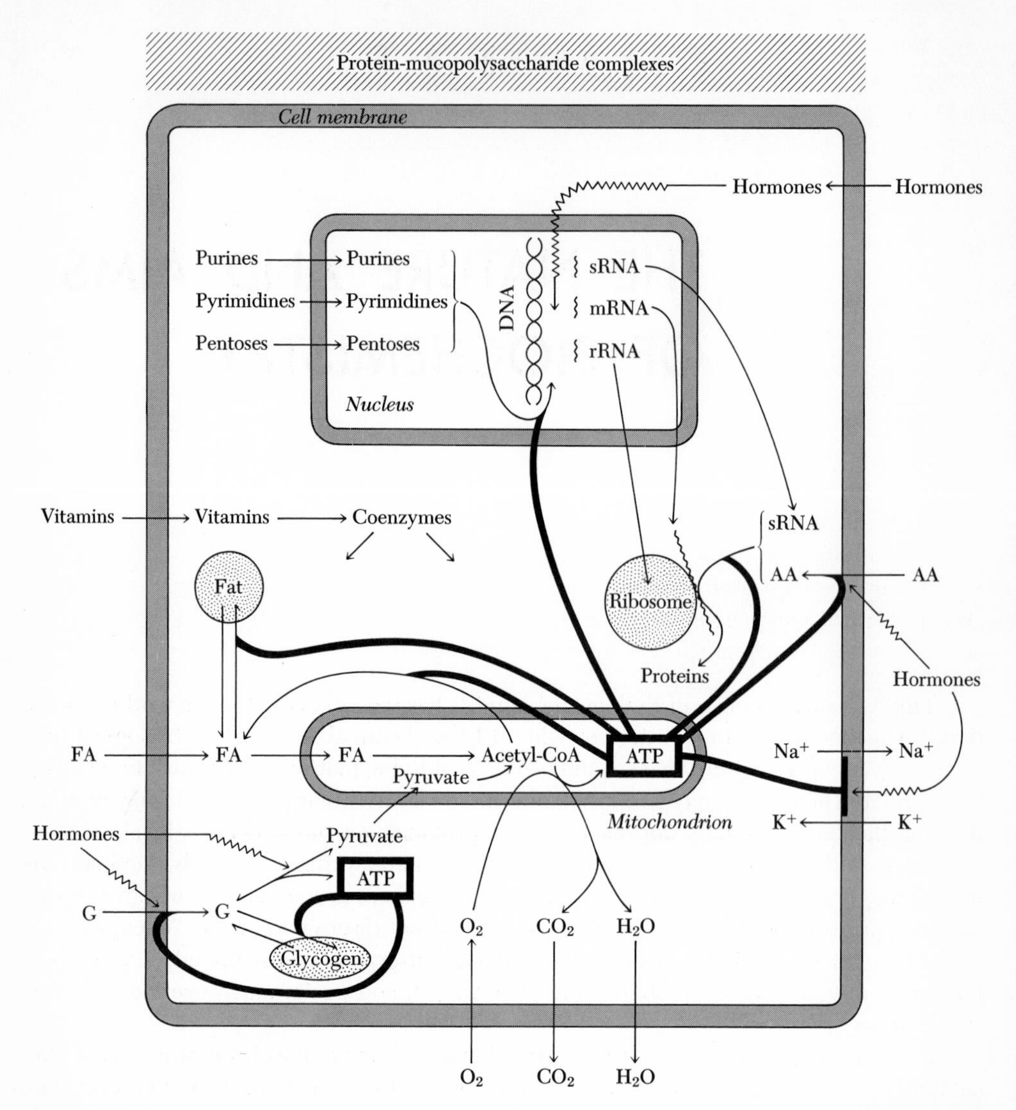

Figure 1-1. Prototype animal cell. *AA,* Amino acids; *Acetyl-CoA,* acetyl-coenzyme A; *ATP,* adenosine triphosphate; *DNA,* deoxyribonucleic acid; *FA,* fatty acids; *G,* glucose; *RNA,* ribonucleic acid (*s,* soluble; *m,* messenger; *r,* ribosomal).

A prototype animal cell is shown, complete with cell membrane, nucleus, and, for simplicity, only one ribosomal particle and one mitochondrion (both greatly exaggerated in size).

In the organism, the cell does not exist in isolation. It is surrounded by extracellular fluid and connective tissue elements rich in protein-carbohydrate (protein-mucopolysaccharide) complexes. The cell membrane consists of lipid-protein (lipoprotein) complexes arranged in layers; a similar membrane surrounds many of the intracellular organelles.

Entering the cell are the major metabolic fuels, glucose (also arising from intracellular glycogen granules and derivable also from certain amino acids) and fatty acids (also arising from intracellular fat globules and derivable also from glucose), and the oxygen required for their combustion. Also entering are many required trace elements (not shown), certain major inorganic ions such as sodium and potassium (in the normal economy of the cell, potassium is maintained at a high internal level and sodium is actively extruded), amino acids (some derivable from glucose), and vitamins (in many cases used for synthesis of coenzymes). Leaving the cell are carbon dioxide, water, and other waste products, as well as products of specific synthetic activities in the case of certain cells (not shown). The transport of many substances across the cell membrane is an active process, requiring the expenditure of metabolic work.

The major source of energy in the cell is the oxidation of glucose and fatty acids to carbon dioxide and water within the mitochondria. Preliminary conversion is required of both classes of metabolites to the stage of acetate (in the form of acetyl-coenzyme A), processes which liberate some useful energy. The major portion of the energy, however, is produced by the further oxidation of acetate units. In the course of this oxidation, hydrogen atoms (or hydrogen ions plus electrons) from the metabolites are passed along a chain of oxidation catalysts containing, among other constituents, a group of heme (iron-porphyrin)-proteins, the cytochromes.

During these intramitochondrial oxidations (and to a lesser extent, in some extramitochondrial oxidations) a compound known as adenosine triphosphate (ATP) is formed, incorporating within its chemical bonds some of the energy liberated in the oxidations. ATP, in turn, can serve as a source of energy for various forms of work: (1) osmotic work in transporting substances (e.g., amino acids and inorganic ions) across cell membranes; (2) mechanical work, such as contraction of muscle fibers (not shown); (3) chemical work, such as synthesis of fatty acids from acetate units, synthesis of polysaccharides from sugars, synthesis of proteins from amino acids, and synthesis of nucleic acids from purines, pyrimidines, pentoses, and phosphate.

The biochemical potentialities of the cell are determined by its genetic composition, encoded in the deoxyribonucleic acid (DNA) of the nucleus. Under the influence of this DNA, several species of ribonucleic acid (RNA) are synthesized and sent from the nucleus to the cytoplasm: (1) ribosomal RNA (rRNA), which together with protein forms the ribosomes, the major site of protein synthesis in the cell; (2) soluble RNA (sRNA), which carries "activated" forms of amino acids to the ribosomes; (3) messenger RNA (mRNA), which provides the patterns or templates for synthesis of proteins with the proper content and sequence of amino acids.

Since the products which are synthesized by the ribosomal system include not only "structural" but also "catalytic" proteins (i. e., enzymes), the final biochemical character of the cell must depend heavily upon the types of mRNA produced. It is of great interest that recent research has demonstrated the influence of cytoplasmic regulatory influences upon the expression of genetic potentialities in the form of mRNA. In addition to metabolites as such, certain hormonal regulators operate in this fashion. Other hormones may act directly upon enzymatic reactions in the cytoplasm, whereas still others appear to affect the transport mechanisms of cell membranes.

This thumbnail sketch should make it obvious that an adequate comprehension of biochemistry necessitates study of the chemistry of carbohydrates, lipids, proteins, nucleic acids, porphyrins, vitamins, hormones, and inorganic substances, followed by study of their transformations within the organism, accompanied by due consideration of the energy exchanges involved and the regulatory mechanisms which coordinate the whole. That is the task which lies ahead.

CHAPTER 2

CHEMISTRY OF CARBOHYDRATES

INTRODUCTION

Definition and Biological Significance

For the purposes of this chapter we may define carbohydrates as polyhydroxylic aldehydes and ketones (monosaccharides), their polymers (oligosaccharides and polysaccharides), reduction products (polyhydric alcohols and cyclitols), oxidation products (aldonic, uronic, and saccharic acids), substitution products (amino sugars), and esters (sulfates and phosphates).

The chief function of carbohydrate in the animal organism is that of a fuel, the degradation of which to carbon dioxide and water represents a major source of energy. In addition, certain products of carbohydrate metabolism, as will be seen later, aid in the breakdown of many foodstuffs, acting as catalysts or promoters of oxidations. When the supply of these carbohydrate metabolites runs low, owing to faulty metabolism, widespread disorders prevail, as in diabetes mellitus. Carbohydrate can also be used as a starting material for the biological synthesis of other types of compounds in the body, such as fatty acids and certain amino acids. A final and more obscure function of carbohydrate is its role in the structure of certain biologically important compounds, such as glycolipids, glycoproteins, heparin, nucleic acids, and other substances which will be mentioned in subsequent discussions.

Types Found in Nature

Quantitatively, starch is the most important carbohydrate in the human diet. It is one of a class of carbohydrates of high molecular weight known as polysaccharides. These materials are characterized by a relatively low solubility in their native state, in keeping with their functions in plants and animals as either storage forms or supporting and protecting structures for the tissues. Some polysaccharides, when freed from other tissue constituents, can be dispersed in colloidal form in water. All are insoluble in aqueous ethanol and organic solvents generally. Starch and cellulose are storage and supporting polysaccharides, respectively, in the plant world, while glycogen represents the storage form of carbohydrate in animals.

Many other carbohydrates of lower molecular weight are found in nature. The mono- and oligosaccharides are crystalline substances, soluble in water and dilute ethanol, insoluble in most organic solvents. Among the oligosaccharides, sucrose, lactose, and maltose are of considerable biological importance. Glucose, fructose, galactose, mannose, ribose, and deoxyribose are examples of monosaccharides which will be discussed in this chapter. It may be appropriate to mention at this point that, regardless of the form in which a carbohydrate happens to be ingested, it must be transformed into a monosaccharide for absorption and metabolism, thus emphasizing the significance of monosaccharides in the animal economy.

The sugar alcohols, acids, and amino sugars are of lesser quantitative importance than the major groups mentioned above. Nevertheless they are involved (either as such, or as constituents of more complex compounds) in metabolic processes.

In recent years it has been shown that phosphorylation of the carbohydrates is a metabolic reaction which must occur before these compounds can be oxidized by the body. The phosphate esters, therefore, represent metabolically active carbohydrates.

CLASSIFICATION AND CONFIGURATION

Classification and Nomenclature

A monosaccharide is a carbohydrate which cannot be broken down to simpler substances by acid hydrolysis. Oligosaccharides and polysaccharides consist of monosaccharide units, combined by the abstraction of the elements of water from each two monosaccharides in the chain. Although no strict dividing line is possible, the term "oligosaccharide" is usually applied to carbohydrates yielding 2 to 10 monosaccharide units on hydrolysis; beyond this, the compounds are called "polysaccharides." Depending on the number of constituent monosaccharide units, the oligosaccharides are called "disaccharides," "trisaccharides," etc.

The characteristic ending in naming mono- and oligosaccharides (commonly called "sugars") is -ose. The portion of the name preceding this, however, reflects the history and origin of the compound more than it does chemical systematics, e.g., lactose (milk sugar). In systematic nomenclature, polysaccharides are named by attachment of the suffix "-an" to the name of the constituent monosaccharide (Table 2-1). Polysaccharides are not usually named systematically; their historical names are generally used.

Length of the carbon chain forms one basis for the classification of the monosaccharides. The simplest compound containing a hydroxyl group and a carbonyl function is glycolic aldehyde, or glycolaldehyde. Containing two carbon atoms, this would be called a diose. Monosaccharides of three to seven carbon atoms are trioses, tetroses, pentoses, hexoses, and heptoses, respectively.

$$\begin{array}{l} \mathrm{H} \\ \mathrm{C{=}O} \\ | \\ \mathrm{CH_2OH} \end{array}$$

Glycolaldehyde

TABLE 2-1. CLASSIFICATION OF THE CARBOHYDRATES

I. Simple monosaccharides
  A. Diose
  B. Trioses
    1. Aldotriose
    2. Ketotriose
  C. Tetroses
  D. Pentoses
    1. Aldopentoses
    2. Ketopentoses
    3. Deoxypentoses
  E. Hexoses
    1. Aldohexoses
    2. Ketohexoses
    3. Deoxyhexoses
  F. Heptoses
II. Acetal derivatives of I.
  A. Glycosides containing aglycons
  B. Oligosaccharides
    1. Disaccharides
      a. Reducing
      b. Non-reducing
    2. Tri-, tetra-saccharides, etc.
  C. Polysaccharides
    1. Homosaccharidic
      a. Pentosans
      b. Hexosans
    2. Heterosaccharidic
      a. Pentosans
      b. Hexosans
      c. Pento-hexosans
III. Substituted, derived, conjugated monosaccharides
  A. Amino sugars
  B. Sugar alcohols
    1. Open-chain polyols
    2. Cyclitols
  C. Sugar acids
    1. Aldonic (glyconic)
    2. Uronic
    3. Saccharic (glycaric)
  D. Amino sugar acids
  E. Esters
    1. Sulfuric
    2. Phosphoric
IV. Polymers of III.
  A. Homosaccharidic
    1. Non-nitrogenous
    2. Nitrogenous
  B. Heterosaccharidic
    1. Non-nitrogenous
    2. Nitrogenous (mucopolysaccharides)
      a. Neutral
      b. Acidic
        (1) Sulfate-free
        (2) Sulfate-containing

Each group of monosaccharides except the diose has the possibility of containing both aldehydic and ketonic members. Thus glyceraldehyde and dihydroxyacetone are an aldotriose and ketotriose in the systematic nomenclature.

Certain "modified" sugars are named from their parent compounds by addition to the parent name of terms designating the type of change in structure involved. Conversion of an alcohol function to a methyl or methylene is thus designated by the prefix "deoxy-" (e.g., ribose $\longrightarrow$ 2-deoxyribose).

Ketoses are often named from the corresponding aldoses by insertion of the syllable "ul-" before the "-ose" suffix (e.g., ribose and ribulose).

A final basis for the classification of the monosaccharides and their derivatives is concerned with stereochemical families of compounds. On this basis, which will be discussed in detail in the following section, compounds are classified as belonging to the D or L series.

An outline of the classification of carbohydrates is given in Table 2-1. It will be explained in later discussions.

Asymmetric Carbon Atoms and Optical Isomerism

A carbon atom bearing four different groups is spoken of as asymmetric. As can be seen in the accompanying diagram, two different spatial arrangements can be made of the groups attached to the central atom, and models of the two arrangements will be found to be non-superimposable. They are, in fact, mirror-images of each other (Fig. 2–2). The

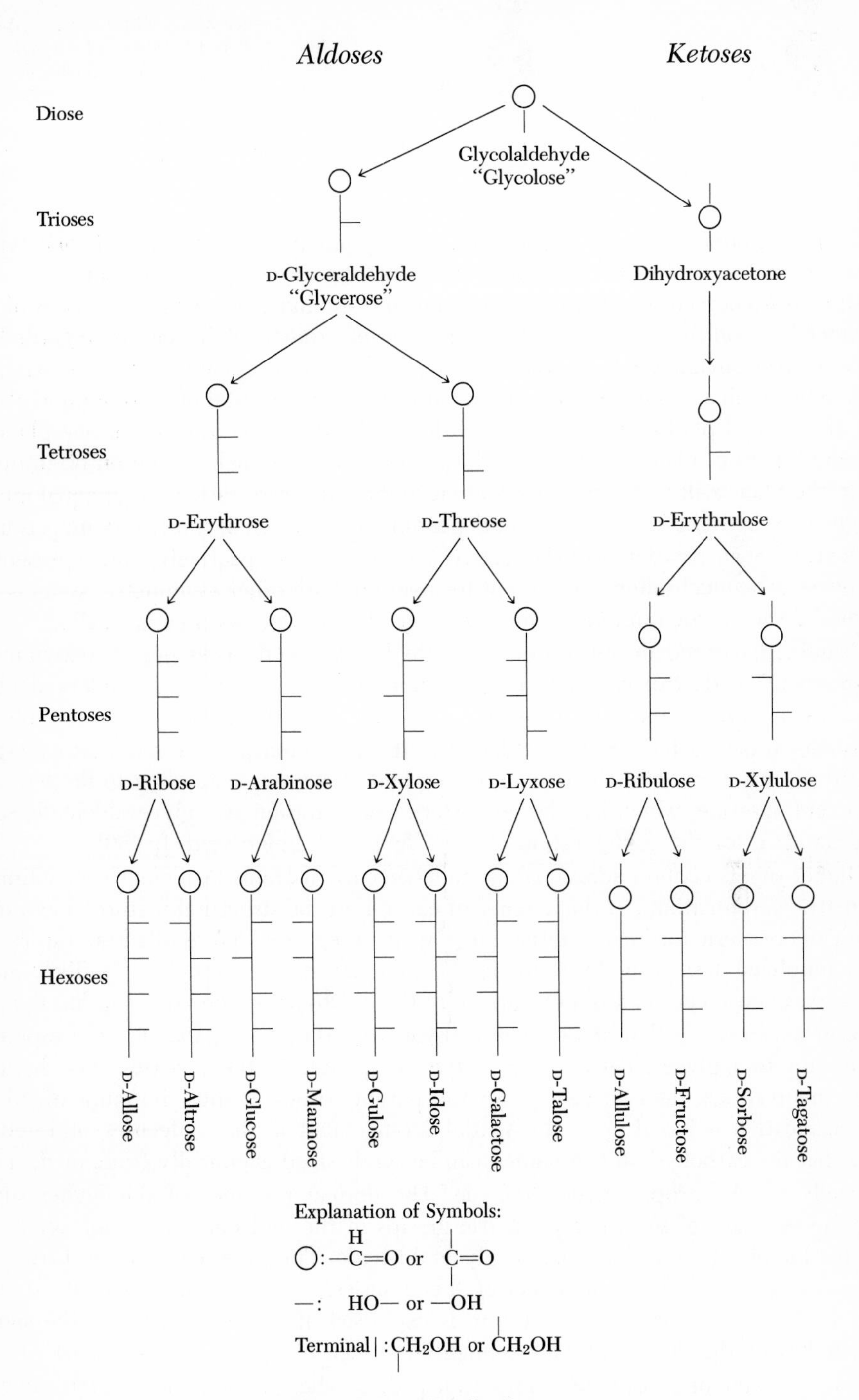

Explanation of Symbols:

○: —C(H)=O or C=O

—: HO— or —OH

Terminal | : CH_2OH or CH_2OH

Figure 2-1. D-Family of sugars.

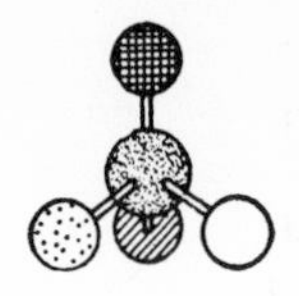

Figure 2-2. Mirror images. (Adapted from Noller: Chemistry of Organic Compounds, ed. 3, W. B. Saunders Company, 1965.)

isomerism exhibited by compounds containing asymmetric carbon atoms is one type of optical isomerism, and is the only type which will be discussed in this book.

Optical isomerism receives its name from the peculiar effect which solutions of such an isomer have on plane polarized light. A beam of ordinary light may be regarded as a bundle of electromagnetic waves vibrating in all directions perpendicular to the axis of the beam. When such a beam is passed through a properly cut crystal of certain minerals or a sheet of a special plastic known as Polaroid, all vibrations except those in one plane are eliminated. If this "plane polarized" light is now passed through a solution of an optical isomer, the plane will be found to be rotated to the left (levorotation) or an equal number of degrees to the right (dextrorotation), depending upon which of the two isomers is under examination. Such rotations are designated (−) and (+), respectively, and represent the only physicochemical difference (except for reaction with other asymmetric systems, e.g., enzymes) between such optical isomers, or "enantiomorphs," as they are called.

Examination of the formula for glyceraldehyde discloses the presence of an asymmetric carbon atom. The dextrorotatory form is customarily written with the secondary alcoholic hydroxyl extending to the right when the aldehyde group is at the top of the molecule. This isomer is designated "D-glyceraldehyde." Its enantiomorph, the levorotatory L-glyceraldehyde, is written with the corresponding hydroxyl group extending to the left. (The amino acid, L-serine, which has the same steric configuration as L-glyceraldehyde, serves as the standard for the configuration of the L-family of amino acids [p. 56].)

Higher sugars contain additional asymmetric carbon atoms. A molecule containing n asymmetric carbon atoms, in the absence of certain special structural features, can exist in 2^n optically isomeric forms. The rather large array of sugars which results from this isomerism is simplified somewhat by dividing the monosaccharides into two families. Sugars whose asymmetric carbon atom farthest from the aldehyde or ketone group has the same spatial arrangement as that of D-glyceraldehyde are called "D sugars;" the corresponding relationship to L-glyceraldehyde places the compound in the L series. The hydroxyl groups involved are then written as for the parent trioses. It must be emphasized that this classification is based upon the spatial arrangement in the molecules, and actually means that the carbohydrates so named can be synthesized chemically from, or degraded chemically to, the proper glyceraldehyde. The optical rotations of the higher sugars, being the resultant of several asymmetric groups in the molecule, need not agree with the direction of rotation of the parent glyceraldehyde. Thus, the naturally occurring glucose and fructose are both members of the D series, but the former is dextrorotatory while the latter is levorotatory. Rotation is expressed, if it is necessary, by the sign + or −, following the designation for configuration, i.e., D(−), D(+), L(−), L(+).

It is a matter of considerable importance that, when a compound which might be expected to contain an asymmetric carbon atom is synthesized by the methods of organic chemistry, an optically inactive product is obtained. In fact, it can be shown that an equimolar mixture of D and L forms, a so-called "racemic mixture," is produced. Nature, however, prefers "asymmetric synthesis," and practically always manufactures only one of the two possible enantiomorphs. This has given rise to the concept that the machinery of biological synthesis, the enzyme system, is itself spatially asymmetric. As is indicated elsewhere (p. 211), the high degree of specificity of enzymes is in agreement with this concept. The carbohydrates found in nature belong, with few exceptions, to the D series, indicating some fundamental spatial similarity in most of the enzyme systems having to do with carbohydrate synthesis in the plant and animal kingdoms.

Cyclic Structures of the Sugars

Up to this point the sugars have been depicted as open-chain polyhydroxylic aldehydes and ketones. However, there is conclusive evidence that, in the natural state, the aldehyde or ketone group exists in a condensed form, as a hemi-acetal, by combination with one of the alcoholic hydroxyl groups in the same molecule. The formation of a hemi-acetal from a simple aldehyde and simple alcohol occurs as follows:

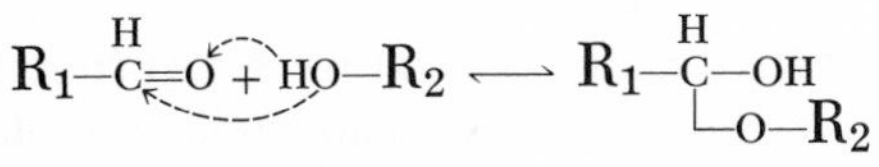

$$R_1-\overset{H}{C}=O + HO-R_2 \longrightarrow R_1-\overset{H}{C}(-OH)-O-R_2$$

If the two reacting groups belong to the same molecule, a cyclic structure must result. If we take the open-chain form of D-glucose, which we may call aldehydo-D-glucose, and condense the aldehyde group on carbon 1 with the alcohol group on carbon 5, as formulated below, two different forms of glucose may be produced. Carbon 1, after the cyclization, has four different groups attached to it, and is therefore an asymmetric carbon atom. If the hydrogen atom of the participating alcohol group catches the carbonyl oxygen atom of the rotating aldehyde group on one side of the chain, the resulting new hydroxyl group will extend to the right, forming α-glucose. The analogous combination, forming the new hydroxyl group on the other side of the chain, produces β-glucose. The two cyclic compounds will have different optical rotations, but they will not be equal in magnitude and opposite in sign, as is the case with enantiomorphs, because the compounds as a whole are not mirror-images of each other. Compounds related in this way are called "anomers," and carbon 1 is called the anomeric carbon atom.

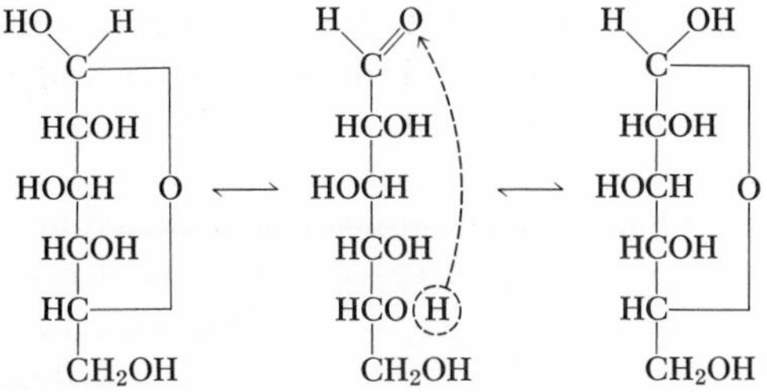

HO H | H O | H OH
C | C | C
HCOH | HCOH | HCOH
HOCH O ⟵⟶ HOCH ⟵⟶ HOCH O
HCOH | HCOH | HCOH
HC | HCO(H) | HC
CH_2OH | CH_2OH | CH_2OH

β-D-Glucose (β-D-Glucopyranose) | Aldehydo-D-glucose | α-D-Glucose (α-D-Glucopyranose)

If ordinary, crystalline glucose (which happens to be the α form) is dissolved in water, a gradual change in optical rotation can be observed, finally arriving at a steady value. This change in optical rotation is called "mutarotation," and represents a conversion, in this case, from α-glucose to an equilibrium mixture of the α and β forms. Pure β-glucose can be prepared in the crystalline state, and when dissolved in water undergoes a similar mutarotation, changing from its characteristic optical rotation to a final value exactly the same as that found in the case of mutarotation of α-glucose. The mechanism of mutarotation probably involves opening of the hemi-acetal ring to form traces of the aldehyde form, then recondensation to the cyclic forms. The aldehyde form is extremely unstable and exists only as a transient intermediate in carbohydrate reactions.

The cyclic forms of glucose described thus far have contained six-membered rings. By analogy with the structure of the compound pyran, such rings are called "pyranose forms." In some cases, carbohydrates are found to contain five-membered rings. These forms are called "furanose," from the parent structure, furan. Pyranose rings are generally more stable than furanose rings.

```
                        CH2
  HC——CH              HC/   \CH
  ||    ||            ||     ||
  HC\  /CH            HC\   /CH
     O                    O
   Furan                 Pyran
```

The student will recall from organic chemistry that a characteristic reaction of aldehydes is the reduction of alkaline copper reagents (Fehling's solution) from the cupric to the cuprous state, with concomitant oxidation of the aldehyde group. Aldose sugars exhibit the same reaction, so that we must assume that the aldehyde group, while apparently blocked in hemi-acetal formation, is still potentially available for certain reactions. There is some evidence that a small amount of the aldehydo sugar is present in solution at all times, in equilibrium with the cyclic forms of the carbohydrate.

The ketose sugars also are found to reduce alkaline copper reagents, in contrast to ordinary ketones. It will be noted that, adjacent to the carbonyl group of the ketoses, there are two alcohol groups. A hydroxyl group and ketone group, when existing side by side, form a grouping known as a ketol, and such a combination acts toward many reagents much like an aldehyde. Both aldoses and ketoses, then, so long as their hemi-acetal forms can revert to the open-chain aldehydo and keto sugars, are "reducing sugars."

Haworth Formulations of Cyclic Sugars

The cyclic structures of glucose shown (p. 9) do not accurately depict the true shape of the molecule. For example, the lengths of the bonds on the ring oxygen atom are grossly exaggerated. Also, the primary alcohol group ($-CH_2OH$) actually should project from the molecule in a direction *trans* to the hydroxyls on C_2 and C_4.

Haworth has suggested that a pyranose sugar be depicted in a "perspective" formula as a hexagon, the lower edge of which is nearest to the reader. Groups projecting to the right or left in the linear formula are shown projecting downward or upward, respectively, from the plane of the hexagon. Furanose sugars are depicted analogously, but as pentagons. For the sake of simplicity, the carbon atoms constituting the corners of the rings are usually omitted.

The transition from open chain to Haworth form may be shown as follows (p. 11): the chain is first folded and the primary alcohol is present in its true steric relation to other groups. The heavy lines designate the edge of the hexagon nearest the reader.

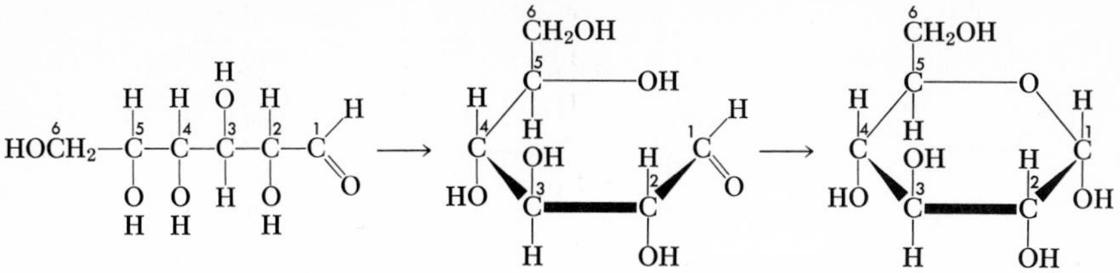

Aldehydo-D-glucose α-D-Glucopyranose

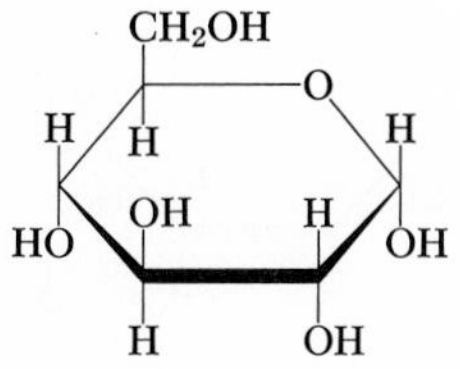

Usual simplified Haworth formula

Since the Haworth formulation presents a truer picture of the molecule, and in addition, permits easier visualization of the structures of oligo- and polysaccharides, it will be used wherever convenient in subsequent discussions.

SIMPLE MONOSACCHARIDES OF BIOLOGICAL IMPORTANCE

Diose

Glycolaldehyde, the structure of which has already been given, differs from the higher aldoses in not containing an asymmetric carbon atom, and in not being truly polyhydroxylic. For these reasons some textbooks have not included this compound among the true carbohydrates. However, recent work has implicated glycolaldehyde in the metabolism of pentoses, providing biological, if not chemical, justification for considering it among the carbohydrates.

Trioses

Both D-glyceraldehyde and dihydroxyacetone occur, in the form of phosphate esters, as intermediates in the fermentation and glycolysis of carbohydrates. They are also the precursors of the glycerol which the organism synthesizes and incorporates into various types of lipids.

Tetroses

A few compounds of this group have been shown to be intermediates in certain phases of carbohydrate metabolism.

Pentoses

The three most important pentoses from the standpoint of animal biochemistry are shown in Figure 2–3. Ribose and deoxyribose are constituents of the nucleic acids, and

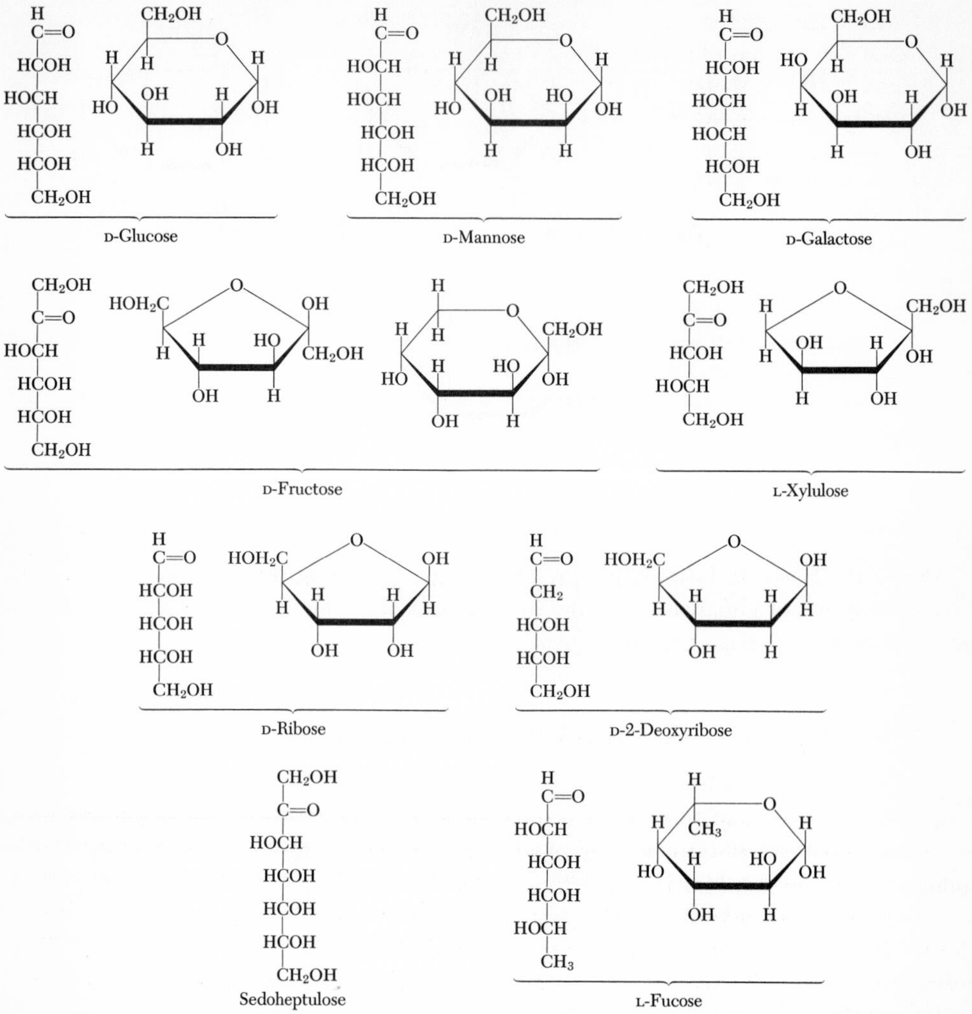

D-Glucose D-Mannose D-Galactose

D-Fructose L-Xylulose

D-Ribose D-2-Deoxyribose

Sedoheptulose L-Fucose

Figure 2-3. Important monosaccharides, open-chain and cyclic formulas. Latter are α-configuration except for fructofuranose, ribose, and deoxyribose, which are shown in their naturally occurring β-forms.

ribose in addition is a part of the structure of certain coenzymes. These two sugars appear to have the furanose ring in their natural state. When combined in nucleic acids and their derivatives, the pentoses are in the β configuration.

L-Xylulose (ketoxylose) is one of the few L sugars found in nature. It is a metabolite of glucuronic acid, and is excreted in the urine of humans afflicted with a hereditary abnormality in metabolism known as pentosuria.

Arabinose, a pentose closely related to ribose, is of importance only in plants. It is frequently used in the student laboratory as a typical pentose because it is readily available and inexpensive.

Hexoses

In addition to glucose, the formulas for which were given previously, other important hexoses are the aldoses, mannose and galactose, and the ketose, fructose.

Glucose and fructose occur in the free state in certain foodstuffs, are found combined with each other in sucrose (ordinary table-sugar), and form the basic units from which many plant and animal polysaccharides are constructed. Older names for these two sugars are dextrose (for glucose) and levulose (for fructose), based on their optical rotations. Fructose is shown with two cyclic forms, fructopyranose being the configuration of the free sugar, while the furanose structure seems to occur whenever fructose exists combined in oligosaccharides and polysaccharides.

D-Galactose is found in the animal organism in the disaccharide, lactose (milk sugar), and in glycolipids known as cerebrosides. Polysaccharides containing mannose are constituents of certain glycoproteins.

Deoxyhexoses have usually been thought of in connection with the plant world. However, the unusual sugar, L-fucose (6-deoxy-L-galactose), occurs in a number of mucopolysaccharides and mucoproteins, including the blood group polysaccharides (p. 799).

Heptoses

Sedoheptulose has been shown to occur as an intermediate in certain phases of carbohydrate metabolism.

ACETAL DERIVATIVES OF THE SIMPLE MONOSACCHARIDES

Acetals

The formation of hemi-acetals was shown previously. The hydroxyl group resulting from this reaction can react with compounds containing a replaceable hydrogen atom, splitting out water and forming compounds known as acetals. It is obvious that, since the hemiacetal forms of the parent sugars can be either α or β, two series of acetals are also possible. Since acetalization blocks any possible opening of the ring to form the aldehydo sugar, the sugar acetals show no mutarotation. Other characteristic reactions of carbonyl groups, such as reduction of alkaline copper reagents, are also absent. Acetals are generally stable toward alkali, but easily hydrolyzed by acids. The many biologically important compounds which are acetal derivatives of the simple monosaccharides will be discussed in the following sections.

Glycosides Containing Non-Sugar Moieties

Sugar acetals are more commonly called glycosides; the acetal linkage is therefore called the glycoside or glycosidic linkage. Two types of glycoside exist. If glycosidic linkages join two or more monosaccharide units ("intersaccharidic glycosides"), the resulting compounds are called "disaccharides," etc., and are discussed in the subsequent sections. There also exist glycosides in which a monosaccharide is linked to a non-sugar moiety (an "aglycon"). Simple glycosides of this type are named from their constituent parts as follows: aglycon—the symbol α or β to indicate the configuration of the original hemiacetal—the parent sugar, replacing the ending "ose" by "oside," and frequently indicating which cyclic form is involved. The full name for the following substance, for example, is methyl α-D-glucopyranoside, commonly abbreviated to methyl α-glucoside:

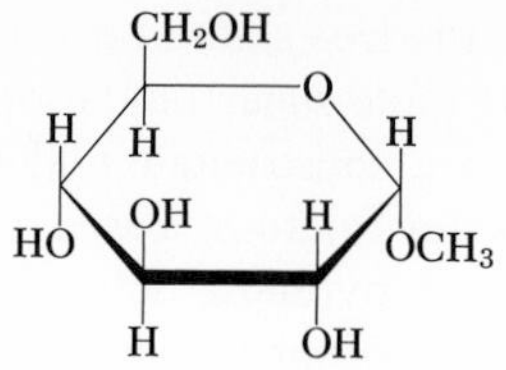

CH₂OH
O
H H H
OH H
HO OCH₃
H OH

In contrast to the simple aglycon, methanol, used above, most of those found in biological products are very complex. Many of the red, violet, and blue pigments found in the plant world are present in their natural state as glycosides, the aglycons being rather complex, heterocyclic compounds. Some glycosides of medical interest contain phenanthrene derivatives as aglycons, such as the cardiac glycosides (from the Digitalis plant) and the saponins (hemolytic poisons, widely distributed in plants). The cerebrosides, glycolipids found especially in the nervous system of animals, contain galactose in a glycosidic linkage. Two of the component parts of the antibiotic, streptomycin, are coupled as a glycoside. Finally, many compounds excreted in the urine of animals, including both foreign substances administered experimentally or therapeutically (e.g., menthol) as well as those found or produced naturally within the organism (certain hormones and their breakdown products), are conjugated as glycosides with a glucose derivative, glucuronic acid.

The glycosides mentioned thus far have involved an aglycon linked to the parent sugar through an oxygen atom. A group of glycosides of great biological importance, the nucleosides, contains nitrogenous bases as aglycons, the bond to the sugar being formed through a nitrogen atom. These glycosides occur in the nucleic acids and some related compounds. The carbohydrate portions of the nucleosides are D-ribose and D-2-deoxyribose. Nucleoside structures are considered in detail elsewhere (p. 109).

Disaccharides

If, instead of being coupled in acetal linkage with an aglycon, a monosaccharide is combined with a second monosaccharide, the result is a disaccharide. Continuation of this process leads to trisaccharides, tetrasaccharides, etc., thus giving rise to the group known as oligosaccharides. Of this group only the disaccharides are of importance in animal biochemistry, and only three disaccharides merit discussion in an elementary textbook: maltose, lactose, and sucrose.

As indicated in Figure 2–4, disaccharides can be named on the same basis as glycosides, simply substituting the name of the corresponding monosaccharide for the aglycon. For completeness, the particular hydroxyl group of the sugar which enters into combination with the glycosidic monosaccharide is indicated by number. In a newer and less awkward system of nomenclature, the sugar contributing the glycoside linkage is considered to be a sugar radical, the glycosyl radical, formed by removing the hydroxyl from the anomeric carbon. The reducing oligosaccharides are named as glycosyl aldoses and the non-reducing oligosaccharides as glycosyl aldosides. If necessary, the terms "glycofuranosyl" and "glycopyranosyl" may be used.

Most oligosaccharides form exceptions to certain generalizations made with respect to acetals, in that they are (with few exceptions) reducing sugars and exhibit mutarotation. Maltose consists of two glucose units, combined in α-glycosidic linkage. A glance at the structure of maltose will reveal that, whereas one of the two potential aldehyde groups is

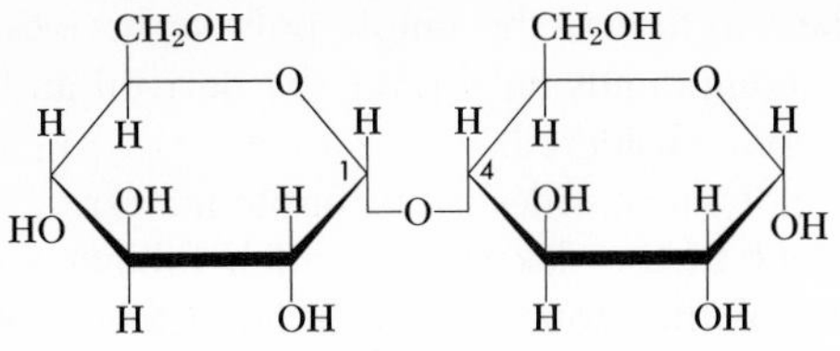

Maltose
4-α-D-Glucopyranose-α-D-glucopyranoside
α-D-Glucopyranosyl-4-α-D-glucopyranose

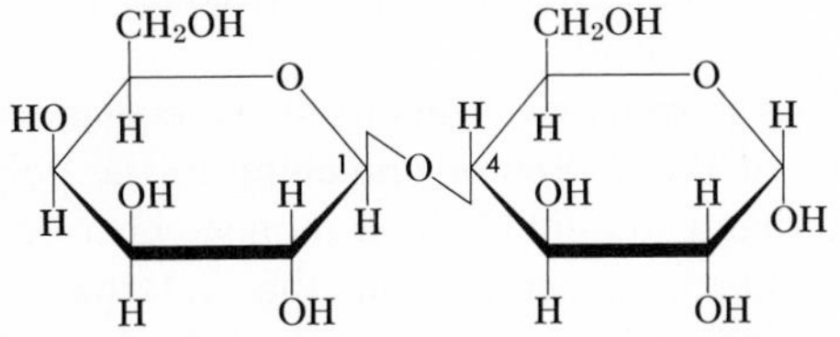

Lactose
4-α-D-Glucopyranose-β-D-galactopyranoside
β-D-Galactopyranosyl-4-α-D-glucopyranose

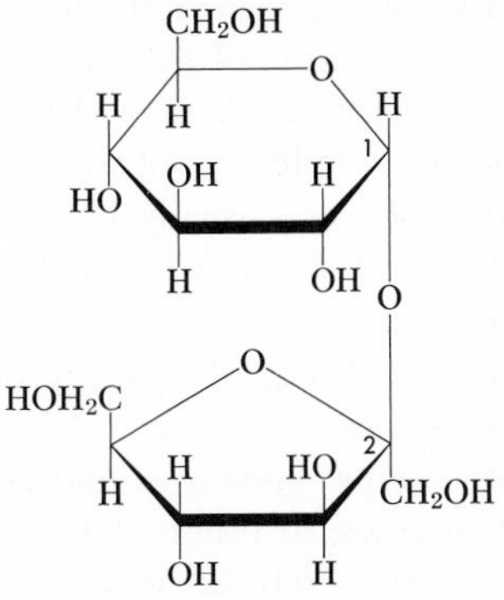

Sucrose
α-D-Glucopyranosido-β-D-fructofuranoside
β-D-Fructofuranosido-α-D-glucopyranoside
β-D-Fructofuranosyl-α-D-glucopyranosyl
α-D-Glucopyranosyl-β-D-fructofuranosyl

Figure 2-4. Important disaccharides.

blocked in the acetal linkage and cannot possibly revert to the open-chain form, there is nothing to prevent the other hemi-acetal group from displaying all of the reactions of free glucose. Maltose is important, not per se, but because it is the product formed when enzymes known as amylases digest starch in the alimentary tract of the animal organism.

Lactose differs from maltose in several respects. It is a galactoside rather than a glucoside, and the disaccharide linkage is of the β configuration. Like maltose, however, it is a reducing sugar and mutarotates. Lactose is the sugar found in mammalian milk, which is one of the few places where galactose occurs in animals.

Sucrose, a disaccharide obtained from sugar cane, sugar beets, and other sources, forms an important constituent of the human diet, both directly and in combination in various commercially prepared foodstuffs. Its structure is rather unusual. In addition to glucose it contains a fructofuranose residue. The intersaccharide linkage is formed by an α-glucoside on one side coupled to a β-fructoside on the other. Both the potential aldehyde and potential ketone groups are blocked by the manner of linkage, hence sucrose is nonreducing and does not undergo mutarotation. Upon hydrolysis, sucrose gives rise to a molecule each of glucopyranose and fructopyranose, the fructose reverting to the more stable ring form in the process. If the optical rotation is followed during the course of the hydrolysis, the initial dextrorotation of the sucrose is observed to decrease gradually, the final mixture actually becoming levorotatory. This is caused by the magnitude of the levorotation of fructose, which is greater numerically than the dextrorotation of glucose, with the result that an equimolar mixture of the two monosaccharides is levorotatory. The hydrolysis of sucrose is therefore called "inversion," and the product is called "invert sugar."

Polymers of the Simple Monosaccharides

Molecules of the molecular magnitude of polysaccharides can be formed from derived and substituted monosaccharides, but the complexities and problems of classification of these substances are such that it would be best to discuss the simple polysaccharides first, leaving the treatment of the more complex compounds until after the derived and substituted monosaccharides themselves have been considered.

The elucidation of the structures of the polysaccharides is no simple matter, and the problems in this field, as will become evident in the discussions which follow, are far from being completely solved. Identification of the monosaccharide constituents of the polysaccharide can usually be accomplished after complete acid hydrolysis of the large molecule to its simplest units. Partial hydrolysis, stopping at the disaccharide stage, will often reveal the manner in which the units are linked together; e.g., the formation of maltose from starch suggests that this polysaccharide is composed of glucose residues, combined through carbon atoms 1 and 4 by an α-glucosidic bond.

A technique known as end-group analysis permits an estimate of molecular weight in certain cases; in others it is an indication of the degree of branching in the polysaccharide chain. It will be readily appreciated that a straight chain of monosaccharide units must possess two terminal residues which differ in structure from the "internal" units. One terminus will be formed by a sugar residue with a potential reducing group, while the other will differ from all other sugars in the chain by containing an extra hydroxyl group. Chemical methods are available for determining the ratio of terminal residues to the total number of units in the chain. For a straight chain this makes possible an estimate of the length of the molecule in terms of monosaccharide units, hence the molecular weight can be calculated. In the case of a branched chain, the average number of monosaccharide units per branch can be determined, but the molecular size must then be found by some other method.

Figure 2–5 illustrates some of the techniques which may be employed. For example, after exhaustive methylation followed by acid hydrolysis, the number of reducing end groups in the polysaccharide is indicated by the amount of 2,3,6-trimethylglucose isolated, the number of non-reducing end groups by the amount of 2,3,4,6-tetramethylglucose isolated, and the number of branching points by the amount of 2,3-dimethylglucose isolated. In a polysaccharide of the type shown in the figure, periodate oxidation produces formaldehyde solely from the reducing end groups, so that the amount of formaldehyde gives an indication of the amount of these groups. If the polysaccharide is highly branched, the number of reducing end groups is small compared to the number of non-reducing end groups, and therefore the amount of formic acid produced by periodate oxidation may be used as indication of the number of groups of the latter type present. More recently, enzymatic methods of end-group analysis have been applied. For example, in one method two enzymes are required, one specific for α-D-1,4-linkages (p. 244) and a second enzyme capable of hydrolyzing the small proportion of branching or α-D-1,6-linkages. From the proportion of products resulting from the action of these two enzymes, the degree of branching and hence the length of the branches can be determined.

Since the polysaccharides are of colloidal dimensions, special physicochemical methods have been developed for the direct determination of their molecular weights. Such techniques as measurement of viscosity, osmotic pressure, light-scattering, and ultracentrifugal sedimentation are among those which have applied. Most of these methods are of considerable importance in protein chemistry also, and are discussed in some detail elsewhere (p. 83 ff.).

The polysaccharides of the simple sugars can be divided into two groups, the homosaccharidic and heterosaccharidic, depending upon whether their constituent monosaccharides are all alike, or are of mixed types. Although some heteropolysaccharides of the mixed

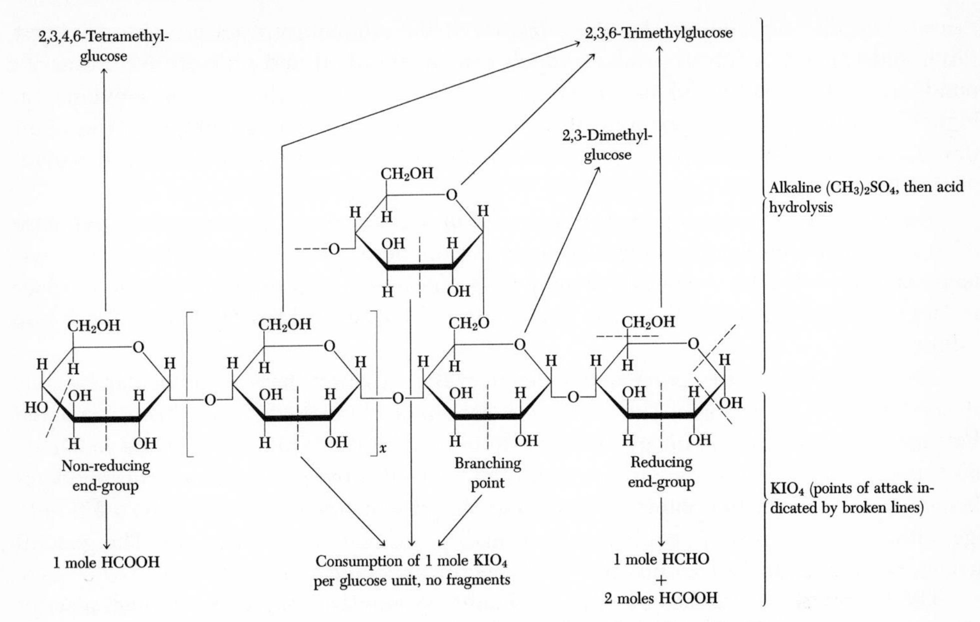

Figure 2-5. Chemical end-group analysis of a polysaccharide.

hexose or hexose-pentose type are found in plants and bacteria, our discussion will be limited to the homosaccharidic group, which includes several familiar and important members.

Polysaccharides may be called "pentosans" or "hexosans," according to the type of monosaccharide unit involved. A more detailed nomenclature specifies the actual sugar, giving rise to terms such as glucans (dextrans), fructans (levans), galactans, mannans, etc. Many dextrans are produced by fungi, yeasts, and bacteria. Levans (inulin), mannans, galactans, and pentosans are widely distributed throughout the plant world. Of all the homosaccharidic polymers of the simple sugars, three glucans are of sufficient economic or biological importance to warrant a more detailed consideration. These are cellulose, starch, and glycogen.

Cellulose acts as a supporting structure for plant tissues. In man it provides bulk when ingested in plant foodstuffs. (Ruminants are able to utilize cellulose, since it is digested by the microorganisms which inhabit their alimentary tracts.) It is of interest that a polysaccharide apparently identical with cellulose is present in a number of lower animal forms and in certain connective tissues of man. By the application of the methods mentioned earlier, it has been determined that cellulose consists of unbranched chains of glucopyranose units, combined through carbon atoms 1 and 4 by a β-glucosidic linkage. Although it is difficult to avoid some degradation of the native cellulose molecules in the course of determining molecular weights, careful studies have indicated that there may be over 3000 glucose residues per molecule of cellulose, resulting in a molecular weight of over half a million. The cellulose fiber consists of bundles of these chains packed side by side, oriented in the direction of the fiber axis. Thus the tensile properties of cellulose, which account for much of the industrial importance of cotton and related materials, are visible manifestations of a type of architecture existing at the molecular level.

Starch differs functionally from cellulose in being a storage form of nutritionally available carbohydrate in plants. Its importance in human nutrition is immeasurably greater than that of cellulose, for the enzymes of the alimentary tract are able to digest starch and convert it into a product which can be absorbed and utilized. As ordinarily found, starch is a mixture of two types of molecules, amylose (linear) and amylopectin (highly branched). The proportions of the two components vary according to the plant source, and there is evidence of variability in structure among the amyloses and amylopectins themselves.

The amylose components of starch consist of a chain of 1,4-linked α-glucopyranose units. Although completely elongated chains of amylose can be prepared, there is evidence that its molecules are usually wound in the form of a helix, with six glucose residues per turn. The molecular weight has been reported to range from 69,000 to about one million.

The amylopectins are larger molecules than the amyloses, having molecular weights of 200,000 to many million. The molecules are highly branched; it has been estimated that one branch is present for every 24 to 30 glucose units. While most of the molecule has the same basic unit as the amyloses, 1,4-linked α-glucopyranoses, some other mode of linkage must occur at the points of branching. At present this is thought to be a 1,6-linkage, although there is some evidence for a small percentage of 1,3-linkages. The general arrangement of branches within the amylopectin molecule is indicated in Figure 2–6.

The hydrolysis of starches by enzymes known as amylases proceeds, through a series of lower molecular weight polysaccharides called "dextrins," to maltose as the final product. Reactions of this type occur in the saliva and in the small intestine of animals.

Just as starch serves as a storage form of carbohydrate in plants, glycogen performs this function in animals. Liver and muscle contain stores of glycogen which are of special importance in intermediary metabolism. The glycogen molecule is similar in many respects to amylopectin (Fig. 2–6), consisting largely of 1,4-linked α-glycopyranoses, with considerable branching (probably involving 1,6-linkages). Small amounts of 1,3-linkages have been reported to exist in glycogen as well as starch. Since the average chain length per branch is about 12 glucose units, the glycogen molecule is even more highly ramified than amylopectin. Determinations of molecular weight have yielded values of 1 to 400 million. There is evidence of considerable heterogeneity in glycogen preparations. Different types of glycogen molecules may be deposited in the tissues of animals, depending on the carbohydrate administered and the manner of administration. Glycogen molecules of abnormal structure appear to occur in certain types of glycogen storage disease (p. 401). It is possible that some of the reported differences in the molecular weight of glycogen are due to differences in methods of extraction, as it is known that reagents used in the extractions differ in their degradative effects on the native molecule.

Although the digestible oligosaccharides and polysaccharides which are ingested as foodstuffs are broken down in the animal organism by a process of hydrolysis, the degradation (and, by reversal, the synthesis) of glycogen within the body involves a reaction with the elements of phosphoric acid, rather than of water. This reaction is called "phosphorolysis," and is discussed in the chapter on the metabolism of carbohydrates (p. 400).

SUGAR ACIDS, AMINO SUGARS, AND THEIR POLYMERS

Aldonic Acids (Fig. 2–7)

Oxidation of the aldehyde group of the aldose sugars to a carboxyl group gives rise to a series of compounds called "aldonic acids." Although these substances are not found in

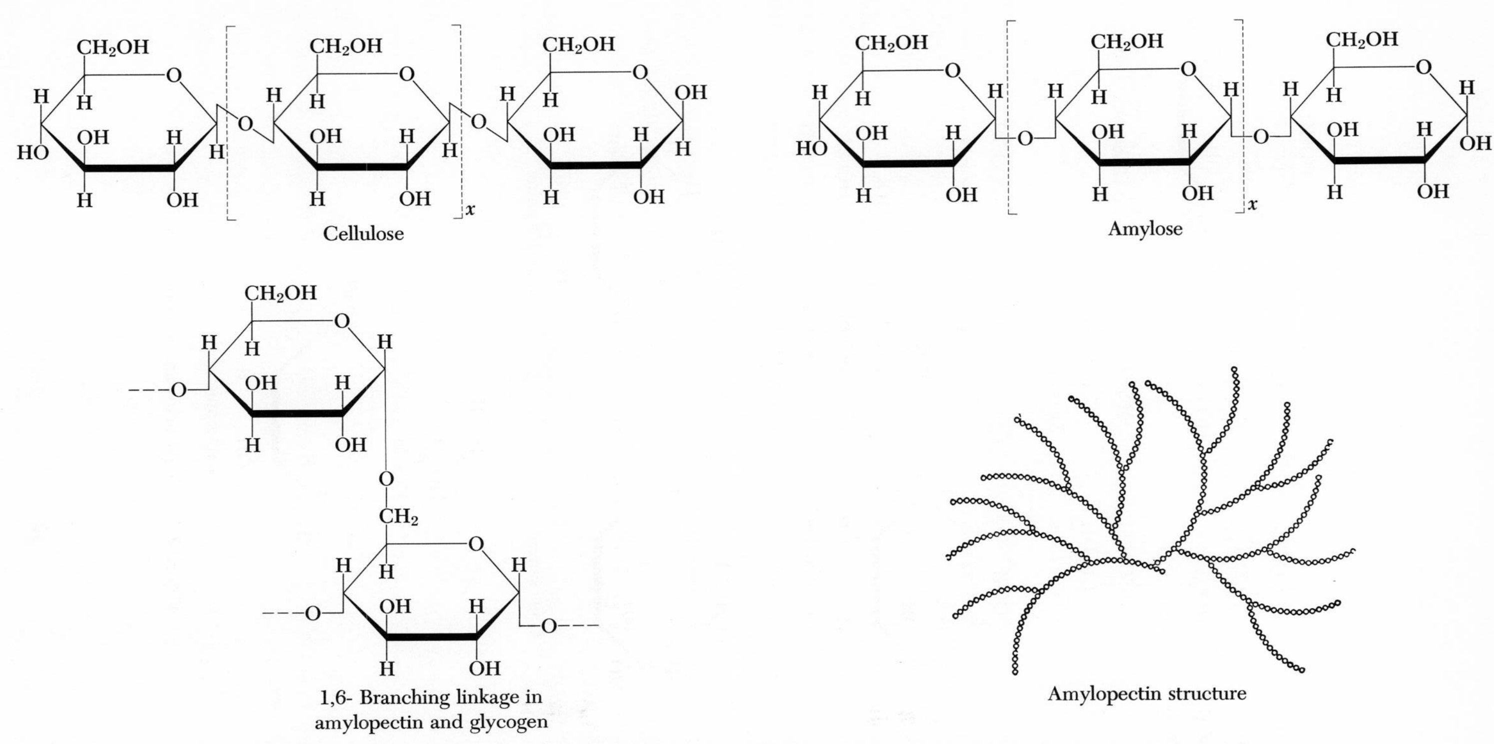

Figure 2-6. Important homopolysaccharides. (Amylopectin structure from Bernfeld: Advances Enzymol. *12,* 1951; Meyer and Bernfeld: Helvet. chim. acta *23,* 1940.)

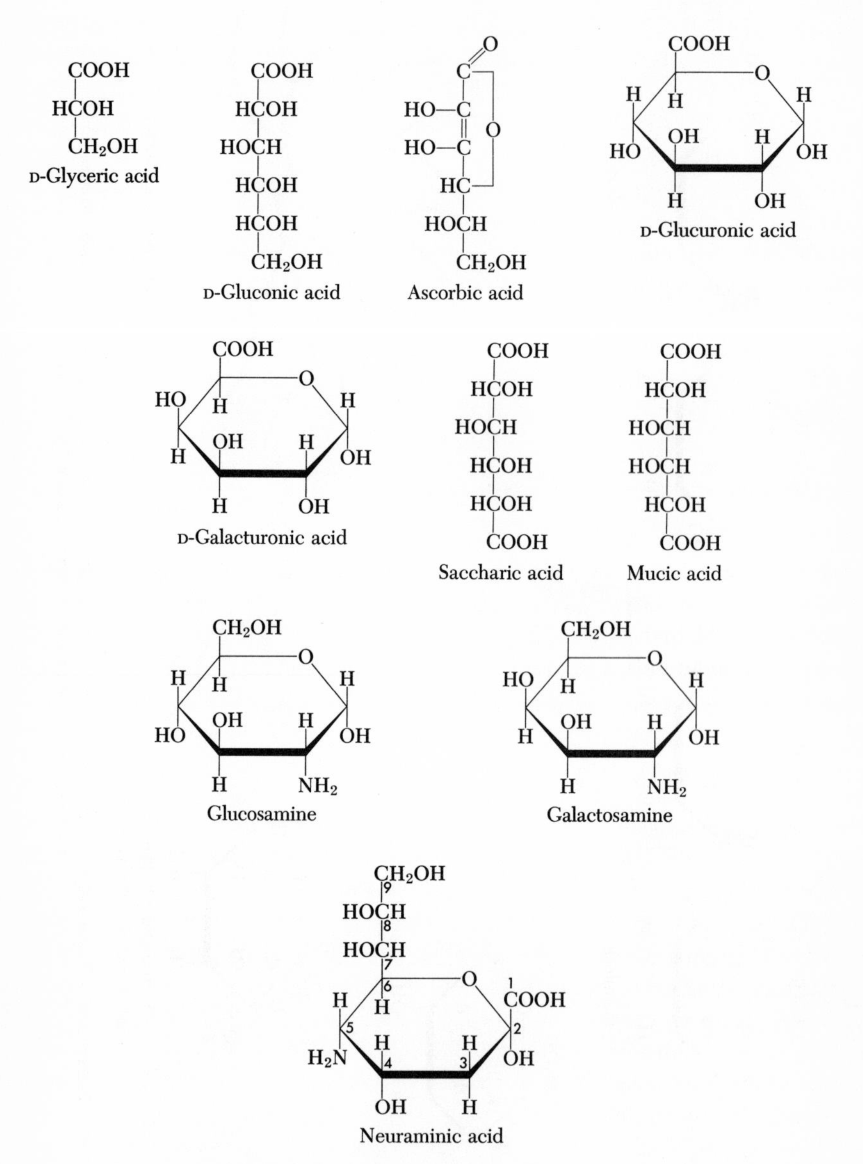

Figure 2-7. Sugar acids and amino sugars.

nature in the free state, some of their derivatives are of biological importance. D-Gluconic acid, in the form of its 6-phosphate ester, can be produced by the action of enzymes on the corresponding glucose ester, and is an important intermediate in the biological synthesis of pentoses.

Glyceric acid, in phosphorylated form, is an intermediate in the transformation of carbohydrate to lactic acid in the organism. Ascorbic acid is the anti-scorbutic vitamin C. It is the enol of the γ-lactone formed from the ketoaldonic acid of an L-hexose.

Uronic Acids

If the aldehyde group of an aldose is left intact, but the primary alcohol at the opposite end of the chain is oxidized to a carboxyl group, a uronic acid results. Glucuronic acid is found in the urine, conjugated (as a glucuronide) to foreign substances which may be administered to the organism, or to breakdown products of these substances, or to quite normal metabolites, such as pregnanediol, which arises from the metabolism of the hormone, progesterone (p. 696). In addition, it is a constituent of certain polysaccharides which will be discussed shortly. Galacturonic acid is found in certain plant and bacterial polysaccharides.

Saccharic Acids

Oxidation at both ends of the monosaccharide molecule produces a saccharic (or glycaric) acid, the group taking its name from the acid derived from D-glucose (also called glucaric acid). Mucic acid, from D-galactose, is often used as a derivative for the identification of that sugar. Although tartaric acid, a plant product, is a member of this group of compounds, the saccharic acids are not of great importance in animal biochemistry.

Amino Sugars (Fig. 2-7)

Two types of amino sugars are of physiological importance. In one, the glycosylamine, the anomeric hydroxyl group is replaced by an amino group. A compound belonging to this group is ribosylamine, a derivative of which is involved in the synthesis of purines (p. 515). The second type of amino sugar is the glycamine or glycosamine, in which alcoholic hydroxyl groups on the sugar molecule are replaced by amino groups. Two naturally occurring members of this group are derived from glucose and galactose by replacing the hydroxyl group on carbon atom 2 of each sugar by a primary amino group. Glucosamine, also called "chitosamine," is the basic unit in the polysaccharide, chitin, which forms part of the integument of arthropods. Galactosamine, also known as chondrosamine, is a part of the complex polysaccharides of connective tissue. Both amino sugars are also found in other polysaccharides which are discussed below. The amino groups of both compounds are often present in the acetylated state.

Amino sugar acids. Neuraminic acid (Fig. 2-7) is the parent compound of a group of substances which occur in a number of mucopolysaccharides and glycolipids (p. 41). Structurally, neuraminic acid appears to be a condensation product of pyruvic acid and mannosamine. Neuraminic acid is unstable and is found in nature in the form of acylated derivatives known as sialic acids, including such compounds as N-acetylneuraminic acid, O,N-diacetylneuraminic acid, and N-glycolylneuraminic acid. A number of nitrogenous oligosaccharides which contain neuraminic acid are found in human milk. Certain bacterial cell walls contain muramic acid, a compound which is structurally a condensation product of glucosamine and lactic acid.

Polymers of the Sugar Acids and the Amino Sugars

Homosaccharidic

An example of the non-nitrogenous members of this group of polymers is pectin, a substance (really a group of substances) present in fruits, having the economically important property of forming gels with sugar at the proper pH. Pectin is composed of D-galacturonic acid units, connected through a 1,4-linkage, probably as α-glycosides, with many of the carboxyl groups present as methyl esters.

The skeletal material of arthropods contains, in addition to protein, a nitrogenous homopolysaccharide called "chitin." This substance consists of D-glucosamine units, acetylated on the amino group, probably linked by 1,4-β-glucoside bonds.

Non-nitrogenous, heterosaccharidic

Among the non-nitrogenous, heterosaccharidic polymers of the substituted and derived sugars are the hemi-celluloses, consisting of hexoses, pentoses, and uronic acids. The plant gums and mucilages have a somewhat similar composition. Some of the pneumococcus polysaccharides and those from the tubercle bacillus also belong to this group.

Nitrogenous, heterosaccharidic (mucopolysaccharides)

Although there is no agreement on classification in this field, the nitrogenous heteropolysaccharides would coincide with what are known as mucopolysaccharides in most systems. They may be subdivided into neutral and acidic groups, and the latter further classified as sulfate-free and sulfate-containing. This system omits, for the sake of simplicity, any reference to the protein moiety which may be coupled to the polysaccharide in nature.

Neutral. Many of the neutral polysaccharides of the various types of pneumococci contain nitrogen, as do the polysaccharides of certain other species of bacteria. Also included in the group of nitrogenous neutral heteropolysaccharides are the blood group substances, those compounds which account for the immunological reactions between bloods of individuals of the same species. These substances contain amino acids or peptides as well as carbohydrates. Four monosaccharides are found in all types of blood group substances regardless of source: galactose, fucose, and acetylated glucosamine and galactosamine. Non-reducing end groups of acetylglucosamine, galactose, and fucose are associated with blood group specificities of A, B, and H, respectively. The amino acid composition of blood group substances is peculiar in that sulfur-containing and aromatic amino acids are absent. Of special importance in animal biochemistry are the nitrogenous, neutral polysaccharides found firmly bound to proteins (p. 54); e.g., ovalbumin contains mannose and glucosamine. Some protein hormones are united to similar polysaccharides. Thyrotropin has been reported to contain glucosamine, galactosamine, mannose, and fucose.

Acidic, sulfate-free. Some nitrogenous acidic polysaccharides found in the animal organism occur in the free state, or as dissociable complexes with proteins, whereas others are firmly bound. Among the sulfate-free polysaccharides found firmly bound to protein are included several fractions of the plasma proteins. One is the acid α_1-mucoprotein, also called oroso-mucoid or acid glycoprotein, which contains galactose, mannose, glucosamine, fucose, and sialic acid. Other similar mucoproteins are found in the α_2-globulins. γ-Globulins have also been reported to contain hexose, hexosamine, fucose, and sialic acid. The gonadotropic hormones ICSH and FSH also contain these carbohydrate components. Galactose, mannose, glucosamine, galactosamine, fucose, and sialic acid are found in chorionic gonadotropin. Prothrombin and mucins of the alimentary tract contain hexose, hexosamine, and sialic acid; fucose is also present frequently in the mucins. The egg-white proteins, ovomucoid and ovomucin, contain reducing sugars, amino sugars, and sialic acid. Cell walls of gram-positive bacteria appear to contain a selection of few amino acids (including, however, the unusual amino acid, diaminopimelic), hexoses, hexosamines, muramic acid, and little lipid. Cell walls of gram-negative bacteria contain more lipid, less hexosamine, and a wider range of amino acids, including diaminopimelic. A notable fact is that some of the amino acids of bacterial cell walls occur in the D-configuration. The surfaces of red cells (and possibly other cells) contain mucopolysaccharides possessing terminal neuraminic acid residues which are susceptible to attack by neuraminidase (sialidase) enzymes contained in influenza virus and possibly other viruses. Such reactions may be involved in the invasion of certain viruses into cells of the respiratory tract. (In addition to the neuraminidase of influenza virus, there is evidence for the presence of this enzyme in the cholera vibrio, Monks' virus, Newcastle disease virus, Clostridium welchii, pneumococcus type 2, and possibly diphtheroid bacilli.)

The mucopolysaccharides of the various mucous membranes throughout the body, as integral parts of mucoproteins, are thought to have a protective influence on the tissues which secrete them. This protection may be exerted against the action of digestive juices or invading microorganisms; in the latter case the possession of "mucolytic" enzymes by certain bacteria may be a matter of some consequence. The "intrinsic factor" involved in the maturation of erythrocytes may be associated with one of the fractions of gastric mucin (p. 261).

Hyaluronic acid, a sulfate-free polysaccharide, is found in the vitreous humor, synovial fluid, skin, umbilical cord, and in general (together with protein and other mucopolysaccharides) forms the so-called "ground substance" of the mesenchyme. Viscous complexes of hyaluronic acid and protein in synovial fluid probably are important in lubrication of the joints. In connection with the present great interest in diseases of the connective tissues, and the function of hormones of the adrenal cortex in relation to these tissues, investigations of the chemistry of hyaluronic acid and related substances are being pursued intensively. The probable role of hyaluronic acid as an intercellular cement has also focused attention on the possibility that invasion by microorganisms may be facilitated by the secretion of hyaluronidases (enzymes hydrolyzing hyaluronic acids), also called "spreading factors." Hyaluronic acid is composed of alternating units of glucuronic acid and N-acetylglucosamine. The structure of the repeating unit in this polymer is shown in Figure 2–8.

Another sulfate-free mucopolysaccharide is chondroitin, found in cornea. It differs from hyaluronic acid only in that it contains acetylgalactosamine in place of acetylglucosamine.

Acidic, sulfate-containing. A sulfate-containing polysaccharide, keratosulfate, is found in costal cartilage and cornea. It consists of equimolar amounts of N-acetylglucosamine, galactose, and sulfate. Of more widespread occurrence are the chondroitin sulfates. Chondroitin sulfates A and C are composed of glucuronic acid and sulfated galactosamine residues. The only structural difference between compounds A and C lies in the position of the sulfate on the galactosamine residue. Chondroitin sulfate B, also called

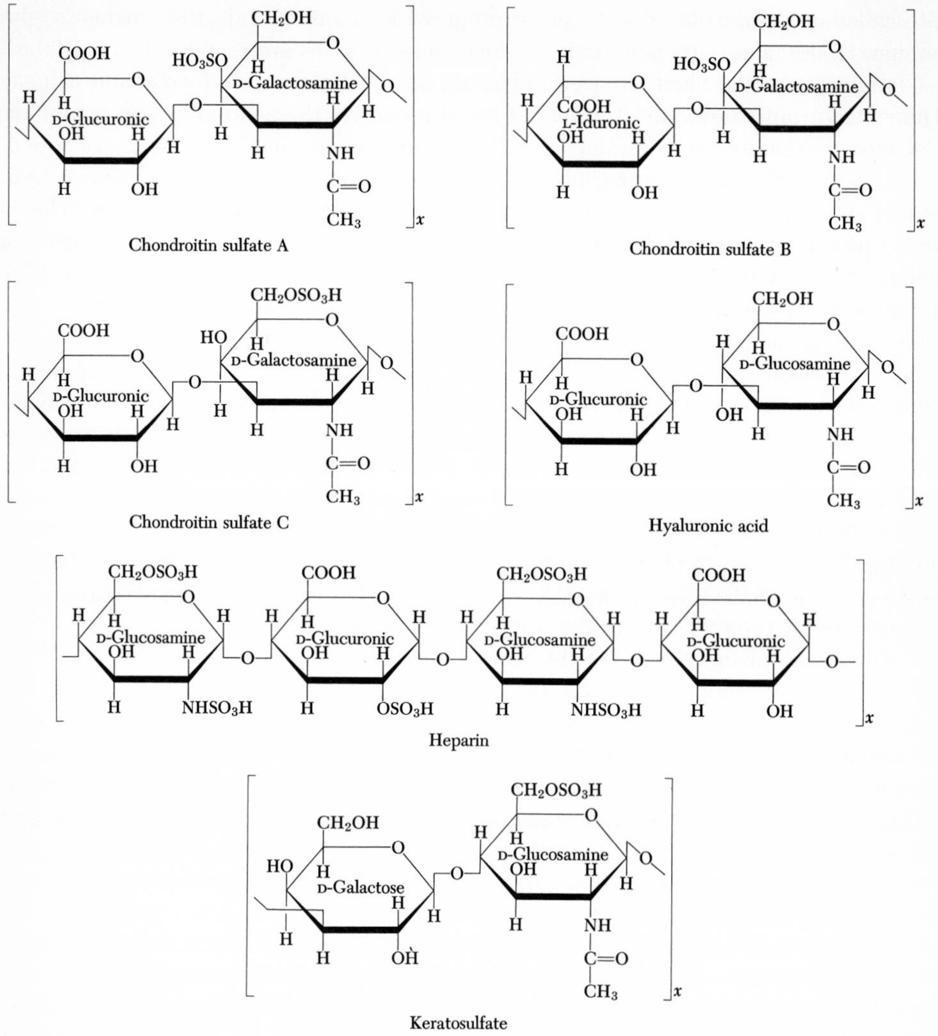

Chondroitin sulfate A

Chondroitin sulfate B

Chondroitin sulfate C

Hyaluronic acid

Heparin

Keratosulfate

Figure 2–8. Mucopolysaccharides.

β-heparin and dermatan sulfate, differs from chondroitin sulfates A and C in having L-iduronic acid as its uronic acid constituent. The chondroitin sulfates are found distributed in many types of connective tissue. Structures of these polysaccharides are shown in Figure 2–8.

Heparin, a widely distributed mucopolysaccharide with blood anticoagulant properties, contains glucosamine and glucuronic acid residues. It differs from the other compounds thus far discussed in that its sulfuric acid component is present not only as ester sulfate, but also in an amide linkage with the amino group of the glucosamine. Furthermore, it contains no acetyl groups. Although the structure of heparin is by no means settled, a tentative formula for one of its repeating units is given in Figure 2–8. A polysaccharide named heparitin sulfate (probably identical to the heparin monosulfate prepared from ox liver or lung) has been isolated from amyloid liver, certain normal tissues such as human and cattle aorta and from the urine, liver, and spleen of patients with gargoylism. This compound has negligible anticoagulant activity, seems to be structurally similar to heparin, but has a lower molecular weight, some of the amino groups carry acetyl groups, and the percentage of sulfate groups is smaller.

According to the older literature, there occurs in gastric mucin a polymer of glucosamine, glucuronic acid, and sulfate, called mucoitin sulfate. Doubt has been expressed concerning its existence.

It is of interest that human milk contains growth factors for Lactobacillus bifidus, a normal inhabitant of the gastrointestinal tract of infants, and that these growth factors are muco-oligosaccharides. The simplest of these is lactose-N-acetylneuraminic acid. Substances of both low and high molecular weight are found. In addition to acidic oligosaccharides, neutral oligosaccharides are found, including several that contain no nitrogen.

SUGAR ALCOHOLS AND CYCLITOLS

Sugar Alcohols

Hydrogenation of the aldoses and ketoses reduces the carbonyl groups to alcohol groups, producing a series of compounds known as the sugar alcohols, the acyclic polyols, or the glykitols. Although the alcohols derived from the hexoses (hexitols) have considerable commercial importance as synthetic intermediates, they are not involved in animal biochemistry and will not be considered here. Actually, the only polyols that are significant from the standpoint of mammalian metabolism are two that are derived from the trioses and pentoses.

Glycerol can be considered a derivative of either glyceraldehyde or dihydroxyacetone. Since its metabolism is closely related to that of the lipids, many of which contain glycerol, discussion of the properties of glycerol is best deferred until the glycerides are considered. It should be pointed out, however, that glycerol has its origin in the carbohydrates, and that its ultimate fate, after removal of attached "lipoid" groups, involves a return to the carbohydrate fold.

D-Ribitol is derived from D-ribose. In combination with a heterocyclic moiety known as flavin, it forms the vitamin, riboflavin, a member of the B-complex. The entire riboflavin molecule, in turn, is found combined with other substances in larger molecules which act as coenzymes (p. 353).

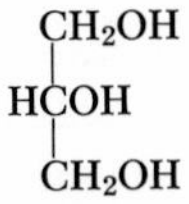

CH_2OH
HCOH
CH_2OH
Glycerol

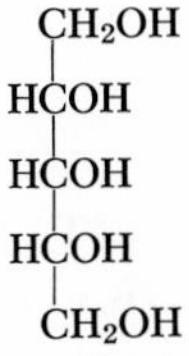

CH_2OH
HCOH
HCOH
HCOH
CH_2OH
D-Ribitol

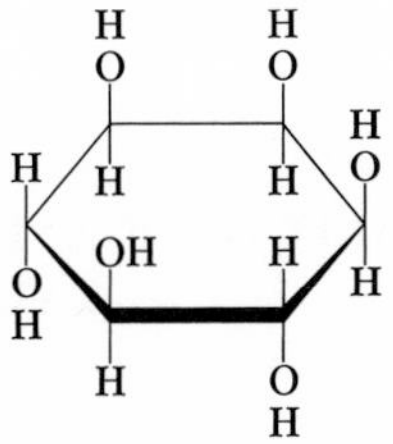

Meso-inositol

Teichoic Acids

Cell walls of various bacteria contain polymers, the teichoic acids, consisting of glycerol or ribitol units linked by phosphate diester groups. Side chains of sugars, amino sugars, and D-alanine are frequently present.

Cyclitols

A number of polyhydroxylated cyclohexane derivatives occur in nature. It is possible that they are formed in plants by cyclization of hexoses. One of the group, inositol, is a B vitamin. Human beings show no definite dietary requirement for this vitamin, since it is readily synthesized by the microorganisms which inhabit the intestines and is abundant in most foods, but it must be supplied in one way or another, for it has certain important functions. It is a constituent of certain phospholipids, and has some regulatory influence on fat accumulation in the liver (p. 504). In plants, it is found in the form of phytin, the calcium-magnesium salt of phytic acid, which is a hexa-phosphoric ester of inositol (p. 204).

PHOSPHORIC ESTERS OF THE SUGARS

Hexose Phosphates

As mentioned previously, the sugars are phosphorylated by the organism preparatory to their oxidation. The most important of the hexose esters are shown in Figure 2–9. Certain derivatives of the hexoses, such as gluconic acid, also form phosphate esters in the course of their metabolism.

Triose Phosphates

It will be shown in the discussion of carbohydrate metabolism that the major pathway of hexose breakdown involves phosphorylation, followed by cleavage into trioses. The triose esters and some of their derivatives which are on this pathway are indicated in Figure 2–9. As can be seen, many of the compounds are closely related to glyceric acid. The change from the state of oxidation of glyceraldehyde to that of glyceric acid represents the first oxidation which occurs in the metabolism of carbohydrates.

Pentose Phosphates

Some esters of D-ribose (and analogous derivatives of deoxyribose) occur as intermediates in pentose metabolism. In addition, such compounds constitute parts of more complex molecules, such as nucleotides, nucleic acids, and coenzymes.

QUALITATIVE AND QUANTITATIVE TESTS FOR CARBOHYDRATES

Chromatography

Carbohydrates may be separated for qualitative identification and quantitative determination by partition chromatography, using either the column or filter paper technique (p. 96). In the latter instance, spatial separation of sugars on the filter paper may be followed by treatment with reagents (frequently of the type used in the furfural-forming tests discussed below) which produce characteristic colors.

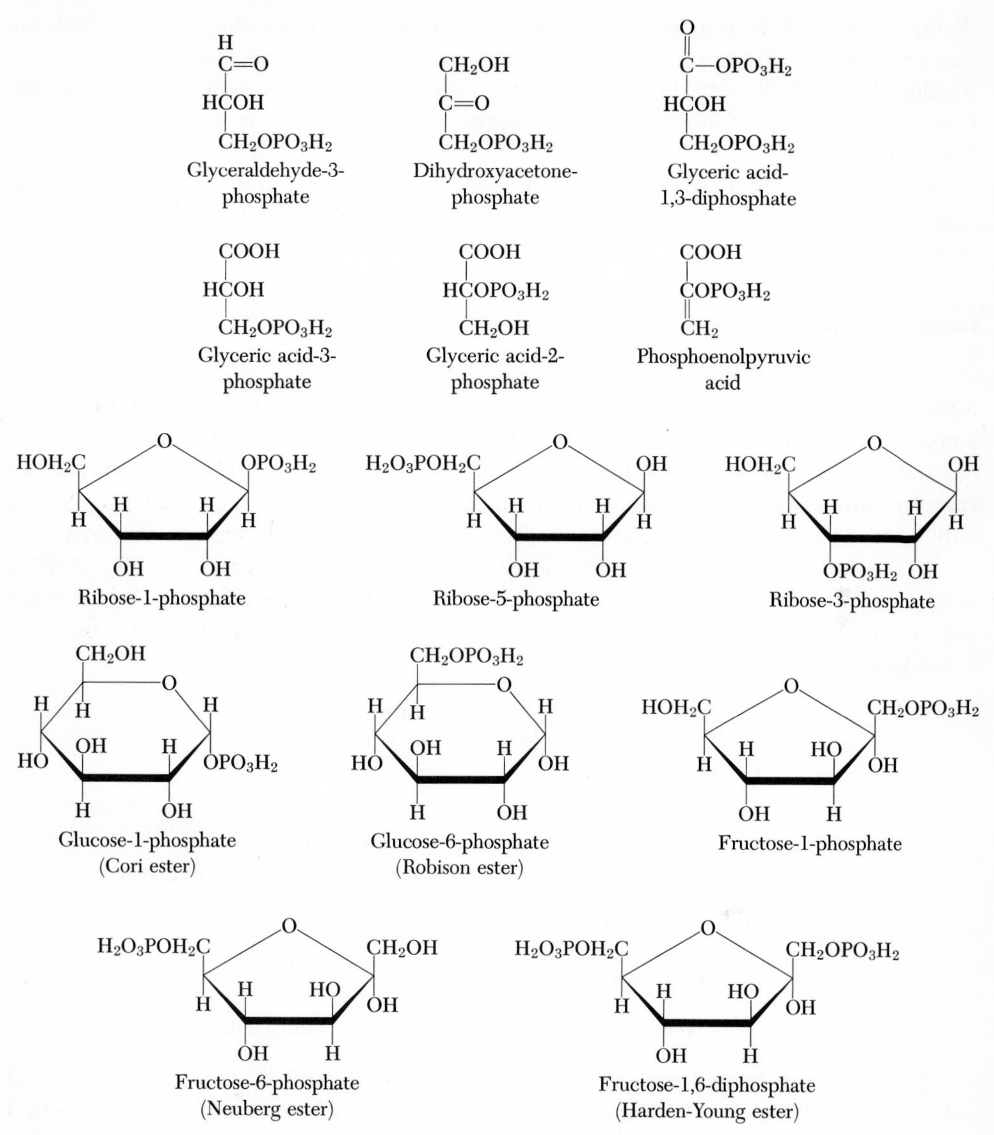

Figure 2-9. Phosphate esters of sugars and related compounds.

Copper and Other Reduction Tests

The most commonly used test for the detection of reducing sugars involves heating the sample with an alkaline reagent containing cupric copper held in solution by some type of complexing agent. Potential aldehyde or ketol groups are oxidized, and the copper is reduced to the red cuprous oxide. Fehling's solution has been largely replaced by the more convenient Benedict's reagent for qualitative tests in clinical laboratories. No equation can be given, since the reaction is not stoichiometric. However, by empirical standardization of the conditions, the reaction can be used for the quantitative determination of reducing sugars. The reduced copper is determined by reaction with phosphomolybdate

(Folin-Wu, Benedict) or arsenomolybdate (Nelson-Somogyi) to produce colors which are measured photometrically. Alternatively, the reduced copper may be titrated iodometrically (Somogyi, Shaffer-Hartmann). Direct reduction of ferricyanide by the sugar has been employed also, followed by photometry (Folin-Malmros) or iodometric titration (Hagedorn-Jensen).

If a slightly acidic copper reagent is used (Barfoed's test) and the time of heating controlled, the reducing monosaccharides give a positive reaction, while the reducing disaccharides do not.

Furfural-forming Tests

Carbohydrates, in the presence of non-oxidizing acids, undergo dehydration to form furfural or hydroxymethyl furfural. Since these aldehydes will condense with aromatic amines and phenols to give intensely colored compounds, furfural formation can be used as a qualitative or quantitative test for carbohydrates. By employing vigorous conditions all carbohydrates can be made to react; the test then becomes general. Under milder conditions only certain classes of compounds will react, thus giving rise to more specific tests.

In the presence of strong sulfuric acid all of the sugars and their polymers give positive reactions. When α-naphthol is the coupling reagent, the test is known as the Molisch reaction. Orcinol, anthrone, and carbazole give similar reactions, and have been used for quantitative estimations.

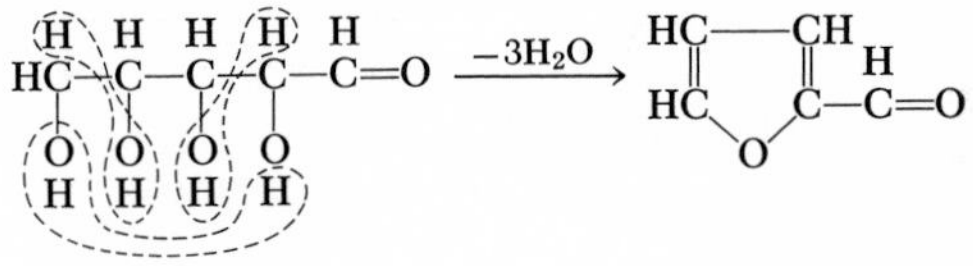

Pentose $\xrightarrow{-3H_2O}$ Furfural

Hexose $\xrightarrow{-3H_2O}$ Hydroxymethyl furfural

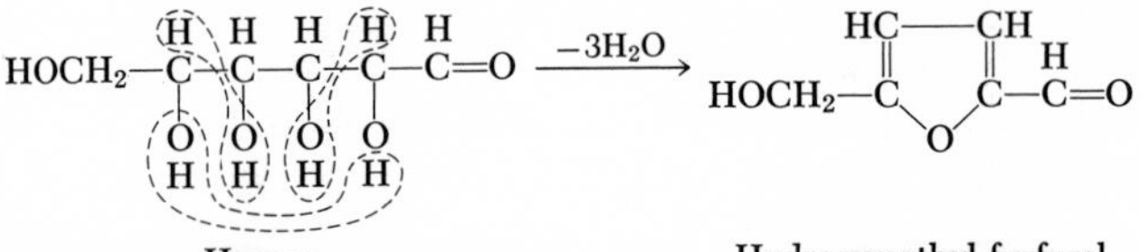

Ketoses, when heated with hydrochloric acid and resorcinol, produce a bright red color (Selivanoff test). Under the conditions of this test any ketoses which may be bound in glycosidic linkages will be liberated to give a positive reaction, e.g., the fructose portion of sucrose.

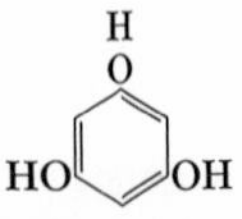

Phloroglucinol 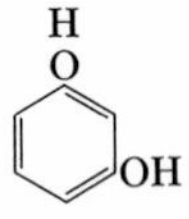 Resorcinol 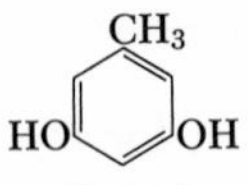 Orcinol 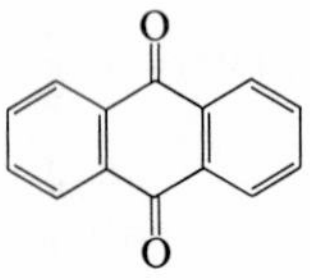 Anthrone

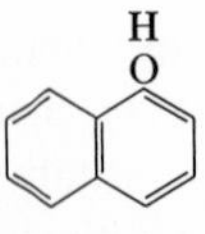

α-Naphthol 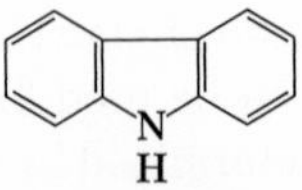 Carbazole 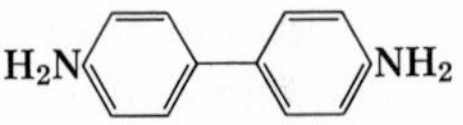 Benzidine

Many tests for pentoses depend upon formation of furfural. Under the usual conditions of the tests, uronic acids are decarboxylated to pentoses, and hence give positive reactions. Galactose is also an interfering factor in many of these tests. Thus, the reaction to Bial's orcinol test is positive for pentoses and galactose (the latter yielding a yellower and muddier green than the former), and under certain conditions for uronic acids. Tollens' phloroglucinol reaction yields positive results with pentoses, uronic acids, and galactose, but only the first two groups of substances result in specific absorption bands in the spectrophotometer. Pentoses and uronic acids both react positively toward Tauber's benzidine reagent.

Tests for deoxypentoses are mentioned in connection with the nucleic acids (p. 118).

Nitric Acid Oxidation

Both the aldehyde and primary alcohol groups of the aldoses are oxidized to carboxyl groups by nitric acid, producing the class of compounds called "saccharic acids" (p. 21). This reaction is often used for the detection and estimation of galactose, because the compound, mucic acid, produced from this sugar, is quite insoluble, in contrast to the other saccharic acids. Under the conditions of the test, galactose-containing glycosides and oligosaccharides (e.g., lactose) are hydrolyzed to give a positive reaction.

Phenylhydrazine

Aldoses and ketoses, so long as they retain their potential carbonyl groups, react with phenylhydrazine just as do the simple aldehydes and ketones, forming phenylhydrazones. However, in the presence of excess reagent a series of complicated reactions takes place, resulting in the introduction of a second phenylhydrazone group at the primary (for ketoses) or secondary (for aldoses) alcohol group adjacent to the original carbonyl group. These products are called "osazones," and are used for identification of the sugars, since they crystallize in characteristic forms. As formulated below, glucose and fructose give the same osazone, since their only structural differences, at carbon atoms 1 and 2, are obliterated by osazone formation. Mannose would also produce the same osazone as glucose and fructose, except that its phenylhydrazone is so insoluble that the reaction usually stops at that poin

HC=O, HCOH, HOCH, HCOH, HCOH, CH_2OH —($H_2N \cdot NH$–C_6H_5)→ HC=N—NH–C_6H_5, HCOH, HOCH, HCOH, HCOH, CH_2OH —(Excess reagent)→

CH_2OH, C=O, HOCH, HCOH, HCOH, CH_2OH —($H_2N \cdot NH$–C_6H_5)→ CH_2OH, C=N—NH–C_6H_5, HOCH, HCOH, HCOH, CH_2OH —(Excess reagent)→

HC=N—NH–C_6H_5, C=N—NH–C_6H_5, HOCH, HCOH, HCOH, CH_2OH

It may be appropriate at this time to point out that reducing properties, mutarotation, and osazone formation all depend upon the presence of a potential aldehyde or ketol group. Blockage of all such groups in a molecule (e.g., sucrose) abolishes all three reactions.

Alkali

Reducing sugars are profoundly affected by alkaline conditions. Isomerizations occur at the carbonyl end of the molecule, resulting in the formation of a mixture of related aldoses and ketoses. More extensive rearrangements may lead to branched-chain acids. Actual fragmentation of the chain to smaller molecules also takes place, leading to what one of the investigators in this field called a "furchtbares Gemisch." Heating an alkaline solution of a reducing sugar in the presence of air produces a visible change, called "caramelization." The solution turns yellow at first, then brown, probably as a result of the condensation of oxidized and fragmented molecules to higher polymers and tars.

Iodine

Certain polysaccharides give characteristic colors when treated with iodine solutions. The amylose fraction of starch, for example, gives a deep blue color, whereas the reaction with amylopectin is red to purple. Although the usual sample of starch handled in the student laboratory contains more amylopectin than amylose, the latter substance combines with much more iodine and produces such an intense color that the "typical" reaction to the iodine test for starch is the appearance of blue color. Hydrolysis of starch proceeds through a series of dextrins of presumably decreasing molecular weight, reacting in the iodine test to give colors changing from blue through violet to red-brown (erythrodextrins) to colorless (achroodextrins). Glycogen gives a red-brown color with iodine, whereas cellulose does not react.

Fermentation and Other Enzymatic Tests

Of the commonly occurring sugars, ordinary bakers' yeast ferments only glucose, fructose, mannose, maltose, and sucrose. It does not attack galactose, lactose, or pentoses appreciably. Since lactose and pentoses sometimes occur in the urine in conditions which have no serious clinical implication, fermentation tests are used to differentiate these cases from *glucosuria*, which may be indicative of diabetes mellitus. Special strains of yeast may be obtained which ferment galactose or pentoses.

The explanation for the fermentability of some sugars and the inertness of others involves the enzymatic make-up of the yeast cell and the concept of the specificity of enzymes. These topics will be discussed in the chapters on enzymes and carbohydrate metabolism.

Glucose is oxidized specifically by a glucose oxidase from fungi; the hydrogen peroxide which is formed can be made to oxidize an aromatic amine (such as *o*-dianisidine) in the presence of peroxidase. The resulting color can be measured photometrically. A galactose oxidase is used similarly.

BIBLIOGRAPHY

GENERAL

Advances in Carbohydrate Chemistry.
Annual Review of Biochemistry.
Florkin, M., and Stotz, E. H. (eds.): Comprehensive Biochemistry, Vol. 5, Carbohydrates, Amsterdam, Elsevier Publishing Company, 1963.
Guthrie, R. D., and Honeyman, J.: An Introduction to the Chemistry of Carbohydrates, New York, Oxford University Press, 1964.
Pigman, W. (ed.): The Carbohydrates, New York, Academic Press, Inc., 1957.

NON-NITROGENOUS, NON-ACIDIC CARBOHYDRATES

Bailey, R. W.: Oligosaccharides, Oxford, Pergamon Press Ltd., 1965.
Bell, D. J.: Natural monosaccharides and oligosaccharides: their structures and occurrence, Chapter 7 in Florkin, M., and Mason, H. S. (eds.): Comparative Biochemistry, New York, Academic Press, Inc., 1962, Vol. 3.
Stacey, M., and Barker, S. A.: Carbohydrates of Living Tissues, London, D. Van Nostrand Company Ltd., 1962.
Staněk, J., Černý, M., Kocourek, J., and Pacák, J.: The Monosaccharides, New York, Academic Press, Inc., 1963.
Staněk, J., Černý, M., and Pacák, J.: The Oligosaccharides, New York, Academic Press, Inc., 1965.
Whistler, R. L., and Smart, C. L.: Polysaccharide Chemistry, New York, Academic Press, Inc., 1953.

NITROGENOUS AND ACIDIC CARBOHYDRATES

Brimacombe, J. S., and Webber, J. M.: Mucopolysaccharides, Amsterdam, Elsevier Publishing Company, 1964.
Clark, F., and Grant, J. K. (eds.): The Biochemistry of Mucopolysaccharides of Connective Tissue (Biochemical Society Symposium No. 20), Cambridge, Cambridge University Press, 1961.
Gottschalk, A.: The Chemistry and Biology of Sialic Acids and Related Substances, Cambridge, Cambridge University Press, 1960.
Jeanloz, R. W.: Recent developments in the biochemistry of amino sugars, Advances Enzymol. *25*:433, 1963.
Kent, P. W., and Whitehouse, M. W.: Biochemistry of the Aminosugars, London, Butterworths Scientific Publications, 1955.
Stacey, M., and Barker, S. A.: Carbohydrates of Living Tissues, London, D. Van Nostrand Company Ltd., 1962.

METHODS

Bouveng, H. O., and Lindberg, B.: Methods in structural polysaccharide chemistry, Adv. Carb. Chem. *15:* 53, 1960.
Colowick, S. P., and Kaplan, N. O. (eds.): Methods in Enzymology, Vol. 3, Preparation and Assay of Substrates, Section 1, Carbohydrates, and supplement Vol. 6, pp. 453–501, Preparation and Assay of Substrates, Section1, Carbohydrates, New York, Academic Press, Inc., 1957 and 1963.
Dische, Z.: New color reactions for determination of sugars in polysaccharides, Methods of Biochem. Analysis 2:313, 1955.
Smith, I. (ed.): Chromatographic and Electrophoretic Techniques, Vol. 1, Chapter 13, New York, Interscience Publishers, Inc., 1960.
Stahl, E. (ed.): Thin-Layer Chromatography, p. 461, New York, Academic Press, 1965.
Whistler, R. L., and Wolfrom, M. L. (eds.): Methods in Carbohydrate Chemistry, Vol. 1, Analysis and Preparation of Sugars, New York, Academic Press, 1962.

CHAPTER 3

CHEMISTRY OF LIPIDS

INTRODUCTION

Definition and Biological Significance

Bloor has defined lipids as "a group of naturally occurring substances consisting of the higher fatty acids, their naturally occurring compounds, and substances found naturally in chemical association with them." Probably the most important role of lipids, from the quantitative viewpoint, is that of fuel. In some respects lipid is even superior to carbohydrate as a raw material for combustion, since it yields more heat per gram when burned, and furthermore can be stored by the body in almost unlimited amount, in contrast to carbohydrate. Some deposits of lipid may exert an insulating effect in the body, while others may provide padding to protect the internal organs. The nervous system is particularly rich in lipids, especially certain types which do not occur normally in such high concentrations elsewhere in the organism, but unfortunately we know little about the functions of these particular substances in the nervous system or other tissues. Some compounds derived from the lipids are important building blocks of biologically active materials; e.g., acetic acid (a normal breakdown product of the fatty acids, as will be seen later) can be used by the body to synthesize the rather complex compound, cholesterol, which in turn can give rise to certain hormones. One of the important functions of dietary lipid is that of supplying so-called "essential fatty acids," compounds which cannot be synthesized by the animal organism. Lipoproteins, compounds of lipids with proteins, may be important constituents of many natural membranes, such as cell walls, and are involved in a number of other phenomena which will be discussed in the following pages.

Forms Occurring in Nature

Most of the lipid material occurring in nature differs from the carbohydrates and the proteins in being insoluble in water and soluble in certain organic solvents (ether, benzene, chloroform, etc.). The fat depots of animals contain mainly neutral fat, by which is meant

TABLE 3-1. CLASSIFICATION OF THE LIPIDS

I. Simple lipids
  A. Fats
  B. Waxes
  C. Glyceryl ether diesters
II. Compound lipids
  A. Phospholipids (phosphatides)
    1. Lecithins
    2. Cephalins
      a. Ethanolamine type
      b. Serine type
    3. Phosphoinositides
    4. Plasmalogens
    5. Phosphatidic acids
    6. Glyceryl ether phosphatides
    7. Sphingomyelins
  B. Glycolipids
    1. Cerebrosides (including sulfolipids)
    2. Globosides
    3. Hematosides
    4. Gangliosides
    5. Glyceroglycolipids
  C. Lipoproteins
III. Derived lipids
  A. Fatty acids
  B. Alcohols
    1. Acyclic
    2. Carotenoid alcohols
    3. Sterols (v. infra: IV, C)
    4. D vitamins
    5. Inositol
  C. Hydrocarbons
    1. Aliphatic, saturated
    2. Carotenoid
    3. Squalene
IV. Substances associated with lipids in nature
  A. Tocopherols
  B. K vitamins
  C. Steroids

esters of glycerol with three fatty acid molecules. In contrast, most cells other than adipose tissue contain much less fat; their lipids consist largely of phospholipids and cholesterol. The brain is particularly rich in cholesterol (largely in the free state), phospholipids, and glycolipids. The lipoproteins have not been thoroughly investigated as a group, but a possible clue to their future importance is given by current researches which have attempted to relate the occurrence of certain lipoproteins in the plasma to atherosclerosis.

CLASSIFICATION

The classification of lipids which we shall follow, a modification of that given by Bloor, is shown in Table 3-1. Simple lipids contain only fatty acids and some type of alcoholic compound. In the fats, the alcohol is glycerol; in the waxes, it is some compound of higher molecular weight, such as cholesterol. Compound lipids contain some chemical group in addition to an alcohol and fatty acids. The two subdivisions currently in use are phospholipids and glycolipids, characterized by their content of phosphoric acid and carbohydrate, respectively. Although the lipoproteins are really members of a class known as conjugated proteins, their chief biochemical interest at present resides in the lipid moiety which is attached to the protein, hence they will be discussed in this chapter.

Further subdivisions of the classes of lipids will be discussed in detail in later sections.

FATS, WAXES, AND THEIR COMPONENTS

Glycerides

The storage lipid of animals and a high percentage of the lipid material in their diet consist of triglycerides or neutral fats. Such compounds consist of three molecules of fatty acid esterified to glycerol. Most of the glycerides found in nature are mixed, that is, R_1, R_2, and R_3 are all different, or only two of the three are the same. The distribution of fatty acids in glycerides is not completely random. Many fats follow the so-called "even distribution" pattern. According to this, an acid will not occur twice in a triglyceride molecule until it occurs once in every other molecule, and will not occur three times until it occurs twice in every other glyceride molecule. Glycerides are named from their constituent fatty acids, beginning at one end of the glycerol molecule, substituting the letter "o" for the acid suffix "-ic," except for the third fatty acid group, which bears the ending "-in." Duplicate or triplicate occurrences of a given fatty acid are also noted. Examples are oleopalmitostearin, oleodipalmitin, and tristearin. The two initial fatty acid moieties may also be named with their "acyl" endings: oleyl-palmityl-stearin.

The fats are characterized by their insolubility in water and their solubility in such solvents as benzene, chloroform, ether, and hot alcohol. Their melting points vary with their constituent fatty acids, shorter-chain or more unsaturated fatty acids tending to impart lower melting points. These facts are of some importance, since fats having melting points much above human body temperature (37° C.) may be poorly digested. Fats which are liquid at room temperature are often called "oils," a term which may cause confusion with certain other natural products.

Hydrolysis of the glycerides proceeds by the addition of the elements of water across the ester linkages, producing glycerol and three fatty acid molecules. In the intestine this process is catalyzed by enzymes, while in the test tube it can be catalyzed by acid or base. The alkaline hydrolysis of fats is a reaction of industrial importance, and is called "saponification" (literally, "soap-making"). The metallic salts of the fatty acids which result from this process are the soaps, those of the alkali metals being soluble soaps, while those of the alkaline earths and heavy metals are insoluble.

$$\begin{array}{l} CH_2{-}O{-}\overset{O}{\overset{\|}{C}}{-}R_1 \\ | \\ CH{-}O{-}\overset{O}{\overset{\|}{C}}{-}R_2 \\ | \\ CH_2{-}O{-}\overset{O}{\overset{\|}{C}}{-}R_3 \end{array} \xrightarrow{3KOH} \left\{ \begin{array}{l} R_1{-}\overset{O}{\overset{\|}{C}}{-}OK \\ R_2{-}\overset{O}{\overset{\|}{C}}{-}OK \\ R_3{-}\overset{O}{\overset{\|}{C}}{-}OK \end{array} \right. + \begin{array}{l} CH_2OH \\ | \\ CHOH \\ | \\ CH_2OH \end{array}$$

Saponification of a triglyceride

Given the appropriate conditions of moisture, light, warmth, oxygen, and possibly catalytic substances, fats containing unsaturated fatty acids undergo a reaction known as autoxidation. This is probably the major factor in the complex of changes in fats called "rancidification." A rancid fat not only has a disagreeable odor and taste, but in addition contains groups of the peroxide type which are quite destructive to the fat-soluble vitamins. The vitamin E group (tocopherols) may act as natural antioxidants and protect the other fat-soluble vitamins from oxidation in the food, in the intestine, or in the tissues (p. 168). In addition to the oxidative aspects of rancidity, some hydrolysis of fatty acid may occur, and some new acid groups may be formed by the oxidative scission of the unsaturated fatty acids at the double bonds.

Glycerol, the alcoholic component of the fats, is closely allied chemically and in biological origin to the carbohydrates, as has been pointed out previously. However, in terms of function and occurrence, it is appropriate to consider glycerol along with the lipids.

Unesterified glycerol is soluble in water and alcohol, insoluble in the "lipid solvents," but these properties are completely masked when the three hydroxyl groups are attached to fatty acid residues. Stepwise hydrolysis of triglycerides yields diglycerides and monoglycerides, compounds which were assumed to occur only as intermediates in the intestinal digestion of fats until recently, when monopalmitin was found in pancreatic tissue. Molecules such as the monoglycerides, having a "lipid-soluble" group at one end and a water-soluble group at the other, act as detergents and emulsifying agents. This may play a useful role in the digestion of fat. Natural compounds of this type have served as models for many of the present synthetic detergents.

The fatty acids found in nature almost always have straight chains and an even number of carbon atoms. (Odd-numbered and branched-chain fatty acids occur in human sebum and depot fat.) The lower fatty acids are soluble in water, but this property decreases with increasing chain length from caproic acid on, so that, as a generalization, we may say that most of the natural fatty acids are insoluble in water. Hot alcohol and the usual fat solvents dissolve the higher fatty acids. The alkali metal salts (sodium and potassium soaps) are soluble in water but not in the fat solvents. Shorter chain length and increasing unsaturation result in fatty acids of lower melting point. Palmitic, stearic, and oleic acids make

1. Saturated

Butyric $CH_3(CH_2)_2COOH$
n-butanoic

Caproic $CH_3(CH_2)_4COOH$
hexanoic

Caprylic $CH_3(CH_2)_6COOH$
octanoic

Capric $CH_3(CH_2)_8COOH$
decanoic

Lauric $CH_3(CH_2)_{10}COOH$
dodecanoic

Myristic $CH_3(CH_2)_{12}COOH$
tetradecanoic

Palmitic $CH_3(CH_2)_{14}COOH$
hexadecanoic

Stearic $CH_3(CH_2)_{16}COOH$
octadecanoic

Lignoceric $CH_3(CH_2)_{22}COOH$
tetracosanoic

2. Unsaturated

Palmitoleic $CH_3(CH_2)_5CH{=}CH(CH_2)_7COOH$
9-hexadecenoic

Oleic $CH_3(CH_2)_7CH{=}CH(CH_2)_7COOH$
9-octadecenoic

Nervonic $CH_3(CH_2)_7CH{=}CH(CH_2)_{13}COOH$
15-tetracosenoic

Linoleic $CH_3(CH_2)_4CH{=}CHCH_2CH{=}CH(CH_2)_7COOH$
9,12-octadecadienoic

Linolenic $CH_3CH_2CH{=}CHCH_2CH{=}CHCH_2CH{=}CH(CH_2)_7COOH$
9,12,15-octadecatrienoic

Arachidonic $CH_3(CH_2)_4CH{=}(CHCH_2CH{=})_3CH(CH_2)_3COOH$
5,8,11,14-eicosatetraenoic

3. Cyclic

$HC{=}CH$
$H_2C \quad CH{-}(CH_2)_{12}COOH$
CH_2

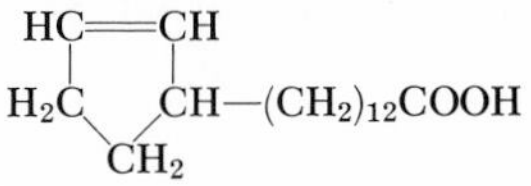

Chaulmoogric
13-[2-cyclopentenyl] tridecanoic

Figure 3-1. Typical fatty acids.

up the bulk of animal depot fat. Human depot fat contains on the average 25 per cent palmitic acid, 6 per cent stearic acid, 7 per cent palmitoleic acid, 50 per cent oleic acid, 8 per cent polyunsaturated 18-carbon fatty acids (almost entirely linoleic and linolenic acids), and 2 per cent higher polyunsaturated fatty acids. The composition of the depot fat is influenced considerably by the composition of the ingested fat. Milk fat contains a relatively higher percentage of the acids of lower molecular weight. (Human milk fat differs from that of the cow in that only small amounts of the lower saturated acids are present, while oleic and linoleic acids occur in higher proportions.) The glycerides of the liver frequently differ from those of the depots in their greater degree of unsaturation.

Chaulmoogric acid, a rather unusual fatty acid of plant origin, is mentioned here because it is one of a group of cyclic fatty acids which are used in the treatment of leprosy. Linoleic, linolenic, and arachidonic acids (polyunsaturated) are sometimes listed as "essential" fatty acids, since there is considerable evidence that they cannot be synthesized by the animal and must therefore be provided in the diet. Cerebrosides of the nervous system contain α-hydroxy fatty acids (p. 40), which also are found in some other tissues in much smaller amounts. The "prostaglandins," compounds present in seminal plasma and certain tissues, are C_{20} fatty acids containing one or more unsaturated linkages, several hydroxyl groups, sometimes a keto group, and a cyclopentane ring at the middle of the chain. These compounds have potent effects on smooth muscle, blood pressure, and fatty acid mobilization. They are discussed further in connection with the metabolism of the polyunsaturated fatty acids, from which they are derived in the body (p. 464).

Waxes

The waxes consist of fatty acids esterified to alcohols other than glycerol. One of the most important of these alcohols is cholesterol, a member of the steroid series. The formula for cholesteryl palmitate, a common wax found in blood plasma, is:

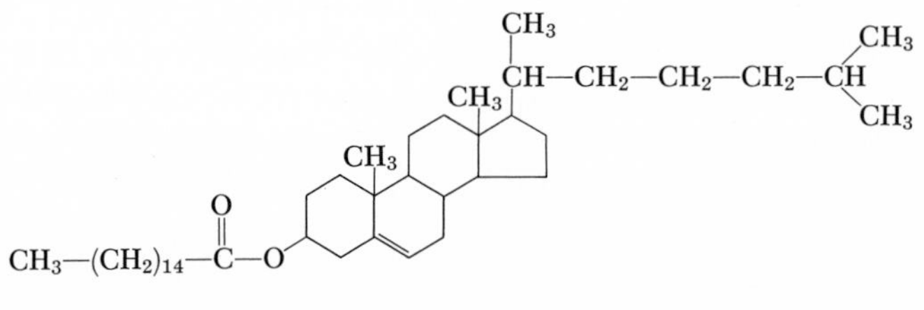

$$CH_3-(CH_2)_{14}-\overset{\overset{O}{\|}}{C}-O-\text{[steroid nucleus with two } CH_3 \text{ groups]}-\underset{\underset{CH_3}{|}}{CH}-CH_2-CH_2-CH_2-CH(CH_3)_2$$

Cholesterol esters occur only in small amounts in animal tissues under normal conditions, except in the adrenal glands and liver. Abnormally high concentrations of cholesterol and its esters are found in the liver, spleen, and other tissues in the condition known as Schüller-Christian disease. Some of the waxes of the skin contain hydroxylated fatty acids esterified with aliphatic alcohols (such as would result from the reduction of the higher fatty acids, e.g., cetyl alcohol from palmitic acid).

Batyl alcohol (stearyl alcohol combined with glycerol at the α position in an ether linkage which forms a stable, non-hydrolyzable union) and other glyceryl ethers have been isolated from saponified lipids of bone marrow, spleen, milk, and arteriosclerotic arteries. Many of these compounds occur naturally in the form of fatty acid diesters. Unsaturated glyceryl ethers of the "plasmalogen" type (p. 39) also have been found in animal tissues as diesters.

PHOSPHOLIPIDS (PHOSPHATIDES)

Lecithins

A typical lecithin consists of glycerol, to which are esterified two fatty acids (frequently at least one is unsaturated) and phosphoric acid, which in turn is attached to the alcohol group of the organic base, choline. There is evidence that previous reports of lecithins containing the phosphorylcholine group on the central hydroxyl of glycerol may have been the result of rearrangement during isolation and analysis. Owing to the number of different fatty acids, many lecithins are obviously possible. Having a diversified complement of fatty acids, the naturally occurring lecithins thus may vary from completely unsaturated to fully saturated types. Although earlier investigations using purely chemical techniques led to contrary conclusions, recent enzymatic procedures indicate that lecithins contain predominantly saturated fatty acids on the α and unsaturated fatty acids on the β position of the glycerol. A similar distribution probably obtains in the case of the triglycerides.

It should be noted that the lecithins and other glycerophosphatides contain an asymmetric carbon atom, centrally located on the glycerol. These compounds are chemically (and biologically) related to L-α-glycerol-phosphate (p. 481), consequently their structural formulas are written with the β-hydroxyl and its substituents extending to the left, when the phosphate ester group is written at the bottom of the formula.

The lecithins are soluble in alcohol and the usual fat solvents, with the exception of acetone. Although not truly soluble in water, they have some affinity for that substance and can be dispersed in it in a colloidal state. Owing probably to their high degree of unsaturation, lecithins decompose rapidly on storage in air (some completely saturated lecithins, however, have been found in various tissues).

Cephalins (Kephalins)

The cephalins differ from the lecithins in composition with respect to the base attached to the phosphoric acid. Two types of cephalins are known. In one the base is ethanolamine (phosphatidyl-ethanolamine); in the other the amino acid, serine (phosphatidyl-serine, seryl-phosphatide). Like the lecithins, many cephalins contain one or two unsaturated fatty acids. Phospholipids occur in liver which are intermediate in structure between the lecithins and cephalins, containing mono- or dimethylated ethanolamine.

Like the lecithins, the cephalins are soluble in most of the fat solvents with the exception of acetone, but differ from the former group by their lower solubility in alcohol. They are unstable in air.

Certain enzymes in snake venoms catalyze the hydrolysis of the unsaturated fatty acid residues from lecithins and cephalins, producing lysolecithins and lysocephalins, compounds with a marked hemolytic action. Certain cephalins may have an accelerating effect on blood coagulation (p. 800).

Phosphoinositides

These compounds have been obtained from the crude cephalin fractions of tissues, and some systems of classification include them among the cephalins, mainly on the basis of solubility. Chemically, however, they are quite distinct from the compounds which we have discussed as cephalins. They are characterized as a group by containing inositol, and are acidic substances. Inositides isolated by several laboratories from soybean, wheat germ, liver, and heart muscle are thought to have structures similar to the lecithins and cephalins, with inositol replacing the base (Fig. 3-2). Some brain diphosphoinositides have this composition, whereas others contain one to three additional phosphate groups esterified on the inositol.

Complex phosphoinositides containing carbohydrates occur in brain, plants, and bacteria; possibly they form a new class of compounds, "phosphoglycolipids."

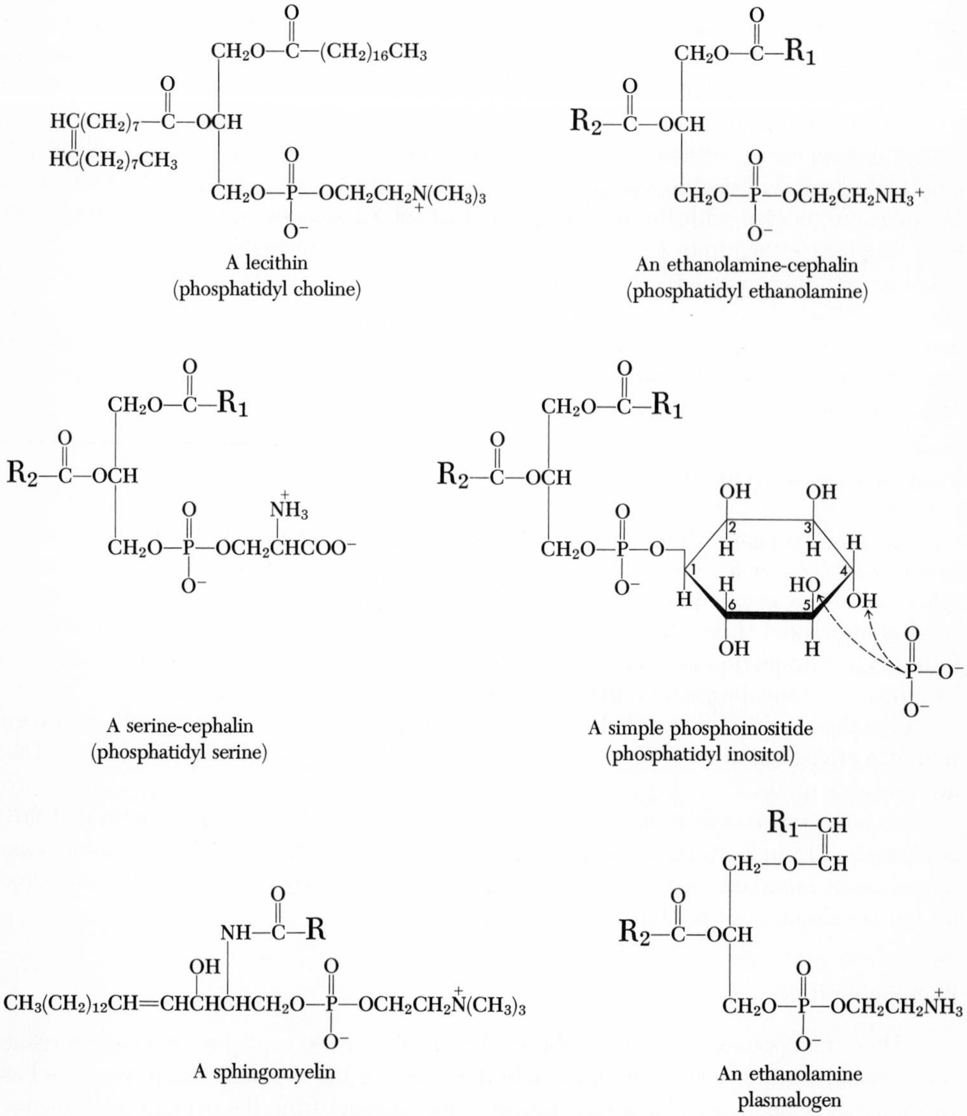

A lecithin
(phosphatidyl choline)

An ethanolamine-cephalin
(phosphatidyl ethanolamine)

A serine-cephalin
(phosphatidyl serine)

A simple phosphoinositide
(phosphatidyl inositol)

A sphingomyelin

An ethanolamine
plasmalogen

Figure 3-2. Phospholipids.

Plasmalogens

These compounds are similar to the lecithin-cephalin group, except that the fatty acid residue in the α or β position is replaced by a fatty aldehyde in an enol-ether linkage to glycerol. Plasmalogens of most tissues are characterized by their content of highly unsaturated fatty acids. As to bases, serine, ethanolamine, and choline are found.

Phosphatides of Saturated Glyceryl Ethers

Animal tissues contain compounds similar to the ethanolamine and choline plasmalogens, but with a saturated ether linkage in the α position of the glycerol.

Phosphatidic Acids and Related Compounds

The phosphatidic acids consist of glycerol, two fatty acid molecules, and phosphoric acid. No base is attached to the phosphoric acid group, which is present in the form of a salt. Although originally discovered in plants, the phosphatidic acids are intermediates in the synthesis of phospholipids and triglycerides in animal tissues (p. 481). (Phosphatidic acids occur in the free state in liver; a few contain the plasmalogen structure.) A related compound called "cardiolipin" has been isolated from the heart. This lipid (used in the serological diagnosis of syphilis) contains two phosphoric acids, three glycerols, and four fatty acid residues.

Sphingomyelins

This class of phospholipid is closely related chemically to the glycolipids, which will be discussed below. The sphingomyelins contain, in addition to phosphorylcholine, a complex base called "sphingosine." A fatty acid is attached to the amino group of the sphingosine in an amide linkage. (N-acyl derivatives of sphingosine are called ceramides, and have been found in the free state in the spleen, the liver, and red cells.) Some sphingomyelins contain the saturated base, dihydrosphingosine. Plant sphingolipids contain the bases "phytosphingosine" and "8:9-dehydrophytosphingosine." These compounds differ from ordinary sphingosine in possessing a second secondary alcoholic hydroxyl group adjacent to the first.

Sphingomyelins are much less soluble in ether than are lecithins and cephalins, and precipitate from the cold solution. They can be dissolved in hot alcohol, from which they also separate on cooling. Like the other phospholipids, they are insoluble in acetone, soluble in benzene and chloroform. They form opalescent suspensions in water. Unlike cephalins and lecithins, sphingomyelins are quite stable in air, due probably to the small amount of monounsaturated and virtual absence of polyunsaturated fatty acids in the latter. Greatly increased concentrations of sphingomyelins (and possibly lecithins) occur in the liver, spleen, and other tissues in a condition known as Niemann-Pick disease.

Phosphatido-peptides

Peptide derivatives of phospholipids have been isolated from a variety of tissues in many species. One such compound contains inositol, phosphate, esterified fatty acids, sphingosine, and amino acids; it appears to be quite active metabolically.

GLYCOLIPIDS

It has been customary in the past to divide the sphingoglycolipids (glycolipids containing sphingosine) into two chemical groups, the cerebrosides and the gangliosides. More recent investigations have revealed a close chemical relationship between these two types of compounds, and in addition have brought to light several families of glycolipids which appear to bridge the gap between the relatively simple cerebrosides and the structurally complex gangliosides. The following discussion utilizes the classification of sphingoglycolipids suggested by Yamakawa.

Figure 3–3 indicates the basic structure found in all "sphingolipids" (phospho- and glycolipids containing sphingosine). The ceramide unit consists of an amino alcohol (sphingosine, icosisphingosine, or their dihydro derivatives) bearing a fatty acid in amide linkage to the amino group. In the sphingomyelins (phospholipids) discussed previously, the terminal hydroxyl of the ceramide is esterified with phosphorylcholine. The ceramide unit of the sphingoglycolipids, on the other hand, is linked glycosidically through the terminal hydroxyl group to one or more sugars, aminosugars, sialic acids, and various combinations thereof.

Cerebrosides

Cerebrosides may be defined as sphingoglycolipids containing only simple sugars, "(oligo-)glycosyl-ceramides." Their composition, disregarding sequence, is indicated by:

$$\text{CERAMIDE-(GLUCOSE)}_m\text{-(GALACTOSE)}_n$$

The first cerebrosides to be discovered, and the only compounds so classified until recently, contain single molecules of hexose (usually galactose) in the carbohydrate moiety. Further classification of this type of cerebroside is based upon the nature of the fatty acid component: kerasin(e) or cerasine contains lignoceric acid; phrenosin(e) or cerebron, cerebronic (α-hydroxylignoceric) acid; nervon, nervonic acid; and hydroxynervon, α-hydroxynervonic acid. Other fatty acids, such as palmitic and stearic, have been found in some cerebrosides. The base in most cerebrosides is sphingosine, although dihydrosphingosine occurs also.

The spleen of patients with Gaucher's disease may accumulate cerebrosides containing galactose, glucose (also reported in normal spleen), or both hexoses in the form of the disaccharide, lactose. This last type of compound, which has the structure ceramide-glucose-galactose, has been called "cytolipin H," and is an immunologically active lipid hapten found in certain tumors, human red cell stroma, and other tissues. Equine red cells contain a ceramide-oligohexoside. A compound having the structure ceramide-(galactose)$_2$ is found in small amounts in the brain in Tay-Sachs disease. A series of related

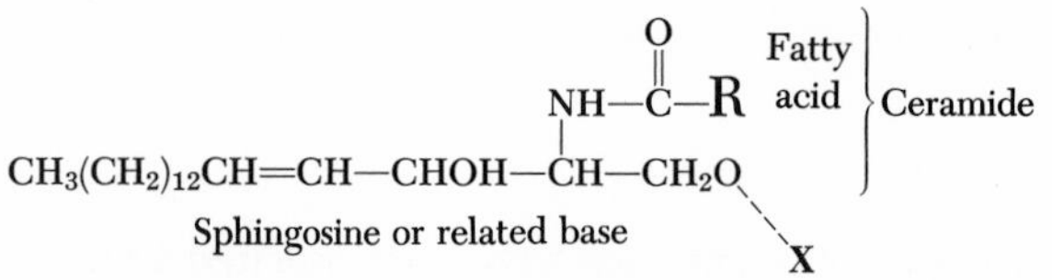

$$\underbrace{CH_3(CH_2)_{12}CH{=}CH{-}CHOH{-}\overset{\displaystyle NH{-}\overset{\displaystyle O}{\overset{\|}{C}}{-}R\ \text{(Fatty acid)}}{\overset{|}{C}H}{-}CH_2O}_{\text{Sphingosine or related base}}{\diagdown}X \quad \text{(Ceramide)}$$

Figure 3-3. General structure of sphingolipids. **X**, carbohydrate moiety in sphingoglycolipids, phosphorylcholine in sphingophospholipids.

cerebrosides isolated from human blood serum, spleen, and liver have the structures: ceramide-glucose, ceramide-glucose-galactose, and ceramide-glucose-$(galactose)_2$.

Sulfolipids or sulfatides have been reported in various tissues. The sulfolipids of brain are probably sulfate esters of kerasin and phrenosin; the sulfate is esterified to the C-3 hydroxyl of the galactose moiety.

Cerebrosides are present in many tissues, but normally in low concentration, except for nervous tissue. Large amounts are found in the white matter of brain and in the myelin sheath of nerves. Abnormally high concentrations occur in liver, spleen, and other tissues in Gaucher's disease.

Globosides

Globosides are sphingoglycolipids containing acetylated aminosugars in addition to simple hexoses. Disregarding sequence, they have the composition:

$$\text{CERAMIDE-(GLUCOSE)}_m\text{-(GALACTOSE)}_n\text{-(N-ACETYLHEXOSAMINE)}_p$$

The aminosugar is usually, but not invariably, galactosamine.

Human serum, spleen, liver, and erythrocytes contain globosides of the composition: ceramide-(glucose)-$(galactose)_2$-(N-acetylgalactosamine). More complex globosides, isolated from human erythrocytes, contain one molecule of glucose, two of N-acetylgalactosamine, and five or six of galactose. The compounds from A(+) and B(+) blood types differ chemically; each specifically inhibits agglutination of red cells of its type by the corresponding antibody. In some animal species the erythrocyte globosides contain both glucosamine and galactosamine.

A globoside of the composition: ceramide-glucose-galactose-N-acetylgalactosamine accumulates in relatively large amounts in the brain in Tay-Sachs disease.

Hematosides

This class of sphingoglycolipids has the general composition:

$$\text{CERAMIDE-(GLUCOSE)}_m\text{-(GALACTOSE)}_n\text{-(SIALIC)}_q$$

Red cell stroma contains hematosides, the sialic acid component of which is N-acetylneuraminic acid in some species, N-glycolyl- in others. Several molecules of hexose are present, along with one to four molecules of sialic acid.

Human brain and spleen also contain compounds of the hematoside type, consisting of a ceramide linked to glucose, one or two molecules of galactose, and one or two molecules of sialic acid.

Gangliosides

The true gangliosides contain the chemical moieties which are common to both globosides and hematosides:

$$\text{CERAMIDE-(GLUCOSE)}_m\text{-(GALACTOSE)}_n\text{-(N-ACETYLGALACTOSAMINE)}_p\text{-(SIALIC)}_q$$

The ceramide base may be sphingosine, dihydrosphingosine, or the C_{20} homolog of sphingosine ("icosisphingosine" or "gangliosine"), in amide linkage with fatty acids of the C_{18}, C_{22}, and C_{24} series.

Glucosamine replaces galactosamine in bovine erythrocyte stroma ganglioside. Human red cell gangliosides appear to contain both glucosamine and galactosamine.

The major gangliosides of brain consist of a ceramide linked to one molecule of glucose, two of galactose, one of N-acetylgalactosamine, and one, two, or three of sialic acid. A monosialo ganglioside containing one molecule of galactose is normally one of a number of minor gangliosides in brain; in Tay-Sachs disease, it occupies a major position. Brain also contains gangliosides with four to six hexose molecules; trisialo compounds of this type are found combined with amino acids in "glycolipopeptides."

A ganglioside with an apparent minimum particle weight of 250,000 has been isolated from brain. Strandin, a crude glycolipid fraction of brain, contains a ganglioside-peptide of particle weight 180,000. It has been suggested that these apparently high particle weights are the result of micelle formation, not true polymerization.

Glyceroglycolipids

Two galactose-containing glycerides have been isolated from brain. One is a galactosyl diglyceride; in the other, one of the fatty acyl residues is replaced by an alkyl ether.

STEROIDS, STEROLS, AND BILE ACIDS

Steroids As a Group

There exists in nature a large group of compounds having in common a structure based on the cyclopentano-perhydrophenanthrene nucleus:

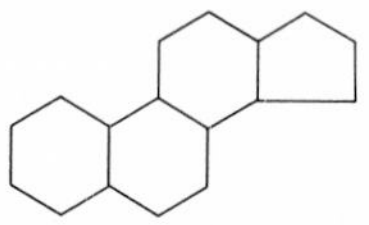

These compounds, the steroids, have greatly diversified physiological properties, despite the basic similarity in chemical structure. The group includes precursors of certain vitamins, hormones of several types, cholesterol (and similar compounds in the plant world), bile acids, certain natural drugs and poisons, and some physiologically inert compounds. Certain of the steroids are found associated with the lipids in nature, either by reason of mutual solubility, or owing to some actual metabolic relationship.

The steroid structure contains many centers of actual or potential asymmetry. The resulting stereoisomerism is of considerable importance, especially in the case of the steroid hormones, since it is closely related to the physiological actions of these compounds. This subject is discussed more fully elsewhere (p. 681).

Sterols

The sterols are the steroid alcohols, one of which, cholesterol, has already been mentioned in connection with the waxes. Cholesterol can be synthesized by the animal body from small fragments, such as acetic acid. Large amounts of cholesterol occur in the free state in the central nervous system, but its function there is unknown at the present time.

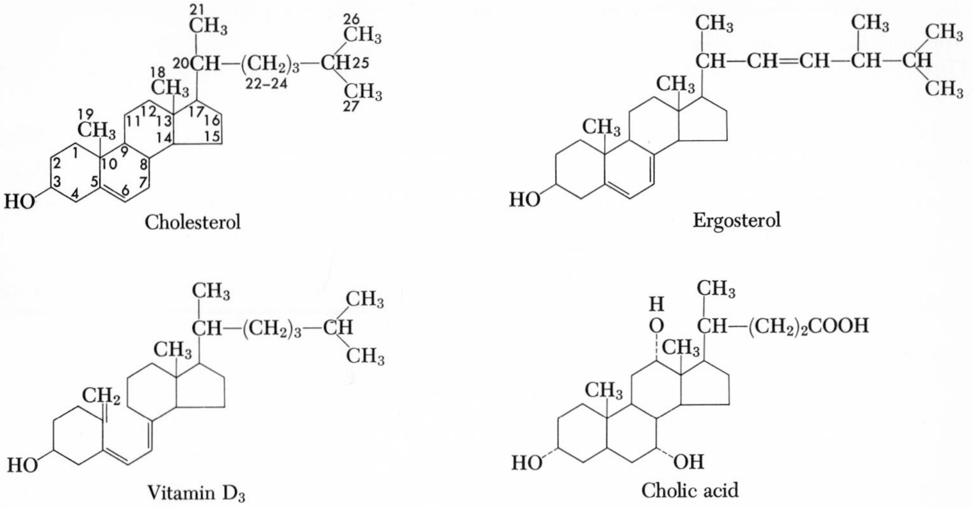

Cholesterol

Ergosterol

Vitamin D_3

Cholic acid

Figure 3-4. Sterols and related compounds.

In certain endocrine glands (e.g., adrenal cortex), cholesterol is the probable parent compound from which steroid hormones are synthesized (p. 704). The participation of cholesterol in gallstone formation has been recognized for many years (p. 268). Cholesterol is an unsaturated alcohol, and in tissues outside of the nervous system (including blood plasma) exists partly in the form of esters with fatty acids. The non-hydroxylic part of the molecule is strictly hydrocarbon in nature, accounting for the solubility characteristics of cholesterol, which are like those of the true lipids.

In the animal body, cholesterol can be converted to 7-dehydrocholesterol. When the latter compound, in the skin, is subjected to ultraviolet radiation (as in sunlight), it is converted to one of the D vitamins, in this case D_3. Ergosterol, a plant sterol differing somewhat in structure from cholesterol, after irradiation acts as a D vitamin in animals. These vitamins and their sterol precursors are discussed more fully elsewhere (p. 159).

Much attention is being directed to cholesterol at the present time, not only because of its close relationship to the other steroids in the body, but also because cholesterol is involved in certain degenerative changes in the arterial wall, known as atherosclerosis, or hardening of the arteries.

Bile Acids

In addition to the steroid nucleus and one or more alcoholic hydroxyl groups, bile acids contain a carboxyl group on the side chain. As found in bile, these compounds are conjugated through their carboxyl groups to an amino acid, glycine, or to a compound called "taurine," which is derived from another amino acid (cysteine). (The formulas of these compounds are discussed later on page 267.) The relationship of bile acids to the lipids is two-fold: on the one hand they are synthesized biologically from cholesterol, hence their ultimate origin is in fragments metabolically derived from fatty acids; on the other, they are important factors in the digestion and absorption of lipids in the intestine. Within the pH range prevailing in the intestine, the bile acids (in their conjugated forms, as stated above) are present as salts. Having an ionic group at one end of the molecule, and a predominantly lipid-soluble nucleus, they are very effective emulsifying agents. This characteristic aids in the digestion of lipids and the subsequent absorption of the less water-soluble products (p. 268).

One of the bile acids, deoxycholic acid, has the unusual property of forming soluble, diffusible complexes with fatty acids. At one time this property was considered important in the absorption of fatty acids from the intestine. However, these complexes (called "choleic acids") are formed only by deoxycholic acid, whereas cholic acid predominates in human bile. Furthermore, *conjugated* deoxycholic acid does not appear to form the choleic acid complexes. At the present time it would appear that the fat-solubilizing action of bile acids, in their natural state, is largely due to their emulsifying abilities.

OTHER SUBSTANCES ASSOCIATED WITH LIPIDS IN NATURE

Carotenoids and Vitamins A (p. 143)

The carotenoid pigments, as can be deduced from the hydrocarbon type of structure, are lipid-soluble, hence they are found associated with lipids in nature. In fact, the yellowish color ascribed to many fats is not due to the fats themselves, but to dissolved carotenoid pigments.

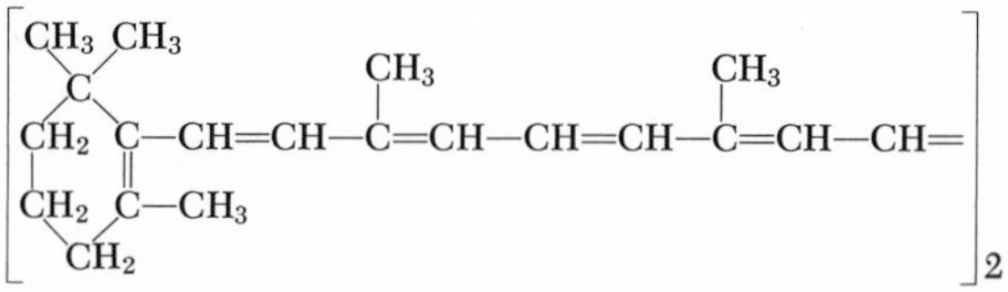

$$\left[\begin{array}{l}
CH_3\ CH_3 \\
\quad\ \ C \qquad\qquad\qquad\quad CH_3 \qquad\qquad\qquad\quad CH_3 \\
CH_2\ \ C{-}CH{=}CH{-}\overset{|}{C}{=}CH{-}CH{=}CH{-}\overset{|}{C}{=}CH{-}CH{=} \\
|\qquad\ \| \\
CH_2\ \ C{-}CH_3 \\
\quad CH_2
\end{array}\right]_2 \quad \beta\text{-Carotene}$$

While the carotenoids themselves are products of the plant world, some of them are important in animal nutrition as precursors of the A group of vitamins, since the animal organism is able to effect the conversion. Carotenoids and A vitamins are classified as lipids in some systems. Vitamin A alcohol occurs in the diet as an ester with fatty acids, and in the body in similar combinations. Combinations of A vitamins with proteins are consequently regarded as lipoproteins. Regardless of fixed classifications, the complexes of proteins with vitamin A or its derivatives are important in the biochemistry of vision, and for convenience these substances will be mentioned along with the "true" lipoproteins in a later section of this chapter.

Vitamins K and E (pp. 169, 166)

The K group of vitamins has little to do with the lipids, aside from solubility considerations. Conditions which prevent proper absorption of lipids from the intestine tend to have a similar effect on the lipid-soluble vitamins. In the case of the K vitamins, at least, a definite state of deficiency can result.

The E vitamins, or tocopherols, are natural antioxidants found dissolved in many vegetable fats, and have the ability to prevent or delay autoxidation of unsaturated fatty acids. These vitamins have no other known connection with the lipids.

LIPOPROTEINS

State of Lipids in Nature

It is probable that many of the substances described in this chapter do not exist as such in their natural state, and represent what the purists would call artifacts of the laboratory. This is a reflection of the primitive state of intracellular biochemistry (and unfortunately the situation is not confined to the lipids). From the available evidence, it appears that many of the lipids are combined with proteins in the tissues. These combinations are called "lipoproteins." The nature of the linkage between the lipid and protein moieties is not known; it is usually stable toward non-polar solvents, such as ether, but frequently can be disrupted by more highly polar substances, such as alcohol. Despite the evidence for the widespread occurrence of lipoproteins, the technical difficulties in handling these materials have been such that, until the very recent introduction of newer physicochemical methods, few members of this group were characterized as chemical entities.

Examples of Lipoproteins

It is widely assumed that the cell membrane is a lipoprotein structure of some type, and, although there is not much direct evidence available, the general properties of cell membranes are at least consistent with this view. Certain of the internal structures of the cell also contain lipids, apparently in combination with proteins. This is the case with visible entities, such as the nucleus and mitochondria, as well as the submicroscopic particles (microsomes).

The thromboplastic protein isolated from lung tissue (p. 800) has been characterized as a lipoprotein. The lipid portion, as in the case of many lipoproteins, consists of more than one type of lipid. Egg yolk contains two lipoproteins known as lipovitellins α and β, (the lipid fraction consists largely of phospholipids along with some triglycerides and sterols) plus a lipoprotein mostly containing triglycerides. A number of bacteria have been shown to contain firmly bound lipids, although it is not certain in some cases whether the lipids are bound to protein or to polysaccharides. Certain animal viruses appear to contain firmly bound lipids also, but this is not true of the viruses thus far isolated from plant sources. The film which stabilizes the fat droplets in milk appears to be a combination of protein and phospholipid.

Most, if not all, of the lipid in blood serum is carried in the form of lipoprotein complexes (pp. 489, 560). The statement also holds for the lipid-soluble vitamins, the carotenoids, and the steroids. Since the presence of lipid causes the lipoprotein molecule to have a lower density than that of ordinary proteins, it is possible, by proper adjustment of the experimental conditions, to force lipoproteins to travel toward the axis instead of toward the periphery of an ultracentrifuge (p. 84). The rate of flotation of a lipoprotein is related to its density, and expressed in S_f units (p. 561). Two major groups of serum lipoproteins may be identified ultracentrifugally: the low density lipoproteins, with densities below 1.063, and the high density lipoproteins, with densities between 1.063 and 1.20. The low density lipoproteins are commonly subdivided into flotation classes of S_f: 0 to 12, 12 to 20, 20 to 100, 100 to 400, 400 to 40,000. The concentrations of one or more of any of these classes may be altered in clinical abnormalities. Individual plasma lipoproteins are discussed in detail in connection with the transport of lipids (p. 489).

By the use of this "flotation" method, certain cholesterol-containing lipoproteins have been implicated in the development of atherosclerosis in experimental animals.

The pigment of the retinal rods, visual purple, is a compound of a protein, opsin, with the aldehyde of vitamin A (retinene), the complex being called "rhodopsin" (p. 148). Owing to the relationship of carotenoids and vitamin A to the lipids, compounds such as rhodopsin are often classed with the lipoproteins.

The lipoproteins have usually been thought of as conjugated proteins, possessing the general properties (e.g., solubility) of proteins. However, a new series of compounds has been isolated from various tissues, having the solubility characteristics of lipids. Probably these substances, which have been named "proteolipids," should be considered primarily as lipids, not as proteins.

QUALITATIVE AND QUANTITATIVE TESTS FOR LIPIDS

Saponification Number

This constant, which is of special value in the identification and characterization of neutral fats, is defined as the number of milligrams of KOH required to saponify one gram of fat. Since three equivalents of KOH ($3 \times 56 = 168$ gm. or 168,000 mg.) are consumed in the saponification of the three ester linkages of each mole of triglyceride, the saponification number will depend on the number of moles of fat per gram. The number of moles per gram is an inverse function of the molecular weight of the fat, which in turn is determined by the chain length of the fatty acids involved. For triglycerides,

$$\text{Saponification number} = \frac{168{,}000}{\text{Gram molecular weight of the triglyceride}}$$

Fats, such as butter, which contain relatively larger amounts of the fatty acids of lower molecular weight, are characterized by higher saponification numbers than are the depot fats.

Iodine Number

This is defined as the number of grams of iodine taken up by 100 grams of fat. Since halogens react by addition to olefinic linkages, the iodine number is a measure of the degree of unsaturation of a fat. For triglycerides consisting largely of C_{18} fatty acids,

$$\text{Iodine number} \approx 90 \times \text{average number of double bonds per fatty acid residue}$$

Highly unsaturated fats, such as linseed oil, have characteristically high iodine numbers.

Osmic acid also reacts with the unsaturated fatty acids, giving dark products. This reaction is used by histologists for the microscopic detection of fat.

Other "Numbers"

Additional constants are also used by chemists to characterize lipids, such as the "Reichert-Meissl number" (a measure of the soluble, volatile fatty acids), the "acetyl number" (a measure of hydroxy acids), and others, but they are of no particular importance to non-specialists in this field.

Acrolein Test

Glycerol, when heated in the presence of a dehydrating agent, such as sodium bisulfate, is converted to the unsaturated aldehyde, acrolein, a compound having the characteristic odor of burned fat. This reaction is positive for glycerol whether in the free state or combined in a fat or phospholipid.

$$\begin{array}{l} \text{H} \\ \text{HC—OH} \\ \text{HC—OH} \\ \text{HC—OH} \\ \text{H} \end{array} \xrightarrow[-2H_2O]{\text{Heat}} \begin{array}{l} \text{H} \\ \text{C=O} \\ \text{CH} \\ \| \\ \text{CH}_2 \end{array}$$

Acrolein

Choline Tests

As a tertiary amine, choline has the property of forming various quaternary salts and addition compounds, such as with Kraut's reagent (a bismuth potassium iodide). These products are frequently brightly colored and serve as tests for the detection of choline. Similar addition compounds are formed by lecithin, owing to the choline contained in the molecule.

Cholesterol Tests

In the Liebermann-Burchard test, a chloroform solution of cholesterol reacts with acetic anhydride and sulfuric acid to form a succession of colors. The nature of the reaction is not known. It is supposedly specific for sterols unsaturated at C5-C6. The Liebermann-Burchard reaction is also used for the quantitative determination of cholesterol, particularly in blood. More recently, cholesterol has also been determined by the purple color which it forms with ferric salts in concentrated sulfuric acid.

Tests for Bile Acids

In the Hammarsten test, an acetic acid solution of the compound to be tested is warmed with concentrated hydrochloric acid, leading to the development of a violet color. The Pettenkofer reaction consists of heating an acetic acid solution of the bile acid with sulfuric acid and furfural, producing a red-purple color. Although these two tests are positive for cholic acid, they are negative for certain other bile acids. A simple clinical test for the presence of bile acids in urine is based upon the ability of these compounds to lower the surface tension of solutions. Thus, finely powdered sulfur is sprinkled on the surface of the urine sample; the powder floats on the surface of normal urine, but due to the lowered surface tension, it sinks through the surface of urine containing bile acids.

Fractionation of Lipids

Lipids are frequently divided into saponifiable and non-saponifiable fractions. Those substances which, after saponification with alkali, are extractable with ether are called non-saponifiable. Glycerol is not soluble in ether, nor are the sodium or potassium soaps of the fatty acids, hence these substances remain in the saponifiable fraction. Compounds which go into the non-saponifiable fraction are the sterols, carotenoids, and related substances. Of course, acidification of a saponified fat will transform the soaps into free fatty acids, which are ether-soluble, but the term "non-saponifiable" refers only to those substances which are ether-extractable while the saponified mixture is alkaline.

Many schemes of fractionation of lipid mixtures into the several groups of lipids are based upon differences in solubility in various organic solvents. For example, lecithins and cephalins can be separated from other ether-soluble lipids by precipitation with acetone.

Good separations of the subgroups of certain families of lipids (e.g., phospholipids) have been achieved with the aid of "reversed phase" paper chromatography and thin layer chromatography (p. 98).

After the preparation of a presumably pure lipid, the question often arises as to the identity of its constituent fatty acids. The separation and identification of the individual components in a mixture of fatty acids have been approached in a number of ways. Fatty acids of lower molecular weight may be separated from those of higher molecular weight by steam distillation, and individual fatty acids may be separated by fractional distillation of the methyl esters. Saturated long-chain fatty acids may be separated from unsaturated acids by the insolubility of the lead salts of the former in alcohol, and saturated and monounsaturated acids may be separated from polyunsaturated acids by the insolubility of the lithium salts of the former group in acetone, by their lesser solubility in organic solvents at low temperatures, and by their more ready formation of addition complexes with urea. Fatty acids may also be fractionated by the standard methods of column chromatography (p. 96), or by the newer technique of vapor phase or gas chromatography.

BIBLIOGRAPHY

GENERAL

Advances in Lipid Research

Annual Review of Biochemistry

Deuel, H. J., Jr.: The Lipids, Their Chemistry and Biochemistry, Vol. 1, Chemistry, New York, Interscience Publishers, Inc., 1951.

Florkin, M., and Stotz, E. H. (eds.): Comprehensive Biochemistry, Vol. 6, Lipids, Amino Acids and Related Compounds, Amsterdam, Elsevier Publishing Company, 1965.

Hanahan, D. J.: Lipide Chemistry, New York, John Wiley & Sons, Inc., 1960.

Hilditch, T. P., and Williams, P. N.: The Chemical Constitution of Natural Fats, New York, John Wiley & Sons, Inc., 1964.

Markley, K. S. (ed.): Fatty Acids, 3 vols., New York, John Wiley & Sons, Inc., 1960, 1961, 1964.

Progress in the Chemistry of Fats and Other Lipids, 6 vols., London, Pergamon Press, 1952 to 1963.

PHOSPHOLIPIDS

Ansell, G. B. and Hawthorne, J. N.: Phospholipids, Amsterdam, Elsevier Publishing Company, 1964.

Hawthorne, J. N.: The inositol phospholipids, J. Lipid Research *1*:255, 1960.

Klenk, E., and Debuch, H.: Plasmalogens, Progr. Chem. Fats and Other Lipids *6*:1, 1963.

Wittcoff, H.: The Phosphatides, New York, Reinhold Publishing Corporation, 1951.

GLYCOLIPIDS

Carter, H. E., Johnson, P., and Weber, E. J.: Glycolipids, Ann. Rev. Biochem. *34*:109, 1965.

Goldberg, I. H.: The sulfolipids, J. Lipid Research *2*:103, 1961.

Law, J. H.: Glycolipids, Ann. Rev. Biochem. *29*:131, 1960.

Svennerholm, L.: The gangliosides, J. Lipid Research *5*:145, 1964.

BILE ACIDS AND STEROLS

Cook, R. P. (ed.): Cholesterol, New York, Academic Press, Inc., 1958.

Fieser, L. F., and Fieser, M.: Steroids, New York, Reinhold Publishing Corporation, 1959.

Florkin, M., and Stotz, E. H. (eds.): Comprehensive Biochemistry, Vol. 10, Sterols, Bile Acids and Steroids, Amsterdam, Elsevier Publishing Company, 1963.

Heftmann, E., and Mosettig, E.: Biochemistry of Steroids, New York, Reinhold Publishing Corporation, 1960.

Klyne, W.: The Chemistry of Steroids, London, Methuen & Company, 1961.

Kritchevsky, D.: Cholesterol, New York, John Wiley & Sons, Inc., 1958.

Shoppee, C. W.: Chemistry of the Steroids, London, Butterworths Scientific Publications, 1964.

LIPOPROTEINS

Freeman, N. K., Lindgren, F. T., and Nichols, A. V.: The chemistry of serum lipoproteins, Progr. Chem. Fats and Other Lipids *6:*215, 1963.

Lindgren, F. T., and Nichols, A. V.: Structure and function of human serum lipoproteins, Chapter 11 in Putnam, F. W. (ed.): The Plasma Proteins, Vol. 2, New York, Academic Press, Inc., 1960.

Searcy, R. L., and Bergquist, L. M.: Lipoprotein Chemistry in Health and Disease, Springfield, Ill., Charles C Thomas, 1962.

METHODS

De Lalla, O. F., and Gofman, J. W.: Ultracentrifugal analysis of serum lipoproteins, Methods of Biochem. Analysis *1:*459, 1954.

Fontell, K., Holman, R. T., and Lambertsen, G.: Some new methods for separation and analysis of fatty acids and other lipids, J. Lipid Research *1:*391, 1960.

Holman, R. T.: Measurement of polyunsaturated fatty acids, Methods of Biochem. Analysis *4:*99, 1957.

James, A. T.: Qualitative and quantitative determination of the fatty acids by gas-liquid chromatography, Methods of Biochem. Analysis *8:*1, 1960.

Marinetti, G. V.: Chromatographic separation, identification and analysis of phosphatides, J. Lipid Research *3:*1, 1962.

McIlwain, H., and Rodnight, R.: Practical Neurochemistry, Chapters 4 and 5, Boston, Little, Brown & Company, 1962.

McKibbin, J. M.: The determination of inositol, ethanolamine and serine in lipids, Methods of Biochem. Analysis *7:*111, 1959.

Radin, N. S.: Glycolipide determination, Methods of Biochem. Analysis *6:*163, 1958.

Sperry, W. M.: Lipide analysis, Methods of Biochem. Analysis *2:*83, 1955.

CHAPTER 4

CHEMISTRY OF PROTEINS

INTRODUCTION

Definition and General Properties

Proteins may be defined as compounds of high molecular weight, consisting largely (or entirely) of chains of α-amino acids united in peptide linkage. The constituent amino acids can be obtained by hydrolysis of the proteins. While the individual amino acids may be considered analogous to the monosaccharides of carbohydrate chemistry, and the true proteins analogous to the polysaccharides, an important difference must be pointed out. The polysaccharides are polymers of a single sub-unit, or of a few types of sub-units at the most, while the proteins contain, in general, some 20-odd individual amino acids, present in characteristic proportions and linked in a specific sequence in each protein. Hence, other things being equal, it is possible for nature to concoct many more different proteins than polysaccharides, a fact which lends fascination as well as difficulty to the problems confronting the protein chemist.

The molecular weights of the proteins vary from about 13,000 to many millions. Most proteins, owing to their molecular size, are not diffusible through membranes such as cellophane, and like the polysaccharides are actually of colloidal dimensions and exhibit the properties associated with the colloidal state of matter. Some are soluble in pure water; some require the presence of salts or small amounts of acid or base to dissolve. One group is soluble in certain concentrations of alcohol, although (with the exception of the recently discovered proteolipids) proteins are generally insoluble in organic solvents. The structural proteins known as scleroproteins are dissolved only by reagents which cause considerable alterations in their structure.

The average protein is a very sensitive individual. In reprisal for its exposure to heat, extremes of pH, surface action, or various reagents, the native protein undergoes a series of changes known as denaturation, resulting in alterations in a number of its properties.

Heat denaturation, under the proper circumstances, proceeds on to a further stage, coagulation, as can be seen in the familiar example of the fried egg.

As will be shown later (p. 72), proteins possess free ionic or charged groups, so that they migrate in an electrical field. Owing to their charges, proteins combine with ionic reagents, in some cases resulting in insoluble compounds. The reaction of the ionic groups on the protein molecule with both hydrogen and hydroxyl ions indicates that proteins are amphoteric, and the fact that these groups in the protein are weak acids results in the setting up of buffer systems, a matter of considerable biological importance.

Certain color reactions (p. 93) are given by the unhydrolyzed protein. One of these is due to the peptide linkages possessed by all proteins; the others are given by reactive chemical groups situated in the amino acid residues.

While the immunochemical reactions of proteins (such as the antigen-antibody reactions) are undoubtedly physicochemical phenomena, not enough is known about them to warrant a discussion in purely chemical terms. They will be considered briefly in connection with antibody synthesis (pp. 561, 562).

Biological Importance

The biochemical significance of proteins cannot be overemphasized. If carbohydrates and lipids, generally speaking, can be considered the fuels of the metabolic furnace, proteins may be regarded as forming not only the structural framework, but also the gears and levers of the operating machinery. Indeed, at the risk of pushing the analogy to extremes, we may regard the protein hormones (which act as regulators of metabolism) as the policy-forming top management of the enterprise.

Such structures as cell walls and various membranes are mainly protein, although frequently coupled or associated with lipids. Connective tissue is composed of chemically rather inert types of proteins, in some cases combined with carbohydrates. The contractile elements of muscle are proteins. Aside from such obviously structural substances as those mentioned, the catalysts which permit the reactions of intermediary metabolism to proceed at a reasonable rate under mild conditions, the enzymes, are known to be protein in nature. Finally, as already pointed out, certain proteins in the body act as hormones, or regulators of metabolism.

Protoplasm may be regarded as a colloidal system of proteins, together with lipids and carbohydrates. With some exceptions, the supply of carbohydrates and lipids may rise or fall, and the cell may flourish or do poorly as a result, but at any rate it survives for some time. If something interferes with the supply of protein, however, the cell inevitably sickens and dies.

CLASSIFICATION OF PROTEINS

Bases for Classification

A system for the classification of proteins which differs slightly from that usually presented in textbooks is given in Table 4-1. It is based on the same characteristics of proteins as the commonly used system, i.e., solubility and composition. That these properties do not provide a perfect system of classification will become evident in what follows.

The three major classes of proteins are the simple proteins, the conjugated proteins, and the derived proteins. Upon hydrolysis the simple proteins yield only amino acids,

TABLE 4-1. CLASSIFICATION OF THE PROTEINS

I. Simple proteins
  A. Albumins
  B. Globulins
  C. Glutelins
  D. Prolamines
  E. Scleroproteins
II. Conjugated proteins
  A. Nucleoproteins
  B. Phosphoproteins
  C. Porphyrinoproteins
    1. Hemoproteins
    2. Chlorophylloproteins
  D. Glycoproteins
  E. Lipoproteins
  F. Flavoproteins
  G. Miscellaneous metalloproteins
III. Derived proteins
  A. Split products of conjugated proteins
    1. Protamines
    2. Histones
    3. Others
  B. Denatured proteins
  C. Hydrolytic products
    1. Proteoses and peptones
    2. Peptides

while the conjugated proteins yield some substance or substances in addition to amino acids. Derived proteins are the products resulting from various rather deep-seated changes in the structure or composition of the native proteins belonging to the first two classes.

With the advance of biochemical research, the line of demarcation between simple and conjugated proteins has become somewhat obscured. A number of proteins previously classified as simple, in fact some which were used as typical examples of that class, have been shown in recent years to contain carbohydrate groups as integral components of their molecules. Still others are in the process of reclassification to such groups as lipoproteins, metalloproteins, etc. Discrepancies in our present classification will be pointed out in the following sections.

The subdivision of the class of simple proteins is based upon solubility. As will be pointed out later, the division into albumins and globulins is quite arbitrary, as a considerable overlap of properties exists between these groups.

Conjugated proteins are further classified according to the nature of the non-protein group which is attached to the molecule, the so-called "prosthetic group." In some systems of classification all proteins with colored prosthetic groups are collectively designated "chromoproteins." There seems to be no rational chemical or biological basis for this practice, hence no such group is included in Table 4-1.

Protamines and histones are frequently included among the simple proteins. Since, however, they occur in nature as the protein moieties of conjugated proteins (especially in nucleoproteins and hemoproteins), it seems best to consider them as "derived." This also permits the creation of a class of split-products of the conjugated proteins, which will include any "artificial" proteins that may be produced by the cleavage of prosthetic groups from conjugated proteins. The denatured proteins and the products of partial hydrolysis of proteins will be discussed in subsequent sections.

It is possible to classify proteins on the basis of criteria other than those mentioned above. Alternative systems could be based upon molecular size, shape, numbers of ionic groups, or biological function. However, despite its defects, the system of classifying proteins according to composition and solubility seems to be the most useful at the present time.

Simple Proteins

Albumins were originally differentiated from globulins by virtue of the solubility of the former in pure water, since the globulins originally studied required the presence of small quantities of salt for their solution. Later, when it was discovered that proteins could be forced out of solution by high concentrations of salt (salting out), a second criterion was established; globulins were proteins which could be precipitated by ammonium sulfate in concentrations of half-saturation or less, whereas albumins required higher concentrations of the salt. Unfortunately for the system of classification, the two criteria do not lead to the same results in all cases. For instance, among the "globulins," as classified by the salting-out method, are many which are soluble in pure water. These have been called "pseudoglobulins" (to distinguish them from "true globulins," or euglobulins). The opposite type of difficulty also occurs, since there are euglobulins (by the water-solubility criterion) which are salted out with the albumins. It is therefore evident that the terms "albumin" and "globulin" have little significance unless the criterion of classification is stated. Unless indicated otherwise, we shall use the criterion of salting out in our discussions of the albumins and globulins.

Probably the best known proteins of the two groups just discussed are egg albumin, plasma albumin, and the plasma globulins. To the confusion of systematists, highly purified egg albumin as well as some fractions of plasma albumin and of the plasma globulins contain firmly bound carbohydrate. While this fact calls for a classification of these substances as glycoproteins, the change-over has not yet been generally accepted.

The glutelins are simple proteins which are insoluble in pure water and dilute salt solutions, but soluble in dilute acids or bases. Glutenin from wheat is an example of this group. It is probable that these proteins, the best characterized of which have been obtained from plants, actually represent mixtures of closely related individuals. Prolamines are proteins which are insoluble in water and absolute alcohol, but soluble in aqueous ethanol (70 to 80 per cent). Examples are zein from corn and gliadin from wheat. The unusual solubility properties of this group of proteins are accounted for by the predominance of non-polar (hydrocarbon-type) groups in the molecule.

The scleroproteins (sometimes called "albuminoids," a poor choice of terminology) form a group with structural and protective functions, and are appropriately characterized by their insolubility in all of the solvents mentioned thus far. There is evidence that reagents which dissolve scleroproteins do so only as a result of fundamental changes in the protein molecules. Typical scleroproteins are keratin from horn, nails, hoofs, and feathers, collagen from tendon, skin, and bone, and elastin from ligament.

Conjugated Proteins

Nucleoproteins are characterized by the possession of prosthetic groups known as nucleic acids. Certain nucleic acids are attached to proteins known as protamines, which are water-soluble, basic proteins, of relatively low molecular weight. Other nucleic acids are found in nature combined with histones, which are also basic proteins, differing from the protamines by their higher molecular weight. The protein moieties of some nucleoproteins are less basic, of higher molecular weight, and more complex than the protamines and histones. The nucleic acids and nucleoproteins are substances of such great biological importance that a separate chapter will be devoted to them.

Phosphoproteins contain phosphoric acid, usually linked as a monoester to the hydroxyl group of serine. Casein of milk is an example of a phosphoprotein.

A number of proteins contain as prosthetic groups certain rather complex heterocylic compounds known as porphyrins, which in turn are usually combined with a metallic atom. In the case of the chlorophylloproteins, the porphyrin is combined with magnesium to form the familiar green compound, chlorophyll, which is widely distributed in the plant world. The hemoproteins contain iron-porphyrins, known as hemes, attached to the protein portion of the molecule. Hemoglobin and myoglobin are examples of hemoproteins, as are a number of enzymes, such as the catalases, peroxidases, and cytochromes.

The prosthetic groups of the glycoproteins are polysaccharides of the heterosaccharidic, nitrogenous type (mucopolysaccharides). Further subdivision of this group of proteins may be based upon the composition of the mucopolysaccharides and the nature of the protein-carbohydrate linkage. It should be noted, however, that much disagreement exists concerning nomenclature in this field. For example, the term "glycoprotein" has been used by some authors to designate one subdivision of this family of substances (cf. (2) below), thus neatly eliminating the logical generic name for the entire family. By analogy with nucleoprotein, lipoprotein, etc., we take the term "glycoprotein" to mean any type of carbohydrate-protein combination. At least three distinct types of such combinations are found in nature:

(1) A number of acidic mucopolysaccharides of fairly high molecular weight, such as hyaluronic acid, keratosulfate, and the chondroitin sulfates, appear to occur in nature as salts of proteins. Such combinations may be called "protein mucopolysaccharidates," the electrostatic nature of the protein-carbohydrate linkage being analogous to that in many nucleoproteins (actually, "protein nucleates").

(2) In contrast to the preceding, certain proteins are found to contain covalently linked carbohydrate. Glycoproteins of this type generally consist of a protein molecule to which are attached a number of prosthetic groups of relatively small size, apparently bound by ester linkages to the side chains of glutamic and aspartic acid residues. The nitrogenous oligo- and polysaccharide moieties may be either neutral (i.e., containing hexoses and acetylated hexosamines) or acidic (containing, in addition, sialic acids). As indicated earlier, certain of the substances classified as simple proteins are really members of this group, e.g., egg albumin. Others are found among the plasma proteins and in the mucous membranes which line the digestive tract. Some hormones such as chorionic gonadotropin and certain of the pituitary hormones are likewise in this category.

(3) The blood group substances are examples of a third category, conveniently called "glycopeptides." The molecules are predominantly mucopolysaccharide chains, to which at various points small peptides are covalently attached.

Lipoproteins are discussed in the chapter on lipids (p. 45) and in connection with the plasma proteins (pp. 489, 560), and are mentioned again at this point only for completeness of classification.

Riboflavin, a member of the vitamin B complex, forms a part of the prosthetic group of a number of proteins, flavoproteins, which act as enzymes in catalyzing biological oxidations. In some cases, riboflavin phosphate as such makes up the prosthetic group; in others a compound known as adenylic acid is combined with the riboflavin phosphate to form the prosthetic group. (Some flavoproteins also contain metals.)

Many conjugated proteins contain metallic atoms. When these metals are parts of more complex prosthetic groups, the proteins are classified according to the complete group. However, there are metalloproteins which contain, so far as can be ascertained, no special non-protein substances other than the metallic atoms themselves. Among such proteins are ferritin (an iron-containing protein), copper-binding and iron-binding plasma proteins, carbonic anhydrase (a zinc-protein enzyme), insulin (a zinc-containing hormone), and certain metal-activated peptidase enzymes. Hemocyanins, the oxygen-transporting blood pigments of many invertebrates, are copper proteins, although it is not certain whether the copper is combined with some more complex group.

Derived Proteins

As mentioned earlier, the protein moieties which result from the removal of prosthetic groups from conjugated proteins may be considered one class of derived proteins. In this category are the protamines from the nucleoproteins of spermatozoa, the histones from the nucleoproteins of the thymus, and the familiar histone, globin, from hemoglobin.

The early literature on derived proteins contained such terms as proteans and metaproteins. These substances are now recognized as denatured proteins, and the terms are obsolete. Denaturation is a phenomenon which can be shown to occur in the case of most proteins; it will be discussed in connection with the steric architecture of proteins (p. 87).

The products of partial hydrolysis of proteins are often classified as derived proteins. One class, the proteoses, were differentiated from another class, the peptones, by the precipitability of the former with ammonium sulfate. Actually, these substances are highly heterogeneous mixtures of molecules of varying molecular weight, and it is questionable whether the terms serve any useful purpose at the present time. Continuation of the process of hydrolysis eventually leads to the production of smaller peptides, many of which have been characterized as chemical individuals.

LEVELS OF STRUCTURAL ORGANIZATION OF PROTEINS

According to some authorities, proteins exhibit four levels of organization. The primary level is concerned with the quantitative amino acid composition of the protein and the sequence of these constituents in the peptide chain. (Some proteins consist of more than one peptide chain, each of which possesses a specific primary level of organization.)

The peptide chains, in turn, may be coiled to a greater or lesser extent in the form of helices, or may exist in more extended form, in either case giving rise to a secondary level of organization.

Interaction between several peptide chains or between parts of the same chain results in a three-dimensional structure of higher order, sometimes stabilized with covalent bonds of the disulfide type. The shape of the protein at this tertiary level of organization, i.e., its "conformation," is correlated with its biological function. Proteins which are destined to form fibers and membranes ("fibrous" proteins) generally (at this level of organization) consist of ropes of peptide chain coils twisted about each other ("coiled coils") or sheets of peptide chains lying side by side. Proteins having other functions may have roughly spherical conformations ("globular" proteins), formed by compact folding of the peptide chains upon themselves.

In the case of certain proteins a still higher level of organization ("quaternary") may exist. Thus, the more or less linear tertiary structures of the fibrous proteins may in turn be packed into linear super-structures, partly by lateral and partly by end-to-end association, giving rise eventually to microscopically visible fibrils and membranes. Where the "molecule" leaves off and the "organelle" begins is a debatable point in such cases. Many globular proteins likewise consist of several tertiary sub-units, combined to form the functional molecule (e.g., hemoglobin).

An alternative nomenclature used by some authors refers to the chain sequence (primary level), chain conformation (secondary and tertiary levels), and sub-unit array (quaternary level).

PRIMARY LEVEL OF ORGANIZATION: THE AMINO ACIDS

Common Structural Features

With the exception of the prolines (which are imino acids), the amino acids which form the building blocks of proteins are characterized by an amino group in a position α to the carboxyl group. The rest of the molecule, represented by "R—," is the source of the variations in structure which differentiate one amino acid from another.

Examination of the formula for an amino acid discloses the fact that the α carbon atom has four different groups attached to it, except for the case where R is H. As a result this carbon atom is asymmetric, with the exception of the simplest amino acid, glycine. In the chapter on carbohydrates it was pointed out that glyceraldehyde was the reference compound for the steric families of sugars. In a similar fashion, serine, an α-amino, β-hydroxy acid, serves as the reference compound for the amino acids. L-Serine has the same steric configuration as L-glyceraldehyde. When the carboxyl groups of the amino acids are placed on top of the diagram, the amino group is written to the left for an L amino acid. The opposite arrangement holds for the D compounds.

$$\begin{array}{c} COOH \\ | \\ NH_2CH \\ | \\ CH_2OH \end{array} \qquad \begin{array}{c} COOH \\ | \\ HCNH_2 \\ | \\ CH_2OH \end{array}$$

L-Serine D-Serine

If necessary, the direction of optical rotation of the amino acids may be indicated by the symbols (+) or (−), following the designation D or L, e.g., D(+), D(−), L(+), L(−). As was emphasized in the case of the carbohydrates, no necessary relation exists between the steric configuration of the amino acids and their optical rotation.

The amino acids which make up the protoplasmic proteins of plants and animals belong to the L stereochemical family. At one time it was thought that only the L amino acids occurred in nature; they were therefore called the "natural" amino acids, and their enantiomorphs were said to be "unnatural." A number of products have been isolated, however, which are proteins or peptides in structure and contain some D amino acids. Many of these substances, which are liberated by microorganisms into the culture medium, are of medical importance as "antibiotics."

The fact that the intracellular proteins of all living creatures examined thus far are composed mostly of L amino acids is evidence for the existence of some common stereochemical configuration in the machinery of synthesis. As was mentioned in connection with carbohydrates, the substances which catalyze biochemical reactions, the enzymes, are known to have a high degree of stereochemical specificity.

Structure of the Amino Acids

The amino acids which are accepted at present as constituents of proteins may be classified in several ways. Figure 4–1 gives one such classification and the structural formulas of the amino acids. In some tabulations the group of basic amino acids is considered one of the chief categories, in which case histidine is included as a basic amino acid. Actually, although its basicity is sufficient to permit its precipitation with certain acidic reagents, it is not comparable to that of arginine or lysine.

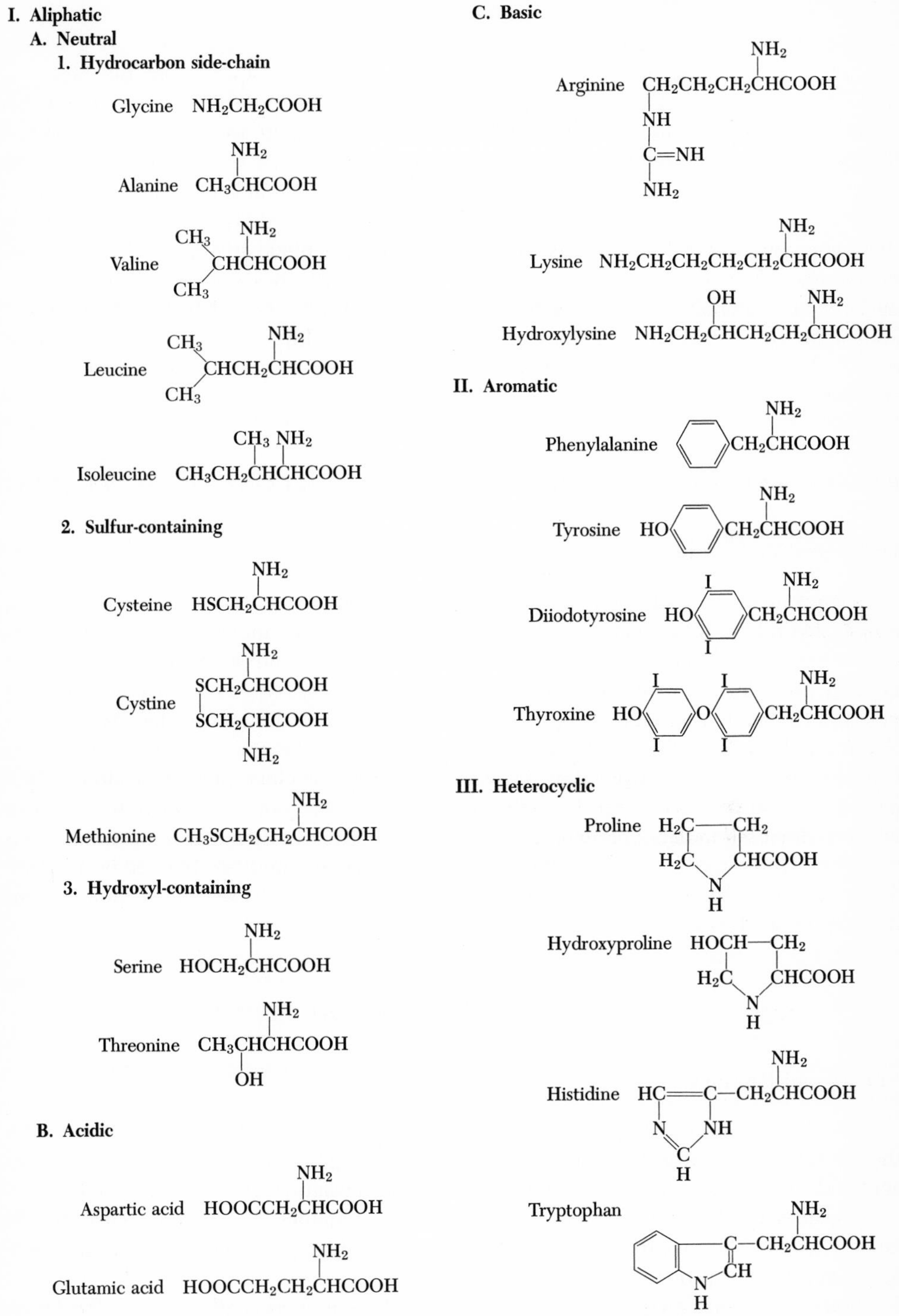

I. Aliphatic

A. Neutral

1. Hydrocarbon side-chain

Glycine NH_2CH_2COOH

Alanine $CH_3CH(NH_2)COOH$

Valine $(CH_3)_2CHCH(NH_2)COOH$

Leucine $(CH_3)_2CHCH_2CH(NH_2)COOH$

Isoleucine $CH_3CH_2CH(CH_3)CH(NH_2)COOH$

2. Sulfur-containing

Cysteine $HSCH_2CH(NH_2)COOH$

Cystine $SCH_2CH(NH_2)COOH$ / $SCH_2CH(NH_2)COOH$ (S–S linked)

Methionine $CH_3SCH_2CH_2CH(NH_2)COOH$

3. Hydroxyl-containing

Serine $HOCH_2CH(NH_2)COOH$

Threonine $CH_3CH(OH)CH(NH_2)COOH$

B. Acidic

Aspartic acid $HOOCCH_2CH(NH_2)COOH$

Glutamic acid $HOOCCH_2CH_2CH(NH_2)COOH$

C. Basic

Arginine $NH_2C(=NH)NHCH_2CH_2CH_2CH(NH_2)COOH$

Lysine $NH_2CH_2CH_2CH_2CH_2CH(NH_2)COOH$

Hydroxylysine $NH_2CH_2CH(OH)CH_2CH_2CH(NH_2)COOH$

II. Aromatic

Phenylalanine $C_6H_5CH_2CH(NH_2)COOH$

Tyrosine $HOC_6H_4CH_2CH(NH_2)COOH$

Diiodotyrosine $HOC_6H_2I_2CH_2CH(NH_2)COOH$

Thyroxine $HOC_6H_2I_2OC_6H_2I_2CH_2CH(NH_2)COOH$

III. Heterocyclic

Proline H_2C—CH_2, H_2C $CHCOOH$, N–H (pyrrolidine ring)

Hydroxyproline $HOCH$—CH_2, H_2C $CHCOOH$, N–H (pyrrolidine ring)

Histidine $HC{=}C{-}CH_2CH(NH_2)COOH$, ring N, NH, C–H (imidazole)

Tryptophan (indole ring) $C{-}CH_2CH(NH_2)COOH$, CH, N–H

Figure 4-1. Classification and structure of amino acids.

Importance of Amino Acids

Although most of this chapter will be devoted to the protein molecule as a whole, the significance of the amino acids must not be underrated, apart from the fact that proteins are built up of amino acids. From the nutritional standpoint, the organism requires amino acids, only certain of which are essential, and can do quite well, generally speaking, if supplied with these compounds instead of proteins. The dietary requirement for proteins exists only because proteins happen to be the form in which amino acids are largely found in nature. During digestion, the ingested proteins are hydrolyzed to amino acids, and it is these compounds which are offered to the tissues via the bloodstream. Furthermore, the amino acids (and possibly peptides) are the substances which are involved in the many anabolic and catabolic reactions of the organism. Few types of biochemical reactions are known in which protein molecules in toto participate, although these few, it must be admitted, include such biologically important phenomena as enzymatic and immunological reactions.

PRIMARY LEVEL OF ORGANIZATION: AMINO ACID CONTENT OF PROTEINS

Determination of Amino Acid Content

Determination of the content of the individual amino acids in a protein involves, usually, hydrolysis, followed by specific analyses for the various amino acids. In many cases, preliminary separation of the amino acids into chemically or physically similar groups or families precedes the final analyses. Some indication of the types of procedures used is given in the section on qualitative and quantitative tests at the end of this chapter.

Typical results. Table 4-2 presents a compilation of these analyses for some of the common proteins. Aside from their importance in the chemical characterization of the proteins, these data have considerable application in the field of nutrition, a matter which is discussed in detail elsewhere (p. 653). Suffice it to say here that some amino acids cannot be synthesized by the animal organism, and therefore must be obtained in the food. The nutritive value of a protein is related to a great extent to its content of these "essential" amino acids.

PRIMARY LEVEL OF ORGANIZATION: THE PEPTIDE CHAIN

Amides and Peptides

The formation of a simple amide from a carboxylic acid and ammonia proceeds by the splitting out of water. An analogous reaction, involving the carboxyl group of one amino acid and the amino group of another, results in the formation of a peptide bond.

Peptides are thus shown to be specialized forms of amides. Their biochemical importance is due to the fact that the peptide bond is the linkage by which amino acids are bound together in proteins.

Since it contains two amino acid residues, the compound synthesized in the lower equation (p. 59) would be called a dipeptide. A repetition of the reaction at either the free amino or free carboxyl group of the dipeptide would give rise to a tripeptide, and so on.

$$\mathrm{R{-}\overset{O}{\overset{\|}{C}}{-}OH + H{-}\underset{H}{N}{-}H \xrightarrow{-H_2O} R{-}\overset{O}{\overset{\|}{C}}{-}NH_2}\ \text{Amide}$$

$$\mathrm{R_1{-}\underset{H}{\overset{NH_2}{C}}{-}\overset{O}{\overset{\|}{C}}{-}OH + H{-}\overset{H}{N}{-}\underset{R_2}{\overset{H}{C}}{-}\overset{O}{\overset{\|}{C}}{-}OH \xrightarrow{-H_2O} R_1{-}\underset{H}{\overset{NH_2}{C}}{-}\boxed{\overset{O}{\overset{\|}{C}}{-}NH}{-}\underset{R_2}{\overset{H}{C}}{-}\overset{O}{\overset{\|}{C}}{-}OH}\ \text{Peptide}$$

Peptide bond

It is obvious that long peptide chains could be built up in this manner, and it is well established that the basic structure of the protein molecule consists of such peptide chains.

Peptides are named by beginning with the amino acid residue which retains its free amino group, substituting the suffix "-yl" for the usual suffix "-ine," and continuing this process through the peptide chain until the amino acid residue containing the free carboxyl group is reached, giving this terminal residue its full chemical name. (If necessary for the particular discussion at hand, the steric families are noted as D or L.)

$$\mathrm{\underset{H}{\overset{NH_2}{HC}}{-}\overset{O}{\overset{\|}{C}}{-}NH{-}\underset{CH_3}{\overset{H}{C}}{-}\overset{O}{\overset{\|}{C}}{-}OH}$$

Glycyl-alanine

$$\mathrm{CH_3{-}\underset{H}{\overset{NH_2}{C}}{-}\overset{O}{\overset{\|}{C}}{-}NH{-}\underset{H}{\overset{H}{C}}{-}\overset{O}{\overset{\|}{C}}{-}OH}$$

Alanyl-glycine

TABLE 4-2. AMINO ACID COMPOSITION OF PROTEINS*

	FOOD PROTEINS				TISSUE PROTEINS			
	GELATIN† (BOVINE BONE)	BOVINE α-CASEIN	OVALBUMIN	ZEIN	HUMAN HEMOGLOBIN	RABBIT MYOSIN	CALF THYMUS HISTONE (TOTAL)	HUMAN SERUM ALBUMIN
Alanine	9.02	2.78	5.36	8.39	8.14	5.19	7.73	—
Amide N	0.24	1.65	1.02	2.98	0.90	1.20	0.71	0.88
Arginine	8.07	3.51	5.13	1.53	3.07	6.59	10.41	5.51
Aspartic Acid	5.79	6.96	8.04	3.98	9.17	7.69	4.43	8.99
Cysteine	0.0	—	1.15	0.70 (Cysteine + Cystine/2)	—	—	0.0	0.7
Cystine/2	0.0	0.37	0.43		0.87	1.20	0.0	4.74
Glutamic Acid	10.18	18.43	14.48	23.61	6.32	19.39	8.52	15.27
Glycine	20.67	1.53	2.32	—	3.43	1.44	3.85	1.22
Histidine	0.62	2.58	2.08	1.17	7.49	2.13	2.19	3.09
Isoleucine	1.33	4.96	6.04	4.31	0.28	13.46 (Isoleucine + Leucine)	3.96	1.47
Leucine	2.98	6.89	7.94	18.21	13.13		7.06	10.27
Lysine	3.82	8.16	5.52	0.0	9.29	10.45	15.21	10.78
Methionine	0.55	2.35	1.57	2.12	1.41	2.99	1.00	1.12
Phenylalanine	2.22	4.15	6.86	6.50	7.06	3.86	2.49	6.95
Proline	13.07	6.95	3.04	8.88	4.22	1.62	3.90	4.30
Serine	3.09	5.30	6.75	5.84	4.56	3.59	4.08	3.06
Threonine	2.00	3.56	3.42	2.93	5.18	4.34	4.64	4.24
Tryptophan	0.0	1.82	1.09	0.14	1.09	0.73	0.0	0.17
Tyrosine	0.21	6.57	3.33	4.72	3.96	3.06	3.32	4.20
Valine	2.34	4.82	5.96	3.37	9.38	2.18	4.90	6.51

* In gm. anhydroamino acid per 100 gm. protein. Data selected from Tristram, G. R., and Smith, R. H.: The amino acid composition of some purified proteins, Adv. Protein Chem. *18*:227, 1963.

† Contains in addition 0.67 gm. hydroxylysine and 11.48 gm. hydroxyproline.

In order to conserve space, the amino acid sequence in peptides is frequently expressed in an abbreviated form, in which each amino acid residue is designated by (usually) the first three letters of its name. Thus, in this system, the two peptides shown (p. 59) would be written: "Gly-Ala" and "Ala-Gly," respectively.

With some 20-odd amino acids to draw upon, it is evident that a tremendous number of positional isomers is possible in a long peptide chain, and that the situation becomes even more complicated in the case of the proteins, with molecular weights running into the thousands or millions. Despite this possibility, it has been established that each protein possesses a specific sequence of amino acids which is under strict genetic control.

Naturally Occurring Peptides and Pseudopeptides

Before considering the general topic of the peptide structure of the proteins proper, a number of simpler compounds of similar structure may be mentioned. The formulas for some of these are given in Figure 4–2.

Glutathione is a tripeptide of glutamic acid, cysteine, and glycine. Aside from the peculiar mode of attachment of the glutamyl group, which in this case involves the γ- instead of the α-carboxyl, glutathione may be considered a true peptide. It is distributed widely in living tissues. The ocular lens contains two sulfur-free tripeptides, closely related to glutathione in structure: ophthalmic (γ-glutamyl-α-aminobutyryl-glycine) and norophthalmic (γ-glutamyl-alanyl-glycine) acids.

Carnosine and anserine are found in muscle. Since they contain the compound β-alanine, which does not belong to the class of α-amino acids, they may be called "pseudopeptides."

The other compounds, since they contain some residues which are definitely not amino acids, also belong to the category of pseudopeptides. They are more closely related to peptides than to amides, however, because in each case one constituent of the compound is either an amino acid or closely related to an amino acid. Pantothenic and folic acids belong to the group of B vitamins. Hippuric acid, phenylacetylglutamine, and dibenzoylornithine are substances which result from the coupling of a foreign substance for excretion from the organism (detoxication). The conjugated bile acids were discussed briefly in the chapter on lipids.

Under proper conditions, carbon dioxide, which may be considered the anhydride of carbonic acid, combines with the amino groups of amino acids or proteins to form "carbamino" compounds:

$$\text{R—NH}_2 + \text{CO}_2 \longrightarrow \text{R—NH—}\overset{\text{O}}{\overset{\|}{\text{C}}}\text{—O}^- + \text{H}^+$$

The resulting linkage bears some resemblance to an amide or peptide bond. The carbamino compounds formed by hemoglobin are important in the transport of carbon dioxide in the bloodstream.

Evidence for Peptide Linkage in Proteins

Up to this point the formulation of proteins as chains of amino acids united in peptide linkage has been stated as a fact. Some of the supporting evidence will now be discussed.

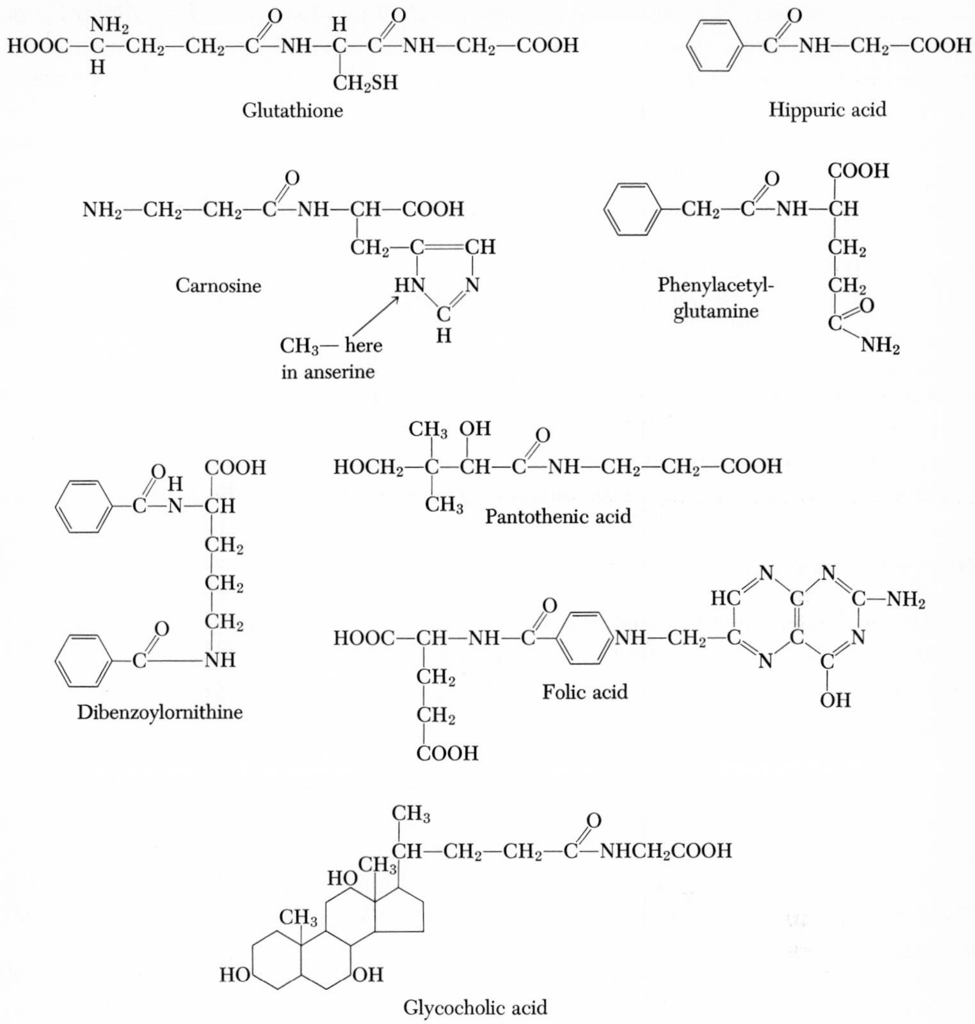

$HOOC-CH(NH_2)-CH_2-CH_2-CO-NH-CH(CH_2SH)-CO-NH-CH_2-COOH$

Glutathione

$C_6H_5-CO-NH-CH_2-COOH$

Hippuric acid

$NH_2-CH_2-CH_2-CO-NH-CH(COOH)-CH_2-(\text{imidazolyl})$

Carnosine

CH_3— here in anserine

$C_6H_5-CH_2-CO-NH-CH(COOH)-CH_2-CH_2-CONH_2$

Phenylacetyl-glutamine

$C_6H_5-CO-NH-CH(COOH)-CH_2-CH_2-CH_2-NH-CO-C_6H_5$

Dibenzoylornithine

$HOCH_2-C(CH_3)_2-CH(OH)-CO-NH-CH_2-CH_2-COOH$

Pantothenic acid

$HOOC-CH(CH_2CH_2COOH)-NH-CO-C_6H_4-NH-CH_2-(\text{pteridinyl; } NH_2, OH)$

Folic acid

$CH_3-CH(\text{steroid; } HO, HO, OH, CH_3, CH_3)-CH_2-CH_2-CO-NHCH_2COOH$

Glycocholic acid

Figure 4-2. Peptides and pseudopeptides.

Proteins react positively to the biuret test (p. 94), giving a color reaction mainly characteristic of compounds containing multiple peptide linkages. Most of the chemical groups other than the peptide linkage which give the biuret reaction can be eliminated from consideration, since they do not occur in proteins. The amino acid, histidine, reacts positively to the biuret test in the free state, but it is easily shown that the response as given by proteins is not due to any appreciable extent to their histidine content. Hydrolysis of a protein to the stage of free amino acids or to a mixture of peptides no larger than dipeptides results in the disappearance of the biuret reaction.

By direct chemical or physical chemical methods, proteins can be shown to possess few free carboxyl and amino groups. During hydrolysis of the protein new amino and carboxyl groups appear, and this liberation of the two types of groups occurs at the same rate for each, as though they were linked together in the protein, mole for mole.

Partial hydrolysis of proteins can give rise to small peptides, e.g., of the dipeptide or tripeptide type. These can be isolated and characterized. Identical peptides can be synthesized by chemical methods of such a nature that it is certain that the constituent amino acid residues of the products are joined in peptide linkages. On the reasonable assumption that the peptides isolated from the hydrolyzed proteins represent true fragments of the original molecules, these original molecules must have contained the same peptide linkages. The crowning achievement of the organic synthetic approach has been the total synthesis of certain polypeptide hormones (oxytocin, vasopressin, MSH, insulin) and the partial synthesis of others (ACTH).

Proteins are hydrolyzed by enzymes which show a high degree of specificity toward the peptide linkage. The demonstration that proteolytic enzymes also hydrolyze esters of certain types does not invalidate the hypothesis under discussion, since the chemical composition of proteins makes it impossible for ester linkages to constitute any appreciable fraction of the total linkages between amino acids.

The absorption spectra of proteins in the infrared and far ultraviolet also provide evidence for the existence of large numbers of peptide bonds in the protein molecule.

Hydrolysis of the Peptide Linkage

Essentially, hydrolysis of a peptide linkage amounts to the addition of the elements of water across the bond, resulting in the formation of a free amino and carboxyl group for each peptide bond split:

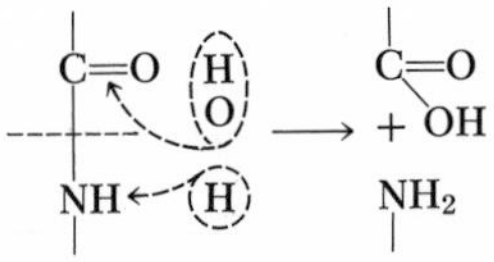

$$\begin{array}{ccc} \mid & & \\ C{=}O & H & \\ \mid & O & \\ \mid & & \\ NH & H & \\ \mid & & \end{array} \longrightarrow \begin{array}{c} \mid \\ C{=}O \\ + OH \\ \\ NH_2 \\ \mid \end{array}$$

The reaction as written proceeds to completion under physiological conditions; the best available evidence indicates that the biosynthesis of peptide bonds does not proceed by simple reversal of the hydrolytic reaction.

Although the equilibrium point of the hydrolytic reaction lies far toward the side of the products, the rate of the reaction is slow in the absence of catalysts. In the laboratory, the hydrolysis of peptides and proteins is effected by heating in the presence of acids or bases as catalysts. The organism carries out the same reaction at moderate temperatures, using enzymes as catalysts.

Complete cleavage of a protein to its constituent amino acids for analytical purposes is usually accomplished in the laboratory by prolonged boiling with aqueous solutions of mineral acids. This procedure has the advantage in that it results in the retention of the natural stereochemical configurations of the amino acids. However, tryptophan is completely destroyed, and cysteine, serine, and threonine are also decomposed to some extent.

The use of boiling alkali in the hydrolysis avoids the destruction of tryptophan. On the other hand, racemization of the amino acids occurs in alkali, as well as the decomposition of some of these compounds including arginine, cysteine, cystine, serine, and threonine.

Hydrolysis by proteolytic enzymes is the gentlest of all available methods, but is seldom used as a laboratory procedure except for special purposes. Outside of the body, enzymatic digestion of proteins proceeds at a slow rate and is generally incomplete. Conditions within the digestive tract, however, permit a rapid and quite complete hydrolysis of ingested proteins. In contrast to the action of acidic or basic catalysts, the peptide linkages are not attacked at random by proteolytic enzymes. The nature of the specificity toward certain linkages will be discussed in Chapters 8 and 9.

While there may be variations in the exact course of hydrolysis of a given protein in the presence of a given hydrolytic catalyst, the general succession of events is believed to be the following:

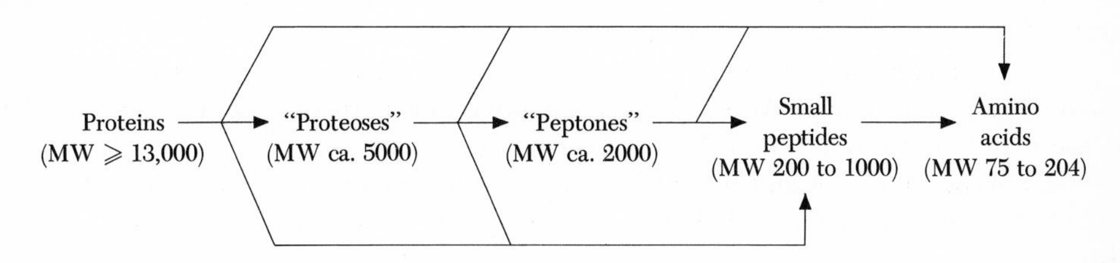

The proteoses and peptones are not chemical individuals, but rather mixtures of ill-defined substances intermediate in molecular weight between the proteins and the smaller peptides. Since terminal as well as central peptide linkages may be hydrolyzed, some free amino acids may be liberated throughout the course of the process, as shown.

Hydrolysates of proteins are currently being used therapeutically. In conditions where digestion is impaired but absorption is satisfactory, the hydrolysate is given orally; should normal intake of food be impossible, intravenous administration of hydrolysates can be used to satisfy the requirements for amino acids for a time.

Sequence of Amino Acids

Although analysis of proteins for their amino acid content has reached a high state of perfection in recent times, this general approach to the problem of protein structure dates back to the earliest years of protein chemistry. Determination of the sequence in which the amino acids occur in the peptide chains of the proteins, however, has been a much more difficult problem to attack. Partial hydrolysis of a protein to the stage of small peptides and determination of the amino acid sequence in the peptides represents one technique which has been used to some extent. However, the lack of information on the original location in the protein of the apparent sequences obtained, and the possibility that the peptides may have undergone rearrangement or "resynthesis" during the hydrolysis, have been advanced as objections to this method. Chemical procedures are available which make it possible to convert to some identifiable derivative those terminal amino acids which bear free amino (N-terminal) or carboxyl (C-terminal) groups, following which the converted fragments can be removed and identified, and the procedure repeated on the next amino acid residue in the sequence. Although these methods are laborious, they offer the opportunity of starting at one end of the protein or the other and methodically working one's way into the interior of the molecule. Most investigators in this field have adopted the abbreviated procedure of conversion of terminal amino acids, partial hydrolysis, and identification of those peptides "labeled" by the conversion procedure.

A method which has been very successful in the case of terminal amino groups is based upon reaction with fluorodinitrobenzene, yielding N-dinitrophenyl derivatives. After hydrolysis the dinitrophenylamino acids, which were originally at the free amino ends of the protein chains, are isolated, identified, and quantitatively determined. The ϵ-dinitrophenyl derivative of lysine is easily separated from the other derivatives and offers no interference. By the use of partial instead of complete hydrolysis, and identification of the dinitrophenyl peptides, this method has been adapted also to the determination of the sequence of amino acids in the protein molecule.

Reaction of N-terminal amino acids with phenylisothiocyanate forms phenylthiocarbamyl derivatives which, on treatment with acid, cyclize to liberate the phenylthiohydantoins of the N-terminal residues. Since the remainder of the peptide chain is set free (but unhydrolyzed) in this reaction, the procedure can be performed repeatedly to yield information on the N-terminal sequence.

The enzyme, leucine aminopeptidase, also has been used for hydrolysis and identification of N-terminal residues. Although its specificity is much broader than the name implies, its use is limited to some extent by resistant peptide linkages.

Carboxypeptidases A and B have been applied in a similar fashion at the C-terminal end of the peptide chain. Problems of specificity complicate the use of this technique also.

Treatment of a protein with hydrazine ("hydrazinolysis") results in the formation of hydrazides of all amino acids except those at C-termini, which are liberated as identifiable free amino acids.

Reduction of an esterified protein with lithium borohydride converts C-terminal amino acids to aminoalcohols, which are readily separated from the remaining amino acids after acid hydrolysis.

Extensive, and, in some cases, complete amino acid sequences have been reported for a number of proteins and polypeptides, including insulin, ribonuclease, cytochrome *c*, tobacco mosaic virus protein, lysozyme, various hemoglobins, myoglobin, and several pituitary hormones.

Parallel sequences containing identical amino acids, with occasional "substitutions," have been found in analogous proteins isolated from different species and in sub-unit peptide chains (e.g., hemoglobin chains α, β, and γ) of the same species. A number of hydrolytic and phosphorolytic enzymes contain parallel sequences of amino acids around their "active sites." All of these findings probably have important evolutionary implications.

PRIMARY LEVEL OF ORGANIZATION: IONIC PROPERTIES OF AMINO ACIDS AND PROTEINS

Although the electrochemical properties of amino acids and proteins may well be discussed as an independent topic, certain aspects of the secondary and higher levels of organization of proteins which are to be considered subsequently require some familiarity with the common ionizable groups of these substances. Furthermore, with the exception of certain ionic groups which may be "masked" by the compact folds of certain types of proteins (p. 89), most of the electrochemical properties of proteins can be discussed without reference to levels of organization higher than the primary.

Electrolytes, pH, and Buffers

Although certain ionic compounds may be encountered among the carbohydrates and lipids, the phenomenon of ionization is the rule rather than the exception among amino acids and proteins. In fact, most of the chemical and many of the biological properties of these substances are explicable only on the basis of their ionic character. In order to provide the necessary background for the consideration of amino acids and proteins as charged particles, a brief summary follows of the elementary principles of electrolytic dissociation and related phenomena.

(*a*) ***Dissociation.*** Many of the chemical compounds encountered in biochemistry exist in solution as undissociated particles. Solutions of these substances have low electrical conductivity, and their colligative properties (those related to the number of particles in solution) can be calculated directly from the molarities of the solutions. As examples, the decrease in the freezing point of water, the increase in the boiling point of water, and the osmotic pressure of such solutions are related to the molar concentration of solute as follows:

$$\Delta^{\circ}_{fp} = 1.86 \times C \qquad \Delta^{\circ}_{bp} = 0.52 \times C \qquad P_{osm} = 22.4 \times C \text{ atmospheres (at } 0^{\circ}\text{ C)}$$

Examples of such substances are glycerol, glucose, urea, and the proteins (at their isoelectric points only; see p. 73).

Solutions of many other chemical compounds, however, exhibit colligative properties which seem to be far in excess of their indicated molarities; in fact, they are practically integral multiples of the molarities. These solutions have a high electrical conductivity, due to the complete ionization of the compounds into charged particles. Substances of this sort are called "strong electrolytes," and include such common laboratory reagents as the mineral acids (hydrochloric, nitric, and sulfuric), many of the common alkalies (or bases) such as sodium hydroxide, potassium hydroxide, and barium hydroxide, and practically all salts. The colligative properties of solutions of these compounds can be calculated, to a fair degree of approximation in dilute solution, by multiplying the molarity by the number of particles resulting from the ionization, and using this figure (known as the osmolarity, or osmolar concentration) in place of the molarity in the formulas given above. For instance, HCl yields two particles, while $BaCl_2$ produces three, so that the osmolarity of the former will be twice, and that of the latter will be three times the indicated molarity.

In addition to non-electrolytes and strong electrolytes a third group of substances exists, called "weak electrolytes." These compounds are intermediate in properties between the two groups already discussed; they conduct the electric current better than do the non-electrolytes but not nearly so well as the strong electrolytes. Their solutions have colligative properties which are in excess of those expected from their molar concentrations, but not so much in excess as to indicate complete dissociation. They are, in fact, partly dissociated or ionized. The calculation of the colligative properties of this group of compounds involves a consideration of the degree of dissociation, which in turn varies with the concentration. While not especially complex, this type of calculation is required so seldom in elementary biochemistry that it will not be considered here. Among the weak electrolytes frequently encountered are fatty acids, lactic acid, acetoacetic acid, ammonium hydroxide, carbonic acid, the ionizable groups on amino acid and protein molecules, and water itself.

(*b*) ***Ionization constants.*** In the ionization of weak electrolytes the ionized particles are in equilibrium with the un-ionized molecules, allowing us to set up (according to the law of mass action) an equilibrium constant, or (as it is frequently called in this case) an ionization or dissociation constant:

$$XY \rightleftharpoons X + Y \qquad K_{diss} = \frac{(X)(Y)}{(XY)}$$

The quantities in parentheses are concentration units of gram moles or gram ions per liter.*

Water, as has been mentioned already, is a weak electrolyte. Its dissociation can be represented as follows:

$$H_2O \longrightarrow H^+ + OH^- \qquad K_{diss} = \frac{(H^+)(OH^-)}{(H_2O)}$$

(For the sake of simplicity, the hydrogen ion will be represented in this book by the classical symbol, H^+, rather than by the more modern hydrated form, H_3O^+. See p. 67.) Since the concentration of water in all ordinary solutions remains practically constant, owing to the very small degree of dissociation and very high concentration, it has been found convenient to incorporate the (H_2O) term into a new constant on the left side of the equation:

$$K_w = (H^+)(OH^-) = 1.0 \times 10^{-14} \ (25° \text{ C})$$

In pure water (that is, containing no acidic or basic substances) the concentrations of hydrogen and hydroxyl ions are equal to each other, hence each is present in a concentration of 10^{-7} moles/liter.

(*c*) ***Hydrogen ion concentration and pH.*** Although the product of the hydrogen and hydroxyl ion concentrations is always 10^{-14}, many solutions contain a large excess of one or the other, so that the expression of the concentration of either ion involves rather unwieldy exponents. A simplified notation has been devised, therefore, which denotes the acidity of all solutions in terms of pH, defined as follows:

$$pH = \log \frac{1}{(H^+)}$$

In this notation a neutral solution will have a pH of 7, a solution containing hydrogen ions in 1 molar concentration will have a pH of 0, while a 1 molar solution of hydroxyl ions (remembering the K_w) will have a pH of 14. An analogous notation for direct expression of hydroxyl ion concentrations would be:

$$pOH = \log \frac{1}{(OH^-)}$$

From the ionization equation for water, the pH and pOH of all solutions are related by:

$$pH + pOH = \log \frac{1}{K_w} = 14$$

In the preceding equation the term "$\log \frac{1}{K_w}$" can be expressed in a notation similar to that used for pH and pOH, namely pK_w (= 14). For convenience the dissociation constants of many weak electrolytes are often expressed in this pK notation.

(*d*) ***Dissociation of weak acids.*** Since the weak electrolytes which are of interest in biochemistry are acids or can be formulated as acids (p. 69), the ionization of this class of

*Strictly speaking, the terms in parentheses in these and other expressions of equilibrium should be thermodynamic "activities" rather than molar concentrations. Actually, in the dilutions encountered in biological systems, the error involved in this simplification is slight. Furthermore, the requisite activity coefficients (which vary with the ionic strength of the solution) are not known in many cases.

compounds requires special attention. Taking the general case of the weak acid HA dissociating* into H^+ and A^-, the equilibrium can be formulated as follows:

$$HA \longleftrightarrow H^+ + A^-$$

$$K_a = \frac{(H^+)(A^-)}{(HA)} \qquad pK_a = \log \frac{1}{K_a}$$

Owing to the reciprocal nature of the mathematical function, the stronger the acid, the smaller the pK_a value.†

(*e*) ***Buffers and the Henderson-Hasselbalch equation.*** A buffer may be defined as a solution which resists the change in pH which might be expected to occur upon the addition of acid or base to the solution. Buffers consist of mixtures of weak acids and their salts or weak bases and their salts. The former type is the more important in biochemistry; its action against added acid or base may be illustrated as follows:

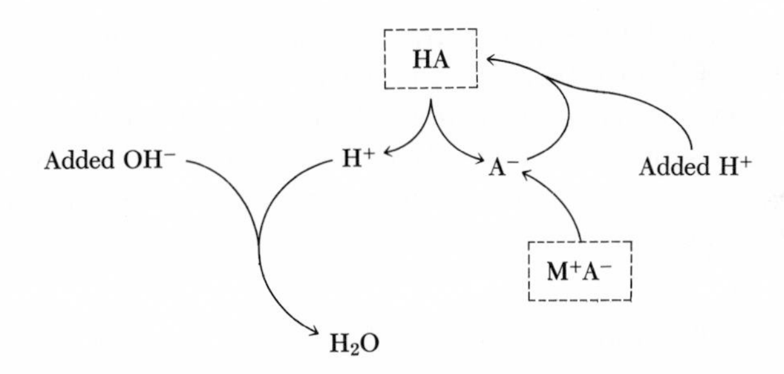

The buffer consists of the weak acid HA and its completely ionized salt M^+A^-. Added hydrogen ions, in the form of a strong acid, combine with anions A^- (largely from the salt component of the buffer) to form the weakly dissociated HA, so that the pH does not become as acid as it would in the absence of the buffer. The capacity to combine with added acid remains so long as there is a supply of the buffer salt in the solution. Added hydroxyl ions, in the form of a strong base, combine with hydrogen ions derived from the acid HA, and form the weakly dissociated water molecule. Hence the pH does not become as alkaline as would otherwise occur. Hydroxyl ions can be buffered as long as some of the acid HA remains to supply hydrogen ions.

The pH of any mixture of a weak acid and its salt can be calculated from the Henderson-Hasselbalch equation, which is readily derived as follows: in any solution of a weak acid, whether its salt is present or not, the usual dissociation constant equation holds true—

$$K_a = \frac{(H^+)(A^-)}{(HA)}$$

---

*It is recognized that for every proton donor there must be a proton acceptor, that in aqueous systems this acceptor is water, that a solvent molecule should be included as a reactant, and that the hydronium ion H_3O^+ is the actual product rather than the free hydrogen ion. However, this concept does not add to our understanding of the biological processes, but merely complicates the equations. Therefore, the simpler view of acid ionization will be adopted.

† It should be noted that K_a and pK_a as derived are thermodynamic constants, valid only at infinite dilution or at measurable concentrations when corrections are made with activity coefficients (cf. p. 66). To avoid calculation of these corrections, the biochemist frequently uses a "working pK," or pK′, in which the corrections are incorporated to allow direct use at usual physiological ionic strengths. These pK's differ numerically from the thermodynamic pK's found in the chemical handbooks.

The dissociation of the average weak acid is so small that the term (HA) can be replaced with the actual, total molarity of the acid dissolved in the solution. Similarly, when the salt of the acid is present, practically all of the anion A^- in the solution can be regarded as coming from the salt, so that the term (A^-) can be replaced by the molarity of salt added. Making the indicated replacements and rearranging terms,

$$\frac{1}{(H^+)} = \frac{1}{K_a} \times \frac{(\text{salt})}{(\text{acid})}$$

Taking logarithms of both sides of the equation,

$$\log \frac{1}{(H^+)} = \log \frac{1}{K_a} + \log \frac{(\text{salt})}{(\text{acid})}$$

or

$$pH = pK_a + \log \frac{(\text{salt})}{(\text{acid})}$$

from which one can calculate the pH of any buffer system from the pK of the acid involved and the salt-acid ratio. It may be pointed out that, when the salt and acid are present in equal concentrations, the pH of the solution is numerically equal to the pK of the acid, since the logarithmic term becomes zero. Buffers are most efficient at pH's near their pK's, and their effective range is commonly said to include pH's 1 (or possibly 2) pH units above and below the pK value.

Amino Acids and Proteins as Charged Particles

(*a*) ***Biological importance.*** The fact that the protein molecule bears electrical charges on its surface is of paramount importance in many biological phenomena. It is probable that the permeability of natural membranes, composed chiefly or entirely of proteins, owes much of its selectivity to the electrical charges in the vicinity of its orifices, especially when the particles approaching the membrane are themselves electrically charged. Interactions between enzyme and substrate, antigen and antibody, and probably hormone and target molecule all involve some reactive portion of the surface of a protein. Evidence is accumulating that the degree and specificity of such reactivity is dependent upon the presence and steric placement of electrically charged groups.

(*b*) ***Titration methods.*** As will be shown later, the electrical charges on amino acid and protein molecules arise from ionizable groups, all of which may be regarded as weak acids. The number and type of each group can be studied by means of titrations with acid and base, acid being used to "back-titrate" those groups which may be in their salt form, while base reacts with those which are present as undissociated acids. The number of groups can be calculated from the stoichiometry of the titration, and the chemical type of each group can be ascertained from the pH range in which it is titrated. A variation of this procedure is the study of the combination with proteins of anions and cations other than H^+ and OH^-, e.g., heavy metal ions and ionic dyestuffs.

(*c*) ***Electrophoresis.*** Except under special circumstances which will be discussed later, amino acids and proteins in solution carry a net positive or negative charge. They therefore migrate in an electrical field toward one electrode or the other. This migration, called "electrophoresis," may be used not only as a tool in theoretical studies of the numbers of charged groups on protein molecules, but also as an analytical method for the quantitative determination of individual proteins in complex natural mixtures, such as blood plasma (pp. 74, 558).

(*d*) ***Charged groups on amino acids.*** The amino acids display, on a simpler and miniature scale, most of the electrical and ionic properties of the proteins. As mentioned earlier, the groups involved may be regarded as weak acids, the term "acid" being defined as any compound or group capable of giving up a hydrogen ion. The form of the group existing after removal of the hydrogen ion will be spoken of as the ionized or "salt" form (called a "conjugate base" in the Brønsted formulation, p. 312). Two types of acid groups must be considered, the cationic acids and the uncharged acids. Since the student may not be familiar with this sort of formulation, especially with the classification of the ammonium ion as an acid, a detailed outline follows of the ionization and titration of both types of acids, in the general form and as specific examples (acetic acid and ammonium ion, respectively):

Cationic Acid, General Formulation	*Specific Example*
Ionization: $ZH^+ \rightleftharpoons Z^0 + H^+$	$NH_4^+ \rightleftharpoons NH_3^0 + H^+$
Titration: $ZH^+ \xrightarrow{Na^+OH^-} Z^0 + Na^+ + H_2O$	$NH_4^+ \xrightarrow{Na^+OH^-} NH_3^0 + Na^+ + H_2O$
Back-titration: $Z^0 \xrightarrow{H^+Cl^-} ZH^+ + Cl^-$	$NH_3^0 \xrightarrow{H^+Cl^-} NH_4^+ + Cl^-$

$$K_a = \frac{(H^+)(Z^0)}{(ZH^+)}$$

Uncharged Acid, General Formulation	*Specific Example*
Ionization: $ZH \rightleftharpoons Z^- + H^+$	$CH_3COOH \rightleftharpoons CH_3COO^- + H^+$
Titration: $ZH \xrightarrow{Na^+OH^-} Z^-Na^+ + H_2O$	$CH_3COOH \xrightarrow{Na^+OH^-} CH_3COO^-Na^+ + H_2O$
Back-titration: $Z^-Na^+ \xrightarrow{H^+Cl^-} ZH + Na^+Cl^-$	$CH_3COO^-Na^+ \xrightarrow{H^+Cl^-} CH_3COOH + Na^+Cl^-$

$$K_a = \frac{(H^+)(Z^-)}{(ZH)}$$

It will be observed that the uncharged acid becomes negatively charged upon ionization or titration, while the cationic acid loses its positive charge and becomes electrically neutral. For the sake of simplicity the anion which must always accompany the positively charged cationic acid group is omitted from the equations.

(*e*) ***Dissociation constants and buffer systems.*** Since all of the groups under consideration are weak acids, ionization constants can be formulated for them, based on the law of mass action. From each K_a a corresponding pK_a can be derived. In Table 4-3 are presented the various acid groups found in amino acids and proteins, together with their salt forms and approximate pK's. Under any circumstances in which one of these groups is present partly in its acid form and partly in its salt form, a buffer system will be set up, the pH of which will follow the Henderson-Hasselbalch equation for that particular group. As with most buffer systems, the effective buffer range or titration range of each group lies within 1 or 2 pH units above and below its pK.

$$pH = pK_a + \log\frac{(\text{salt form})}{(\text{acid form})}$$

(*f*) ***Zwitterions.*** From the numerical values of the pK's, it would be expected that, at pH's around neutrality, carboxyl groups should exist in their salt forms, while ammonium groups should retain their hydrogen ions and exist in cationic form. An amino acid in approximately neutral solution, therefore, cannot have the uncharged structure assigned to it by the classical organic chemists. Instead, it exists as a doubly charged molecule (in the case of those amino acids having only two ionizable groups), containing one positive and one negative charge, and hence is electrically neutral. Such a structure is called a zwitterion (hybrid ion) or dipolar ion.

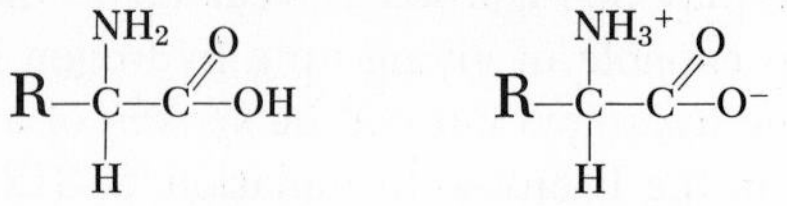

$$\underset{\text{Classical structure}}{R{-}\overset{NH_2}{\underset{H}{C}}{-}C(=O){-}OH} \qquad \underset{\text{Zwitterion}}{R{-}\overset{NH_3^+}{\underset{H}{C}}{-}C(=O){-}O^-}$$

The reaction of the zwitterion with acid represents a back-titration of the carboxyl group, leading to the formation of an organic molecule bearing a net positive charge. Bases, on the other hand, react with the ammonium group of the zwitterion, removing its titratable hydrogen and resulting in the formation of an organic molecule bearing a net negative charge. Each of these reactions can be reversed by the use of the appropriate reagent:

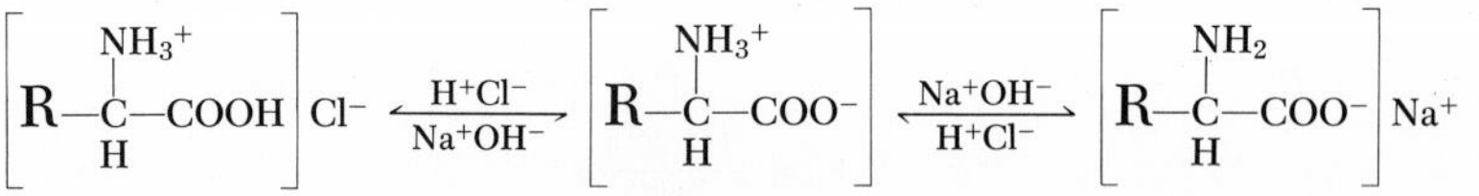

$$\left[R{-}\overset{NH_3^+}{\underset{H}{C}}{-}COOH\right]Cl^- \underset{Na^+OH^-}{\overset{H^+Cl^-}{\rightleftharpoons}} \left[R{-}\overset{NH_3^+}{\underset{H}{C}}{-}COO^-\right] \underset{H^+Cl^-}{\overset{Na^+OH^-}{\rightleftharpoons}} \left[R{-}\overset{NH_2}{\underset{H}{C}}{-}COO^-\right]Na^+$$

The fact that an amino acid (or a protein) can react with both acid and base places it in the category of amphoteric substances.

That pH at which the amino acid molecule bears a net charge of zero is known as the isoelectric point. At that pH the compound will not migrate in an electrical field. The amino acid carries a net positive charge at pH's acid to its isoelectric point, a net

TABLE 4-3. BUFFER GROUPS OF PROTEINS

ACID TYPE	GROUP	ACID FORM	SALT FORM	LOCATION	APPROX. pK
Uncharged	Carboxyl	—COOH	$—COO^-$	End-group	3.5
	Carboxyl	—COOH	$—COO^-$	Aspartyl- and glutamyl side-chains	4.0
	Phenol	>C—OH	$>C—O^-$	Tyrosine	10.0
	Sulfhydryl	—SH	$—S^-$	Cysteine	10.0
Cationic	Imidazolium	HC═C— / $\overset{+}{HN}$ NH / C / H (ring)	HC═C— / N NH / C / H (ring)	Histidine	7.0
	Ammonium	$—NH_3^+$	$—NH_2$	α-Amino end-group	8.0
	Ammonium	$—NH_3^+$	$—NH_2$	ε-Amino of lysine	10.0
	Guanidinium	—NH—C(=$\overset{+}{N}H_2$)—NH_2	—NH—C(=NH)—NH_2	Arginine	12.5

negative charge at pH's basic to its isoelectric point, and migrates toward the cathode and anode respectively. The isoelectric pH is frequently symbolized by pI.

From what has been said, it is obvious that even the simplest amino acids contain two potential buffer systems. If the pH of the solution is acid to the pI of the amino acid, but not so acid that all of it is in its positively charged form, then a buffer system will exist in which the (+) form is the acid, and the zwitterion (±) is the salt. A second buffer system exists on the basic side of the pI, with the zwitterion now acting as the acid (the hydrogen donor), and the negatively charged form (−) as the salt. Each buffer system can be described by its appropriate Henderson-Hasselbalch equation, using the pK's for the groups involved. The pK's of amino acids are customarily designated by numerical subscripts, taken in the order of decreasing acidity (or increasing pK value). Thus, in the simple amino acids, pK_1 refers to the —COOH group and pK_2 to the $—NH_3^+$ group. In this case the pI is related to the pK's by:

$$pI = \frac{pK_1 + pK_2}{2}$$

Taking the case of glycine as an example, $pK_1 = 2$, $pK_2 = 10$, hence $pI = 6$.

The dicarboxylic amino acids (glutamic, aspartic) contain three ionizable groups, characterized by three pK's (pK_1, carboxyl; pK_2, carboxyl; pK_3, ammonium), and hence can act as buffers in three pH ranges. Since the charged forms, beginning at the extreme acid side, may be symbolized by:

$$\left[\begin{array}{l}—COOH\\ —COOH\\ —NH_3^+\end{array}\right. \xleftarrow{}\, pK_1 \xrightarrow{} \left[\begin{array}{l}—COO^-\\ —COOH\\ —NH_3^+\end{array}\right. \xleftarrow{}\, pK_2 \xrightarrow{} \left[\begin{array}{l}—COO^-\\ —COO^-\\ —NH_3^+\end{array}\right. \xleftarrow{}\, pK_3 \xrightarrow{} \left[\begin{array}{l}—COO^-\\ —COO^-\\ —NH_2\end{array}\right.$$

and since the contribution of the third ionization to the isoelectric form is negligible, the pH at the isoelectric point may be calculated from:

$$pI = \frac{pK_1 + pK_2}{2}$$

A similar equation applies to tyrosine and cysteine, since the pK's of the phenolic —OH and the —SH (pK_3's) are numerically greater than the pK of the ammonium group (pK_2). Analogous reasoning applied to the diamino acids (histidine, lysine, arginine) (pK_1, carboxyl; pK_2 and pK_3, ammonium or other "onium") leads to the equation:

$$pI = \frac{pK_2 + pK_3}{2}$$

From these relationships and the numerical values of the pK's involved, it can be understood why solutions of the isoelectric forms of the "acidic" and "basic" amino acids have pH's below and above 7.0, respectively, and why histidine is not as "basic" as lysine or arginine.

(*g*) ***pH Titration curves.*** If 1 gram molecular weight of a simple amino acid in its most positively charged form (i.e., the product of treatment of 1 mole of the isoelectric form with one equivalent of acid) is titrated with standard base, and equivalents of base used are plotted against the resulting pH at each point, a buffer curve is obtained of the type shown in Figure 4–3. At the beginning of the curve, all of the amino acid is in the (+) form. As base is added, some of the COOH groups are titrated to the salt

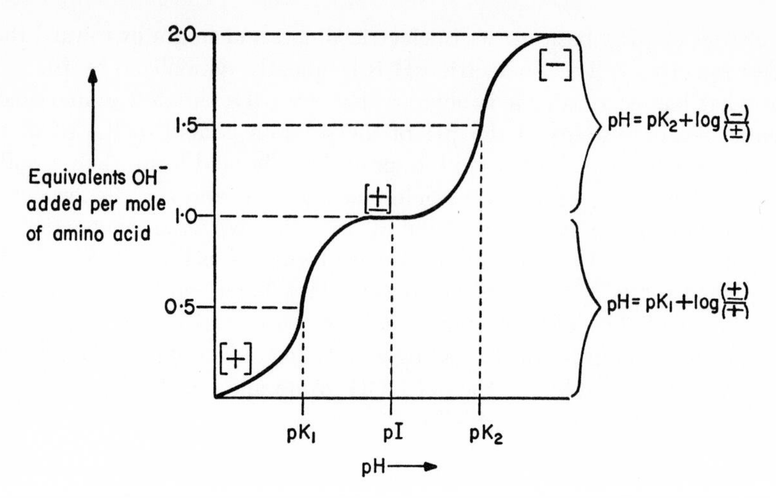

Figure 4-3. pH titration curve of a monoamino-monocarboxylic acid.

form, in this case, the (±), hence a buffer system is set up. It can be seen that there is a resistance to change in pH, especially around the middle of this part of the titration. When half an equivalent of base has been added, there is as much salt form as acid form present, so that, from the Henderson-Hasselbalch equation describing this part of the curve, $pH = pK_1$. At the end of the addition of the first equivalent of base, all of the amino acid is in the zwitterion form. Here the pH is in the neighborhood of the pI, and practically no buffer action is exerted. Further addition of base converts some of the $—NH_3^+$ groups of the zwitterion (now acting as a H^+ donor, or acid) to the salt form, $—NH_2$, or (−) for the whole molecule. A second buffer system is thus produced. The midpoint of this part of the titration corresponds to $pH = pK_2$. Upon addition of the complete two equivalents of base to the amino acid, all of it will be present in the (−) form. Any part or all of the titration just described can be reversed by the addition of equivalent amounts of acid.

Amino acids with three titratable groups will yield a triple instead of a double sigmoid curve. However, if two of the groups are close to each other in pK value (e.g., two carboxyls), the curves may fuse and the separation between the two may be obscured. Nevertheless, each group will still require an equivalent of base for its titration.

(*h*) ***Charged groups on proteins.*** Since amino acids are united through their amino and carboxyl groups to form the long polypeptide chains of proteins, it follows that most of these groups must be blocked from participation in buffer reactions. This raises the problem of explaining the well-established buffering properties of proteins. Two sources of titratable groups are found in proteins, the end groups and the side-chain groups. Aside from the case of a cyclic structure, each peptide chain, no matter how long, must have a beginning and an end. The few amino and carboxyl groups thus located account for only a minor part of the buffering properties of proteins. More important are the side-chain groups. Those amino acids which contain three titratable groups can be linked to other amino acids in a peptide chain through their α-amino and carboxyl groups, thus tying them up "fore and aft," and still have an unblocked group projecting out to the side, a "side chain."

A sample peptide containing end groups and typical side-chain groups, with approximate pK values indicated, is given on the next page:

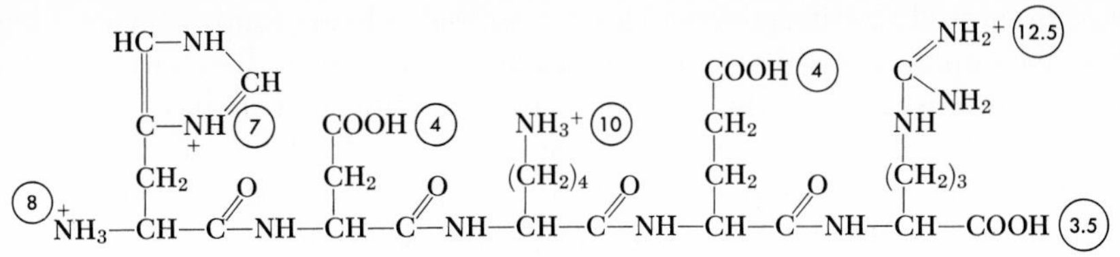

```
                                                                         NH2+ (12.5)
   HC—NH                                                                //
   ‖    \                                            COOH (4)          C
   ‖     CH                                          |                 | \
   ‖    //                                           |                 |  NH2
   C—NH (7)       COOH (4)        NH3+ (10)          CH2               NH
   |  +           |               |                  |                 |
   CH2    O       CH2    O        (CH2)4    O        CH2    O          (CH2)3
(8)|     //       |     //        |        //        |     //          |
 +NH3—CH—C—NH—CH—C—NH—CH—C—NH—CH—C—NH—CH—COOH (3.5)
```

This peptide is shown in its most positively charged form. Titration with base will involve first the end-group carboxyl and the side-chain carboxyls of aspartic and glutamic acid, setting up buffer systems around pH 4. In the neutral range the imidazolium side chain of histidine is most important. On the alkaline side, the end group ammonium will be titrated, followed by that in the side chain of lysine. Finally, at the extreme basic end of the titration, the guanidinium side chain of arginine is reached. Obviously such a peptide will be able to buffer over a wide pH range.

(*i*) ***Ionic states of proteins.*** Proteins represent, from the acid-base standpoint, nothing more than peptides of the above type, but of much higher molecular weight. Their buffering properties are due to the same groups; there are simply more of them. In solutions acid to their isoelectric points, proteins bear a net positive charge. On the basic side of the pI, the net charge is negative. By definition, that pH at which the net charge is zero is the pI. If we regard the ammonium group as characteristic of all the cationic acid groups in the protein, and the carboxyl as representative of the uncharged acids, then a simplified, diagrammatic formulation of the statements just made can be indicated as follows:

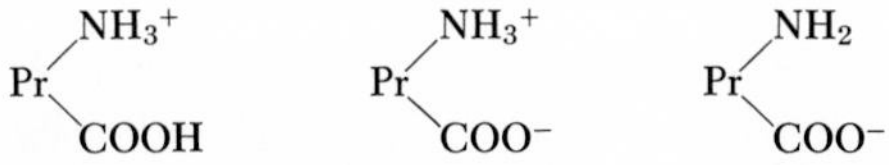

$$\mathrm{Pr}\begin{matrix} \diagup NH_3^+ \\ \diagdown COOH \end{matrix} \qquad \mathrm{Pr}\begin{matrix} \diagup NH_3^+ \\ \diagdown COO^- \end{matrix} \qquad \mathrm{Pr}\begin{matrix} \diagup NH_2 \\ \diagdown COO^- \end{matrix}$$

$$\mathrm{pH} < \mathrm{pI} \qquad\qquad \mathrm{pH} = \mathrm{pI} \qquad\qquad \mathrm{pH} > \mathrm{pI}$$

At the pI of a protein its migration in an electrical field (electrophoresis) will obviously be at a minimum. Other properties of proteins which pass through minima at or near the pI are osmotic pressure, solubility, and viscosity. Since anions will combine most readily with the (+) form of a protein, and cations with the (−) form, the combination of proteins with ions of both types should be at a minimum when the protein is in its isoelectric state.

The numerical value of the pI is characteristic for each individual protein, in the presence of specified types and concentrations of salts, being primarily the resultant of the number of ionizing groups of each type present and their pK's. Although proteins are known with pI's located throughout the entire pH range, the majority of soluble proteins found in animal tissues and fluids have pI values slightly on the acid side of pH 7. Since most animal tissues and fluids have a slightly alkaline pH (7.4), these proteins are normally found in their negatively charged forms. The foregoing statements mean, in effect, that most proteins have a slight excess of groups with pK values on the acid side.

The isoelectric point of a protein may vary somewhat with changes in the composition and concentration of salts in the medium. These variations are caused by combination of the protein with ions other than hydrogen. Extrapolation to infinite dilution of isoelectric points measured at various salt concentrations yields the "isoionic point," a pH at which the protein is not only electrically neutral, but also uncombined with extraneous ions.

Although most of the titratable end groups and side-chain groups which are known to occur in a given protein, based on amino acid analysis, appear in their normal positions on the pH titration curve when the protein is treated with acid or base, a few seem to exhibit altered pK values, and some may not titrate at all (if precautions are taken to avoid denaturation). These peculiarities are explained by intergroup bonding and masking effects which are due to the folding of the peptide chain into secondary and tertiary structures.

(*j*) ***Proteins as buffers.*** A survey of the pK's of the various ionizing groups reveals that few will operate as buffers in the physiological pH range. Those few ammonium groups which are located at the ends of peptide chains may contribute to physiological buffer action, but only to a small extent. Actually, the imidazole group of histidine is the most important buffer at pH's around neutrality, a fact which has received insufficient emphasis in the past.

The biological significance of the charged state of proteins was mentioned briefly at the beginning of this section. No less important is the buffer function of proteins. As the result of reactions of intermediary metabolism, various acids are produced in significant amounts normally, and in excessive amounts in certain abnormal conditions. The proteins of the tissues and those of the blood (especially hemoglobin) are as important in buffering these acids as the inorganic buffers such as phosphate and bicarbonate, which are frequently given much more attention. Abnormalities in which excessive alkalinity occurs in the body also bring into play the operation of protein buffers along with other types.

(*k*) ***Electrophoresis of proteins.*** Since proteins differ in their isoelectric points, they will generally bear net charges of different magnitudes at any given pH. As a result, the individual components of a mixture of proteins will migrate at different velocities in an electrical field. Advantage is taken of this phenomenon in the procedure of electrophoretic analysis, which has many applications. For the purpose of illustration, the analysis of plasma proteins is quite suitable, especially from the viewpoint of its practical application in medical research.

If the pH of plasma is adjusted, by addition of a proper buffer, to a value alkaline to the isoelectric points of all the plasma proteins, they will all carry negative charges, but of different magnitudes. Passage of an electric current through the solution will then cause the proteins to migrate toward the positively charged electrode (anode) at characteristically different rates. If a solution of protein-free buffer is carefully layered over the protein solution before the current is turned on, then the migration of the proteins under the impetus of the electric current can be made to proceed into the protein-free solution, a "moving boundary" of proteins being produced. Examination of this boundary reveals a succession of proteins, traveling at velocities, related to their net charges. The actual spatial distribution of the proteins in the boundary can be followed by optical scanning methods which take advantage of the fact that solutions of proteins have higher refractive indices than the protein-free solution. Electrophoresis equipment available at present for the moving boundary technique permits visual or photographic scanning diagrams to be produced, resulting in curves of refractive index increment per increment in distance against linear distance in the boundary. The area under the curve for each migrating component is a measure of the total amount of that particular protein present in the mixture. An electrophoretic diagram of normal serum is shown in Figure 4–4.

In the technique of "zone electrophoresis," proteins or other charged molecules migrate in an electrical field set up across a strip of filter paper, cellulose acetate, or slab of starch gel (or other porous supporting medium) saturated with buffer. The results of

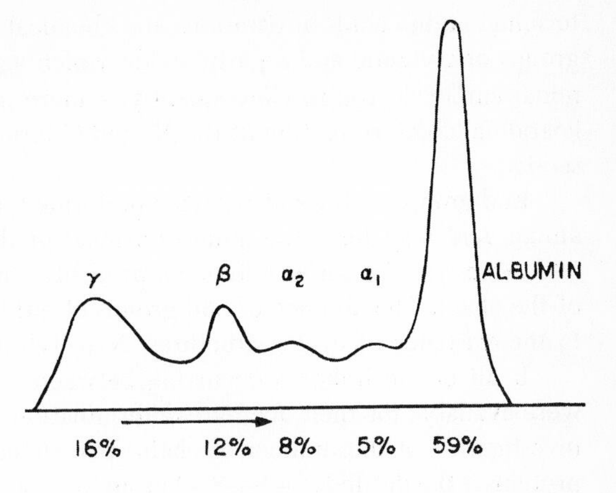

Figure 4-4. Electrophoresis of human serum at pH 8.6. Refractive index increments in moving-boundary method (upper) and stained fractions separated by paper electrophoresis (lower). Percentages indicate fractions of total protein. (Prepared by F. W. Putnam for Encyclopaedia Britannica, from G. R. Cooper in The Plasma Proteins, Vol. 1, Academic Press, Inc., 1960.)

this technique differ from those of free electrophoresis in that actual spatial separation of the individual protein fractions occurs. Zone electrophoresis has the advantages of being a microtechnique, requiring relatively simple and inexpensive apparatus, and being less time-consuming than the conventional methods.

In "immunoelectrophoresis," a mixture of proteins is subjected to zone electrophoresis in a gel, following which a preparation containing antibodies to one or more of the proteins in the mixture is allowed to diffuse into the gel at right angles to the direction of electrophoresis. Interactions between specific antigenic proteins and their antibodies result in identifiable zones of precipitation.

(l) ***Reversible combination of proteins with heavy metal ions.*** Although the combination of negatively charged protein molecules with heavy metal ions has been known for many years, the reaction as commonly carried out resulted in alteration of the fine structure of the protein (denaturation), making impossible the regeneration of the protein in its native state. Recent advances in this field, however, utilizing zinc ions under carefully controlled conditions, have resulted in procedures useful in the separation and isolation of plasma proteins. These methods are supplementary to the fractionation of plasma proteins with alcohol at low temperatures, discussed elsewhere (p. 86).

SECONDARY LEVEL OF ORGANIZATION

Number of Chains per Molecule

If the molecular weight of a protein is known, the number of peptide chains per molecule can be determined, theoretically, from the number of terminal amino or carboxyl groups. This technique may be called "end-group analysis," by analogy with the somewhat similar procedure used in the field of carbohydrate chemistry. Complications are caused by the side-chain amino groups of lysine, which behave much like the α-amino groups of terminal amino acids in titrations and chemical reactions, and by the side-chain carboxyl groups of glutamic and aspartic acids, which again are scarcely distinguishable from terminal carboxyl groups. Consequently, a more practical approach involves actual identification and determination of the N- and C-terminal residues, as discussed in the previous section.

End-group analyses of proteins performed up to this time indicate that virtually any amino acid may form the amino terminal of the peptide chain. Although the data are less extensive, the same statement probably can be made concerning the carboxyl end of the chain. The absence of end groups of either or both types in certain proteins is due to the existence of cyclic structures, N-acetyl, or carboxyl amide linkages.

If all of the linkages occurring between peptide chains were known, and methods were available for their accurate determination, a powerful tool would be at hand for the investigation of the number of chains per molecule. The major covalent cross-linkage in proteins is the disulfide (—S—S—) group of cystine. (Diester phosphate and pyrophosphate cross-linkages may occur in certain phosphoproteins.) Other forces which hold peptide chains together seem to be of the non-covalent type, and are determinable only to a rough degree of approximation. Furthermore, the linkages which bind chain to chain often serve as intra-chain bonds in folded secondary structures, introducing an element of ambiguity into the interpretation of the data. Hence, the direct analytical approach to this problem is usually replaced or at least supplemented by chemical or physicochemical techniques which specifically cleave the linkages in question, followed by ultracentrifugal, chromatographic, or electrophoretic separation of the sub-units.

By the use of such procedures, it has been shown that the "A" peptide chain of insulin is joined to the "B" chain by two disulfide linkages, forming a closed ring; in the "A" chain itself there exists a disulfide-containing loop which forms a ring of 20 atoms, a structure shared also by the posterior pituitary hormones, oxytocin and vasopressin (pp. 723, 746).

Conformation of the Peptide Chain at the Secondary Level

Three forms of the peptide chain appear to exist. The least organized is the more or less fully extended, randomly oriented chain found in denatured proteins (p. 87). Intra- and inter-chain stabilizing forces are minimal.

Silk fibroin and the β or extended forms of keratin and synthetic polypeptides contain almost fully extended peptide chains arranged in "pleated sheets" (Fig. 4–5*B* and *C*). The adjacent chains, which run in the same ("parallel") or alternate ("antiparallel") directions, are stabilized by hydrogen bonds (Fig. 4–8) between opposing carboxyl oxygen and imino hydrogen atoms of adjacent peptide linkages.

A still more highly organized form of the peptide chain occurs in unextended synthetic polypeptides, fibrous proteins in the unextended configuration (α-keratin, myosin, fibrinogen), and to a variable extent in the globular proteins. This is the right-handed α-helix of Pauling and Corey (Fig. 4–5A), consisting of 3.6 amino acid residues per turn, stabilized by intra-chain hydrogen bonds between the carboxyl oxygen of each peptide linkage and the imino hydrogen of the third following peptide linkage along the helix. Due to its unusual composition (high content of glycine and the prolines), the secondary structure of collagen consists of a special type of left-handed helix.

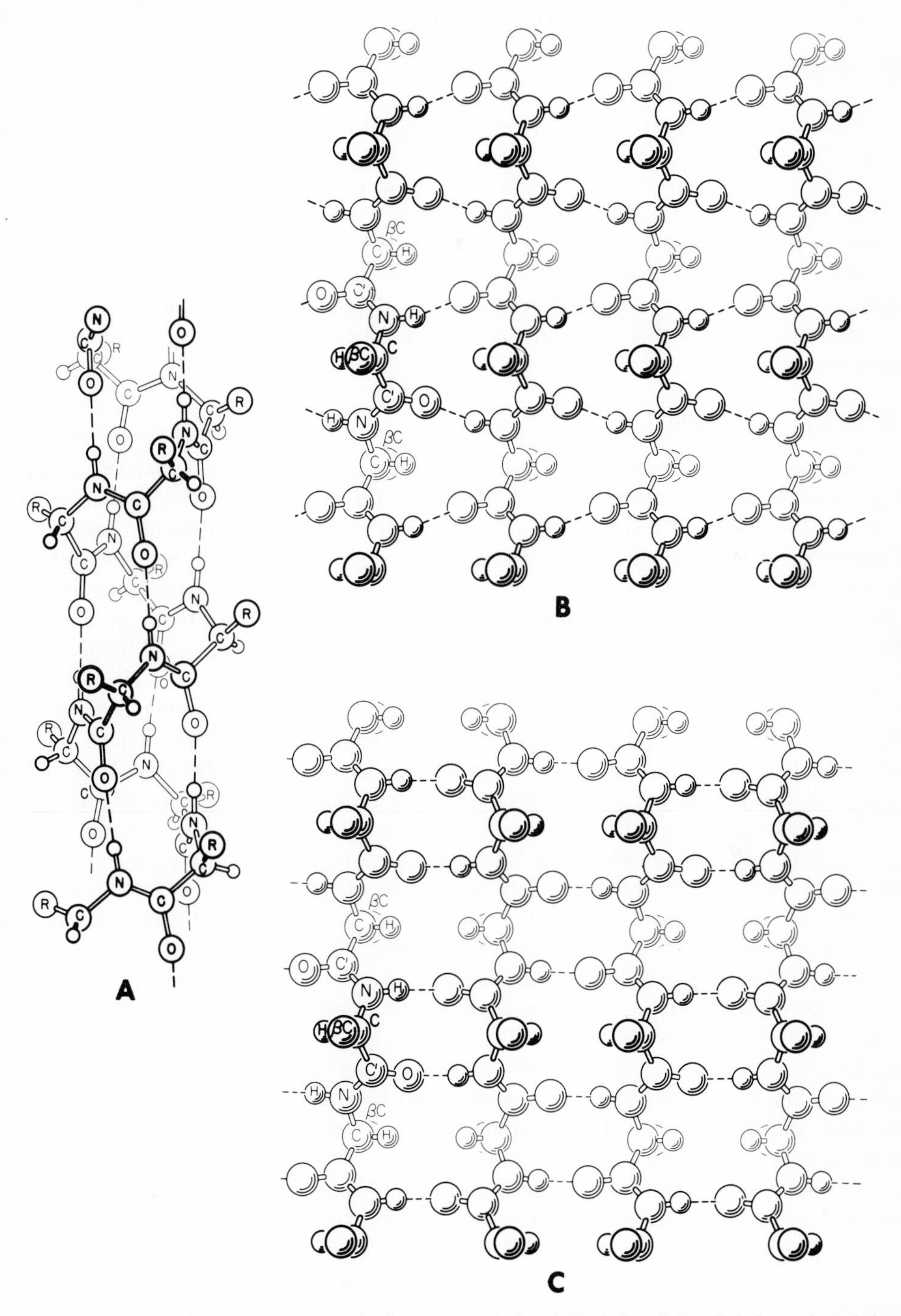

Figure 4-5. Conformations of peptide chains. *A*, Right-handed α-helix. *B*, Parallel-chain pleated sheet. *C*, Antiparallel-chain pleated sheet. (From Pauling: The Nature of the Chemical Bond, ed. 3, Cornell University Press, 1960.)

TERTIARY AND QUATERNARY LEVELS OF ORGANIZATION: SHAPE AND SIZE

The Shape of Protein Molecules

Such phenomena as the attraction of substrate to the enzyme surface, and hormone molecule to target molecule, indicate the importance of the shape of protein molecules to their several biological functions. In addition to catalytic proteins of the types mentioned, the structural proteins which form fibers and membranes must also obviously have shapes in keeping with the tasks which they are called upon to perform. As another example, when foreign proteins find their way into the bloodstream, the process by which plasma γ-globulins are synthesized is modified so as to produce antibody globulins which are altered in shape so that they can combine with the foreign proteins and remove them from circulation.

Methods of Investigation

(*a*) ***Streaming birefringence.*** One of the methods for determining the shape of proteins depends on a property known as streaming birefringence, or double refraction of flow. If a beam of light is passed through a sheet of Polaroid, a solution of a protein, and a second sheet of Polaroid with an orientation at right angles to the first, the light will be cut off provided that the protein solution has no effect on the plane polarized light coming from the first sheet (see polarimetry of carbohydrates, p. 8). If the protein molecules in question are spherical, they will have no effect* on the polarized light, whether the solution is at rest or in motion. Even elongated molecules do not affect the light while their solution is at rest, since the molecules are distributed in random orientation in space. If the solution is in motion, however, as in streaming through the stem of a funnel, the elongated molecules tend to orient themselves lengthwise in the axis of the stream (Fig. 4–6). This partial orientation has the effect of adding another type of polarization to the light passing through the solution, so that now the light is visible even through the second sheet of Polaroid, which has been kept with its axis at right angles to the first. From measurements of this phenomenon of streaming birefringence it is possible to calculate the ratio of the length of the long axis to that of the short axis of the protein molecule, frequently designated as the "axial ratio."

(*b*) ***Viscosimetry and dielectric dispersion.*** Two other methods of determining the axial ratio which also depend on orientation of elongated molecules are viscosimetry and dielectric dispersion. The presence of rodlike particles in a solution would be expected to interfere with its flow through an orifice to a greater extent than the presence of spherical particles, hence some relation may be expected between the asymmetry of a protein molecule and the viscosity of its solutions, although calculations of the axial ratio from such data are complicated by the degree of hydration of the protein, a factor which is seldom known accurately. The method of dielectric dispersion, on the other hand, depends on the fact that proteins are charged particles and will tend to orient themselves, like electrical dipoles, in an electrical field (Fig. 4–7). The time taken for the molecule to orient itself is a function of its asymmetry, which frequently can be calculated with considerable precision from measurements of the dielectric properties of protein solutions.

---

*This is not strictly true, since proteins are optically active. However, the effects under consideration are above and beyond this optical activity.

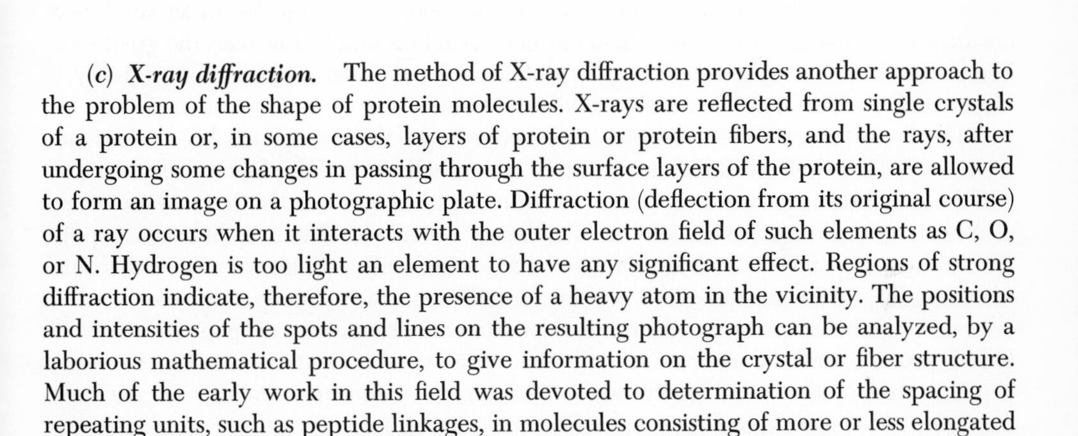

Figure 4-6. Streaming birefringence.

Figure 4-7. Dielectric dispersion.

(*c*) ***X-ray diffraction.*** The method of X-ray diffraction provides another approach to the problem of the shape of protein molecules. X-rays are reflected from single crystals of a protein or, in some cases, layers of protein or protein fibers, and the rays, after undergoing some changes in passing through the surface layers of the protein, are allowed to form an image on a photographic plate. Diffraction (deflection from its original course) of a ray occurs when it interacts with the outer electron field of such elements as C, O, or N. Hydrogen is too light an element to have any significant effect. Regions of strong diffraction indicate, therefore, the presence of a heavy atom in the vicinity. The positions and intensities of the spots and lines on the resulting photograph can be analyzed, by a laborious mathematical procedure, to give information on the crystal or fiber structure. Much of the early work in this field was devoted to determination of the spacing of repeating units, such as peptide linkages, in molecules consisting of more or less elongated peptide chains of the helical or extended-chain type. More recent work, particularly on globular proteins, has increased the resolution of detail so that individual atomic groups of amino acid side chains can be identified. The sheer bulk of mathematical calculations involved would have made investigations impossible before the advent of the electronic computer.

(*d*) ***Electron microscopy.*** What may be considered a direct "picture" of the protein molecule is furnished by the electron microscope. This instrument is analogous to the light microscope, but uses beams of electrons instead of light, and electrical or magnetic fields in place of glass lenses. Magnification of about 100,000× is commonly available, with even greater power possible. Insofar as drying of the specimen and subjecting it to a high vacuum do not produce artifacts, the electron photomicrograph is a true picture of the dimensions and shape of the object under observation. At the present time the resolving power of the instrument unfortunately limits its use to proteins of very high molecular weight, such as viruses.

Forces Stabilizing the Tertiary Organization

The final shapes of the proteins found by the methods previously discussed are the result of specific spatial arrangements of the secondary peptide structures into conformations of a higher order of organization, the tertiary. (In certain cases, several tertiary sub-units combine to form a quaternary array.)

Either intra- or inter-chain linkages, or both, may participate, depending upon whether the tertiary structure is formed of one or several individual peptide chains. Examples of the bonds involved are shown in Figure 4–8.

It is not certain at this time whether phosphate diester (or pyrophosphate) bonds play a significant role in the tertiary structure of phosphoproteins. All of the phosphate in α-casein is believed to be orthophosphate. It is of interest that "runs" of three or more consecutive phosphoryl-serine units have been found in phosphoproteins.

The only covalent cross-linkage for which firm evidence is available is the disulfide bond, formed by oxidative union of two cysteine side chains. Although not as stable as the peptide linkage, this bond is more stable than the non-covalent bonds to be discussed, and withstands conditions (e.g., denaturation) in which the non-covalent bonds are cleaved. Disulfide linkages may occur between cysteine residues of the same or different peptide chains.

The non-covalent linkages which participate in the stabilization of the tertiary organization include the hydrogen, ionic, and hydrophobic bonds. As might be anticipated, non-covalent cross-linkages are weaker than covalent, bond for bond. However, the great number of the former which may exist per protein molecule lends considerable stability to the tertiary structure, at least under mild conditions.

The importance of the hydrogen bond between peptide groups has been mentioned previously. These linkages stabilize the intra-chain α-helix (secondary level of organization) and the inter-chain pleated sheet structures (which can be considered both on the secondary and tertiary level of organization). Similar bonds occur within helices between peptide carboxyl oxygen and the hydrogen atoms linked to oxygen or nitrogen in the side-chains of serine, threonine, histidine, and tyrosine. Stabilization of the compact tertiary folds of helices in globular proteins, lateral and end-to-end association of peptide chains in fibrous proteins, and the union of several tertiary sub-units in quaternary arrays in certain proteins are probably significantly aided by hydrogen bond cross-linkages of the types mentioned as well as those between amino acid side chains.

The existence of net charges in the side chains of many amino acids in the physiological pH range (p. 69) provides another source of cross-linkage, the ionic, coulombic, electrostatic, or salt-bridge type of bond. Such linkages would be expected between pairs of anionic (glutamate, aspartate, C-terminal carboxylate) and cationic (arginine, lysine, histidine, N-terminal ammonium) groups. However, the number of such linkages appears to

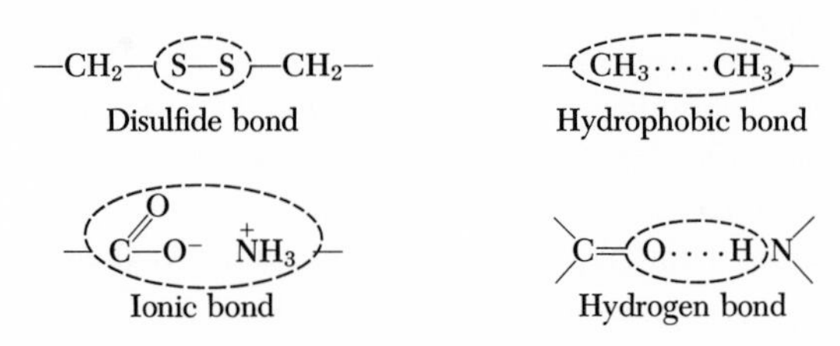

Figure 4–8. Intra- and inter-chain cross-linkages in proteins.

be relatively small, since most polar groups (which seem to lie largely in "exposed" positions in the tertiary structure) interact strongly with the solvent molecules (water).

At the present time much attention is being given a third type of non-covalent cross-linkage, the hydrophobic or apolar bond. This bond depends upon forces of the van der Waals type, and may be expected to occur between side chains composed of aliphatic and aromatic hydrocarbon residues. Hydrophobic bonds may contribute greatly to the stabilization of tertiary structures.

In addition to the foregoing, it is obvious that the conformation of a protein in its natural aqueous environment must also be influenced by interactions with solvent molecules. Such phenomena with polar groups are well known, as has been mentioned previously. The nature and extent of interaction between water and hydrophobic side chains, however, is the subject of some controversy at this time.

Results: Shapes of Protein Molecules

Using the various methods mentioned, it is possible to classify the proteins found in nature into two groups, the fibrous and the globular. For the purpose of this classification an arbitrary dividing line between the two groups may be set at an axial ratio of 10. Proteins having a length/width ratio under 10 will be considered globular, while those with ratios over 10 will fall into the fibrous class.

(*1*) ***Fibrous proteins.*** A typical fibrous protein consists of a more or less elongated peptide chain or a group of such chains. Each chain may be extended or helically coiled along its length. X-ray diffraction studies indicate the presence of amorphous regions in which the chains are distributed in random fashion in space, interspersed with "crystalline" regions in which the adjacent chains are arranged with much the same regularity as that found in the true crystal.

Keratin, a protein found in hair, wool, and skin, has a fibrous structure. As found in nature it is in the form of coiled (α-helical) peptide chains, with cross-linkages between adjacent chains of the —S—S— type, formed from the amino acid cystine. The keratin helices are believed to be twisted about each other to form "coiled coils," a typical conformation of structural proteins. Stretching of the keratin fiber causes unfolding of the natural, or α-keratin configuration, to form the elongated β-keratin, which may have the parallel-chain, pleated-sheet structure (p. 76), or may be a mixture of the parallel and antiparallel. A good deal of the stability of keratin is due to the disulfide linkages, which are cleaved only by vigorous reagents. Silk fibroin contains extended chains, in the antiparallel pleated sheet configuration, causing them to be rather inelastic. Collagen, the major protein of connective tissue, consists of three peptide chains, two of which are identical, the third different, in amino acid composition. Each chain is a left-handed helix, the three helices being wound about each other in a right-handed "super helix" of shallow pitch. Fibrinogen, an elongated molecule found in blood plasma, forms clots of fibrin by increasing its chain length even further by head-to-tail coupling, accompanied by formation of a dense network of cross-linkages. These changes are preceded by cleavage of "fibrinopeptides" under the influence of thrombin (p. 801). The muscle proteins myosin and actin, and their complex, actomyosin, form a fibrous system which represents the mechanical basis of muscle contraction.

(2) ***Globular proteins.*** The typical globular protein consists of a rather compactly folded or coiled peptide chain or group of chains. In these compounds the axial ratios are usually well under 10, and frequently are only about 3 or 4. X-ray diffraction studies

indicate a high degree of regularity in structure. Most of the easily crystallizable proteins fall into this group, as might be expected from the regularity which is required in true crystal structures.

It appears that the secondary structure of globular proteins involves the α-helix. However, because of the rather compact shape of the globular proteins, the helices must be tightly folded or looped. There is evidence that globular proteins do not consist entirely of α-helical structures. Estimates of the extent of helical coiling in proteins, based upon measurements of optical rotatory dispersion, X-ray diffraction, and rates of exchange between atoms of hydrogen and deuterium, vary from a figure of 12 per cent in silk fibroin to a value of 81 per cent helix in ovalbumin.

Regardless of its actual detailed conformation, there is much evidence from many fields of investigation that the native globular protein is rather compactly folded, to the extent that certain functional groups known to occur in the protein are not available for ordinary chemical reactions. Many of these groups, such as the phenolic group of tyrosine, the sulfhydryl group of cysteine, and the disulfide group of cystine, often detectable only with difficulty in the native protein, become easily detectable when the protein is denatured. These matters are discussed in more detail in the section on denaturation (p. 87).

Figure 4–9 illustrates the tertiary conformation of the globin moiety of myoglobin, which is quite similar to the globin sub-units in the quaternary array of hemoglobin (p. 124).

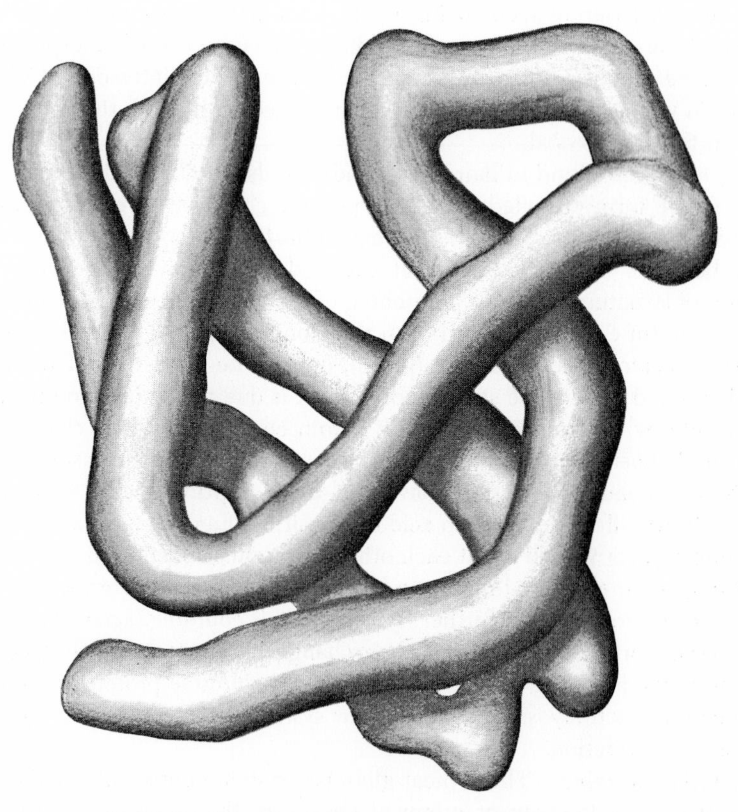

Figure 4–9. Typical conformation of peptide chain in a globular protein, after myoglobin structure of Kendrew et al. and hemoglobin structure of Perutz et al.

The myoglobin molecule consists of one peptide chain. The sausage-like structure in the drawing is actually a hollow tube, the straight segments of which are α-helical. In addition to the corners, several other non-helical segments also exist, including one at the carboxyl end of the chain (upper left). Side chains of the amino acids, and the iron-porphyrin ring, two features which are omitted from the drawing for simplicity, result in virtual filling of the internal space in the actual molecule; only a few molecules of water are trapped inside.

Most of the polar side chains of myoglobin are located on the outside surface of the molecule; all of these appear to be hydrated. A few polar side chains are "buried" in the interior, where they are not detectable by methods which suffice for their surface brethren. The interior of the molecule appears to be largely a region of non-polar side chains, closely packed and interacting by van der Waals forces. Calculations suggest that these hydrophobic bonds may be quantitatively more important than hydrogen and ionic bonds in stabilization of the tertiary structure. Details concerning the heme group and heme-linked histidine residues of myoglobin and hemoglobin are discussed elsewhere (p. 129).

Insulin, a hormone of the pancreas, belongs to the globular class of proteins. The "sub-unit" of insulin, having a molecular weight of 6000, consists of two peptide chains joined by disulfide linkages (p. 723). As found in the crystalline state or in solution, insulin is an aggregate of two to eight of these sub-units. Many of the components of the albumin and globulin fractions of the blood plasma are globular proteins (for properties, see p. 560).

The Size of Protein Molecules: Colloidal Properties

(*a*) ***Importance.*** To those proteins with an obvious structural purpose in life, large size is an advantage which needs no special explanation. The protein components of fibers, membranes, and other "insoluble" structures are examples of this group. Among the soluble proteins, large size first of all limits diffusibility, thus keeping a protein at its workbench, instead of allowing it to wander throughout the body. (Some proteins, however, are definitely nomadic as part of their function, e.g., the protein hormones.) The really striking advantage of colloidal dimensions is best seen when we consider those proteins which have catalytic functions, such as enzymes, antigens and antibodies, and probably hormones. In order to perform certain operations on smaller molecules, it is necessary for biocatalysts first of all to attract the smaller victims to their surfaces, and one of the chief attributes of colloidal particles is a large surface area, facilitating the phenomenon of adsorption. Also, the particular chemical reaction which is to be catalyzed by the protein, such as cleavage in two of a substrate at some specific linkage, requires an intense electrical field, strong enough to react with the linkage being attacked, and with its (+) and (−) charges at exactly the proper positions in space. Of all the substances available in nature, none but the proteins can meet these specifications.

(*b*) ***Osmotic pressure.*** In order to investigate the molecular sizes of the proteins, it is necessary to use methods of physical chemistry which have been developed especially for colloidal systems. One of the simplest of these, in principle, is the measurement of osmotic pressure. A highly diagrammatic representation of an apparatus for this purpose is given in Figure 4–10. The inverted thistle tube has firmly sealed over its large end a membrane such as cellophane, which is freely permeable to water (solvent), but impermeable to the protein being investigated (solute). A known weight of the protein is dissolved in water and the solution used to fill the inverted thistle tube to the index mark. The open end of this tube is then attached to a pressure gauge and gas tank, and the thistle tube

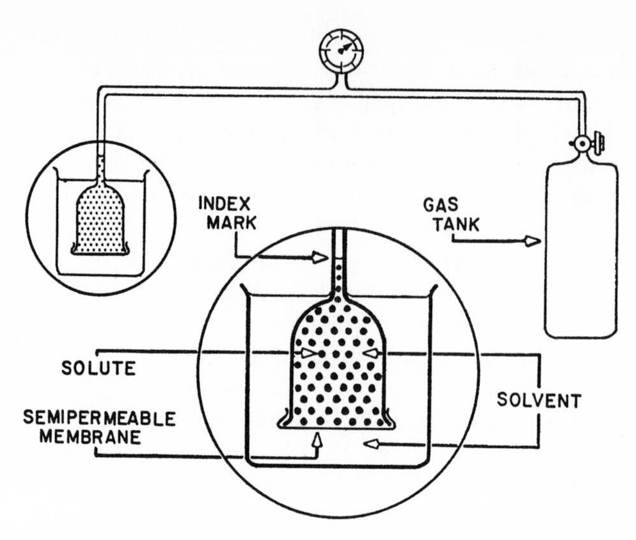

Figure 4-10. Osmotic pressure.

is immersed in water. On the solvent side of the membrane the water molecules are uninhibited and pass through the orifices of the membrane at the maximum rate fixed by the conditions of the experiment. On the solution side of the membrane, movements of the water molecules are inhibited by the presence of the protein molecules, which by the nature of the membrane must remain on the inside of the thistle tube. The activity of the water molecules inside the tube is thus less than that of the water on the outside, the former molecules pass through the orifices to the outside at a slower rate than those coming in, and a net influx of water into the tube tends to occur. This influx can be prevented by applying pressure to the inner solution from the gas tank, adjusting the pressure so that the solution in the thistle tube remains at the level of the index mark. The pressure required to accomplish this, read on the pressure gauge, is numerically equal to the pressure tending to force water into the thistle tube, hence it is a measure of the osmotic pressure. Under ideal conditions a protein solution of 1 molar concentration will exert an osmotic pressure of 22.4 atmospheres at 0° C, so that the molecular weight of the protein can be calculated from its osmotic pressure and weight concentration.

(*c*) ***Ultracentrifugation.*** Although the proteins are large molecules, their size is not such as to make them settle out under the influence of gravity. By increasing the gravitational force, however, as in an ultracentrifuge, proteins can be forced to sediment at rates related to their molecular weights. By the use of optical scanning devices such as those described in connection with electrophoresis, the migrating boundaries of individual proteins in a mixture can be observed while the ultracentrifuge is in operation (Fig. 4-11). The results of ultracentrifugal analysis can be used not only for the calculation of molecular weights, but also for the demonstration of the presence of several components in a mixture of proteins. Its use for quantitative analysis of mixtures is limited by its resolution, which is much inferior to that obtained by electrophoresis. One recent analytical application, however, has arisen in connection with the plasma lipoproteins (p. 489), some of which are thought to be related to the occurrence of atherosclerosis. By adjusting the density of plasma samples to the proper value, lipoproteins (which have a rather low density due to the lipid component) can be made to migrate toward the axis of rotation in an ultracentrifuge, this procedure being one of flotation rather than sedimentation.

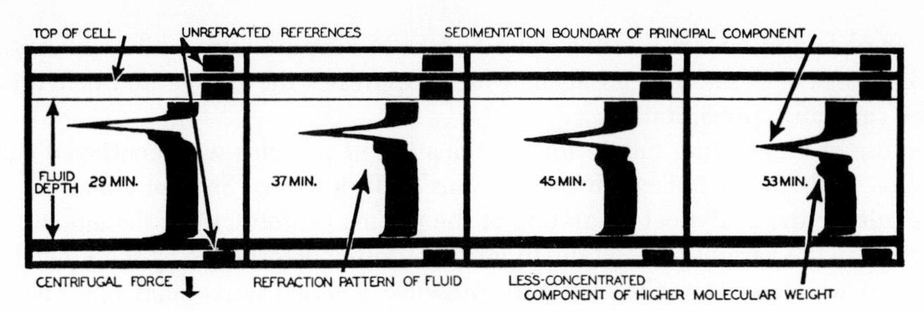

Figure 4-11. Ultracentrifugation of commercially prepared γ-globulin. (Spinco Division, Beckman Instruments, Inc.)

(*d*) ***Light-scattering.*** Colloidal substances exhibit the Tyndall effect; that is, a beam of light projected through such systems becomes visible to the observer owing to the scattering of light from the colloidal particles at right angles to the incident beam. Advantage may be taken of this effect in determining the molecular weight of proteins, for a simple relationship exists between the molecular weight, concentration, and turbidity of colloidal systems when the results are extrapolated to zero concentration.

Other methods which have been used for determination of the molecular weights of proteins include free diffusion and X-ray diffraction. To some extent the electron microscope also furnishes information on the approximate dimensions of the largest protein molecules.

(*e*) ***Molecular weights.*** Table 4-4 summarizes the currently accepted molecular weights of some typical proteins. Under certain conditions some of the proteins listed appear to have molecular weights higher or lower than those given in the table. The former circumstance is the result of aggregation, the latter of dissociation, both of which are of common enough occurrence to be disturbing factors in any attempt to fix a "true" molecular weight for those proteins subject to such behavior.

(*f*) ***Fractionation by salting out.*** Many of the methods for fractionation of proteins are based primarily on considerations of molecular size. For example, the proteins are forced out of solution by increasing concentrations of salt in an order which, roughly, proceeds from the larger to the smaller protein molecules. This method of "salting out" proteins probably depends upon several physical phenomena, the two most important of which are a suppression of the charge on the surface of the protein by the salt ions of opposite charge, and a removal of the shell of water from around the protein molecule by the competition of the ions of the salt for that water. Since the surface charge and

TABLE 4-4. MOLECULAR WEIGHTS OF PROTEINS*

Insulin	6000 (monomer)	Hemoglobin	68,000
Ribonuclease	13,000	Urease	480,000
Cytochrome *c*	13,000	Thyroglobulin	630,000
Lactalbumin	17,400	Myosin	840,000
Myoglobin	17,500	Actomyosin	4 million
Bence Jones proteins	35,000 and 37,000	Tobacco mosaic virus	40 million
β-Lactoglobulin	38,000	Lung thromboplastin	167 million
Pepsin	39,000	Influenza virus	200 to 322 million
Ovalbumin	44,000		

* Physical data on plasma proteins are tabulated elsewhere (p. 560).

the water of hydration are the two chief factors in keeping hydrophilic colloids in suspension, it is easy to see how an agent which suppresses the charge and dehydrates the particles can cause precipitation.

The use of ammonium sulfate for fractionation of proteins was mentioned earlier in connection with the classification of albumins and globulins. Sodium sulfate is a more suitable salt for the analytical separation of the plasma proteins, since the amount of protein present in the various precipitates or filtrates is often determined by the Kjeldahl nitrogen method, which could not be used in the presence of added ammonium ions. The original sodium sulfate procedure (Howe) gave results which have been found to disagree with those obtained by electrophoretic analysis. Modifications of this method have corrected these errors by readjustment of the concentrations of sodium sulfate used in each step (p. 559).

(*g*) ***Fractionation by solvents.*** Although salting out is a useful procedure, both for analytical purposes and for the isolation and purification of proteins on a laboratory scale, the subsequent removal of the added salt presents a difficult problem, particularly when it is desired to prepare such materials as plasma protein fractions on a pilot-plant or industrial scale for clinical use. The development of the method of alcohol fractionation at low temperatures, together with the procedure of drying protein precipitates in vacuo from the frozen state (freeze-drying, or lyophilization), has provided a satisfactory solution to this problem.

The addition of alcohol to an aqueous system lowers its dielectric constant, which means, in effect, that the electrical forces between charged particles in the solution are increased, thus reducing the solubilities of substances such as proteins. At high alcohol concentrations the dehydration of the protein molecules also may be a contributing factor. Whatever the underlying phenomena may be, it has been adequately demonstrated that proper adjustment of the pH, alcohol concentration, temperature, protein concentration, and total salt concentration (usually kept at low levels) makes possible a more selective separation of the constituent proteins of a mixture than can be achieved by the older salting-out method. The deleterious effects which alcohol can have on proteins (see under "denaturation," p. 87) are minimized by conducting the fractionations at low temperatures and removing the water and alcohol from the protein fractions in a vacuum while these substances are in a frozen state. In certain of the procedures the dielectric constant is increased, when desired, by the addition of glycine to the system. Some of the more recent fractionations have made use of the insoluble complexes formed by proteins with zinc ions.

While the initial fractionation of plasma, following the above procedures, does not result in homogeneous proteins, it can be supplemented by further separations to secure many of the proteins of each crude fraction in a pure state. Furthermore, the crude fractions have many clinical uses. For instance, one fraction is used for the preparation of fibrin film and fibrin foam, which find application in surgery. Plasma albumin, the most important fraction of the blood in the treatment of shock, nephrosis, and cirrhosis, has been made available in concentrated form. Antibodies are largely found in the γ-globulin fraction, which is used to confer passive immunity to certain infectious diseases (measles and hepatitis). Blood typing has been greatly aided by the preparation of concentrated agglutinins from the plasma of appropriate donors.

(*h*) ***Dialysis.*** The colloidal dimensions of proteins, in addition to providing the physical basis for fractionation procedures such as salting out, also make possible certain other techniques which are useful in the laboratory and even have their counterparts in biological systems. Dialysis, for example, involves the removal of smaller, crystalloidal particles from proteins (or other colloids) by selective diffusion through a membrane of appropriate permeability (Fig. 4–12). Thus, the salts used in precipitation of a protein can

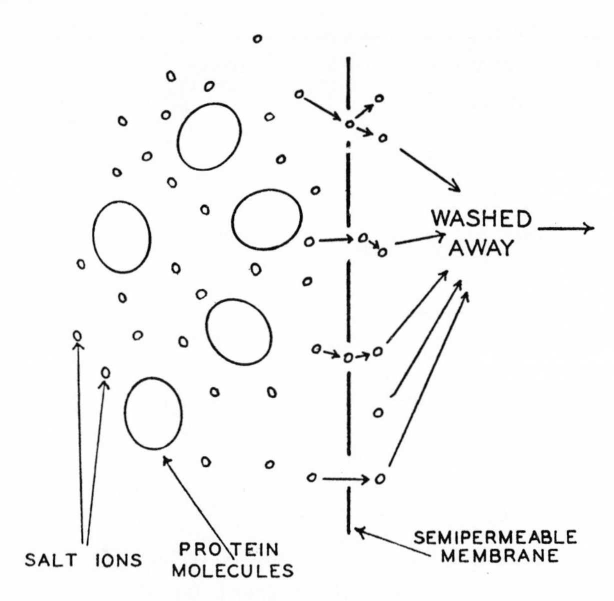

Figure 4-12. Dialysis.

be removed by suspending the protein and salts in water inside of a cellophane sack, immersing this sack in a large volume of water, and changing the outside water until no more salt ions are detected, having been washed out. This desalting can be accelerated by electrodialysis, in which the protein is placed in the central chamber of a series of three, the compartments being separated by cellophane membranes. Electrodes are placed in the two outer chambers, and a current of electricity is passed through the system, causing rapid migration of diffusible ions (salts only) out of the central chamber. Another variation of dialysis is ultrafiltration, which is dialysis under pressure, the water and crystalloids being forced through the semipermeable membrane (in this case, firmly supported to withstand the pressure) by the application of positive pressure from above the solution or of suction from below, or both simultaneously.

The non-dialyzability of proteins is of importance in certain biological situations, such as the filtration process across the glomerular membranes of the kidney, the passage of interstitial fluid across the capillary wall, osmotic equilibration between tissue cells and extracellular fluid, and the Donnan equilibrium which controls the distribution of diffusible ions across the membrane of the red cell.

(*i*) ***Molecular sieves.*** This technique, which represents a sorting out of molecules according to molecular size by differential permeability into a gel, will be discussed in connection with chromatography (p. 98).

DISRUPTION OF THE HIGHER LEVELS OF ORGANIZATION: DENATURATION

Characteristics

Denaturation may be defined as a disruption of the secondary, tertiary, and, where applicable, quaternary organization of a protein, due to the cleavage of non-covalent

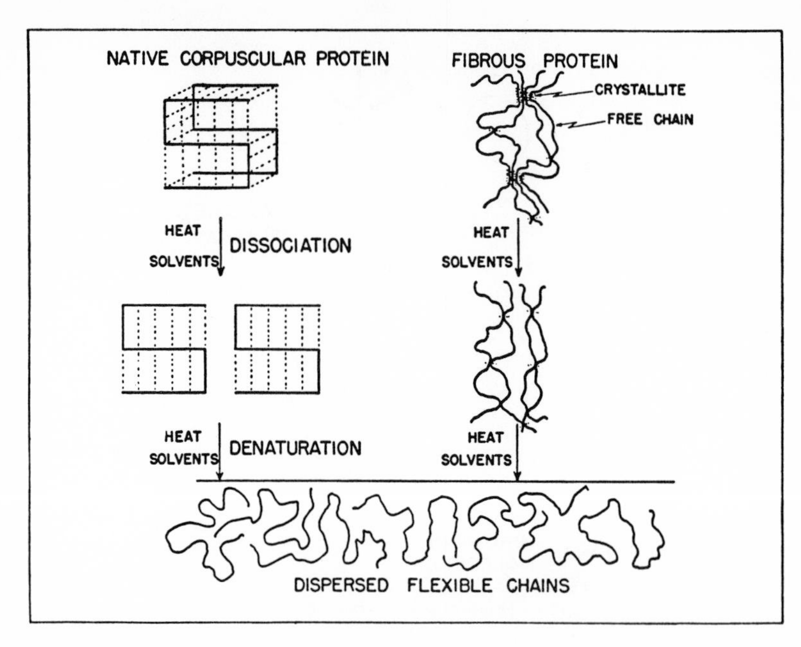

Figure 4–13. Denaturation of globular (corpuscular) and fibrous proteins. (Adapted from Lundgren: Advances in Protein Chemistry, Vol. 5, Academic Press, Inc., 1949.)

bonds. This disorganization results in alteration of the chemical, physical, and biological characteristics of the protein. Figure 4–13 illustrates the type of change involved in going from the organized structures of globular or fibrous proteins to the dispersed, flexible chains of the denatured state. The quaternary array, where such exists, dissociates into its component sub-units, these tertiary structures unfold, and helical secondary structures, if present, also unwind to yield, finally, randomly oriented polypeptide chains. Complete dispersion of chains or complete dissociation of certain intra-chain segments may not occur if these units are linked by covalent disulfide bridges, which ordinarily are not cleaved in denaturation.

Although it would seem unlikely that such changes could be reversible, since the native state of most proteins is characterized by a very specific organization, it has been found, nevertheless, that conversion of certain denatured proteins into forms practically indistinguishable from their native forms can take place. This suggests that the native conformation of the protein may be the most thermodynamically stable form, and that, given a specific sequence of amino acids, the polypeptide chain spontaneously folds into the "native" secondary and tertiary conformations (and these associate to form quaternary arrays, if necessary). If true, this hypothesis could have important implications for the mechanism and genetics of protein synthesis (p. 556).

Since denaturation consists of a series of events, it is evident that various degrees of denaturation may occur, depending upon the severity of treatment given to the protein.

Denaturing Agents

Many agents can cause denaturation. Included in the list are physical agents such as heat, surface action, ultraviolet light, ultrasound, and high pressure, and chemical agents such as organic solvents, acids and alkalies, urea and guanidine, and detergents. It is probable that the denaturing action involves a disturbance by these reagents of the hydrophobic linkages between non-polar side chains in the protein. Urea and guanidine probably interfere with the hydrogen bonds between peptide linkages, forming hydrogen bonds of their own with these linkages. (An action by these agents on hydrophobic linkages also has been suggested.) Acids and bases probably attack directly the hydrogen bonds in the secondary and tertiary structure of the proteins, although it has also been suggested that great electrostatic repulsions would be expected between different parts of a protein molecule when the protein is at a pH far from its isoelectric point, sufficing to disrupt secondary and tertiary structures.

Chemical Alterations

Among the altered chemical properties of the denatured protein is its greatly decreased solubility at its isoelectric point. Many proteins which are quite soluble over the entire pH range, and merely exhibit decreased solubility when isoelectric in their native state, become highly insoluble at that pH upon denaturation. As a result of the unfolding process in denaturation, many chemical groups which were rather inactive owing to shielding in the native state become exposed and more readily detectable. Among these are the sulfhydryl group of cysteine, the disulfide group of cystine, the phenolic group of tyrosine, and several others.

Physical Alterations

A further consequence of the conversion of the compact, native structure to the dispersed chains of the denatured proteins is an increase in the viscosity of the solution. Simultaneously, the rate of diffusion of the protein molecules decreases, as might be expected. The altered conformation of the denatured protein also results in increased flow birefringence and levorotation. Many proteins, especially of the globular type, can be crystallized in the native state. Since the formation of a crystal depends upon a high degree of organization of the molecules, it is not surprising that denatured proteins cannot be crystallized.

Biological Alterations

Increased digestibility by proteolytic enzymes has been found in the case of certain denatured proteins. The most marked alterations in biological properties, however, are suffered by those proteins which in the native state had some specific biological function. For instance, enzymatic or hormonal activity is usually destroyed by denaturation. The antigenic or antibody functions of proteins are frequently altered as well.

Denaturation, Flocculation, Coagulation

If a protein is denatured by heat at a pH relatively far removed from its isoelectric point and in the virtual absence of salts, the solution may undergo no very obvious change, although chemical or physical tests will reveal the presence of denatured protein. Adjustment of the pH of the solution to the isoelectric point of the protein will cause it to precipitate, for which process the specific term "flocculation" is used. The flocculation of a denatured protein is reversible in the sense that adjustment of the pH to some value above or below the isoelectric range results in solution of the precipitate. Flocculation is obviously a simple clumping together of the dispersed chains of denatured protein when the forces of mutual repulsion are at a minimum. If a denatured, flocculated protein is heated, the clumped chains become matted together in a mass which is insoluble, not only at the pI, but over the entire pH range. This process is known as coagulation. Among other reactions, heat coagulation may involve formation of new cross-linkages between peptide chains, probably of the disulfide type. Heat denaturation of a protein at its pI results in an apparently direct coagulation, but this is only the final, visible manifestation of a series of changes which includes denaturation and flocculation. The relationship between these phenomena can be illustrated as follows:

$$
\begin{array}{ccccc}
\text{pH} < \text{pI} & & \text{pH} = \text{pI} & & \text{pH} > \text{pI} \\
\text{Pr}^{+}_{\text{native}} & \underset{\text{OH}^-}{\overset{\text{H}^+}{\rightleftharpoons}} & \text{Pr}^{0}_{\text{native}} & \underset{\text{H}^+}{\overset{\text{OH}^-}{\rightleftharpoons}} & \text{Pr}^{-}_{\text{native}} \\
\text{(soluble)} & & \text{(soluble)} & & \text{(soluble)} \\
\Big\downarrow \text{Heat} & & \Big\downarrow \text{Heat} & & \Big\downarrow \text{Heat} \\
 & & \text{Pr}^{0}_{\text{denatured}} & & \\
 & & \text{(flocculated, coagulated)} & & \\
 & & \Big\uparrow \text{Heat} & & \\
\text{Pr}^{+}_{\text{denatured}} & \underset{\text{H}^+}{\overset{\text{OH}^-}{\rightleftharpoons}} & \text{Pr}^{0}_{\text{denatured}} & \underset{\text{OH}^-}{\overset{\text{H}^+}{\rightleftharpoons}} & \text{Pr}^{-}_{\text{denatured}} \\
\text{(soluble)} & & \text{(flocculated)} & & \text{(soluble)} \\
\text{pH} < \text{pI} & & \text{pH} = \text{pI} & & \text{pH} > \text{pI}
\end{array}
$$

Applications and Importance

Denaturation is usually something to be avoided. The methods employed by the protein chemist and the enzymologist in the preparation of their materials involve extreme precautions which are designed to subject the protein as little as possible to conditions other than those it encounters in its native environment. Maintenance of low temperatures, avoidance of extremes of pH, elimination of toxic heavy metals from reagents and apparatus, and precautions against shaking and frothing are some of the conditions which come under consideration. Conversely, deproteinization of a solution is frequently achieved by heat coagulation of the proteins, or by precipitation under denaturing conditions with organic solvents or other reagents. A qualitative test for albumin in the urine involves acidification to the pI of the protein and heat coagulation.

QUALITATIVE AND QUANTITATIVE TESTS FOR AMINO ACIDS AND PROTEINS

Reactions of Constituent Groups

(a) Carboxyl Groups

(*1*) ***Salt formation.*** Among the many recognized reactions of carboxyl groups, that of forming salts with cations is of considerable importance in the case of amino acids and proteins. The combination of these substances with basic dyes, the precipitation of proteins by cationic detergents, and some of the precipitations of proteins with heavy metal cations (insofar as the —SH group is not involved) are apparently due to direct union of the cationic reagent with the anionic groups of the protein. Carboxylate anions form the majority of such groups in the average protein. Proteins combine best with cationic reagents when the proteins themselves are anionic, i.e., on the basic side of their isoelectric points.

(2) ***Back-titration.*** The direct titration of carboxylate anions back to the undissociated acid form is seldom practical, owing to the extremely acidic end-point. Such titrations can be performed, however, by utilizing the considerable increase in pK_1 which occurs upon the addition of certain solvents to the aqueous system.

(b) Amino Groups

(*1*) ***Formol titration.*** Free amino groups in amino acids and proteins can be estimated by a technique known as formol titration. The reaction which occurs between amino groups and formaldehyde is:

$$R{-}\underset{}{\overset{NH_3^+}{\overset{|}{C}H}}{-}COO^- \rightleftharpoons R{-}\overset{NH_2}{\overset{|}{C}H}{-}COO^- + H^+$$

$$\Big\downarrow \begin{matrix}H\\HC{=}O\end{matrix}$$

$$R{-}\overset{NH{-}CH_2OH}{\overset{|}{C}H}{-}COO^-$$

$$\Big\downarrow \begin{matrix}H\\HC{=}O\end{matrix}$$

$$R{-}\overset{N(CH_2OH)_2}{\overset{|}{C}H}{-}COO^-$$

An equilibrium always exists between the zwitterion form of an amino acid and the anionic form plus a hydrogen ion, this equilibrium representing the ionization of the cationic ammonium group. Formaldehyde reacts with the uncharged amino group, forming N-methylol or N,N-dimethylol derivatives, thus shifting the ionization equilibrium to the right by removing one of the products of the reaction. In effect, the addition of formaldehyde to a solution of an amino acid or protein decreases the pK_2 of the ammonium groups, making them stronger acids. The formol titration of glycine is shown in Figure 4–14, superimposed upon the ordinary pH-titration curve for purposes of explanation. An initially isoelectric solution of glycine is titrated with standard base to the phenolphthalein end point in the presence of formaldehyde. Owing to the decrease of pK_2 from 9.6 to about 7 in the presence of formaldehyde, the ammonium group is completely titrated at pH of 9, instead of at 11. Hence, the effect of formaldehyde is to place the titration of ammonium groups in the convenient range of the usual indicators, and also to avoid the complications due to absorption of atmospheric CO_2 which occurs at a pH as alkaline as 11.

(2) ***Van Slyke nitrous acid method.*** Free amino groups react with nitrous acid to form hydroxyl groups and liberate gaseous nitrogen.

$$R{-}\overset{NH_2}{\overset{|}{C}H}{-}COOH \xrightarrow{HNO_2} R{-}\overset{OH}{\overset{|}{C}H}{-}COOH + N_2 + H_2O$$

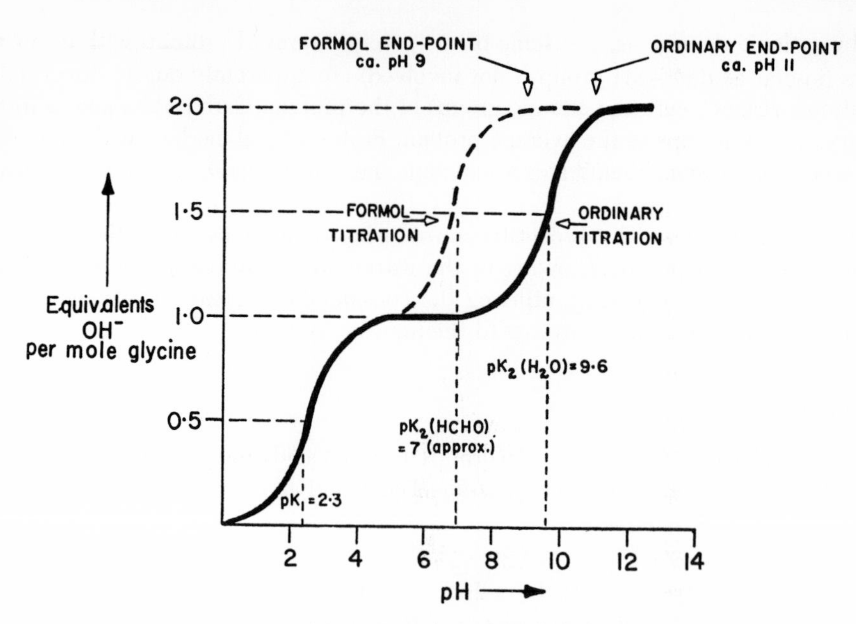

Figure 4-14. Formol titration of glycine.

Volumetric or manometric measurement of the nitrogen is the basis of the Van Slyke method for the estimation of amino groups. As in the case of formol titration, *free* amino groups are measured, regardless of the attachments of the carboxyl groups, so that both methods can be used to determine the number of such amino groups in peptides and proteins.

(3) ***Ninhydrin reaction.*** Ninhydrin (triketohydrindene hydrate) undergoes an oxidation-reduction reaction with free amino groups, oxidatively deaminating them to carbonyl groups and ammonia. The reduced form of the ninhydrin couples with the ammonia and the residual ninhydrin to give rise to a blue-violet dye:

$$-\overset{NH_2}{\underset{H}{C}}- + \text{C}_6\text{H}_4(\text{C=O})_2\text{C(OH)}_2 \longrightarrow -\overset{O}{\overset{\|}{C}}- + \text{C}_6\text{H}_4(\text{C=O})(\text{C}-\text{O}^-)\text{=C(OH)} + NH_3$$

$$\text{C}_6\text{H}_4(\text{C=O})_2\text{C(OH)}_2 + H\text{-}N\text{-}H + \text{(HO)C=C(O}^-\text{)(C=O)C}_6\text{H}_4 \xrightarrow{-3H_2O} \text{C}_6\text{H}_4(\text{C=O})_2\text{C=N-C=C(O}^-\text{)(C=O)C}_6\text{H}_4$$

This is the essence of the ninhydrin *color* reaction, which is positive for all free amino groups, whether in amino acids, peptides, or proteins. In the case of free amino acids, which possess a free carboxyl group adjacent to the amino group, a further reaction takes place, causing decarboxylation of the amino acid to CO_2 and the next lower aldehyde, in addition to the liberation of ammonia and the color reaction. This *decarboxylating* ninhydrin reaction is negative for peptides and proteins. Quantitative methods based on the ninhydrin reactions may measure the NH_3, CO_2, or the colored complex, depending on the purpose of the analysis.

(*4*) ***Anionic precipitants.*** Various anionic reagents react with the cationic groups of the protein molecule, such as the ammonium, imidazolium, and guanidinium groups. The precipitation of proteins by anionic detergents, metaphosphate, trichloroacetate, tungstate, picrate, ferrocyanide, and anionic dyes involves such a reaction. Combination of a protein with an anion is best effected when the protein itself is cationic, i.e., on the acid side of its isoelectric point.

(*5*) ***Fluorodinitrobenzene.*** Amino groups combine with fluorodinitrobenzene to yield N-dinitrophenyl derivatives. This reaction has already been mentioned as a means of labeling and locating the terminal amino acids of proteins.

$$R{-}NH_2 \xrightarrow{NO_2C_6H_3(NO_2)F} R{-}NH{-}C_6H_3(NO_2)_2 + HF$$

(*6*) ***Carbamino reaction.*** The free amino groups of proteins can condense with carbon dioxide, forming carbamino compounds.

$$R{-}NH_2 + CO_2 \longrightarrow R{-}\overset{H}{N}{-}\overset{O}{\overset{\|}{C}}{-}O^- + H^+$$

Such compounds of the plasma proteins and, to an even greater extent, of hemoglobin are concerned in the transport of carbon dioxide in the blood.

(c) R— Groups

(*1*) ***Millon's reagent.*** Millon's reagent, a mixture of mercuric and mercurous nitrates and nitrites, produces a red color when heated with compounds containing phenolic groups, such as tyrosine. The reaction probably involves mercuration and nitration or nitrosation. It is given by tyrosine whether free or combined in proteins.

(*2*) ***Xanthoproteic reaction.*** In the xanthoproteic reaction the sample is heated with concentrated nitric acid, cooled, and made alkaline. In the presence of either tyrosine or tryptophan, yellowish nitro compounds are formed by the action of the nitric acid on the aromatic or heterocyclic rings. The nitro compounds are converted to orange-colored salts by the alkali. Under the usual conditions of the test the simple benzene ring of phenylalanine is not reactive enough to respond.

(*3*) ***Folin's phenol reagent.*** Folin's phenol reagent (a phosphomolybdotungstic acid) in alkaline solution undergoes reduction to a blue form in the presence of tyrosine or tryptophan. The reaction is not very specific, since many easily oxidizable substances can interfere.

(*4*) ***Hopkins-Cole reaction.*** In the presence of acid, many aldehydes condense with the indole ring of tryptophan to yield colored products. The original Hopkins-Cole procedure, applied as a qualitative test, calls for mixing the sample with a solution of glyoxylic acid (an aldehyde-acid, its structure being an aldehyde group attached to a carboxyl group), then carefully layering concentrated sulfuric acid under the mixture. The presence of tryptophan is indicated by the appearance of a violet ring at the interface.

(*5*) ***Bromine-water reaction.*** Free tryptophan in weakly acidic solution produces a pink color with bromine water. The reaction is said to be due to halogenation of the tryptophan. It differs from most of the other color tests for this amino acid in being positive only when the tryptophan is free, not combined in a protein.

(6) ***Pauly reaction.*** Histidine and tyrosine couple with diazotized sulfanilic acid in alkaline solution, forming red products which are doubtless azo dyes.

(7) ***Sakaguchi reaction.*** In the Sakaguchi reaction, arginine develops a red color when treated with α-naphthol and sodium hypochlorite or hypobromite.

(8) ***Alkali-labile sulfur.*** Protein sulfur which is present as sulfhydryl or disulfide groups (cysteine and cystine) can be detected by the formation of lead sulfide when alkaline solutions of the protein are heated with lead acetate. The sulfur of methionine is not alkali-labile.

(9) ***Nitroprusside reaction.*** Free sulfhydryl groups, as in cysteine, some proteins, and glutathione (in its reduced form), react with sodium nitroprusside in ammoniacal solution to produce a red color. Ammonium sulfate intensifies the reaction. Disulfide groups (as in cystine) give a positive reaction only after reduction to sulfhydryl groups.

(d) Peptide linkage

Substances containing two or more peptide linkages produce a blue-violet color with dilute copper solutions in a strong alkali. This is called the biuret reaction, after the compound biuret, which happens to give the test. The color is due to a complex between the cupric ion and two adjacent peptide chains. According to recent determinations, the ratio of copper to peptide nitrogen is 6 in the case of most proteins. This is explained, as can be seen in the accompanying formula, by coordination of the copper with a peptide nitrogen and formation of a covalent bond to the oxygen of the enolized form of the next peptide linkage, the process occurring symmetrically in two adjacent peptide chains. The structure of the α-helix (p. 76) prevents the third peptide linkage in each chain from participating in this or the subsequent copper linkage, hence the N/Cu ratio of 6 for the two adjacent chains and the bulk protein. (Serum globulin has a ratio of 5.)

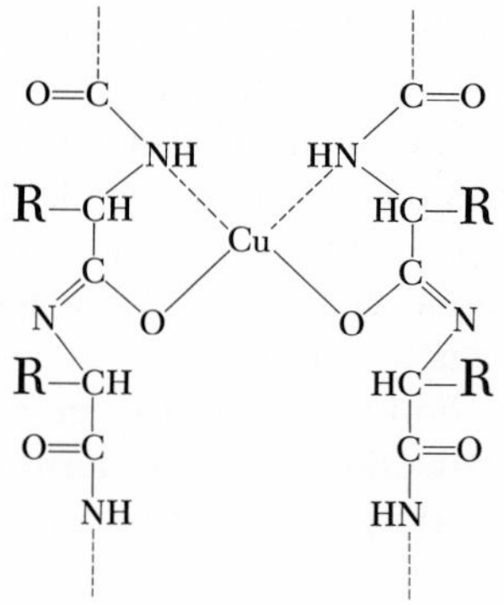

```
      |                     |
     O=C                   C=O
         \                /
          NH          HN
    R—CH     \      /     HC—R
      |        \  /         |
      C         Cu          C
    //  \      /  \       /  \\
   N     O               O     N
    \                         /
    R—CH                   HC—R
      |                     |
     O=C                   C=O
      |                     |
      NH                   HN
      |                     |
```

Although many substances other than peptides and proteins give a positive reaction to the biuret test, these substances, for the most part, do not occur in nature. The amino acid histidine, however, gives a positive reaction.

(e) Total Nitrogen

All of the nitrogen of a protein, whether in peptide linkage or not, can be determined by the Kjeldahl method. This involves digestion with concentrated sulfuric acid, usually in the presence of certain catalytic substances to hasten the reaction. The carbonaceous matter is entirely oxidized and the nitrogen is left in the form of ammonium sulfate. Alkalinization and distillation of the ammonia into a known excess of standard acid, followed by titration of the residual acid, complete the procedure. In an alternate procedure, the ammonia resulting from the Kjeldahl digestion is allowed to react directly with Nessler's reagent (a potassium mercuric iodide), forming a colored compound which is matched against standards in the colorimeter.

SEPARATION AND DETERMINATION OF AMINO ACIDS (WITH SOME APPLICATIONS TO PROTEINS)

(a) Methods of Fischer, Dakin, Van Slyke, and Others

One of the earliest methods for the determination of the amino acids in the protein hydrolysate was that of Emil Fischer, who fractionally distilled the ethyl esters of the amino acids in vacuo. Butyl alcohol was used by Dakin to separate certain groups of amino acids from others. Fractionation of the amino acids into neutral (monoamino, monocarboxylic), basic (diamino), and acidic (dicarboxylic) groups, followed by application of the Van Slyke nitrous acid method, was another of the earlier attempts at separation and estimation of the amino acids arising from the hydrolysis of proteins. These techniques are seldom if ever used at the present time.

(b) Electrodialysis

By passing an electric current through a mixture of amino acids which is in the central compartment of a three-part apparatus, with each part separated from the others by a semipermeable membrane, it is possible to cause a differential migration of amino acids from one compartment to another. The charges carried by the amino acids can be regulated by proper adjustment of the pH, so that, for instance, diamino acids can be collected at the cathode, and dicarboxylic acids in the anodic compartment, while the monoamino monocarboxylic acids remain in the central compartment.

(c) Solubility Product

Few reagents are known which specifically precipitate single amino acids quantitatively. However, even semiquantitative precipitations would be expected to follow the solubility-product law, which states that the product of the concentrations of the two substances (amino acid and precipitant) in equilibrium with the precipitate will be a constant. The application of this principle to amino acid determinations involves, essentially, two determinations of this constant on two separate aliquots of the sample containing different quantities of precipitant, resulting in what amounts to two simultaneous equations in two unknowns.

(d) Isotope Dilution and Isotope Derivative Methods

The amount of any constituent in a mixture can be ascertained by adding to the mixture a known quantity of the compound to be determined, but differing from the normal substance by being labeled with an isotopic atom. Isolation of the compound in a pure state (the isolation need not be quantitative) and determination of the degree of dilution of the original isotopic reagent with non-isotopic compound lead directly to the calculation of the quantity of the latter which must have been present in the sample. Another isotopic technique involves the preparation of labeled derivatives of the amino acids in a mixture, using an isotopic acylating reagent, for example. A known excess of unlabeled derivative of one particular amino acid is then added to the mixture, re-isolated, and the amount of original amino acid in the mixture calculated from the isotope content of the purified derivative.

(e) Chromatography

Chromatography may be defined as a technique in which the components of a mixture are caused to migrate at different rates through an apparatus which involves equilibration of compounds between a stationary and a moving phase. The four types of chromatography in current use are adsorption, partition, ion-exchange, and molecular sieve chromatography, to use a classification based upon the physical forces underlying each type. The result obtained in chromatographing a sample is called a chromatogram.

It should be emphasized that, although chromatography is discussed at this point, its application is by no means restricted to the amino acids. In fact, there are few groups of biologically important compounds the fractionation of which has not been facilitated by this technique.

(*1*) ***Adsorption.*** In adsorption column chromatography a powdered adsorbent, such as charcoal, aluminum oxide, silica, or the like, is packed into a vertical glass tube, usually as a slurry in the solvent to be used later. The mixture to be resolved is added to the top of the column in a small amount of solvent. Larger amounts of pure solvent are then passed through the column by the use of either pressure from above the column or suction from below. The rate of migration of any compound through the column is determined by the balance between its affinity for the solvent and its adsorption by the solid phase. It is possible, by the judicious choice of solvent mixtures and adsorbents, to effect many separations which would be impossible by ordinary chemical means. Figure 4–15 shows three colored components of a mixture which have separated and are traveling down a

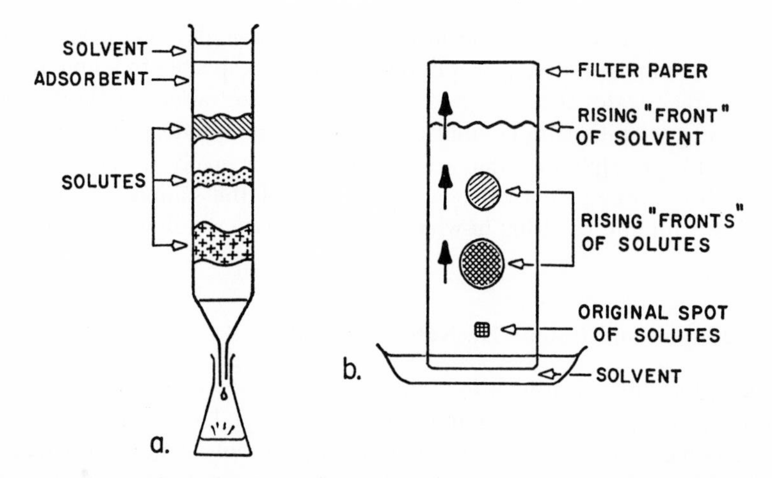

Figure 4–15. *a,* Adsorption column chromatography. *b,* Paper partition chromatography.

column at different rates. By changing receivers, these fractions can be collected separately as they leave the bottom of the column. Colorless substances are frequently separated by collecting many small fractions in succession from the column, testing each fraction chemically or by other means, and combining all fractions containing single components.

Instead of packing the adsorbent in a column, it may be deposited on a sheet of glass ("thin-layer" chromatography). The techniques of applying the sample, allowing the solvent to traverse the system, and subsequently detecting the separated compounds, are similar to those used in paper partition chromatography.

Although there are exceptions (polypeptides and some small proteins), generally adsorption chromatography has not been successful with proteins. Its major applications have been in the areas of amino acids, lipids, steroids, sugars, and similar compounds of relatively low molecular weight.

(2) ***Partition.*** In adsorption chromatography the forces of adsorption between the stationary phase and the solutes in the moving phase are of utmost importance. Partition chromatography, on the other hand, uses the solid part of the system as a mere support (in theory, at least) for a stationary liquid phase. One type of partition chromatography makes use of the same columnar arrangement as that discussed for adsorption. The stationary phase may consist of wet starch or wet silica gel, for example, and the solutes, dissolved in the appropriate organic solvent, undergo a series of multiple partitions between the stationary and moving solvent phases as they travel down the column. The overall effect is that of an infinite number of extractions carried out in a succession of infinitesimal separatory funnels. If side effects are left out of consideration, the major physical basis of this form of chromatography is the partition coefficient of each solute between the stationary solvent (e.g., water) and the moving solvent.

In addition to columnar techniques, powders for liquid-liquid partition also may be used on thin-layer plates.

The technique of "counter-current distribution" is closely related, although not usually classified as a chromatographic method. It involves successive partition of the solute(s) between two liquid phases in a series of modified separatory funnels.

A very useful form of partition chromatography substitutes a sheet of filter paper for the usual column. The stationary phase consists of water adsorbed to the cellulose fibers of the paper. A small amount of sample is spotted near one end of the strip of paper, the end dipped into an appropriate solvent mixture, and the solvent allowed to travel through the paper by capillarity. At the end of the desired period of time the position of the solvent "front" is marked and the paper is dried. Spraying the paper with the proper reagent (e.g., ninhydrin for amino acids) then reveals the various constituents of the mixture as separate spots. The ratio of the distance traveled by any particular substance to that covered by the solvent is known as the ratio of the "fronts," or R_f, and is usually quite constant for each substance in a particular solvent. At times this simple or "one-dimensional" paper chromatogram is unable to separate some of the constituents of a complex mixture. In that case the sample is placed in one corner of a square sheet of paper which is chromatographed in one direction with one solvent system, then turned and run with another solvent system in a direction at right angles to the first, producing a "two-dimensional" chromatogram.

Slight differences in the composition of analogous proteins in different species are readily detected by the so-called "fingerprinting technique," in which the mixture of peptides, produced by partial enzymatic hydrolysis of the protein, is subjected to paper chromatography in one dimension, and paper electrophoresis at right angles to this direction, resulting in satisfactory separations of small peptides and amino acids.

The cellulose-water stationary phase of the usual paper chromatogram is unsatisfactory for most lipid-soluble substances. In such cases "reversed phase" paper chromatography is used, in which the paper (acting merely as an inert support) is impregnated with a non-polar phase such as silicic acid or petrolatum, and the more polar phase is represented by the moving solvent.

Gas-liquid partition chromatography is a useful technique for substances which are stable at whatever temperatures are required for volatilization. Columns generally are rather long, narrow tubes (coiled to conserve space) packed with an inert supporting medium which is coated with a non-volatile, liquid stationary phase. The sample is injected into a stream of carrier gas (e.g., helium), which, after passage through the column, comes in contact with some type of sensor which detects changes in gas composition. Although initially restricted to such obviously volatile substances as low molecular weight hydrocarbons, alcohols, aldehydes, and fatty acids, gas chromatography has more recently been applied with some success to certain thermostable derivatives of sugars and amino acids.

As in the case of adsorption, partition chromatography in its various forms has been successful mainly with substances of lower molecular weight, not with proteins.

(3) ***Ion-exchange.*** The ion-exchange resins are polymers which contain functional groups that are capable of undergoing exchange reactions with ions. Cation exchangers contain such groups as phenols, carboxyls, or sulfonic acids. Anion exchangers are organic bases, or amines. Amino acids bearing an appropriate charge can be deposited on a column of the proper type of resin by an exchange reaction with the functional groups of the resin, while other amino acids pass through the column. The deposited amino acids can then be displaced from the column by using strong solutions of the proper acids or bases. Ion-exchange resins have been deposited on paper; these preparations have the same general uses as ion-exchange columns, but on a smaller scale. The techniques resemble those of paper partition chromatography.

Ionic substances of high molecular weight, such as proteins and nucleic acids, appear to be unable to penetrate the dense, cross-linked structure of synthetic ion-exchange resins; most of the successful separations reported with this technique have involved proteins of relatively small size. On the other hand, chemical insertion of anionic and cationic functional groups into the relatively open, fibrous structure of a natural polymer, such as cellulose, has resulted in the production of materials (cellulose ion-exchangers) which are currently enjoying great success in the field of protein separation. Cellulose ion-exchangers are used in the form of powder (columns or thin-layer plates) or paper sheets.

(4) ***Molecular sieving (gel filtration).*** A type of "three-dimensional dialysis" can be carried out by filtration of a mixture of solutes through a column of gel particles, into the internal matrix of which only molecules of a limited size and compact shape can penetrate readily. Dextrans of varying chain length and degree of artificial cross-linkage provide gels with graded ability to take up (and hence retard the rate of migration down the column of) molecules of various sizes. "Desalting" of protein solutions is accomplished readily; the salts penetrate the gel and leave the column after the protein (which enters the gel matrix less readily, if at all). By appropriate choice of gel, proteins of different molecular weights can be separated from each other.

Chemical incorporation of anionic and cationic groups has produced a series of ion-exchange dextran gels, the functions of which are a combination of ion exchange and molecular sieving.

It may be appropriate to point out, at the conclusion of this discussion of chromatography, that although the various techniques have been classified by the *major* physical phenomenon occurring in each case, "side effects" due to other phenomena almost always intrude. Adsorption, for example, is involved to some extent in any form of chromatography in which the sample comes in contact with a solid phase of great surface area (powders, gels, paper sheets).

(f) Chemical Reactions

Many of the color reactions which were discussed in connection with the functional groups of proteins and amino acids have been adapted to the quantitative determination of those amino acids bearing such groups. Some of these reactions are specific enough for one amino acid so as to require no preliminary separation of the amino acid in question from other constituents of natural mixtures.

(g) Microbiological and Enzymatic Methods

Some microorganisms require for growth preformed amino acids in their culture media. The extent of growth in a medium complete except for the amino acid being determined can therefore be used for the estimation of that amino acid in a sample added to such a test system.

Specific enzymes which decarboxylate certain amino acids are present in some species of bacteria. The quantity of CO_2 evolved in these reactions can be measured manometrically.

Detection and Determination of Protein

(a) Heat Coagulation

Albumin is often detected in pathological urine by the appearance of a coagulum on heating. The addition of weak acetic acid to the heated sample will intensify the protein precipitate by moving the pH of the urine closer to the pI of the albumin, while any basic phosphates which may be precipitated by the heat will redissolve when acidified. Heat coagulation is sometimes used for the gravimetric determination of proteins. Complications are introduced by the necessity of removing inorganic salts and all lipids from the coagulum before drying and weighing.

(b) Precipitating Agents

In Heller's ring test, protein in urine is detected qualitatively by layering the urine over concentrated nitric acid and observing the ring of acid-denatured protein which appears at the interface of the two liquids. Other reagents, such as sulfosalicylic acid, have been used to determine the degree of proteinuria by turbidimetry, but the methods lack accuracy.

(c) Specific Gravity

The specific gravity of plasma or serum is dependent in large part on its protein content. A method for the determination of plasma proteins has been based on this fact, and involves timing the rate at which a drop of plasma falls through a column of organic solvents of a density slightly less than that of plasma. Both plasma and whole blood proteins have been determined by observing the flotation or sedimentation of a drop of the sample in copper sulfate solutions of graded density.

(d) Refractive Index

The index of refraction of protein solutions is greater than that of water by an amount which is proportional to the concentration of protein. Serum has been analyzed by this method, although it is said to be less sensitive than the falling-drop method mentioned above.

(e) Electrophoresis

This method has been discussed in connection with the properties of proteins as electrically charged particles (p. 74).

(f) Chromatography

Those forms of chromatography which may be used for the separation of proteins have been mentioned previously.

(g) Chemical Determination of Constituent Groups

Protein is widely determined by the Kjeldahl method which was discussed earlier. Assuming a nitrogen content of 16 per cent for the average protein, the percentage of nitrogen in the sample is multiplied by 6.25 to obtain the protein content.

The biuret color reaction has been adapted to the quantitative determination of protein. It is rapid and quite accurate, but requires calibration against some "absolute" method, such as the Kjeldahl, although salt-free, crystalline, bovine serum albumin of known moisture content also may be used as a photometric standard.

Folin's phenol reagent has been used for the colorimetric determination of plasma proteins. However, since it is actually a method for the amino acid, tyrosine, it must be standardized against a sample of the same protein as will occur in the samples to be tested. Any variation in the tyrosine content of the samples will invalidate the method.

BIBLIOGRAPHY

GENERAL

Advances in Protein Chemistry
Annual Review of Biochemistry
Florkin, M., and Stotz, E. H. (eds.): Comprehensive Biochemistry, Vol. 7, Proteins (Part 1), and Vol. 8, Proteins (Part 2) and Nucleic Acids, Amsterdam, Elsevier Publishing Company, 1963.
Greenstein, J. P., and Winitz, M.: Chemistry of the Amino Acids, 3 vols., New York, John Wiley & Sons, Inc., 1961.
Haurowitz, F.: Chemistry and Function of Proteins, New York, Academic Press, Inc., 1963.
Meister, A.: Biochemistry of the Amino Acids, Vol. 1, Chapter 1, New York, Academic Press, Inc., 1965.
Neurath, H. (ed.): The Proteins, 4 vols., New York, Academic Press, Inc., 1963 to 1966.
Schröder, E., and Lübke, K.: The Peptides, 2 vols., New York, Academic Press, Inc., 1965 and 1966.

COMPOSITION, STRUCTURE, PHYSICAL CHEMISTRY

Cohn, E. J., and Edsall, J. T. (eds.): Proteins, Amino Acids, and Peptides as Ions and Dipolar Ions, New York, Reinhold Publishing Corporation, 1943.

Edsall, J. T., and Wyman, J.: Biophysical Chemistry, Vol. 1, New York, Academic Press, Inc., 1958.
Joly, M.: A Physico-Chemical Approach to the Denaturation of Proteins, New York, Academic Press, Inc., 1965.
Scheraga, H. A.: Protein Structure, New York, Academic Press, Inc., 1961.
Šorm, F.: Identical and analogous peptide structures in proteins, Advances Enzymol. *24:*415, 1962.
Tristram, G. R., and Smith, R. H.: The amino acid composition of some purified proteins, Adv. Protein Chem. *18:*227, 1963.

METHODS

Alexander, P., and Block, R. J. (eds.): A Laboratory Manual of Analytical Methods of Protein Chemistry, 3 vols., New York, Pergamon Press, 1960 and 1961.
Bailey, J. L.: Techniques in Protein Chemistry, Amsterdam, Elsevier Publishing Company, 1962.
Bier, M. (ed.): Electrophoresis: Theory, Methods, and Applications, New York, Academic Press, Inc., 1959.
Bradstreet, R. B.: The Kjeldahl Method for Organic Nitrogen, New York, Academic Press, Inc., 1965.
Porath, J.: Cross-linked dextrans as molecular sieves, Adv. Protein Chem. *17:*209, 1962.
Schachman, H. K.: Ultracentrifugation in Biochemistry, New York, Academic Press, Inc., 1959.
Smith, I. (ed.): Chromatographic and Electrophoretic Techniques, 2 vols., London, William Heinemann Medical Books Ltd., 1960.
Stahl, E. (ed.): Thin-Layer Chromatography, New York, Academic Press, Inc., 1965.

SPECIFIC TYPES OF PROTEINS

Allen, F. W.: Ribonucleoproteins and Ribonucleic Acids, Amsterdam, Elsevier Publishing Company, 1962.
Boeri, E.: Non-porphyrin metalloproteins, in Florkin, M., and Stotz, E. H. (eds.): Comprehensive Biochemistry, Vol. 8, p. 38, Amsterdam, Elsevier Publishing Company, 1963.
Bonner, J., and Ts'o, P. (eds.): The Nucleohistones, San Francisco, Holden-Day, Inc., 1964.
Busch, H.: Histones and Other Nuclear Proteins, New York, Academic Press, Inc., 1965.
Felix, K.: Protamines, Adv. Protein Chem. *15:*1, 1960.
Gottschalk, A.: Glycoproteins and glycopeptides, in Florkin, M., and Stotz, E. H. (eds.): Comprehensive Biochemistry, Vol. 8, p. 17, Amsterdam, Elsevier Publishing Company, 1963.
Gurd, F. R. N.: Lipoproteins, in Florkin, M., and Stotz, E. H. (eds.): Comprehensive Biochemistry, Vol. 8, p. 3, Amsterdam, Elsevier Publishing Company, 1963.
Harrington, W. F., and von Hippel, P. H.: The structure of collagen and gelatin, Adv. Protein Chem. *16:*1, 1961.
Lehmann, H., and Huntsman, R. G.: Hemoglobin and myoglobin, in Florkin, M., and Stotz, E. H. (eds.): Comprehensive Biochemistry, Vol. 8, p. 55, Amsterdam, Elsevier Publishing Company, 1963.
Partridge, S. M.: Elastin, Adv. Protein Chem. *17:*227, 1962.
Putnam, F. W. (ed.): The Plasma Proteins, Vol. 1, Isolation, Characterization, and Function, New York, Academic Press, 1960.
Searcy, R. L., and Bergquist, L. M.: Lipoprotein Chemistry in Health and Disease, Springfield, Ill., Charles C Thomas, 1962.

CHAPTER 5

CHEMISTRY OF NUCLEOPROTEINS, NUCLEIC ACIDS, AND NUCLEOTIDES

INTRODUCTION

Terminology

From the standpoint of protein chemistry, the nucleoproteins are a class of conjugated proteins, the prosthetic groups of which are the nucleic acids. As is the case with many other types of conjugated proteins (lipoproteins, glycoproteins, etc.), the chemical and biological properties of the prosthetic groups are at the present time the major objects of attention.

Two major chemical types of nucleoproteins have been found in nature, differing from each other in many respects. However, the difference which underlies the current system of nomenclature concerns the nature of the sugar contained in the nucleic acid moiety of the nucleoprotein. In one type of nucleoprotein the sugar is a pentose, which has been shown to be D-ribose in all cases which have been investigated to the point of isolation and final identification. The nucleic acid containing this sugar is called "pentosenucleic acid" (PNA) or "ribonucleic acid" (RNA), and the nucleoprotein is named accordingly. The second type of nucleoprotein contains a deoxypentose. Where this sugar has been identified definitely, it has proved to be D-2-deoxyribose. The corresponding nucleic acid is called "deoxypentosenucleic acid" or "deoxyribonucleic acid" (DNA).

In the early days of nucleic acid chemistry, RNA was isolated from yeast. It was thought to be restricted to the plant world, and was called "yeast nucleic acid" or "plant nucleic acid." DNA was obtained from fish sperm and thymus gland, and was called "thymonucleic acid" or "animal nucleic acid," in accordance with its assumed distribution in nature. Both types of nucleic acid have since been found in all living cells, rendering the older terminology obsolete. The term "nucleic" or "nucleo-" is derived from the early erroneous belief that nucleic acids and nucleoproteins occurred only in the nuclei of cells. At the present time this term refers to a chemically defined class of substances, irrespective of source or location in nature.

Biological Importance

The present great interest in the nucleoproteins and nucleic acids, after a period of virtual stagnation, is at least partly the result of the demonstration by research workers in many apparently unrelated fields of biology that these substances are of prime importance in connection with certain of the major problems under investigation in their respective disciplines.

There appears to be a rather direct connection between nucleoproteins and genetics. Several of the intranuclear structures in cells, including the chromosomes, contain or are entirely composed of nucleoproteins. Conclusive evidence now exists that the genes, the determinative units of inheritance which are associated with chromosomes, are deoxyribonucleic acids. Substances have been discovered in bacterial cells which can transform one genetic type of bacterium into another genetic strain. Chemically, they have proved to be deoxyribonucleic acids.

The participation of the intranuclear nucleoproteins in such processes as mitosis and meiosis seems to be matched by the involvement of the extranuclear nucleoproteins in protein synthesis in the cytoplasm. Evidence that the synthesis of protein in the cytoplasm is under the eventual control of nuclear events has made the subject of the interrelations between the various nucleoproteins of the cell a matter of concern to workers in the fields of embryology, growth, protein metabolism, and cancer.

The viruses of plants, bacteria (bacteriophages), and animals contain nucleoproteins. Some of the simplest viruses seem to be purely nucleoprotein; others are of more complex composition.

Certain substances which are chemically similar to the sub-units of which the nucleic acids are composed (nucleotides, to be discussed later) exist in the free state in cells. Some of these are important in the energy transfers characteristic of living organisms, while others act as cofactors to the enzymes whose catalytic activities promote the reactions which provide the energy.

NUCLEOPROTEINS

Nucleoprotamines

These substances are found only in fish sperm. Although they are the most easily prepared nucleoproteins from this source, there is evidence that the sperm nucleus from which they are obtained also contains nucleoproteins of a more complex type.

The nucleic acid components of the nucleoprotamines are of the deoxyribose type. Protamines, the protein moieties of these substances, are proteins by courtesy only, since they are of relatively low molecular weight (of the order of 5000). Owing to their high content of basic amino acids (such as arginine) the protamines have isoelectric points in the strongly basic pH range, and are therefore positively charged in the usual physiological environment. The protamines contain no tyrosine or tryptophan. The sequence of amino acids appears to be characterized by repeated oligopeptides of arginine separated by one or more residues of neutral amino acids. Arginine appears to be the C-terminal residue. Most protamines have a proline N-terminus, although alanine and serine also seem to occur at this site. When combined with nucleic acids, the secondary structure of the protamines is a more or less extended form rather than the α-helix.

As will be indicated later, the nucleic acids have isoelectric points in the strongly acid range, and are negatively charged at the pH of the cell. The linkage between the anionic nucleic acid and the cationic protamine is saltlike in character. It can be disrupted by mineral acid, which acts as a displacing agent for the nucleic acid, or even by such neutral salts as NaCl, which undergoes a double replacement reaction with the "protamine nucleate." It has been proposed that the polypeptide chain of the protamine is wrapped helically around the double helix of DNA (Fig. 5–4), with the arginine residues (the major basic amino acid of the protamine) forming salt linkages with the phosphate groups of the DNA. Indeed, in many preparations of fish sperm nucleoprotamine, the ratio of arginine to phosphate is approximately 1.

Nucleohistones

Certain varieties of fish sperm contain in their nuclei somewhat more complex nucleoproteins than the nucleoprotamines. These are the nucleohistones, which are also found in the sperm of animals, the avian erythrocyte, and somatic cell nuclei in general.

The nucleohistones are combinations of deoxyribonucleic acids with histones, which are basic proteins like the protamines, but of higher molecular weight. The histones also differ from the protamines in containing a greater variety of amino acids, including tyrosine. Although histones have been fractionated into "very lysine-rich," "slightly lysine-rich," and "arginine-rich" subgroups, there is considerable evidence that these preparations themselves are heterogeneous. The situation is complicated by the ease with which histones undergo degradation (enzymatic, for example) during the isolation procedures. Certain data indicate that over one-half of the histone in the nucleohistone complex has a secondary structure of the α-helix type. It is believed, although not unanimously, that histones, like protamines, are wrapped around a core of DNA. As in the case of nucleoprotamines, the linkage between nucleic acid and protein in the nucleohistones is of the salt type.

Both nucleoprotamines and deoxynucleohistones are confined in their distribution to the cell nucleus, where they are found in close association with the chromosomes.

Higher Nucleoproteins

By this term is meant those nucleoproteins in which the nucleic acid is combined with a protein of greater complexity than the protamines or histones. It is a general, but not invariable, rule that such combinations are not cleaved as easily as the saltlike linkages discussed previously. It seems possible that covalent bonds may be involved in these cases. For example, RNA of yeast and several types of animal cells contains a small percentage of peptide-like material which can be removed only by hydrolysis.

In addition to the nucleoprotamines and nucleohistones containing DNA, the cell nucleus also may contain RNA-proteins. The chromosomes, for instance, contain significant amounts of RNA, possibly in combination with non-basic proteins. Outside of the chromosomes, nuclear RNA is found also in the nucleolus, in association with lipids and proteins which are not as yet characterized.

The cytoplasm of the cell, in contrast to the nucleus, contains mainly RNA-proteins. A large part of the cytoplasmic ribonucleoproteins seems to be incorporated in the particulate fractions which can be isolated by differential centrifugation. RNA is found affiliated with proteins, lipids, and other constituents in both the "large particle" or mitochondrial fraction and the "small particle" or microsomal fraction. The bulk of the cellular RNA is contained in the microsomal particles called "ribosomes," which are involved in protein synthesis. As pointed out later, these particles contain two ribonucleic acids and a large number of slightly basic proteins of relatively low molecular weight. The soluble RNA in the particle-free portion of the cytoplasm, which also participates in protein synthesis, appears to be in loose association with soluble cytoplasmic proteins. There is evidence that a rather labile "messenger" or "template" RNA is formed in the nucleus and migrates into the cytoplasm to the ribosomes. Little is known of its chemistry or possible combination with protein. Ribosomal, soluble, and messenger RNA are frequently designated rRNA, sRNA (or tRNA, t = transfer) and mRNA, respectively.

Small amounts of DNA have been found in the mitochondria, where this substance apparently plays a role in intramitochondrial synthesis of RNA and protein.

The viruses are submicroscopic particles or "molecules" which are responsible for many infectious diseases of animals and plants. Although they possess many of the properties of "lifeless" matter (e.g., some can be crystallized), they have the peculiar characteristic of reproducing themselves inside the cells of the host. All of the plant viruses isolated thus far contain ribonucleoproteins, and many have been shown to contain no other significant components. Some animal viruses contain DNA, some RNA. Most bacterial viruses (bacteriophages) contain DNA, but a few have been found recently which contain RNA. Certain viruses contain, in addition to protein, polyamines (spermidine, putrescine, and others) which neutralize part of the anionic groups of the nucleic acids. The animal viruses and bacteriophages are generally more complex in composition than the plant viruses. They frequently contain lipids and carbohydrates, and seem to resemble in some ways the particles found in cytoplasm.

Evidence from the electron microscope indicates that tobacco mosaic virus consists of nucleic acid enclosed in a helical shell of protein. The structure appears to involve discs of protein molecules stacked like a cylinder of lock-washers, with a helically twisted strand of RNA inside. Other viruses have equally distinctive architecture, but all appear to share one common characteristic, namely a nucleic acid core protected by an external coat of protein.

NUCLEIC ACIDS

Composition

The nucleic acids, prosthetic groups of the nucleoproteins, are substances of high molecular weight, containing phosphoric acid, sugars, and purine and pyrimidine bases. The major products of complete hydrolysis of the two types of nucleic acids are listed in Table 5-1. In addition to the different sugars, the two types are distinguished by the pyrimidine bases which they contain, for while both contain cytosine, the uracil of RNA is replaced by thymine in DNA.

The subject of nucleic acid composition has been complicated by recent findings to the effect that (a) in addition to the major constituents listed in Table 5-1, many commonly occurring nucleic acids contain small amounts of unusual components; (b) familiar components may occur in unusual linkages; and (c) certain nucleic acids may contain unusual components as major constituents. Methylcytosine occurs in traces in various deoxyribonucleic acids of animal origin and in larger amounts in wheat germ DNA. In DNA of bacteriophages T_2, T_4, and T_6 of Escherichia coli, cytosine is completely replaced by

TABLE 5-1. MAJOR PRODUCTS OF HYDROLYSIS OF COMMON NUCLEIC ACIDS

RNA	DNA
H_3PO_4	H_3PO_4
Ribose	Deoxyribose
Adenine	Adenine
Guanine	Guanine
Cytosine	Cytosine
Uracil	Thymine

hydroxymethylcytosine, whereas the DNA of B. subtilis phage SP8 contains 5-hydroxymethyluracil and that of B. subtilis phage PBS2 contains uracil itself, both replacing thymine. The soluble RNA of the cytoplasm appears to be characterized by containing small amounts of methylated constituents, such as 2′-O-methylribose, thymine (methyluracil), 1-methyl-adenine, 2-methyl-adenine, N^6-methyl-adenine, N^6, $N^{6'}$-dimethyl-adenine, 1-methyl-guanine, 7-methyl-guanine, N^2-methyl-guanine, and N^2, $N^{2'}$-dimethyl-guanine. (N^6-methyl-adenine is also found in DNA of E. coli.) The unusually linked 5′-ribosyluracil (pseudouridine) also is found mainly in soluble RNA, some fractions of which contain, in addition, hypoxanthine and dihydrouracil.

The structural formulas for the two sugars of the nucleic acids are shown below. They exist in their furanose forms in the nucleic acids.

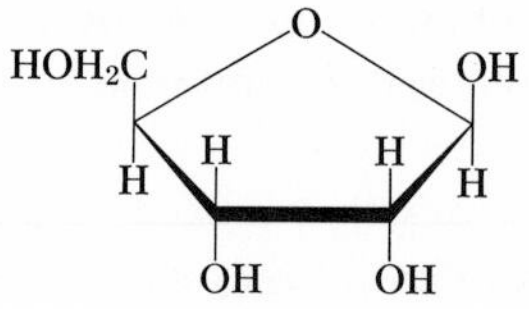

Ribose

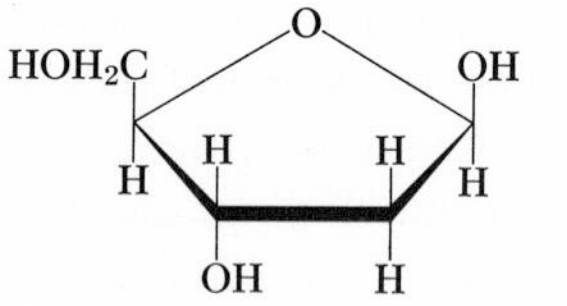

Deoxyribose

Adenine and guanine are the two major purine components of the nucleic acids. The numbering system for the purine skeleton is indicated in the formulas below. Both compounds are capable of undergoing keto-enol tautomerism; they are shown in their enol forms. The amino groups of adenine and guanine can act as cationic acids in a manner similar to these groups found in amino acids, but the aromatic character of the purine ring causes a shift of the pK values toward the acid side (adenine 3.7, guanine 2.5, as found in the nucleic acids). The enolic hydroxyl group of guanine behaves as an uncharged acid with a pK of 9.3.

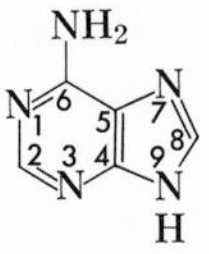

Adenine

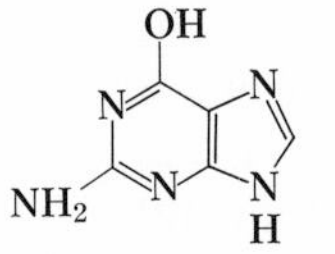

Guanine

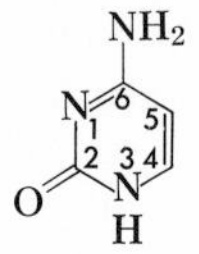

Cytosine

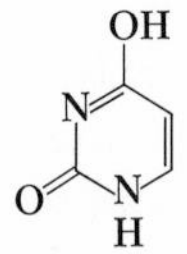

Uracil

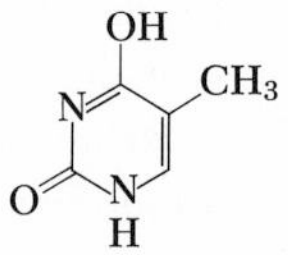

Thymine

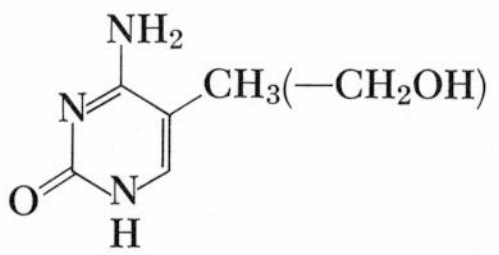

Methyl-(or hydroxymethyl-) cytosine

The structural formulas and numbering system for the pyrimidine bases of the nucleic acids are on page 106. Here again, keto-enol tautomerism is possible. The structures are shown in their enol forms except for positions 2 and 3, since a hydrogen atom is required at position 3 to accommodate a linkage which occurs in the nucleic acids. The amino group of cytosine (and probably methylcytosine) has a cationic acid pK of 4.4, while the enolic hydroxyl groups of uracil and thymine have pK's of 9.3 and 10.0, respectively.

In any nucleic acid structure containing doubly esterified phosphoric acid, the remaining acid group of the phosphoric acid would be expected to have a pK less than 2 (0.7 to 1.6). Singly esterified phosphoric acid would have one acidic group with a pK less than 2 (the "primary" dissociation), and one with a pK of about 6.5 (the "secondary" dissociation of phosphoric acid).

The nucleic acids are amphoteric substances which contain a preponderance of acid groups with low pK values, resulting in isoelectric points far on the acid side (probably about pH 1). At physiological pH's the nucleic acids exist in their anionic forms, thus they can easily combine with the cationic forms of proteins to produce saltlike compounds.

$O{=}P{-}OH$		$O{=}P{-}O^-$		$O{=}P{-}O^-$		$O{=}P{-}O^-$
$\boxed{NA}{-}NH_3^+$	$\longleftrightarrow$	$\boxed{NA}{-}NH_3^+$	$\longleftrightarrow$	$\boxed{NA}{-}NH_2$	$\longleftrightarrow$	$\boxed{NA}{-}NH_2$
$C{-}OH$		$C{-}OH$		$C{-}OH$		$C{-}O^-$
(soluble)		(insoluble)		(soluble)		(soluble)

$|\leftarrow pH < pI \rightarrow|\leftarrow pH = pI\ ca.\ 1 \rightarrow|\leftarrow pH\ 5\ to\ 8 \rightarrow|\leftarrow pH\ 8\ to\ 12 \rightarrow|$

Table 5-2 lists some determinations of the quantitative base composition of typical nucleic acids (see minor bases, pp. 105–6). It should be noted that all nucleic acids contain

TABLE 5-2. BASE COMPOSITION OF NUCLEIC ACIDS

NUCLEIC ACID	MOLAR RATIOS OF BASES, ADENINE = 1.00				
	ADENINE	THYMINE OR URACIL	GUANINE	CYTOSINE	OTHER
DNA:		(THYMINE)			
Human thymus	1.00	0.95	0.64	0.64	
Human sperm	1.00	1.02	0.62	0.60	
Human spleen	1.00	1.01	0.72	0.67	
Human liver	1.00	1.00	0.64	0.66	
Wheat germ	1.00	0.99	0.83	0.62	Methylcytosine 0.22
Yeast	1.00	1.05	0.60	0.55	
Escherichia coli	1.00	1.00	1.09	1.10	
M. tuberculosis	1.00	1.1	1.6	1.9	
Vaccinia virus	1.00	1.0	0.70	0.68	
Bacteriophage T5	1.00	1.02	0.64	0.64	
Bacteriophage T2r$^+$	1.00	1.0	0.56	—	Hydroxymethyl cytosine 0.52
Phage ϕX174	1.00	1.31	1.06	0.82	
RNA:		(URACIL)			
Calf thymus nuclear ribosomes	1.00	0.91	1.6	1.4	
Calf thymus nucleolar fraction (mRNA?)	1.00	1.1	0.86	0.73	
Rat liver cytoplasmic ribosomes	1.00	1.5	2.0	1.4	
Yeast sRNA, alanine-specific	1.00	1.7	2.8	2.5	Pseudouridylate 0.3
Yeast sRNA, tyrosine-specific	1.00	0.79	1.4	1.2	Pseudouridylate 0.2
Tobacco mosaic virus	1.00	0.88	0.85	0.62	

a mole of sugar and of phosphate for each mole of base. Insofar as DNA is concerned, each species seems to synthesize molecules having the same gross composition in all tissues, but differing from the DNA of other organisms. This finding is in accord with the current belief that DNA is the carrier of genetic information for most organisms, the exceptions being the RNA viruses. As would be expected from the genetic complexity of most forms of life, the DNA isolated from each organism (with the possible exception of certain bacteriophages) is a heterogeneous mixture of molecules. It has been suggested that two general types of DNA exist, one with a preponderance of adenine and thymine (found in animal tissues and yeast), and one with an excess of guanine and cytosine (characteristic of certain bacteria and some insect viruses). Of great importance in connection with the secondary structure of deoxyribonucleic acid are the following generalizations concerning composition: on a molar basis, purines = pyrimidines, guanine = cytosine (including methyl- and hydroxymethyl-), adenine = thymine, and 6-amino groups = 6-keto groups (i.e., adenine + cytosine = guanine + thymine). The only DNA listed in Table 5-2 which deviates significantly from these rules is that from bacteriophage ϕX174; the explanation for this will be given subsequently.

In general, the composition of RNA appears to exhibit few regularities, although there is a tendency for the 6-amino bases to equal the 6-keto bases (adenine + cytosine = guanine + uracil). Ribonucleic acid is found in several locations within the cell, each site being characterized by a type (which in turn is frequently a very heterogeneous mixture) of ribonucleic acid subserving a specific metabolic function and differing chemically from the RNA found at other sites (Table 5-2). Several different types of RNA occur in the nucleus of the cell in small amounts, and some is found in the mitochondria of the cytoplasm. However, most of the RNA of the cell (80 to 90 per cent) exists in the ribosome particles of the cytoplasm; these particles and the composition of the RNA contained therein are remarkably similar in different forms of life. The soluble RNA ("amino acid transfer" RNA) of the cytoplasm (10 to 20 per cent of the total cellular RNA) is quite heterogeneous, since there are at least as many types of soluble RNA molecules as there are species of amino acids in the cell (p. 554). This fraction of the cytoplasmic RNA, and to a lesser extent also the ribosomal RNA, is characterized by its content of methylated "minor constituents" and 5-ribosyluracil (p. 106). Little is known at this time of the chemistry of so-called "messenger RNA" (p. 105), except that its base composition and sequence must have a special relation to that of the DNA of the same cell (p. 528).

Tobacco mosaic virus RNA is one of the few molecularly homogeneous ribonucleic acids known at this time, perhaps because it serves a genetic function in the virus and consequently is analogous to (but genetically simpler than) the nuclear DNA of the animal cell.

Primary Structure

As in the case of the proteins, the structure of the nucleic acids can be discussed on successively higher levels of organization. The primary level of organization refers to the structures of the "monomeric" units (mononucleotides) and the covalent linkages which unite them in the "polymeric" polynucleotides or nucleic acids. Each polymeric strand is in turn arranged in a specific steric conformation, giving rise to a secondary level of organization. As will be seen subsequently, in the case of DNA this secondary organization overlaps the tertiary, which is concerned with inter-strand linkages.

Hydrolysis of the nucleic acids under appropriate conditions liberates a group of compounds known as nucleotides, consisting of purine or pyrimidine bases linked to sugars, which in turn are esterified with phosphoric acid. These nucleotides are the sub-units from which the polymeric nucleic acids are constructed. Further hydrolysis of the nucleotides gives rise to the nucleosides, compounds of sugar and nitrogenous base. The nucleosides and nucleotides, respectively, are named as follows: from adenine, adenosine and adenylic acid (the presence of deoxyribose can be indicated by the prefix "deoxy"); from guanine, guanosine and guanylic acid; from cytosine, cytidine and cytidylic acid; from uracil, uridine and uridylic acid; from thymine and *deoxyribose*, thymidine and thymidylic acid.

By choosing appropriate methods of hydrolysis, nucleotides having the structures of either nucleoside-3′- or nucleoside-5′-phosphates may be obtained from DNA (Fig. 5–1). Deoxyribose, in furanose form, is attached to positions 9 and 3 of the purines and pyrimidines, respectively, in β-glycosidic linkage. Two interesting diphosphate esters have been isolated from DNA, thymidine-3′,5′-diphosphate and deoxycytidine-3′,5′-diphosphate. All of the evidence available indicates that the chief, if not the only, inter-nucleotide linkage in the nucleic acids is an ester bond between phosphoric acid and sugar hydroxyl groups. In the case of DNA, the structures of the nucleotides which have been isolated would seem to implicate positions 3′ and 5′ of the deoxyribose as the sites of esterification.

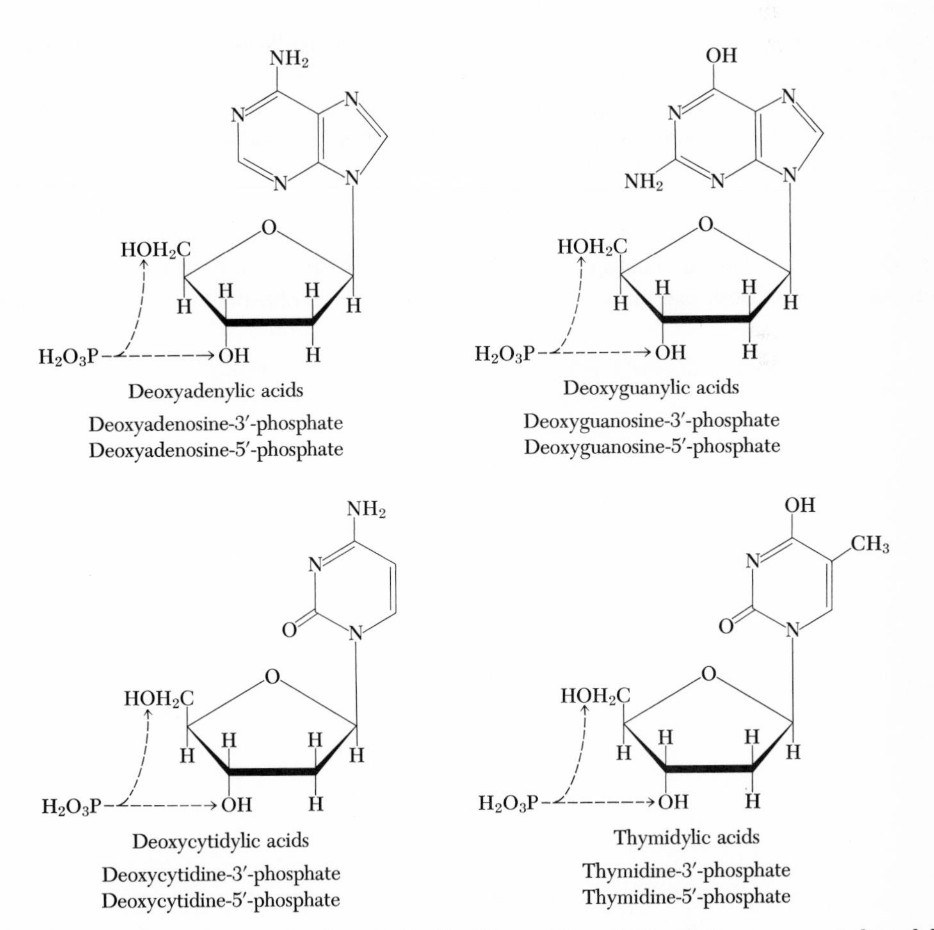

Figure 5–1. Major nucleotides found in DNA. Possible positions of phosphate group are indicated by broken lines.

A polynucleotide can be constructed in which the phosphate group of each nucleotide subunit is attached to the sugar of the adjacent nucleotide, as shown in Figure 5–2. There is evidence that DNA possesses such a structure, since the amino and enolic hydroxyl groups of the purines and pyrimidines can be shown to be free, no free sugar hydroxyl groups can be found, and essentially all of the phosphoric acid groups react like "primary" phosphate in titrations.

Physical measurements on DNA preparations indicate high molecular weights and great asymmetry, in agreement with the concept of a long-chain molecule having few if any branching points. Molecular weights have been reported ranging from a few million to many million; determination of the "true" values for DNA are complicated by the heterogeneity of the isolated preparations, a tendency for the molecules to aggregate, and, in the opposite direction, a tendency for the long, native chains to cleave even under mild shearing stress.

Little is known of the sequence of nucleotides in the primary structure of DNA, except that it is neither random nor a repetition of purine-pyrimidine alternating patterns. Clusters of purine and of pyrimidine nucleotides are known to occur. As indicated subsequently, the sequence of nucleotides has a bearing on the tertiary level of organization in DNA, with the wider implication that this sequence is the form in which genetic information is carried (p. 556).

Considering the primary structure of RNA, a glycosidically-bound ribofuranose molecule would appear to offer the possibility of three locations for attachment of phosphate, the 2′-, 3′-, or 5′-hydroxyl groups. Although mixtures of nucleoside 2′- and 3′-phosphates have been produced from RNA by some hydrolytic techniques, and nucleoside 5′-phosphates by others, it appears that the 2′-phosphates are artifacts arising from cyclic 2′,3′-phosphate esters which occur as intermediates. It may be concluded, then, that the internucleotide linkages of RNA are the same as those in DNA, namely alternating 3′- and 5′-phosphates. The major nucleotides occurring in RNA are shown in Figure 5–3. In addition, soluble (and to a lesser extent, ribosomal) RNA contains the phosphate ester of the unusual

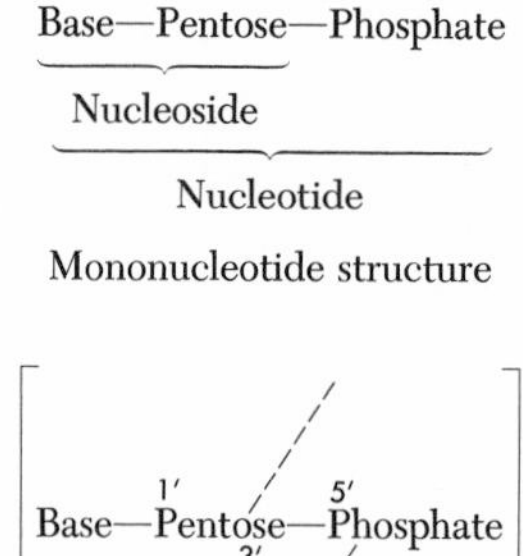

Figure 5–2. Structure of mono- and polynucleotides.

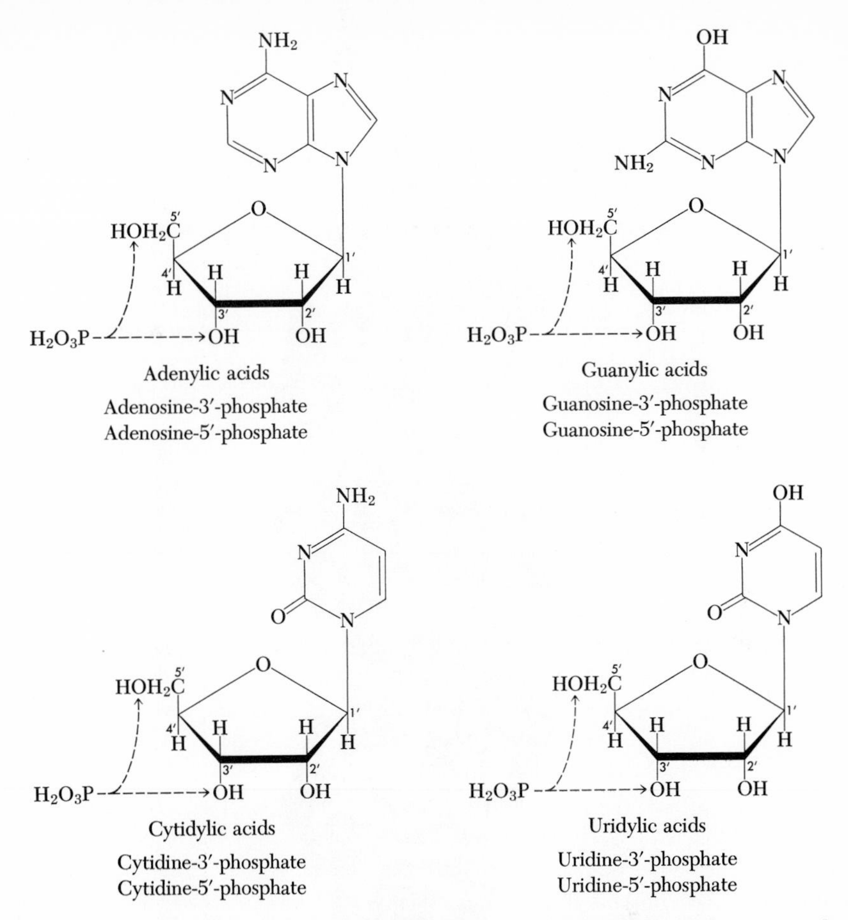

Figure 5-3. Major nucleotides found in RNA. Possible positions of phosphate group are indicated by broken lines.

nucleoside, 5-ribosyluracil (pseudouridine), as well as a number of minor methylated constituents (p. 106). Otherwise, the positions of attachment of sugar, purines, pyrimidines, the configuration of the glycosidic bond, and the cyclic form of the sugar, all appear to be the same as in DNA.

Despite the availability of the 2′-hydroxyl group, RNA does not appear to be branched by phosphate linkages at this position. All available evidence points to a long-chain, unbranched molecule. Molecular weights are different for each type of RNA found in the cell, and are best discussed subsequently in connection with their macromolecular structures.

The generalizations concerning our lack of information on nucleotide sequence in DNA apply also to RNA, compounded by the multiplicity of species of the latter. However, all types of soluble RNA active in transferring amino acids for protein synthesis (p. 554) contain, on the terminus to which the amino acid is attached, the sequence cytidylic-cytidylic-adenylic. The opposite terminus is usually guanylic, sometimes adenylic, and occasionally uridylic. It is probable that the nucleotide sequence of most (if not all) types of RNA bears some relationship to the nucleotide sequence of some fraction of the DNA in the same cell (p. 528).

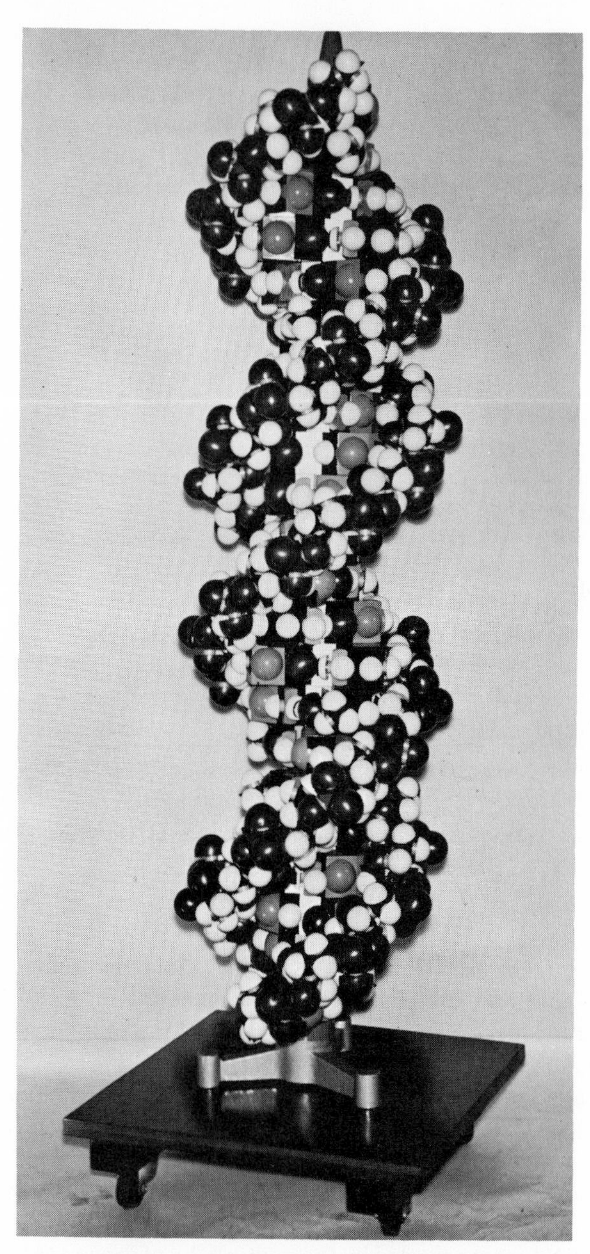

Figure 5-4. A 6-foot tall DNA structure assembled from Ealing-Courtauld atomic models, comprising 22 base pairs and two complete turns of the double helix. (Copyright, The Ealing Corp.)

Secondary and Tertiary Levels of Organization

It is currently believed that DNA possesses the structure proposed by Watson and Crick (Fig. 5–4). According to this suggestion, DNA is a two-stranded structure, consisting of two polynucleotide chains twisted about each other in a double helix. There are ten nucleotides in each chain per rotation of the helix, the period being 34 Å. Both chains are right-handed helices and run in opposite (antiparallel) directions. Titration results require that the bases of one helix be hydrogen-bonded to the bases of the other helix, while general dimensions of the structure suggested by X-ray diffraction require the matching of a large base on one chain with a small base on the other. These conditions are satisfied by pairing adenine with thymine, and guanine with cytosine (Fig. 5–5), an equivalence which also agrees with the analytical data on the composition of DNA. The two nucleotide strands are thus complementary to each other; the sequence of bases in one chain fixes the sequence of bases in the other, an arrangement with implications for genetics (p. 531). The planes of the purine and pyrimidine bases, which project inward from the sugar-phosphate external framework, are perpendicular to the long axis of the helix. Close stacking of these bases permits electron interaction between each base and those immediately preceding and following it. The resulting hydrophobic bonds contribute significantly to the stability of the helix, and incidentally lower the ultraviolet absorption coefficients of the bases (p. 117) below the levels found in free mononucleotides (hypochromic effect). It is of interest that certain dyes (some of which are mutagenic) and polycylic hydrocarbons (some of which are carcinogenic) possessing planar conformations can combine with DNA by intercalation between adjacent layers of bases.

Bacteriophage ϕX174 contains an unusual deoxyribonucleic acid, which, in its nonreplicative phase, consists of a single strand in the form of a closed ring. Since no base-pairing is involved, this DNA deviates from the rules governing equalities of base content (p. 108). A double-stranded form of the DNA occurs during replication of the phage.

On the basis of various physicochemical methods it has been concluded that RNA has a much less ordered structure than DNA, although recent investigations give evidence

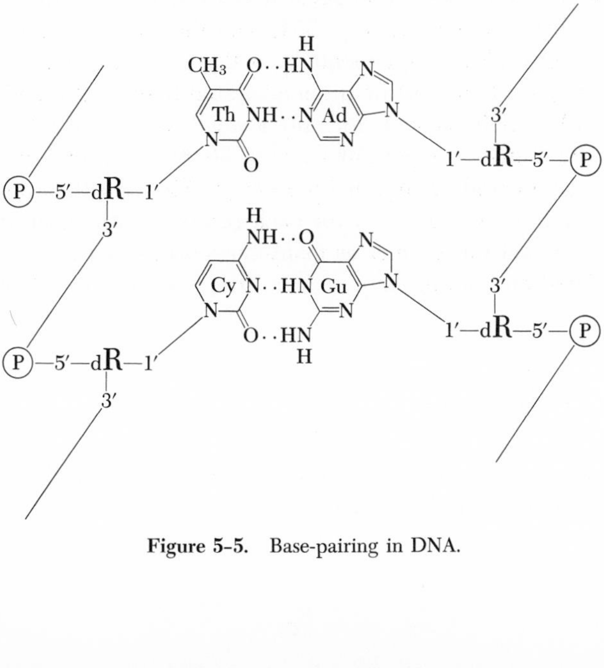

Figure 5-5. Base-pairing in DNA.

of hydrogen-bonding between bases and appreciable double-helix content. (Base-pairing of the adenine of RNA, in contrast to DNA, involves uracil rather than thymine.) Since most types of RNA are single-stranded, formation of double-helical regions can occur only by folding back of the RNA strand upon itself. Lacking the complete complementarity of the two strands of DNA, such double helix formation in RNA can occur only in isolated sections along the chain. The secondary structure of many species of RNA, then, consists of such helical regions connected by randomly oriented polynucleotide segments. Under certain conditions a tertiary rodlike structure is formed by close packing of the helical regions, the long axes of the helices being perpendicular to that of the rod.

In the particle of tobacco mosaic virus, a single RNA chain (molecular weight, 2.1×10^6) is wound helically within a long, tubelike structure composed of some 2200 protein sub-units. When in solution and freed from the constraint of the protein, the nucleic acid tends to form secondary and tertiary structures similar to those described in the previous paragraph.

Although there are ribosomal particles in the nucleus of the cell, and possibly also within the mitochondria, most of the ribosomes are found in the cytoplasm in the "microsome" fraction isolated by ultracentrifugation (p. 225). Each particle consists of a larger and smaller sub-unit, the union of which appears to depend upon Mg^{++} and the high intracellular K^+ concentration. The larger and smaller moieties, contain, respectively, single-stranded RNA molecules of molecular weight 1.12 to 1.34×10^6 and 0.39 to 0.56 $\times 10^6$ in various organisms, along with approximately 20 and 10 separate protein molecules of relatively low molecular weight. In contrast to viral particles, ribosomes do not possess a protein shell; the proteins are rather uniformly distributed in the densely packed particles along with the RNA, which has appreciable helical structure.

"Soluble" or amino acid-transfer RNA, which accounts for some 10 to 20 per cent of total cellular RNA, consists of a mixture of many species, as noted previously. Molecular weights are low (25,000 to 30,000), since these molecules contain only about 75 nucleotides. Although the evidence is not entirely conclusive, it has been suggested that these small, single-stranded nucleic acids are folded back upon themselves in the shape of a hairpin, the two sides of which are then twisted to form a double helix of about $3\frac{1}{2}$ turns, with base-pairing between sides. Non-helical regions include the free ends, one of which is involved in transfer of amino acids (p. 554), and the "loop" region, which is believed to contain three nucleotides complementary to three in messenger RNA (p. 555). This loop region also may contain most of the methylated bases and pseudouridine of sRNA.

Messenger RNA, which accounts for only a small fraction of total cellular RNA, appears to have a wide range of molecular weights (30,000 to several millions), as might be expected from its postulated biological function (p. 554). On theoretical grounds, there should exist a specific messenger RNA for each protein synthesized in the cell, and the messenger should contain three times as many nucleotides as the number of amino acid residues in the related protein. In point of fact, little is known of mRNA chemistry at this time.

Denaturation and Hybridization

The highly organized secondary and tertiary structures of nucleic acids render these molecules susceptible to much the same type of disorganization as in the case of proteins.

Although nucleic acids are denatured by extremes of pH, exposure to low ionic strength, or treatment with such reagents as urea, trichloroacetate, and thiocyanate, much of the current work in this field has centered on thermal denaturation.

As in the case of proteins, heating of solutions of nucleic acids results in cleavage of hydrogen bonds and hydrophobic linkages, leading to disorganization of the secondary and tertiary structures. The changes are followed conveniently by the concomitant increase in ultraviolet absorption of the bases (hyperchromic effect).

Thermal denaturation of ribonucleic acids causes dissociation of any existing tertiary side-by-side packing of helical regions, followed or accompanied by unwinding of the helices themselves, finally resulting in formation of randomly oriented chains. In the case of DNA, the final stages of thermal denaturation involve, in addition to the changes already enumerated, complete dissociation of the double strands.

Slow cooling ("annealing") of thermally denatured ("melted") nucleic acids permits reversal of the denaturation to occur, even to the extent of re-forming the double helices of DNA. On the other hand, rapid cooling ("quenching") prevents this relatively slow and complex process from taking place, thus preserving the nucleic acid in its denatured form.

Advantage may be taken of the reversal phenomenon to produce hybrid nucleic acids. Thus, if two different DNA preparations from genetically closely related organisms are heat-denatured separately, quenched, then heated together to a temperature somewhat below that required for complete denaturation and annealed slowly, mutual recognition of complementary sequences, base-pairing, and construction of double helical structures will occur between strands originating from the different sources. These hybrids are most easily recognized by their behavior during centrifugation in a density gradient, particularly if the two components are labeled with different isotopes.

Prior partial fragmentation of one of the two DNA preparations permits hybrid formation even with limited areas of complementarity, allowing recognition of rather distant genetic relationships. This procedure has obvious applications in the fields of taxonomy, anthropology, and the study of evolutionary development.

Hybridization between DNA and RNA also occurs, and permits identification of any species of the latter which are complementary in base sequence to the genetic material of the same cell. This technique is being used currently to search for the rather elusive "messenger" RNA.

FREE NUCLEOTIDES OF BIOLOGICAL IMPORTANCE

Adenylic System

In addition to the nucleotides which are integral components of the nucleic acids, a number of compounds exist in the free state in tissues, having nucleotide or near-nucleotide structures. These compounds have catalytic functions, act in conjunction with enzyme systems, and probably have no direct metabolic connection with the nucleic acids.

Adenosine monophosphate (also called muscle adenylic acid), adenosine diphosphate, and adenosine triphosphate act as carriers or transfer agents for phosphate groups, a function intimately bound up with the energetics of the living cell (p. 380). An unusual cyclic phosphate, adenosine-3′,5′-cyclophosphate, is involved in the activation of the enzyme, phosphorylase (p. 400).

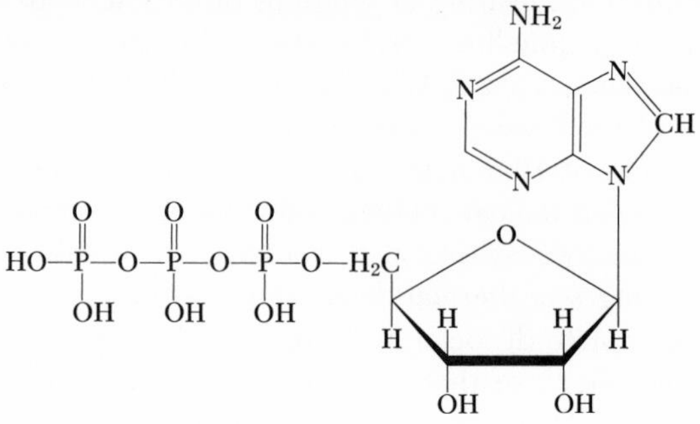

NH_2

N N CH N N

O

HO—P(=O)(OH)—O—P(=O)(OH)—O—P(=O)(OH)—O—H_2C

H H H H

OH OH

Adenosine monophosphate (AMP)

Adenosine diphosphate (ADP)

Adenosine triphosphate (ATP)

Coenzymes

The topic of coenzymes is discussed in detail elsewhere (p. 214). Word formulas of a number of coenzymes which are structurally related to the nucleotides are shown below. A more complete tabulation of nucleotide-like coenzymes is presented in connection with their metabolism (p. 524).

Adenine—ribose—PO_4—PO_4—ribose—nicotinamide
Diphosphopyridine nucleotide (DPN)
or, Nicotinamide adenine dinucleotide (NAD)

Adenine—ribose—PO_4—PO_4—ribose—nicotinamide
(ribose) | PO_4
Triphosphopyridine nucleotide (TPN)
or, Nicotinamide adenine dinucleotide phosphate (NADP)

Flavin—ribitol—PO_4
Flavin mononucleotide (FMN)

Flavin—ribitol—PO_4—PO_4—ribose—adenine
Flavin adenine dinucleotide (FAD)

Uracil—ribose—PO_4—PO_4—glucose
Uridinediphosphate-glucose (UDPG)

Adenine—ribose—PO_4—PO_4—pantothenate
(ribose) | PO_4 (pantothenate) | thiolethylamine
Coenzyme A

The two nicotinamide adenine dinucleotides, flavin adenine dinucleotide, and flavin mononucleotide are concerned with biological oxidations (p. 351). Uridinediphosphate-glucose takes part in the reaction which transforms galactose-1-phosphate to glucose-1-phosphate (p. 254). Transacylations (p. 230) of many types involve coenzyme A.

Miscellaneous Nucleosides and Nucleotides

A nucleoside containing uric acid and ribose is found in the red cells. Its function has not been elucidated. A portion of the vitamin B_{12} molecule is known to have a nucleotide-like structure (p. 199).

The mono-, di-, and triphosphates of the purine and pyrimidine nucleosides and deoxynucleosides occur in the free state in liver and other tissues.

CHEMICAL TESTS ON NUCLEIC ACIDS AND THEIR COMPONENTS

Preparation of Nucleic Acids

Nuclear material may be separated from cytoplasmic contaminants by mincing tissues in approximately isotonic NaCl, centrifuging, and washing the precipitate with isotonic NaCl. DNA may be extracted from the precipitate as nucleoprotein with concentrated salt solutions, water, or anionic detergents. Free DNA is obtained after denaturation of the protein by any one of several methods, e.g., shaking with chloroform.

The soluble isotonic NaCl extracts mentioned above contain RNA, which can be precipitated as nucleoprotein at pH 4.5, dissolved in $NaHCO_3$ solution, and deproteinized with chloroform or alcohol. RNA also may be precipitated from cold 2M guanidine hydrochloride solution, in which the denatured protein remains in a soluble state.

DNA and RNA can be separated directly from minced (homogenized) tissue by extraction with phenol. RNA appears in the aqueous phase, leaving DNA and protein in the phenol.

Due to the molecular heterogeneity of the nucleic acids extracted from any source, it is frequently desirable to fractionate further each preparation of DNA or RNA. Nucleic acids have been fractionated by precipitation as metallic salts (Ca^{++}, Ba^{++}, Mg^{++}) in the presence of alcohol, precipitation as salts of quaternary ammonium cations, differential centrifugation in a density gradient, and chromatography on columns of methylated serum albumin or on columns or sheets of cellulose ion-exchangers. Counter-current distribution has been employed in the fractionation of the low molecular weight "soluble RNA."

Determination of Nucleic Acids

The individual purines and pyrimidines have characteristic absorption spectra, the maxima being located in the range, 240 to 270 mμ. Owing to their content of these bases, nucleic acids exhibit an absorption maximum at 260 mμ, which is of such intensity that the nucleic acids can be detected readily even in the presence of protein, which has a maximum around 280 mμ (owing to the amino acids, tyrosine and tryptophan). Use has been made of this intense absorption in the intracellular localization (and estimation) of the nucleic acids by photomicrography in the ultraviolet, employing a quartz microscope.

A frequently used procedure (Schmidt-Thannhauser) for the estimation of the amounts of the two types of nucleic acids present in tissues involves the removal of acid-soluble phosphorus compounds, followed by removal of phospholipids. The residue is treated with dilute alkali, which degrades RNA to soluble nucleotides without so affecting DNA. Acidification then causes precipitation of DNA together with degraded proteins. Phosphorus determinations on this precipitate and on the soluble nucleotides from RNA in the filtrate permit calculation of the amounts of the nucleic acids of each type present in the original tissue.

In the Ogur-Rosen technique, RNA is solubilized by prolonged treatment with cold dilute perchloric acid, whereas the residual DNA is dissolved by heating in stronger perchloric acid. The nucleic acids in the two fractions are determined by UV absorption.

Separation of the two types of nucleic acid is not required in the method of Schneider, in which RNA and DNA are extracted with hot trichloroacetic or perchloric acid, which simultaneously denatures the protein and hydrolyzes both nucleic acids to nucleotides or free bases. The mixture is then analyzed for pentose and deoxypentose by the usual colorimetric methods.

Determination of Purines and Pyrimidines

DNA may be completely hydrolyzed to yield free bases by heating under appropriate conditions with hydrochloric, perchloric, or formic acid. RNA is more difficult to hydrolyze, but yields free bases on heating with perchloric acid, a mixture of purine bases and pyrimidine nucleotides with dilute sulfuric or hydrochloric acid, and purine and pyrimidine nucleotides on treatment with dilute alkali at moderate temperatures.

The free bases are readily separated by paper chromatography located on the paper by scanning under an ultraviolet lamp, the spots cut out, eluted, and the purines or pyrimidines determined by spectrophotometry in the ultraviolet.

Nucleotides are easily separated by paper electrophoresis, ion-exchange column chromatography, or cellulose ion-exchangers in sheets or thin-layer plates.

Sugars

The usual tests for pentoses can be applied to the detection and determination of ribose. Bial's orcinol reaction is often so used.

Deoxypentoses produce a blue color when heated with diphenylamine in a mixture of acetic and sulfuric acids (Dische reaction), a pink color with cysteine and sulfuric acid (Stumpf), a red color with tryptophan and perchloric acid (Cohen). Deoxyribonucleic acids are often located in histological tissue preparations by the Feulgen reaction, a test based on the use of the Schiff fuchsin-sulfurous acid reagent following a preliminary acid treatment of the tissue.

BIBLIOGRAPHY

INTRODUCTORY TEXTBOOKS

Davidson, J. N.: The Biochemistry of The Nucleic Acids, New York, John Wiley & Sons, Inc., 1965.
Hutchinson, D. W.: Nucleotides and Coenzymes, London, Methuen & Company, 1964.
Potter, V. R.: Nucleic Acid Outlines, Vol. 1, Structure and Metabolism, Minneapolis, Burgess Publishing Company, 1960.

ADVANCED TREATISES, MONOGRAPHS, AND SYMPOSIA

Bonner, J., and Ts'o, P. (eds.): The Nucleohistones, San Francisco, Holden-Day, Inc., 1964.
Busch, H.: Histones and Other Nuclear Proteins, New York, Academic Press, Inc., 1965.
Chargaff, E., and Davidson, J. N. (eds.): The Nucleic Acids, 3 vols., New York, Academic Press, Inc., 1955 to 1960.
Florkin, M., and Stotz, E. H. (eds.): Comprehensive Biochemistry, Vol. 8, Part B, Nucleic Acids, Amsterdam, Elsevier Publishing Company, 1963.
Jordan, D. O.: The Chemistry of Nucleic Acids, Washington, Butterworths, 1960.
Michelson, A. M.: The Chemistry of Nucleosides and Nucleotides, London, Academic Press, 1963.
Spirin, A. S.: Macromolecular Structure of Ribonucleic Acids, New York, Reinhold Publishing Corporation, 1964.
Steiner, R. F., and Beers, R. F., Jr.: Polynucleotides, Amsterdam, Elsevier Publishing Company, 1961.

REVIEWS

Annual Review of Biochemistry
Brawerman, G., and Shapiro, H. S.: Nucleic acids, Chapter 4 in Florkin, M., and Mason, H. S. (eds.): Comparative Biochemistry, Vol. 4, New York, Academic Press, Inc., 1962.
Davidson, J. N., and Cohn, W. E. (eds.): Progress in Nucleic Acid Research [and Molecular Biology], 3 vols., New York, Academic Press, Inc., 1963 and 1964.
Felix, K.: Protamines, Adv. Protein Chem. *15:*1, 1960.
Fox, J. J., and Wempen, I.: Pyrimidine nucleosides, Adv. Carb. Chem. *14:*283, 1959.
Montgomery, J. A., and Thomas, H. J.: Purine nucleosides, Adv. Carb. Chem. *17:*301, 1962.
Peacocke, A. R.: The structure and physical chemistry of nucleic acids and nucleoproteins, Progr. Biophys. & Biophys. Chem. *10:*55, 1960.
Phillips, D. M. P.: The histones, Progr. Biophys. & Biophys. Chem. *12:*211, 1962.

METHODS

Allen, F. W.: Ribonucleoproteins and Ribonucleic Acids, Preparation and Composition, Amsterdam, Elsevier Publishing Company, 1962.
Cantoni, G. L., and Davies, D. R. (eds.): Procedures in Nucleic Acid Research, New York, Harper & Row, Publishers, Inc., 1966.
Colowick, S. P., and Kaplan, N. O. (eds.): Methods in Enzymology, Vol. 3, Preparation and Assay of Substrates, Section 5, Nucleic Acids and Derivatives, and supplement Vol. 6, pp. 645–815, Preparation and Assay of Substrates, Section 4, Nucleic Acids, Coenzymes, and Derivatives, New York, Academic Press, Inc., 1957 and 1963.
Webb, J. M., and Levy, H. B.: New developments in the chemical determination of nucleic acids, Methods of Biochem. Analysis *6:*1, 1958.

CHAPTER 6

CHEMISTRY OF HEMOGLOBIN, PORPHYRINS, AND RELATED COMPOUNDS

INTRODUCTION

The compounds to be discussed in this chapter have a unique biochemical significance. Unlike the carbohydrates or lipids, they are not used for fuel by living organisms. Although certain of the substances under consideration are proteins (conjugated), they have no structural significance in the cell, nor do they exert the subtle control over the pattern of metabolism that is attributed to nucleoproteins and their derivatives. Rather, the hemoproteins, i.e., conjugated proteins bearing iron-porphyrin prosthetic groups, are concerned directly or indirectly in facilitating the reaction which is the basis of practically all bioenergetics, the union of oxygen and hydrogen to form water (p. 346).

Hemoglobin is the carrier of atmospheric oxygen from the lungs to the interior of the body. The oxygen may be stored temporarily in muscle attached to another hemoprotein, myoglobin. The combination of the oxygen from the air with hydrogen of metabolic substrates to form water is catalyzed by another group of hemoproteins, the cytochromes and cytochrome oxidase. Ancillary roles in biological oxidations are played by the catalases and peroxidases, enzymes which, like the cytochromes, contain heme prosthetic groups. The vital importance of the hemoproteins is illustrated by the fact that inhibition of the oxygen transport system (hemoglobin) by carbon monoxide, or inhibition of the oxygen utilization system (cytochromes) by cyanide, results in rapid death of the organism.

Detailed consideration of the role of chlorophyll in the photosynthetic reactions of plants lies outside the province of this discussion. However, it may be noted in passing that chlorophyll (a magnesium-porphyrin) is concerned in the catalysis of the cleavage of water into hydrogen and oxygen, whereas the hemoproteins (iron-porphyrin proteins) are involved in the reverse reaction. Evidently the derivatives of porphyrins are of wide significance in comparative biochemistry, from the initial fixation of solar energy in green plants to its eventual utilization by man.

Understanding of the carriage of gases or the catalysis of oxidations by the hemoproteins requires a comprehension of certain aspects of their chemistry. It may be helpful in this regard to consider first the chemistry of the prosthetic groups (porphyrins, hemes), secondly the hemoproteins themselves, primarily hemoglobin, and finally certain of their metabolic degradation products (bile pigments).

CHEMISTRY OF PORPHYRINS

Structures and Nomenclature

As indicated in Figure 6–1, porphyrins are cyclic compounds composed of four pyrrole units linked by methyne (—CH=) bridges. All porphyrins may be regarded as derivatives of porphin, a cyclic tetrapyrrole containing no substituent side chains. The biological precursor of the porphyrins is a monopyrrole with acetic and propionic acid side-chains, porphobilinogen (p. 609). Other side chains found in the natural porphyrins are indicated in Figure 6–2, together with their symbols which will be used hereafter for convenience.

The uroporphyrins, so called because originally discovered in urine (but not restricted to that medium), are tetra-acetic, tetrapropionic porphins. Of the four possible isomers that can be constructed with two types of substituents, only two are found in nature, designated uroporphyrins I and III. The Type I uroporphyrin bears its substituents in alternating sequence, whereas this order is reversed in the fourth pyrrole unit of uroporphyrin III.

Decarboxylation of the acetic acid side chains of the uroporphyrins produces the coproporphyrins (so called because of their original isolation from feces, but also found

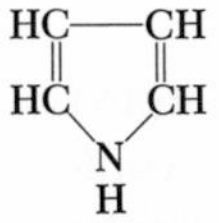

Pyrrole

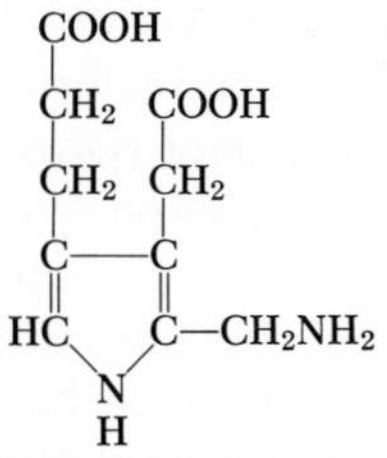

Porphobilinogen, the monopyrrole precursor of porphyrins

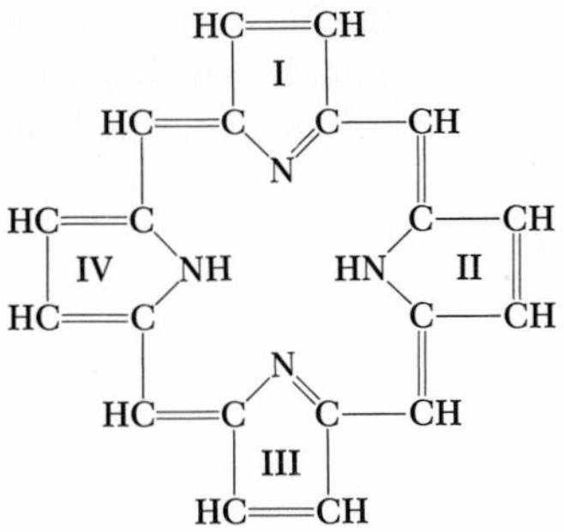

Porphin

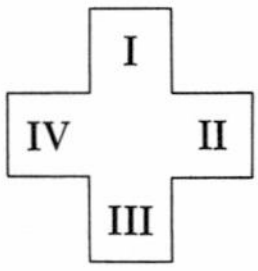

Simplified version of porphin ring to be used in further discussions

Figure 6–1. Basic pyrrole and porphyrin structures.

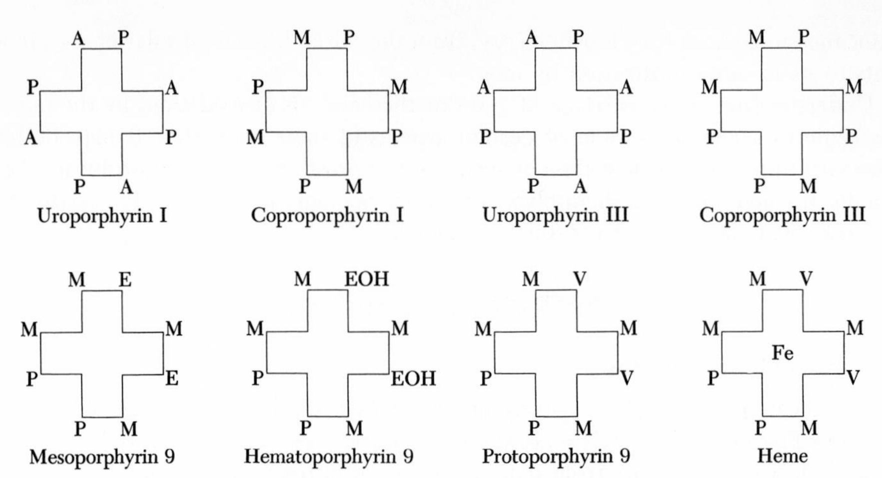

Figure 6-2. Naturally occurring porphyrins. *A*, Acetic—CH_2COOH. *E*, Ethyl—CH_2CH_3. *EOH*, Hydroxyethyl—$CHOHCH_3$. *M*, Methyl—CH_3. *P*, Propionic—CH_2CH_2COOH. *V*, Vinyl—$CH{=}CH_2$.

in urine), tetramethyl, tetrapropionic porphins. Again, only Types I and III are found in nature.

The remaining porphyrins illustrated in Figure 6-2 contain three rather than two types of substituent groups. Although derived biologically from the Type III porphyrins (p. 610), these latter compounds are designated as Type 9 (or IX), since they are related chemically to the ninth member of a series of 15 parent porphins containing three types of substituent groups.

Mesoporphyrin 9 (tetramethyl, diethyl, dipropionic porphin) may be regarded as derived from coproporphyrin III by decarboxylation of two propionic acid groups. Conversion of the two ethyl groups of mesoporphyrin 9 to hydroxyethyl groups produces hematoporphyrin 9 (tetramethyl, bishydroxyethyl, dipropionic porphin). Dehydration of the hydroxyethyl groups in turn forms protoporphyrin 9 (tetramethyl, divinyl, dipropionic porphin), the parent porphyrin of the hemoproteins. For example, insertion of an atom of iron into protoporphyrin 9 produces heme, the prosthetic group of hemoglobin and, indeed, of most hemoproteins.

Evidence is available indicating the occurrence of porphyrins containing numbers of carboxyl groups intermediate between uro- (eight) and copro-(four) porphyrins. Compounds bearing three carboxyl groups may also be expected to occur. Current systems of porphyrin nomenclature make no provision for such compounds.

In addition to the various types of porphyrins enumerated thus far, reduction products known as "porphyrinogens" are intermediates in the biosynthesis of porphyrins and occur among the normal excretory products. Such compounds, which are readily oxidized to the porphyrins proper, contain reduced "bridge" carbons, i.e., methylene instead of methyne:

H_2C — CH_2 — N H — NH — HN — H N — H_2C — CH_2

Physical Properties

The porphyrins have characteristic absorption spectra. This absorption of light at the violet end of the spectrum is so intense that the compounds themselves are red. Solutions of the porphyrins in organic solvents or mineral acids exhibit a red fluorescence under ultraviolet irradiation. This property is used for qualitative detection and quantitative determination of these compounds. The porphyrinogens are colorless and do not fluoresce.

In general, porphyrins are more readily soluble in certain organic solvents than in water. Porphyrins containing larger numbers of carboxyl groups exhibit decreased solubility in organic solvents and increased solubility in water. Owing to the different numbers of carboxyl groups contained in the various porphyrins, differential extractions are possible from organic solvents with aqueous phases of appropriate pH. The porphyrins and their methyl esters may also be separated and identified by paper chromatography. For preparative purposes, the esters may be separated by column adsorption chromatography.

Chemical Properties

Owing to their carboxyl groups, the common porphyrins readily form salts. Of these, the ammonium salts are the most soluble in water, those of sodium the least. The presence of pyrrole nitrogens as well as carboxyl groups makes the natural porphyrins amphoteric compounds, with isoelectric points at pH 3 to 4.5. Consequently, at physiological pH's the porphyrins bear negative charges, and may be expected to couple readily to basic proteins (cationic at neutral pH).

The carboxyl groups of porphyrins are readily esterified. Most of the isolations of these substances from natural sources have involved preliminary conversion to methyl esters.

The nitrogen atoms of the pyrrole nuclei are able to form complexes with certain metals, the metal occupying a central position in the porphyrin ring. Although copper, zinc, and possibly other metals are found combined with porphyrins in nature, the complexes with iron are of greatest biological importance. The iron-porphyrins ("hemes") in turn combine with proteins, simpler organic compounds, and, in some cases, gases. These important phenomena are discussed below.

Oxidizing agents convert the porphyrinogens to the corresponding porphyrins. Iodine, and exposure to oxygen and light are frequently used for this purpose. Hydrogen peroxide is less satisfactory. The reduction of porphyrins to porphyrinogens may be effected readily with sodium amalgam or potassium borohydride.

CHEMISTRY OF HEMES

Coordination of Iron

Both ferric and ferrous iron tend to form hexavalent coordination complexes. Insertion of a ferrous ion into the center of protoporphyrin 9 results in ejection of the two protons attached to the pyrrole nitrogen atoms with formation of an uncharged iron-porphyrin complex. Since the iron is coordinated with only the four pyrrole nitrogen atoms, room is available for two additional coordinating groups. The complex of ferrous iron and protoporphyrin ("ferroprotoporphyrin") unites with two electrically neutral groups of the "oxygen" or "nitrogen" type, i.e., H_2O, CO, O_2, NH_3, pyridine, imidazole, HN_3 (hydrazoic acid), $NH_2—NH_2$ (hydrazine), NH_2OH (hydroxylamine), HCN, NO, CH_3NC.

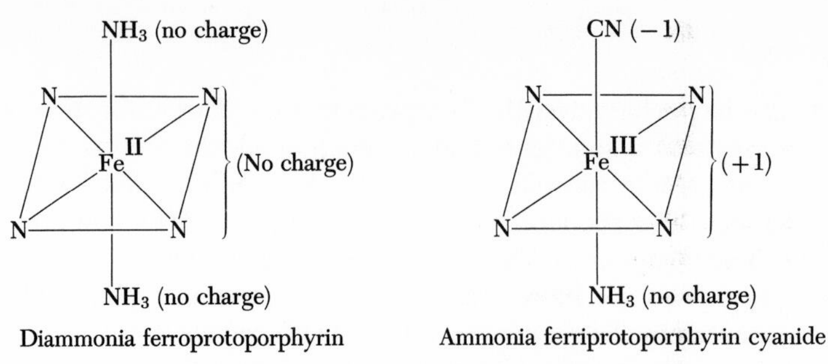

Figure 6–3. Coordination in ferro- and ferri-hemes.

Insertion of a ferric ion into the protoporphyrin ring ("ferriprotoporphyrin") results in a complex bearing a residual positive charge. Completion of the hexavalent coordination in this case is consequently accomplished by union of ferriprotoporphyrin with one uncharged and one anionic group. Typical of the latter category are OH^-, N_3^-, CN^-, and F^-.

A simplified diagram of the coordination systems under consideration is presented in Figure 6–3. The four nitrogen atoms of the pyrrole units occupy a plane with the iron; the two additional coordinating groups lie above and below that plane. The bonds between the iron and the pyrrole nitrogen atoms may be covalent or electrovalent, depending on the specific compound involved. This matter is discussed later in connection with hemoglobin and gas transport.

The combination of an iron porphyrin with two nitrogenous groups is sometimes called a hemochromogen or hemochrome. A particularly complex example of this type is the coordination of heme (ferroprotoporphyrin) with imidazole residues of histidine in the globin moiety of hemoglobin (discussed on page 129).

CHEMISTRY OF HEMOGLOBIN

General Physical Properties

Hemoglobin has a molecular weight of about 68,000, and consists of the protein, globin, to which are attached four heme groups. Studies by the method of X-ray diffraction indicate that hemoglobin has a nearly spherical shape of dimensions 50*h*, 55*w*, 64*l* Å (Fig. 6–4). The molecule consists of four peptide units, arranged in tetrahedral configuration. The four peptide chains may be further subdivided into pairs (α and β), the members of each pair having identical chemical composition. The pairs resemble each other in steric configuration, but are not identical. Furthermore, the steric configurations of both pairs resemble that of myoglobin (p. 82). The heme groups lie in pockets on the surface of the molecule, each pocket being formed by folds in one of the peptide chains.

Varieties of Human Hemoglobin

It has been known for many years that fetal hemoglobin differs from that of the adult by its greater resistance to alkaline denaturation. More recent investigations have shown that, although the molecular weights are similar, fetal hemoglobin differs from the adult pigment also in oxygen affinity and electrophoretic mobility. Fetal hemoglobin is usually replaced by adult hemoglobin more or less completely in the infant by the end of the first

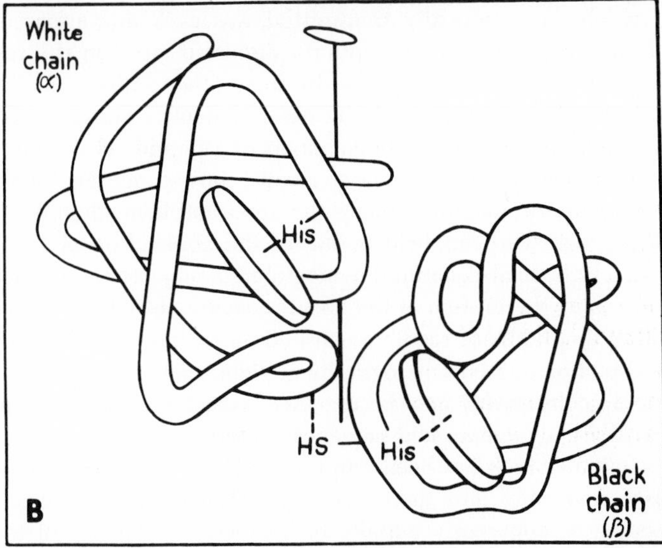

Figure 6-4. *A*, Model of hemoglobin, with heme groups of two peptide chains nearest observer shown as gray discs. Other pair of chains partly visible at rear. *B*, Configuration of two nearest chains. (From Perutz et al.: Nature *185*:416, 1960. See also Perutz: Science *140*:863, 1963.)

year. However, this pigment occurs in adults in some types of anemia. Of the four peptides in fetal hemoglobin, one pair is identical with that designated as α in normal adult hemoglobin. The other pair of peptide chains, designated γ, differs from both types of adult hemoglobin peptide chains. Fetal hemoglobin is commonly designated hemoglobin F.

Normal adult hemoglobin, or hemoglobin A, contains two pairs of peptide chains, designated α and β, respectively. Recently, normal adult hemoglobin has been found to be heterogeneous in electrophoresis. In addition to the major component, now designated A_1, a slowly migrating fraction is found, designated A_2, accounting for approximately 2.5 per cent of the total. This substance differs from both hemoglobins A_1 and F in containing, in addition to a pair of α chains, a pair differing from both β and γ types, designated δ. An electrophoretically fast fraction also appears, amounting to between 3 and 10 per cent of the total. Although designated A_3, it appears to be an altered form of A_1, found chiefly in old red cells.

From the standpoint of evolutionary theory, it is of interest to look for homologous amino acid residues and sequences among the individual peptide chains of the hemoglobins and myoglobin, all of which have a very similar conformation. Myoglobin and the hemoglobin α chains share relatively few homologous residues, suggesting early evolutionary divergence. On the other hand, α and β chains contain some 60 homologous residues, despite a difference in chain length (141 vs. 146 residues, respectively). Even closer relationships are seen between β and γ chains (two-thirds of residues homologous), and between β and δ (only 7 or 8 differences). It has been suggested that the δ chains originated rather recently in evolution, perhaps coincidentally with the emergence of the primates.

In addition to normal adult and fetal hemoglobins, more than 30 abnormal types have been described thus far. The occurrence of these abnormal hemoglobins, which are best differentiated by their characteristic electrophoretic mobilities, has given rise to the concept of "molecular disease," according to which an aberrant metabolic process forms a molecule different from the normal in shape, composition, or electrical charge. These abnormalities, which are genetically transmitted, are each due apparently to a single mutant gene, resulting (with a few exceptions, discussed later) in the replacement of a single amino acid residue of hemoglobin A_1 by some other amino acid. The substitutions frequently involve replacement of acidic by basic or neutral amino acids, and since this change in structure occurs in both of the members of a peptide chain pair (either α or β), a considerable difference in electrical charge results, thus accounting for the observed differences in electrophoretic mobility among the abnormal hemoglobins.

Much of the progress in this field is due to the application of the "fingerprinting technique," in which the heat-denatured hemoglobin is subjected to the action of trypsin, which specifically splits the protein at the 26 sites occupied by lysine and arginine molecules. The resulting peptides are readily separated on rectangular filter paper by electrophoresis in one direction and chromatography at right angles. In this way, peptides containing "abnormal" constituents may be detected, isolated, and their constituent amino acids and eventually their amino acid sequences determined.

Another technique which has been employed is "hybridization." At low pH, hemoglobins dissociate reversibly into their four constituent peptide chains. Neutralization results in reassociation, apparently initially to homogeneous dimers of the types α_2 and β_2, then to mixed tetramers, i.e., $\alpha_2\beta_2$. If a mixture of isotopically labeled hemoglobin A_1 and a sample of an abnormal hemoglobin is subjected to this process, it is possible to determine whether the α-like or β-like chain of the abnormal hemoglobin is exchangeable with the analogous chain of A_1, thus locating the abnormality in the non-exchangeable chain. Alternatively, an abnormal hemoglobin may be hybridized with a second abnormal hemoglobin, the defective locus of which is known. If the two hemoglobins are abnormal in different chains, a new species of doubly abnormal hemoglobin will be formed.

Table 6-1 lists the normal and a number of the abnormal hemoglobins, along with their chain composition, in terms of α and β pairs, and information on the specific amino acid abnormality. It will be noted that the abnormal substituent sometimes occurs in the α peptide chains, sometimes in the β. An additional type of abnormality involves formation

TABLE 6-1. DIFFERENCES IN COMPOSITION OF HUMAN HEMOGLOBINS

HEMOGLOBIN TYPE	PROBABLE CHAIN COMPOSITION	DIFFERENCES FROM HEMOGLOBIN A (A_1)*
$A_{(1)}$	$\alpha_2{}^A\beta_2{}^A$	————
A_2	$\alpha_2{}^A\delta_2{}^{A_2}$	δ replaces β
F	$\alpha_2{}^A\gamma_2{}^F$	γ replaces β
Barts	$\gamma_4{}^F$	Four γ^F chains
C	$\alpha_2{}^A\beta_2{}^C$	Lys replaces Glu in β residue No. 6 (same locus as S)
D_α St. Louis ($G_{Philadelphia}$, $G_{Bristol}$)	$\alpha_2{}^{D\text{ St. Louis}}\beta_2{}^A$	Lys replaces AspN in α residue No. 68
D_{Punjab} (Chicago, Cyprus)	$\alpha_2{}^A\beta_2{}^{D\text{ Punjab}}$	GluN replaces Glu in β residue No. 121 (same locus as O_{Arabia})
E	$\alpha_2{}^A\beta_2{}^E$	Lys replaces Glu in β residue No. 26
$G_{Honolulu}$ (Singapore, Hong Kong)	$\alpha_2{}^{G\text{ Honolulu}}\beta_2{}^A$	GluN replaces Glu in α residue No. 30
$G_{San\ Jose}$	$\alpha_2{}^A\beta_2{}^{G\text{ San Jose}}$	Gly replaces Glu in β residue No. 7
H	$\beta_4{}^A$	Four β^A chains (may be accompanied by $\delta_4{}^{A_2}$)
I	$\alpha_2{}^I\beta_2{}^A$	Asp replaces Lys in α residue No. 16.
M_{Boston}	$\alpha_2{}^{M\text{ Boston}}\beta_2{}^A$	Tyr replaces His in α residue No. 58
$M_{Saskatoon}$ (Emory)	$\alpha_2{}^A\beta_2{}^{M\text{ Saskatoon}}$	Tyr replaces His in β residue No. 63 (same locus as Zürich)
$M_{Milwaukee}$	$\alpha_2{}^A\beta_2{}^{M\text{ Milwaukee}}$	Glu replaces Val in β residue No. 67
Norfolk	$\alpha_2{}^{\text{ Norfolk}}\beta_2{}^A$	Asp replaces Gly in α residue No. 57
$O_{Indonesia}$	$\alpha_2{}^{O\text{ Indonesia}}\beta_2{}^A$	Lys replaces Glu in α residue No. 116
O_{Arabia}	$\alpha_2{}^A\beta_2{}^{O\text{ Arabia}}$	Lys replaces Glu in β residue No. 121 (same locus as D_{Punjab})
S	$\alpha_2{}^A\beta_2{}^S$	Val replaces Glu in β residue No. 6 (same locus as C)
Zürich	$\alpha_2{}^A\beta_2{}^{\text{Zürich}}$	Arg replaces His in β residue No. 63 (same locus as $M_{Saskatoon}$)

* Residues numbered from N-terminus.

of tetramers of a single type of peptide chain (γ_4, β_4, or δ_4). Finally, a hemoglobin not included in the table, Hb-Lepore$_{Boston}$, contains normal α chains, but instead of normal β chains there occur hybrids, the first 10 or 11 residues from the N-terminal being of the δ type, the rest β. This has been interpreted as resulting from non-homologous crossing-over between corresponding points of the β and δ genes.

Hemoglobin S derives its name from the fact that red cells containing it, when deoxygenated, change in shape from a disc to a sickle-shape, caused by the insolubility of hemoglobin S in its deoxygenated form, resulting in the formation of tactoids* and distortion of the shape of the red cell. Certain interesting chemical features of the hemoglobins M are discussed on p. 132.

Individuals who are heterozygous (bearing a single gene) for hemoglobin A and an abnormal hemoglobin are said to have the particular "trait" related to the abnormal hemoglobin. The red cells of these individuals contain both hemoglobin A and the abnormal hemoglobin, the former usually constituting more than 50 per cent of the total. Individuals who are homozygous (bearing a double complement of genes) for an abnormal hemoglobin are said to have the "anemia" or "disease" related to the abnormal hemoglo-

*Doubly-refracting, concentrated masses of rodlike particles.

bin. In these cases the synthesis of hemoglobin A is completely suppressed, although hemoglobin F frequently appears along with the abnormal hemoglobin. Individuals have been described who are heterozygous for two abnormal hemoglobins, in which case both abnormal hemoglobins are present in the red cell, hemoglobin A is absent, and fetal hemoglobin is present in some cases. A genetically transmitted condition known as thalassemia results in a decrease in the rate of synthesis of hemoglobin A, but does not, in itself, cause the production of an abnormal hemoglobin. (It has been suggested that the mutation causing thalassemia involves an "operator" rather than a "structural" gene (p. 765), and that there may occur both α and β operator defects.) Homozygosity in the gene causing this condition results in what is known as thalassemia major (simple heterozygosity for thalassemia = thalassemia minor). Individuals who are heterozygous for the thalassemia gene may also be heterozygous in the gene for an abnormal hemoglobin, resulting in conditions such as sickle-cell thalassemia disease, etc. In these conditions the red cells of the individual exhibit an absence or considerable decrease in the amount of hemoglobin A, and a relative increase in the amount of the abnormal hemoglobin and of hemoglobin F. The geographical distribution of the abnormal hemoglobins is of considerable interest to anthropologists, since certain of these pigments appear to predominate in specific ethnic groups.

Acid-Base Properties

As in the case of other proteins, the ionizable groups which are operative in hemoglobin at physiological pH are chiefly the imidazole side chains of histidine, possibly supplemented to a slight extent by certain of the amino end groups. The isoelectric point (pI) of hemoglobin is approximately 6.8, varying somewhat with the salt concentration in the solution.

Owing to its large content of histidine (approximately 35 such groups per molecule) and its high concentration in whole blood, hemoglobin is a very effective buffer. It is probable, in fact, that hemoglobin is responsible for most of the buffering efficacy of blood which is not accounted for by bicarbonate. Certain special aspects of the acid-base properties of the hemoglobin histidines are discussed below, in connection with gas transport.

Transport of Gases by Heme Groups of Hemoglobin

(*a*) ***Combination with oxygen.*** The physiological importance of hemoglobin derives chiefly from its ability to combine reversibly with oxygen. The gas is taken up readily at high partial pressures (e.g., in the lungs) and is released as readily at low oxygen pressures (e.g., in the tissues), thus providing an effective system for the transport of oxygen from the atmosphere to the cells of the body.

Under conditions of constant temperature, salt concentration, and pH, the degree of saturation of hemoglobin with oxygen is a function of the partial pressure of the gas, a plot of one variable versus the other producing a sigmoid curve (p. 285). At constant partial pressure of oxygen, the extent of combination of the gas with hemoglobin is decreased by (1) increased temperature, (2) increased acidity (decrease in pH), and (3) increased salt concentration.

(*b*) ***Heme-heme interactions.*** Each molecule of hemoglobin (molecular weight 68,000) contains four heme groups, each of which is capable of combining with a molecule of oxygen. The hemes are apparently not altogether independent; combination of oxygen with one heme group increases the oxygen affinity of the other heme groups, the enhancement of affinity increasing in a regular fashion as each oxygen is bound, with the exception of the last step, where a much greater change seems to occur. It is believed that these heme-heme interactions are responsible for the sigmoid shape of the oxygenation curve referred to above. In this connection, it is of interest that the oxygenation curve of myoglobin, which contains only one heme group, is hyperbolic rather than sigmoid.

Since the heme groups of hemoglobin are distant from each other, the mechanism of heme-heme interactions is not clear. Of possible relevance is recent evidence which indicates that a change in conformation accompanies oxygenation, involving a somewhat closer packing of the β chains.

(*c*) ***Heme-linked groups.*** As mentioned previously, the affinity of hemoglobin for oxygen decreases with decrease in pH (in the physiological range). The converse effect occurs also; oxygenation of hemoglobin results in a liberation of hydrogen ions into the solution. The biological significance of these effects is discussed elsewhere (Bohr effect, p. 287). We are concerned here with their chemical basis.

The interrelation of oxygenation and ionization suggests the presence in hemoglobin of ionizable groups located in sufficient proximity to the heme rings to be influenced by the state of oxygenation. Such groups are designated "heme-linked." Present information on the detailed structure of hemoglobin identifies these groups as the imidazole rings of histidine residues No. 87 and No. 92 in the α and β chains, respectively.

The state of affairs existing at a single heme in hemoglobin during oxygenation is illustrated in Figure 6–5. In the unoxygenated (frequently but erroneously called "reduced") hemoglobin molecule, bonds between the ferrous iron and the four pyrrole nitrogen atoms, the imidazole, and the sixth coordinating group (shown here as water) are essentially ionic in character. For reasons of simplification, only one of the several possible resonance structures is shown for the imidazole ring, the cationic "inium" group of which ionizes with a pK of 8.25.

Displacement of the water molecule by oxygen results in a number of alterations in the heme and heme-linked group, but it should be noted that, despite its direct attachment to oxygen, the iron of oxygenated hemoglobin ("oxyhemoglobin") remains in the ferrous state. Oxygenation causes the former ionic linkages to become covalent. In addition, the strongly electron-attracting character of oxygen tends to cause certain electron displacements along the lines shown in the figure. Liberation of a proton from the acid group is facilitated as a result, since ionization of a hydrogen amounts to, essentially, stripping a

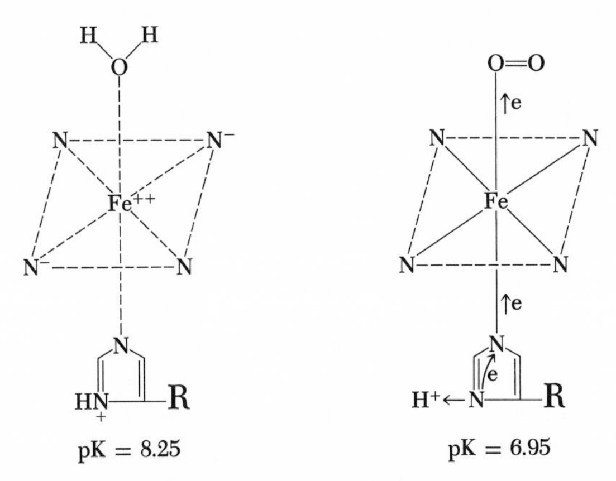

Figure 6–5. Heme-linked groups.

hydrogen atom of its electron. The inium group, therefore, becomes a stronger acid (pK = 6.95).

Since the oxygenation-deoxygenation and ionization-deionization reactions are both true equilibria, their relation has a two-sided character. That is to say, not only does oxygenation increase the ionization of the heme-linked group, but also any condition which facilitates the ionization (e.g., higher pH) likewise favors the oxygenation. The physiological applications of these effects are considered in connection with respiration.

Evidence has been obtained for the existence of a second heme-linked group in hemoglobin. This group is believed also to be an imidazole, but farther removed from the iron than the group already discussed, and consequently interacting only weakly with the heme group. The histidine residue has been identified tentatively as No. 58 in the α chain and No. 63 in the β. Although not close enough to bind directly to the iron atom, the imidazole ring appears to be within hydrogen-bonding distance of the water molecule coordinated with the iron in deoxygenated hemoglobin. Oxygenation of the heme group *increases* the pK of this imidazole from 5.30 to 5.90, hence this effect tends to oppose that previously described, but to only a slight extent. With the aid of the Henderson-Hasselbalch equation, it can be calculated that the net result of the changes in the pK's of the two heme-linked imidazoles is the liberation of approximately 0.6 mEq. of H^+ at each oxygenated heme, assuming a pH of 7.25 within the erythrocyte.

(*d*) ***Combination with carbon monoxide.*** Hemoglobin combines with carbon monoxide ("carboxyhemoglobin") much as it does with oxygen, but with several hundred times the affinity. The effects on the character of the linkages and on the heme-linked groups are the same as in the formation of oxyhemoglobin. Sufficiently high partial pressures of oxygen can reversibly displace carbon monoxide from hemoglobin. It has been suggested that the competition of these two gases for hemoglobin may be regarded as an example of biological antagonism.

Carbamino Compound Formation

All proteins bearing free amino groups can combine with carbon dioxide under appropriate conditions, forming carbamino compounds (p. 93). Although small amounts of CO_2 are carried by the plasma proteins in carbamino form, most of the CO_2 transported in this manner is combined with hemoglobin (p. 291).

It is commonly stated that deoxygenated hemoglobin is capable of carrying more carbamino-CO_2 than oxyhemoglobin. However, the amino groups responsible for this combination are probably distributed over the globin molecule, and cannot be considered "heme-linked" as are the histidine imidazoles discussed previously. The phenomenon is probably due, not directly to the oxygenation-deoxygenation reaction, but to the concomitant alteration in the number of sites available for the uptake of the hydrogen ions liberated in carbamino compound formation.

Oxidation-Reduction Properties of Hemoglobin

Throughout all of the reactions discussed thus far, the iron of hemoglobin has remained in the ferrous form. Treatment of hemoglobin with certain oxidants (e.g., ferricyanide) converts it to methemoglobin, in which the iron is ferric. Traces of methemoglobin may exist normally in the erythrocyte; clinically, significant "methemoglobinemia" is found as

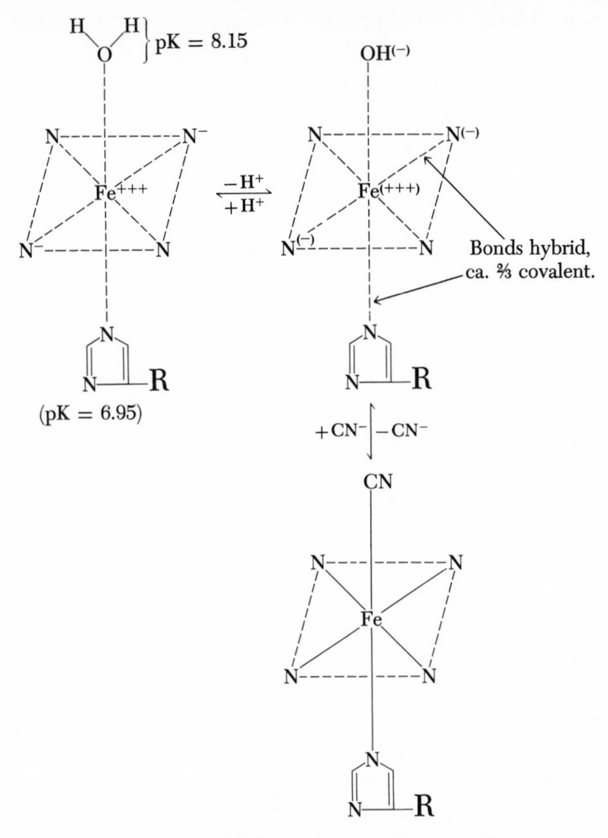

Figure 6-6. Methemoglobin and its cyanide.

a result of the ingestion of or exposure to certain substances, viz., chlorates, nitrites, phenacetin, acetylsalicylic acid, sulfonamides, aromatic amines, and aromatic nitro compounds, and in hereditary methemoglobinemias such as the hemoglobin M diseases (p. 132).

The oxidation of hemoglobin to methemoglobin is reversible. In vitro, reducing agents such as $Na_2S_2O_4$ (dithionite) are effective; in vivo, it is probable that the glycolytic system (p. 424) of the erythrocyte is responsible for the reduction.

Owing to the valence of the iron, the heme groups of methemoglobin bear unit positive charges. A number of consequences ensue (Fig. 6-6). The pK of the major heme-linked imidazole discussed previously takes on the value that it has in oxyhemoglobin (6.95), influenced by the positive charge of the iron. (In the figure, this group is shown ionized, as it largely would be at physiological pH.) In addition, the coordinated water molecule, also influenced by the positive charge of the iron, is enabled to lose a hydrogen ion, thus becoming a new acid group (pK = 8.15). Although the bonds in methemoglobin are ionic, liberation of a hydrogen ion from the water molecule to form the corresponding hydroxide results in partial conversion of the bonds to the covalent form (estimated to be two-thirds covalent in this case). At physiological pH's, a significant fraction of methemoglobin exists as the hydroxide.

In contrast to hemoglobin, methemoglobin cannot combine with O_2 or CO. Having net positive charges, however, the heme groups of methemoglobin can combine with various anions. The combination with cyanide (cyanmethemoglobin; bonds entirely covalent) is of considerable interest (Fig. 6–6). Methemoglobinemia is sometimes induced clinically in the treatment of cyanide poisoning, since the methemoglobin will compete for the cyanide with the cytochrome system of the tissues (p. 364), which otherwise might be inhibited to the point of causing death; such treatment obviously must be prompt to be effective.

In the hemoglobin M diseases (Table 6-1, p. 127), two of the four heme groups may be permanently fixed in the ferric state and hence unable to carry oxygen. The second (weakly) heme-linked histidine (p. 130) is replaced by a tyrosine in hemoglobins M_{Boston} (residue α-58) and $M_{Saskatoon}$ (residue β-63). Apparently the phenolate group coordinates strongly with the ferric iron and prevents its reduction by the enzyme system of the red cell. A slightly different situation, which, however, leads to the same result, is found in hemoglobin $M_{Milwaukee}$, in which a valine at position β-67 is replaced by glutamic acid. Since position β-67 is separated from β-63 by three residues, the glutamate side chain is aligned in the same direction from the α-helix (p. 76) as the histidine imidazole on β-63. Evidently the carboxylate anion complexes the ferric iron just as does the phenolate anion mentioned previously.

Sulfhemoglobin

This is a pigment of uncertain structure, formed by the action of H_2S on oxyhemoglobin. It is found in the blood after administration of aromatic amines or sulfur, in severe constipation, and in certain types of bacteremia. The formation of sulfhemoglobin involves the production of H_2S in the intestine by bacterial action on protein. This H_2S is normally excreted or oxidized after absorption. Sulfhemoglobinemia results from the presence in the blood of either excessive quantities of H_2S or compounds (aromatic amines) which catalyze the formation of sulfhemoglobin from the normal traces of H_2S in the body.

Interconversions of the Major Hemoglobin Derivatives

Figure 6–7 illustrates the interrelations which exist among the more important derivatives of hemoglobin, indicating the common and systematic names of each compound and the means of interconversion. Table 6-2 lists the absorption bands in the visible range of the major hemoglobin derivatives. The absorption spectra and interconversion reactions are often used for identification of these compounds.

Deoxygenated hemoglobin, oxyhemoglobin, and carbon monoxide hemoglobin are readily interconverted by displacement of one gas by another at appropriate partial pressure, or by the use of reagents which combine specifically with one gas. Oxyhemoglobin may react further with H_2S to form sulfhemoglobin.

Oxidation of hemoglobin produces methemoglobin; the reaction can be reversed by reducing agents. Methemoglobin combines with cyanide, forming cyanmethemoglobin.

Denaturation of hemoglobin under proper conditions produces a compound in which ferroprotoporphyrin is united with denatured globin. This compound readily undergoes autoxidation to the ferric derivative.

If hemoglobin is heated with glacial acetic acid in the presence of NaCl, denatured globin is split off from the prosthetic group, which undergoes oxidation to the ferric state, producing ferriprotoporphyrin chloride (heme chloride, or hemin). This product forms characteristic crystals which may be used in the detection of hemoglobin.

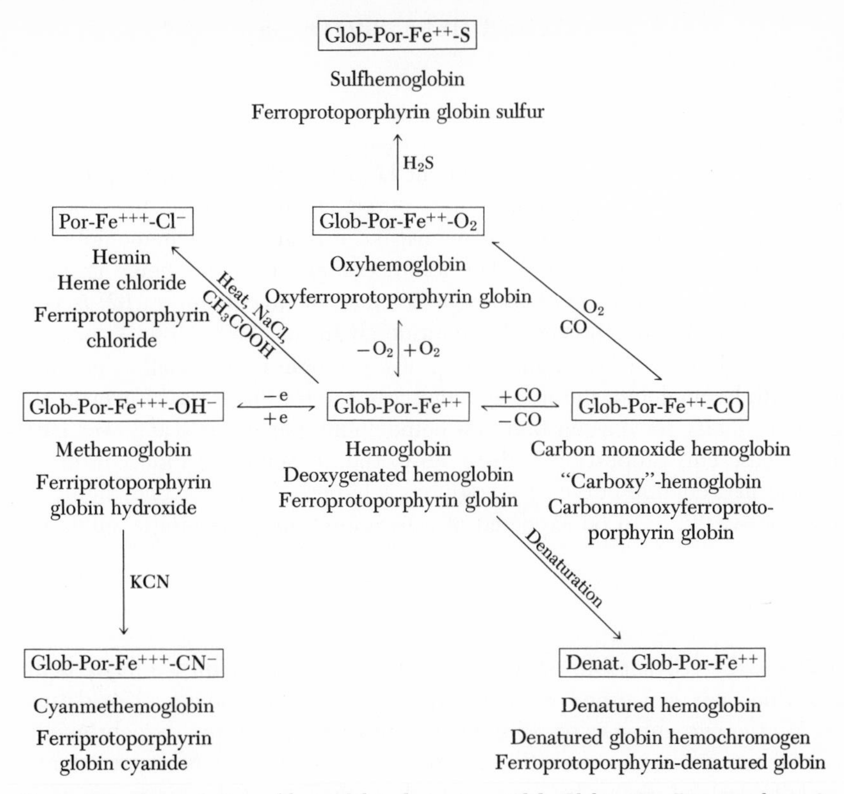

Figure 6-7. Interrelations of hemoglobin derivatives. *Glob*, Globin. *Por*, Protoporphyrin 9.

The term "hematins" is sometimes used to denote the products obtained by treatment of hemoglobin with acid or alkali, usually for purposes of quantitative determination. "Acid hematin" consists of a colloidal system of hemin (heme chloride) and denatured globin. "Alkaline hematin" solutions contain heme hydroxide (salt formation also occurring on the propionic acid groups of the porphyrin) and probably also denatured globin and its hemochromogen.

Table 6-2. Absorption of Visible Light by Hemoglobin and Derivatives

	Absorption bands, wavelengths in $m\mu$					
	Violet (400–475)	Blue (475–510)	Green (510–575)	Yellow (575–590)	Orange (590–620)	Red (620–700)
Hemoglobin	430		555			
Oxyhemoglobin	412–415		540–542	576–578		
Carbon monoxide-hemoglobin	418		538–540 568–572			
Methemoglobin						
pH < 7	405–407	500				630
pH > 7	411		540	577	600	
Cyanmethemoglobin	412–416		540			
Sulfhemoglobin					620	

OTHER HEMOPROTEINS

Myoglobin

Muscle contains an intracellular pigment known as myoglobin. Its prosthetic group is iron protoporphyrin 9; the protein moiety differs chemically from the globin of hemoglobin. In certain respects, myoglobin seems like a quarter of a hemoglobin molecule, i.e., its molecular weight is about 18,000 and it contains only one heme group. Furthermore, the spatial conformation of the peptide chain of myoglobin (p. 82) is very similar to, but not identical with, the α and β peptide chains of hemoglobin A (p. 124).

Oxygen combines with the heme group of myoglobin in essentially the same manner as it does with hemoglobin, the iron remaining in the ferrous state. However, myoglobin has a greater affinity for oxygen than has hemoglobin, particularly at lower partial pressures of the gas. This property is well suited to the physiological functions of myoglobin (p. 430). The oxygenation curve of myoglobin is hyperbolic rather than sigmoid; as indicated previously, this is to be expected of a hemoprotein containing a single heme.

Cytochromes

(*a*) ***General.*** All aerobic organisms contain a group of intracellular hemoprotein enzymes which are concerned with the major pathway of biological oxidations. These catalysts are the cytochromes (p. 359). One member of the group, cytochrome oxidase, is the terminal catalyst in the sense that it effects the direct union of oxygen with the electrons initially derived from substrates. The other members of the group are go-betweens, transferring electrons from other enzyme systems to the cytochrome oxidase. The cytochrome system is present chiefly in the mitochondria. In contrast to the hemoproteins discussed previously, cytochrome oxidase and the other members of the cytochrome group undergo repetitive oxidation and reduction of the iron as an integral feature of their function.

A major impediment to the study of the cytochromes has been the fact that these compounds exist in the mitochondria in the form of lipoprotein complexes. Only recently has it been possible to solubilize the cytochromes and fractionate or separate one from the other. The most successful technique in this connection appears to be the use of bile salts, which probably dissociate the cytochromes from their lipid complexes.

There are three major groups of cytochromes in the cell, differing in their prosthetic groups. The *a* cytochromes contain a porphyrin which differs from protoporphyrin in that one of the methyl groups is replaced by a formyl, and one of the vinyl groups by an α-hydroxyalkyl group. The *b* cytochromes contain protoporphyrin 9. In the *c* cytochromes, the two vinyl side chains of protoporphyrin have undergone an addition reaction with two thiol groups of cysteine residues of the protein, thus forming two thioether linkages.

These differences in prosthetic groups result in corresponding differences in absorption spectra. Thus, the reduced forms of the *a* cytochromes of animal tissues exhibit an α absorption band near 600 mμ, no β absorption band, and a γ (Soret) absorption band near 450 mμ. The *b* cytochromes of animal tissue have α absorption bands near 560 mμ, β absorption bands near 530 mμ, and γ absorption bands near 420 or 430 mμ. The corresponding bands for the *c* cytochromes are 550, 520, and 415. On oxidation, the α and β bands disappear, and the remaining γ bands shift toward the ultraviolet.

(*b*) ***Cytochromes a: Cytochrome Oxidase.*** It has been postulated for some time, on the basis of spectral data, that two cytochromes *a* exist, cytochrome *a* proper, said to be simply an electron-transferring cytochrome similar to the others in the chain, and cytochrome a_3, the terminal oxidase which reacts with molecular oxygen. The major proof for the existence of two cytochromes *a* is the observation that combination with carbon monoxide appears to cause partial, not complete, changes in the absorption bands allocated to cytochrome *a*, thus suggesting that two components account for the normal absorption bands of cytochrome *a*, but that one of these components, a_3, forms a carbon monoxide compound with a spectrum different from that of the free pigment. Although only one type of heme can be isolated from "cytochrome oxidase," a preparation of cytochrome *a* which is free of a_3 has been reported, thus substantiating the belief in the existence of two different hemoproteins.

Cytochrome oxidase (or cytochrome *a*) is found solely in the mitochondria. The solubilized form has been reported to have a molecular weight of 72,000 or 93,000, to require the presence of phospholipids for maximum oxidation of reduced cytochrome *c*, and to have an oxidation potential of +0.29 volt. Copper appears to be an integral part of the molecule and to be concerned in its function.

The exact nature of the reaction between cytochrome oxidase and oxygen is not known, beyond the fact that the ferrous oxidase reduces the oxygen, becoming ferric in the process. The ferrous form of cytochrome oxidase resembles hemoglobin in its ability to combine with carbon monoxide; the ferric form resembles methemoglobin in combining with cyanide. Both types of unions effectively prevent the oxidase from performing its normal function, and, in fact, almost completely inhibit oxidative metabolism in aerobic organisms.

(*c*) ***Cytochromes b.*** Mitochondrial cytochrome *b* has an oxidation potential of +0.04 volt in the mitochondria, −0.34 volt when free. The microsomes contain a cytochrome designated b_5 or *m*. Its physiological function is unknown at the present time. A "cytochrome 556," probably identical with b_5, and its corresponding reductase have been isolated from mitochondria.

(*d*) ***Cytochromes c.*** In contrast to cytochrome oxidase, which clings tenaciously to the particulate matter of the cytoplasm, cytochrome *c* is readily prepared in a soluble state. It has a molecular weight of 12,000 to 12,350 and contains one heme group. Cytochrome *c* exists exclusively in the mitochondria, and has an oxidation potential of +0.26 volt. Cytochrome c_1 or *e* has been found in heart and skeletal muscle. Its water-soluble form has a molecular weight of about 380,000. Cytochrome c_1 has an oxidation potential of +0.22 volt.

Catalases and Peroxidases

These hemoprotein enzymes catalyze either the decomposition of peroxide or its oxidation of secondary substrates (p. 365). Liver catalase has a molecular weight of 225,000 and contains four heme groups. The various peroxidases which have been studied differ from each other in molecular weight and in absorption spectra, all of which exhibit the bands of iron porphyrins, but nevertheless differ from each other. The various peroxidases probably contain different porphyrins. In the case of horseradish peroxidase, the prosthetic group is known to be iron protoporphyrin 9. All catalases and peroxidases contain trivalent iron, which is believed to remain in the oxidized state during the enzyme reactions. These enzymes are inhibited by cyanide, but not by carbon monoxide.

CHEMISTRY OF BILE PIGMENTS

Structure and Nomenclature

The major pathway of catabolism of hemoglobin results in the formation of open-chain tetrapyrroles known as bile pigments, the structures of which are indicated in Figure 6–8. All of the compounds in this group may be regarded as derived from a hypothetical parent compound (proto-)bilane. As can be seen from its structure, protobilane could be formed (hypothetically, only) by opening the ring of protoporphyrin 9 between pyrrole units I and II, eliminating the methyne carbon atom at that point by oxidation, and reducing all remaining methyne linkages to methylenes. Since the substituents on the pyrroles are the same as in protoporphyrin, this parent bilane bears the prefix, "proto-," which is understood if not indicated explicitly. Reduction of the vinyl side chains to ethyl groups (as in mesoporphyrin) produces mesobilane, the parent of certain of the bile pigments.

Oxidation of a methylene linkage (the central such group in naturally occurring compounds) in a bilane produces a bilene. A similar alteration in two methylene groups (as found in animals, the outer two) forms a biladiene, whereas oxidation of all three results in a bilatriene. Reduction of the outer unsaturated linkages in both external pyrrole rings of a bilane or bilene produces the corresponding tetrahydro derivative.

It is currently believed that the initial bile pigment formed from the degradation of hemoglobin is biliverdin, a (proto-)bilatriene. Subsequent reduction of a methyne group produces bilirubin, a biladiene. (Bilirubin is conjugated by the liver as glucuronide and sulfate, in which form it appears in the bile.) Conversion of the vinyl groups of bilirubin to ethyl groups places the compound in the "meso" family, the result being mesobilirubin, a mesobiladiene. The reduction probably proceeds in a step-wise fashion, the result of reducing one vinyl group being dihydrobilirubin. Further reduction, in this case at the methyne linkages, forms mesobilirubinogen, a mesobilane. This reaction probably also proceeds step-wise, the intermediate being dihydromesobilirubin. Stercobilinogen, a tetrahydromesobilane, is formed by hydrogenation of the two outer pyrrole nuclei. A third bilane, of somewhat uncertain origin and structure, is d-urobilinogen, a tentative formula for which is shown in Figure 6–8. Mesobilirubinogen, stercobilinogen, and d-urobilinogen are collectively designated "bilinogens" or "urobilinogens" in clinical biochemistry. By oxidation of the central methyne group of each of these compounds there are formed, respectively, i-urobilin (a mesobilene), stercobilin (a tetrahydromesobilene), and d-urobilin, which together are known as "bilins" or, confusingly, "urobilins." As in the case of the porphyrins, the prefixes "uro-" and "sterco-" indicate sources originally used in the isolation of these compounds, and do not exclude their occurrence in other tissues, body fluids, or excreta. The prefixes "i-" and "d-" are derived from the optical rotations of the compounds concerned. Mesobilirubinogen and its corresponding i-urobilin are optically inactive, d-urobilinogen and d-urobilin are, respectively, slightly and very dextrorotatory, while stercobilinogen and stercobilin, although not concerned in this nomenclature, are levorotatory. It should be emphasized that this nomenclature is irregular, and that i-urobilin and d-urobilin are in no sense isomers.

The bilifuscins are dipyrroles which are related to the bile pigments, but are anabolic in origin (p. 619). Possible formulas for mesobilifuscins are as follows:

M E M H P
O= N =CH– N =O
H H

P H M M E
O= N –CH= N =O
H H

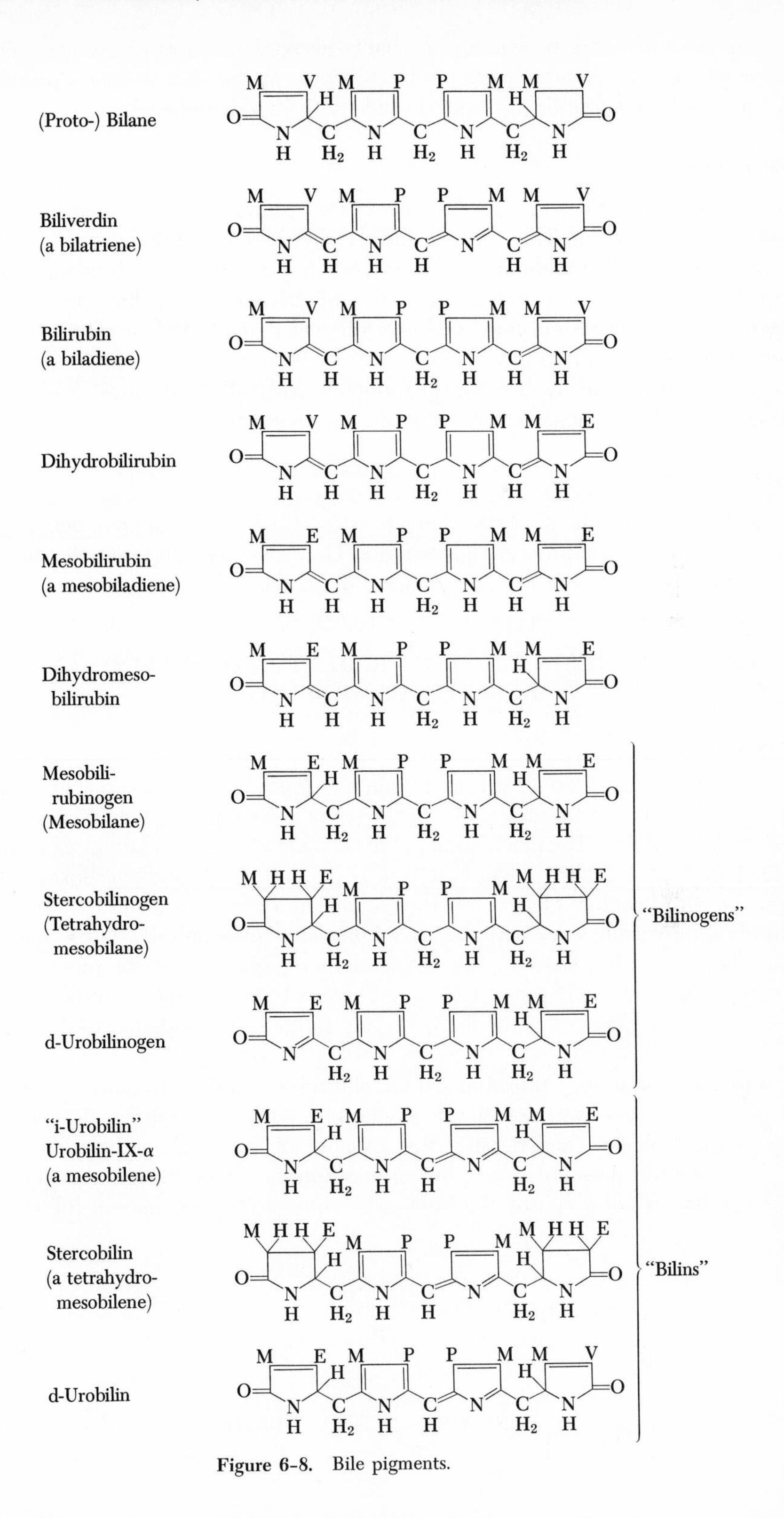

Figure 6-8. Bile pigments.

These compounds are dark brown, and probably account for most of the color of feces. The major part of the mesobilifuscins in feces occurs as the chromogens, "promesobilifuscins," in which compounds the central methyne bridge is reduced.

Physical Properties

The colors of the bile pigments depend on the number of unsaturated linkages and their degree of conjugation. Thus, bilanes and tetrahydrobilanes (bilinogens) are colorless, bilenes and tetrahydrobilenes (bilins) are yellow, biladienes of the type occurring in animals (bilirubin, mesobilirubin) are orange, and the bilatrienes (biliverdin) are blue-green.

The free acid forms of bilirubin and biliverdin and their Ba and Ca salts are insoluble in water (the Ca salt of bilirubin is found in certain types of biliary calculi). The Na and K salts are water-soluble, as are the glucuronide and sulfate conjugates of bilirubin. Certain organic solvents (e.g., ethanol) dissolve the free acids.

Chemical Properties

Certain bile pigments produce characteristic colors on oxidation, coupling with diazonium salts, or condensation with aldehydes. They may also form metallic salts which fluoresce. These reactions are discussed more fully in the following section.

CHEMICAL TESTS ON BILE PIGMENTS, PORPHYRINS, AND RELATED COMPOUNDS

Bile Pigments

(*a*) ***Oxidation tests.*** Treatment of certain bile pigments with nitric acid containing nitrous acid results in the formation of a sequence of colors: green, blue, violet, red, and yellow (Gmelin reaction). The mechanism of the reaction involves oxidation of the pigment to the bilatriene (green, blue) stage, followed by conversion of methyne linkages to carbonyl groups with eventual cleavage of the chain. The reaction is given by bilirubin and mesobilirubin. Biliverdin, since it is already a bilatriene, gives only the later stages of the reaction. Other oxidation tests for bile pigment (more specifically, for pigments of the bilirubin type), such as the Huppert-Cole and Fouchet tests, depend on initial isolation or concentration of the pigment as the Ba or Ca salt, followed by oxidation to the biliverdin stage.

(*b*) ***Azo dye formation.*** Bilirubin and mesobilirubin couple with diazotized sulfanilic acid to give an azo dye (van den Bergh reaction, p. 616). The reaction involves initial cleavage of the molecule, and requires the presence of a central methylene (—CH_2—) group (i.e., biliverdin does not react), but in addition has other structural requirements, since the reaction is not given by the bilinogens. A suggested mechanism follows:

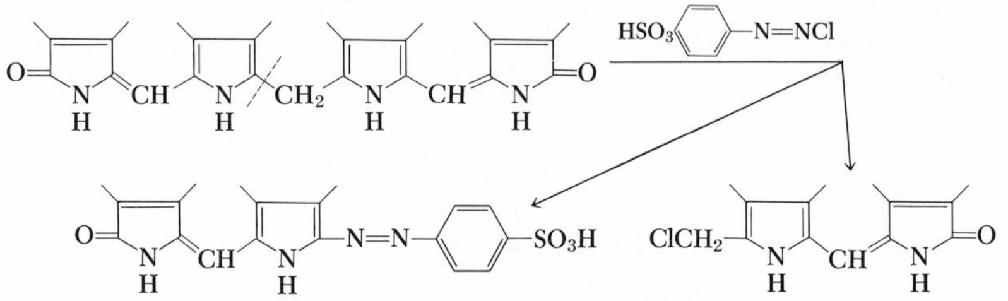

The resulting azo dye is blue-violet in strong acid, red at pH's between 2.0 and 5.5, and green above 5.5. In the presence of excess reagent, both halves of the bile pigment react to give two dye molecules.

Production of color within one minute after mixing serum and diazotized sulfanilic acid is known as the "prompt, direct" van den Bergh reaction, and is obtained with bile and with serum in obstructive and hepatocellular jaundice. Rapid formation of the azo dye only upon the addition of alcohol or caffeine characterizes the "indirect" reaction, given by the bilirubin found in serum of normal subjects or those with hemolytic jaundice. "Direct-reacting" bilirubin is now known to be conjugated as a glucuronide or sulfate. Unconjugated bilirubin is responsible for the "indirect" type of reaction. The difference between the two types of reactions is largely due to the differences in aqueous solubility of the various reacting species of bile pigment.

(*c*) ***Aldehyde condensation.*** The bilinogens (mesobilirubinogen, stercobilinogen) condense with Ehrlich's aldehyde reagent (*p*-dimethylaminobenzaldehyde) in acid solution to give a red color, probably involving condensation (with dehydration) of the aldehyde carbonyl with the active central methylene group of the bilinogens. The colored product formed from the bilinogens is soluble in organic solvents, in contrast to that formed by porphobilinogen, a metabolic precursor of the porphyrins.

(*d*) ***Fluorescence of Zn complexes.*** The bilins (stercobilin, urobilin) exhibit a brilliant green fluorescence when treated with alcoholic zinc acetate (Schlesinger reaction). This fluorescence is easily differentiated from that produced by various drugs which may be excreted in the urine or feces, since the former disappears on acidification.

Determination of Urinary Porphyrins

Before proceeding with the analysis, it is usually advisable to convert precursors of uroporphyrin (e.g., porphobilinogen) and precursors of coproporphyrin (e.g., coproporphyrinogens), to their respective porphyrins, conversions which may be effected by the use of heat and oxidizing agents. Coproporphyrins are then extracted with ethyl acetate from the urine which has been adjusted to a pH of 4 to 6, at which pH the uroporphyrins remain in the aqueous phase. The coproporphyrins may be determined fluorimetrically, after extraction from the ethyl acetate with 1.5N hydrochloric acid. The uroporphyrins, which remained in the original aqueous phase, may be adsorbed on aluminum oxide, from which they may be eluted with 1.5N hydrochloric acid for fluorimetric measurement.

Porphyrins bearing different numbers of carboxyl groups, as well as Types I and III isomers, have been separated also by various chromatographic techniques.

Porphobilinogen

Porphobilinogen may be distinguished from other substances which react with Ehrlich's reagent to form a red color as follows: (1) whereas most other compounds develop their color mostly after the addition of excess sodium acetate, porphobilinogen develops its maximum color on addition of Ehrlich's reagent alone; (2) in contrast to urobilinogen and other substances, porphobilinogen and its colored reaction product are not extracted by *n*-butyl alcohol; (3) heating in dilute acid converts porphobilinogen to uroporphyrin, which may be detected by its characteristic reactions.

δ-Aminolevulinic Acid

Although this compound (an intermediate in porphyrin synthesis) does not give a reaction with Ehrlich's reagent directly, it may be converted, by reaction with acetylacetone, to a pyrrole which does give this reaction.

Pseudoperoxidase Reaction

Heme compounds, free or combined with protein, catalyze the oxidation of organic substrates (particularly phenols and aromatic amines) by hydrogen peroxide. The reaction is similar to that catalyzed by the true peroxidases (p. 365), differing only in being thermostable. With proper precautions, the pseudoperoxidase reaction may be used as a test for blood, depending in that case on the very high concentration in blood of heme in the form of hemoglobin.

Separation of Hemoglobin Variants

In addition to the electrophoretic techniques mentioned previously (p. 126), ion exchange column chromatography also has been employed for the separation of abnormal and minor normal hemoglobins.

Determination of Hemoglobin

Methods for the quantitative determination of this important hemoprotein fall into four groups, based on: (1) the gas-transporting function of hemoglobin; (2) its iron content; (3) the color (light absorption) of hemoglobin itself or of its derivatives; (4) its general properties as a blood protein.

(*a*) ***Gasometric methods.*** Since the heme groups of hemoglobin combine stoichiometrically with oxygen or carbon monoxide, accurate analytical methods have been devised in which the blood sample is saturated with the chosen gas. The quantity of gas combined with the sample is then determined (by pressure or volume) by liberation through conversion of the hemoglobin to methemoglobin (which cannot combine with these gases). One gram of hemoglobin combines with 1.36 ml. of O_2 or CO (standard temperature and pressure), or, conversely, each milliliter of gas taken up by the sample is equivalent to 0.736 gm. of hemoglobin. These methods are designated "oxygen (or carbon monoxide) combining capacity."

(*b*) ***Iron determination.*** Since hemoglobin contains 0.34 per cent iron (1 gm. hemoglobin = 3.4 mg. Fe), determination of the iron content of a blood sample would permit calculation of the hemoglobin content if no non-hemoglobin iron were present. Actually, only traces of non-hemoglobin iron are present in blood, so that a determination of total iron is practically equivalent to a determination of hemoglobin. The iron is ordinarily liberated from the hemoglobin and determined colorimetrically with thiocyanate or thioglycolate.

(*c*) ***Colorimetric and spectrophotometric methods.*** Direct measurement of light transmission (at 540 or 576 mμ) of blood samples suitably diluted with weak alkali yields results that are satisfactory for clinical purposes. Increased accuracy can be obtained by the use of a spectrophotometer instead of the ordinary photoelectric colorimeter, but the method even then is probably not as accurate as those discussed in groups (a) and (b).

Conversion of the hemoglobin to cyanmethemoglobin and determination of the latter by colorimetric or spectrophotometric means has been suggested as a particularly accurate modification of this group of methods. In any case, the colorimetric or spectrophotometric methods require comparison with standard samples or reliance on previous calibrations.

Conversion of the hemoglobin in the blood sample to acid or alkaline "hematin" and measurement of the resulting color against standards is the basis of certain widely used clinical methods (e.g., the Sahli "acid hematin" method). These methods are not very precise.

(*d*) ***Protein determination.*** Theoretically, the quantity of hemoglobin in blood could be determined by the difference between analyses for total blood protein and plasma protein (since hemoglobin accounts for almost all of the protein within the red cell), using standard methods. In practice, such a procedure would be too time-consuming. However, the copper sulfate specific gravity method represents this approach in an abbreviated form (p. 99).

BIBLIOGRAPHY

GENERAL

Lemberg, R., and Legge, J. W.: Hematin Compounds and Bile Pigments, New York, Interscience Publishers, Inc., 1949.

PORPHYRINS

Falk, J. E.: Porphyrins and Metalloporphyrins, Amsterdam, Elsevier Publishing Company, 1964.

Florkin, M., and Stotz, E. H. (eds.): Comprehensive Biochemistry, Vol. 9, Part A, Pyrrole Pigments, Amsterdam, Elsevier Publishing Company, 1963.

Rimington, C., and Kennedy, G. Y.: Porphyrins: structure, distribution, and metabolism, Chapter 12 in Florkin, M., and Mason, H. S.: Comparative Biochemistry, Vol. 4, New York, Academic Press, Inc., 1962.

Schwartz, S., Berg, M. H., Bossenmaier, I., and Dinsmore, H.: Determination of porphyrins in biological materials, Methods of Biochem. Analysis *8*:221, 1960.

BILE PIGMENTS

Gray, C. H.: The Bile Pigments, London, Methuen & Company, 1953.

Gray, C. H.: Bile Pigments in Health and Disease, Springfield, Ill., Charles C Thomas, 1961.

HEMOGLOBIN AND MYOGLOBIN

Braunitzer, G., Hilse, K., Rudloff, V., and Hilschmann, N.: The hemoglobins, Adv. Protein Chem. *19*:1, 1964.

Ingram, V. M.: Hemoglobin and its Abnormalities, Springfield, Ill., Charles C Thomas, 1961.

Ingram, V. M.: The Hemoglobins in Genetics and Evolution, New York, Columbia University Press, 1963.

Lehmann, H., and Huntsman, R. G.: Haemoglobin and myoglobin, Chapter 1, Section D, p. 55, in Florkin, M., and Stotz, E. H. (eds.): Comprehensive Biochemistry, Vol. 8, Amsterdam, Elsevier Publishing Company, 1963.

Rossi Fanelli, A., Antonini, E., and Caputo, A.: Hemoglobin and myoglobin, Adv. Protein Chem. *19*:74, 1964.

Wyman, J., Jr.: Linked functions and reciprocal effects in hemoglobin: a second look, Adv. Protein Chem. *19*:224, 1964.

HEME ENZYMES

Paul, K. G.: Heme compounds in enzyme catalysis, Chapter 16 in Boyer, P. D., Lardy, H., and Myrbäck, K. (eds.): The Enzymes, Vol. 3, New York, Academic Press, Inc., 1960. See also Vol. 8, 1963.

CHAPTER 7

VITAMINS

THE FACT that normal nutrition cannot be maintained in animals receiving diets containing only purified proteins, carbohydrates, lipids, and minerals was recognized at least 30 years before the existence of substances now known as vitamins was actually demonstrated. Such clinical observations as the prevention and cure of scurvy by citrus fruit juices and of beriberi by rice polishings also strongly suggested the nutritional importance of then unknown dietary factors. The names of Hopkins, Osborne, Mendel, and McCollum are associated with fundamental observations in this field (1912 and 1913) which resulted in the establishment of this class of substances, originally designated "accessory food factors." Funk (1912) demonstrated the presence of basic nitrogen in a substance extracted from rice polishings and yeast, which was curative for pigeon beriberi. He applied the term "vitamine," i.e., an amine essential for life, to this substance. This designation (minus the terminal "e" to avoid the implication that they are amines, as a class) has since been employed to designate this category of "accessory food factors," which have come to be recognized as playing vital roles in nutrition and in certain fundamental metabolic processes.

Vitamins have been defined as organic compounds, occurring in natural foods, either as such or as utilizable precursors, which are required in minute amounts for normal growth, maintenance, and reproduction, i.e., for normal nutrition and health. They differ from other organic foodstuffs in that they do not enter into the tissue structure and do not undergo degradation for purposes of providing energy. They were originally classified according to their solubility in water or fats and alphabetically, e.g., fat-soluble A and D, water-soluble B and C. The list of members of the vitamin family has grown considerably; most of them have been identified chemically and many have been synthesized. With establishment of the chemical structure of a vitamin, alphabetical designations have become unnecessary; with elucidation of its specific metabolic functions, even the term "vitamin" becomes superfluous, except as an indication of its occurrence in nature and exogenous requirement. For example, several of the B vitamins are known to serve as coenzymes in fundamentally important metabolic reactions, and the functional activity of others, perhaps of all, may ultimately be found to be due to their influence on or participation in enzyme systems.

Demonstration of their chemical nature led in many instances to the discovery that several structurally related substances may possess similar vitamin activities. The terms "isotels" and "vitamers" have been suggested for such substances; e.g., activated 7-dehydrocholesterol (vitamin D_3) and activated ergosterol (vitamin D_2) are isotels, or D vitamers.

Although procedures are available for quantitative determination of most of the known vitamins, especially in foods, clinical evaluation of nutritional status with respect to vitamins is often difficult and the available methods unsatisfactory. This is particularly true during the usually long latent period of progressing deficiency which precedes the appearance of frank symptoms and signs. Various types of diagnostic procedures may be employed for this purpose:

1. The concentration of the vitamin or one of its metabolites may be determined in the blood or urine.
2. The curve of concentration in the blood or excretion in the urine may be measured after administration of a standard test dose of the vitamin. This is the so-called "saturation test" procedure, based on the assumption that subsaturation of the tissues with the vitamin will result in a subnormal rise in the blood and subnormal excretion in the urine under conditions of the test.
3. Quantitative determinations may be made of the vitamin content of tissues obtained at biopsy (e.g., liver, muscle).
4. Evidence of certain types of deficiency may be obtained by microscopic studies, e.g., of mucosal scrapings in vitamin A deficiency.
5. Certain consequences of specific deficiencies may be demonstrated by biophysical methods, e.g., impaired dark adaptation in vitamin A deficiency and increased capillary fragility in ascorbic acid deficiency.
6. In the case of certain vitamins, deficiency may manifest itself in some characteristic derangement of metabolism which can be measured quantitatively, e.g., elevation of blood pyruvate in thiamine deficiency, and increase in serum alkaline phosphatase, hypophosphatemia and hypocalcemia in vitamin D deficiency.
7. Of great diagnostic value is the prompt relief of clinical manifestations of suspected deficiency upon administration of adequate amounts of the vitamin in question.

The usefulness of each of these procedures for the detection of deficiency varies in the case of different vitamins, and few of them are entirely satisfactory for any vitamin. Biochemical studies in this connection are most valuable when used in conjunction with other types of data, e.g., clinical and dietary.

VITAMINS A

Vitamin A derives its alphabetical designation from the fact that, although not isolated until some years later, it was the first substance to be placed in this category of nutritionally essential factors (in 1913). It was originally recognized as a substance present in egg yolk and butter fat, which if absent from the diet of rats resulted in their failure to maintain normal growth. This growth factor was designated "unidentified dietary factor fat-soluble A."

It was found also that rats deprived of this substance developed rather characteristic eye changes, viz., dryness (xerophthalmia) and inflammation of the conjunctiva, ulceration, edema and opacity of the cornea (keratomalacia), eventuating in blindness. These were preventable by administration of small amounts of cod-liver oil. The resemblance of this condition to xerophthalmia and keratomalacia occurring in children (and also adults) on restricted diets (largely vegetable) was noted. It was then shown that this clinical disorder responded promptly to administration of foods rich in vitamin A.

Chemistry

Vitamin A is a derivative of certain carotenoids (p. 44), which are hydrocarbon (polyene) pigments (yellow, red) widely distributed in nature. The most important of these carotenoid precursors, designated provitamins A, are α-, β-, and γ-carotene, which are $C_{40}H_{56}$-hydrocarbons, and a monohydroxy-β-carotene ($C_{40}H_{55}OH$), termed "cryptoxanthin." The structure of β-carotene is indicated in Figure 7–1. It is a symmetrical molecule, containing two terminal β-ionone rings (A and B), connected by an 18C hydrocarbon chain with 11 conjugated double bonds. The three other provitamins A differ from β-carotene only in the nature of ring B (Fig. 7–1). Such compounds are subject to *cis-trans* isomerization and, when considered from a three-dimensional standpoint, there are a large number (148) of possible stereoisomers of the four provitamins named. Only a few of these have been investigated as to biological activity. In general, the *trans*-isomers are most active with respect to growth, liver storage, and vaginal cornification, whereas only the *cis*-form of vitamin A aldehyde is involved in the synthesis of rhodopsin. It is obvious that isomerization must occur in vivo to a considerable extent.

The general structural relation of vitamin A to β-carotene may be indicated as follows (Fig. 7–1): (1) β-carotene contains two β-ionone rings, vitamin A one; (2) β-carotene ($C_{40}H_{56}$) contains 40 C atoms, vitamin A 20 ($C_{20}H_{29}OH$); (3) β-carotene has 11 conjugated double bonds in the hydrocarbon chain, vitamin A five; (4) vitamin A has a terminal primary alcohol group, whereas β-carotene has no such group.

Two molecules of vitamin A are formed by symmetrical oxidative scission of β-carotene.

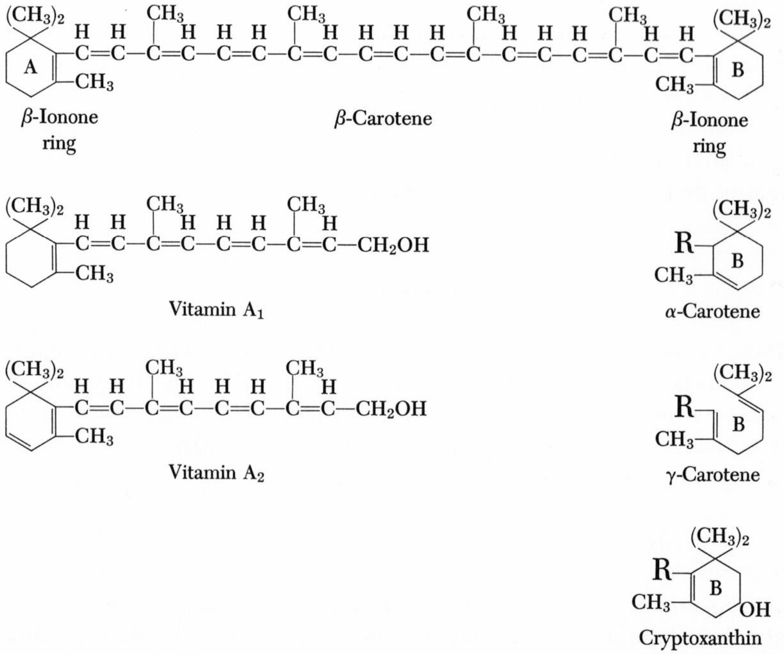

β-Ionone ring — β-Carotene — β-Ionone ring

Vitamin A_1 — α-Carotene

Vitamin A_2 — γ-Carotene

Cryptoxanthin

Figure 7–1. Structures of provitamins A and vitamins A. The symbol "R" attached to the B rings of the provitamins refers to the remainder of the molecule, which is identical with that of β-carotene.

TABLE 7-1. RELATIVE VITAMIN A ACTIVITIES OF CERTAIN NATURALLY OCCURRING PIGMENTS (PROVITAMINS A)

PROVITAMIN	β-IONONE RINGS	RELATIVE A ACTIVITY
all-*trans*-β-Carotene	2	100
all-*trans*-α-Carotene	1	53
all-*trans*-γ-Carotene	1	27
mono-*cis*-β-Carotene (neo-β-Carotene B)	2	53
di-*cis*-β-Carotene (neo-β-Carotene U)	2	38
Cryptoxanthin	1	57

Oxidation of the central double bond may produce as intermediate an aldehyde, which is subsequently reduced to the alcohol (vitamin A). Similar splitting of α- or γ-carotene, or cryptoxanthin, containing only one β-ionone ring, gives rise to only one molecule of the vitamin, no vitamin A activity being associated with the portion of the molecule which does not contain a β-ionone ring. The approximate relative biological activities of these provitamins are indicated in Table 7-1.

Vitamin A occurs in nature in different forms. The usual form, vitamin A_1, described above, predominates, except in the livers (and other tissues) of certain fresh-water fishes; in these, another type predominates, designated "vitamin A_2," which shows an absorption band at 693 mμ when treated with antimony trichloride, whereas A_1 shows a band at 620 mμ. Vitamin A_2 differs from A_1 apparently in having an additional unsaturated linkage in the ring, i.e., a double bond between Carbons 3 and 4 (Fig. 7–1). Its biological activity is approximately 40 per cent of that of vitamin A_1. A stereoisomer of vitamin A_1, "neovitamin A," is apparently a *cis-trans*-form, vitamin A being an all-*trans*-form. Neovitamin A has about 70 to 80 per cent of the biological activity of vitamin A.

By virtue of its alcoholic structure, vitamin A can form esters and can be oxidized to an aldehyde. The vitamin occurs in fish liver oils as mixtures of the free alcohol and esters of fatty acids. The aldehyde is presumably an intermediate in the formation of the vitamin from its carotenoid precursors. Moreover, "retinene," an intermediate in the rhodopsin (visual purple) cycle (p. 148), has been identified as vitamin A aldehyde.

Vitamin A and the provitamins are practically insoluble in water and are very soluble in most fat solvents. Vitamin A is referred to, therefore, as a "fat-soluble vitamin." One of the most important of the physical properties of this vitamin and its precursors is their spectral absorption, which is useful in their identification and quantitative determination. Individual carotenoids differ in their absorption maxima.

Both provitamins and vitamins A are destroyed by oxidation and by exposure to light, vitamin A being more stable than carotene. Both are protected by the presence of antioxidants, e.g., α-tocopherol (vitamin E). They are not thermolabile, but heat accelerates their destruction in the presence of oxygen. The vitamin A content of foods is not affected by canning or freezing, but is lowered by dehydration.

Occurrence and Food Sources

Whereas carotenoids are present in both plant and animal tissues, vitamin A occurs only in animals. It is generally believed that the carotenoids found in animals are derived from the food, although the possibility of their formation in the animal organism has not been excluded. If true, this is a unique situation, in which a vitamin is formed only by animals from precursors formed only by plants. β-Carotene has been found in the corpus luteum, placenta and adrenals in man.

The provitamin carotenoids are the chief dietary source of vitamin A. They are widely distributed throughout the plant kingdom, in which they represent an important class of pigments (yellow-red). There is a parallelism between greenness, i.e., chlorophyll content, and vitamin A activity in leafy vegetables, but the nature of this relationship is not clear. Yellow-colored vegetables and fruits, e.g., corn, sweet potatoes, carrots, tomatoes, apricots, yellow peaches, etc., are also rich in carotenoid provitamins. The most important animal food sources of vitamin A are whole milk, butter, and egg yolk. The vitamin A potency of butter fat (milk), which contains both β-carotene and vitamin A_1, varies in different breeds of cattle and with the carotenoid content of the feed. Colostrum has a higher content (both carotene and vitamin A) than has mature milk. This is true also of human milk, which can be enriched by ingestion of vitamin A.

The livers of certain fish contain higher concentrations of vitamin A than do any other tissues; consequently, fish liver oil concentrates are commonly used therapeutically. The livers of marine fishes contain vitamin A_1 and those of fresh-water fishes A_2. The concentration in halibut liver oil (1.5 per cent) may be 150 times and in tuna liver oil (4.5 per cent) 450 times that in cod liver oil (0.01 per cent). However, these ratios vary widely in similar types of fish in different regions. The liver of the polar bear is very rich in vitamin A.

Assay

The bioassay procedure for vitamin A is based upon the acceleration of growth produced in young rats given a basal diet nutritionally complete except for vitamin A or its precursors. When β-carotene was found to be a provitamin A, it was adopted as a reference standard. Crystalline vitamin A acetate is also used for this purpose. The International Unit (I.U.) (also U.S.P. unit) is defined as the amount of vitamin A equivalent in effect to 0.6 μg. of pure crystalline β-carotene. A satisfactory grade of cod liver oil (unconcentrated) contains at least 600 I.U./gm.

Absorption

Vitamin A and its carotene precursors are absorbed in the small intestine. It is believed that the simultaneous presence of tocopherols and other antioxidants protects them against destruction in the intestinal lumen. Dietary vitamin A is chiefly in the form of esters, which are hydrolyzed in the lumen to free vitamin A alcohol and fatty acid. The vitamin apparently undergoes re-esterification in the intestinal epithelial cells and in the liver, for it appears in the blood in the ester form promptly, regardless of the form in which it is administered. The maximum blood level is attained four to five hours after a single large dose (130 mg.). The blood carotene level reaches a maximum about seven to eight hours after oral administration of carotene.

Being fat-soluble, vitamin A and carotene are absorbed from the intestine more or less well according to the adequacy of lipid absorption. Because of its solubility in mineral oil, absorption of carotene is diminished by the presence of this oil, being carried out with it in the feces. Absorption of vitamin A is not affected significantly.

Storage and Intermediary Metabolism

Carotenoids which contain a β-ionone ring (α-, β-, γ-carotene, cryptoxanthin) are capable of transformation into vitamin A, as indicated previously. The intestinal epithelium is the major site of this conversion, at least in certain species, but it apparently occurs in other tissues. The liver may be the principal site in man.

About 95 per cent of the vitamin A reserve of the body is held in the liver, chiefly in ester form (combined with fatty acids), a small amount being present in other tissues, e.g., kidney (not in man), lactating breast, adrenals, lung, intestine. Under normal conditions, vitamin A is stored chiefly in the liver cells; after ingestion of large amounts it enters the Kupffer cells also. In subjects with liver damage, the capacity for storage and apparently also for formation of vitamin A from carotene is impaired and concentration of this vitamin in the blood is decreased. The hepatic storage capacity is comparatively low in young infants, increasing with age. The quantity stored in the liver varies in different species, but is largely dependent upon the antecedent diet. About 70 per cent of a single large dose of vitamin A may be recovered from the liver of the rat, which can store enough in a few days of adequate intake to satisfy its requirement for months. On the other hand, less than 10 per cent of a similar dose can be recovered from the liver of the guinea pig, which is very sensitive to deficiency in vitamin A. The storage capacity in man is apparently relatively large. Nothing is known concerning the catabolic mechanisms.

Mobilization and Circulation

The blood plasma contains both vitamin A and carotenoid pigments (as lipoprotein complexes). The former is present chiefly in the free state (alcohol) except after ingestion of large amounts of vitamin A or its carotene precursors, when the ester form appears in the blood. Under normal conditions, the levels of both substances in the blood are maintained by transformation of carotene to vitamin A and mobilization of the latter from the hepatic stores. The mechanism which regulates this mobilization is not clear.

Reported values for vitamin A and carotenoids in the blood of normal subjects vary widely, owing in part to differences in methods employed, several of which have proved unsatisfactory. The following figures appear to be acceptable: vitamin A, 18 to 60 μg. (60 to 200 I.U.) per 100 ml. serum; carotenoids, 100 to 300 μg. per 100 ml. serum, carried mainly in the β-lipoprotein fraction.

Excretion

The urine contains no vitamin A or carotene except after administration of excessive amounts. Under normal conditions only very small quantities are excreted in the feces. Administration of mineral oil, especially in young children, may cause excessive loss of carotene in the feces. Considerable amounts of vitamin A and carotene are present in milk, the concentration being greatest in colostrum and decreasing gradually over the period of lactation. Human colostrum possesses about twice as much vitamin A activity as early milk, the latter, providing 2400 to 4000 I.U. daily, being considerably richer in this factor than cow's milk. The vitamin A content of milk is increased by ingestion of added amounts of vitamin A during pregnancy, but not by similar doses of carotene.

Functions

With the exception of its role in relation to certain visual processes, the functions of vitamin A in the organism are suggested chiefly indirectly, by changes which occur in the presence of deficiency in this factor.

Vitamin A and Vision

The retina contains two types of receptor cells: (1) cones, which are specialized for color and detail vision in bright light; (2) rods, which are specialized for visual acuity in dim light (night vision). Light waves, striking these receptors, produce chemical changes which, in turn, give rise to nerve impulses that pass to the brain. Vitamin A plays an essential role in the photochemical phase of this process.

Visual acuity of the rod cells (vision in dim light) is dependent upon their content of a photosensitive pigment, rhodopsin or visual purple (in land and marine vertebrates), a dissociable combination of a protein, "opsin," and "retinene$_1$" (vitamin A_1 aldehyde). In fresh-water vertebrates (fishes, lampreys, and certain larval amphibia), rhodopsin is replaced by "porphyropsin," a combination of opsin and retinene$_2$ (vitamin A_2 aldehyde). The cones contain, in addition to rhodopsin, a similar pigment, "iodopsin" (visual violet), which functions in color discrimination and visual acuity in bright light. This substance differs from rhodopsin in its protein component (photopsin).

Under the influence of light, rhodopsin is converted to unstable orange products which undergo chemical change to a yellow mixture of *trans*-retinene and opsin. *Trans*-retinene is inactive in the resynthesis of rhodopsin; it must first be converted to the active *cis*-isomer (Fig. 7–2). In vitro, this can be accomplished by exposure to blue, but not to yellow light, which is not absorbed by retinene. The absorption spectrum of retinene, maximal at 385 mμ, extends into the violet and blue, but is negligible in and beyond the green. In the eye, however, this isomerization pathway is relatively unimportant, for the *trans*-retinene is promptly transformed to *trans*-vitamin A, its carbonyl group being reduced to the primary alcohol by retinene reductase (alcohol dehydrogenase) and NADH. The *trans*-vitamin A, which too is inactive in rhodopsin synthesis, is passed into the bloodstream.

In the course of resynthesis of rhodopsin, which occurs in dim light and in the dark, the active *cis*-vitamin A enters the retina from the blood and is oxidized to *cis*-retinene by reverse action of retinene reductase (alcohol dehydrogenase) in the presence of NAD. The *cis*-retinene couples with opsin to form rhodopsin; this reaction is exergonic, thereby

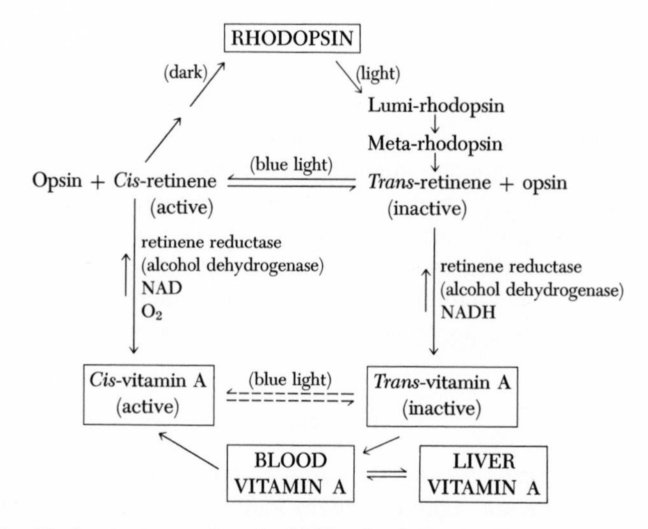

Figure 7–2. Rhodopsin-vitamin A cycle. (Hubbard and Wald: J. Gen. Physiol. *36:*269, 1952.)

serving to drive continuous oxidation of vitamin A to retinene by promptly removing the latter from the reaction mixture.

The visual process therefore involves continual removal of the active vitamin A isomer from the blood by the retina, which returns the inactive isomer to the circulation. Vitamin A isomerizes in the body, the four likely isomers (p. 145) probably being in equilibrium in the organism, ensuring an adequate supply of the active form.

Visual defects in deficiency (nyctalopia). One of the earliest functional defects induced by vitamin A deficiency is impairment of dark adaptation. Bright light causes bleaching of rhodopsin, which must be resynthesized in the dark, chiefly from vitamin A reaching the retinal rods via the bloodstream, before normal visual acuity in dim light is possible. Individuals having vitamin A deficiency are consequently unable to see clearly in dim light (nyctalopia). In mild deficiency there may be merely delay in the development of visual acuity in the dark following a period of exposure to bright light (delayed rhodopsin synthesis).

Reproduction

In vitamin A deficient rats, although litters may be produced, fertilization or implantation often fails. Synthesis or release of androgen by the testis may be interfered with. Fetal resorption or growth retardation and death may occur early in pregnancy, owing to placental injury. In other instances, gestation is prolonged, the fetuses being at times excessively large. Dental abnormalities are apparent soon after birth; cardiovascular and other anomalies occur in the fetuses and newborn.

Epithelium

In many species, including man, vitamin A appears to be necessary for the morphological and functional integrity of epithelial cells of the skin and many mucous membranes. Deficiency is characterized chiefly by keratinizing metaplasia of these structures and its consequences. The skin is characteristically dry, scaly, and rough (follicular hyperkeratosis). Keratinization of the epithelium of the lacrimal glands leads to dryness of the eyes, with consequent irritation and conjunctivitis.

Small, triangular, silvery or pearly, foamlike spots (Bitot's spots) appear in the conjunctiva just lateral, at times also medial, to the cornea. These are due to keratinization of the conjunctival epithelium. Vision is impaired as a result of keratinization of the epithelium of the cornea which, in severe deficiency, becomes edematous, infiltrated with leukocytes, cloudy, and softened (keratomalacia). These changes, together with the frequently associated secondary infection resulting from dryness and irritation, may lead to blindness and perforation of the cornea.

Keratinizing metaplasia of the epithelium in the nose, accessory nasal sinuses, pharynx, and tracheobronchial tree may lead to irritation and lowering of local resistance of these structures to infection. Similar changes in the mucosa of the lower urinary passages in the rat lead to calculus formation, the desquamated cells forming a nidus on which calcium salts precipitate out of the urine. There is no evidence that this mechanism operates in urinary lithiasis in man.

Vitamin A deficiency results in keratinization of the vaginal epithelium in rats, with a decrease in leukocytes and eventual replacement of the normal cyclic changes by the phase of complete cornification (diestrus smear). The presence of estrogen is necessary for the production of this effect.

Bones and Teeth

In addition to its requirement for normal growth, which it shares with other vitamins, vitamin A plays a role in the construction of normal bone. In several species, vitamin A deficiency results in slowing of endochondral bone formation and decreased osteoblastic activity, the bones becoming cancellous, losing their fine structural details. This is associated with defective synthesis of chondroitin sulfate, which may be due to inability to form phosphoadenosine phosphosulfate, the active sulfate donor (p. 587). In vitamin A deficient puppies, and to a lesser extent in rabbits and rats, there is a decrease in the inside dimensions of the skull cavity, and reduction in the marrow cavities of long and flat bones. This is apparently caused by defective resorption of previously formed bone, but also in part perhaps by actual overgrowth of bone. The vitamin appears to be involved in control of the activities of osteoblasts and osteoclasts. The most striking result of these bone changes is impingement upon and degeneration of certain cranial and spinal nerves, mainly those carrying afferent fibers. In addition, lesions of the central nervous system and increased cerebrospinal fluid pressure occur because of continued growth of nervous tissue within the smaller bone casing (skull and spine).

Vitamin A apparently accelerates the normal growth sequences, including both deposition and resorption processes, required for orderly formation of normal bone structure. Dental defects appear in the newborn rats of vitamin A deficient mothers, the enameloblasts being keratinized, with consequent thinning of the enamel and the appearance of chalky patches (underlying dentin) resembling those seen in fluorosis (p. 646). Odontoblasts may atrophy and tooth growth cease. The normal orange-brown color of the outer layer of the incisors may be lost and the teeth may be deformed.

Deficiency in Man

Present understanding of the role of vitamin A in human nutrition is reflected in the following statements (A.M.A. Council on Pharmacy):

1. Vitamin A is specific for the cure and prevention of xerophthalmia, nyctalopia (night blindness), and hemeralopia (day blindness).

2. Vitamin A is essential to the normal structure and behavior of epithelial tissue, e.g., the epithelium covering the skin, and forming the lining of the nasal sinuses and respiratory tract, mouth, pharynx, entire digestive tract, and the genitourinary tract. It prevents follicular hyperkeratosis of the skin.

3. Vitamin A is a growth factor.

To these may be added an apparently important role in regulation of osteoblastic and osteoclastic activity, although there is little information on this point in human deficiency states.

Vitamin Interrelationships

The occurrence of manifestations of vitamin K deficiency in animals receiving excessive amounts of vitamin A is referred to elsewhere (p. 151), as is the effect of vitamin E (and other antioxidants) in preventing destruction of vitamin A in the intestine. It has been reported that rats deficient in vitamin A exhibit certain manifestations which resemble those of vitamin C deficiency (to which the rat is very resistant), viz., red, swollen gums, changes in the molars, joint swelling, and bleeding from the lacrimal glands. These symptoms, which may be accompanied by a drop in the blood vitamin C content, disappear after administration of vitamin C.

Detection of Deficiency in Man

The most important clinical manifestations of vitamin A deficiency in man are: (1) xerophthalmia, i.e., thickening and loss of transparency of the bulbar conjunctiva, with yellowish pigmentation and occasionally Bitot's spots; (2) follicular conjunctivitis; (3) keratomalacia, i.e., softening of the cornea with, in advanced cases, ulceration and necrosis; (4) impairment of dark adaptation, progressing to night blindness (nyctalopia); (5) follicular hyperkeratosis of the skin.

The clinical manifestations and their prompt response to administration of adequate amounts of vitamin A constitute the best available means of diagnosis. No reliable procedures are available for detecting subclinical deficiency states. The following objective methods have been investigated: (1) determination of the concentration of vitamin A and carotene in the blood; (2) the dark adaptation test; (3) examination of scrapings of the bulbar conjunctiva and vagina (and other mucous membranes).

Vitamin A content of blood. The concentration of vitamin A in the blood (plasma or serum) is not a reliable index of the status of vitamin A nutrition, although extremely low values (below 40 I.U./100 ml.) may be regarded as indicative of deficiency. There is no satisfactory consistent correlation between the blood vitamin values and the presence or severity of the various clinical deficiency manifestations. The plasma carotene level is of still less diagnostic value. It reflects the immediate past intake of carotenoids, falling promptly after their exclusion from the diet and rising promptly following their readministration. A zero value is compatible with normal nutrition inasmuch as there is no consistent relationship between the level of plasma carotene and the quantity of vitamin A in the organism.

Dark adaptation test. The biophotometer has been employed to test the speed of visual adaptation to dim light after a period of exposure to bright light. Although night blindness is an important manifestation of vitamin A deficiency, the general experience has been that the dark adaptation test does not satisfactorily reflect subclinical levels of vitamin A deficiency and that biophotometer readings do not parallel the concentration of the vitamin in the blood. The time of development of significant impairment of dark adaptation in subjects on a diet low in vitamin A and carotenoids varies widely, from several days to many months. Moreover, conditions other than vitamin A deficiency may cause this phenomenon.

Examination of scrapings. In established A deficiency, keratinized epithelial cells may be demonstrated in scrapings from the bulbar conjunctiva and the vagina. These changes generally occur rather late, being preceded usually by subjective evidence of impaired dark adaptation. This procedure is therefore of little clinical value.

Effects of Excess of Vitamin A

Acute symptoms may follow ingestion of very large amounts of vitamin A. These include drowsiness, sluggishness, severe headache, vomiting, and peeling of the skin about the mouth and elsewhere. This syndrome has been recognized by Eskimos as occurring after eating the livers of polar bears and arctic foxes, which are extremely rich in vitamin A.

Continued intake of excessive amounts, especially in children, produces roughening of the skin, irritability, coarsening and falling of the hair, anorexia, loss of weight, headache, vertigo, hyperesthesia, occasionally hepatomegaly, splenomegaly, hyperlipemia and hemorrhages (in some species), and certain rather characteristic skeletal changes, accompanied by high levels of vitamin A in the plasma. The hemorrhagic manifestations are associated with hypoprothrombinemia, and may be prevented by simultaneous administration of vitamin K. This effect may be due to interference with bacterial synthesis of vitamin K in the intestine; it does not occur in chicks.

The skeletal changes are the result chiefly of acceleration of the normal bone growth sequences, with simultaneous increase in the processes of resorption (osteoclasis) and cortical bone deposition (hyperostosis). In children, there is early closure of the epiphyses and retardation of growth. Young rats and guinea pigs fed large amounts of vitamin A may show an equivalent of a year's growth in a few weeks, the new bone being inadequately mineralized and fracturing easily. Weanling rats fail to grow, have difficulty in walking and pain in the extremities, with fractures and associated hemorrhages.

Infants may tolerate daily doses of about 200,000 I.U. of vitamin A for a year, but develop symptoms with 500,000 I.U. daily for even brief periods. On this basis the toxic daily dose for adults would be between 1,000,000 and 3,000,000 I.U.

Carotenemia

Increase in the plasma carotenoid concentration above a level which varies in different individuals (carotenemia) results in a yellow or yellow-orange discoloration of the skin. Apparently the dermal epithelium is colored by carotene excreted by sebaceous glands. This condition may occur in normal subjects after protracted ingestion of large amounts of carotenoid-rich vegetables and is not uncommon in diabetics, for similar dietary reasons. In contrast to jaundice, the conjunctivae and urine are not discolored. The condition is harmless and disappears promptly when the carotene intake is reduced.

Vitamin A Requirement

In subjects receiving diets virtually devoid of vitamin A and carotene, it was found that the blood vitamin A concentration was maintained by daily doses of 2500 I.U. of vitamin A esters, and that clinical evidences of deficiency did not appear. It was concluded that adequate safety is provided by a daily intake (normal adults) of 2500 I.U. of preformed vitamin A or, in the form of carotene, 4000 I.U. in oily solution, 7500 I.U. as green vegetables, or 12,000 I.U. as boiled sliced carrots.

It is generally considered that the adult requirement is 25 to 55 I.U./kg. body weight for preformed vitamin A and about twice these amounts, or more, if the sole source is carotene. Because of the fact that the requirement is increased by an increase in metabolic rate, children require relatively more than adults (Table 24-1, p. 650). The National Research Council recommendations for normal subjects receiving an otherwise adequate mixed diet are: adults, 5000 I.U.; during pregnancy (latter half), 6000 I.U.; during lactation, 8000 I.U.; children under 1 year, 1500 I.U., increasing to 5000 I.U. at adolescence.

The requirement is increased in hepatic disease, with the possible attendant impairment of storage of vitamin A and of its formation from carotene. An increased supply should also be provided in the presence of increased metabolic rates, as in fever and thyrotoxicosis. Faulty absorption may occur in chronic diarrhea, and specifically in sprue and celiac disease (steatorrhea) because of defective fat absorption.

VITAMIN C (ASCORBIC ACID)

In the early days of ocean navigation, scurvy was one of the most prevalent and dreaded diseases to which sailors were subject, owing to the unavailability of fresh foods for long periods of time. It was also prevalent during wars and famines, and among inmates of prisons, asylums, and almshouses. The curative value of oranges, lemons, and certain herbs ("scurvy grass") was recognized as early as the sixteenth century, but it was not until the middle 1700's that the effectiveness of this method of control was widely publicized.

Upon introduction of the vitamin concept in the early 1900's, suspicion was aroused that scurvy might be a vitamin deficiency disease. Experimental production of this condition in guinea pigs laid the basis for systematic research in this direction, culminating (1927 to 1933) in the isolation of "hexuronic acid" from adrenal cortex, cabbage, and lemon juice; its identification as the antiscorbutic principle; demonstration of its chemical structure; and its synthesis.

Chemistry

Ascorbic acid is an enediol-lactone of an acid with a configuration similar to that of the sugar, L-glucose (Fig. 7–3). It is a comparatively strong acid (e.g., stronger than acetic acid), owing to dissociation of the enolic hydrogen at C-3, not to the carboxyl group, which is tied up in lactone form. Inasmuch as it contains two asymmetric C-atoms (C-4 and C-5), two pairs of optically active isomers are possible. The D-forms are generally inactive as antiscorbutic agents. Naturally occurring vitamin C is L-ascorbic acid.

Its most important and prominent chemical property is its strong reducing activity. This depends on the liberation of the H atoms from the enediol-hydroxyl groups (on C-2 and C-3), the ascorbic being oxidized to dehydroascorbic acid (Fig. 7–3) (e.g., by air, H_2O_2, $FeCl_3$, iodine, quinones, methylene blue, silver nitrate, ferricyanide, 2,6-dichlorophenol indophenol). This reaction is readily reversible by reducing agents, in vitro (e.g., by H_2S) and in vivo (e.g., by HS-compounds, such as glutathione). In alkaline, neutral, or slightly acid solutions (above pH 5), dehydroascorbic acid undergoes hydrolysis, with splitting of the lactone ring, to form diketogulonic acid, which is biologically inactive. This reaction is irreversible in vivo, but can be reversed in vitro by hydrogen iodide. Diketogulonic acid readily undergoes further irreversible oxidation to oxalic and L-threonic acids (Fig. 7–3).

Oxidative destruction of ascorbic acid is accelerated by increasing pH (increased tendency toward hydrolysis of the lactone ring), by light (especially in presence of flavins), and by silver and cupric ions (ascorbic acid oxidase is a copper-protein enzyme). These facts are of practical importance in relation to the vitamin C activity of processed foodstuffs (below).

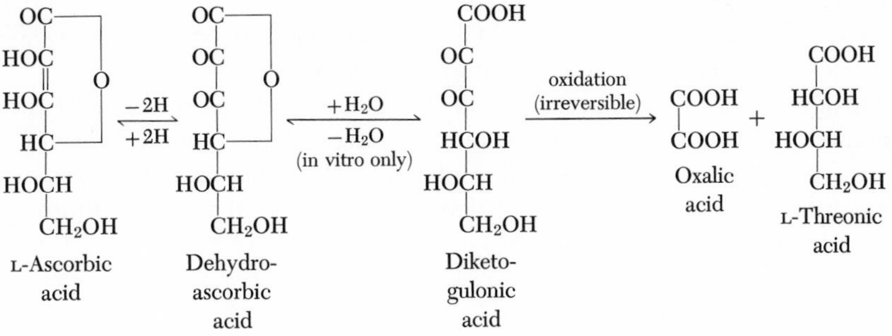

OC—, HOC, ‖, HOC, HC—, HOCH, CH_2OH (ring O): L-Ascorbic acid
$\underset{+2H}{\overset{-2H}{\rightleftarrows}}$
OC—, OC, OC, HC—, HOCH, CH_2OH (ring O): Dehydroascorbic acid
$\underset{-H_2O \text{ (in vitro only)}}{\overset{+H_2O}{\rightleftarrows}}$
COOH, OC, OC, HCOH, HOCH, CH_2OH: Diketogulonic acid
$\xrightarrow{\text{oxidation (irreversible)}}$
COOH, COOH: Oxalic acid + COOH, HCOH, HOCH, CH_2OH: L-Threonic acid

Figure 7–3. Metabolism of ascorbic acid.

Occurrence and Food Sources

Ascorbic acid is distributed widely throughout the plant and animal kingdoms. Animal tissues contain rather small amounts, the highest concentrations occurring generally in metabolically highly active organs (e.g., endocrine glands, liver). Considerable amounts may be present in human milk (75 mg./liter) and less in cow's milk (22 mg./liter), varying with the intake.

Ascorbic acid is present in all living plant cells, the largest amounts being usually in the leaves and flowers, i.e., in actively growing parts. It cannot be demonstrated in dry seeds, but appears immediately upon germination. In most tissues, ascorbic acid (reduced form) occurs in equilibrium with its oxidized form, dehydroascorbic acid, in varying proportions. As indicated elsewhere (p. 156), both of these forms are biologically active but the products of further degradation (hydrolysis, oxidation) are not. Consequently, provision must undoubtedly be made for maintaining a large proportion of the vitamin in the reduced form, e.g., by such reducing agents as HS-compounds, present in all cells.

Important dietary sources of ascorbic acid include leafy vegetables, green peas and beans, peppers, certain tubers (potatoes, turnips), tomatoes, and citrus and other fruits (oranges, lemons, limes, grapefruit, cantaloupe, strawberries, bananas). Because of its water-solubility and its susceptibility to irreversible oxidative degradation to inactive compounds, considerable amounts of ascorbic acid may be lost during cooking, processing, and storage procedures. Boiling and heating (in air) involves loss by extraction by the cooking water and oxidation. Activity, which diminishes rapidly during ordinary drying, wilting, chopping, crushing, or storage, may be preserved by (1) low-temperature storage before processing, (2) quick preheating (to destroy oxidative enzymes), and (3) exclusion of oxygen (by N or CO_2) during processing (e.g., canning, drying, freezing). The vitamin C in milk is usually destroyed by pasteurization or evaporation as usually conducted.

Assay

Ascorbic acid may be determined by bioassay or by chemical procedures. Although the former are the most specific and accurate, they have been largely replaced by the latter for practical reasons.

Bioassay. The guinea pig is the test animal of choice, because of its extreme sensitivity to dietary lack of vitamin C. (The albino rat is unsuitable because of its immunity to the development of scurvy.) The animals are given a vitamin C-free diet, on which they develop scurvy in two to three weeks. Various procedures determine the minimum amount of test material required to (1) protect against or (2) cure gross scorbutic manifestations (e.g., weight-loss, joint-tenderness, edema, hemorrhage, etc.), or (3) prevent characteristic scorbutic changes in dental structure (development of incisor odontoblasts).

One unit of vitamin C (I.U. or U.S.P. unit) is defined as equivalent to 0.05 mg. of pure ascorbic acid, i.e., 1 mg. of ascorbic acid = 20 units.

Chemical methods. The procedures in common use are based on one or the other of two principles: (1) measurement of the rate or extent of reduction of certain oxidizing agents, e.g., methylene blue, 2,6-dichlorophenol indophenol; (2) measurement of the colored complex formed by coupling of dehydroascorbic acid with 2,4-dinitrophenylhydrazine and treatment with strong H_2SO_4.

Absorption, Distribution, Circulation

Only man, other primates, and guinea pigs, of the many species investigated, are unable to synthesize ascorbic acid; the entire human requirement must consequently be supplied by the diet. Ascorbic acid is absorbed readily from the small intestine, peritoneum, and subcutaneous tissues. It is widely distributed throughout the body, in local concentrations roughly paralleling the metabolic activity of the tissue, in the following descending order: pituitary, corpus luteum, adrenal cortex, thymus (young), liver, brain, gonads, spleen, thyroid, pancreas, salivary glands, lung, kidney, intestinal wall, heart, skeletal muscle, blood. Ascorbic acid is supplied to the fetus from the maternal circulation, passing the placental barrier readily. The concentration in umbilical cord blood is higher than in the maternal blood, suggesting that the placenta may be able to concentrate the vitamin.

There is no evidence that any particular organ or tissue serves as a storage reservoir. That the body does contain mobilizable reserve stores of ascorbic acid is indicated, however, by the fact that clinical manifestations of scurvy develop in man only after several months on an ascorbic acid-free diet.

Normal human blood plasma contains about 0.6 to 1.5 mg. ascorbic acid per 100 ml. Under adequate dietary conditions the concentration in the erythrocytes is one to two and one-half times, and in the white blood cells and platelets ("white layer") 20 to 40 times that in the plasma.

Metabolism, Excretion

In the rat, it has been shown that the carbon chain of glucose is utilized for synthesis of ascorbic acid (Fig. 7–4). No synthesis occurs in man, other primates, and the guinea pig, owing presumably to inability to convert ketogulonolactone to ascorbic acid.

The vitamin exists in the body largely in the reduced form (ascorbic acid), in rever-

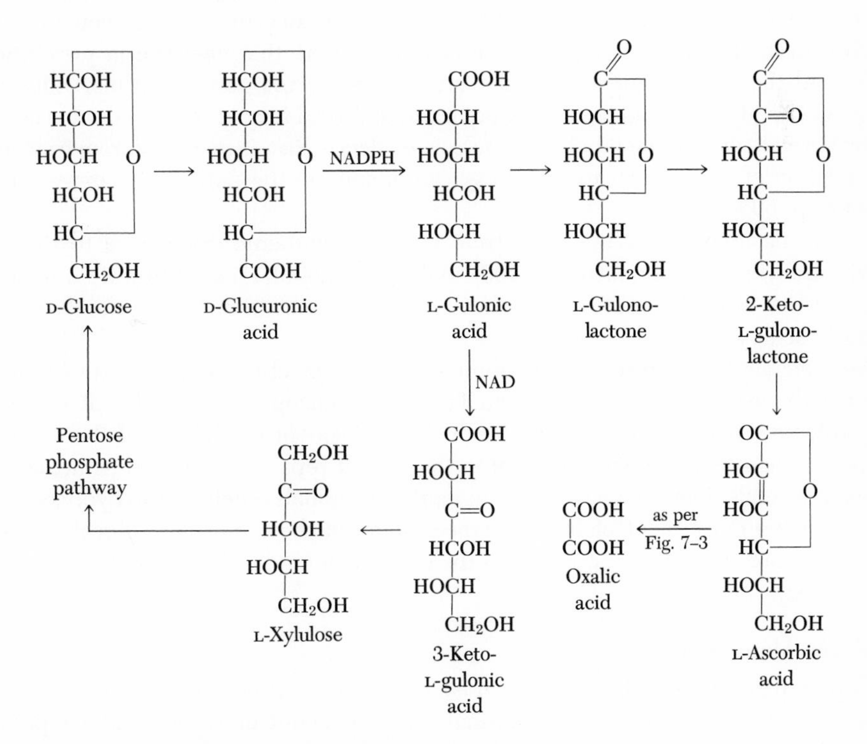

Figure 7–4. Biosynthesis and catabolism of ascorbic acid.

sible equilibrium with a relatively small amount of dehydroascorbic acid (oxidized form) (Fig. 7–3). Under conditions of normal dietary intake (75 to 100 mg.), about 50 to 75 per cent of ingested ascorbic acid undergoes metabolic conversion to inactive compounds. The remainder is excreted, as such, in the urine. It is also present in milk in active form. The chief terminal metabolites in the rat and guinea pig are CO_2 and oxalic acid. Decarboxylation of ascorbic acid does not occur in man, the chief terminal metabolites being oxalic acid and diketogulonic acid, which are excreted in the urine.

Functions

The fundamental role played by ascorbic acid in metabolic processes is not known. The fact that it is very sensitive to reversible oxidation (ascorbic acid $\rightleftharpoons$ dehydroascorbic acid) suggests that it may be involved in cellular oxidation-reduction reactions, perhaps serving as a hydrogen transport agent.

Inasmuch as the oxidized (dehydro-) form is irreversibly hydrated to the inactive diketogulonic acid (Fig. 7–3), preservation of vitamin activity must involve some mechanism which maintains a large proportion of the vitamin in the reduced form (ascorbic acid). Such reducing agents as sulfhydryl compounds, including glutathione, cysteine and HS-proteins, have been suggested as possibly implicated in this connection. Reversible oxidation of ascorbic acid may be accomplished by a number of tissue catalysts, e.g., the cytochrome system, peroxidases, ascorbic acid oxidase (plants), polyphenol oxidases, hemochromogens, and adrenochrome. Evidence against the view that ascorbic acid functions as a major respiratory catalyst is the fact that the tissues of scorbutic animals do not show a decreased respiratory capacity and their O_2 consumption is not increased by addition of the vitamin.

Scorbutic guinea pigs and premature infants given a high-protein (or tyrosine or phenylalanine), ascorbic acid-deficient diet excrete *p*-hydroxyphenylpyruvic and *p*-hydroxyphenyllactic acids in the urine. Administration of ascorbic acid corrects this condition. However, the amount required is much larger than that effective in prevention of scurvy, and the abnormality of tyrosine metabolism occurs only when markedly excessive quantities of the amino acid are administered. Ascorbic acid is not regarded as essential for normal tyrosine metabolism. There is evidence that it may be a requirement for hydroxylation of tryptophan to 5-hydroxytryptophan, on the pathway of biosynthesis of serotonin (p. 595).

It may be involved in the conversion of pteroylglutamic (folic) acid to the active formyl tetrahydrofolic derivative (p. 198), and in the mobilization of iron from its storage form, ferritin. Disturbances of these functions may contribute to the development of anemia in scurvy.

Ascorbic acid is required for functional activities of fibroblasts and osteoblasts, and consequently for formation of collagen fibers and mucopolysaccharides of connective tissue, osteoid tissue, dentin, and the intercellular "cement substance" of the capillaries. This requirement is particularly critical in the case of repair of damaged tissue, as in the healing of wounds. The collagen formed in scorbutic animals is deficient in hydroxyproline, a characteristic constituent of this substance. Many of the important clinical manifestations of vitamin C deficiency are directly dependent upon abnormal development of these tissues.

Deficiency Manifestations—Scurvy

Guinea pigs, the standard species used for demonstrating ascorbic acid deficiency, exhibit characteristic histological abnormalities after about one week and symptoms in about two weeks on a vitamin C-free diet. The term "scurvy" is applied to the characteristic features resulting from failure of certain specialized cells, i.e., fibroblasts, osteoblasts, odontoblasts, to promote normal deposition of collagen, osteoid, and dentin. Formation of ground substance (mucopolysaccharides) is also impaired. The earliest histological changes include alteration in osteoblasts and odontoblasts. The animals lose appetite and weight, their joints become swollen and tender (subperiosteal hemorrhage), and they assume the "scurvy" position, lying flat with the hindlegs extended. There may be enlargement of the costochondral junctions, hemorrhages in the gums, and loosening and fracture of the teeth.

Symptoms appear in man only after a much longer period of ascorbic acid privation (four to five months). They include: hyperkeratotic papules over the buttocks and calves (specificity?); petechial, subcutaneous, subperiosteal, and internal hemorrhages; pain on movement; swelling at ends of long bones and at costochondral junctions; hyperemia, swelling, sponginess, tenderness, retraction and bleeding of the gums, leading in severe scurvy to secondary infection and loosening and falling of the teeth; edema, pallor, anemia; delayed wound healing; defective formation of the teeth in children; roentgenographic signs of defective skeletal structure, most of which are not specific.

Detection of Deficiency in Man

Advanced scurvy is readily diagnosed, but is rarely seen. Detection of subclinical deficiency is difficult, as is demonstration of ascorbic acid deficiency as a cause of various clinical conditions. As in the case of vitamin deficiencies generally, prompt improvement following administration of ascorbic acid constitutes the most reliable evidence that deficiency in this substance had contributed to the development of the condition in question. Certain objective methods have been proposed for the demonstration of subclinical deficiency states. They include: (1) the concentration of ascorbic acid in the blood; (2) urinary excretion of ascorbic acid; (3) urinary excretion following administration of the vitamin (saturation test); (4) intradermal test for ascorbic acid; (5) capillary fragility test.

Blood ascorbic acid. The plasma ascorbic acid concentration falls relatively promptly after removal of the vitamin from the diet, approaching zero in 40 to 80 days. Usually, when the plasma values fall below 0.3 mg./100 ml. the concentration in the leukocytes and platelets begins to decrease, and when the former reaches 0.1 mg./100 ml. the latter may be assumed to be seriously reduced. As a rule, recognizable clinical manifestations of scurvy appear only after this degree of depletion has been reached. Consequently, decrease in ascorbic acid of the "white blood cell-platelet layer" or, less significantly, of whole blood, is a more reliable index of the scorbutic nature of clinical signs than is a fall in the plasma ascorbic acid concentration.

Urine ascorbic acid. Urinary excretion of ascorbic acid decreases rather promptly following lowering of the intake and does not therefore reflect the nutritional status of the organism in this regard. Test procedures which embody the "tissue saturation" principle are perhaps more useful clinically. These saturation tests are based upon the principle that if the tissues contain an adequate amount of ascorbic acid, i.e., are "saturated" with the vitamin, a certain proportion of an administered test dose will be excreted in the urine. If the tissues are "undersaturated" they will retain an abnormally large proportion of the test dose, and a subnormal amount will be excreted in the urine. A number of different procedures and dosages have been employed, with rather equivocal results. The chief difficulty has been in the establishment of normal values because of the wide range of individual variation. Such saturation tests may be valuable under carefully controlled conditions.

Intradermal test. This consists in the intradermal injection of 2,6-dichlorophenolindophenol and determination of the time required for decolorization (reduction) of this dye. Abnormally long persistence of the blue color in the cutaneous wheal is regarded as indicative of tissue subsaturation with ascorbic acid. This procedure is not very reliable.

Capillary resistance (fragility) test. This is designed to disclose, by the application of mechanical stress, increased fragility of the capillary walls. This is generally ascribed to defective formation of the intercellular capillary cement substance, but increased activity of the hyaluronidase-hyaluronic acid system may be involved. A positive reaction may be obtained before the defect manifests itself spontaneously by petechial or other hemorrhages. The mechanical stress is applied in the form of either negative (cupping) or positive (tourniquet) pressures.

These procedures are of value in the diagnosis of ascorbic acid deficiency, but, unfortunately, capillary fragility may be increased in other conditions. They are useful chiefly as screening procedures, a normal (negative) response constituting evidence against serious ascorbic acid deficiency.

Vitamin and Hormone Interrelationships

In rats, vitamin A deficiency is accompanied by a sharp decrease in blood and tissue ascorbic acid, followed by the appearance of rather characteristic scorbutic manifestations. The latter disappear after administration of ascorbic acid. The nature of this relationship is not clear; it has been suggested that loss of protection (i.e., by antioxidant action of vitamin A) against oxidative degradation of ascorbic acid may be involved.

Reference is made elsewhere (p. 156) to the possible role of ascorbic acid in the conversion of pteroylglutamic (folic) acid to the formyl-tetrahydrofolic derivative (folinic acid). In this connection, severe deficiency in ascorbic acid in human infants and in monkeys may be accompanied by a megaloblastic type of anemia, relieved by folinic acid or large amounts of folic acid.

The increase in size (and decrease in cholesterol) of the adrenal glands in scorbutic guinea pigs may be due in part to stress, but exceeds that produced by inanition due to other causes. Administration of adrenocorticotropic hormone (ACTH) results in a prompt decrease in the relatively high concentration of ascorbic acid in the adrenal cortex of normal animals. This response is so striking that it is used as the basis for a sensitive method of bioassay of ACTH (p. 739). The urinary excretion of 11-oxygenated adrenal cortical hormones is increased in scorbutic guinea pigs. The nature of the relationship between ascorbic acid and adrenal cortical hormones is not understood.

Effects of Excess Ascorbic Acid

Administration of large amounts of ascorbic acid are not known to produce deleterious effects in man. In rats, dehydroascorbic acid, in enormous doses (1.5 gm./kg.), produces permanent diabetes identical with that produced by alloxan (destruction of beta cells of islands of Langerhans) (p. 444). This action is prevented by immediately antecedent intravenous injection of sulfhydryl compounds (cysteine, glutathione) as in the case of alloxan, which resembles dehydroascorbic acid in chemical structure.

Ascorbic Acid Requirement

A daily intake of about 100 mg. is adequate to maintain the plasma ascorbic acid concentration at about 1 mg./100 ml. in normal adults. Official recommended minimal daily intakes are: children, 30 mg. (infants under one year) to 80 mg. (adolescence); adults, 75 mg.; pregnant women, 100 mg.; during lactation, 150 mg. The requirement is increased in the presence of infections, owing apparently to an increased rate of destruction of the vitamin. Increased urinary excretion, with depletion of the tissue reserves, has been seen after prolonged ether anesthesia.

VITAMINS D

The curative value of cod liver oil in rickets (rachitis) was demonstrated in 1822, and the possible relation of absence of sunlight to the occurrence of this disease was suggested in 1890. However, the demonstration of the true nature of this condition necessarily had to await the development of the vitamin concept. The remedial action of cod liver oil in rickets was first attributed to the presence of vitamin A, until it was shown that milk, which contains this vitamin, did not prevent rickets in infants. In 1920, this disorder was produced experimentally in rats, by special diets, and shortly thereafter (1922) the antirachitic component of cod liver oil, later designated "fat-soluble vitamin D," was separated from vitamin A by destroying the latter by heating and oxidation.

In 1924 it was shown that antirachitic activity could be induced in certain foods by ultraviolet irradiation. It was soon demonstrated that this phenomenon occurred in the sterol fraction of the foodstuff, specifically in ergosterol, which has no antirachitic activity prior to irradiation. This discovery was followed, during the next 15 years, by isolation of this vitamin in pure form, and by demonstration of its chemical structure and of the existence of other forms of vitamin D. The most important of these originates in animal species from 7-dehydrocholesterol, corresponding to that originating in plants from ergosterol.

Chemistry

The inactive natural precursors of the D vitamins, the corresponding provitamins, are cyclopentanophenanthrene derivatives, classified as steroids. At least 10 such substances are known, differing only in the hydrocarbon side chain; only two of these have been found to occur in nature, ergosterol (provitamin D_2) and 7-dehydrocholesterol (provitamin D_3), the former in plants, the latter in animals (Fig. 7–5). Other provitamins D are mainly of chemical rather than biological interest. All provitamins D possess certain essential structural characteristics: (1) —OH group at C-3; (2) two conjugated double bonds (between C-5 and C-6 and between C-7 and C-8); (3) a hydrocarbon chain at C-17. None has been completely synthesized, but 7-dehydrocholesterol has been prepared from cholesterol and 7-dehydrositosterol from sitosterol (soybean oil).

Each D vitamin has the same empirical formula as its corresponding provitamin, i.e., they are isomers. Transformation from the inactive to the active forms is accomplished physiologically by the ultraviolet rays present in sunlight, or artificially, by ultraviolet irradiation (275 to 300 mμ), and α, β, γ, and other similar types of radiation. The photochemical activation process results only in an intramolecular rearrangement, not an oxidation, with opening of ring B between C-9 and C-10, conversion of the methyl group (—CH_3)

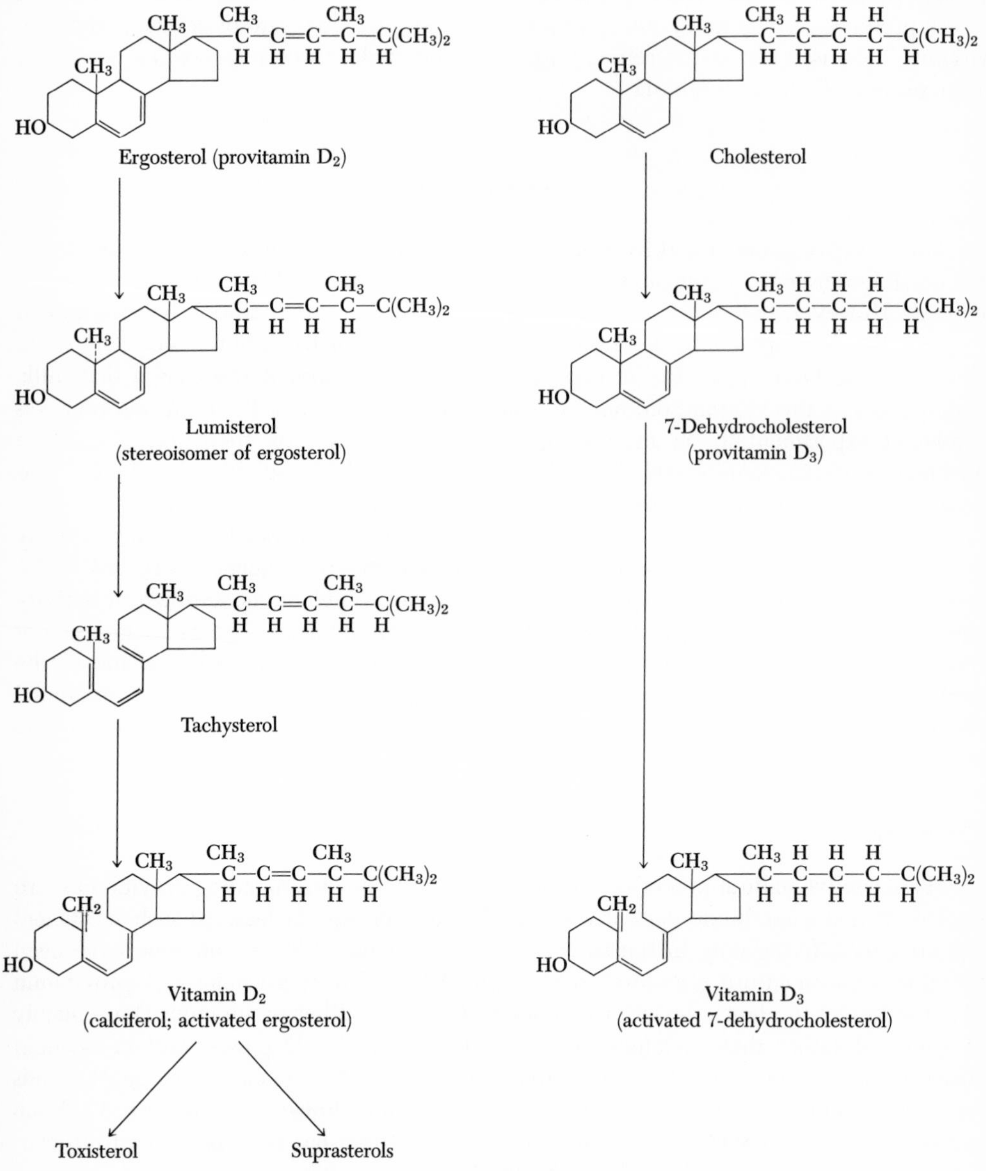

Ergosterol (provitamin D_2)

Lumisterol
(stereoisomer of ergosterol)

Tachysterol

Vitamin D_2
(calciferol; activated ergosterol)

Toxisterol

Suprasterols

Cholesterol

7-Dehydrocholesterol
(provitamin D_3)

Vitamin D_3
(activated 7-dehydrocholesterol)

Figure 7-5. Pathways of synthesis of vitamins D_2 and D_3.

at C-10 to a methylene (=CH_2) group, and hydrogenation of C-9 (Fig. 7–5). Vitamin D activity requires these structural characteristics in addition to those specified above for the provitamins. The alcohol group (—OH at C-3) must be free or, if esterified, capable of being hydrolyzed in the organism. The only forms of importance in human nutrition are activated ergosterol (calciferol; vitamin D_2) and activated 7-dehydrocholesterol (vitamin D_3). Both of these have been isolated in pure form.

The process of photochemical activation involves a series of irreversible reactions with the formation of compounds intermediate between the provitamin and the vitamin. Prolonged irradiation may result in decomposition of the latter. Thus, ergosterol, on irradiation, passes through the stages of "lumisterol$_2$" (a stereoisomer of ergosterol) and "tachysterol$_2$" (opening of ring B) before forming vitamin D_2 (calciferol). Overirradiation of the latter produces toxisterol$_2$ and suprasterol$_2$. The other provitamins D yield similar series of photochemical derivatives. Apart from the vitamins themselves, these substances have no significant antirachitic activity, with the exception of certain toxisterols, which have toxic, calcifying properties out of proportion to their antirachitic potency. A reduction product of tachysterol (Fig. 7–5), dihydrotachysterol, is only slightly antirachitic, but exerts a powerful hypercalcemic effect on oral administration, its action resembling that of the parathyroid hormone. It has therefore been used in the treatment of hypoparathyroidism (tetany) (p. 730), and is sometimes referred to as A.T. 10 (antitetany compound No. 10).

The vitamins D and their provitamins are soluble in fat solvents and practically insoluble in water. They are therefore included among the "fat-soluble vitamins." The several provitamins have rather characteristic and virtually identical ultraviolet absorption spectra, as have vitamins D_2 and D_3. Vitamin D, crystalline or in vegetable-oil solution, is quite stable if kept anaerobically in the dark. It is resistant to oxidation and to heat (in neutral solution). This relative stability as compared to vitamin A permitted its original identification as an entity separable from the latter in cod liver oil.

Occurrence and Food Sources

Ergosterol is widely distributed in plants. It makes up 90 to 100 per cent of the sterols of yeast, which is the most practical source of this provitamin. It has also been found in animal species (snail, earthworm, chicken egg, milk), perhaps of dietary origin. Ergosterol (non-activated) is of no dietary nutritional value since it is not absorbed well from the intestine. It differs in this respect from calciferol (activated ergosterol), which is readily absorbed. 7-Dehydrocholesterol is the characteristic provitamin D in the higher animals and man. It is believed to be formed in the intestinal mucosa from cholesterol, passing to the skin, where it undergoes activation to vitamin D_3 by the action of solar ultraviolet rays.

Vitamin D is present in plants in relatively insignificant amounts. Although it is distributed widely in various animal species, largely as vitamin D_3, very few natural foods contain enough to provide an adequate amount of vitamin D in the diet. Of common foods, egg yolk (chicken) is perhaps richest in this factor, averaging about 300 I.U./100 gm. Values for cow's milk range from 5 to 45 I.U./quart, for butter 8 to 60 I.U./100 gm., while human milk contains about 60 I.U./quart (colostrum about 150 I.U./quart). Other foods contain only negligible quantities, with the exception of fish, in which the highest concentrations of vitamin D occur, chiefly in the liver. There is an enormous species difference in this regard: e.g., cod liver oil contains about 100 I.U./gm., halibut-liver oil about 1200 I.U./ gm., bluefin tuna liver oil about 40,000 I.U./gm. For practical purposes, however, edible portions of fish, as of other foods, cannot be relied upon for an adequate daily supply of this vitamin.

It is advisable to supply the entire requirement as a dietary supplement, unless artificially enriched milk or bread is used. The vitamin D content of milk can be increased by (1) irradiation of the milk, (2) addition of calciferol or of fish liver oil concentrates, and (3) feeding irradiated yeast to cows. The most useful preparations for dietary supplementation are the highly active fish liver oil concentrates and solutions of calciferol in oil (viosterol).

Assay

Physical and chemical procedures are of limited value in the quantitative determination of vitamin D in body fluids. These include spectrophotometry, chromatography, and the antimony trichloride reaction, which are of value, however, in distinguishing between various forms of vitamin D and their precursors and, possibly, in quantitative procedures applied to foodstuffs and preparations employed therapeutically.

Two types of bioassay procedure are in common use; these involve comparison of the amounts of test material and standard vitamin D preparations required (1) to induce healing of rickets in rats, or (2) to maintain normal bone ash levels in chicks. The former is employed chiefly in determining the potency of materials intended for human use; the latter is applied in assays of poultry feed, because of the relative insensitivity of fowl to vitamin D_2. In the rat, the process of healing (calcification) of the characteristically decalcified zone in the epiphyseal region of the tibia, radius, or ulna (zone of provisional calcification) is followed either histologically ("line test;" U.S.P. procedure) or roentgenographically. Another procedure, based on measurement of radioactivity in the paw of the rat after being given P^{32}, is simpler and more sensitive.

One International Unit (I.U.) or U.S.P. unit of vitamin D is defined as represented by the activity of 0.025 μg. of pure crystalline vitamin D_2 (calciferol), which, therefore, has an activity of 40,000 I.U./mg. (rat assay). Vitamins D_2 and D_3 apparently are about equally active (D_3:D_2 = 1.5) in man (and other mammals), although vitamin D_3 may have a potency in the chick as much as 100 times that of vitamin D_2. Distinction between the two is therefore important in poultry but not in human nutrition.

Absorption, Storage, Excretion

Although plant sterols, including ergosterol, are poorly absorbed from the intestinal tract, irradiated ergosterol is readily absorbed in the small intestine and also from the skin surface. Being fat-soluble, its absorption from the bowel is enhanced by factors which favor fat absorption, including an adequate quantity of bile salts.

Little is known about the intermediary metabolism of vitamin D. Adequate liver function is apparently necessary for optimal antirachitic activity. This may be related to the fact that the liver is the chief site of storage of vitamin D, although significant amounts are stored also in the skin and brain and small amounts in the lungs, spleen, and bones. However, in mammals, the amount stored in the liver is distinctly limited, and is small as compared with fish. Nevertheless, although only about 15 per cent of an administered dose of calciferol can be recovered from the liver, a single dose exerts a therapeutic influence in rickets for periods of weeks or even months. A small amount may be excreted in the bile, but is apparently largely reabsorbed in the intestine. None is eliminated in the urine. The major portion is converted to as yet unidentified metabolites. The vitamin D content of milk reflects the intake; e.g., ingestion of a single large dose (600,000 I.U.) increased the concentration in the milk (human) from about 10 I.U./liter to 1000 I.U./liter in one day, the level being still elevated (100 I.U./liter) after one month.

Functions

The overall effect of vitamin D is to increase the availability and retention of calcium and phosphate and their utilization for proper mineralization of the skeleton. All of the actions that contribute to production of these effects are not known, but they probably include the following:

(1) Vitamin D promotes absorption of calcium from the intestine.

(2) Intestinal absorption of phosphate is apparently increased. This does not appear to be dependent entirely on increased calcium absorption. However, there is an increase in serum phosphate and in skeletal uptake of P^{32} in rats on a phosphate-free diet, possibly suggesting an effect other than on phosphate absorption.

(3) Vitamin D is necessary for proper growth, perhaps through its action in promoting endochondral growth of long bones and mineralization of the "zone of provisional calcification" (antirachitic action).

(4) It promotes mineralization of the skeleton in both adult and growing organisms, in part by providing an adequately balanced supply of available calcium and phosphate in the body fluids. Some other mechanism is involved, however, for rachitic cartilage does not calcify upon incubation in rachitic serum to which calcium and phosphate have been added to bring them to normal concentrations, whereas it does calcify readily if normal serum is used.

(5) Certain of the characteristic effects of parathyroid hormone are produced only in the presence of an adequate supply of vitamin D. This applies to the actions of the hormone in increasing absorption of calcium from the intestine and its mobilization from the bones, and perhaps also in increasing urinary excretion of phosphate.

(6) It lowers the pH in the colon, cecum, and distal ileum, the urinary pH increasing simultaneously. This may be, in part at least, secondary to increased absorption of calcium, decreasing the base of the intestinal contents.

(7) It counteracts the inhibitory effect of calcium ions on the hydrolysis of phytate (inositol hexaphosphate). In adequate amounts and in the presence of a high calcium intake, it suppresses the anticalcifying and rachitogenic effect of phytate. The mechanism of action is unknown.

(8) Vitamin D in physiological doses increases the citrate content of bone, blood, and other tissues, as well as urinary excretion. This suggests possibly increased synthesis or decreased oxidation of citrate.

Mechanism of Action

It is believed that vitamin D acts by promoting the transport of calcium and, probably secondarily, of phosphate into the bloodstream from the bones, intestinal lumen, and perhaps the renal tubule. The mechanism whereby this is accomplished has not been established. According to one current view, it exerts an action directly upon cellular and subcellular membranes. Other possibilities are suggested by the observation that actinomycin D, which inhibits production of mRNA and, therefore, protein biosynthesis, also inhibits the action of vitamin D in inducing a rise in serum calcium and increased intestinal transport of calcium. This effect is independent of the action of the antibiotic in inhibiting the hypercalcemic response to the parathyroid hormone (p. 733). The concept has been proposed that the vitamin may enhance transport of calcium by inducing biosynthesis either of a calcium-translocating enzyme or of some structural component of the membranes.

Deficiency Manifestations

Rickets, osteomalacia. Vitamin D deficiency during the period of skeletal growth results in rickets (rachitis), with a characteristic defect in endochondral bone growth and mineralization of the "zone of provisional calcification" of long bones (junction of epiphysis and diaphysis) and corresponding areas of flat bones. This lesion cannot occur in fully grown bones, the characteristic skeletal manifestation of deficiency in adults being a type of defective mineralization of osteoid tissue termed "osteomalacia."

Under normal conditions, the narrow plate of epiphyseal cartilage, containing transverse rows of cartilage cells in orderly arrangement, is supported by bone on the epiphyseal side and by marrow capillaries on the diaphyseal side. Growth is accomplished by continual proliferation of the row of cartilage cells bordering the epiphysis and simultaneous degeneration of those bordering the diaphysis, the degenerating cells being absorbed and invaded by capillaries and osteoblasts, which accomplish mineralization of the newly formed osteoid tissue in a narrow, dense, even, transverse line (zone of provisional calcification). In vitamin D deficiency these cells continue to proliferate but do not undergo orderly degeneration. Capillaries do not enter this zone in a regular fashion and mineralization is scanty and uneven. The cartilaginous area enlarges unevenly and imperfectly mineralized osteoid tissue and chondro-osteoid trabeculae are formed irregularly. Similar changes occur in all developing bones (defective mineralization of osteoid tissue), as in the cancellous portions of long bones, along the lacunae in the cortex, and in the tables of the skull. In adult, non-growing bones, mineralization of osteoid tissue throughout the skeleton may be impaired. The roentgenographic picture of these lesions is rather characteristic.

The phenomena attending bone growth in vitamin D deficiency result in enlargements at the ends of long bones, which, being abnormally pliable, are rather readily bent by the forces of muscle-pull and weight-bearing, with consequent deformities. The cranial sutures are widened and the fontanelles remain open; other cranial deformities develop as a result of external and internal pressure. Other characteristic deformities include enlargement of the costochondral junctions ("rachitic rosary"), "chicken breast," lateral sternal depressions, kyphosis, bowlegs and other distortions of the legs, pelvic deformities, and "potbelly."

In the rat, the rachitogenic effect of hypovitaminosis D is influenced considerably by the quantities and proportions of calcium and phosphate in the diet. At any given level of vitamin D deficiency the development of rickets is facilitated by lowering of the intake of these elements and by increase in the dietary Ca:P ratio above 2:1 (ratio in milk, 1.3:1). The latter effect is apparently related to the fact that, on low phosphate intake, large amounts of calcium prevent adequate phosphate absorption. A similar rachitogenic effect may be produced in the rat by administration of excessive amounts of other cations which form insoluble, and therefore poorly absorbable, phosphates, e.g., beryllium, aluminum, lead, iron, magnesium, strontium.

There can be little doubt that vitamin D deficiency is responsible for the production of rickets in children. However, there is no precise information as to whether the other dietary features indicated above as influencing the development of this condition in the rat are also operative in man. Clinical experience suggests that factors which promote absorption of calcium or phosphate from the intestine exert a beneficial influence in rickets, e.g., increased acidity of the intestinal contents (p. 632), and absence of excessive amounts of phytic acid (p. 632).

Metabolic manifestations of deficiency. Vitamin D deficiency results in decreased net retention of calcium and inorganic phosphate in the organism. The mineral content of the bones is diminished, the water and organic matter being correspondingly increased. The bones have a lower calcium, phosphate, and carbonate content and a higher magnesium content. Urinary excretion of calcium and phosphate falls and fecal excretion increases. The serum inorganic phosphate concentration usually falls, whereas the serum calcium usually remains within normal limits for some time; in advanced deficiency it, too, decreases, often to markedly hypocalcemic levels (infantile tetany). The serum alkaline phosphatase activity increases, usually in proportion to the severity of the skeletal defect.

The sequence of events is believed to be as follows:

(1) There is decreased intestinal absorption of calcium, resulting in tendency toward decrease in serum calcium and decrease in urine calcium.

(2) The tendency toward decrease of the serum calcium concentration is counteracted by increased mobilization of calcium from the labile deposits in the skeleton. In addition, the parathyroids are stimulated to increased activity (also hyperplasia). However, the effectiveness of parathyroid hormone in increasing the serum calcium concentration diminishes with increasing deficiency of the vitamin.

(3) Increase in urinary excretion of phosphate may be due in part to a direct effect of vitamin D deficiency in decreasing renal tubular reabsorption of phosphate. In the early stages of the deficiency it may be contributed to also by increased parathyroid activity.

(4) Increase in fecal phosphate may result, in part at least, from diminished absorption due to the excess of unabsorbed calcium in the bowel (unfavorable $Ca:PO_4$ ratio).

(5) As deficiency progresses, the available mobilizable mineral reserves of the skeleton may become depleted to the extent that the serum calcium level cannot be supported adequately. In addition, there is decreasing effectiveness of the parathyroid hormone both in promoting absorption of calcium from the intestine and its mobilization from the bones. Hypocalcemia then develops and, if of sufficient degree, is manifested clinically by neuromuscular hyperexcitability (infantile or osteomalacic tetany).

(6) Decreased mineralization of the bones, both generalized and, in growing long bones, also in the zone of provisional calcification, results in softening and deformities. This strain constitutes a stimulus to proliferation of osteoblasts, which form alkaline phosphatase. The local increase in this enzyme is reflected in increased alkaline phosphatase activity in the blood.

All of the above manifestations are reversed promptly after administration of adequate amounts of vitamin D, calcium, and phosphate. The increased alkaline phosphatase activity is usually the last abnormality to disappear.

Demonstration of Vitamin D Deficiency

This depends on the presence of (1) suggestive clinical manifestations, (2) characteristic roentgenographic abnormalities, and (3) metabolic aberrations. The most important of the latter are: (1) hypophosphatemia; (2) increased serum alkaline phosphatase activity; (3) normal or decreased serum calcium; (4) decreased urinary and increased fecal excretion of calcium and phosphate. Prompt response to specific therapy, except in cases of so-called "vitamin D-resistant rickets," is of great diagnostic importance.

Effects of Excess Vitamin D

Vitamin D is well tolerated in doses many times the normal requirement. However, seriously deleterious effects may be produced by extremely large amounts (500 to 1000 times the normal requirement). The early symptoms are due chiefly perhaps to the induced hypercalcemia (increased intestinal absorption of calcium and increased skeletal mobilization). These include anorexia, thirst, lassitude, constipation, and polyuria, followed later by nausea, vomiting, and diarrhea. Hyperphosphatemia may occur.

Increased urinary excretion of calcium and phosphate may lead to urinary lithiasis and the hypercalcemia and hyperphosphatemia may lead to metastatic calcification. The kidneys, arteries, bronchi, pulmonary alveoli, muscles, and gastric mucosa are principally involved. Renal failure may develop, leading to death. In growing children there may be excessive mineralization of the zone of provisional calcification at the expense of the diaphysis, which undergoes demineralization (with extremely large doses). In adults, too, with large doses there is excessive resorption of bone. Certain clinical disorders have been attributed to states of hypervitaminosis D due to increased sensitivity to the vitamin rather than to excessive intake. These include sarcoidosis and "idiopathic hypercalcemia" of children.

Requirement

Exogenous vitamin D is required throughout the period of skeletal growth, i.e., to adult life. The following recommendations have been made (National Research Council): infants (under 1 year) 400 to 800 I.U. daily; children and adolescents (up to 20 years) 400 I.U. These recommendations presuppose adequate intakes of calcium and phosphorus (milk) and no excess of phytate-containing cereals (oatmeal) (p. 632). The requirement for adults is not known. It is generally believed that, with adequate exposure to sunlight, sufficient amounts of vitamin D are formed in the skin to provide for normal nutrition in this regard if the intake of calcium and phosphorus is satisfactory. Daily supplements of 400 to 800 I.U. should be provided during the last half of pregnancy and throughout the period of lactation.

VITAMINS E (TOCOPHEROLS)

The presence, in the non-saponifiable fraction of certain fats, of a nutritional essential other than vitamins A and D was demonstrated in 1922. In addition to its requirement for normal growth, male rats and chicks deprived of this factor became sterile; female rats and birds with this dietary deficiency failed to produce normal progeny. Inclusion of the missing principle in the diet prevented these conditions and its administration to females early in pregnancy resulted in normal gestation and normal fetal development. This factor was therefore designated "fat-soluble vitamin E," and the "antisterility" or "fertility" vitamin. It was subsequently found that a rather specific type of muscle dystrophy occurred in certain species rendered deficient in this factor. Subsequently, a group of compounds, designated "tocopherols" (*tokos* = childbirth; *phero* = to bear; *ol* = alcohol), were shown to possess vitamin E activity and were identified as the active principles in foodstuffs. They were also found to be potent antioxidants. Despite the similarity of several of the deficiency manifestations in experimental animals to conditions occurring in man, there is little convincing evidence that vitamin E deficiency is a factor in the pathogenesis of the latter or that its administration is of therapeutic value.

Chemistry

The vitamins E, or "tocopherols," may be regarded as possessing a hypothetical "tocol" nucleus (Fig. 7–6). Seven naturally occurring tocopherols have been identified,

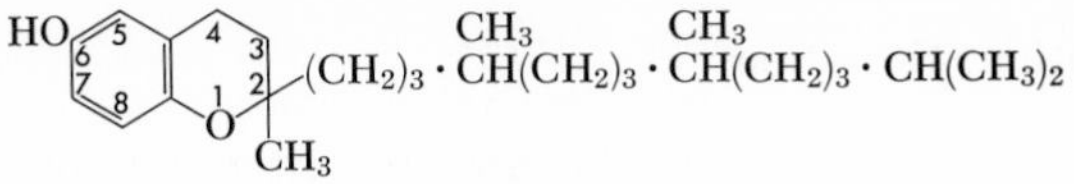

HO ... $(CH_2)_3 \cdot \overset{CH_3}{CH}(CH_2)_3 \cdot \overset{CH_3}{CH}(CH_2)_3 \cdot CH(CH_3)_2$, CH_3

"Tocol"

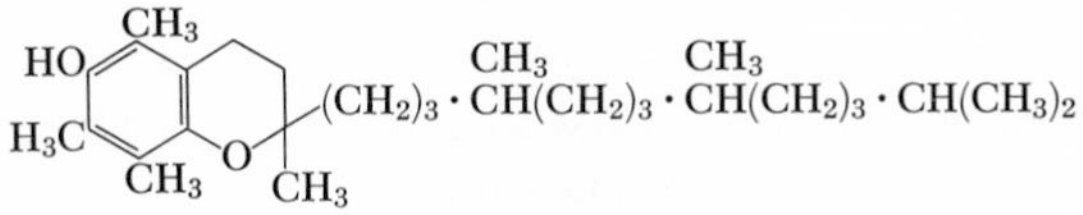

α-Tocopherol
(5,7,8-trimethyltocol)

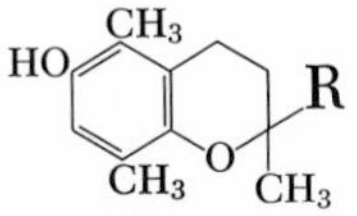

β-Tocopherol
(5,8-dimethyltocol)

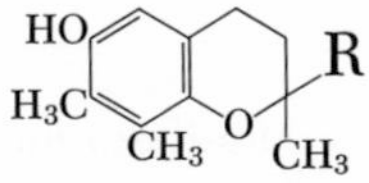

γ-Tocopherol
(7,8-dimethyltocol)

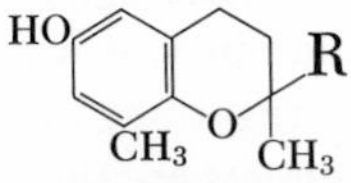

δ-Tocopherol
(8-methyltocol)

Figure 7–6. Vitamins E (tocopherols).

differing from one another in the number or position or both of methyl groups on the chroman portion (ring) of the "tocol" nucleus (Fig. 7–6). The presence of the phenolic hydroxyl group permits the formation of esters. Both the free tocopherols and their esters are insoluble in water and soluble in fat solvents. The vitamins E are therefore designated "fat-soluble vitamins."

Perhaps the most striking chemical property of the tocopherols is their antioxidant activity, due to the phenolic hydroxyl group at C-6 in the ring (Fig. 7–6). Because of their extreme susceptibility to oxidation, they protect less susceptible compounds by breaking up the chain of oxidation reactions. This is the basis for their important commercial use as inhibitors of the oxidation of fats (also carotenes and vitamin A), and perhaps for their physiological importance. δ-Tocopherol is the most potent of the vitamins E in antioxidant activity, followed in order by γ-, β-, and α-tocopherols. This is the reverse of the order of certain aspects of their biological activity in certain species (e.g., antisterility action in the rat).

Occurrence and Food Sources

The tocopherols occur in nature predominantly in plants. α-Tocopherol is the most abundant. All green plants contain considerable amounts (e.g., lettuce, alfalfa), vegetable fats being the richest natural source (e.g., wheat-germ oil and other seed-germ oils). Only small amounts are present in olive and coconut oils. Animal tissues contain relatively small amounts, which vary considerably, however, especially in the liver, in relation to the dietary intake. The same is true of egg yolk. Milk is generally poor in this factor, human milk containing more than cow's milk and colostrum more than later milk. The tocopherol content of animal fats is quite low, but may be raised somewhat by increasing the intake.

Absorption, Distribution, Excretion

Free tocopherols (and esters) are readily absorbed from the small intestine; bile acids are apparently necessary for absorption. The amount in the blood varies with the intake; the average level in man is 1.0 mg./100 ml. serum, carried chiefly in the α-lipoprotein fraction. They are widely distributed throughout the body, but the relatively small amounts in all tissues and in the feces suggests that the tocopherols may undergo rapid and extensive destruction in the gastrointestinal tract and tissues.

Under ordinary dietary conditions, there is no significant excretion of tocopherols in urine or feces. Milk contains small amounts. When large excesses are fed, some appears in the feces, but only traces in the urine.

Functions, Deficiency Manifestations

Despite the accumulation of considerable information regarding the structure and chemical and biochemical actions of the tocopherols, and the biological consequences of deficiency in these compounds, their physiological role in mammalian organisms is not known. There is no certainty that vitamin E is a nutritional requirement for man.

There are two diverging views regarding the role of tocopherols in mammalian metabolism. According to one, their effects are due solely to their non-specific antioxidant properties. According to the other, in addition, they serve a specific metabolic function not related to their antioxidant actions. There is evidence to support both views. Moreover, the order of activity of the four tocopherols in certain of their biological actions (e.g., "antisterility") is the reverse of that of their antioxidant potencies.

Functions based on antioxidant action. The antioxidant action of the tocopherols is probably responsible for its sparing action on vitamin A and carotene, which are particularly sensitive to oxidative destruction in the presence of unsaturated fats. This protective effect of vitamin E, which is enhanced by the presence of other antioxidants, e.g., ascorbic acid, is probably exerted mainly in the intestinal tract, but also perhaps in the tissues.

The increased in vitro O_2 uptake of the muscles and body fat of vitamin E-deficient animals is reduced by pre-treatment with the vitamin or by its addition in vitro. According to some, this increased oxygen consumption results from uninhibited peroxidation of unsaturated fatty acids.

Highly unsaturated fatty acids, e.g., those in cod liver oil, cause peroxidation and brown pigmentation of the adipose tissue of rats and chicks; this is prevented by administration of tocopherols. These fatty acids (in enameloblasts) are responsible also for the dental depigmentation of vitamin E-deficient rats, normal pigmentation being restored by administration of tocopherols.

Oral administration of tocopherols prevents the massive hepatic necrosis produced experimentally in rats by feeding certain brands of yeast as the sole dietary source of protein (deficient in sulfur-containing amino acids). Protection is also afforded by administration of cystine or certain selenium-containing compounds (p. 646). The functional relation of vitamin E to these substances is not clear. Vitamin E also prevents the liver injury induced by feeding excessive amounts of cod liver oil or diets containing artificially purified proteins.

The development of encephalomalacia (cerebellar disorder) and an "exudative diathesis" in chicks maintained on diets containing cod liver oil and deficient in vitamin E is probably due to the toxic action of abnormal oxidation products of highly unsaturated fatty acids. These conditions are prevented by administration of tocopherols.

Vitamin functions. The most prominent manifestations of vitamin E deficiency occur in certain rodent species (rat, rabbit, guinea pig) and fall into two general categories: (1) gonadal and reproductive functions; (2) muscle metabolism and structure.

In male rats deprived of vitamin E the seminiferous epithelium (germ cells) undergoes irreversible degenerative changes at the onset of sexual maturity, leading to permanent sterility. Similar changes may occur in the guinea pig, but not in the mouse.

In the female rat, vitamin E deficiency does not affect the ovary, since the processes of estrus, ovulation, conception, and implantation of the fertilized ovum are normal. However, the fetus does not develop normally, dying *in utero* and undergoing resorption. This phenomenon is apparently due to placental abnormalities, chiefly of a vascular nature, which interfere with the nutrition of the fetus. Administration of vitamin E within the first 10 days after conception results in normal gestation and fetal development.

There is no satisfactory evidence that vitamin E deficiency is a factor in the production of sterility or spontaneous abortion in man, or that tocopherol therapy exerts a favorable influence in these conditions.

The most common manifestation of vitamin E deficiency in a number of species (e.g., rat, rabbit, hamster, young guinea pig, calf, lamb, duckling) is muscle dystrophy, a degenerative change in the skeletal muscles, leading to necrosis, edema, inflammation, and fibrosis. This is accompanied by weakness or paralysis. Similar changes may occur in smooth muscle (uterus, heart) in certain species. In vitamin E-deficient rabbits, creatine is lost from the muscles and increases in the liver, blood, and urine before the appearance of morphological damage. The characteristic muscle lesions, with paralysis, occur also in the young born to vitamin E-deficient mothers. These metabolic and morphological abnormalities can be prevented or cured by administration of tocopherols.

The muscle lesions of experimental vitamin E deficiency resemble closely those of certain muscular dystrophies in man, the pathogenesis and etiology of which are unknown. However, there is no evidence that vitamin E deficiency is a factor in these clinical conditions or that tocopherol therapy exerts a beneficial influence.

There is evidence that a metabolite of tocopherol, perhaps tocopherolactone, plays a role in the biosynthesis of coenzyme Q (ubiquinone), at least in certain tissues. This action is not shared by other potent antioxidants.

Requirement

Whereas vitamin E is a dietary essential for certain species (e.g., rat, rabbit, guinea pig, dog, chick), there is no conclusive evidence that deprivation of this factor results in any demonstrable abnormality in man. The human requirement, if any, is therefore not known. It has been estimated that the average daily diet should contain about 30 mg. of mixed natural tocopherols.

VITAMINS K

These are the most recently recognized members of the group of fat-soluble vitamins. A hemorrhagic syndrome was observed (1929) in chicks raised on an artificial diet low in lipids, which did not respond to administration of any of the then known vitamins. The hemorrhagic manifestations were associated with a blood-clotting defect (1934) which was shown to be due to deficiency in prothrombin (1935). The term "vitamin K" (Koagulations-

Vitamin) was applied to the missing factor, which was later (1939) identified as a naphthoquinone. It was subsequently found that vitamin K activity was exhibited by a number of naturally occurring and synthetic compounds possessing a quinonoid ring structure.

The great practical importance of this vitamin arose out of the observation that certain common hemorrhagic disorders in man are dependent upon hypoprothrombinemia (e.g., in obstructive and hepatocellular jaundice; in the newborn; in certain intestinal disorders). Administration of vitamin K was found to be strikingly effective in controlling the hemorrhagic diathesis in many of these conditions.

Chemistry

The several substances, natural and synthetic, with vitamin K (antihemorrhagic) activity are naphthoquinones (Fig. 7–7). It has been suggested that the effectiveness of these compounds in this connection may be related to their capacity for forming 2-methyl-1,4-naphthoquinone ("menadione"), which is then alkylated with digeranylpyrophosphate to form vitamin K_2 (20C side chain), the active compound.

Two naturally occurring vitamins K have been identified. Vitamin K_1 (phylloquinone), isolated originally from alfalfa, has a phytyl chain attached at position 3 of the menadione nucleus (2-methyl-3-phytyl-1,4-naphthoquinone). Vitamin K_2 (farnoquinone), isolated originally from putrid fish meal, has a longer, difarnesyl chain attached at position 3 (2-methyl-3-difarnesyl-1,4-naphthoquinone). Phthiocol, a constituent of tubercle bacilli possessing slight vitamin K activity, has an —OH substituent at the 3 position (2-methyl-3-hydroxy-1,4-naphthoquinone). Menadione (2-methyl-1,4-naphthoquinone), because of its high activity, is the most important of the synthetic vitamins K, a number of which have been prepared. Vitamin K_1 has also been synthesized.

Activity is apparently related to the presence of the methyl group at the 2 position in the quinonoid ring. Substitution of the 2-methyl group by other alkyl radicals or by hydrogen results in marked decrease in activity. Less striking alterations are produced by substitutions in the 3 position, activity being favored by branching of the side chain.

The natural vitamins K are "fat-soluble vitamins," i.e., they are insoluble in water and are quite soluble in most fat solvents. The synthetic forms, lacking the long hydrocarbon chain, are somewhat soluble in water, but not sufficiently so for practical purposes. However, the hydroquinones of the vitamins K form esters (disulfate, diphosphate, diacetate) which are more soluble (water), less irritating, and more stable than the parent compounds, although less active. Certain of these are available and satisfactory for parenteral administration, e.g., 2-methyl-1,4-naphthohydroquinone-3-sodium sulfonate; 4-amino-2-methyl-1-naphthol hydrochloride.

The K vitamins are fairly stable to heat, but are readily destroyed by light, alkali, and alcohol. They have rather characteristic ultraviolet absorption patterns which are useful in their identification.

Occurrence and Food Sources

Both of the natural vitamins K occur principally in the plant kingdom. Vitamin K_1 is present chiefly in green leafy tissues (e.g., alfalfa, spinach), but has also been found in cauliflower, cabbage, kale, tomatoes, soybeans, rice bran, and oat shoots.

Vitamin K_2 is a product of the metabolism of most bacteria (but not yeasts, molds, or fungi), including the normal intestinal bacteria of most higher animal species. It is therefore present in the feces even when vitamin K is absent from the diet. Its presence in

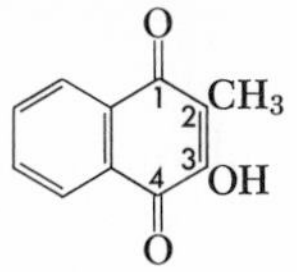

Phthiocol
(2-methyl-3-hydroxy-1,4-naphthoquinone)

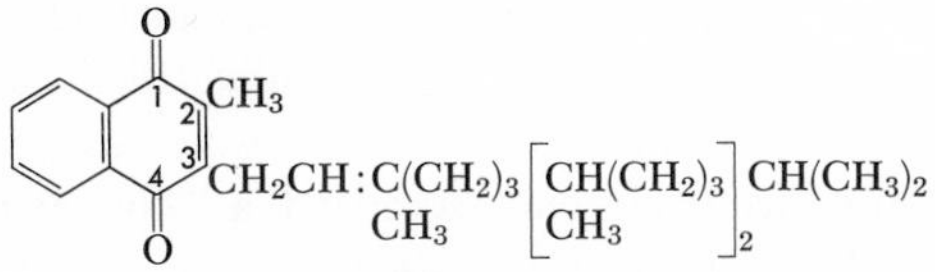

Vitamin K_1
(2-methyl-3-phytyl-1,4-naphthoquinone)

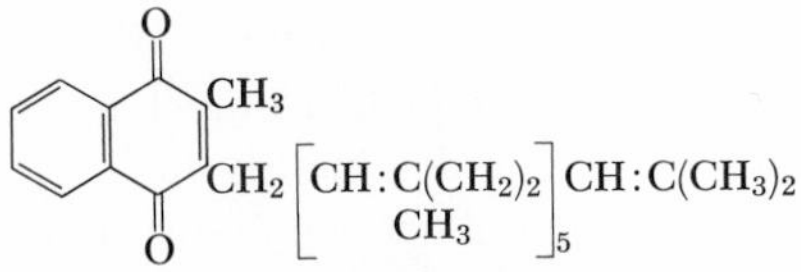

Vitamin K_2
(2-methyl-3-difarnesyl-1,4-naphthoquinone)
Farnoquinone

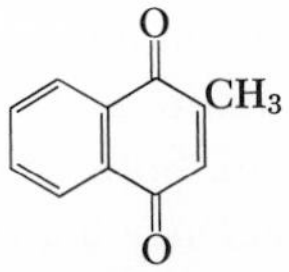

Menadione
(2-methyl-1,4-naphthoquinone)

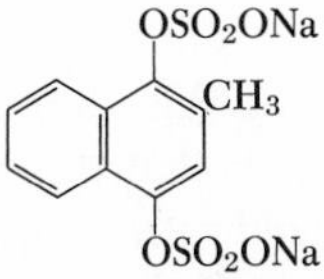

2-Methyl-1,4-naphthohydroquinone disulfate, Na salt

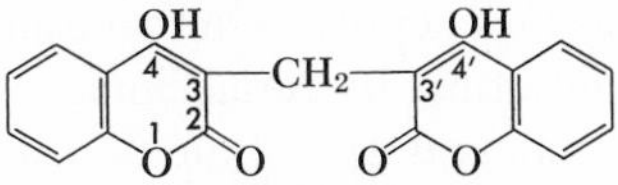

Dicumarol
3,3′-methylene-bis(4-hydroxycoumarin)

Figure 7-7. Vitamins K and Dicumarol, a vitamin K antagonist.

large amounts in putrid fish meal, from which it was originally isolated, is due to the luxuriant growth of bacteria in this material. The generally small amounts of vitamin K in animal tissues and products (milk, egg yolk) are of both dietary and intestinal bacterial origin.

Dietary supply of this factor is of little practical importance under ordinary circumstances, because adequate amounts are synthesized by the normal intestinal bacteria. An exogenous supply may become important, however, in individuals in whom growth of intestinal bacteria is inhibited (by certain antibiotics and sulfonamides) for therapeutic purposes (e.g., preliminary to surgical operations on the gastrointestinal tract).

Assay

Because of the important function of vitamin K in the formation of prothrombin, the assay procedure employed originally was based upon the effect of the test material on the "plasma prothrombin time" of K-deficient chicks. Activity was expressed as "curative units." In view of the availability of pure 2-methyl-1,4-naphthoquinone, vitamin K activity is expressed most satisfactorily in relation to the biological effect of a given amount of this substance. There are no international or U.S.P. standards for vitamin K. A convenient standard of reference is the activity (on "prothrombin time") of 1 μg. of 2-methyl-1,4-naphthoquinone (menadione), which is about three times as active as vitamin K_1. The latter is also commonly used as a reference standard, a "Thayer-Doisy unit" being represented by the activity of 1 μg. of pure vitamin K_1.

Absorption, Metabolism, Excretion

A normal diet contains an abundance of vitamin K. It is also formed by intestinal bacteria (chiefly E. coli) in amounts adequate to meet normal requirements. Being fat-soluble, its absorption, which occurs predominantly in the jejunum, by way of the lymphatics, is influenced by factors which affect the absorption of lipids. Adequate amounts of bile salts must be present for optimal absorption, a fact of great importance in relation to the hemorrhagic manifestations of biliary obstruction. Absorption is diminished by large amounts of liquid petrolatum.

Vitamin K has not been found consistently in the bloodstream in significant amounts. During pregnancy, it apparently passes readily from the mother to the fetus. The capacity of the organism for storing this vitamin is extremely limited, at least in experimental animals, and evidence suggests that this is true also of man. Both vitamin K and prothrombin are utilized or metabolized rather rapidly, so that deficiency manifestations appear after a relatively brief period of deprivation (24 to 48 hours in rats).

Vitamin K is apparently not excreted in the urine or bile. It has been found in the milk of women receiving adequate amounts of the vitamin. Rather large quantities may be present in the feces; whereas this may represent actual excretion by the intestinal mucosa, a more probable source is the intestinal bacterial flora.

Administration of excessive amounts of vitamin A results, in certain species, in hypoprothrombinemia and hemorrhagic manifestations which are prevented by simultaneous administration of vitamin K. It is believed that this effect may be due to interference with bacterial synthesis of vitamin K in the intestine.

Function

Vitamin K is essential for the formation of proconvertin, plasma thromboplastin component (Factor IX), Stuart's factor (Factor X) and prothrombin by the hepatic cells, the mechanism of its action being unknown, perhaps serving as a coenzyme or activator. The methods commonly employed for measuring prothrombin measure activity, and do not distinguish, for example, between prothrombin, Ac-globulin, and convertin (p. 800). All of these appear to be affected in liver damage. The principal overall effect of vitamin K is to shorten the prothrombin time.

The wide distribution in nature of substances with vitamin K activity, including species (e.g., vegetables) in which they perform no clotting function, suggests that they may serve some more fundamental metabolic function. It has been postulated that vitamin K (or a derivative) is an essential component of the respiratory mechanism of the cell, participating in electron transfer in the oxidative chain and also perhaps in the associated phosphorylations (p. 382). The fact that Dicumarol, a vitamin K antagonist, causes uncoupling of oxidative chain phosphorylations has suggested that vitamin K may also be involved in the coupling mechanism. There is as yet no conclusive evidence that it is involved in these mechanisms in mammalian cells.

Deficiency

Vitamin K deficiency can be induced by dietary restriction in several species (chick and other birds, rat, mouse, rabbit). In man, because of adequate synthesis of the vitamin by intestinal bacteria, deficiency rarely results from dietary inadequacy. The low plasma prothrombin activity which occurs consistently in the newborn, during the first few days of life, is attributed to vitamin K deficiency, due in part to inadequacy of the intestinal bacterial flora, and in part perhaps to inadequate bile flow and intestinal hypermotility, with consequent poor absorption. If sufficiently low, this may result in "hemorrhagic disease of the newborn." This is prevented by administration of vitamin K to the mother during the last few days of pregnancy or during labor.

Deficiency manifestations result usually from conditions which interfere with (1) absorption of the vitamin from the intestine, (2) its utilization in prothrombin formation or activation, or (3) its production by intestinal bacteria. The latter is accomplished by drugs (certain sulfonamides and antibiotics) which inhibit growth of bacteria in the intestinal tract. Inadequate absorption may occur in association with an external bile fistula and biliary obstruction (absence of adequate amount of bile salts in intestine), chronic diarrhea or steatorrhea (ulcerative colitis, tuberculous enteritis, sprue, celiac disease), gastrocolic fistula, intestinal obstruction, etc. Deficient utilization may occur in association with hepatocellular damage, the liver cells being unable to synthesize prothrombin (or proconvertin) despite an adequate supply of vitamin K. This situation is not one of vitamin K deficiency but rather deficient prothrombin activity, due to impaired liver function. The characteristic manifestations of vitamin K deficiency are due to inadequate formation (or activation) of plasma proconvertin and prothrombin, essential components of the blood clotting mechanism (p. 800). When the plasma prothrombin activity falls to 30 to 40 per cent of normal, clot formation is demonstrably delayed. When it falls below 20 per cent of normal, subcutaneous, intramuscular, and internal hemorrhage may occur as a result of otherwise insignificant trauma, and uncontrollable bleeding may follow minor abrasions and cuts. This was formerly a frequent cause of death following operations on patients with obstructive jaundice. In the absence of serious liver damage, the bleeding can now be effectively prevented or controlled by administration of vitamin K.

Vitamin K deficiency can be induced in rats by inclusion of dihydroxystearic acid in the diet. Although not bacteriostatic or bactericidal, this substance blocks intestinal synthesis of the vitamin, presumably by displacing a precursor from the enzyme system involved. A similar state of hypoprothrombinemia, correctable by administration of vitamin K, can be produced by certain structural analogues of the vitamin, e.g., bishydroxycoumarin (Dicumarol) and α-tocopherol quinone. These apparently are examples of biological antagonism (competition), discussed elsewhere (p. 664).

Requirement

From what has been said previously, it is obvious that there is no dietary requirement (human) for vitamin K under physiological conditions. An exogenous supplement is required under the circumstances indicated as potential causes of vitamin K deficiency. Only small amounts are required, e.g., 1 to 2 mg. of menadione or its equivalent, daily.

VITAMINS B (VITAMIN B COMPLEX)

In the early period of vitamin investigations, the term "water-soluble vitamin B" was applied to the factor, present in rice polishings, bean extracts, yeast and liver, which if deficient in the diet results in beriberi. At that time (before 1920), two other vitamins were recognized, "fat-soluble A" and "water-soluble C," and shortly thereafter another, "fat-soluble D," was identified as distinct from vitamin A. The multiple nature of "vitamin B" soon became obvious, and the numerical designations, B_1, B_2, etc., were applied to the various components of the "vitamin B complex." As soon as their chemical nature or structures were established, they were given more descriptive names.

As information accumulated regarding the occurrence and functions of these substances, it became increasingly evident that, in contrast to other known vitamins (e.g., A, C, D), they are nutritional essentials for all forms of life, from the lowly yeasts, molds, and bacteria to man. It has been shown that several are essential components (coenzymes) of fundamentally important intracellular enzyme systems (e.g., thiamine, riboflavin, niacin, pantothenic acid, pyridoxine). The same may prove to be true of other B vitamins. This concept has been emphasized by Williams, who regards them as essential parts of the metabolic machinery of all cells, their strictly nutritional function being of secondary importance. He includes among the B vitamins those organic substances which are present in all living cells, act catalytically, and function nutritionally for at least some of the higher animals. Some of these indispensable factors may be synthesized by man and are therefore not dietary essentials.

Although whether a substance is or is not regarded as a B vitamin is of little consequence, it is desirable that some uniformity be maintained in this connection, if only for purely academic purposes. The following are generally accepted as B vitamins: (1) thiamine; (2) riboflavin; (3) niacin and niacinamide; (4) pantothenic acid; (5) pyridoxine, pyridoxal, pyridoxamine; (6) biotin; (7) the folic acid group (pteroylglutamic acid; "folinic acid"); (8) vitamin B_{12} (cobalamin; cobamide; anti-pernicious anemia [extrinsic] factor); (9) α-lipoic acid. There is no agreement about the inclusion in this category of inositol and choline. We shall concern ourselves here mainly with the significance of these substances in mammalian organisms, particularly in man.

Thiamine

Beriberi, a disabling condition that was endemic for centuries in the Orient and Pacific islands, was the first disorder to receive the designation of a "deficiency disease." Eijkman (1897) showed that an analogous condition could be produced in hens by feeding polished rice, and could be cured or prevented by adding rice polishings (pericarp and germ) to the diet. It was shortly found that extracts of rice polishings (or of beans) cured beriberi in human subjects and this disease was therefore identified with deficiency in some factor removed from the rice grains in the process of milling. Thirty years later (1926) the factor, thiamine, was isolated from rice polishings, and about 10 years thereafter its chemical structure was established and its total synthesis accomplished.

Chemistry

Free thiamine is a basic substance containing a pyrimidine and a thiazole ring. It is generally prepared as a chloride-hydrochloride (Fig. 7–8), soluble in water (1 gm./1 ml.) and 95 per cent ethanol (1 gm./100 ml.) but not in fat solvents. In this form it is acid in aqueous solution owing to dissociation of the HCl; it is rather resistant to heat (boiling or autoclaving) in solutions below pH 3.5, but loses activity above pH 5.5 (hydrolysis). The relative heat stability of thiamine in foods, under ordinary conditions of preparation, may be due to the fact that much of it is in combined form. However, its high solubility may result in considerable loss in the cooking water. The thiamine content of vegetables is well preserved by freezing and by storage below 0° C.

By virtue of its basic characters, it forms a number of salts and esters which possess equal vitamin activity on a molar basis. The most important ester is the pyrophosphate (reacting with the alcoholic —OH on the thiazole ring) (Fig. 7–8), which serves as the prosthetic group (cocarboxylase) for metabolic reactions involving decarboxylation of certain α-keto acids and for the transketolase reaction (p. 417).

Thiamine and its pyrophosphate undergo both oxidation and reduction. Treatment in vitro with mild oxidizing reagents (e.g., potassium ferricyanide) results in the formation of thiochrome (Fig. 7–8). This reaction forms the basis of one of the methods for quantitative determination of thiamine. Reduction (e.g., by hydrosulfite) results in irreversible loss of vitamin activity.

Biosynthesis

Thiamine is a nutritional requirement for all plant and animal species. It is synthesized by all higher plants, but to only a limited extent in the dark, and by many bacteria, yeasts, and molds. There may be a certain degree of symbiosis in this connection between plants and soil microorganisms, particularly during the initial stages of growth of seed-

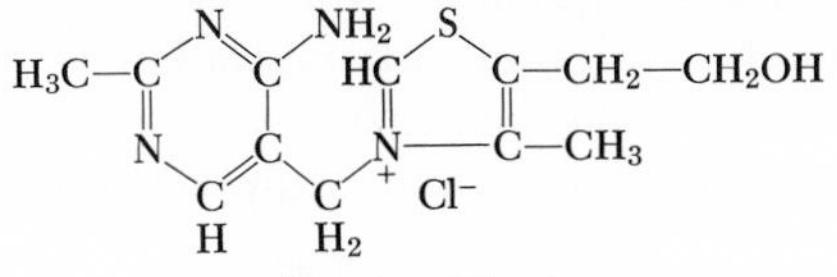

Thiamine chloride

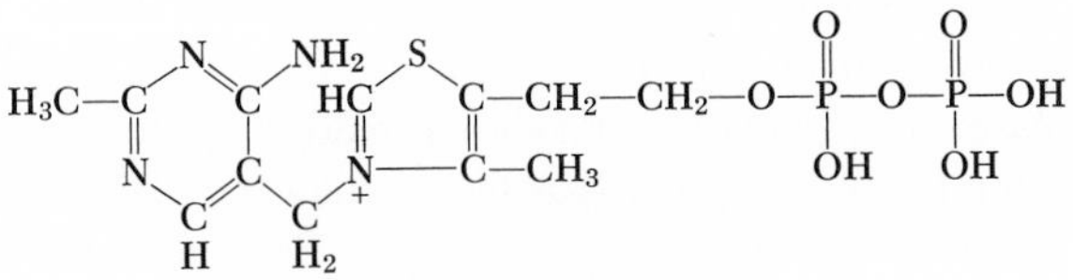

Thiamine pyrophosphate
(cocarboxylase)

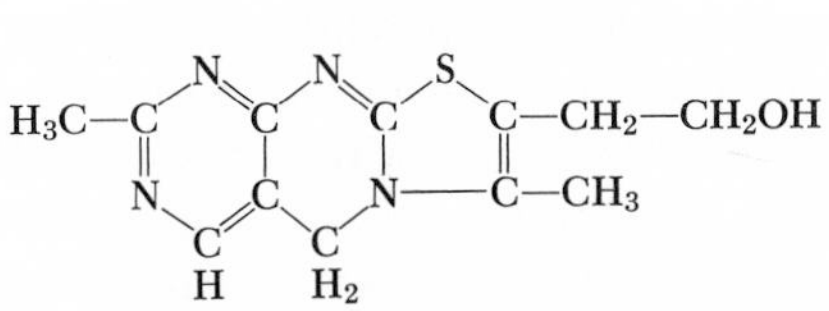

Thiochrome

Figure 7-8. Thiamine and derivatives.

lings. It is apparently not synthesized in significant amounts in animal tissues. The most important source of this vitamin for man and other animals is dietary although certain ruminants (sheep, cattle) may obtain their total requirement from intestinal bacterial synthesis.

Certain plants and microorganisms can synthesize thiamine if the pyrimidine component alone is supplied, others if the thiazole portion alone is supplied, while others require neither of these components in a preformed state. The final steps in the synthesis involve: (a) coupling of the pyrimidine and thiazole monophosphate (methylene bridge); (b) hydrolysis of the latter, forming the free base (thiamine); (c) pyrophosphorylation of the latter with ATP, forming thiamine pyrophosphate. Cocarboxylase activity is exhibited by thiamine pyrophosphate, not by the free base. Cells of several tissues contain enzymes capable of phosphorylating thiamine in the presence of ATP, or if coupled with enzymatic reactions in which reactive phosphate compounds are formed (pp. 379 to 387).

Metabolism of Thiamine

Free thiamine is absorbed readily from the small intestine, but the pyrophosphate (cocarboxylase) is not. The bulk of the dietary vegetable thiamine is in the free state. It is actively phosphorylated to cocarboxylase in the liver and, to a lesser extent, in other tissues (muscle, brain), including nucleated red blood cells.

It is present in the blood plasma and cerebrospinal fluid in the free state (about 1 μg./100 ml.). The largest portion of the blood thiamine, which ranges from 6 to 12 μg./100 ml., is in the blood cells as the pyrophosphate, in protein combination. Since free thiamine (base) is readily diffusible and the pyrophosphate is not, the plasma thiamine probably represents the transport form (inactive) of the vitamin, which undergoes phosphorylation upon entrance into tissue cells, including nucleated red blood cells in the bone marrow.

The capacity of the organism for storing thiamine is limited. It is present in both free and combined forms, mainly the latter, in the heart, liver, and kidneys, and, in lower concentration, in skeletal muscle and brain. Administration of thiamine may result in an increase in the tissues, within certain limits. However, on a thiamine-free diet, the tissue content is depleted within a short time, emphasizing the desirability of providing an adequate daily supply.

Cocarboxylase, formed within the cell, unites with protein apoenzymes to form carboxylases, one of which (pyruvic carboxylase) contains magnesium. The pyrophosphate group is apparently involved in this union.

The pyrophosphate linkage in cocarboxylase is readily hydrolyzed by tissue pyrophosphatases, free thiamine being liberated. However, when the coenzyme is combined with the apoenzyme it is quite resistant to such hydrolysis; thiamine is released from this combination through the action of proteolytic enzymes.

If normal amounts of thiamine are ingested (1 to 2 mg. daily), about 10 per cent is excreted in the urine. The remainder is apparently partly phosphorylated and utilized for carboxylase action and partly degraded to neutral sulfur compounds and inorganic sulfate. Neither the enzyme nor the metabolic pathways are known. If large amounts are given, the excess is largely excreted in the urine. All of the urinary thiamine is in the free form. Normal subjects on an adequate intake excrete at least 50 μg. daily in the urine. That present in the feces is probably largely of bacterial origin (large intestine). It is secreted in the milk as a thiamine-protein complex and, in certain species (e.g., goat), as mono- and diphosphothiamine.

Occurrence and Food Sources

Thiamine is distributed widely throughout the plant kingdom, occurring in the highest concentrations usually in the seed, but also being present in the leaf, root, stem, and fruit. In cereal grains, it is concentrated in the outer germ and bran layers (e.g., rice polishings), which are often discarded during milling processes (e.g., of wheat flour and rice). The following are good dietary sources of this vitamin: peas, beans, whole cereal grains, bran, nuts, prunes, gooseberries, killed yeast. Whole-wheat bread is a good source; white bread is now commonly made from thiamine-enriched flour, and is therefore satisfactory from this standpoint.

Thiamine is present in most animal tissues. Of those which are commonly used as foods, ham and pork are particularly rich in this factor, beef, liver, and eggs also supplying considerable amounts. Milk, although containing comparatively low concentrations, is an important dietary source because of the large quantities consumed.

Assay

An International Unit (I.U.) (also U.S.P. unit) of thiamine is equal to 3 μg. of thiamine hydrochloride.

Thiamine may be determined quantitatively by (1) chemical (fluorometric; colorimetric) or (2) bioassay (microbiological; rat curative test) procedures. Although certain of the latter are more sensitive, they have been largely replaced by the former, for practical reasons.

Functions

Thiamine pyrophosphate (diphosphothiamine; TPP; DPT), the active form of the vitamin, is a cofactor (coenzyme), together with α-lipoic acid, in reactions involving decarboxylation of the α-keto acids, pyruvic and α-ketoglutaric acids (pp. 409, 411). The enzymes catalyzing these reactions are termed "carboxylases" and the coenzyme (DPT) "cocarboxylase." Cocarboxylase is not involved in decarboxylation of carboxyl groups beta to the keto group. Biotin is involved in the latter type of reaction (β-decarboxylation) (p. 413).

Thiamine pyrophosphate is also a coenzyme for the transketolase reaction, a step in the phosphogluconate oxidative pathway of carbohydrate metabolism (p. 417).

Deficiency Manifestations

In its severe form, formerly endemic in the Orient, and occurring elsewhere during periods of severe malnutrition (postwar), thiamine deficiency results in the condition known as beriberi. This is characterized by cardiovascular and neurological manifestations, and, in some cases, edema ("wet" beriberi).

Cardiovascular manifestations include palpitation, dyspnea, cardiac hypertrophy and dilatation, progressing to congestive heart failure (hepatic and pulmonary congestion, peripheral edema).

Neurological manifestations are predominantly those of an ascending, symmetrical, peripheral polyneuritis, accompanied, at times, by an acute hemorrhagic polioencephalitis (Wernicke's encephalopathy).

Edema may occur ("wet" beriberi), due probably in part to congestive heart failure and in part to protein undernutrition (low plasma albumin). Anorexia is an early symptom. There may be gastric atony, with diminished gastric motility and nausea. Fever and vomiting occur in advanced stages.

The fully developed clinical picture of beriberi is seldom encountered in the western world except, at times, in famine areas. Manifestations of thiamine deficiency are usually mild, with anorexia, nausea, cardiovascular symptoms, and evidence of early peripheral neuritis.

In most animals, thiamine deficiency produces symptoms resembling these of beriberi, described above, with certain important additional features. In the rat, after about two weeks on a thiamine-free diet, the heart rate decreases from about 500 beats to about 250 to 300 beats per minute (bradycardia). This phenomenon has been used as a basis for a bioassay procedure for thiamine. Pigeons develop a rather characteristic, rigid, retraction of the head (opisthotonus), which sign has also been employed in bioassay procedures. A type of spastic paralysis (Chastek paralysis) has been observed in foxes on a raw fish diet, characterized by extreme, boardlike rigidity, with retraction of the head. This has been attributed to the presence of a thiamine-splitting enzyme (thiaminase) in the raw fish.

The important biochemical features of thiamine deficiency include: decreased levels of thiamine and cocarboxylase in the blood and urine; increased concentrations of pyruvic and lactic acids in the blood; decreased uptake of oxygen by thiamine-deficient brain tissue (in glucose or pyruvate), reversible, in vitro, by addition of thiamine ("catatorulin effect"). The decreased oxygen uptake is probably due to blocks in the conversion of pyruvate to acetate (p. 409) and of ketoglutarate to succinate (p. 411), for which cocarboxylase is required. In thiamine-deficient rats, pentose sugars accumulate in the red blood cells as a result of retardation of the transketolase reaction.

Demonstration of deficiency in man. The prompt response of symptoms to specific (thiamine) therapy is of great diagnostic significance. Supportive evidence is furnished by the demonstration of subnormal levels of thiamine and cocarboxylase, or increased concentrations of pyruvic and lactic acids in the blood. It has been suggested that the blood pyruvate-lactate levels are of greater diagnostic significance if studied in relation to the blood sugar concentration after administration of glucose. Rather extensive use has been made of saturation tests, a lower urinary excretion of thiamine and cocarboxylase after administration of a test dose occurring in thiamine-deficient than in normal subjects.

Requirement (Table 24-1, p. 650)

The estimated daily thiamine requirement (dietary) for adults is 0.5 mg. for each 1000 Calories, i.e., 1.0 and 1.5 mg. for diets providing 2000 and 3000 Calories, respectively, with a minimum of 1 mg. The actual requirement is probably related more directly to the carbohydrate content than to the caloric value of the diet. Recommended daily intakes for children range from 0.4 mg. for infants to 1.3 mg. for pre-adolescents (10 to 12 years).

The requirement for thiamine may be increased under the following circumstances: anoxia (shock, hemorrhage); serious illness or injury; during oral administration of antibiotics; during refeeding of markedly undernourished subjects; increased caloric expenditure (e.g., fever, hyperthyroidism).

Riboflavin

Certain substances exhibiting a strong yellowish-green fluorescence, isolated from egg white, milk, liver, plants, and other sources, were found (1933) to stimulate the growth of rats. These were called "ovoflavin," "lactoflavin," "hepatoflavin," and "verdoflavin," respectively, until it was found that they were probably the same substance. It was demonstrated shortly thereafter that this pigment was also contained in the "yellow enzyme" discovered (1932) by Warburg and Christian in yeast. Its relation to cellular oxidation mechanisms was thereby established. The original designation, "lactoflavin," was changed to "riboflavin" when its constitution became known. Synthesis of riboflavin was accomplished in 1935.

Chemistry

Riboflavin is an orange-yellow compound containing D-ribitol (a ribose alcohol) and a heterocyclic substance, isoalloxazine (flavin) (Fig. 7–9). The 1-carbon of the ribityl group is attached at the 9 position of isoalloxazine (6,7-dimethyl-9-(1′-D-ribityl)-isoalloxazine).

Riboflavin is quite stable to heat in neutral and acid, but not in alkaline solutions. Aqueous solutions are unstable to visible and ultraviolet light, this instability being increased by heat and alkalinity. On exposure to light, the ribityl residue is split off, with

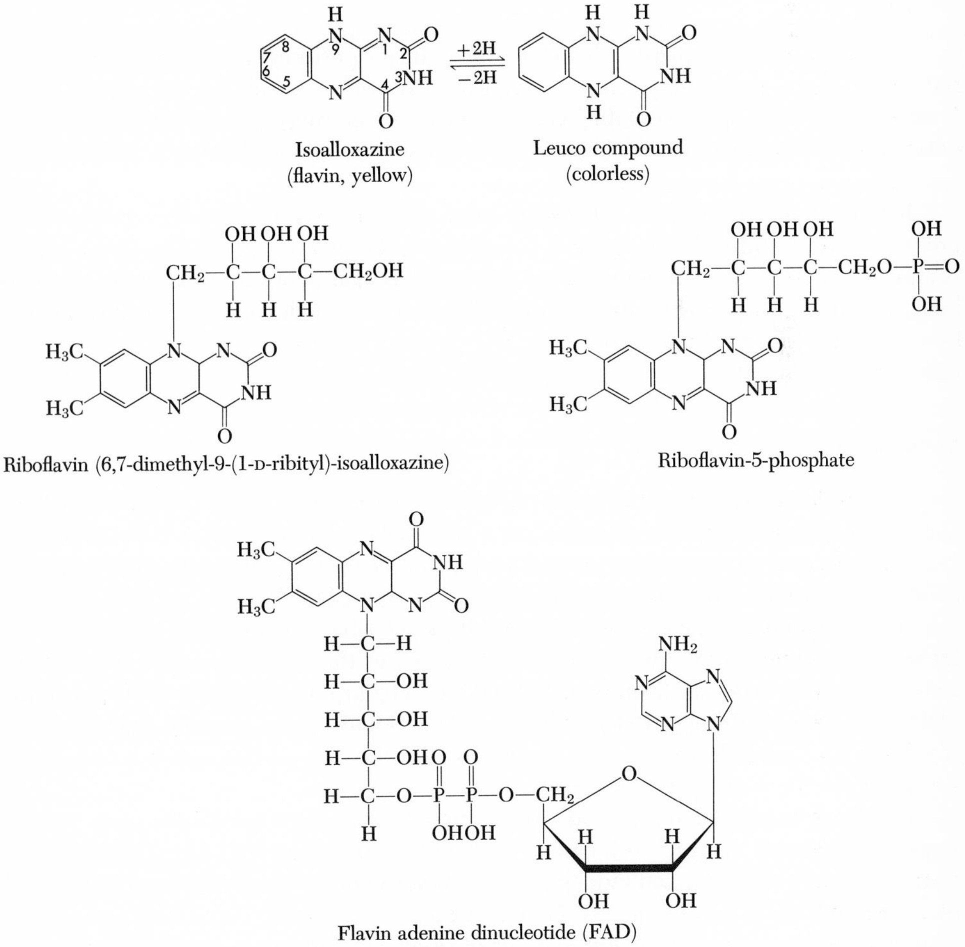

Isoalloxazine (flavin, yellow) $\underset{-2H}{\overset{+2H}{\rightleftharpoons}}$ Leuco compound (colorless)

Riboflavin (6,7-dimethyl-9-(1-D-ribityl)-isoalloxazine)

Riboflavin-5-phosphate

Flavin adenine dinucleotide (FAD)

Figure 7–9. Riboflavin and related compounds.

the formation, in alkaline solution, of a yellow, chloroform-soluble pigment, "lumiflavin," and, in acid or neutral solution, of a similar compound, called "lumichrome." This reaction is irreversible. Riboflavin readily undergoes reversible reduction to a colorless substance, "leucoriboflavin" (Fig 7–9). This phenomenon is probably related to the important function of riboflavin as a component of enzyme systems catalyzing cellular oxidation-reduction reactions (p. 353).

The biologically active forms in which riboflavin serves as the prosthetic group (coenzyme) of a number of enzymes are phosphorylated derivatives: (1) flavin mononucleotide (riboflavin phosphate), and (2) flavin adenine dinucleotide (FAD) (Fig. 7–9). The acidic properties imparted by addition of phosphoric acid influence their capacity for combining with the protein apoenzymes. This union apparently occurs through both this acid group and the imide N of the isoalloxazine nucleus, forming linkages with basic and acidic groups of the proteins. These compounds (holoenzymes) are termed "flavoproteins" (p. 54). In most instances they are readily dissociable in acid solution into their apoenzyme (protein) and prosthetic (coenzyme; flavin nucleotide) components; the latter can be removed by dialysis.

Biosynthesis

All higher plants synthesize riboflavin, the younger portions containing more than the older (e.g., leaves more than stems). Young leaves are richer in this factor than old leaves. Most ungerminated seeds contain little riboflavin, which increases during the process of germination. Riboflavin occurs in nature in the free form and as the mono- and dinucleotides, as such, or as flavoproteins.

It is synthesized also by most yeasts, fungi, and bacteria, but not by animals, which are therefore completely dependent on extrinsic sources for their riboflavin supply. Ruminants (cow, goat) can obtain all of their requirement from intestinal bacteria, none being required in the diet. In man, on the other hand, although considerable amounts may be formed by intestinal microorganisms, the quantity absorbed is not adequate to maintain normal nutrition.

Metabolism

The flavin nucleotides are readily absorbed in the small intestine. Free riboflavin apparently undergoes phosphorylation as a prerequisite to absorption. The mono- and dinucleotides can apparently be formed in the tissue cells also, since the normal requirements can be met by parenteral administration of free riboflavin.

Human blood plasma contains 2.5 to 4.0 μg. of riboflavin per 100 ml., about two-thirds as the dinucleotide, the bulk of the remainder as the mononucleotide. The concentration in erythrocytes has been reported as 15 to 30 μg./100 gm., and in leukocytes (plus platelets) as about 250 μg./100 gm. These values remain quite constant even in severe riboflavin deficiency. Determination of riboflavin in the blood is not useful in the clinical evaluation of the state of riboflavin nutrition.

Riboflavin is present in all tissue cells, principally as the nucleotides (coenzymes), a variable proportion of which is bound as flavoprotein (holoenzymes). The highest concentrations occur in the liver and kidneys, but the tissue content is not increased significantly by administration of large amounts. Certain tissues (e.g., muscle) may retain considerable quantities in the presence of manifestations of riboflavin deficiency. Riboflavin is secreted in the milk, 40 to 80 per cent being in the free state, increasing with increased intake. It is also present in perspiration (10 μg./hour). The riboflavin content of the feces (free and nucleotides) tends to remain quite constant (500 to 750 μg. daily), and is presumably largely of bacterial origin. The urinary excretion (mainly free, but up to 50 per cent nucleotide) varies with the intake. Under ordinary dietary conditions (1 to 2 mg. riboflavin), the daily urinary excretion is about 10 to 20 per cent of intake (0.1 to 0.4 mg.). When larger amounts are administered, as much as 50 per cent may be eliminated in the urine. The bulk of the dietary riboflavin is metabolized in the body, largely to unknown compounds. The capacity of the organism for utilizing and retaining riboflavin is reduced in the presence of a negative nitrogen balance (e.g., low protein intake, excessive protein catabolism). It would appear that flavoproteins are more labile than most other body proteins.

Occurrence and Food Sources

Riboflavin, being an essential component of many biological oxidation-reduction systems, is widely distributed in nature. It is probably present in all plant and animal cells, but very few common foodstuffs contain large amounts. Comparatively high concentrations occur in yeasts and fermenting bacteria. Appreciable amounts are present in liver (2 to 3 mg./100 gm.), kidney, crab meat, whole grain, dry beans and peas, nuts, milk, eggs, meats, and green leafy vegetables. In tissues, it occurs largely as the mono- (riboflavin phosphate) or dinucleotide (isoalloxazine-adenine-dinucleotide; FAD), usually probably bound to proteins (apoenzymes). Milk contains free riboflavin. The riboflavin of different foodstuffs is not equally available upon ingestion. Drying (e.g., yeast) and cooking may increase its availability.

Assay

Riboflavin can be determined quantitatively by (1) biological (animal curative), (2) microbiological (most sensitive), and (3) chemical (chromatographic; fluorometric; colorimetric) procedures.

Functions

Riboflavin, in the form of the mono- and dinucleotides, acts as the prosthetic group (coenzyme) of several enzymes (flavoproteins) involved in biological oxidation-reduction reactions. These enzymes serve as bridges over which hydrogen atoms can pass between two other molecules (p. 353). The flavoprotein enzymes catalyze many fewer reactions and exhibit much more hydrogen-acceptor specificity than do the pyridinoprotein enzymes (containing nicotinamide as a prosthetic group) (p. 359). Moreover, the redox potential of riboflavin is intermediate between the relatively low values of its H donors (organic metabolites; nicotinamide) and the higher values of its H acceptors (cytochromes; oxygen). Consequently, the majority of biological reactions catalyzed by flavoprotein enzymes proceed effectively only in one direction; i.e., from organic substrates as the original H donors to molecular oxygen as the ultimate H acceptor. In its reduction and oxidation, riboflavin alternately accepts and releases two H atoms, being reversibly transformed to leucoriboflavin (Fig. 7–9).

The reactions catalyzed by flavoproteins may be divided into two groups:

1. Reactions in which the enzyme removes hydrogen directly from a primary substrate (organic metabolite). The latter include D-amino acids, L-amino acids, glycine, L-hydroxyacids, aldehydes, purines (xanthine, hypoxanthine).

2. Reactions in which the enzyme removes hydrogen, not from the primary substrate, but from an intermediate carrier, e.g., a reduced pyridine nucleotide system (NADH; NADPH) (p. 353).

The individual reactions in which the flavin nucleotides function as H-carriers and the mechanisms involved are considered elsewhere (pp. 353, 357). In a few of these the mononucleotide (riboflavin phosphate) is involved, in the majority the dinucleotide (FAD).

Deficiency Manifestations

As is the case with other B vitamins, the effects in man of deficiency in riboflavin are not very well defined, because clinical (i.e., dietary) deficiency in this factor is almost inevitably accompanied by deficiencies in other B vitamins. However, certain symptoms in subjects with multiple deficiencies (e.g., pellagra, beriberi) respond quite specifically to administration of riboflavin, and are presumably due to lack of this factor.

The most important and consistent symptoms of riboflavin deficiency in man are lesions of the mouth, tongue, nose, and eyes, with weakness, lassitude, and, less consistently, skin lesions. They include: redness and shiny appearance of the lips; lesions at the mucocutaneous juncture at the angles of the mouth, leading to painful fissure (cheilosis); painful glossitis, the tongue assuming a red-purple (magenta) color; seborrheic dermatitis (scaly, greasy desquamation) chiefly about the ears, nose, and nasolabial folds.

Similar lesions occur in experimental animals: dermatitis, with roughening or loss of hair (alopecia) (rat, mouse, pig, dog, monkey); conjunctivitis, cataract, vascularization, opacity and ulceration of the cornea (rat, mouse, dog, pig); incoordination and paralysis of the legs (myelin degeneration) (rat, mouse, dog, monkey, pig); lymphopenia (rat); anemia (rat, dog, monkey); and congenital malformations (rat).

Protein synthesis is impaired in severe riboflavin deficiency. Since protein malnutrition interferes with utilization and retention of riboflavin, these are therefore mutually limiting factors.

Demonstration of deficiency in man. This depends mainly on recognition of characteristic symptoms and the response to adequate specific therapy. Determination of the blood level or urinary excretion of riboflavin is of no diagnostic value. Saturation tests may be useful if adequately standardized. Normal subjects excrete at least 20 per cent of a test dose (3 mg.) during the subsequent 24 hours.

Requirement (Table 24-1, p. 650)

The human requirement for riboflavin is not known exactly, but it is related to the degree of protein utilization, both factors being interdependent. The recommended daily intake is as follows: adults, 1.5 to 1.8 mg., depending on weight; women in the latter half of pregnancy, 2.0 mg.; during lactation, 2.5 mg.; infants, 0.6 mg.; children, 1.0 to 1.8 mg., and 2 to 2.5 mg. during adolescence.

The requirement for riboflavin may be increased under the following circumstances: after severe injury or burn; increased protein catabolism; during acute illness and early convalescence. This is apparently related to the active participation of riboflavin in anabolic processes.

Niacin (Nicotinic Acid)

Pellagra is a serious disease which has for centuries occurred in endemic and epidemic forms in various regions and was quite common in the southern United States. It was clearly demonstrated as early as 1912 (Goldberger) that it originated in some dietary inadequacy, the exact nature of which was not clear. It was also shown (1917) that a condition in dogs, called "canine blacktongue," had much in common with human pellagra. In 1937, Elvehjem isolated nicotinic acid and nicotinamide from liver extract and showed that they were highly effective in curing canine blacktongue. Shortly thereafter their curative effect in clinical pellagra was reported.

Nicotinic acid was first derived from nicotine in 1867, and it had been isolated from yeast and rice bran as early as 1912, with no appreciation of its nutritional significance. However, in 1935, Warburg and Christian had demonstrated the participation of nicotinamide in cellular oxidation systems as a hydrogen-transport agent. This observation, together with the development of knowledge regarding riboflavin, emphasized the possible role of certain vitamins as essential components of fundamentally important intracellular enzyme systems. The term "niacin" (and "niacinamide") was adopted officially to avoid the implication of a functional or pharmacological resemblance to the alkaloid nicotine.

Chemistry

Nicotinic acid (niacin) is pyridine 3-carboxylic acid (Fig. 7–10). It derives its name from the fact that it can be prepared by oxidation of nicotine, although it differs strikingly from the latter in its pharmacological effects. It occurs in tissues principally as the amide (nicotinamide; niacinamide; pyridine 3-carboxylic acid amide), in which form it enters into physiologically active combination.

In tissues, nicotinamide is present largely as a dinucleotide, the pyridine N being linked to a ribose residue. Two such compounds are known: (1) nicotinamide adenine dinucleotide (coenzyme I; cozymase; codehydrogenase; NAD; DPN) containing nicotinamide, two molecules each of D-ribose and phosphoric acid, and one of adenine (Fig. 7–10); (2) nicotinamide adenine dinucleotide phosphate (coenzyme II; NADP; TPN), differing from NAD in that it contains an additional molecule of phosphoric acid.

These coenzymes are soluble in water, stable in acid but not in alkali, and exhibit characteristic absorption maxima in the ultraviolet which shift upon reduction (e.g., 260 mμ for NAD, 340 mμ for NADH). This fact is of importance in demonstrating participation of this factor in biological oxidation reactions.

Occurrence and Food Sources

Nicotinamide and its combined forms (NAD, NADP) are distributed widely in plant and animal (only combined) tissues. As is true of other B vitamins, nicotinamide is present in cereal grains in highest concentration in the germ and pericarp (bran), which are often discarded in the milling process (e.g., wheat, rice). Yeast (brewers' and bakers') is particularly rich in this factor (also beer and ale). Important food sources include liver, kidney, meats, fish, legumes (peas, beans, lentils), certain nuts, certain green vegetables, coffee, tea, and whole-wheat, rye, and artificially enriched white bread. Fruits, milk, and eggs are generally poor sources.

Biosynthesis

Tryptophan is a precursor of nicotinic acid in many plant and animal species, including man. Kynurenine, 3-hydroxyanthranilic acid and quinolinic acid are intermediates in the biosynthetic pathway (p. 596). Pyridoxal phosphate is a cofactor in this reaction

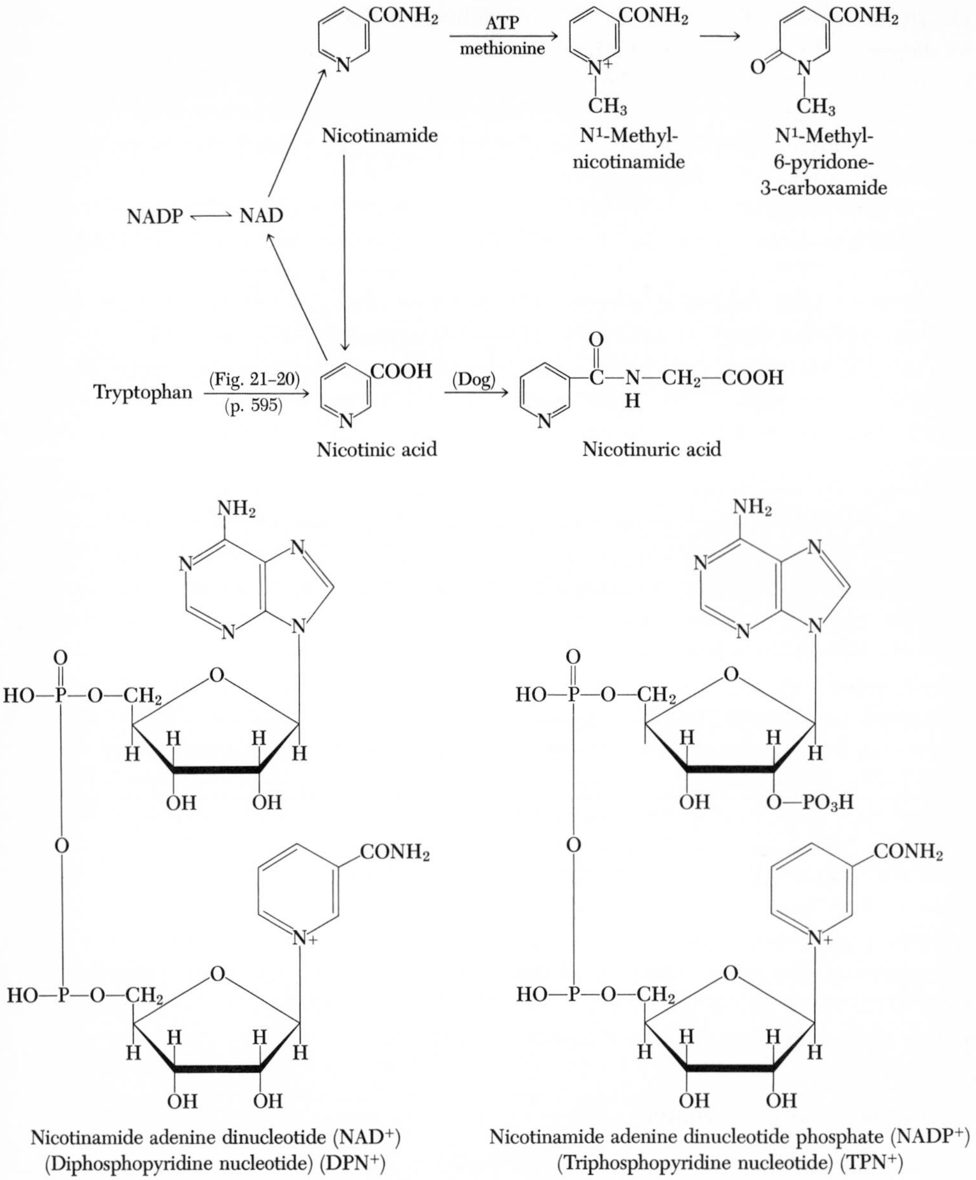

Nicotinamide → (ATP, methionine) → N^1-Methylnicotinamide → N^1-Methyl-6-pyridone-3-carboxamide

NADP ⟷ NAD

Tryptophan → (Fig. 21-20) (p. 595) → Nicotinic acid → (Dog) → Nicotinuric acid

Nicotinamide adenine dinucleotide (NAD^+)
(Diphosphopyridine nucleotide) (DPN^+)

Nicotinamide adenine dinucleotide phosphate ($NADP^+$)
(Triphosphopyridine nucleotide) (TPN^+)

Figure 7-10. Metabolism of nicotinamide. Structures of niacin-containing coenzymes.

sequence (p. 189). In higher animals, tryptophan (also hydroxyanthranilic acid) can substitute nutritionally for nicotinic acid and, in man also, administration of tryptophan is followed by increased urinary excretion of niacin metabolites (viz., N^1-methylnicotinamide).

This synthesis can be accomplished by animal tissues (e.g., rat liver) and also by certain intestinal bacteria. The latter can also apparently form nicotinic acid from other amino acids, i.e., glutamic acid, proline, ornithine, and glycine (Fig. 7-10). The dietary supply of this vitamin is therefore supplemented by its synthesis in tissues, and perhaps to a limited extent also by intestinal bacteria, in the presence of adequate provision of proteins rich in tryptophan. The increased niacin requirement incident to a high corn diet is due to the low tryptophan content of zein (maize protein). Nicotinamide is apparently not formed directly from nicotinic acid; it is formed by degradation of NAD through the action of diphosphopyridine nucleotidase (p. 525). In higher organisms, the bulk of the intracellular nicotinamide is in the form of the dinucleotide coenzymes, NAD and NADP. These are synthesized by intracellular enzymes from nicotinic acid, ribose, ATP, and glutamine (p. 525).

Metabolism

Nicotinic acid and its amide are absorbed from the intestine, the concentration in the blood plasma rising promptly after oral administration of large doses (20 mg.). Stated values for human blood are as follows: (1) whole blood, total nicotinic acid activity, 0.2 to 0.9 (av. 0.6) mg./100 ml.; (2) erythrocytes, total nicotinic acid activity, 1.3 mg./100 ml.; (3) plasma, total nicotinic acid activity, 0.025 to 0.15 (av. 0.075) mg./100 ml. Most of the nicotinic acid (or amide) in the blood is in the erythrocytes, presumably as coenzyme. The values in the blood are not altered significantly in severe niacin deficiency (i.e., in pellagra), and their determination is therefore of no value in the detection of clinical deficiency states.

The metabolism of the pyridine nucleotides (NAD, NADP) is considered elsewhere (p. 525).

Normal adults, on a normal diet, excrete both nicotinic acid and nicotinamide in the urine (0.25 to 1.25 mg., and 0.5 to 4 mg. daily, respectively). However, the major urinary metabolite is a methylated derivative, N^1-methylnicotinamide, which exhibits a bluish-white fluorescence in alkaline butanol in the ultraviolet. There may also be variable amounts of oxidation products of the latter, N^1-methyl-6-(and 4-)pyridone-3-carboxylamide (Fig. 7–10). These processes of methylation and oxidation occur in the liver. In the dog, the major urinary metabolite is nicotinuric acid (nicotinoyl glycine). In rats, administration of large amounts of nicotinic acid or nicotinamide may produce fatty liver, which is prevented by simultaneous administration of methionine, choline, or betaine (p. 505). This phenomenon is apparently due to diversion of methyl groups for the formation of N^1-methylnicotinamide. In plants, nicotinic acid undergoes N-methylation to trigonelline, the reaction being reversible.

Traces of nicotinamide are present in sweat. Small amounts are secreted in human milk, increasing from less than 0.05 mg. on the first day post partum to about 3.0 mg. on the tenth day (intake 16.5 mg. daily). Somewhat larger amounts are present in cow's milk.

Assay

Nicotinic acid can be determined by chemical and microbiological methods.

Functions

NAD and NADP function as prosthetic groups (coenzymes) for a large number of dehydrogenases (pyridinoproteins) (p. 353). The respective apoenzymes generally exhibit a distinct preference, if not an absolute requirement, for one or other of these factors. In most instances, the added hydrogen atoms (NADH; NADPH) are transferred to the riboflavin component of flavoprotein enzymes (p. 359), with the regeneration of NAD and NADP (p. 360).

The pyridinoprotein enzymes catalyze many more dehydrogenation reactions and exhibit much less hydrogen-acceptor specificity than do the flavoprotein enzymes (containing riboflavin as a prosthetic group) (p. 358). They differ from the latter also in that the redox potentials of the systems with which they are associated usually fall in the same range as those of the pyridine-coenzymes themselves. Consequently, the reactions catalyzed by these enzymes are frequently reversible under physiological conditions, e.g., with changes in the relative concentrations of reacting metabolites in the cell, or with changes in the ratio between the oxidized and reduced forms of the coenzymes.

Pharmacological Action

Unlike most vitamins, niacin and niacinamide, being pyridine derivatives, have rather marked pharmacological actions when given in relatively large doses. Both have a stimulating effect on the central nervous system. In therapeutic doses, nicotinic acid, but not nicotinamide, produces pronounced, transient vasodilatation, with flushing of the face, neck, and arms. This is accompanied by an increase in peripheral blood flow and skin temperature, with a frequently uncomfortable sense of warmth and, at times, burning and itching. There is a wide individual variation in this regard. Nicotinic acid (not nicotinamide) may reduce the plasma lipid concentration in certain cases of hyperlipemia, the mechanism being unknown.

Deficiency Manifestations

Certain of the most characteristic features of human pellagra (*pelle* = skin; *agra* = rough) are due to niacin deficiency, although the complete picture, as it occurs clinically, is dependent upon a multiple B vitamin deficiency. The cardinal symptoms of this condition have been referred to as the three "D's," i.e., dermatitis, diarrhea, and dementia. Despite the known vital role played by nicotinamide in a variety of oxidation-reduction reactions, the manifestations of deficiency cannot be correlated with the known functions of the vitamin.

The skin lesions typically involve areas exposed to sunlight and subjected to pressure, heat, chafing, and other types of trauma or irritation. These include the face, neck, dorsal surfaces of the wrists and forearms, the elbows, knees, breasts, and perineum. The skin becomes reddened, later brown, thickened, and scaly.

Gastrointestinal manifestations include: anorexia, nausea, vomiting, abdominal pain, with alternating constipation and diarrhea, the latter becoming intractable later; gingivitis and stomatitis, with reddening of the tip and margin of the tongue, which becomes swollen and cracked; achlorhydria in about 40 per cent of cases; thickening and inflammation of the colon, with cystic lesions of the mucosa, which later becomes atrophic and ulcerated; possible development of fatty liver.

Cerebral manifestations include: headache, irritability, forgetfulness, confusion, insomnia, vertigo, anxiety, depression, and other mental symptoms ranging from those of mild psychoneuroses to severe psychoses (hallucinations, delusions, mania).

General effects include: inadequate growth (children), loss of weight and strength, anemia (which may be due to associated deficiency in other B vitamins), and dehydration and its consequences (resulting from diarrhea). Niacin deficiency is aggravated by a low tryptophan intake, i.e., by diets low in protein or those in which corn furnishes the bulk of the protein.

Because of the extensive biosynthesis of niacin, niacin deficiency can be induced in certain animals only by diets deficient in protein (i.e., in tryptophan) as well as in the vitamin. The most characteristic picture develops in the dog, the outstanding feature being a condition known as "canine blacktongue," in which the mouth is dark red, with necrotic lesions in the mucosa.

Demonstration of deficiency in man. In its fully developed form the clinical picture is rather characteristic and response to administration of adequate doses of nicotinic acid or nicotinamide is prompt and dramatic. The diagnosis is usually made easily on the basis of clinical features and response to specific therapy.

Available diagnostic laboratory tests, although useful, are not entirely reliable. The most promising are based on the "saturation" principle (p. 157), in which the urinary excretion of N^1-methylnicotinamide is measured following administration of a standard test dose of nicotinic acid or nicotinamide. The amount excreted is subnormal in niacin deficiency. As is true of most "saturation tests," difficulty is encountered chiefly in the establishment of normal standards.

Requirement (Table 24-1, p. 650)

In view of present knowledge of the influence of dietary tryptophan on the nicotinic acid requirement, previous estimates of the latter must be regarded as provisional. With a completely adequate diet, ranging from 2000 to 4500 Cal., a daily niacin intake (adults) of 17 to 21 mg. has been recommended. Suggested values for children range from 6 mg. for infants to 17 mg. for pre-adolescents (10 to 12 years).

The requirement for niacin is increased under the following circumstances: increased caloric intake or expenditure; acute illness and early convalescence; after severe injury, infection, and burn.

Pyridoxine (Vitamin B_6)

With the identification of thiamine and riboflavin in the early 1930's, the multiple nature of what had been designated "vitamin B" began to be apparent. A rather characteristic dermatitis in rats, called "acrodynia," had previously been attributed to the pellagra-preventive (P-P) factor. It was soon found, however, that niacin had no preventive or curative effect on this lesion. The missing responsible substance (rat antidermatitis factor) was designated "vitamin B_6" (György). Within a few years (1938, 1939) it was isolated (yeast and liver), its chemical structure established, and its synthesis accomplished. This factor was named "pyridoxine." This term is now used as a group designation for naturally occurring pyridine derivatives possessing vitamin B_6 activity. Derivatives containing substituents in the 4-position are designated as follows: CH_2OH, pyridoxol; CHO, pyridoxal; CH_2NH_2, pyridoxamine.

Chemistry

Pyridoxol is 2-methyl-3-hydroxy-4,5-di(hydroxymethyl)-pyridine (Fig. 7–11). It occurs in nature in association, perhaps in equilibrium, with an aldehyde (pyridoxal) and an amine (pyridoxamine) form. All three forms exhibit "vitamin B_6" activity, which, however, actually resides apparently in phosphorylated derivatives, pyridoxal phosphate and pyridoxamine phosphate. These forms occur in nature largely in combination with protein (apoenzymes). The phosphorylation apparently involves the hydroxymethyl group (position 5 in the pyridine ring).

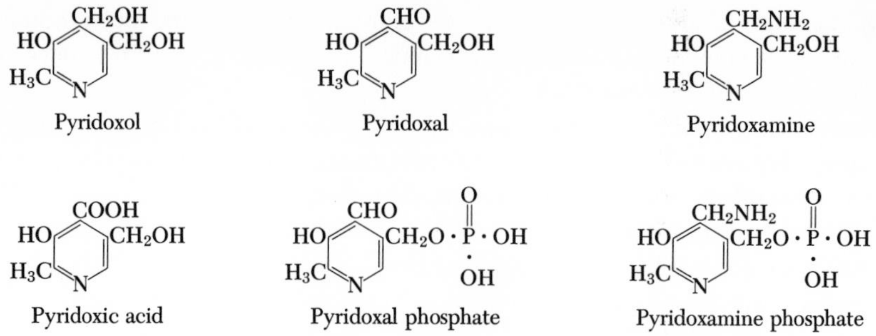

Pyridoxol

Pyridoxal

Pyridoxamine

Pyridoxic acid

Pyridoxal phosphate

Pyridoxamine phosphate

Figure 7-11. Pyridoxine and derivatives.

Occurrence and Food Sources

In common with other members of the vitamin B group, vitamin B_6 is distributed widely in animal and plant tissues. Foodstuffs containing relatively large amounts include yeast, rice polishings, the germinal portion of various seeds and cereal grains, and egg yolk. Moderate amounts are present in liver, kidney, muscle, and fish, and relatively low concentrations in milk. The highest concentrations occur in royal jelly (bee).

Although pyridoxol, pyridoxal, and pyridoxamine are nutritionally interchangeable in animals, this is not the case in all plants and microorganisms, the predominating form varying in different strains, certain of which, for example, cannot convert the base (pyridoxol) to the active aldehyde (pyridoxal). These substances are generally present as phosphorylated derivatives bound to their protein apoenzymes.

Assay

Chemical, biological, and microbiological methods are available, the last named being the most satisfactory and the most widely employed.

Biosynthesis and Metabolism

The B_6 vitamins are formed by many microorganisms, and probably also plants, but the precursors and pathways are not known. In certain dry seeds, e.g., wheat and rice, which are metabolically inactive, pyridoxol is present as a relatively inactive storage form, whereas pyridoxal and pyridoxamine predominate in metabolically active tissues. Phosphorylation to the functioning forms is apparently accomplished readily (ATP). Pyridoxol is synthesized by intestinal bacteria in several animal species, but the extent to which it is available from this source in man is questionable. Pyridoxol, pyridoxal, and pyridoxamine are nutritionally interchangeable in man, the base being apparently converted to the functionally active phosphorylated aldehyde and amine derivatives.

Although pyridoxal and pyridoxamine are excreted in the urine in small amounts (0.5 to 0.7 mg. daily), the major urinary metabolite (about 3 mg. daily) is the biologically inactive 4-pyridoxic acid (2-methyl-3-hydroxy-5-hydroxymethylpyridine-4-carboxylic acid) (Fig. 7-11). When large amounts (70 to 80 mg.) of either of the three vitamin forms are administered, 30 to 70 per cent may be excreted unchanged. Pyridoxal and pyridoxamine are also secreted in milk and sweat.

Functions

The demonstrated functions of vitamin B_6 are concerned principally with the metabolism of amino acids. In animals, the three fundamental vitamin forms, pyridoxol, pyridoxal, and pyridoxamine, are equally effective nutritionally, suggesting that they are all readily interconvertible or convertible to some functional form or forms. The active coenzyme is pyridoxal phosphate (Fig. 7–11), produced by phosphorylation (ATP) of pyridoxal.

Reversible interconversion of pyridoxal and pyridoxamine in the process of transamination has been postulated (p. 234).

Pyridoxal phosphate is a coenzyme in a number of mammalian enzyme systems catalyzing important reactions in the intermediary metabolism of amino acids: (1) transamination (cotransaminase), i.e., the reversible transfer of an α-amino group between an amino acid and an α-keto acid (p. 234); (2) decarboxylation (codecarboxylase) of at least two amino acids, viz., 3,4-dihydroxyphenylalanine (dopa) and glutamic acid (p. 582); (3) conversion of 3-hydroxykynurenine to 3-hydroxyanthranilic acid, a step in the pathway of formation of nicotinic acid from tryptophan (p. 596); (4) interconversion of glycine and serine, involving also tetrahydrofolic acid as a cofactor (p. 576); (5) transsulfurase and thionase reactions, converting homocysteine and cystathionine to cysteine (p. 584).

Pyridoxal phosphate is apparently a cofactor in the transformation of linoleic to arachidonic acid (p. 464), the mechanism of its action being unknown. It is a requirement also for synthesis of sphingosine (from serine).

Extensive functions have been demonstrated in mold and bacterial enzyme systems, e.g., in decarboxylation of several α-amino acids and in the synthesis of tryptophan from indole and serine (reversible).

It has been suggested that pyridoxine is involved in the active transport of amino acids and certain metallic ions across cell membranes, based on the following observations: (1) it can form chelate complexes with amino acids and metals; (2) it facilitates the entrance of amino acids into ascites tumor cells in vitro; (3) the concentration of amino acids in cells of pyridoxine-deficient animals is subnormal; (4) entrance of certain (but not all) metallic ions into ascites tumor cells is accelerated in the presence of pyridoxal and certain amino acids.

Deficiency Manifestations

Epileptiform convulsions in infants have been attributed to pyridoxine deficiency. These may possibly be related to lowered activity of glutamic acid decarboxylase, for which pyridoxal phosphate is a cofactor, and consequent lowering of the concentration of γ-aminobutyric acid in the brain (p. 784). Reports of symptomatic improvement following its administration in a number of clinical disorders in adults have not been convincing. These include: multiple B vitamin deficiency states (e.g., pellagra, beriberi), nausea and vomiting of pregnancy, dermatoses, certain types of anemia and neutropenia, epilepsy, X-ray sickness, paralysis agitans, pseudohypertrophic muscular dystrophy, etc. However, deficiency manifestations, especially neuritis, follow administration of the pyridoxine antagonists, deoxypyridoxine and isonicotinylhydrazide (isoniazid), the latter being used commonly in the treatment of tuberculosis.

The general manifestations of vitamin B_6 deficiency in species requiring this vitamin include inadequate growth or failure to maintain weight, anemia, leukopenia, skin lesions, nervous system symptoms, and evidence of interference in tryptophan metabolism. All of these do not occur in every species.

In the rat, the most characteristic feature is a form of dermatitis (acrodynia), involving the paws, tail, nose, mouth, and ears, with scaliness, loss of hair, and swelling. Similar lesions occur in acute deficiency in adult but not in young mice nor in other species.

Epileptiform seizures (excitement, convulsions, coma), with degenerative changes in the nervous system, occur in the dog, rat, pig, and chick. Monkeys exhibit ataxia and pigs a "goose-step" type of gait. Pyridoxine appears to be essential for normal neuronal function, deficiency being accompanied by a variety of neuropathies, e.g., myelin degeneration, in several species, including man. This may be related to its suggested functions in lipid metabolism.

Anemia occurs in the monkey, dog, pig, chick, and duck, but not in the rat. There is evidence of impaired synthesis of protoporphyrin and an increased amount of iron in the blood plasma and tissues. Poikilocytosis is a prominent feature in cattle. Lymphoid tissue (e.g., thymus, spleen) undergoes rapid involution in mice with pyridoxine deficiency.

Interference in tryptophan metabolism is reflected in increased urinary excretion of xanthurenic acid and decreased excretion of kynurenic acid (p. 596) and nicotinic acid metabolites following administration of tryptophan. Manifestations of pyridoxine deficiency are exaggerated by administration of tryptophan or a high protein diet (increased pyridoxine requirement). Atherosclerosis has been reported in the monkey. In certain species, pyridoxine deficiency may result in increased urinary excretion of endogenous oxalate (cat, rat), renal calculi of calcium oxalate (rat), and nephrocalcinosis (cat). This phenomenon is apparently related to an influence of pyridoxine in the metabolism of glycine, a source of endogenous urinary oxalate (p. 577).

Requirement

In the absence of known manifestations of vitamin B_6 deficiency in man (except infants), no accurate statement can be made regarding the dietary pyridoxine requirement. A daily intake of 2 mg. has been recommended on the basis of animal requirements. This should perhaps be increased when the protein intake is unusually high.

Pantothenic Acid

It had been recognized (1934) that a factor was present in liver and yeast which was necessary for the prevention of a rather characteristic dermatitis in chicks (chick antidermatitis factor), distinct from the rat antidermatitis factor (which proved to be pyridoxine). This unknown substance was referred to as the "filtrate factor," because it could be separated from pyridoxine by adsorbing the latter on fuller's earth.

This factor was found (1939) to resemble pantothenic acid, which had been shown (1933) to be essential for the normal growth of yeast. In a short time (1940) its chemical identity was established and its synthesis accomplished.

Chemistry

Pantothenic acid consists of β-alanine in peptide linkage with a dihydroxydimethylbutyric acid (Fig. 7–12). The free acid is soluble in water and is destroyed (hydrolyzed) by acid or alkali; it is thermolabile. Its sodium and calcium salts are fairly soluble in water, and are somewhat more stable to heat than the free acid.

In tissues, this vitamin is apparently present almost entirely in the form of coenzyme, designated coenzyme A (CoA), largely perhaps bound to proteins (apoenzymes). It may

$$CH_2OH \cdot C(CH_3)_2CHOH \cdot CO \cdot NH \cdot CH_2CH_2COOH$$
Pantothenic acid

$$\underset{\text{Aspartic acid}}{HOOC \cdot CHNH_2 \cdot CH_2 \cdot COOH} \xrightarrow{-CO_2} \underset{\beta\text{-Alanine}}{CH_2NH_2 \cdot CH_2COOH}$$

$$\underset{(\alpha\text{-ketoisovaleric acid})}{HC(CH_3)_2COCOOH} \longrightarrow \underset{\substack{\text{Pantoic acid} \\ (\alpha\text{-}\gamma\text{-dihydroxy-}\beta\text{-dimethyl-butyric acid})}}{CH_2OHC(CH_3)_2CHOHCOOH}$$

$$\beta\text{-Alanine} + \text{Pantoic acid} \longrightarrow \text{Pantothenic acid}$$

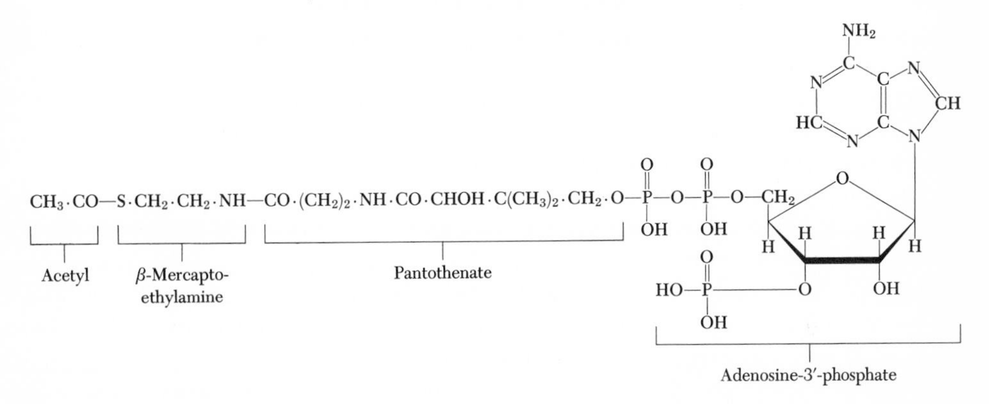

Figure 7-12. Structures of pantothenic acid and acetyl-CoA, and suggested pathway of biosynthesis of pantothenic acid.

be released from this combination by certain proteolytic enzymes, certain phosphatase preparations, and a liver enzyme system. The structure of coenzyme A (A = acetylation) has been established; the structural formula, as indicated in Figure 7-12, represents pantothenate, joined on the one hand to adenosine phosphate by a pyrophosphate bridge, and on the other hand in peptide linkage with β-mercaptoethylamine. The terminal thiol group of the latter component is apparently the reactive center of the CoA molecule, e.g., reacting with acetate to form acetyl-CoA (Fig. 7-12). The naturally occurring forms of the coenzyme probably include the reduced —SH form, oxidized —S—S— forms, and combinations of the —SH form with various metabolites, e.g., acetate, succinate (p. 473).

Occurrence and Food Sources

Pantothenic acid, mainly perhaps in bound forms, is present in all living tissues. Yeast, liver, kidney, eggs, wheat and rice bran, peanuts, and peas contain relatively large amounts; milk, beef, pork, lamb, chicken, certain fish, wheat, rye, oats, and sweet potatoes moderate amounts; most vegetables and fruits are rather poor sources. It is interesting that the richest known source of pantothenic acid is royal jelly (also rich in biotin and pyridoxine), which is responsible for the development of queen bees from bee larvae. The significance of this fact is not clear, since this vitamin alone cannot accomplish this metamorphosis.

Assay

No adequate chemical procedure is available for assay of pantothenic acid. Satisfactory microbiological methods are based on measurement of the degree of stimulation of growth of a strain of Lactobacillus arabinosus, as determined by increase in turbidity of the culture or increase in lactic acid production (titration).

Biosynthesis and Metabolism

In many microorganisms (molds, yeasts, bacteria), pantothenic acid is synthesized by direct coupling of β-alanine and pantoic acid (Fig. 7–12). β-Alanine is apparently formed by decarboxylation of aspartic acid, and pantoic acid from α-ketoisovaleric acid, via α-ketopantoic acid. The first step in the subsequent formation of coenzyme A is conjugation of pantothenic acid with cysteine. The initial series of reactions, i.e., synthesis of pantothenic acid, occurs only in microorganisms; the subsequent steps occur also in mammalian tissues. Tetrahydrofolic acid (p. 201) is a requirement for conversion of α-ketoisovalerate to α-ketopantoate (hydroxymethylation reaction).

The concentration of pantothenic acid in whole blood is 15 to 45 (av. 30) μg./100 ml.; it is somewhat higher in the cells than in the plasma. It is present in all tissues in small amounts, the highest concentrations occurring in liver (40 μg./gm. dry weight) and kidney (30 μg./gm.). These values decrease in depleted animals and can be increased above normal by administration of large amounts of the vitamin. It is secreted in the milk (200 to 300 μg./100 ml.) and sweat (3 to 4 μg./100 ml.).

The products of catabolism of pantothenic acid are not known. Under ordinary dietary conditions about 2.5 to 5 mg. are excreted daily in the urine. Normal subjects excrete (urine) about 10 per cent of an orally administered dose of calcium pantothenate within four hours. As much as 60 per cent may be recovered in the urine after intravenous injection.

Functions

Pantothenic acid is required by all animal species studied; microorganisms that are not able to effect its synthesis require an exogenous supply.

Its only demonstrated metabolic function is as a component of coenzyme A. It is therefore concerned with a number of fundamentally important metabolic reactions involving transfer of acyl groups (e.g., acetyl, butyryl, succinyl). The role of CoA in these vital reactions is considered in detail elsewhere (p. 473).

Pantothenic acid appears to be involved in adrenocortical activity, being essential to the formation of adrenocortical hormones from "active" acetate (acetyl-CoA) and cholesterol (p. 704). Pantothenic acid-deficient animals have reduced levels of adrenal cholesterol, liver glycogen, and blood glucose, and higher adrenal weights and adrenal ascorbic acid concentrations than normal animals. The adrenal functional response to stress (e.g., anoxia, formalin injection, cold) is impaired. These effects may be related perhaps to the hemorrhagic necrosis of the adrenal cortex which occurs in severe deficiency in the rat.

Deficiency Manifestations

No manifestations of pantothenic acid deficiency have been recognized in man. This may be due, in part at least, to its widespread distribution in foodstuffs and possibly, although to a limited degree, to its synthesis by intestinal bacteria. However, certain symptoms attributed to deficiency in other members of the vitamin B complex may be due to lack of this factor.

Apart from such general effects as inadequate growth, failure to maintain weight, decreased reproductive capacity (rat, hen), and fatty liver, the manifestations of pantothenic acid deficiency in experimental animals cannot be correlated readily with its known metabolic functions. Changes in the skin and hair occur in a number of species. These include: dermatitis (rat, chick) and scaling of the paws and tail (rat); loss of hair (alopecia) (rat, mouse, pig), which may be a reflection of a more complicated multiple B vitamin deficiency, e.g., inositol, biotin; circumocular (spectacle) alopecia (also in inositol deficiency); graying of the hair (rat, fox, monkey), due to atrophy of the hair apparatus and cessation of melanin deposition; depigmentation of feathers in chicks.

Nervous system manifestations include: myelin degeneration of peripheral nerves and degenerative changes in posterior root ganglia and dorsal fibers, leading to paralysis of hind quarters (mouse, dog) and uncoordinated, "goose-stepping" gait (pig); convulsions, coma (dog).

Gastrointestinal manifestations include gastritis and enteritis, with ulceration and bloody diarrhea. Fatty liver occurs in dogs and rats.

Anemia develops (monkey, dog, pig, rat) and, in severe cases, hypoplasia of the bone marrow. Hemorrhages occur beneath the skin and in the kidneys and adrenal cortex (rat). The development of "blood-caked whiskers" in rats is due to deposition of porphyrin, secreted by the harderian glands and excreted through the nasolacrimal ducts. A similar condition has been induced in rats by severe water restriction. There may also be epistaxis and ocular exudates.

Requirement

The human requirement for pantothenic acid is not known. Daily intakes of 5 to 12 mg. per 2500 Cal. have been recommended. This should perhaps be increased in the presence of severe stress (e.g., acute illness, burns, severe injury, etc.), especially when antibiotics are being given, because of the possible occurrence of adrenocortical exhaustion in states of pantothenic acid deficiency.

BIOTIN

Elucidation of the nutritional significance of biotin developed from investigations in different directions. It had been known for some years that diets rich in raw egg white produced a rather characteristic train of symptoms in the rat and chick. Cooked egg white was without effect and administration of liver or yeast protected against the toxic action of raw egg white. This protective substance was called "vitamin H."

It was recognized that yeast extracts, egg yolk, liver, and other substances contained a factor, distinct from the then known vitamins, which stimulated the growth of certain strains of yeast. This factor was called "biotin." It was also known that a factor, called "coenzyme R," was a growth essential for the nitrogen-fixing organism, Rhizobium, in the root nodules of legumes.

In 1940, it was demonstrated (György) that biotin, vitamin H, and coenzyme R were identical. The toxic factor in raw egg white was identified as a basic protein, avidin, which combines with and inactivates biotin. The chemical structure of biotin was established in 1942 (du Vigneaud) and its synthesis accomplished in 1943.

Chemistry

Biotin is a heterocyclic, S-containing, monocarboxylic acid (Fig. 7–13). There are apparently two forms (at least) with essentially identical biological activities, α-biotin (egg yolk) and β-biotin (liver), differing in the nature of the side chain.

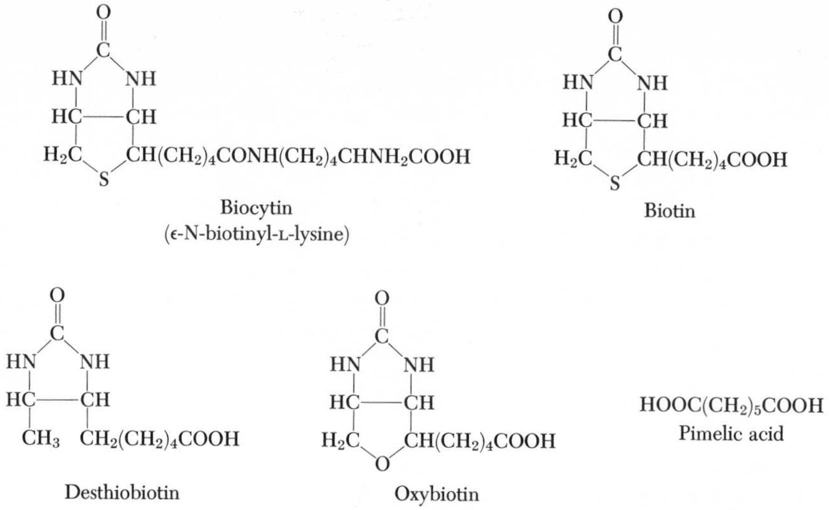

O
‖
C
HN NH
HC—CH
H_2C $CH(CH_2)_4CONH(CH_2)_4CHNH_2COOH$
S

Biocytin
(ε-N-biotinyl-L-lysine)

O
‖
C
HN NH
HC—CH
H_2C $CH(CH_2)_4COOH$
S

Biotin

O
‖
C
HN NH
HC—CH
CH_3 $CH_2(CH_2)_4COOH$

Desthiobiotin

O
‖
C
HN NH
HC—CH
H_2C $CH(CH_2)_4COOH$
O

Oxybiotin

$HOOC(CH_2)_5COOH$
Pimelic acid

Figure 7-13. Biotin and related substances.

Desthiobiotin and oxybiotin (Fig. 7-13) are biologically active in certain strains of yeast and bacteria, the former probably being converted to biotin (yeast), the latter being utilized as such (also by certain animals, e.g., chick).

By analogy with other B vitamins, biotin might be expected to occur in nature in active combined forms (i.e., coenzymes). There are indications that this is the case. One such form, biocytin, has been identified as ε-N-biotinyl-L-lysine (Fig. 7-13). A considerable portion of the biotin-active material in tissues cannot be extracted with water, suggesting its presence in some firmly bound form, probably to protein apoenzymes. Avidin, a basic protein present in egg white, forms a very stable, biologically inactive complex with biotin.

Occurrence and Food Sources

Biotin is distributed widely in nature in both plant and animal tissues. It occurs chiefly in a water-soluble form in most plant materials (except cereals and nuts), and mainly in a water-insoluble form in animal tissues and products and in yeast. Foodstuffs particularly rich in biotin include egg yolk, liver, kidney, milk, and yeast. Exceptionally large amounts are present in royal jelly (bee).

Assay

Animal assay methods have been used, but microbiological assay procedures are employed most extensively.

Biosynthesis and Metabolism

Biotin is synthesized by many bacteria, yeasts, and fungi. There is evidence that, in green plants, it may be formed in the leaf, and that the roots receive at least part of their supply from soil microorganisms. Probably much of the biotin requirement of animals, including man, is supplied by its synthesis by intestinal bacteria. This is indicated by the facts that (1) animals excrete considerably more biotin than is contained in the diet, and (2) biotin deficiency can be produced only by inhibiting growth of intestinal bacteria (sulfonamides, antibiotics), or by oral administration of avidin (raw egg white), which inactivates biotin. Pimelic acid is a possible precursor, and desthiobiotin a probable intermediate (Fig. 7-13).

Biotin may be stored to a limited extent in the liver and kidneys and is excreted in the urine and feces. It is also secreted in the milk. Normal adults on an adequate diet excrete 10 to 180 μg. daily in the urine and 15 to 200 μg. in the feces. Fecal excretion probably represents unabsorbed material. The amount in the urine increases promptly following administration of biotin. The exact nature of the urinary excretion products has not been determined. At least some of it (biologically active) is in a form which does not combine with avidin.

Functions

The physiological importance of biotin is suggested by its virtually universal distribution in plant and animal tissues. Biotin is the prosthetic group of certain enzymes that catalyze CO_2 transfer reactions, i.e., CO_2 fixation and β-decarboxylation. In mammalian tissues, these include the following: (a) acetyl-CoA carboxylase, which catalyzes carboxylation of acetyl-CoA to form malonyl-CoA (fatty acid biosynthesis, p. 459); (b) propionyl-CoA carboxylase, which catalyzes transformation of propionyl-CoA to methylmalonyl-CoA (formation of succinyl-CoA, p. 413); (c) pyruvic acid carboxylase, which catalyzes transformation of pyruvic acid to oxaloacetic acid (p. 413). Biotin is also involved in the production of acetoacetate from leucine (carboxylation of β-methylcrotonyl CoA, p. 580). Urea formation is impaired in the liver of biotin-deficient animals, owing to a decreased rate of conversion of ornithine to citrulline; the role of the vitamin in this connection is believed to be indirect.

Deficiency Manifestations

Biotin deficiency may be induced in experimental animals by inclusion of large amounts of raw egg white in the diet. The active component is a basic protein, "avidin," which combines stoichiometrically with biotin, preventing its absorption from the intestine. This complex is non-dialyzable and the biotin is not released by proteolytic enzymes. Avidin is destroyed by light and heat (i.e., cooked egg white is inactive).

The physiological significance of avidin is not clear. It is present in the albumin-secreting portion of the oviduct (hen), being increased by administration of estrogen and progesterone. The occurrence of large amounts of biotin in egg yolk and of avidin in egg white suggests some metabolic relationship, possibly of importance in reproduction. Biotin is required for normal reproduction in fowl and mice.

Manifestations of biotin deficiency, induced by feeding raw egg white or intestinal antibiotic agents, include: dermatitis (rat, pig, fowl); "spectacle-eyed" appearance (circumocular alopecia) in rats; thinning or loss of fur (alopecia) (mouse, pig, monkey); graying of black or brown fur (mouse, monkey); perosis (slipped-tendon disease in fowl); paralysis, chiefly of hind quarters (dog, cow, rat).

Human subjects given diets containing a minimal amount of biotin and large amounts of raw egg white (30 per cent of total calories) developed the following symptoms, beginning after five to seven weeks: dermatitis of the extremities, pallor of skin and mucous membranes, depression, lassitude, somnolence, muscle pains and hyperesthesia, anorexia, and nausea. There were anemia and hypercholesterolemia. All manifestations were relieved by administration of biotin.

Requirement

Because of its abundant supply by intestinal bacteria, a dietary source of biotin is of little nutritional significance except under unusual circumstances. It may assume importance during periods of oral administration of therapeutic agents which inhibit growth of intestinal bacteria (certain sulfonamides, antibiotics). Deficiency manifestations induced in human subjects by feeding large amounts of raw egg white disappeared rapidly when 100 to 300 μg. of biotin were injected daily.

Folic Acid and Vitamin B_{12}

Substances with vitamin B_{12} activity (cobalamins; anti-pernicious anemia factor) are related functionally to folic acid (pteroylglutamic acid). It seems advisable, therefore, to consider the chemistry and metabolism of these two types of substances separately, and subsequently to discuss their functions and deficiency manifestations jointly.

Folic Acid

Early studies in different fields had demonstrated the presence in liver, yeast, and certain green leafy vegetables of substances required for normal growth and nutrition of certain microorganisms and animal species. These received various designations, but when it was recognized that they are identical, the term "folic acid" (*folium* = leaf) was applied.

Chemistry (Fig. 7-14)

The designation "folic acid" is applied to a number of compounds which contain the following chemical groups: (1) a pteridine nucleus (pyrimidine and pyrazine rings), (2) *p*-aminobenzoic acid, and (3) glutamic acid. Pterin compounds are widely distributed in nature. That present in folic acid is 2-amino-4-hydroxy-6-methylpterin, joined through a methylene linkage to the amino group of *p*-aminobenzoic acid. The latter, originally regarded as a B vitamin, is now regarded as existing in nature and functioning solely as a component of the folic acid group of compounds. Acetyl-PABA occurs in the blood and urine, presumably a metabolite of folic acid. The designation "pteroyl" is applied to the "pteridyl-methylene-PABA" moiety. The amino group of *p*-aminobenzoic acid is in peptide linkage with glutamic acid. Folic acid, as it occurs in liver, is pteroylmonoglutamic acid. It occurs in nature also in the form of two polyglutamic acid conjugates, containing three and seven glutamic acid residues, respectively.

Pteroylmonoglutamic acid is liberated from these conjugates by enzymes called "conjugases." The active coenzyme form of the vitamin is the tetrahydro-derivative (tetrahydrofolic acid). Because of their lability, these occur naturally only in small amounts, being present mainly in the form of N-5 formyl or N-5 methyl derivatives (Fig. 7-14).

Biosynthesis and Metabolism

What information is available concerning the mechanism of biosynthesis of folic acid has been derived mainly from studies in microorganisms. Folic and tetrahydrofolic acids can be synthesized by most microorganisms (e.g., intestinal bacteria in man and rat)

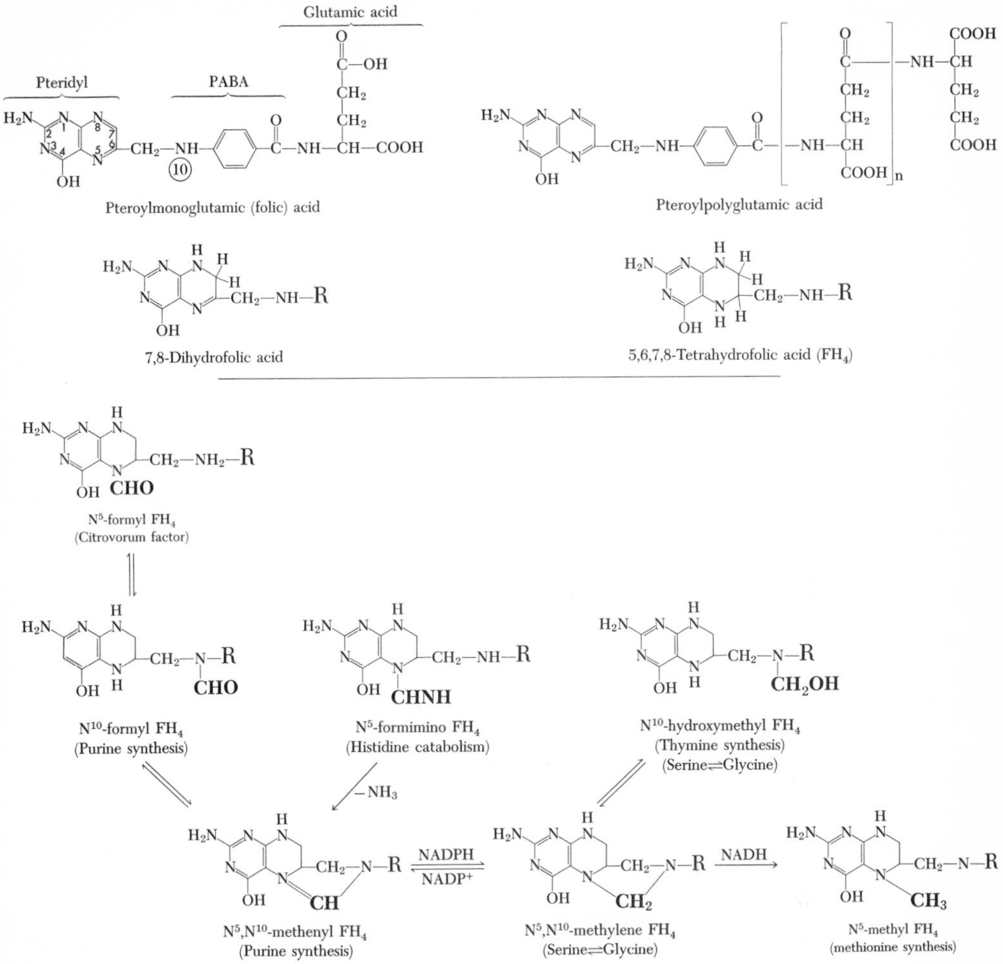

Glutamic acid
Pteridyl
PABA
Pteroylmonoglutamic (folic) acid
Pteroylpolyglutamic acid
7,8-Dihydrofolic acid
5,6,7,8-Tetrahydrofolic acid (FH_4)
N^5-formyl FH_4 (Citrovorum factor)
N^{10}-formyl FH_4 (Purine synthesis)
N^5-formimino FH_4 (Histidine catabolism)
N^{10}-hydroxymethyl FH_4 (Thymine synthesis) (Serine⇌Glycine)
$-NH_3$
NADPH
$NADP^+$
NADH
N^5,N^{10}-methenyl FH_4 (Purine synthesis)
N^5,N^{10}-methylene FH_4 (Serine⇌Glycine)
N^5-methyl FH_4 (methionine synthesis)

Figure 7-14. Folic acid and related substances. (Adapted from Beck, W. S.: New England J. Med. *266:*765, 1962.)

grown on simple synthetic media. There is evidence that, in the presence of ATP and CoA, PABA reacts with glutamic acid to form *p*-aminobenzoyl-glutamic acid. The latter can react with a pterin to produce pteroylmonoglutamic acid (folic acid). There is evidence that the pterin moiety may be derived from guanosine. Certain microorganisms require *p*-aminobenzoic acid for the formation of folic acid, synthesis of which may be blocked by sulfonamide (p. 665), i.e., by competitive inhibition. This is not the case in animals, including man, which are not known to have an independent requirement for PABA. It is believed that the primary end-product is dihydrofolic acid, not folic acid, the latter occurring in nature only because of the lability of the reduced compounds to oxidation. Dihydrofolate is reduced to tetrahydrofolate by dihydrofolate reductase. Conversion of folic acid to tetrahydro-derivatives is accomplished by folic acid reductase. NADPH is the hydrogen donor in these reactions and ascorbic acid is apparently a requirement.

Tetrahydrofolic acid serves as a carrier of one-carbon units in metabolic reactions involving transfers of these units. These carrier forms differ only in the nature of the one-carbon unit (methyl, formyl, hydroxymethyl, formimino) and the site of its attachment to the tetrahydrofolic acid molecule. (N^5,N^{10}). Two of the compounds probably exist chiefly as anhydro-derivatives, which are perhaps their active forms, i.e., hydroxymethyl-tetrahydrofolate as N^5,N^{10}-methylene-tetrahydrofolate, and formyl-tetrahydrofolate as N^5,N^{10}-methenyl-tetrahydrofolate (Fig. 7–14).

Administration of pteroylglutamic acid results in increased urinary excretion of tetrahydrofolic acid. The liver and kidneys are apparently active in this process, which is stimulated by ascorbic acid. Conversely, subjects with scurvy (ascorbic acid deficiency) excrete relatively small amounts of tetrahydrofolic acid in the urine, even after administration of folic acid. Moreover, a megaloblastic anemia (p. 158) occurs in scorbutic monkeys, which is corrected by administration of small amounts of tetrahydrofolic acid more readily than by large amounts of folic acid.

Tetrahydrofolic acid may be liberated from inactive conjugates (polyglutamic acid forms) by enzymes (conjugases) apparently identical with those which liberate pteroylmonoglutamic acid from its conjugated forms.

Under average dietary conditions, adults excrete 2.0 to 6 γ daily in the urine and 130 to 550 γ in the feces. The total amount excreted is four to seven times that contained in the diet (40 to 90 γ), the major portion obviously being contributed by intestinal microorganisms.

Occurrence

Compounds exhibiting folic acid activity are distributed widely in nature, being present in many animal and plant tissues and microorganisms. They are particularly abundant in green leafy vegetables, yeast, and liver; other green vegetables, kidney, beef, and wheat are also good sources.

Assay

Folic acid activity may be assayed in animals (growth of rat, chick) or microorganisms. The microbiological methods, which are generally preferred, usually employ Lactobacillus casei and Streptococcus fecalis as test organisms. The growth response of S. fecalis may be measured turbidimetrically and that of L. casei by titration of the increment in lactic acid.

Requirement

Nothing is known regarding human quantitative requirements for folic acid or its derivatives. This is due mainly to the fact that most if not all of our needs in this connection are supplied by synthesis of these factors by intestinal bacteria. The requirement is apparently increased during pregnancy, lactation, and early infancy (active growth).

Vitamins B_{12} (Cobalamins) (Anti-pernicious Anemia Extrinsic Factor)

It has been recognized for many years that certain animal proteins contain a growth factor (or factors) not present in vegetable foods nor in yeasts. This was termed the "animal protein factor" (APF). In 1948, a crystalline substance was isolated from liver which was found to produce clinical remission in patients with pernicious anemia and was apparently the "antipernicious anemia factor." The same substance was isolated from cultures of several microorganisms, and the material from both sources was found to possess "animal growth factor" activity in rats and chicks. As is the case with other vitamins, a number of closely related substances occur in nature possessing varying degrees of vitamin B_{12} activity. The presence of cobalt as an essential component of the molecule gave rise to the designation "cobalamins" or "cobamides" for compounds in this category.

Chemistry

The structure of cyanocobalamin (cyanocobamide), the generally available form of vitamin B_{12}, is depicted in Figure 7–15. It consists essentially of: (1) a nucleotide (5,6-dimethylbenzimidazole-1-α-D-riboside-3-phosphate), esterified through the phosphate to (2) aminopropanol, which, in turn, is attached to the propionic acid side chain of ring D of (3) a macrocyclic residue reminiscent of porphyrins (p. 121), two of the pyrrole rings of which are linked directly rather than by a methene bridge; (4) cobalt (trivalent), which occupies the center of this porphyrin-like structure ("corrin" ring system), is attached by coordinate linkages to nitrogen atoms of the latter, and also to (5) cyanide and the azole ring of the nucleotide (1). The cyanocobamides do not occur in nature in appreciable amounts; they are formed in the process of chemical isolation of the vitamin.

Apart from (a) the base component of the nucleotide and (b) the cyanide, the remainder of the molecule is common to all known substances with B_{12} activity. The CN ion may be replaced by hydroxyl (B_{12a}; hydroxocobalamin), nitrite (B_{12c}; nitritoco-

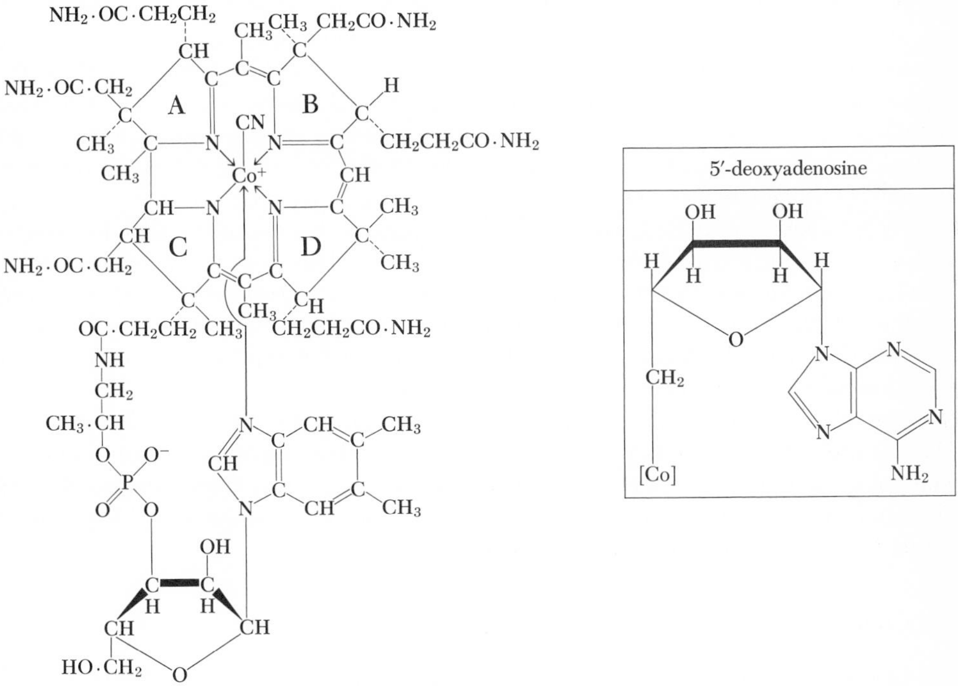

Figure 7-15. *I*, Structure of vitamin B_{12} (cyanocobalamin). *II*, In the cobamide coenzyme, 5′-deoxyadenosine replaces the CN of cyanocobalamin in covalent linkage to Co. (Adapted from Beck: New England J. Med. *266:*765, 1962.)

balamin), chloride (chlorocobalamin), or sulfate (sulfatocobalamin), all of which possess comparable activities. Members of the B_{12} group have been found in pig and calf manure, and in sludge from sewage plants; the 5,6-dimethylbenzimidazole of cyanocobalamin may be replaced by benzimidazole, 5-hydroxybenzimidazole, adenine, 2-methyladenine, hypoxanthine, or 2-methyl-hypoxanthine.

Compounds with vitamin B_{12} activity occur in animal tissues in conjugated form (with polypeptides). One of their important properties is the capacity for binding with protein, e.g., the "intrinsic factor," a phenomenon which plays an important role in absorption of the vitamin from the intestine.

Compounds with vitamin B_{12} activity occur in bacteria and animal tissues chiefly in the form of cobamide coenzymes. These differ structurally from cyanocobalamin (Fig. 7–15) mainly in that cyanide is replaced by 5-deoxyadenosine, which is attached to the central cobalt atom through the 5′- carbon atom of the deoxypentose component of the nucleoside by a covalent bond. The cobamide coenzymes probably exist in several forms, at least three of which have been identified, differing from one another with respect to the benzimidazole portion of the B_{12} molecule.

Biosynthesis and Metabolism

Cobamide compounds with vitamin B_{12} activity are synthesized by many soil microorganisms and by certain other bacteria. They are not synthesized by higher plants or animal tissues. The many types of microorganisms that are dependent upon an exogenous supply of these substances provide a basis for microbiological assay of the vitamin.

The porphyrin-like moiety (corrin ring) can be synthesized by certain microorganisms from δ-aminolevulinic acid, itself formed from glycine and succinate (p. 608). This portion of vitamin B_{12} and porphyrins have similar mechanisms of synthesis. Additional methyl groups arise from the methyl group of methionine. The aminopropanol moiety is formed by decarboxylation of threonine. The mechanism of biosynthesis of the dimethylbenzimidazole moiety has not been established. Certain bacterial enzyme systems can transform vitamin B_{12} to its coenzyme form, the adenine moiety of the added deoxyadenine nucleoside of the latter being contributed by ATP. However, it has not been established that the vitamin is a necessary intermediate in the biosynthesis of the coenzyme.

Vitamin B_{12} ("extrinsic factor") is not absorbed from the intestine in the absence of the "intrinsic factor," a non-dialyzable, thermolabile substance present in normal gastric juice and saliva, the precise nature of which is unknown, but which has mucoprotein characteristics. Pertinent information in this connection is presented elsewhere (p. 202). There is little precise information regarding its intermediary metabolism. After ingestion (man) of even large amounts (10 mg.), no vitamin B_{12} activity is detectable in the urine. This vitamin is excreted in the urine, however, after intravenous injection. It is present in the milk, the quantity increasing with increased B_{12} intake.

Occurrence

Substances with vitamin B_{12} activity are present in liver, eggs, milk, meats, and fish. The liver is apparently an important storage site. However, after feeding vitamin B_{12} (chick), the highest concentrations have been found in the kidneys, somewhat less in the liver, pancreas, and heart muscle, and low concentrations in skeletal muscle. Minute amounts are probably present in all animal cells. Peculiarly, unlike other B vitamins, B_{12} is not found in significant quantities in green plants and yeasts.

Assay

Microbiological and chemical assay procedures are available. The latter are based either on (1) determination of 5,6-dimethylbenzimidazole released by hydrolysis of the vitamin, or (2) determination of CN released from cyanocobalamin. Vitamin B_{12} may also be assayed on the basis of the hematological response of patients with pernicious anemia in relapse.

Requirement

Parenteral administration of as little as 1 γ of vitamin B_{12} daily can maintain a patient with pernicious anemia in complete remission. Several times this amount should perhaps be provided in order to insure absorption of an adequate quantity from the intestine (ileum). Although vitamin B_{12} is synthesized by intestinal bacteria, probably little if any is available to man from this source because it is produced largely in the colon, where its absorption is questionable.

Functions of Folic Acid and Vitamin B_{12}

The functional forms of these factors serve as coenzymes in certain important biological mechanisms concerned mainly with growth, development, and hemopoiesis. They are concerned specifically in the formation and utilization of single carbon units for synthetic purposes. This subject is concerned in detail elsewhere (p. 588). It will suffice here merely to outline the most important types of reactions in which these factors appear to be involved.

Reactions Involving Folic (Tetrahydrofolic) Acid

Tetrahydrofolates are the active cofactors in metabolic reactions involving one-carbon units. These include formyl (—CHO), hydroxymethyl (—CH_2OH), methyl (—CH_3), and formimino (—CH=NH) groups. These are attached to the N atoms at the 5 or 10 positions of the pteroyl structure or both (p. 197). Tetrahydrofolic acid is therefore concerned in several important reactions involving one-carbon units. These include interconversion of glycine and serine (p. 576), biosynthesis of purines (p. 515), and synthesis of methyl groups for formation of methionine and thymine. Methyltetrahydrofolic acid provides the methyl group for these methylation reactions but its transfer to homocysteine to form methionine involves also vitamin B_{12} (p. 589).

Reactions Involving Vitamin B_{12}

Cobamide coenzyme is required for conversion of methylmalonyl-CoA to succinyl-CoA by methylmalonyl-CoA isomerase. This is an important step in the major pathway of utilization of propionic acid, i.e., its conversion to succinate (p. 472). Coenzyme B_{12} is required also for a similar isomerase reaction, interconversion of glutamate and β-methylaspartate (glutamate isomerase) and also for conversion of diols to deoxyaldehydes (diol dehydrase), both of which occur only in bacterial systems. A B_{12}-containing protein is a requirement for methylation of homocysteine by 5-methyltetrahydrofolate to produce methionine in animal tissues. This reaction represents one of the important functional interrelationships between folic acid and vitamin B_{12}. There is indirect evidence that vitamin B_{12} functions in conversion (reduction) of ribonucleotides to deoxyribonucleotides.

Role in Hemopoiesis

Folic acid and vitamin B_{12} exert important effects on hemopoiesis. These are apparently related basically to the functions of these factors in nucleic acid biosynthesis. Their functions in this connection are reflected most clearly in the hematological abnormalities that characterize clinical and experimental states of deficiency in these factors, which are outlined elsewhere (p. 203).

The precise manner in which they act cannot be stated, nor can the functional relation of folic acid to vitamin B_{12}. Both act to promote development of cells of the erythroid series beyond the megaloblast stage. Inadequacy in vitamin B_{12} results in accumulation of megaloblasts in the bone marrow (arrested development) and a macrocytic type of anemia, accompanied by other features characteristic of pernicious anemia. The hematological abnormalities are corrected either by vitamin B_{12} (parenteral) or by folic acid (but not always completely by the latter). On the other hand, similar hematological manifestations resulting from folic acid deficiency are corrected by this substance but often not by vitamin B_{12}. The reasons for these similarities and differences in action are not understood. Vitamin B_{12} (but not folic acid) stimulates local maturation of megaloblasts when introduced into the bone marrow (or in marrow cultures).

Vitamin B_{12} and "Intrinsic Anti-Pernicious Anemia Factor"

According to current concepts, pernicious anemia is due to deficiency in vitamin B_{12} ("extrinsic factor"), which, under physiological conditions, is required for normal erythropoiesis beyond the stage of megaloblasts. This factor is therefore termed the "erythrocyte maturation factor," deficiency in which results in a megaloblastic type of bone marrow (p. 203).

Normal gastric juice contains a non-dialyzable thermolabile substance, the "intrinsic factor," which combines with vitamin B_{12}, the "extrinsic factor," to form a complex. The intrinsic factor has not been identified, although all active preparations have the characteristics of a mixture of mucoproteins.

Ingestion of vitamin B_{12} by patients with pernicious anemia results in excretion in the feces (unabsorbed) of 70 to 95 per cent of the amount ingested, as compared to 5 to 30 per cent of that ingested by normal subjects or by those with pernicious anemia given normal gastric juice simultaneously. No hematological effect is produced in the first instance (except with very large doses), whereas a prompt response occurs in the latter case. Vitamin B_{12}, given parenterally in minute doses (1 γ daily), is effective in producing complete remission in patients with pernicious anemia. These observations indicate that a factor present in normal gastric juice, i.e., the intrinsic factor, is required for absorption of vitamin B_{12}, i.e., extrinsic factor, from the intestine. This factor is absent from the gastric juice in pernicious anemia. The mechanism of its action is not known.

Manifestations of Deficiency of Folic Acid and Vitamin B_{12}

Vitamins of the folic acid and B_{12} groups are essential for normal growth of microorganisms and many animal species (e.g., man, monkey, rat, pig, guinea pig, dog, fowl).

Their growth effects are particularly striking in rapidly developing tissues, such as embryonic and hemopoietic, and certain types of neoplasms.

Deficiency in folic acid is produced in experimental animals most readily in two ways: (1) by feeding certain sulfonamides, which inhibit growth of intestinal bacteria (by blocking PABA utilization) and, therefore, folic acid synthesis; (2) by administration of certain inhibitory analogs of folic acid (e.g., aminopterin) (p. 674). Abnormalities of blood formation are outstanding clinical features of folic acid deficiency. Other manifestations include growth retardation, weakness, lethargy, reproduction difficulties (infertility [female], fetal resorption, congenital abnormalities), and inadequate lactation. The bone marrow shows evidences of arrested development of all elements (erythroid, myeloid, thrombocytes). Megaloblasts and myeloblasts accumulate at the expense of more mature cells, viz., erythroblasts, normoblasts, and myelocytes. The number of megakaryocytes decreases. The peripheral blood picture reflects these production defects, being characterized by one or more of the following, depending mainly on the degree of deficiency: a macrocytic type of anemia, at times with normoblasts, erythroblasts, and megaloblasts; granulocytopenia, occasionally with myelocytes; thrombocytopenia.

On the basis chiefly of prompt response to specific replacement therapy, the following clinical conditions have been attributed to folic acid deficiency:

(1) Nutritional macrocytic anemia (dietary deficiency).

(2) Megaloblastic anemia of infancy (dietary deficiency).

(3) Megaloblastic anemia of pregnancy (mechanism unknown; relative deficiency?).

(4) Macrocytic anemia in liver disease (inadequate storage or conversion?).

(5) Megaloblastic anemia in celiac disease and sprue (inadequate absorption) (also of B_{12}).

(6) Macrocytic anemia after extensive intestinal resection (inadequate absorption).

Vitamin B_{12} is usually not very effective in the treatment of these conditions (except sprue and celiac disease) in the majority of cases. On the other hand, folic acid produces improvement in the hematological abnormalities of vitamin B_{12} deficiency, although often not completely. It is also apparently required for a full response to vitamin B_{12}. However, folic acid has no beneficial effect on the neurological manifestations of B_{12} deficiency, for the prevention or treatment of which this vitamin is specifically required (i.e., in pernicious anemia).

The general and hematological manifestations reviewed above occur also in experimental and clinical vitamin B_{12} deficiency. In addition, other important features appear, particularly in man: (1) mucosal atrophy and inflammation of the tongue (glossitis), mouth (stomatitis), and pharynx (pharyngitis); (2) degenerative lesions of the posterior and lateral columns of the spinal cord (combined system disease), resulting in peripheral sensory disturbances, hyperactive reflexes, ataxia, and paralysis. These, with the hematological manifestations, comprise the clinical picture of pernicious anemia. In its spontaneously occurring form in man, this is due usually to absence of intrinsic factor in the gastric juice (atrophy of gastric mucosa) and consequent lack of intestinal absorption of adequate amounts of vitamin B_{12}.

Pernicious anemia may occur also following total gastrectomy (removal of intrinsic factor) and extensive resections of small intestine (decreased absorptive surface). The therapeutic response in certain patients with celiac disease and sprue (idiopathic steatorrhea) suggests defective absorption of vitamin B_{12}, as well as of folic acid, in these conditions. A megaloblastic type of anemia, responsive to vitamin B_{12} therapy, occurs in infestation with the fish tapeworm (Diphyllobothrium latum), which takes up unusually large amounts of the vitamin, creating a deficiency in the host.

INOSITOL

Inclusion of inositol in the category of vitamins rests mainly on the relatively few manifestations of deficiency that develop in mice (and possibly rats), and on the fact that it is a growth essential for certain strains of yeasts, molds, and fungi. On the other hand, it occurs in animal and plant tissues (phosphatides) in much larger amounts than do substances classified as vitamins. Moreover, no catalytic function has yet been demonstrated for inositol. Its status as a B vitamin is therefore questionable.

Chemistry

Inositol is a cyclic compound, hexahydroxycyclohexane (empirical formula $C_6H_{12}O_6$). It may be regarded as a cyclicized glucose, the aldehyde group of which has been converted to a secondary alcohol group, with linkage of carbon atoms 1 and 6 (p. 11). The term is applied to a group of stereoisomers (at least nine), four of which have been identified in biological materials, and three others synthesized. These are sometimes referred to as "the inositols." The form occurring most commonly in nature, the only isomer shown to have important biological activity, is commonly designated "myo-," "meso-," or "*i*-inositol," or simply "inositol." It has two *meta*-positioned OH groups in one spatial plane and the other four in a different plane with respect to the cyclohexane ring.

Inositol

Because of its alcoholic nature it forms esters, the most important of which, biologically, are the phosphoric acid esters, which are distributed widely in nature. The hexaphosphoric acid ester is "phytic acid." One of the important chemical properties of phytic acid is its capacity for forming highly insoluble salts with calcium and magnesium (phytin) in the intestine, thus diminishing absorption of these elements (p. 632) (rachitogenic action).

Occurrence and Food Sources

Inositol is present in many plants, microorganisms, and animal tissues, occurring sometimes in free, but mainly in combined, forms. Hexaphosphoric acid esters comprise the bulk of the latter, usually in the form of mixed calcium and magnesium salts (phytin). These may account for as much as 85 per cent of the phosphorus of seeds and cereal grains, in which they occur in high concentrations (also mono-, di-, and triphosphoric acid esters). Inositol occurs in animal tissues, mainly in combination with phosphoric acid, but as esters containing less than six phosphate groups (except avian erythrocytes). Highest concentrations of inositol in man are found, in decreasing order, in brain, stomach, kidney, spleen, and liver; smaller amounts are present in blood, muscle (high in heart muscle), and other tissues.

Inositol is present in plants (e.g., soybeans) as a constituent of phosphatides ("inositides") (p. 38), replacing glycerol as the polyalcohol component. Inositides have been found also in yeasts, tubercle bacilli, brain and spinal cord (cephalins), and liver.

Biosynthesis and Metabolism

The structural relation of inositol to glucose raises the possibility of a metabolic relationship between these substances. This may be of a dual nature: (1) glucose (by cyclization) may serve as a precursor in the synthesis of inositol; (2) inositol may be converted to glucose in the body. Evidence on both points is suggestive but inconclusive, at least for animals. Inositol has been found to alleviate ketosis (rat) produced by dietary carbohydrate restriction and to give rise to small amounts of glucose (up to 7 per cent) in phlorizinized rats. There is evidence also of conversion of inositol to glucuronates.

Free inositol is readily absorbed from the intestine, as are inositol-containing phosphatides. Salts of the phosphoric acid esters are also absorbed, the monophosphate apparently more rapidly than free inositol. It is probable that phytates (hexaphosphates) are at least partially hydrolyzed in the intestine, the extent varying in different species and with different diets. Phosphorus from this source is partially utilizable by man. In certain species (e.g., mouse, rat), synthesis by intestinal bacteria provides an adequate and available supply of inositol to the organism. This is possibly the case also in man.

Functions, Actions, Deficiency Manifestations

Apart from the fact that inositol is a component of certain phosphatides, there is little precise knowledge of its physiological actions (if any) or functions. Certain aspects of its possible role in nutrition are suggested by the consequences of experimentally induced deficiency and by its influence on cholesterol metabolism and liver fat.

No manifestations attributable to inositol deficiency have been recognized in man. In the mouse, inositol deficiency causes loss of hair, growth retardation, and even death. In certain strains, pantothenic acid is necessary, and in other strains *p*-aminobenzoic acid, in addition to inositol, for prevention of the alopecia.

Lipotropic action **(*p. 503*).** Rats fed low-protein, fat-free diets containing B vitamins other than inositol develop fatty liver which is prevented or corrected by administration of inositol. Addition of fat to the diet prevents this lipotropic effect of inositol, whereas choline is effective under such circumstances.

The mechanism underlying the lipotropic action of inositol is not clear. The fact that it is a component of certain phosphatides suggests that this may be an important factor in this connection, as is believed to be the case with choline. It has been suggested that inositol, glycerol, and cholesterol, all of which form esters with fatty acids, may compete with one another for combination with the latter or with certain fatty acids preferentially.

α-Lipoic Acid

The water-insoluble fraction of liver (also yeast) remaining after removal of known B vitamins contains certain bacterial growth factors. One of these was originally designated the "pyruvate oxidation factor" (POF) because it is required for oxidative decarboxylation of pyruvate by Streptococcus fecalis. The term "protogen A" was applied to a factor necessary for the growth of the protozoan, Tetrahymena gelii. A factor that can replace acetate for growth of Lactobacillus casei was called "L. casei acetate factor." The substance responsible for these actions is 6,8-dithio-octanoic acid (6-thioctic acid), called "α-lipoic acid."

$$\begin{array}{ccc} & H_2 & \\ & C & \\ H_2C & & CH(CH_2)_4COOH \\ | & & | \\ S & \text{---} & S \end{array}$$

α-Lipoic acid

Lipoic acid is a necessary cofactor in oxidative decarboxylation of α-keto acids, e.g., of pyruvate (forming acetyl-CoA) and α-ketoglutarate (forming succinyl-CoA). In these reactions, lipoic acid functions in conjunction with thiamine pyrophosphate and serves as an acyl-generating, an acyl-transferring, and a hydrogen-transferring agent (p. 361).

Choline (p. 504)

There seems to be no justification for regarding choline as a vitamin, although it was originally considered a member of the B complex. The manifestations associated with choline deficiency are apparently mainly reflections of deficiency in labile methyl groups (p. 588) and, perhaps, of the role of choline as a structural component of phosphatides (p. 37). Choline has a wide distribution in nature, chiefly in lecithin, the largest amounts occurring in nervous tissue, egg yolk, liver, kidney, and heart. Acetylcholine plays an important role in the transmission of nerve impulses (p. 785).

The most important manifestations of choline deficiency in mammalian species are (a) fatty liver, (b) hemorrhagic necrosis of the kidney, (c) anemia, and (d) hypoproteinemia. The last two, which may lead to edema, may also occur in the rat under certain experimental conditions.

Fatty liver occurs in several species maintained on choline-deficient, low-methionine, high-fat diets (p. 503). The mechanism of its production is not clear, but it may be related to the occurrence, in choline-deficient animals, of: (a) reduction in the rate of turnover of tissue phospholipids, and (b) depression of in vitro oxidation of long-chain fatty acids. In some cases this condition may lead to cirrhosis of the liver and, occasionally, malignancy.

Weanling rats given a choline-deficient diet develop, within a few days, a usually fatal hemorrhagic necrosis of the kidneys, preceded by accumulation of fat in the renal tubular epithelial cells and vascular stasis. The underlying mechanism is not known, but it, too, may be related to the role of choline in lipid metabolism.

BIBLIOGRAPHY

GENERAL

Annual Review of Biochemistry.
Annual Review of Physiology.
Bourne, G. H., and Kidder, G. W.: Biochemistry and Physiology of Nutrition, Vols. 1 and 2, New York, Academic Press, Inc., 1953.

Brown, G. M.: Biosynthesis of water-soluble vitamins and derived coenzymes, Physiol. Rev. *40*:331, 1960.
Follis, R. H., Jr.: Deficiency Disease, Springfield, Ill., Charles C Thomas, 1958.
Goodwin, T. W.: The Biosynthesis of Vitamins and Related Compounds, New York, Academic Press, Inc., 1963.
Heinz Handbook of Nutrition, New York, McGraw-Hill Book Co., 1965.
Jolliffe, N., ed.: Clinical Nutrition, New York, Paul B. Hoeber, Inc., 1962.
Recommended Dietary Allowances, Pub. 1146, National Academy of Sciences, Washington, D.C., 1963.
Sebrell, W. H., Jr., and Harris, R. S.: The Vitamins, 3 volumes, New York, Academic Press, Inc., 1954.
Vitamins and Hormones (annual volumes), New York, Academic Press, Inc.
Wagner, A. F. and Folkers, K.: Vitamins and Coenzymes, New York, Interscience Publishers, Inc., 1964.

VITAMIN A

General references.
Deuel, H. J., Jr.: The Lipids. Their Chemistry and Biochemistry, Vol. 1, Chemistry, New York, Interscience Publishers, Inc., 1951, p. 667.
Karrer, P., ed.: Symposium on vitamin A, Vitamins and Hormones *18*:291, 1960.
Lowe, J. S., and Morton, R. A.: Some aspects of vitamin A metabolism, Vitamins and Hormones *14*:97, 1956.
Mackinney, G.: Carotenoids and Vitamin A, in Greenberg, D. M. (ed.): Metabolic Pathways, Vol. 1, New York, Academic Press, Inc., 1960, p. 481.
Moore, T.: Vitamin A, Amsterdam, Elsevier Publishing Co., 1957.
Wald, G.: Vision, Federation Proc. *12*:606, 1953.

VITAMIN C

General references.
Bourne, G. H.: Vitamin C and Bone, in Bourne, G. H. (ed.): The Biochemistry and Physiology of Bone, New York, Academic Press, Inc., 1956, p. 539.
Burns, J. J.: Ascorbic Acid, in Greenberg, D. M. (ed.): Metabolic Pathways, Vol. 1, New York, Academic Press, Inc., 1960, p. 341.
Burns, J. J., ed.: Vitamin C, Ann. New York Acad. Sci. *92*:1, 1965.
King, C. G.: Vitamin C, J.A.M.A. *142*:363, 1950.
Knox, W. E.: Symposium 11, International Congress Biochemistry, 4th Meeting, Vienna, 1958.
Meiklejohn, A. P.: Physiology and biochemistry of ascorbic acid, Vitamins and Hormones *11*:62, 1953.

VITAMIN D

General references.
Albright, F., and Reifenstein, E. C., Jr.: Parathyroid Glands and Metabolic Bone Disease, Baltimore, Williams & Wilkins Company, 1948.
Deuel, H. J., Jr.: The Lipids: Their Chemistry and Biochemistry, Vol. 1, Chemistry, New York, Interscience Publishers, Inc., 1951, p. 739.
Harris, L. J.: Vitamin D and Bone, in Bourne, G. H. (ed.): The Biochemistry and Physiology of Bone, New York, Academic Press, Inc., 1956, p. 581.
Jeans, P. C.: Vitamin D, J.A.M.A. *143*:177, 1950.
Nicolaysen, R.: Physiology of calcium metabolism, Physiol. Rev. *33*:424, 1953.
Wilson, D. R.: Studies in hypophosphatemic vitamin D-refractory osteomalacia in adults, Medicine *44*:99, 1965.

VITAMIN E

General references.
Deuel, H. J., Jr.: The Lipids: Their Chemistry and Biochemistry, Vol. 1, Chemistry, New York, Interscience Publishers, Inc., 1951, p. 373.
Hickman, K. C. D., and Harris, P. L.: Tocopherol interrelationships, Advances Enzymol. *6*:469, 1946.
Karrer, P., ed.: Symposium on vitamin E, Vitamins and Hormones *20*:375, 1962.

VITAMIN K

General references.
Dam, H.: Vitamin K, Vitamins and Hormones *6*:28, 1948.
Deuel, H. J., Jr.: The Lipids: Their Chemistry and Biochemistry, Vol. 1, Chemistry, New York, Interscience Publishers, Inc., 1951, p. 829.
Isler, O., and Wiss, O.: Chemistry and biochemistry of the K vitamins, Vitamins and Hormones *17*:54, 1959.

B VITAMINS (GENERAL)

General vitamin references.
Robinson, F. A.: The Vitamin B Complex, New York, John Wiley & Sons, Inc., 1951.
Symposia on Vitamin Metabolism, Nutrition Symposium Series Nos. 12 and 13, New York, The National Vitamin Foundation, 1956.

Williams, R. J., Eakin, R. E., Beerstecher, E., Jr., and Shive, W.: The Biochemistry of B Vitamins, New York, Reinhold Publishing Corporation, 1950.

THIAMINE

General B vitamin references.
Jansen, B. C. P.: The physiology of thiamine, Vitamins and Hormones *7*:84, 1949.
Wuest, H. M., ed.: Unsolved problems of thiamine, Ann. New York Acad. Sci. *98*:383, 1962.

RIBOFLAVIN

General B vitamin references.

NIACIN (NICOTINIC ACID)

General B vitamin references.
Handler, P.: Symposium 11, International Congress Biochemistry, 4th Meeting, Vienna, 1958, Preprint No. 9.
Krehl, W. A.: Niacin in amino acid metabolism, Vitamins and Hormones *7*:111, 1949.

PYRIDOXINE

General B vitamin references.
György, P., ed.: International symposium on vitamin B_6, Vitamins and Hormones *22*:361, 1964.
Snell, E. E.: Chemical structure in relation to biological activities of vitamin B_6, Vitamins and Hormones *16*:78, 1958.

PANTOTHENIC ACID

General B vitamin references.
Lipmann, F.: On chemistry and function of coenzyme A, Bacteriol. Rev. *7*:1, 1953.

BIOTIN

General B vitamin references.
Lichstein, H. C.: Functions of biotin in enzyme system, Vitamins and Hormones *9*:27, 1951.
Mistry, S. P. and Dakshinamurti, K.: Biochemistry of biotin, Vitamins and Hormones *22*:1, 1964.
Terroine, T.: Physiology and biochemistry of biotin, Vitamins and Hormones *18*:1, 1960.

FOLIC AND FOLINIC ACID GROUPS AND VITAMIN B_{12}

General B vitamin references.
Beck, W. S.: The metabolic functions of vitamin B_{12}, New England J. Med. *266*:708, 765, 814, 1962.
European Symposium on Vitamin B_{12} and Intrinsic Factor, Stuttgart, Germany, Ferdinand Enke Verlag, 1961.
Glass, J. B. J.: Gastric intrinsic factor and its function in the metabolism of vitamin B_{12}, Physiol. Rev. *43*:529, 1963.
Huennekens, F. M., Osborn, M. J., and Whiteley, H. R.: Folic acid coenzymes, Science *128*:120, 1958.
Hutchings, B. L., and Mowat, J. H.: The chemistry and biological action of pteroylglutamic acid and related compounds, Vitamins and Hormones *6*:1, 1948.
Hutner, S. H., Nathan, H. A., and Baker, H.: Metabolism of folic acid and other pterin-pteridine vitamins, Vitamins and Hormones *17*:2, 1959.
Johnson, A. W., and Todd, A.: Chemistry of vitamin B_{12}, Vitamins and Hormones *15*:1, 1957.
Jukes, T. H.: Pteroylglutamic acid and related compounds, Physiol. Rev. *28*:51, 1948.
Perlman, D., ed.: Vitamin B_{12} coenzymes, Ann. New York Acad. Sci. *112*:547, 1964.
Petering, H. J.: Folic acid antagonists, Physiol. Rev. *32*:197, 1952.
Shive, W.: B-vitamins involved in single carbon unit metabolism, Federation Proc. *12*:639, 1953.
SubbaRow, Y., et al.: Folic acid, Ann. New York Acad. Sci. *48*:255, 1946.
Weissbach, H. and Dickerman, H.: Biochemical role of vitamin B_{12}, Physiol. Rev. *45*:80, 1965.

INOSITOL

General B vitamin references.
Hawthorne, J. N.: The biochemistry of the inositol lipids, Vitamins and Hormones *22*:57, 1964.

α-LIPOIC ACID

Bessey, O. A., Lowe, H. J., and Salomon, L. L.: Water-soluble vitamins, Ann. Rev. Biochem. *22*:545, 1953, p. 598.
Kidder, G. W. (Chairman): Symposium on the metabolic role of lipoic acid, Federation Proc. *13*:695, 1954.
Reed, L. J.: Biochemistry of lipoic acid, Vitamins and Hormones *20*:1, 1962.

CHAPTER 8

ENZYMES

INTRODUCTION

THE MAJOR task of metabolism is to provide energy for the maintenance of life. This is accomplished by degrading chemical compounds of relatively high potential energy to products of low potential energy. The energy evolved in such processes is collected, stored, and utilized by the cell for those functions, the totality of which we call "life."

Certain limitations are placed upon the chemical reactions of the body, owing to the necessity of preserving a "physiological" environment in the tissues. Thus, the pH cannot vary far from neutrality (in many parts of the body a pH of 7.4 is maintained), temperatures cannot exceed 37° or 38° C., and corrosive or poisonous reagents must not be used. The oxidation of a fatty acid to carbon dioxide and water in the test tube is not a gentle process; extremes of pH, high temperatures, and corrosive chemicals are required. Yet, in the body, such a reaction goes on smoothly and rapidly under the restricted conditions enumerated above. This remarkable state of affairs is explained by the presence in the body of a group of powerful catalysts, the enzymes.

The phenomenon of catalysis can be explained by referring to the diagram in Figure 8–1. *A* represents a molecule which can undergo cleavage to the products *C*. Since *A* is at a higher potential energy level than *C*, the conversion $A \rightarrow C$ should be spontaneous and occur with the liberation of energy. Actually, the fact that a reaction is spontaneous does not guarantee that it will proceed at a significant rate. The conversion of the reactant to the products requires rupture of the bond which connects the two parts of the original molecule. Final cleavage of this bond is preceded by a "loosening" process, involving transformation of the molecule *A* to the form *B*, often called the "activated complex." Since the activated molecule *B* is at a somewhat higher potential energy level than *A*, it is obvious that an initial "push" must be given to *A* before any reaction can occur.

In any large collection of molecules, some will have higher energies than others, owing to energy transfers between molecules and for other reasons. Hence, at ordinary temperatures and in the absence of other influences, certain molecules of the *A* type will acquire enough energy to reach the activated state. The conversion to *C* will proceed, but possibly at a slow rate. The addition of a catalyst to the system will speed up the reac-

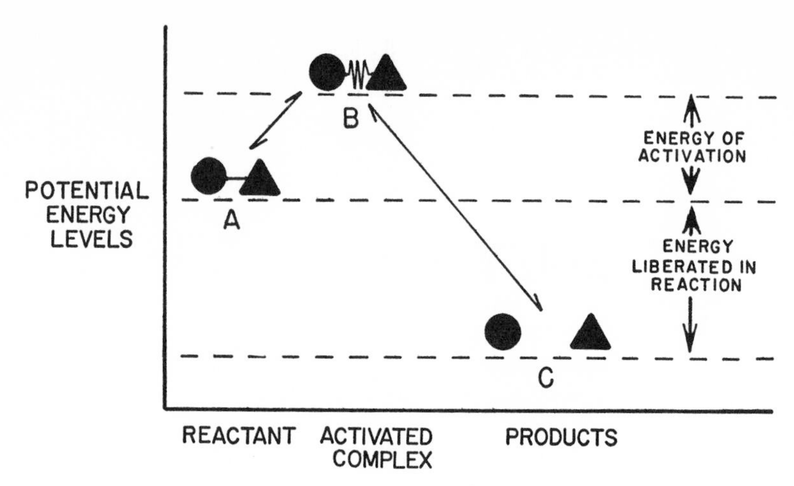

Figure 8-1. Activation of reactants.

tion, facilitating the conversion of *A* to *B* by actually lowering the amount of energy required in the initial "push" to reach the activated state.

As shown in the diagram, it is possible for the products of the reaction to recombine and re-form the reactant. Since this requires an input of energy equal to that liberated in the forward reaction, plus an extra increment of energy for activation, the rate of this reverse reaction will be low. At equilibrium, therefore, the ratio of products to reactant will be high in this particular example. The point of equilibrium is determined by the potential energy difference between the reactant and the products. Catalysts do not affect the position of this equilibrium; they merely hasten its attainment, since they influence equally the transformation of either reactant or products to the activated complex.

Although this discussion is confined to catalysis and does not attempt to cover chemical kinetics in general, it may be pointed out that factors in addition to the energy of activation enter into the determination of the rate of a reaction. In particular, a steric or probability factor is involved, which is a function of the degree of structural disorder or "randomness" of the activated state compared to that of the reactants.

Although the catalysts in non-living systems seem to possess a variety of chemical structures (hydrogen ions, spongy platinum, etc.), all enzymes which have been secured in a pure state have proved to be proteins. They therefore exhibit all of the attributes of proteins, such as denaturation and precipitation with salts, solvents, and other reagents, and are of colloidal dimensions. Many enzymes belong to the class of simple proteins, while others contain firmly bound non-protein groups, hence are conjugated proteins. The digestive enzymes are liberated into the digestive tract from the cells which synthesize them, and are called "extracellular enzymes." Most other enzymes are intracellular. The specific nomenclature of enzymes is discussed in a later section.

GENERAL MECHANISMS OF ENZYME ACTION

Enzyme-Substrate Combination

The substrate is the compound the chemical transformation of which is catalyzed by the enzyme. It seems quite possible that all catalytic reactions involve a temporary union of the substrate with the catalyst. At any rate, there is direct evidence that such combinations occur in the case of enzymatic catalysis. These compounds of enzyme and substrate, many of which have been shown to involve actual covalent bonding, sometimes are stable enough to isolate. They are frequently called "Michaelis" complexes, since combinations of this sort were postulated by Michaelis and coworkers in their theoretical analysis of enzyme kinetics. After formation of the Michaelis complex, some sort of "activation" of the substrate takes place while it is still situated on the enzyme surface. The activated complex referred to in the previous section probably exists as this sort of combination when a catalyst is present. Figure 8–2 illustrates the concepts involved. The enzyme (a protein) has on its surface a reactive site into which the substrate can fit. Due to one or more of several possible causes, the bond in the substrate is "activated" to the point of rupture, liberating the reaction products into the solution and thus regenerating the original enzyme molecule. In this way one enzyme molecule can catalyze the transformation of many substrate molecules.

The exact role played by the enzyme, or more specifically by its catalytically active site(s), in the foregoing sequence of events is still uncertain. Among the functions which have been proposed is the "proximity-orientation" effect, in which the catalytically active and the binding sites of the enzyme orient properly and bring into close proximity with each other the various reactants, including substrate, cofactors, and any acceptor molecules which may be required. Formation of a covalently bound intermediate, when it occurs, may be one aspect of this function. In place of, or in addition to, this covalent binding, chemical groups in the enzyme may induce non-covalent electron polarization in the substrate, leading to labilization of bonds. Due to one or both of the foregoing factors, distortion or "strain" may occur in the substrate. From a contrary viewpoint, evidence has been offered which suggests that the catalytically active and binding sites of the enzyme are flexible to some extent, and that an "induced fit" of enzyme to substrate occurs.

One characteristic which distinguishes enzymes from the usual catalysts in non-living systems is their high degree of specificity. Hydrogen ions, for instance, will catalyze with complete impartiality the hydrolysis of glycosides and that of peptides, whereas totally different enzymes are required for these two reactions. In addition, the enzymes show considerable specificity toward the groups surrounding the bond which is split or formed, even to the point of requiring a certain stereochemical configuration (e.g., D and L isomerism). It is obvious that this specificity must be due to the chemical nature of the groups at the site of action on the enzyme surface, to their disposition in space, and to the nature of their electrical charges.

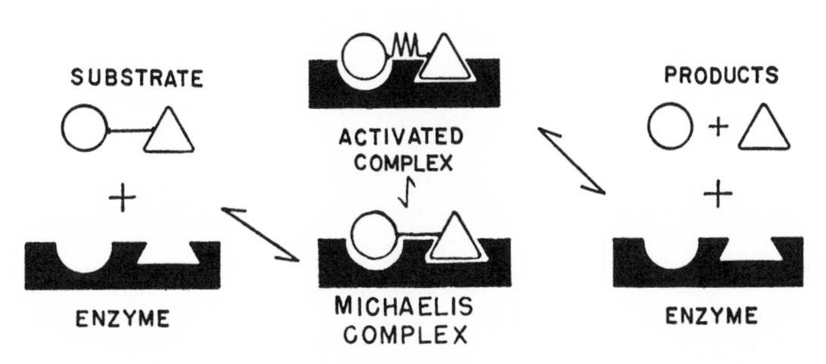

Figure 8–2. Enzyme action.

Intensive investigations are being conducted at the present time on the nature of the groups at the active site, and on the intimate mechanism of combination with substrate. Through the use of certain inhibitors which phosphorylate (diisopropylfluorophosphate) or acylate the group which normally combines with substrate at the active site, it has been found that the hydroxyl group of serine appears to be involved in the case of a number of endopeptidases, esterases, and mutases. In fact, in a number of these cases, the sequence of amino acid residues surrounding the serine is identical. Other studies, however, implicate the imidazole side chain of histidine in the active site. It has been suggested that folding of the peptide chains in the tertiary organization of the enzyme may bring an imidazole residue in close proximity to a serine hydroxyl, resulting in the formation of a hydrogen-bonded structure, thus providing both an acidic and a basic group as required by current theories of hydrolysis. Other combinations which have also been proposed for the active sites of hydrolytic enzymes include the thiol ester, acyl-imidazole, and acyl-phenolic bonds. It should be noted that the combination of an acidic and a basic group, each with its characteristic pK value, is in agreement with the explanation proposed for the effect of pH on the reaction rates of enzyme systems.

Investigation of a number of enzymes has revealed that many contain only one catalytically active site per enzyme molecule. A few seem to contain several sites, sometimes as many as four.

Mechanism of Action of a Typical Enzyme: Acetylcholine Esterase

Hydrolysis is one of the most common reactions catalyzed by enzymes. Broadly speaking, this reaction may also be considered a transfer of a chemical group to water as an acceptor. Although hydrolytic enzymes (hydrolases) and transferring enzymes (transferases) are separated for purposes of classification, there is every indication that the same fundamental mechanism underlies their actions. Furthermore, under appropriate conditions, hydrolases are able to transfer chemical groups to acceptors other than water, and transferases often catalyze hydrolysis as a side reaction. Therefore, detailed consideration of a typical hydrolase (the esterase hydrolyzing acetylcholine) may serve as an example of the sort of mechanism which may be expected to occur during the action of a great number of enzymes.

From the cationic group required of substrates and many inhibitors, it has been con-

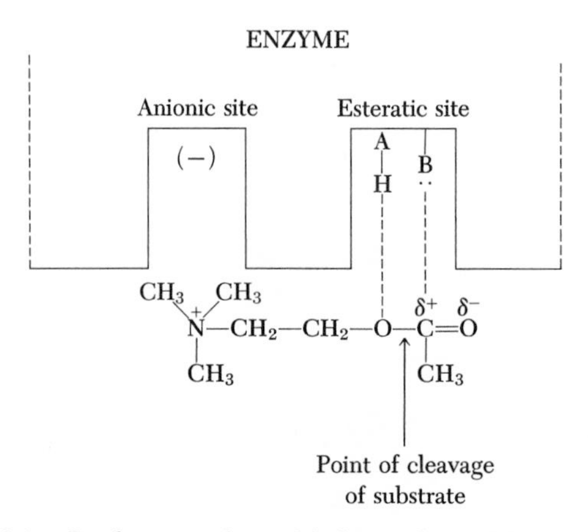

Figure 8-3. Combination of acetylcholine and acetylcholine esterase.

cluded that one of the important binding sites on the esterase surface is anionic. Binding forces of the van der Waals type between the methyl groups of the substrate and hydrocarbon groups of the enzyme also are important in this area. Consideration of the electronic mechanism of ester hydrolysis, permissible structures of substrates, and the structures of certain types of inhibitors (fluorophosphates, p. 668) leads to the surmise that the site of hydrolysis (the "esteratic" site) is located about 5.1 Å from the anionic site and contains two groups, one acidic (proton donor) and one basic (proton acceptor, electron donor). Studies of the pH dependence of the reaction rate have led to calculation of the pK's of these groups as 10.5 and 6.5. Consequently, the combination of acetylcholine and its esterase may be illustrated as in Figure 8–3. (The small positive and negative charges indicated for the acyl carbon and carbonyl oxygen atoms of the substrate, respectively, are those familiar from electronic considerations of organic structure and reactivity.)

The normal hydrolytic reaction may be pictured as occurring in two steps, as follows:

(1)

$$\begin{array}{cc} \mathrm{A} & \\ \mathrm{H} & \ddot{\mathrm{B}} \\ \vdots & \vdots \\ \mathrm{O}- & \mathrm{C{=}O} \\ | & | \\ \mathrm{R} & \mathrm{CH_3} \end{array} \rightleftharpoons \begin{array}{c} \mathrm{A^-} \\ \\ \mathrm{H} \\ | \\ \mathrm{O} \\ | \\ \mathrm{R} \end{array} + \begin{array}{c} \mathrm{B} \\ | \\ \mathrm{C{=}O} \\ | \\ \mathrm{CH_3} \end{array}$$

(2)

$$\begin{array}{ccc} \mathrm{A^-} & & \\ \vdots & & \mathrm{B} \\ \vdots & & + \,| \\ \mathrm{H{-}O} & \cdots & \mathrm{C{=}O} \\ | & & | \\ \mathrm{H} & & \mathrm{CH_3} \end{array} \rightleftharpoons \begin{array}{cc} \mathrm{A} & \\ \mathrm{H} & \ddot{\mathrm{B}} \\ & \\ \mathrm{O}- & \mathrm{C{=}O} \\ | & | \\ \mathrm{H} & \mathrm{CH_3} \end{array}$$

The acid group of the esteratic site donates a proton to the electron-rich (basic) alcoholic oxygen atom, thus liberating the alcohol, choline, while the carboxyl carbon atom of the acetyl group, rendered slightly positive by the electron shift toward the carboxyl oxygen, is subject to nucleophilic attack by the basic group of the esteratic site, which becomes acetylated. In the second step, the carboxyl carbon atom shifts its linkage from the basic group B to the basic oxygen atom of a water molecule, while simultaneously a proton from the water molecule re-protonates the acidic group of the esteratic site. Thus, acetic acid is liberated and the esteratic site is returned to its former state. The water molecule which participates in this second step may be replaced by other acceptors, such as hydroxylamine (NH_2OH).

Many inhibitors of acetylcholine esterase are themselves esters, and it has been demonstrated that their acyl moieties combine with the basic group just as does acetyl. The organic phosphates (p. 668), which are used as insecticides and have been suggested as war gases ("nerve gases"), are particularly effective inhibitors of this enzyme, since their action is almost irreversible. This is because the product of their acylation (actually phosphorylation by substituted phosphoric acids) of site B reacts extremely slowly with water.

Observations that the inhibitor groups could be transferred rapidly to acceptors other than water (such as hydroxylamine) led to the testing of a compound containing, in addition to a good acyl acceptor group, an appropriately located quaternary nitrogen to facilitate binding to the anionic site:

$$\begin{array}{l} \quad\;\; \text{(pyridine ring)} - \overset{\mathrm{H}}{\mathrm{C}}{=}\mathrm{NOH} \\ \quad\;\; \mathrm{N^+} \\ \quad\;\; | \\ \quad\;\; \mathrm{CH_3} \quad \mathrm{I^-} \end{array}$$

This compound, 2-pyridine aldoxime methiodide (2-PAM), not only reactivates acetylcholinesterase inhibited by organic phosphates in vitro, but also has proved to be an effective antidote to the "nerve gases" in experimental animals, particularly when combined with atropine (p. 669) for the protection of peripheral receptors.

Insofar as the identity of the chemical groups at the anionic and esteratic sites is concerned, no conclusions can be drawn. Although the pK of one of the esteratic groups is close to that of the imidazole side chain of histidine, the alcoholic side chain of serine appears to be the site of attachment of the phosphoryl group of the organo-phosphate inhibitors.

If we can regard acetylcholine esterase as typical of many hydrolases and transferases, then a few tentative generalizations can be formulated:

(1) There exist(s) on the surface of the enzyme one (or a few) catalytically active site(s) of dimensions approximating those of the substrate, or of the susceptible part of the substrate.

(2) One part of the site is concerned primarily with binding of the substrate, the nature of the binding probably varying with each enzyme and substrate, being electrostatic or non-polar, or both.

(3) At the appropriate distance from the binding site is the catalytic or reactive site proper, containing, among others, a group which can form a covalent bond with a cleavable portion of the substrate.

(4) The intermediate compound of enzyme plus substrate-fragment reacts with an acceptor molecule, transferring the substrate-fragment to the acceptor (which is water in the case of the hydrolases).

Coenzymes and Prosthetic Groups

Certain enzymes require for their function the presence of certain organic, dialyzable, thermostable compounds. If such a compound is rather firmly attached to the enzyme protein it is usually called a "prosthetic group," as in the case of other conjugated proteins. The group or compound is called a "coenzyme" if its attachment to the protein is not very firm. Certain coenzymes seem to exist in the free state in solution, contacting the enzyme protein only at the instant of reaction. The distinction between prosthetic groups and coenzymes is therefore quantitative, not qualitative, and is related to the magnitude of the equilibrium constant describing the dissociation of the smaller group from the enzyme protein. This general state of affairs is illustrated in Figure 8–4. The term "apoenzyme" is sometimes used for the protein portion of the system, which becomes a "holoenzyme" when combined with coenzyme.

Certain coenzymes of nucleotide structure were described in the chapter on nucleic acid chemistry. Many coenzymes, especially those concerned with biological oxidations, contain members of the B complex group of vitamins in their structures. In any case, they are much smaller molecules than proteins, so that they can be removed from their apoenzymes by dialysis if they are at all dissociable. Their resistance to heat makes it possible to prepare them conveniently, freed from their apoenzymes, by simply heat-denaturing the proteins in the preparation.

The function of the coenzyme in the enzymatic reaction is to assist in the cleavage of the substrate by acting as an acceptor for one of the cleavage products, as shown in Figure 8–5. The substrate and apoenzyme form a complex, but in the presence of the coenzyme. When the bond in the substrate becomes activated, one of the cleavage products (usually a small fragment of the entire substrate molecule) is transferred directly to

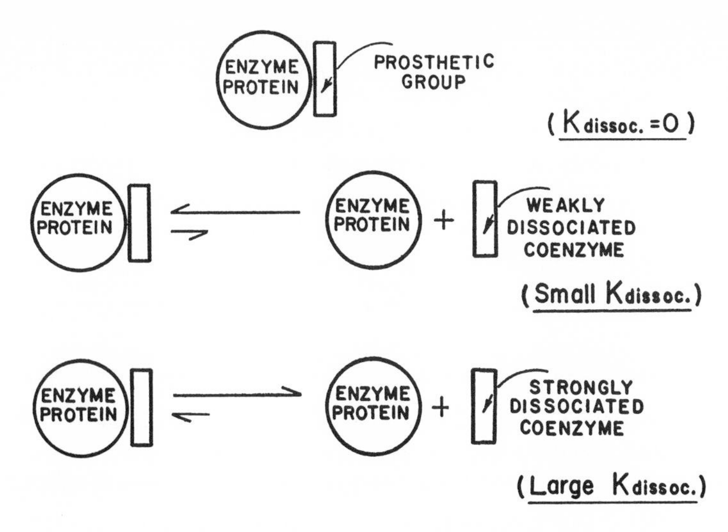

Figure 8-4. Coenzymes and prosthetic groups.

the coenzyme, which has an appropriate receptor site in its structure. What is left of the substrate now dissociates from the apoenzyme. The fragment which is attached to the coenzyme is either liberated as such or passed on to other enzyme systems for additional changes; in either case the coenzyme is regenerated. Both apoenzyme and coenzyme are then able to repeat the same cycle of events, hence it can be said that both act catalytically. A prosthetic group acts in an analogous fashion, the only difference being that the acceptor of the substrate fragment remains attached to the surface of the apoenzyme.

In the discussions which follow in this chapter and that on biological oxidations, it will be noted that coenzymes generally exhibit a much less restricted range of specificity

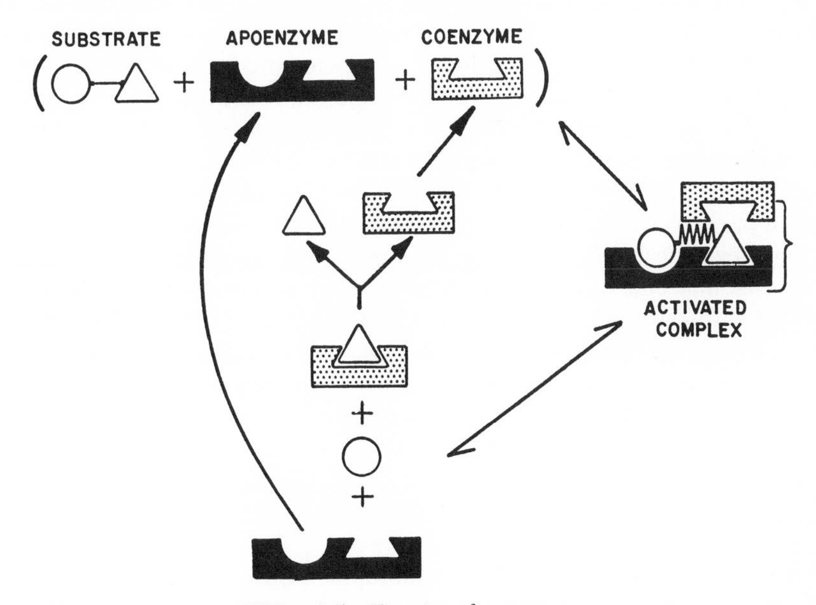

Figure 8-5. Function of coenzymes.

than do the apoenzymes with which they cooperate. By way of explanation, it has been suggested that the apoenzyme must attract the entire substrate molecule to its surface, so that the active site contains groups which are relatively specific for portions of the substrate molecule in addition to the particular region undergoing modification. The coenzyme, on the other hand, is charged with the task of combining with the particular group or fragment that is to be liberated in the reaction, and consequently exhibits much less specificity toward the rest of the molecule. Appropriate examples of these phenomena may be seen among the transaminases (p. 234) and the dehydrogenases (p. 357), among others.

Specific Ion Activators

When the requirement of certain enzyme systems for dialyzable cofactors is examined, it is found that specific inorganic ions are necessary for the reaction to proceed. Thus, many reactions involving phosphorylation seem to require magnesium ions, while the action of various peptide-splitting enzymes requires cobalt, manganese, magnesium, or zinc ions. It is probable that many of the apoenzymes in these cases are actually metalloproteins with rather loosely bound metallic ions.

In those cases in which the function of the metal in an enzyme system has been well established, it seems to be directly concerned in the reaction. The metallic component of certain oxidative enzyme systems (Cu, Fe) may undergo valence changes in accepting electrons from substrates which are being oxidized. In the peptide-splitting systems, the metallic ion joins with groups on the substrate molecule (chelation) and assists the protein part of the enzyme system in activating that bond of the substrate which is to be cleaved. The requirement of certain enzymes for univalent ions, such as K^+, is difficult to explain.

Pre-enzymes (Zymogens, Proenzymes)

Certain enzymes are synthesized in an inactive state, in which condition they are known as proenzymes, zymogens, or pre-enzymes (the name recommended by the International Union of Biochemistry). The conversion of these substances to active enzymes is effected by agents which are more or less specific. One pre-enzyme is transformed to an active enzyme by hydrogen ions, another by a specific activating enzyme which is synthesized for that purpose, and a third by a proteolytic enzyme which happens to be found in its vicinity in the gastrointestinal tract. In many instances the active enzyme, once formed, can itself act as an activator of its own pre-enzyme, an autocatalytic reaction. Most of the known cases of pre-enzyme synthesis occur among the digestive enzymes. It is becoming evident that most cases of pre-enzyme activation involve the removal from the pre-enzyme molecule of an inhibitory or blocking peptide moiety. Although it cannot be stated with certainty, it is probable that the synthesis of these digestive enzymes in an inactive form is a strategem employed by the cell to avoid intracellular degradative action. The pre-enzymes, together with any fully active enzymes which are also destined for secretion by the cell, are transferred from the site of synthesis (ribosomes) to zymogen granules for "export" and subsequent liberation.

Iso(en)zymes

Certain enzymes appear to exist in multiple forms; e.g., lactate dehydrogenase (p. 405) is found in five electrophoretically distinct fractions. Each electrophoretic species of lactate dehydrogenase is a tetramer containing specific proportions of two parent units, H (readily prepared from heart) and M (readily prepared from skeletal muscle), viz., H_4, H_3M, H_2M_2, HM_3, and M_4. The various forms differ in catalytic ability, heat lability, amino acid composition, and immunological properties. Each cell appears to be able to synthesize both sub-units (H and M), the synthesis of each being under its own genetic control. In the course of cellular differentiation, varying amounts of the two sub-units are produced, resulting in a distinctive pattern of electrophoretic species in each mature tissue. Lactate dehydrogenase species with higher proportions of H are maximally active at low, and inhibited by high, pyruvate concentrations. Such characteristics would tend to channel the metabolism of pyruvate into the aerobic degradative system of the Krebs cycle rather than into the formation of lactate (p. 408). It is of interest that such species of the dehydrogenase, which would be an advantage to an aerobic tissue, do indeed predominate in such organs as heart. On the other hand, lactate dehydrogenase species containing higher proportions of the M sub-unit are quite active even at high pyruvate concentrations, thus channelling much of the pyruvate into the lactate, or anaerobic pathway. Lactate dehydrogenase species of this type appear to be more plentiful in skeletal muscle, a tissue in which rapid bursts of energy are required during relatively anaerobic states.

Whether the foregoing findings with regard to cellular differentiation are general or peculiar to lactate dehydrogenase is not known, although other isoenzyme systems also appear to be under genetic control.

PHYSICAL FACTORS INFLUENCING THE RATE OF ENZYMATIC REACTIONS

Time

As an enzymatically catalyzed reaction proceeds, its rate may decrease because of reversal of reaction from increased concentration of product, inactivation of enzyme, formation of inhibitory substances, and various other factors in addition to simple depletion of substrate. To avoid these complications, enzymologists frequently restrict their study of reaction rates to the initial stages of the reaction, where perhaps no more than 10 per cent of the substrate has been consumed.

In the assay of enzyme activity in tissues and body fluids, the determination of initial reaction rates frequently is carried out in the presence of high concentrations of substrate, sufficient to saturate the enzyme. Under such conditions, the reaction rate is independent of substrate concentration (a so-called "zero-order" reaction), and is simply equal to a constant:

$$v = k$$

The amount of substrate consumed over a period of time is given by:

$$\Delta(S) = k\,\Delta t$$

Such reaction rates may be expressed in terms of quantity of substrate consumed per unit time; it has been suggested that an appropriate unit of activity would be μmoles per minute. The course of purification of an enzyme may be followed by determining the *specific* activity, in terms of μmoles substrate utilized per minute per milligram protein.

In many enzyme reactions which involve a single substrate at relatively low concentration, the reaction rate at any given time is proportional to the instantaneous concentration of substrate (a "first-order" reaction):

$$v = k(S)$$

Hence the rate of reaction decreases as the concentration of substrate falls. Integration of the above rate equation and conversion to decimal logarithms produces the following relation between the concentration of substrate (S) at any given time, t, and the initial concentration of substrate $(S)_0$ at zero time:

$$\log (S) = \log (S)_0 - \frac{kt}{2.303}$$

Therefore, the concentration of substrate decreases logarithmically with time, an "exponential" type of relationship also applicable to the decay of radioactive isotopes.

Many enzyme reactions do not follow simple zero- or first-order kinetics, particularly when the substrate concentration is neither very high nor low. The more general treatment required in these cases is given in the section, "Concentration of Substrate."

Dependence of the rate on the concentrations of two or more substrates results in reactions of higher order. This subject will not be pursued further, beyond noting that the enzymologist frequently can reduce such reactions to first- or zero-order for purposes of study by arranging conditions so that the concentrations of one or more substrates are held constant or are sufficiently high to saturate the enzyme.

Temperature

The rate of most chemical reactions, catalyzed or not, increases as the temperature is raised. Enzyme-catalyzed reactions follow the general rule, but with the added complication that, as proteins, the enzymes are adversely affected by elevated temperatures. As a result of the two competing factors, a plot of the rate of an enzymatic reaction versus the temperature exhibits a maximum, as shown in Figure 8–6A. Since most animal enzymes begin to be denatured at a significant rate at temperatures over 40° C., the optimum temperature in experiments of moderate duration is frequently found to be near or somewhat below 40° C. As might be expected, the optimum temperature is decreased with increase in the duration of the incubation.

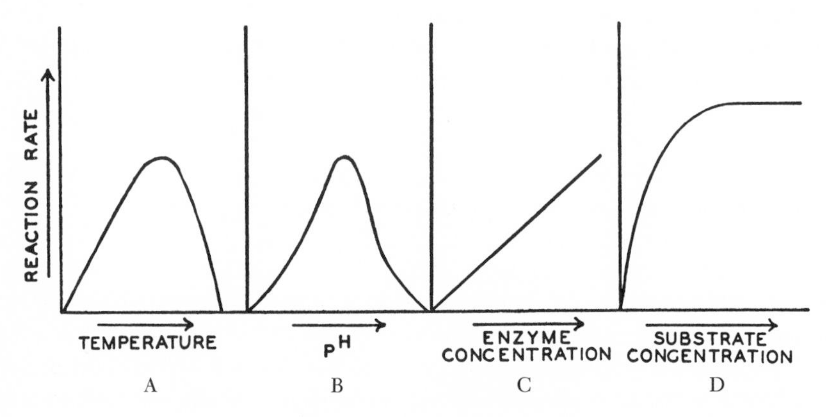

Figure 8–6. Effects of various factors on reaction rate.

pH

Enzymes, being proteins, cannot withstand the action of strong acid or base. However, even over the pH range in which inactivation does not occur, enzymes exhibit optima in their activity (Fig. 8–6*B*). In the case of an enzyme which attacks non-ionic substrates, the optimum pH is constant for the several substrates. The optimum in the curve, then, must correspond to some particular configuration of electrical charges at the reactive sites of the enzyme protein, in which condition the action on the substrate is most efficient. As in the case of the temperature effect, the very existence of an optimum in the curve suggests the action of two opposing forces. In the case of the pH effect, it has been suggested that at least two ionizable groups are involved at the active site, having different pK's, an idea which is in agreement with recent theories concerning the chemical groups at the active site. Ionized substrates will themselves vary in electrical properties over the pH range, so that enzymes attacking such substances often show pH optima which differ from one substrate to another. In these examples the peak in the curve must be a resultant, or compromise, between the most efficient, charged states of the enzyme and substrate.

Concentration of Enzyme

The velocity of a catalyzed reaction is proportional to the concentration of catalyst. Figure 8–6*C* indicates that this generalization holds true for enzymatic reactions. It is possible that the rates of certain metabolic reactions may be limited by the localization of certain enzyme systems in discrete particles in the cell, as in the mitochondria, allowing the reaction to proceed only to the extent that substrate can diffuse into the region of the enzyme. In this way a reaction can be limited in rate throughout the cell, except in regions of high concentrations of enzyme. This localization is most appropriate if a succession of enzymes is required to effect a given metabolic transformation, and if all such enzymes are localized in the same region. Such a situation actually obtains in nature (p. 225).

Concentration of Substrate

With a fixed amount of enzyme, it would be expected that the reaction rate should be proportional to the substrate concentration. This is true up to a point, but as shown in Figure 8–6*D*, a limiting concentration is reached, beyond which increase in substrate concentration causes no further increase in the rate of the reaction. The explanation of this situation is illustrated by the diagrams in Figure 8–7. Four molecules of a hypothetical enzyme, each containing one active site, are shown combining with a substrate at three concentration levels, each double the preceding. At the lowest concentration of substrate, only a few of the active sites in the solution are occupied by substrate molecules at any instant. Increasing the substrate concentration has the effect of increasing the coverage of active sites, until a concentration is reached which "saturates" these sites. Higher concentrations will permit no greater reaction rate than was possible with the limiting concentration, since the reaction can proceed only as rapidly as active sites become available.

The hypothesis of an enzyme-substrate complex may be utilized to derive a general relationship between the concentration of substrate and the reaction rate of enzymatic reactions, known as the Michaelis-Menten equation. In the following discussion, it will be assumed that the enzyme and substrate combine reversibly to form a complex, that this

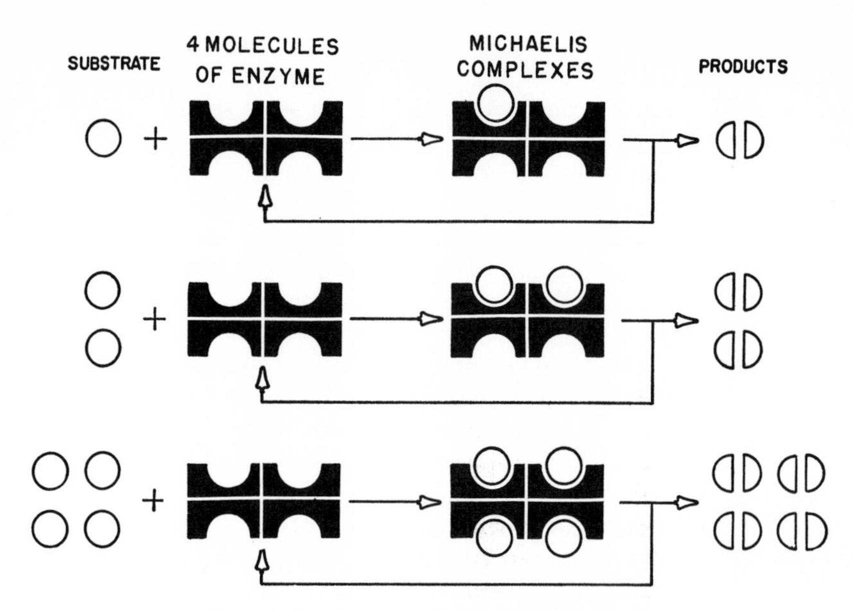

Figure 8-7. Saturation of enzyme with substrate.

complex decomposes to enzyme and products in a reaction, the reversal of which need not be considered during the early stages of the reaction, that the velocity of this initial reaction is proportional to the concentration of the enzyme-substrate complex, and that, after a very rapid initial formation, the concentration of the enzyme-substrate complex remains in a steady state for the period of reaction under consideration. The overall reactions may then be described by the equations:

$$E + S \underset{k_{-1}}{\overset{k_{+1}}{\rightleftharpoons}} ES \overset{k_{+2}}{\rightarrow} E + \text{Products}$$

Since, according to the assumptions, the velocity of the reaction is expressed by

$$v = k_{+2}(ES)$$

it is necessary to derive an expression for the concentration of the enzyme-substrate complex, ES. According to the law of mass action, the rate of formation of ES is proportional to the concentrations of E and S. Since the amount of substrate combined with enzyme is only a minute fraction of the total, the total concentration of substrate may be used to represent the concentration of free substrate. However, in the case of the enzyme, an appreciable fraction of the total enzyme may be involved in the enzyme-substrate complex, so that the free enzyme concentration must be represented by the difference between the total enzyme concentration (E), and the concentration of the enzyme-substrate complex. The rate of formation of ES is then given by

$$k_{+1}[(E) - (ES)](S)$$

The enzyme-substrate complex may break down in two ways, in the direction of the products, and in the direction of the reactants. The rate of breakdown of ES may therefore be expressed as the sum of these two reactions, i.e., by the sum of the products of the concentration of ES and the rate constants in the respective two directions:

$$k_{-1}(ES) + k_{+2}(ES)$$

According to the assumption of a steady state mentioned above, the rate of breakdown is equal to the rate of formation of ES:

$$k_{-1}(ES) + k_{+2}(ES) = k_{+1}[(E) - (ES)](S)$$

Solving for (ES), we obtain the equation

$$(ES) = \frac{(E)(S)}{\frac{k_{-1} + k_{+2}}{k_{+1}} + (S)}$$

Having derived an expression for the concentration for ES, we now return to our assumption that the velocity of the reaction may be expressed by the product of this concentration and the rate constant, k_{+2}

$$v = \frac{k_{+2}(E)(S)}{\frac{k_{-1} + k_{+2}}{k_{+1}} + (S)}$$

This equation may be simplified in two ways. First, the term involving the three rate constants may be replaced by a new constant, K. This is frequently called the Michaelis constant and designated K_m. A second simplification follows from earlier considerations, namely, that as (S) increases sufficiently to saturate the enzyme, the velocity approaches a maximum value, which may be considered a constant, characteristic of the system for any given concentration of enzyme. In more strictly mathematical terms, and referring to the above equation, it will be noted that if (S) becomes large enough mathematically so that $\frac{k_{-1} + k_{+2}}{k_{+1}}$ can be ignored in comparison, then this maximum reaction rate will be equal to $k_{+2}(E)$. Designating this maximum velocity by V, and making the indicated replacements, we arrive at the final Michaelis-Menten equation:

$$v = \frac{V(S)}{K_m + (S)}$$

A number of interesting deductions may be made from this equation. For example, if we set $v = \frac{1}{2}V$, then $(S) = K_m$, meaning that the Michaelis constant is equal numerically to that substrate concentration which allows the reaction to proceed at one-half the maximum velocity. Furthermore, for very large and very small values of (S), the Michaelis-Menten equation reduces to the rate equations for zero- and first-order kinetics, respectively.

Earlier methods of deriving the Michaelis-Menten equation led to the conclusion that the constant K_m was the dissociation constant of the enzyme-substrate complex and was therefore an inverse measure of enzyme-substrate affinity. According to the more sophisticated "steady-state" approach, $K_m = (k_{-1} + k_{+2})k_{+1}$, which is equivalent to the dissociation constant k_{-1}/k_{+1} only if k_{+2} is negligible in comparison to k_{-1}. Although the last two rate constants may have this relationship in some cases, such cannot be a general expectation. Consequently, K_m must now be regarded only as a useful parameter for each enzyme, giving the substrate concentration for half-maximum velocity, and thus suggesting appropriate concentrations of substrate for various desired reaction rates. Mathematically, it also may be considered an upper limit of the true dissociation constant, approaching the latter as k_{+2} becomes smaller.

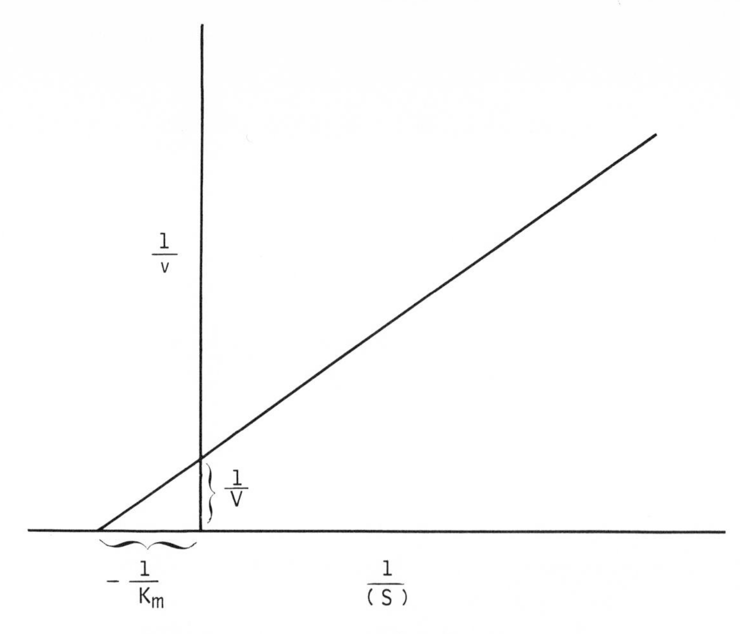

Figure 8-8. Lineweaver-Burk double reciprocal plot.

Determination of important physical constants of an enzyme system, such as V and K_m, would be difficult from the curve that would be obtained by plotting v against (S). However, taking reciprocals of both sides of the Michaelis-Menten equation, we find

$$\frac{1}{v} = \frac{K_m}{V} \cdot \frac{1}{(S)} + \frac{1}{V}$$

This resembles the simple algebraic equation, $y = ax + b$, where a is the slope of a straight line, b is the intercept on the y axis when $x = 0$, and x, the intercept on the x axis when $y = 0$, is $-b/a$. In the case of the reciprocal Michaelis-Menten equation, a plot of $1/v$ against $1/(S)$ gives a straight line, the slope of which is K_m/V, the y intercept is $1/V$, and the x intercept is $-1/K_m$. This so-called Lineweaver-Burk double reciprocal plot, an example of which is shown in Figure 8-8, not only allows relatively easy determination of V and K_m, but also may be used to differentiate certain types of inhibition of enzyme systems (pp. 660, 662).

Concentration of Cofactors

If an enzyme requires for its activity the presence of a dissociable cofactor, such as an inorganic ion or a coenzyme, the rate of the reaction will vary with the concentration of the cofactor. In many cases a limiting concentration is found, as was discussed above for the substrate. The explanation in these cases is similar: whatever active sites on the enzyme surface may be reserved for the cofactors are then saturated.

INHIBITION OF ENZYME REACTIONS

Types of Inhibitors

Since enzymes are proteins, any agents which denature proteins will inactivate enzymes. Such inactivations are quite non-specific and reveal nothing concerning the nature of enzyme action. Certain chemical agents block specific groups in the enzyme protein. This type of inhibition is still considered non-specific, inasmuch as the groups being blocked are common to many enzymes. However, it frequently does indicate that particular chemical groups in the protein fabric are concerned in the action of the enzyme.

Specific inhibitors differ from the foregoing in that they exert their action on only one enzyme, or a small group of related enzymes. The mechanism of the inhibition is specifically related to the structure and action of the enzyme involved, not to some group or property common to all proteins. The target of action of this type of inhibitor may be the coenzyme or prosthetic group, the specific ion activator, the site of combination of substrate and enzyme on the enzyme surface, or some adjacent site otherwise necessary for the action of the enzyme.

Sulfhydryl Inhibitors

Among the non-specific inhibitions, those which involve sulfhydryl groups of the enzymes are perhaps the most thoroughly studied. Many, but not all, enzymes contain sulfhydryl groups derived from the side chains of cysteine residues. Blockage or chemical transformation of these groups results in inhibition of the enzymes. In several cases there is definite evidence that the sulfhydryl groups take part in the combination of enzyme and substrate, accounting for their essentiality. Several types of sulfhydryl inhibitors are shown in the accompanying formulas.

Oxidants such as ferricyanide convert sulfhydryl groups to disulfides; iodoacetate and similar agents block the groups by alkylation; while mercury and other heavy metal ions form mercaptides with them. The vesicant war gas, Lewisite, and the arsenical drugs exert their characteristic actions by combination with sulfhydryl groups. Poisoning by heavy metals or arsenicals has been treated successfully with 2,3-dimercaptopropanol (British Anti-Lewisite, or BAL), the sulfhydryl groups of which compete with the protein's sulfhydryl groups for the toxic substance.

Triose phosphate dehydrogenase (glyceraldehyde-3-phosphate dehydrogenase, p. 403) is an example of an enzyme which is especially sensitive to sulfhydryl reagents.

$$2RSH \xrightarrow[-2H]{\text{Ferricyanide}} R\text{—S—S—}R$$

$$RSH \xrightarrow[-HI]{ICH_2COOH} R\text{—S—}CH_2COOH$$

$$2RSH \xrightarrow[-2H^+]{Hg^{++}} R\text{—S—Hg—S—}R$$

$$2RSH \xrightarrow[-2HCl]{\substack{Cl_2As\text{—}CH{=}CHCl \\ \text{(Lewisite)}}} \begin{matrix} R\text{—S} \\ R\text{—S} \end{matrix}\!\!>\!As\text{—}CH{=}CHCl$$

$$\begin{matrix} CH_2\text{—SH} \\ | \\ CH\text{—SH} \\ | \\ CH_2OH \\ \text{(BAL)} \end{matrix} \xrightarrow[-2HCl]{\text{Lewisite}} \begin{matrix} CH_2\text{—S} \\ | \\ CH\text{—S} \\ | \\ CH_2OH \end{matrix}\!\!>\!As\text{—}CH{=}CHCl$$

Sulfhydryl inhibitors

Inhibitors Acting on Coenzyme, Prosthetic Group, or Ion Activator

Reagents blocking essential groups of coenzymes are relatively specific. As was mentioned earlier, pyridoxal phosphate is the coenzyme (among other functions) for a number of amino acid decarboxylases of bacterial and animal origin. The aldehyde group of this coenzyme would be expected to combine with various carbonyl reagents, an expectation which is fulfilled by the finding that these decarboxylases are inhibited by cyanide, hydrazine, hydroxylamine, and semicarbazide. (The lack of effect of most of these inhibitors on the transaminases remains to be explained.)

Cytochrome oxidase, an important oxidative enzyme containing an iron-porphyrin prosthetic group, is inhibited by cyanide, azide, and carbon monoxide, all of which prevent the reaction of the metal in the prosthetic group with molecular oxygen.

Enolase (phosphopyruvate hydratase), a magnesium-activated enzyme, in the presence of phosphate buffer is inhibited by fluoride.

Inhibition Due to Metabolic Antagonism

In addition to the specific inhibitions mentioned in the preceding section, a special variety of specific inhibition has been studied intensively in recent years, which is due to the structural similarity of certain inhibitors to normal substrates. The classic example of this type is the inhibition of succinate dehydrogenase by malonate.

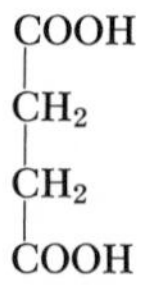

$$\begin{array}{c} COOH \\ | \\ CH_2 \\ | \\ CH_2 \\ | \\ COOH \\ \text{Succinic acid} \end{array} \qquad \begin{array}{c} COOH \\ | \\ CH_2 \\ | \\ COOH \\ \text{Malonic acid} \end{array}$$

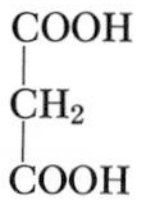

The structural similarity of malonic acid to the normal substrate misleads the enzyme into accepting the inhibitor at the active sites on its surface, thus displacing succinic acid and retarding the rate of conversion of succinic to fumaric acid. Inhibitors such as malonic acid are known as metabolic antagonists or substrate analogs. In many cases the reaction of the enzyme with both analog and substrate is freely reversible, both substances compete for the active sites on the enzyme, and the degree of inhibition depends solely on the ratio of the concentrations of inhibitor to substrate, and not on the absolute concentration of either. Under such conditions the inhibition is said to be competitive. Owing to the importance attached to the phenomenon of metabolic antagonism in recent years, it is discussed in a separate chapter.

Enzymes and Drug Action

In order that drugs may alter the metabolism of an animal or a microorganism, it is almost certain that their action must concern enzymes directly or indirectly. Narcotics, for example, are known to depress the activity of dehydrogenase systems, probably by disrupting the organization of the lipoprotein matrix of the oxidative chain. Many other drugs are known to be metabolic antagonists, sulfhydryl inhibitors, or metal-complexing agents. Considerable effort is being expended at the present time by workers in the fields of chemotherapy and pharmacology in relating their empirical findings to a rational enzymological basis.

THE INTRACELLULAR LOCALIZATION OF ENZYMES

Cytochemical Studies

In the techniques of histo- or cytochemistry a section of tissue is incubated with a substrate and the reaction products are located by microscopic observation, usually after conversion to some easily detectable precipitate. Alkaline phosphatase, for example, is detected by allowing a tissue section to incubate in buffered glycerophosphate containing lead salts. The liberated phosphate is precipitated in situ as lead phosphate, which is then converted to lead sulfide for easy visualization. By use of this technique with duodenal epithelium, alkaline phosphatase was found to be concentrated in the cuticular border, with significant amounts also apparently in the nuclei and in the region of the Golgi apparatus.

Differential Centrifugation

By the application of special grinding procedures to tissues it is possible to prepare "homogenates" which consist of nuclei, cytoplasmic particles, the soluble portion of the cytoplasm and some debris composed of cell membrane fragments and a few intact or partially disrupted cells. Individual fractions of this mixture can then be isolated by the technique of differential centrifugation. Many studies at the present time are concerned with the distribution of enzymes among the following fractions: a nuclear fraction, isolated by low-speed centrifugation; the "large granules" or mitochondria of the cytoplasm, spun down at intermediate speeds; the "small granules" or microsomes, requiring very high speeds for their isolation; the "supernatant" fraction, containing what is assumed to be the clear ground-substance of the cytoplasm, also referred to as the cell sap or "soluble" fraction. The mitochondrial fraction has been shown to be heterogeneous, containing, in addition to the mitochondria proper, particles called "lysosomes," intermediate in size between the mitochondria and the microsomes. The microsomal fraction is also heterogeneous, being derived from the fragmentation of the endoplasmic reticulum, and consisting partly of fragments of the reticular membrane, partly of dense bodies rich in ribonucleoprotein, called "ribosomes."

By use of these techniques, nuclei of liver and kidney cells have been found to contain few enzymes. Both liver and kidney nuclei appear to be lacking in succinate dehydrogenase, a key enzyme in the oxidative catabolism of many foodstuffs. However, a certain amount of protein synthesis can occur in the nucleus, as does the replication of deoxyribonucleic acid and the synthesis of ribonucleic acid, the latter process being the source of most, if not all, of the cytoplasmic RNA.

In terms of percentage, most of the glycolytic system of liver is found in the "supernatant" fraction, along with the enzymes of the "pentose-shunt" pathway. The supernatant fraction of liver is also the major site of certain transaminases, peptidases, phosphorylases, the enzymes of the major pathway of fatty acid synthesis, and most of the enzymes which catabolize purines.

The lysosomes are the major site of localization of acid phosphatase, cathepsin, deoxyribonuclease, and ribonuclease (both with acid pH optima) and β-glucuronidase. The lysosomes are peculiar particles in that they exhibit no enzyme activity while intact, but when their membranes are ruptured by any one of various procedures, all of the enzymes contained within are released in a soluble form. A particle, formerly thought to be lysosomal, but now recognized as a distinct entity, appears to be the locus of urate oxidase (uricase), D-amino acid oxidase, and catalase.

Cytochrome oxidase and the enzymes associated with the tricarboxylic acid cycle are largely concentrated in the mitochondria of liver cells. Also concentrated in the mitochondria are the enzymes of oxidative phosphorylation, and the oxidative degradation of fatty acids.

The microsomal fraction of liver, in addition to a number of phosphatases, esterases, and other enzymes, has been shown to be the site of triglyceride synthesis, certain phases of phospholipid and glycolipid metabolism, and hydroxylase systems which are important in the detoxication of lipid-soluble foreign compounds. Although microsomal fractions contain certain cytochromes and cytochrome reductases, they do not contain the entire oxidative chain, since they lack, among other things, cytochrome oxidase.

Certain metabolic pathways appear to require the collaboration of several intracellular fractions. Both mitochondria and soluble phase are necessary for the synthesis of urea and heme, whereas the formation of cholesterol involves the soluble phase and the microsomal fraction. Although some protein synthesis occurs within the nuclei and mitochondria, the bulk of intracellular protein is formed by reactions which take place partly in the soluble phase, partly on the ribosomal particles of the microsomal fraction.

The present tendency is to regard the mitochondria as the aerobic "powerhouse" of the cell, containing the enzymes required for energy production in a closely knit organization, so set up that the substrate is efficiently passed on from one stage of catabolism to the next. The more primitive, anaerobic production of energy by glycolysis is left to the unorganized soluble phase of the cytoplasm. The ribosomal particles are concerned with the final stage of synthesis of proteins, including the enzymes. Lysosomes probably are "scavengers" which degrade substances taken into the cell in insoluble, particulate form. Since most enzymes which are found in the nucleus are present in relatively small amounts, it is believed that the nucleus contributes little to the total metabolic activities of the cell, its chief function probably being the regulation of metabolic patterns by the transfer of genetic information from DNA to RNA and thence to the cytoplasmic area. These topics are discussed again elsewhere (p. 531).

REGULATION OF ENZYME ACTION

Enzymology and the study of intermediary metabolism have reached a state of maturity in which it is no longer fruitful to regard the cell as a bag of enzymes acting randomly. The survival of the cell, the organism, and, indeed, the species requires an elaborate system of checks and balances to insure optimum operational efficiency. Much current investigation is devoted to the study of these regulatory mechanisms. The importance of this topic justifies more detailed exposition (v. Chapter 27, p. 758). The brief discussions which follow are included solely to round out this chapter on enzymes with some introductory material on the "biology" of these catalysts.

It may be noted that, in addition to the regulatory mechanisms discussed below, the intracellular localization of enzymes (cf. preceding section) also plays a part. The Pasteur effect (p. 416) may be an example.

Influence of Hormones on Enzymes

The facts that hormones act in very low concentrations and that their action amounts to a rather specific type of control over metabolic events have led to the hypothesis that the targets of hormonal action are the enzymes. Actually, it has been very difficult to obtain definitive evidence on this point. The injection of a hormone into an intact animal is frequently followed by a change in the activity of one or more enzyme systems, as assayed in the excised tissues of the animal. In such experiments the action of the hormone could be the result of increased synthesis or destruction of the enzyme, removal or addition of inhibitory substances or cofactors, or simply changes in tissue permeability, all of which are rather far removed from the enzymatic reaction proper (although it is entirely possible that the action of hormones proceeds by just such mechanisms). The same general ambiguities attend experiments performed with tissue slices.

Attempts to demonstrate hormonal action of a physiological type in soluble enzyme systems have not been notably successful. It has been found that natural estrogens activate a "transhydrogenase" of vaginal tissue. However, it is doubtful that this effect is the basis of estrogen action, since synthetic estrogens do not have this action. Furthermore, there is evidence that this enzyme is not primarily a transhydrogenase, but rather a steroid dehydrogenase with broad coenzyme (NAD, NADP) specificity. The apparent effect of epinephrine and glucagon on the activation of phosphorylase is now known to be indirect, the actual activator being the mononucleotide, adenosine-3′,5′-phosphate (cyclic 3,5-AMP). This same compound apparently also plays a part in the activation of adrenal phosphorylase by ACTH. Several dehydrogenases are inhibited by steroid hormones; in some cases this has been shown to be due to a disturbance of the secondary or tertiary structure of the enzyme protein. Whether the effect is "physiological" is not known.

Some investigators have come to the conclusion that the action of hormones is "morphologic," i.e., that their target is the cell wall or the limiting membrane of an intracellular particle (e.g., mitochondrion) or some structural unit therein. Adrenal cortical steroids have a stabilizing influence on the lysosomal membrane. Suppression of release of undue quantities of degradative enzymes may underlie the anti-inflammatory action of these hormones. In connection with membrane functions, there is evidence that some hormones (e.g., insulin) may primarily influence membrane transport mechanisms.

Adrenal oxysteroids act as "inducers" (v. infra), i.e., they stimulate the synthesis of new enzyme molecules, particularly those concerned in gluconeogenesis (p. 423). There is evidence that thyroid hormones also may act as "inducers" rather than "uncouplers" under physiological conditions (p. 384).

Enzymes and Genetics

There is abundant evidence that the general enzymatic pattern of the cell is under genetic control. Whereas much of the modern evidence on this score is provided by studies on bacteria and fungi, relevant data from "inborn errors of metabolism" in man have been available since the beginning of this century.

In the case of many enzymes there seems to be a rather strict "nuclear" control of the enzyme content of the cell, and the offspring of a given cell appear to inherit enzyme patterns in precise, mendelian fashion. This has led to the "one gene–one enzyme" hypothesis, according to which a gene controls the elaboration of only one enzyme. An organism lacking a given gene will be deficient in the corresponding enzyme and will exhibit a block at the point in the sequence of metabolic events at which that enzyme operated. This metabolic block frequently results in the accumulation and excretion of an unmetabolized compound.

In other cases, however, the enzymatic pattern of a cell seems to be influenced by factors outside the nucleus. The very presence of a substrate, for instance, sometimes elicits the synthesis of an enzyme which can attack that substrate. The existence of these adaptive or inducible enzymes has led to the theory that the nuclear genes are responsive to cytoplasmic factors, such as the presence or absence of substrates. The "inducer," which may be the substrate or compounds chemically related to it, is said to react with a nuclear "repressor" system, which normally inhibits the expression of the gene controlling the synthesis of the enzyme in question. Genetic information may then be sent to the cytoplasmic centers of protein synthesis (via "messenger RNA"). The new enzyme molecules are synthesized from the usual raw materials, and only those enzymes may be induced, the formation of which is permitted by the genetic constitution of the cells. As noted in the previous section, certain hormones may act as inducers. Finally, the presence, in the cytoplasm, of unnecessarily large amounts of the end-product of a metabolic sequence may reinforce the nuclear repressor system and cut off synthesis of an enzyme catalyzing an early step in that sequence, an effect not to be confused with the "feedback" mechanism discussed in the next section.

The present consensus seems to be that, although the enzymatic potentialities of the cell are determined in mendelian fashion by the nuclear genes, determination of the fruition of these potentialities is under considerable cytoplasmic (and environmental) influence.

Self-Regulation of Enzyme Reactions

In addition to the regulation of enzymatic reaction rates by intracellular localization, hormonal influences, genetic factors and enzymic induction, as well as such obvious factors as control of the concentration of substrates and cofactors, it has been shown that many enzymatic reactions are inhibited by the products of the reaction. Of even greater interest is the discovery that, in long sequences of enzyme reactions, an early reaction in the sequence may be inhibited by accumulation of the product of a reaction late in the sequence. This type of control, an example of "negative feedback," is very economical for the cell, since it relieves the cell of the necessity of performing a number of intermediary reactions when the final product is no longer needed.

CLASSIFICATION AND NOMENCLATURE OF ENZYMES

Introduction

When enzymes were first discovered they were given various "unsystematic" names by their discoverers, such as pepsin, trypsin, ptyalin, etc. In more recent times enzymes have been designated by the suffix "-ase," preceded by a term which indicates either the general nature of the substrate, the actual name of the substrate, the type of reaction catalyzed, or a combination of several of these facts.

There is no perfect method for the classification of enzymes. However, a scheme which serves most purposes is presented in Table 8-1, based upon recommendations of the Enzyme Commission of the International Union of Biochemistry (I.U.B.). The enzymes are classified first according to the general type of chemical reaction catalyzed, and, secondly, by the type of bond split or formed, the type of chemical group removed or transferred, or in some cases by a simple subclassification of the general reaction type. Main classes and sub-classes are indicated by index numbers. In the complete I.U.B. classification, a third index number is used for more detailed subdivision of the sub-class,

TABLE 8-1. I.U.B. CLASSIFICATION OF ENZYMES (CONDENSED)

1. Oxidoreductases	4. Lyases,
2. Transferases,	acting on following bonds:
transferring following groups:	4.1 C-C
2.1 One carbon	4.2 C-O
2.2 Aldehydic or ketonic residues	4.3 C-N
2.3 Acyl	4.4 C-S
2.4 Glycosyl	4.5 C-halide
2.5 Alkyl or related	5. Isomerases
2.6 Nitrogenous	5.1 Racemases and epimerases
2.7 Phosphorus-containing	5.2 *Cis-trans* isomerases
2.8 Sulfur-containing	5.3 Intramolecular oxidoreductases
3. Hydrolases,	5.4 Intramolecular transferases
acting on following bonds:	5.5 Intramolecular lyases
3.1 Ester	6. Ligases,
3.2 Glycosyl	forming following bonds:
3.3 Ether	6.1 C-O
3.4 Peptide	6.2 C-S
3.5 Other C-N bonds	6.3 C-N
3.6 Acid anhydride	6.4 C-C
3.7 C-C	
3.8 Halide	
3.9 P-N	

and finally a fourth figure designates the serial number of the specific enzyme in the fourth sub-class.

Along with the system of classification, the Enzyme Commission has devised a system of nomenclature, embodying recommendations for both "systematic" and "trivial" names for enzymes. Although the "systematic" names specify the nature of the substrate and of the reaction with great precision, they tend to be rather awkward for general use. Consequently, we shall usually refer to enzymes by their recommended "trivial" names, which in most cases are identical with or very similar to those which have been commonly used in recent years.

General Classes of Enzymes

Oxidoreductases catalyze reactions of oxidation and reduction. Although these reactions involve transfer of hydrogen atoms or electrons, most systems of classification have placed the oxidoreductases in a category of their own, rather than with the "transferases." This seems justified, in view of the special complexities and peculiarities of biological oxidation, to which topic we devote a separate chapter. The transferases catalyze the transfer or shift, from one molecule to another, of a chemical group which is not present in the free state during the transfer. The nature of the group transferred forms the basis for the subclassification of these enzymes.

The hydrolases are those enzymes which catalyze the reaction of hydrolysis, that is, the direct addition of the elements of water across the bond, which is cleaved. A logical subdivision of this group of enzymes can then be made according to the type of linkage which is hydrolyzed.

Lyases catalyze the addition or removal of some chemical group of a substrate, without hydrolysis, oxidation, or reduction. They differ from the transferring enzymes in that the group in question is liberated in the free state (or taken up from the free state), not merely passed on to become a part of another molecule directly. Lyases are subclassified by the type of linkage cleaved or formed during the reaction.

The isomerases catalyze intramolecular reactions or rearrangements which result in no net change in the empirical formula of the substrate, i.e., there is no net gain or loss of electrons. The great variety of enzymes in this group necessitates a subclassification based largely on the types of reactions involved.

Ligases, pronounced with a short "i," (or synthetases) are a relatively new class of enzymes. They catalyze the linkage of two molecules coupled with the cleavage of a pyrophosphate bond in adenosine triphosphate (ATP) or similar compound.

TRANSFERASES

Transfers of 1-Carbon Units

Transmethylation (Table 8-2) is a reaction which is of special concern in the fields of lipid and amino acid metabolism. Only two methylating agents are of physiological significance in the animal organism, betaine (an oxidation product of choline) and "activated" methionine (S-adenosylmethionine). As indicated in Table 8-2, the latter agent is involved in almost all transmethylations. These matters are discussed in greater detail elsewhere (p. 588).

Transferases exist for 1-carbon units which are on a higher oxidation level than the methyl group, namely formyl (formate), formimino, and hydroxymethyl (formaldehyde). The general coenzyme which transports these units is tetrahydrofolic (tetrahydropteroylglutamic) acid (p. 197). In addition to the multiple nature of the units involved, it will be noted from the table that additional complexities result from the several positions which these groups may occupy on the coenzyme, as well as their varied states of hydration. Sources of these groups and examples of their utilization will be indicated in connection with various phases of the metabolism of amino acids, purines, and pyrimidines.

Ornithine transcarbamoylase, which is involved in urea synthesis, catalyzes transfer of a residue in which the carbon atom is on the oxidation level of carbon dioxide. The analogous aspartate transcarbamoylase participates in pyrimidine synthesis.

Transfer of Aldehydic and Ketonic Residues

Transaldolase (dihydroxyacetone transferase) and transketolase (glycolaldehyde transferase) take part in a number of important interconversions in the area of pentose metabolism (p. 416).

Transacylases

Although in strict chemical parlance the term "acyl" includes formyl, in the biochemical sense the metabolism of formyl groups is more closely bound up with the metabolism of methyl and formaldehyde groups than it is with the metabolism of other carboxylic acids; transfer of formyl groups has already been discussed in connection with transfer reactions of 1-carbon units. Transacylation will be regarded herein as covering the transfer reactions of acetic and higher carboxylic acids.

The transfer of acetyl fragments from one molecule to another is a reaction which,

Table 8-2. Transfer of 1-Carbon Units

ENZYME	REACTION	OCCURRENCE
Nicotinamide transmethylase	S-Adenosylmethionine + nicotinamide ⟶ S-adenosylhomocysteine + N^1-methyl-nicotinamide	Liver
Guanidoacetate transmethylase	S-Adenosylmethionine + guanidoacetate ⟶ S-adenosylhomocysteine + creatine	Liver
Norepinephrine transmethylase	S-Adenosylmethionine + norepinephrine ⟶ S-adenosylhomocysteine + epinephrine	Adrenals
Histamine transmethylase	S-Adenosylmethionine + histamine ⟶ S-adenosylhomocysteine + 1-methylhistamine	Various tissues
Catechol transmethylase	S-Adenosylmethionine + various catechols ⟶ S-adenosylhomocysteine + O-methylcatechols	Various tissues
Betaine homocysteine transmethylase	Betaine + homocysteine ⟶ dimethylglycine + methionine	Liver
Serine transhydroxymethylase	Serine + FH_4* $\overset{**}{\longleftrightarrow}$ glycine + 5,10-anhydrohydroxymethyl-FH_4	Liver
Glutamate transformiminase	Formiminoglutamate + FH_4 ⟶ 5-formimino-FH_4 + glutamate	Liver
Aminoimidazolecarboxamide ribotide transformylase	Aminoimidazolecarboxamide ribotide + 10-formyl-FH_4 ⟶ formamidoimidazolecarboxamide ribotide + FH_4	Liver
Glycinamide ribotide transformylase	Glycinamide ribotide + 5,10-anhydroformyl-FH_4 ⟶ formylglycinamide ribotide + FH_4	Liver
Ornithine transcarbamoylase	Carbamoyl-phosphate + ornithine ⟶ phosphate + citrulline	Liver
Aspartate transcarbamoylase	Carbamoyl-phosphate + aspartate ⟶ phosphate + carbamoyl-aspartate (ureidosuccinate)	Various tissues

* FH_4, Tetrahydrofolic acid
** Pyridoxal phosphate required

to some extent at least, is involved in the metabolism of all classes of foodstuffs. It has been found that all transacetylations follow a common pattern. In a "donor" reaction, such as the first one shown in Table 8-3, an acetyl group is transferred from the donor molecule to a coenzyme of acetylations.

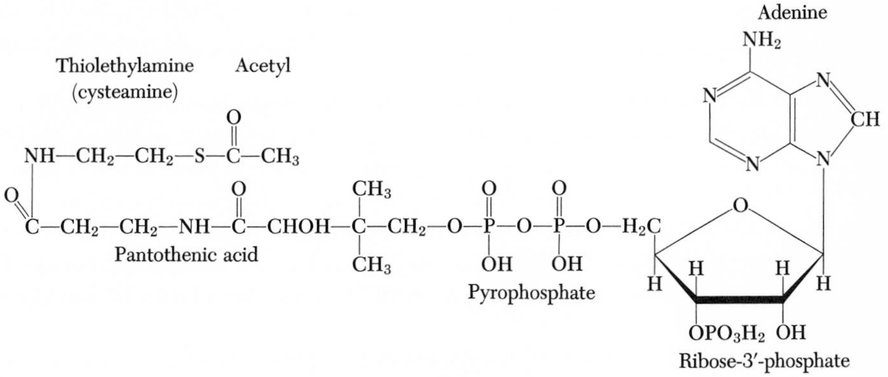

Adenine
NH_2
Thiolethylamine (cysteamine)
Acetyl
$NH—CH_2—CH_2—S—C(=O)—CH_3$
$C(=O)—CH_2—CH_2—NH—C(=O)—CHOH—C(CH_3)_2—CH_2—O—P(=O)(OH)—O—P(=O)(OH)—O—H_2C$
Pantothenic acid
Pyrophosphate
OPO_3H_2 OH
Ribose-3′-phosphate

Acetyl-CoA

TABLE 8-3. TRANSACYLASES

ENZYME	REACTION	OCCURRENCE
β-Ketoacyl-CoA transacetylase	β-Ketoacyl-CoA + CoA ⇌ Acyl(-C_2)-CoA + Acetyl-CoA	Liver
Acetoacetyl-CoA transacetylase (thiolase)	Acetyl-CoA + Acetyl-CoA ⇌ Acetoacetyl-CoA + CoA	Liver, heart
Choline transacetylase	Acetyl-CoA + choline ⟶ Acetyl-choline + CoA	Nervous tissue
Arylamine transacetylase	Acetyl-CoA + sulfonamide ⟶ Acetylsulfonamide + CoA	Liver
Glycine transacylase	Benzoyl-CoA + glycine ⟶ Hippurate + CoA	Liver, kidney
Phosphate transacetylase	Acetyl-CoA + phosphate ⇌ Acetylphosphate + CoA	Bacteria
Glycerophosphate transacylase	Palmityl-CoA + α-glycerophosphate ⟶ Phosphatidic acids + CoA	Liver
Lipoate transacetylase	Acetyl-CoA + dihydrolipoate ⇌ CoA + 6-S-acetyl-dihydrolipoate	Liver
Glucosamine transacetylase	Acetyl-CoA + glucosamine ⟶ N-acetylglucosamine + CoA	Liver
Diglyceride transacylase	Fatty acyl-CoA + diglyceride ⟶ triglyceride + CoA	Liver, adipose tissue

(A major source of acetyl groups, in addition to the β-keto acids from fatty acids, is provided by the oxidation of pyruvic acid derived from carbohydrate catabolism; this reaction is rather complex and is not included in this section.) In a second reaction an acceptor molecule takes up the acetyl fragment, regenerating the free coenzyme. A variety of acceptor reactions is shown in Table 8-3.

The participation of coenzyme A in the transfer of acyl groups other than acetyl has been demonstrated, viz., butyryl, succinyl, and benzoyl. It seems, therefore, that acetylation is but one special instance of a more general reaction, acylation, and that coenzyme A is involved in all cases. Furthermore, it is established that most donor reactions are preceded by activation reactions in which the acyl compound is activated by ATP, the acyl-adenylate thus resulting often transferring its acyl group to coenzyme A for utilization in a donor reaction.

Transglycosylases

Certain of these enzymes are also known as phosphorylases, because originally it was believed that the reaction which they catalyzed could be considered a "phosphorolysis," that is, the addition of the elements of phosphoric acid across the attacked bond, by analogy to hydrolysis. However, it has been shown for some of these enzymes (and generalized to the remainder) that the actual reaction mechanism consists of the transfer of the glycosidic portion of the substrate from its linkage thereon to some sort of linkage with the enzyme, from which location it is passed on to form another glycosidic linkage with an acceptor molecule.

In the case of the glucan phosphorylases or amylophosphorylases (frequently designated simply as "phosphorylases," since they were the first enzymes of this class to be investigated), as shown in Table 8-4, a terminal glycosidically linked glucose molecule is detached from a linear polysaccharide chain (1-4 bonds) and transferred to phosphate to form glucose-1-phosphate. This type of reaction is the major pathway in the breakdown of glycogen in the animal body. Additional information concerning activation and inactivation of the phosphorylases is given elsewhere (p. 400).

Although the phosphorylase reaction can be made to operate reversibly in vitro, under physiological conditions, the equilibrium lies toward the side of degradation of the glycogen. It is currently believed that the synthesis of glycogen is due to the activity of another reversible system, the physiological balance of which leans toward the side of synthesis. This system involves the enzyme uridinediphosphate-glucose-glycogen transglucosylase, which transfers a glucosyl residue from the uridine nucleotide to the nonreducing terminus of a polysaccharide primer. Since the formation of glycogen requires branching of the chains, and since the previously mentioned enzymes synthesize only molecules of the amylose type, the cooperation of various "branching enzymes" is required. These transform 1,4-linkages to 1,6-linkages by transferring part of a 1,4-glucan chain from a 4- to a 6-position, yielding the necessary branching points for a molecule of the amylopectin or glycogen type.

Phosphorylases operating in much the same way as the glucan phosphorylases are known which have as substrates the nucleosides of various purines and pyrimidines. It is quite probable that the hydrolytic breakdown of nucleosides described in the older literature was in reality due to the phosphorylases of this group, especially since many of the experiments were performed in phosphate buffers.

Table 8-4. Transglycosylases

ENZYME	REACTION	OCCURRENCE
α-Glucan phosphorylase (transglucosylase)	$(\alpha\text{-1,4-G})_n + PO_4^* \rightleftharpoons (\alpha\text{-1,4-G})_{n-1} + \text{G-1-P}$	Muscle, liver, heart, brain, plants
UDP-glucose-glycogen transglucosylase	$\text{UDP-G} + (\alpha\text{-1,4-G})_n \rightleftharpoons \text{UDP} + (\alpha\text{-1,4-G})_{n+1}$	Liver, skeletal muscle, heart
α-Glucan-branching transglycosylase	1,4-linkages $\longrightarrow$ 1,6-linkages	Muscle, liver, heart, brain, plants
Purine nucleoside phosphorylases	Purine nucleoside + PO_4 $\rightleftharpoons$ purine + ribose-1-P Purine deoxynucleoside + PO_4 $\rightleftharpoons$ purine + deoxyribose-1-P	Liver, thymus
Pyrimidine nucleoside phosphorylases	Pyrimidine nucleoside + PO_4 $\rightleftharpoons$ pyrimidine + ribose-1-P Pyrimidine deoxynucleoside + PO_4 $\rightleftharpoons$ pyrimidine + deoxyribose-1-P	Kidney, bone marrow, liver
UDP-galactose-glucose transgalactosylase	UDP-Gal + G-1-P $\rightleftharpoons$ UDP + lactose-1-P	Mammary gland
UDP transglucuronylase	UDP-glucuronate + phenols or acids $\rightleftharpoons$ UDP + glucuronides	Liver, kidney, gastric mucosa
Phosphoribosyl pyrophosphate amidotransferase	Phosphoribosyl-pyrophosphate + glutamine $\longrightarrow$ phosphoribosylamine + glutamate + pyrophosphate	Liver
Methionine adenosyl transferase	ATP + Met $\longrightarrow$ S-adenosyl-Met + PO_4 + PP	Liver

* PO_4, inorganic orthophosphate

Various types of transglycosylation are now recognized, many of which, such as the two examples shown in the table, depend upon uridine nucleotide coenzymes. The phosphoribosyl pyrophosphate transferase catalyzes an unusual reaction, the transfer of a glycosyl linkage from pyrophosphate to nitrogen, forming an aminosugar derivative which is used in the synthesis of purines (p. 515).

The adenosyltransferase is an important enzyme, since it "activates" methionine by converting it into a form capable of transferring methyl groups. A singular feature of the reaction is the loss of both ortho- and pyrophosphate groups from the ATP.

Transfer of Alkyl and Related Groups

The synthesis of cholesterol involves several reactions in which two isoprenoid pyrophosphate derivatives condense with the splitting out of pyrophosphate, forming larger isoprenoid derivatives. The participating enzyme has been named "prenyltransferase."

Transaminases and Related Enzymes

The transfer of an amino group from an amino acid to a keto acid, forming a new amino and keto acid in the process, is one of the more important general reactions of protein metabolism. The two enzymes listed first in Table 8-5 are the most widespread and active of the transaminases, but a large number of amino acids other than alanine and aspartate are known to react with ketoglutarate in various tissues. Originally, it was thought that one member of each transaminating system must be dicarboxylic, but enzyme systems are now known which can catalyze transaminations between alanine and several monocarboxylic keto acids.

In those cases in which a coenzyme has been shown to participate in a transaminase system, it has proved to be pyridoxal phosphate. A suggested mechanism for the role of this coenzyme in the reaction is shown below:

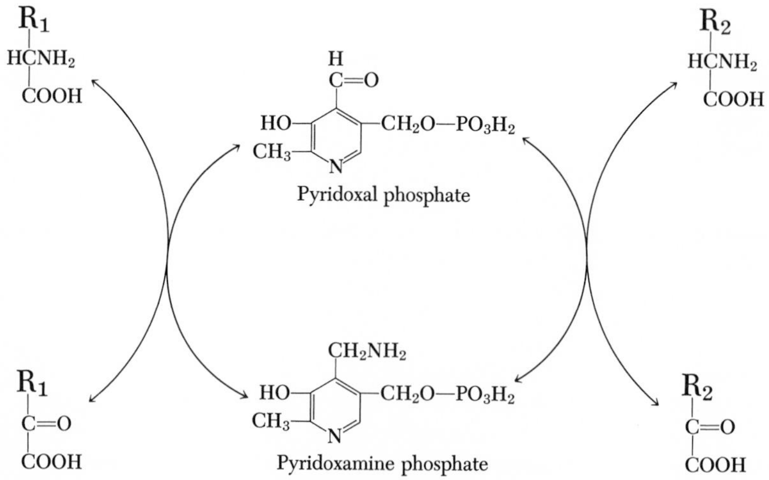

R_1—$HCNH_2$—COOH

H—C=O; HO—, CH_3—, —CH_2O—PO_3H_2 (pyridine ring, N)

Pyridoxal phosphate

R_2—$HCNH_2$—COOH

R_1—C=O—COOH

CH_2NH_2; HO—, CH_3—, —CH_2O—PO_3H_2 (pyridine ring, N)

Pyridoxamine phosphate

R_2—C=O—COOH

An unusual transamination has been described, involving the transfer of the α-amino group of glutamine. An α-ketoacid amide is the product. Asparagine undergoes a similar reaction. The γ-aminobutyrate transaminase presents an example of transamination of a γ-amino acid, in this case being concerned with the metabolism of a compound probably

TABLE 8-5. TRANSAMINASES

ENZYME	REACTION	OCCURRENCE
Alanine (formerly glutamic-pyruvic) transaminase	Alanine + ketoglutarate ⇌ pyruvate + glutamate	Muscle, liver
Aspartate (formerly glutamic-oxaloacetic) transaminase	Aspartate + ketoglutarate ⇌ oxaloacetate + glutamate	Heart, muscle, brain, liver, kidney, testis
Various amino acid-ketoglutarate transaminases	Amino acid + ketoglutarate ⇌ keto acid + glutamate	Liver, heart, kidney
Alanine-keto acid transaminase	Alanine + keto acid ⇌ pyruvate + amino acid	Liver
Glutamine-keto acid transaminase	Glutamine + keto acid ⇌ α-ketoglutaramate + amino acid	Liver, kidney
γ-Aminobutyrate transaminase	γ-Aminobutyrate + ketoglutarate ⇌ succinic semialdehyde + glutamate	Brain

involved in the control of synaptic transmission in the brain. Additional examples of unusual types of transamination are mentioned in connection with the metabolism of amino acids (p. 568).

It may be noted in passing that serum levels of certain transaminases (e.g., aspartate) are elevated in patients with heart or liver damage.

Related formally to the transaminases is the renal enzyme, transamidinase, which transfers an amidine residue from arginine to glycine, forming ornithine and guanidoacetate, the latter being a precursor of creatine.

Transphosphorylases

Transfers of phosphate groups from one molecule to another are of great metabolic importance, especially in the case of carbohydrates. The transphosphorylases are listed in Table 8-6.

The phosphomutases catalyze what would appear on the surface to be a series of intramolecular migrations of phosphate groups. Actually, these reactions are intermolecular and involve a group of rather unusual coenzymes. The mechanisms of two of these systems are shown below:

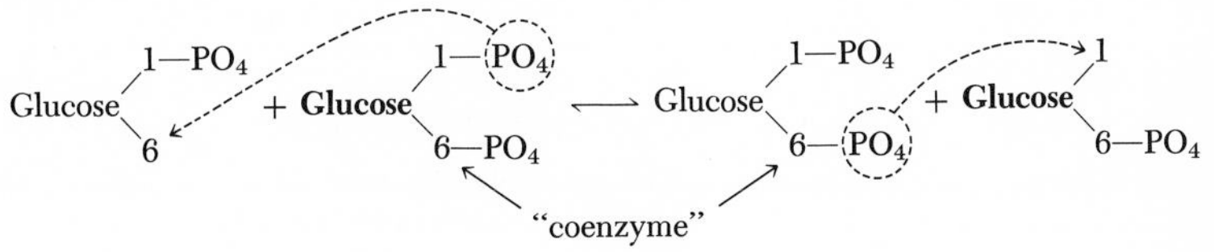

Glucose(1—PO4, 6) + **Glucose**(1—PO4, 6—PO4) ⟷ Glucose(1—PO4, 6—PO4) + **Glucose**(1, 6—PO4)

"coenzyme"

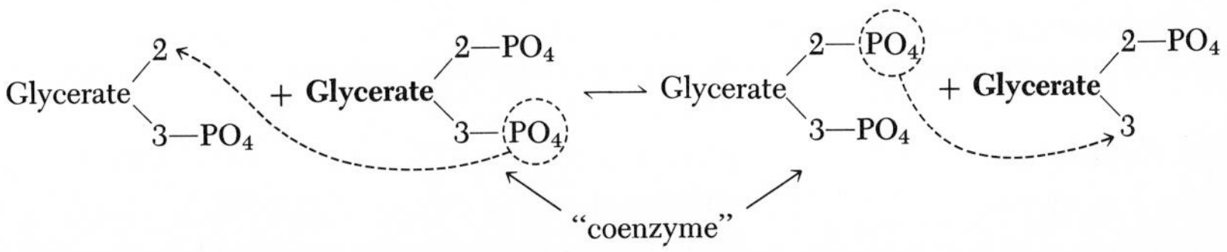

Glycerate(2, 3—PO4) + **Glycerate**(2—PO4, 3—PO4) ⟷ Glycerate(2—PO4, 3—PO4) + **Glycerate**(2—PO4, 3)

"coenzyme"

Transfers of phosphate groups between the adenylic system of compounds (p. 115) and other molecules are catalyzed by the kinases, a group of enzymes which may be subdivided on the basis of reversibility of reaction. (For an explanation of the differences in reversibility,

TABLE 8-6. TRANSPHOSPHORYLASES

ENZYME	REACTION	OCCURRENCE
Phosphomutases		
Phosphoglucomutase	G-1-P $\rightleftharpoons$ G-6-P	All tissues
Phosphoglyceromutase	Glyc-COOH-3-P $\rightleftharpoons$ Glyc-COOH-2-P	All tissues
Phosphoribomutase	R-1-P $\rightleftharpoons$ R-5-P	Liver
"Reversible" kinases		
Phosphoglycerate kinase	Glyc-COOH-3-P + ATP $\rightleftharpoons$ Glyc-COOH-1,3-P + ADP	All tissues
Pyruvate kinase	Pyruvate + ATP $\rightleftharpoons$ Phosphoenolpyruvate + ADP	All tissues
Adenylate kinase (myokinase)	AMP + ATP $\rightleftharpoons$ ADP + ADP	Muscle, heart, brain, liver
Nucleoside monophosphate kinase	Ribosemononucleotides + ATP $\rightleftharpoons$ nucleoside diphosphates + ADP	Liver
Creatine kinase	Creatine + ATP $\rightleftharpoons$ Creatine-P + ADP	Muscle
Diphosphoglycerate-creatine kinase	Creatine + 1,3-diphosphoglycerate $\rightleftharpoons$ creatine-phosphate + 3-phosphoglycerate	Muscle
Carbamate kinase	2ATP + (CO_2 + NH_3) $\rightleftharpoons$ carbamoyl-phosphate + 2ADP + PO_4	Liver
Phosphomevalonate kinase	ATP + 5-phosphomevalonate $\rightleftharpoons$ 5-pyrophosphomevalonate + ADP	Yeast
"Irreversible" kinases		
Hexokinase	{Glucose, Fructose, Mannose} + ATP $\longrightarrow$ {G-, F-, M-} 6-P + ADP	Brain
Glucokinase	G + ATP $\longrightarrow$ G-6-P + ADP	Muscle, liver
Fructokinase	F + ATP $\longrightarrow$ F-1-P + ADP	Liver, intestinal mucosa, (muscle?)
Galactokinase	Gal + ATP $\longrightarrow$ Gal-1-P + ADP	Liver, brain
Phosphofructokinase	F-6-P + ATP $\longrightarrow$ F-1,6-P + ADP	Muscle
Phosphoglucokinase	G-1-P + ATP $\longrightarrow$ G-1,6-P + ADP	Muscle
Adenosine kinase	Adenosine + ATP $\longrightarrow$ AMP + ADP	Kidney, liver
Ribokinase	R + ATP $\longrightarrow$ R-5-P + ADP	Liver
Glycerol kinase	Glycerol + ATP $\longrightarrow$ α-Glycerophosphate + ADP	Liver, kidney
Diglyceride kinase	ATP + diglyceride $\longrightarrow$ phosphatidic acid + ADP	Brain
Mevalonate kinase	ATP + mevalonate $\longrightarrow$ 5-phosphomevalonate + ADP	Yeast, liver
Ribosephosphate pyrophosphokinase	R-5-P + ATP $\longrightarrow$ PP-1-R-5-P + AMP	Liver
Transferases involving substituted phosphate		
Desamido-NAD pyrophosphorylase	Nicotinic acid ribotide + ATP $\rightleftharpoons$ desamido-NAD + PP	Liver
FAD pyrophosphorylase	FMN + ATP $\rightleftharpoons$ FAD + PP	Liver, kidney, yeast
Sulfate-adenyl transferase	ATP + sulfate $\rightleftharpoons$ AMP-sulfate + PP	Liver
Uridyl transferases	UTP + sugar-1-P $\rightleftharpoons$ UDP-sugar + PP	Liver
Cytidyl transferases	CTP + (choline or ethanolamine)-P $\rightleftharpoons$ CDP-(choline or ethanolamine) + PP	Liver

TABLE 8-6. TRANSPHOSPHORYLASES (*Continued*)

ENZYME	REACTION	OCCURRENCE
Transferases involving substituted phosphate (Continued)		
Phosphoryl-(choline or ethanolamine) transferases	CDP-(choline or ethanolamine) + α,β-diglyceride ⟶ CMP + phospholipid (lecithin or cephalin)	Liver
	CDP-choline + ceramide ⟶ sphingomyelin + CMP	Liver
RNA phosphorylase	Nucleoside-DP + (RNA-primer) ⇌ (RNA-primer)-nucleoside-MP + P	Bacteria, sperm
RNA nucleotidyltransferase (polymerase)	Ribonucleoside-TP's ⟶ RNA + PP	All tissues
DNA nucleotidyltransferase (polymerase)	Deoxynucleoside-TP's ⟶ DNA + PP	All tissues

see p. 379). The sub-group of reversible kinases is of importance in the production and storage of energy from the anaerobic breakdown of carbohydrate, while the irreversible group functions largely in the preparation of the carbohydrate substrates for this breakdown, which requires phosphorylated intermediates. An unusual kinase has been described which transfers the carboxyl phosphate of 1,3-diphosphoglycerate directly to creatine without going through the adenylic system. This enzyme is found in skeletal but not in heart muscle. Several reversible kinases are involved in the general metabolism of nucleotides, whereas one, the carbamate kinase, is of importance in the synthesis of urea and pyrimidines.

Enzymes of the hexokinase type have the role of initiating carbohydrate catabolism. Other irreversible kinases are of importance in the metabolism of fats and phospholipids (e.g., the various glycerol kinases) and steroid synthesis (e.g., the mevalonate kinase).

A final category of transphosphorylases includes enzymes catalyzing the transfer, not of phosphate groups as such, but of substituted phosphate. In most, but not all, cases the group transferred is some type of nucleoside phosphate. These rather complex reactions are of considerable importance in intermediary metabolism, and will be discussed in detail in their proper context.

The International Union of Biochemistry system classifies ribonuclease as a phosphotransferase, because of the intermediary formation of cyclic phosphate esters. Since this is a digestive enzyme having an overall hydrolytic action, it will be considered a hydrolase in this chapter (p. 242).

Transfer of Sulfur-Containing Groups

The first enzyme of Table 8-7 catalyzes a reaction which detoxifies cyanide. Some of the sulfatations performed by the second group of enzymes also are detoxications (e.g., conjugation of phenols with sulfate), whereas others are involved in the synthesis of biologically useful products, such as acidic polysaccharides. The CoA-transferase provides for certain tissues a pathway for "activation" and subsequent utilization of acetoacetate.

TABLE 8-7. TRANSFER OF SULFUR-CONTAINING GROUPS

ENZYME	REACTION	OCCURRENCE
Thiosulfate sulfurtransferase (Originally, rhodanese)	Thiosulfate + cyanide ⟶ sulfite + thiocyanate	Liver, kidney
Various sulfotransferases (phenols, arylamines, steroids, polysaccharides)	Phosphoadenosine phosphosulfate + acceptor ⟶ adenosine-3′,5′-P + acceptor-sulfate	Various tissues
β-Ketoacid CoA-transferase	Succinyl-CoA + acetoacetate ⇌ succinate + acetoacetyl-CoA	Heart, muscle

HYDROLASES

Some of the common types of biologically important hydrolytic reactions are shown in Figure 8–9.

Carboxylic Ester Hydrolases

The hydrolysis of esters is catalyzed by a group of enzymes called "esterases," which are listed in Table 8-8 with their typical substrates and their occurrence. By carboxylic

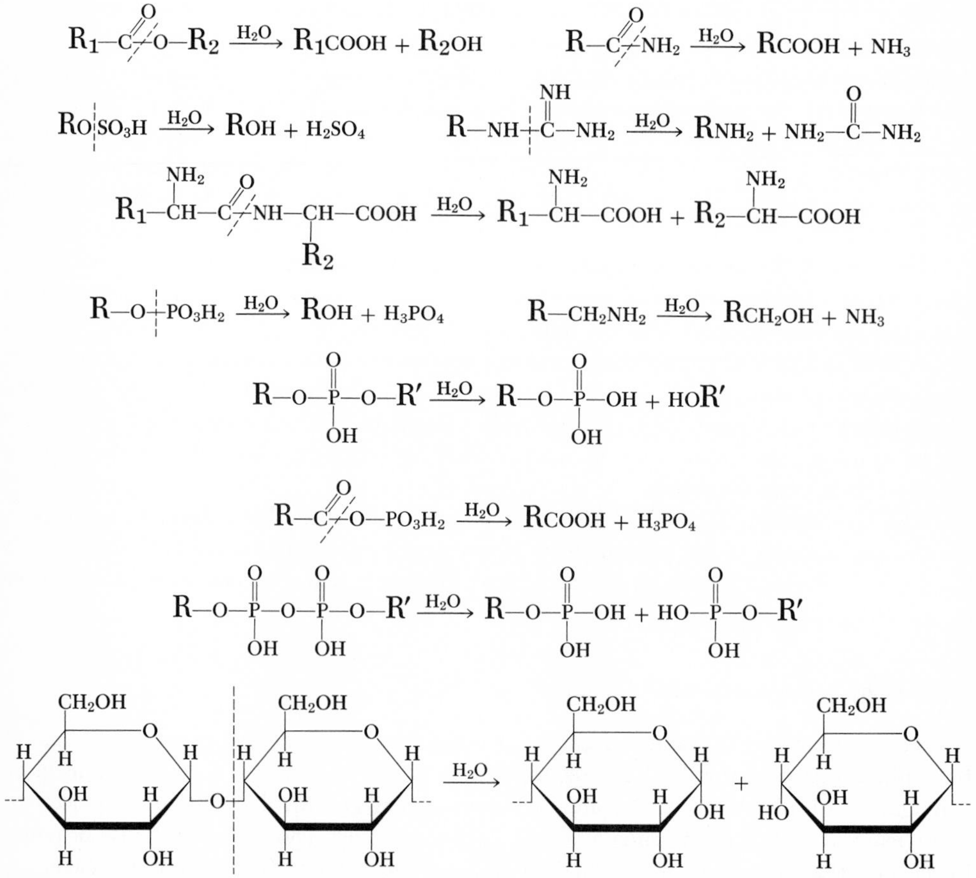

$$R_1{-}\overset{O}{\overset{\|}{C}}{-}O{-}R_2 \xrightarrow{H_2O} R_1COOH + R_2OH \qquad R{-}\overset{O}{\overset{\|}{C}}{-}NH_2 \xrightarrow{H_2O} RCOOH + NH_3$$

$$RO|SO_3H \xrightarrow{H_2O} ROH + H_2SO_4 \qquad R{-}NH{-}\overset{NH}{\overset{\|}{C}}{-}NH_2 \xrightarrow{H_2O} RNH_2 + NH_2{-}\overset{O}{\overset{\|}{C}}{-}NH_2$$

$$R_1{-}\overset{NH_2}{\overset{|}{C}H}{-}\overset{O}{\overset{\|}{C}}{-}NH{-}\underset{R_2}{\underset{|}{C}H}{-}COOH \xrightarrow{H_2O} R_1{-}\overset{NH_2}{\overset{|}{C}H}{-}COOH + R_2{-}\overset{NH_2}{\overset{|}{C}H}{-}COOH$$

$$R{-}O|PO_3H_2 \xrightarrow{H_2O} ROH + H_3PO_4 \qquad R{-}CH_2NH_2 \xrightarrow{H_2O} RCH_2OH + NH_3$$

$$R{-}O{-}\underset{OH}{\underset{|}{\overset{O}{\overset{\|}{P}}}}{-}O{-}R' \xrightarrow{H_2O} R{-}O{-}\underset{OH}{\underset{|}{\overset{O}{\overset{\|}{P}}}}{-}OH + HOR'$$

$$R{-}\overset{O}{\overset{\|}{C}}{-}O{-}PO_3H_2 \xrightarrow{H_2O} RCOOH + H_3PO_4$$

$$R{-}O{-}\underset{OH}{\underset{|}{\overset{O}{\overset{\|}{P}}}}{-}O{-}\underset{OH}{\underset{|}{\overset{O}{\overset{\|}{P}}}}{-}O{-}R' \xrightarrow{H_2O} R{-}O{-}\underset{OH}{\underset{|}{\overset{O}{\overset{\|}{P}}}}{-}OH + HO{-}\underset{OH}{\underset{|}{\overset{O}{\overset{\|}{P}}}}{-}O{-}R'$$

$$(\text{glucose unit, } CH_2OH)\,{-}O{-}\,(\text{glucose unit, } CH_2OH) \xrightarrow{H_2O} (\text{glucose unit, } CH_2OH)\,{-}OH + HO{-}\,(\text{glucose unit, } CH_2OH)$$

Figure 8–9. Common types of biologically important hydrolytic reactions.

ester hydrolases is meant those enzymes which catalyze the hydrolysis of the esters of carboxylic acids. Triglycerides are hydrolyzed by lipases (the fatty acid residues on the α-hydroxyls of the glycerol are cleaved preferentially), whereas simple esters, such as ethyl butyrate, are split most readily by another esterase which has a quite different distribution in animal tissues (carboxylesterase). Other esterases have been described which hydrolyze, respectively, acetic esters and esters of phenols. A specific enzyme, lipoprotein lipase, hydrolyzes triglycerides which are attached to lipoproteins. This enzyme, which is important in the "clearing action" on lipemic plasma, is activated by heparin. Gluconolactonase is an example of an esterase which hydrolyzes a lactone, which is an internal ester. Acetylcholine, a compound of considerable physiological importance, is hydrolyzed by a number of enzymes. One type has a higher affinity for its natural substrate than for any other ester, and is called "acetylcholine esterase." Other esterases are known which attack choline esters more actively than the non-choline esters, but differ from the previously mentioned enzyme in their affinity for various substrates; these enzymes are designated "choline esterases." Since acetylcholine is concerned in the chemical mediation of the transmission of nervous impulses, the physiological function of acetylcholine esterase is thought to be the rapid destruction of the substrate, thus allowing for single rather than continuous nervous discharges. Specific inhibitors of this enzyme have been used in therapy for many years (parasympathomimetics, p. 668). Cholesterol esters are split by an enzyme which has a rather wide distribution. Phospholipase A (formerly lecithinase A) removes one fatty acid molecule (probably an unsaturated one) from lecithins and cephalins, producing the lysolecithins and lysocephalins, from which the remaining fatty acid is removed by phospholipase B (formerly lecithinase B).

Thiolester Hydrolases (Formerly Deacylases)

This relatively new class of esterases consists of those enzymes which hydrolyze the linkage of a carboxyl group with a thiol or sulfhydryl group, the latter usually being a portion of the coenzyme A or glutathione molecule. Since the bonds which are hydrolyzed are of the "high-energy" type (p. 376), and are formed only with the expenditure of chemical work, the action of these enzymes appears to be largely disadvantageous to the organism. Possibly they are concerned in the balance between utilization and production of energy in the body. The acetoacetyl-CoA hydrolase is involved in the production and accumulation of acetoacetic acid which occurs in the liver in certain circumstances.

Sulfatases

Certain natural substrates as well as some of the products of intestinal putrefaction are coupled with sulfuric acid by the tissues. The hydrolysis of these sulfate esters is catalyzed by the sulfatases, a group of enzymes about which very little is known. The physiological significance of these enzymes is not at all certain.

Phosphatases

The phosphatases comprise a large group of enzymes, many of which are involved in important phases of digestion or intermediary metabolism. They can be divided for convenience into the monoesterases and diesterases, the substrates for which are singly or doubly esterified phosphoric acid, respectively. Each of these groups seems to be subdivided into two sub-groups, one of low and one of high specificity. As can be seen in the

Table 8-8. Esterases

CLASS OR INDIVIDUAL ENZYME	TYPICAL SUBSTRATE	OCCURRENCE
I. Carboxylic ester hydrolases		
Carboxylesterase	Simple aliphatic esters	Liver, muscle
Acetylcholine esterase	Acetylcholine	Nervous tissue, muscle, red cell
Choline esterase	Various choline esters	Serum, pancreas
Cholesterol esterase	Cholesterol esters	Blood, pancreas, liver, kidney, spleen, intestinal mucosa
Phospholipase A	Lecithin, cephalin	Pancreas, liver, kidney, heart, muscle, adrenals
Phospholipase B	Lysolecithin, lysocephalin	Pancreas, etc.
Lipase	Fats	Stomach, pancreas
Lipoprotein lipase	Triglyceride attached to plasma lipoproteins	Heart, adipose tissue, serum
Gluconolactonase	δ-Gluconolactone-6-phosphate	Liver
II. Thiolester hydrolases (thiolesterases)		
Acetyl-CoA hydrolase	Acetyl-CoA	Heart
Succinyl-CoA hydrolase	Succinyl-CoA	Heart
Fatty acyl-CoA hydrolase	Fatty acyl-CoA	Liver, brain, kidney
Glutathione thiolesterase	Glutathione thioesters	Brain, liver
Acetoacetyl-CoA hydrolase	Acetoacetyl-CoA	Liver
III. Sulfatases		
Arylsulfatase	Aromatic sulfate esters	Liver, adrenal, kidney
Glycosulfatase	Carbohydrate esters	Mollusk livers
IV. Phosphatases (phosphohydrolases)		
A. Phosphomonoesterases of low specificity		
Alkaline phosphatases (pH 8.6 to 9.4)	Many alcoholic or phenolic monoesters	Plasma, bone, kidney, intestinal mucosa, mammary gland
Acid phosphatases (pH 5.0 to 6.0)	Many alcoholic or phenolic monoesters	Liver, prostate, spleen, kidney, red cell
B. Phosphomonoesterases of higher specificity		
Glucose-6-phosphatase	Glucose-6-phosphate	Liver, kidney, intestine
Hexosediphosphatase	Fructose-1,6-diphosphate	Liver, kidney
5′-Nucleotidase	5′-Nucleotides (adenosine-5′-phosphate, inosine-5′-phosphate)	Testis, retina, nervous tissue, prostate, sperm, posterior pituitary
Phosphoprotein phosphatase	Casein, etc.	Spleen, liver, kidney, etc.
Phosphorylase phosphatase (PR-enzyme)	Phosphorylase a ⟶ phosphorylase b + phosphate	Liver, muscle
Phosphoserine phosphatase	Phosphoserine	Liver
Phosphatidate phosphatase	Phosphatidic acids	Liver, other tissues
C. Phosphodiesterases		
Glycerophosphoryl-choline diesterase	-Glyceryl-phosphoryl┼choline	Pancreas, intestinal mucosa, kidney, liver, brain
Phospholipase C	-Glyceryl┼phosphorylcholine	Pancreas, intestinal mucosa, kidney, liver, brain

TABLE 8-8. ESTERASES (*Continued*)

CLASS OR INDIVIDUAL ENZYME	TYPICAL SUBSTRATE	OCCURRENCE
C. Phosphodiesterases (*Continued*)		
Oligonucleotide phosphodiesterases	Form nucleoside-5′-phosphates from end of poly- and oligo-nucleotides and -deoxy-nucleotides bearing free 3′-OH group	Snake venom, kidney, liver, intestinal mucosa, lung
Oligonucleotide phosphodiesterases	Form 3′-phosphates from above compounds, from end bearing free -5′-OH group	Spleen, thymus, lung, muscle
Extracellular ribonuclease	RNA	Pancreas
Intracellular (acid) ribonuclease	RNA	Most tissues
Intracellular (alkaline) ribonuclease	RNA	Most tissues
Extracellular deoxyribonuclease (DN-ase I)	DNA	Pancreas
Intracellular deoxyribonucleases	DNA	Spleen, thymus, liver

table, the phosphomonoesterases of low specificity are called "alkaline" or "acid" phosphatases, according to their pH optima. The alkaline phosphatases, in addition to their role in hydrolysis of phosphate monoesters in the digestive tract, may play an important part in the calcification of bones and teeth. The alkaline phosphatase level in plasma is increased markedly in certain diseases of bone and in obstructive jaundice. Among the various acid phosphatases, that of the prostate is of special medical significance, since metastasizing cancer of the prostate often results in high levels of this enzyme in the plasma, where it is normally found in minimal amounts. It is possible to differentiate serum acid phosphatase of prostatic from that of other origin by the susceptibility of the former to inhibition by tartrate.

While the phosphatases mentioned thus far show little preference for specific substrates, a few exhibit much more limited activity. The glucose-6-phosphatase and hexosediphosphatase of liver and kidney, for instance, are quite specific for glucose-6-phosphate and fructose-1,6-diphosphate, respectively. They are both important in the anaerobic phase of carbohydrate metabolism. Most so-called "nucleotidases," especially those of the intestinal tract, have turned out to be identical with the non-specific phosphomonoesterases on closer investigation. However, a nucleotidase specific for adenosine-5′-phosphate (or its deaminated derivative) has been found in certain tissues. Specific enzymes appear to catalyze the removal of phosphate groups from phosphoproteins, examples being a phosphatase which attacks phosphoproteins such as casein, and another which inactivates the enzyme, phosphorylase, which is concerned in glycogen metabolism. The phosphatases hydrolyzing phosphoserine and phosphatidic acids play roles in the biosynthesis of serine and triglycerides, respectively.

The phosphoryl-choline and the glyceryl-phosphate linkages which occur in some phospholipids are hydrolyzed by specific diesterases. The general term "nuclease" is sometimes used to include all enzymes concerned in the hydrolysis of nucleic acids. Two general classes seem to exist, exo- and endo-nucleases. The former class is represented by two types of relatively non-specific oligonucleotide phosphodiesterases, each of which attacks a different end of an oligonucleotide chain and forms different products, as indicated in the table. The hydrolysis of internal diester linkages in nucleic acids in the gastrointestinal tract is catalyzed by endonucleases (nucleodepolymerases) which are secreted by the pancreas, these enzymes being designated in Table 8-8 as extracellular ribonuclease and deoxyribonuclease, respectively. The action of these enzymes is not a simple random attack upon all the diester linkages in the substrates. It has been shown that pyrimidine-containing fragments are split off preferentially during the action of pancreatic ribonuclease, which appears to involve cyclic 2′,3′-phosphate esters as intermediates, as in the alkaline hydrolysis of RNA. The products are largely pyrimidine nucleoside-3′-phosphates and a purine-rich, resistant "core." On the other hand, pancreatic deoxyribonuclease produces a mixture of mono- and oligo-nucleotides terminating in 5′-phosphate linkages. Presumably, the unhydrolyzed diester linkages remaining after the action of pancreatic ribonuclease and deoxyribonuclease are attacked by the non-specific phosphodiesterases mentioned previously. Intracellular ribonucleases having acidic and basic pH optima also exist, but have not been well characterized. Certain intracellular deoxyribonucleases appear to catalyze the same type of reaction as the pancreatic enzyme (so-called "Type I" DN-ase), whereas others ("Type II"), particularly one found in spleen, produce nucleotides having 3′-phosphate terminal linkages.

Glycosylases (Glycosidases)

The second large group of hydrolytic enzymes includes those which attack glycosidic linkages. As indicated in Table 8-9, they may be divided into two sub-groups, the first being those enzymes which are specific for the simple glycosides and the oligosaccharides, the second comprising those enzymes which attack the polysaccharides. Enzymes hydrolyzing carbohydrates are sometimes collectively called "carbohydrases."

α- and β-Glycosidic linkages are hydrolyzed by different groups of enzymes. Among the α-glycosidases are a number of α-glucosidases with rather broad specificity, to one or more of which the name "maltase" has been applied in the past. There is no evidence of a specific "sucrase" in mammalian tissues or digestive juices, although one of the α-glucosidases (α-glucosidoinvertase) attacks sucrose more rapidly than maltose. An enzyme of this type is sometimes called an "invertase," from its catalysis of the inversion of sucrose (p. 15). The invertase of yeast differs from that of animal tissues; the former is a β-fructosidase, whereas the latter has its specificity directed toward the α-glucosidic half of the substrate molecule. Various β-glucosides and β-galactosides are hydrolyzed by enzymes which have been called "β-glucosidases" and "β-galactosidases," but there is still some controversy over the separate existence of these two groups, at least in animal tissues. In any case, the disaccharide lactose is hydrolyzed by whatever system attacks β-galactosides generally, not by a specific lactase. The nicotinamide-β-riboside bond appears to be hydrolyzed by a specific enzyme which attacks the coenzyme, NAD (DPN).

β-Glucuronidase, an enzyme attacking the glycosidic linkage in natural and synthetic glucuronides, has been implicated in estrogen metabolism and in the process of cell division and multiplication. The level of this enzyme in various tissues is increased by administration of estrogens, a finding which may be correlated with the conjugation of estrogens with glucuronic acid in the body. Increased amounts of the enzyme have also been found in certain tumors.

Of the various enzymes which catalyze the hydrolysis of the homopolysaccharides, the

TABLE 8-9. GLYCOSIDASES

ENZYME	SUBSTRATE	OCCURRENCE
I. Simple glycosidases		
A. α-Glycosidases		
α-Glucosidase ("maltase")	Various α-glucosides including maltose and sucrose	Intestinal juice
α-Glucosidoinvertase ("sucrase")	Various α-glucosides including maltose and sucrose	Intestinal juice
B. β-Glycosidases		
β-Glucosidase	Various β-glucosides	Kidney, liver, intestinal mucosa
β-Galactosidase ("lactase")	Various β-galactosides	Kidney, liver, intestinal mucosa
β-Glucuronidase	β-Glucuronides	Spleen, liver, endocrines
NAD nucleosidase	Nicotinamide-┼-ribose-pyrophosphate-ribose-adenine	Spleen, brain, erythrocytes
II. Polysaccharidases and oligosaccharidases		
A. Homopolysaccharidases		
Exoamylases (β-amylases)	Starch, glycogen	Higher plants
Endoamylases (α-amylases)	Starch, glycogen	Saliva, pancreas, blood, muscle, liver
B. Oligosaccharidases		
Oligo-1,6-glucosidase	α-1,6 Linkages of dextrins	Intestinal mucosa
Dextrin-1,6-glucosidase	α-1,6 Linkages of glycogen	Liver, muscle
C. Heteropolysaccharidases (Mucopolysaccharidases, mucases)		
Hyaluronidase	Hyaluronate, chondroitin sulfates	Testis
Muramidase (lysozyme)	Polysaccharides of Micrococcus lysodeikticus	Nasal secretions, egg white, spleen
Heparinase	Heparin	Kidney, liver
Neuraminidase (sialidase)	Terminal sialic residues in mucopolysaccharides or mucooligosaccharides	Influenza virus, Vibrio cholerae

amylases are most important in mammalian metabolism, since their substrates include the starches and glycogen. In the body, except in the digestive tract, glycogen is broken down by phosphorolysis, not hydrolysis. (Although intracellular amylases have been described, such as that in liver, it is not believed that these enzymes play a significant role in intermediary metabolism.) There are two types of amylases, differing considerably in their modes of action. The exoamylases or β-amylases are found chiefly in the higher plants. They produce β-maltose from the substrate, appear to attack the ends of the polysaccharide chains, form no non-fermentable products and cause only a slow decrease in the viscosity of starch solutions. Amylose is split completely, amylopectin and glycogen only at the end chains up to the branching points. Salivary and pancreatic amylases belong to the group of endoamylases or α-amylases. These enzymes attack the interior of polysaccharide chains, forming products of the α-configuration. Although some reducing sugar and fermentable substances are produced throughout the reaction, the main course of events is the breakdown of the polysaccharides first to dextrins (accompanied by marked reduction in the viscosity of the solution), followed by a slower phase of maltose formation. The animal amylases require the presence of chloride or related anions for their activity. Since the action of the amylases is limited to α-1,4-glucosidic linkages, the 1,6- branch points in amylopectin and glycogen are hydrolyzed by other enzymes, such as the oligo-1,6-glucosidase. (An intracellular 1,6-glucosidase hydrolyzes the branch points left after the action of phosphorylase on glycogen.) Preparations of salivary or pancreatic amylase will not attack raw starch, although this substance is known to be well utilized by the intact organism. It has been suggested that auxiliary enzymes are present in the pancreatic juice, enabling the organism to digest this substrate.

As was pointed out in the chapter on carbohydrate chemistry, the nitrogenous heteropolysaccharides (mucopolysaccharides) are the only members of this group which need be considered in animal metabolism. Hyaluronic acid is hydrolyzed by hyaluronidase. Since hyaluronic acid acts as an intercellular cement, the fact that certain pathogenic microorganisms possess hyaluronidases has been thought to be related to their invasiveness. Attempts have also been made to relate hyaluronidase to the fertilization of the ovum and to the invasiveness of malignant cells, but these hypotheses are not widely held at the present time. Nevertheless, with the present interest in hyaluronic acid and disorders of the mesenchyme, an important role for hyaluronidase will probably be established eventually.

Micrococcus lysodeikticus contains, in its cell wall, a mucopolysaccharide which is hydrolyzed by muramidase (lysozyme), an enzyme found in egg white and in the nasal secretions. No metabolic role has as yet been shown for this enzyme.

Specific enzymes hydrolyzing the chondroitin sulfates and related compounds have yet to be isolated from animal tissues. These substrates are attacked by testicular hyaluronidase. A partially purified heparinase has been prepared from liver.

Neuraminidase (sialidase) may be of importance in the attack of certain microorganisms, including viruses, on tissues protected by a coating of mucin.

Hydrolases Acting on Ethers

The only known enzyme in this category is a thioether hydrolase found in liver, which attacks S-adenosylhomocysteine, the residue which remains after S-adenosylmethionine has performed a transmethylation.

Peptidases

Peptide linkages are hydrolyzed by a large group of enzymes, sometimes called "proteases," listed in Table 8-10. There are two subdivisions of the peptidases: the exopeptidases are limited in their action to terminal peptide bonds, whereas the endopeptidases can hydrolyze peptide linkages whether terminal or in the interior of the peptide chain. The specificity of the peptidases is further determined by the nature of the side-chain groups in the amino acid residues on either side of the peptide linkage.

Carboxypeptidase A, an exopeptidase, is synthesized by the pancreas in the form of a zymogen which is converted to the active enzyme by the action of trypsin. The highly purified, crystallized enzyme contains zinc in firm combination. As indicated by its name, it requires the presence of a free carboxyl group on the amino acid residue which contributes its amino group to the peptide linkage being attacked. Peptides containing the amino acid termini indicated in the table are hydrolyzed with the greatest speed; others are attacked more slowly. The closely related carboxypeptidase B has a similar action, but is specific for basic amino acid residues.

Leucine aminopeptidase is found in the intestinal mucosa and many other tissues.

Table 8-10. Peptidases

ENZYME	SUBSTRATE	OCCURRENCE
I. Exopeptidases		
Carboxypeptidase A	—NH—CHR—CO¦NH—CHR′—COOH phenylalanine tyrosine tryptophan leucine	Pancreas
Carboxypeptidase B	—NH—CHR—CO¦basic amino acids	Pancreas
Leucine amino-peptidase	NH_2CHR—CO¦NH—CHR′—CO—leucine	Intestinal mucosa
Aminotripeptidase	NH_2CHR—CO¦NH—CHR′—CO— —NH—CHR″—COOH	Intestinal mucosa, thymus, muscle
Glycylglycine dipeptidase	Glycyl¦glycine	Muscle, uterus
Glycylleucine dipeptidase	Glycyl¦leucine	Muscle, intestinal mucosa, uterus
Prolidase, imidodipeptidase	Glycyl¦proline	Intestinal mucosa, muscle
Prolinase, iminodipeptidase	Prolyl¦glycine	Intestinal mucosa
Carnosinase, aminoacyl-histidine dipeptidase	β-alanyl¦L-histidine (carnosine) glycyl¦L-histidine -L-alanyl¦L-histidine -D-alanyl¦L-histidine	Kidney
Alanylglycine dipeptidase	Alanyl¦glycine	Intestinal mucosa
Cysteinylglycine dipeptidase	Cysteinyl¦glycine	Liver, muscle, kidney
II. Endopeptidases		
Pepsin, parapepsins	-glutamyl¦tyrosyl- -glutamyl¦phenylalanyl- -cysteinyl¦tyrosyl- -tyrosyl¦cysteinyl-	Gastric mucosa
Gastricsin	Proteins	Gastric mucosa
Rennin	Casein	Gastric mucosa
Trypsin	-arginyl¦ -lysyl¦	Pancreas
Chymotrypsin, chymotrypsin B	-tyrosyl¦ -phenylalanyl¦ -tryptophanyl¦ -methionyl¦	Pancreas
Pancreatopeptidase E (formerly, elastase)	Peptide bonds adjacent to neutral amino acid residues	Pancreas
Renin	Hypertensinogen	Kidney
Thrombin	Fibrinogen	Serum
Plasmin	Fibrin	Serum
Cathepsin A	Carbobenzoxy-glutamyl¦tyrosine	Spleen, liver, kidney
Cathepsin B	Benzoyl-arginyl¦amide	Spleen, liver, kidney
Cathepsin C	Glycyltyrosyl¦amide	Spleen, liver, kidney
Enteropeptidase (formerly, enterokinase)	Trypsinogen	Intestinal juice

Magnesium or manganese can play the role of ion activator. Leucyl peptides are hydrolyzed more readily, but not exclusively. In contrast to the preceding enzymes, leucine aminopeptidase requires a free amino group for its action. The enzyme formerly called cathepsin III is probably identical with leucine aminopeptidase.

Aminotripeptidase hydrolyzes the peptide linkage adjacent to the free amino group of a number of tripeptides, although it is necessary that the distal carboxyl group also be free. This enzyme has little or no action on dipeptides or tetrapeptides. It is not certain at present whether it requires any metallic ion for activation.

The existence of a general dipeptidase was assumed for many years, but the evidence accumulated in recent times makes it probable that a multiplicity of dipeptidases exists, each characterized by its own specificity. Thus, glycylglycine dipeptidase hydrolyzes the peptide named and practically no other. It requires cobalt or manganese ions. Glycylleucine dipeptidases are found in several tissues, that from rabbit muscle and hog intestinal mucosa being activated by manganese, whereas the corresponding enzymes from rat muscle or human uterus require zinc. Prolidase and prolinase are apparently distinct enzymes, although both are activated by manganese. Carnosinase is the name given to the enzyme which hydrolyzes carnosine, a peptide occurring in rather large quantities in animal tissues. As indicated in the table, the action is not entirely specific. Either zinc or manganese can serve as activator. Enzymes attacking certain alanine dipeptides are known, although they have not been well characterized as yet. Cysteinylglycine dipeptidase is probably involved in the breakdown of glutathione, which proceeds in two stages, the first being removal of the γ-glutamyl residue from the tripeptide.

Pepsin is the most thoroughly studied of all the endopeptidases. It is secreted by the gastric mucosa in the form of the inactive pepsinogen, which is converted to pepsin under the influence of hydrogen ions, and also by the autocatalytic action of pepsin itself. The conversion involves the splitting off of an inhibitor, a basic peptide of 3242 molecular weight as well as five neutral peptides having a total molecular weight of 4000. It is of interest that pepsinogen has an isoelectric point of pH 3.7, while pepsin is anionic even at pH 1.0. This difference is probably accounted for by the nature of the inhibitor. Pepsin also has a lower molecular weight than pepsinogen, the difference being explained by the removal of the peptides. Pepsin contains no special prosthetic groups other than a molecule of phosphoric acid. Its specificity is directed toward those peptide linkages formed by the amino groups of phenylalanine or tyrosine, the action being accelerated by the presence of a carboxyl group (glutamic acid) in the immediate vicinity. Recently such combinations as cysteinyl-tyrosyl- and tyrosyl-cysteinyl- have been shown to be suitable substrates also. The hydrolysis of proteins by pepsin exhibits a pH optimum in the range 1.5 to 2.5. Pepsin also possesses a milk-clotting action (see rennin, below), with an optimal pH of about 5.

Rennin is an enzyme found in the stomach of the young mammal, formed by the activation by hydrogen ions of the zymogen, prorennin. Although pure rennin has definite proteolytic activity, with an optimum pH of 3.7 when hemoglobin is the substrate, the chief interest in this enzyme centers about its milk-clotting activity. Under the influence of rennin, casein is converted to paracasein (pH optimum for this reaction, 5.4), which in the presence of calcium ions flocculates out of solution as a curd. Despite much effort extending over many years, the exact nature of the casein-paracasein conversion is not known.

There have been a number of attempts to establish the existence, in the stomach, of proteolytic enzymes other than pepsin and rennin. Of these, gastricsin appears to be well established as a separate entity; its specificity toward linkages within the proteins which it attacks is not known. The parapepsins resemble pepsin in specificity. There is evidence for a total of three pepsin-like enzymes in the human gastric mucosa; one of these may be identical with gastricsin.

The pre-enzyme trypsinogen, secreted by the pancreas, is converted to trypsin by another enzyme, enteropeptidase (enterokinase), which is found in the small intestine. The process involves cleavage of a peptide bond near the N-terminal portion of the trypsinogen molecule, resulting in the liberation of a peptide having the structure: Val-$(Asp)_4$-Lys. The optimal pH range for this conversion extends from 6.0 to 9.0. Trypsin can also be formed autocatalytically from trypsinogen. In this case the reaction proceeds optimally at pH 7 to 8. The activation of trypsinogen is greatly accelerated by calcium salts. The pH optimum for the hydrolysis of proteins by trypsin varies somewhat with different substrates, but is usually found around pH 8. It is of interest that denatured proteins are hydrolyzed much more readily than those in the native state. Trypsin specifically attacks those peptide linkages containing the carboxyl groups of arginine or lysine. Pancreatic extracts, soybeans, egg white, and blood contain trypsin inhibitors which are proteins or polypeptides.

A second proteolytic enzyme originating in the pancreas is chymotrypsin, so named from its powerful milk-clotting action. Its pre-enzyme, chymotrypsinogen, is converted to the active enzyme by trypsin, a process thought to involve the opening of internal peptide bonds in the zymogen molecule as well as liberation of a basic peptide. Several alternate pathways of activation are open to chymotrypsinogen, resulting in different products or mixtures of products. In what is probably the major pathway of activation, a cyclic portion of the peptide structure of the zymogen is opened by the cleavage of a peptide link between an isoleucine residue and the arginine residue in the sequence leucyl-seryl-arginine, forming π-chymotrypsin. This first step is catalyzed by trypsin. The second step, which is catalyzed by chymotrypsin itself, involves removal of a seryl-arginine group from the sequence mentioned in π-chymotrypsin, forming Δ-chymotrypsin. The optimum pH for proteolysis by chymotrypsin is about the same as that for trypsin. There is considerable difference in specificity, however, the action of chymotrypsin being directed toward peptide linkages containing the carboxyl groups of aromatic amino acids, tryptophan, or methionine. Chymotrypsinogen B, which accompanies ordinary chymotrypsinogen (type "A") in pancreatic juice, is activated to chymotrypsin B, an enzyme with the same specificity as type A.

Elastin, a connective tissue protein, is hydrolyzed by an enzyme from the pancreas formerly called elastase (now pancreatopeptidase E), now recognized as an endopeptidase with some specificity toward amino acid residues with electrically neutral side chains. Renin (not to be confused with rennin), a proteolytic enzyme produced in the kidney, acts upon its substrate, hypertensinogen, a peptide-like material found in serum, to form hypertensin (angiotonin), a vasopressor substance. Thrombin and plasmin are discussed further in connection with other factors concerned in the process of blood coagulation.

Intracellular proteolytic enzymes known as cathepsins are widely distributed throughout animal tissues. They are presumably responsible for the autolysis undergone by the tissues after death. In life, the cathepsins may function in the continual breakdown of tissue protein which is known to occur, and which, together with the counterbalancing synthetic reactions, forms the mechanism underlying the "dynamic state" of body proteins. The cathepsins exhibit a range of individual specificities comparable to that of the extracellular proteinases.

Hydrolases Acting on C-N Bonds Other than Peptide (Amidases and Related Enzymes)

Some of the more important amidases and related enzymes are shown in Table 8-11. Under the influence of urease, urea, the diamide of carbonic acid, is hydrolyzed to a

TABLE 8-11. AMIDASES AND RELATED ENZYMES

ENZYME	SUBSTRATE OR REACTION	OCCURRENCE
Urease	$H_2N \vdots CO \vdots NH_2$	Bacteria, yeasts, molds, plants, mollusks
Asparaginase	$HOOC—CHNH_2—CH_2—CO \vdots NH_2$	Yeast, serum
Glutaminase	$HOOC—CHNH_2—CH_2—CH_2—CO \vdots NH_2$	Plants, liver, kidney, brain, spleen, bacteria
Arginase	$NH_2—C{:}NH \vdots NH—CH_2—CH_2—CH_2—CHNH_2—COOH$	Liver, mammary gland, testis, kidney
Ω-amidase	α-Ketoglutaramate or α-ketosuccinamate	Liver
Formamidase	Formylkynurenine	Liver
Dihydropyrimidinase	Dihydropyrimidines ⟶ β-ureido acids	Liver
β-Ureidases	β-Ureido acids ⟶ β-amino acids + CO_2 + NH_3	Liver
Imidazolonepropionase	Imidazolone propionate ⟶ N-formimino-L-glutamate	Liver
Aminoacylase I	N-acylamino acids (except aspartate)	Kidney
Aspartoacylase (formerly, aminoacylase II)	N-acylaspartates	Kidney
Acyl-lysine deacylase	ε-N-acyl-lysines	Kidney
5′-Adenylic acid deaminase	6-Amino¦purine-ribose-5′-phosphate	Muscle, nerve, erythrocytes
3′-Adenylic acid deaminase	6-Amino¦purine-ribose-3′-phosphate	Spleen, kidney, liver
Guanylic acid deaminase	2-Amino¦6-hydroxypurine-ribose-5′-phosphate	Liver
Adenosine deaminase	6-Amino¦purine-ribose	Kidney, liver, muscle, heart, nerve, intestinal mucosa
Guanosine deaminase	2-Amino¦6-hydroxypurine-ribose	Brain, pancreas, liver, spleen
Cytidine deaminase	6-Amino¦2-hydroxy-pyrimidine-ribose	Liver, kidney
Guanine deaminase (formerly, guanase)	2-Amino¦6-hydroxypurine	Liver, pancreas, spleen, kidneys

molecule of carbon dioxide and two molecules of ammonia, these products forming ammonium carbonate in solution. Urease is predominantly a member of the plant world. Its current importance in biochemistry derives largely from its use as an analytical reagent in the determination of blood urea. Urease was the first enzyme to be crystallized.

The amides, asparagine and glutamine, are ubiquitous in both plant and animal kingdoms. Much of the glutamic and aspartic acid found in proteins is actually present in the form of the amides. In addition, both amides appear to function as temporary stores of ammonia, which is quite toxic to the cells and cannot be allowed to remain in the free state. When required, the ammonia is set free by the appropriate hydrolytic enzyme. In the kidney, for example, the hydrolysis of glutamine by glutaminase provides much of the urinary ammonia which plays an important role in the regulation of "acid-base" balance. This enzyme was formerly designated glutaminase I, in order to differentiate it from a supposed glutaminase II, which required keto acids for its action. The latter has since been shown to be a mixture of two enzymes, one a transaminase which forms an α-keto acid amide, which in turn is the substrate for a true amidase discussed below.

The amidine group of arginine is split off under the influence of arginase (an amidinase) to yield (after a spontaneous rearrangement) urea and ornithine. This reaction is the final step in the ornithine cycle, a metabolic mechanism used by many organisms for the synthesis of urea from the nitrogen derived from the catabolism of protein.

The ω-amidase hydrolyzes the amides resulting from the action of specific transaminases upon glutamine and asparagine. Formamidase is involved in the metabolism of tryptophan. In the course of pyrimidine metabolism, dihydropyrimidines are formed. These intermediates are hydrolyzed to β-ureido acids, which are hydrolyzed in turn to β-amino acids, by enzymes related to the amidases. Another enzyme related to the amidases opens the heterocyclic ring of imidazolone propionate, a metabolite of histidine. The kidney contains a number of amino acid deacylases, one of wide and two of narrower specificity.

Although deamination of amino acids in animal tissues proceeds via an oxidative route, or by the mechanism known as transamination, removal of the amino group from purines and pyrimidines and their derivatives is catalyzed by hydrolytic enzymes. The aminopurines and aminopyrimidines may be classified chemically as cyclic amidines, thus placing the hydrolases which remove their amino groups in a category related to the amidases. Adenine (as the nucleoside, or nucleotide) is converted to the corresponding derivatives of the hydroxy-compound, hypoxanthine, while guanine and cytosine form xanthine and uracil, respectively. The deaminated nucleotide formed from 5′-adenylic acid is known as inosinic acid, and may be produced in some of the side reactions of muscle contraction. It is possible that enzymes of this type exist for all purines and pyrimidines bearing amino groups, but this group of hydrolases has not been studied in detail in animal tissues.

Hydrolases Acting on Acid Anhydride Bonds

Table 8-12 lists those hydrolases specific for the anhydride bond. It will be noted that all substrates of enzymes of this class recognized up to this time involve phosphoric acid as one or both of the participants in the susceptible linkages. The physiological significance of trimetaphosphatase is unknown at present. Many tissues contain an inorganic pyrophosphatase activity, which, by maintaining a low level of pyrophosphate, may aid in converting certain reversible "activating" reactions (which yield pyrophosphate) to practically irreversible types. Evidence has been presented that "inorganic pyrophosphatase" may be identical with the well-known glucose-6-phosphatase.

Adenosinetriphosphatases (ATPases) rarely, if ever, appear to be concerned solely with the simple hydrolysis of the terminal pyrophosphate bond of the substrate, although this is the overall reaction. For one thing, ATPases are associated with formed elements, such

TABLE 8-12. HYDROLASES ACTING ON ACID ANHYDRIDE BONDS

Trimetaphosphatase	$(HPO_3)_3$	Liver, kidney
Inorganic pyrophosphatase	$H_4P_2O_7$	Wide distribution
ATPases	ATP	Wide distribution
Nucleosidediphosphatase	Nucleoside diphosphates (IDP, GDP, UDP, R-5-PP)	Liver, kidney
Nucleotide pyrophosphatase	Pyrophosphate bond of dinucleotides (FAD, NAD)	Liver, kidney
Acyl phosphatase	Acyl phosphates, probably acyl adenylates	Muscle, liver, kidney

as intracellular structures or cell membranes. Myosin ATPase is associated with the mechanism of muscle contraction, mitochondrial ATPase with (probably) the mechanism for securing energy from biological oxidations, and "microsomal" and membrane ATPases (many of which are activated by ions of the alkali metals, such as Na^+) with (possibly) ion concentration and transport across membranes.

Terminal pyrophosphate linkages in certain nucleoside diphosphates, and central pyrophosphate linkages in dinucleotide coenzymes are hydrolyzed by two enzymes found in liver and kidney. Mixed anhydride linkages of carboxylic acids and phosphoric acid or substituted phosphoric acid (adenylic acid), which represent "activated" forms of certain metabolites, are hydrolyzed by an acyl phosphatase. Such degradative reactions may play a role in maintaining the balance between anabolism and catabolism in the cell.

Other Hydrolases

Several hydrolases are known which do not fit into the above classes. These include (a) fumarylacetoacetate hydrolase, involved in tyrosine metabolism, an enzyme acting on a C-C linkage; (b) an alkylhalidase of unknown significance, acting on C-halide bonds; (c) phosphoamidase, a P-N cleaving hydrolase which attacks phosphocreatine, phosphoarginine, and other phosphoamides.

LYASES

(De)hydratases

The dehydratases and other lyases are listed in Table 8-13. Enolase is an enzyme of importance in the anaerobic metabolism of carbohydrate, while fumarase and aconitase are involved in the aerobic phases of the oxidation of carbohydrate as well as other foodstuffs. The enolase reaction is of special importance in bioenergetics, since it results in the formation of a "high-energy" phosphate bond (p. 376). Enolase requires magnesium for its action, and is inhibited by fluoride.

Serine, homoserine, and threonine are deaminated by a rather unusual reaction. A molecule of water is removed from the β- (or γ-) hydroxyl group and a hydrogen atom on the α-carbon. In the case of homoserine, the double bond then shifts to the α-β position. The resulting amino-acrylic acid derivative spontaneously hydrolyzes to yield a molecule of ammonia and the keto acid. Pyridoxal phosphate is the coenzyme of all three systems. Serine dehydratase also catalyzes the synthesis of cystathionine from serine and homocysteine, whereas homoserine dehydratase also splits cystathionine into cysteine, α-ketobutyrate, and ammonia.

Carbonic anhydrase is a zinc-containing enzyme, inhibited by rather low concentrations of the sulfa drugs. Its catalysis of the reversible hydration of CO_2 is of great importance in gas transport in the blood and secretion of acid by the kidney.

Enoyl-CoA hydratase (crotonase) is important in the metabolism of fatty acids.

(De)sulfhydrases and Related Lyases

Reactions analogous to the dehydrations of serine, homoserine, and threonine are undergone by cysteine and homocysteine (the amino acid resulting from the demethylation of methionine), except that H_2S is removed instead of H_2O. Pyridoxal phosphate is again the coenzyme. The "glyoxalase I" reaction shown in the table is the first of two steps; methyl glyoxal is condensed with glutathione under the influence of an enzyme to form a thioester; in the second step, the complex is broken down in a slow spontaneous reaction, or more rapidly in the presence of a second enzyme, forming the hydroxy acid and regenerating the glutathione. It is of interest that the lactic acid thus produced is of the D configuration, whereas L-lactic acid is formed in the normal anaerobic metabolism of carbohydrate. Although methyl glyoxal is in all probability not a normal intermediate, it may be formed in small quantities by the spontaneous decomposition of triose phosphates; the glyoxalase reaction may then have a "mopping up" function.

Non-oxidative (De)carboxylases

Many decarboxylations of amino acids to the corresponding amines occur in the intestine as the result of bacterial action. A few such reactions are also catalyzed by enzymes in the tissues. The coenzyme for many bacterial and mammalian amino acid decarboxylases is pyridoxal phosphate.

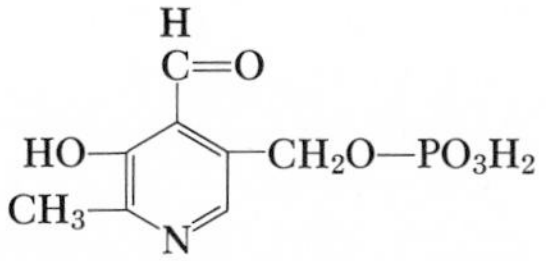

H
C=O
HO— —$CH_2O—PO_3H_2$
CH_3— N

Tyrosine is decarboxylated in a reaction the metabolic importance of which remains to be seen. γ-Aminobutyrate, the product of glutamate decarboxylation, appears to be an inhibitor of synaptic transmission in the central nervous system. 3,4-Dihydroxyphenyalanine (abbreviated "dopa") decarboxylase is involved in the synthesis of epinephrine (adrenaline) and melanin from tyrosine. Decarboxylation of histidine gives rise to the potent pharmacological agent, histamine. A serum vasoconstrictor and neurohormone, serotonin (5-hydroxytryptamine), is formed from a derivative of tryptophan. Cysteic acid, an oxidation product of cysteine, decarboxylates to taurine, a compound found conjugated to certain bile acids. A more important pathway to taurine is via hypotaurine, which is formed by the decarboxylation of cysteine sulfinate.

A number of keto acids are decarboxylated non-oxidatively. The pyruvate decarboxylase of plants is included in the table for the sake of contrast; the normal decarboxylation of this substrate in animal tissues is oxidative. Thiamine pyrophosphate ("cocarboxylase") acts as the sole coenzyme for the non-oxidative, and, in association with other cofactors, for the oxidative reaction (p. 409).

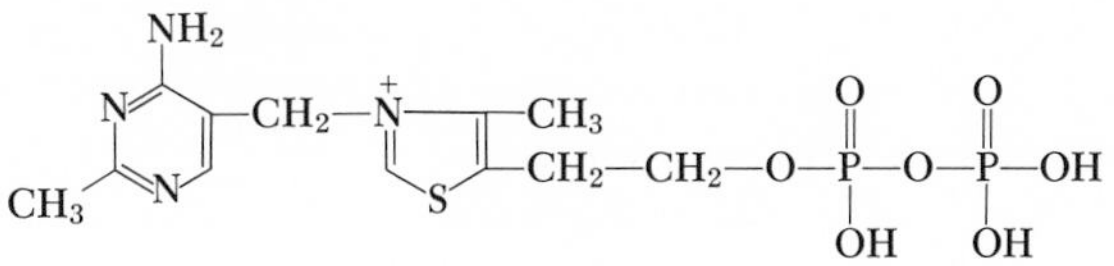

NH_2
N —CH_2—$\overset{+}{N}$— —CH_3
O O
—CH_2—CH_2—O—P—O—P—OH
CH_3 N S
OH OH

By coupling decarboxylation with the appropriate interconversions of compounds containing "high-energy" bonds (p. 376), the reaction can be made reversible, as in the case of phosphopyruvate carboxylase.

Orotidylate decarboxylase is a key enzyme in the synthesis of pyrimidines.

TABLE 8-13. LYASES

ENZYME	REACTION	OCCURRENCE
(De)hydratases		
Phosphopyruvate hydratase (enolase)	2-Phosphoglycerate $\underset{+H_2O}{\overset{-H_2O}{\rightleftharpoons}}$ phosphoenolpyruvate	All tissues
Fumarate hydratase (fumarase)	Fumarate $\underset{-H_2O}{\overset{+H_2O}{\rightleftharpoons}}$ malate	All tissues
Aconitate hydratase (aconitase)	Citrate $\underset{+H_2O}{\overset{-H_2O}{\rightleftharpoons}}$ *cis*-aconitate	All tissues
	Isocitrate $\underset{+H_2O}{\overset{-H_2O}{\rightleftharpoons}}$ *cis*-aconitate	
Serine dehydratase (formerly, cystathionine synthetase)	Serine $\xrightarrow{-H_2O}$ pyruvate + NH_3	Liver
Threonine dehydratase	Threonine $\xrightarrow{-H_2O}$ α-ketobutyrate + NH_3	Liver
Homoserine dehydratase (formerly, cystathionase)	Homoserine $\xrightarrow{-H_2O}$ α-ketobutyrate + NH_3 Cystathionine ⟶ cysteine + α-ketobutyrate + NH_3	Liver, kidney, pancreas
Carbonic anhydrase (carbonate dehydratase)	$H_2CO_3 \longleftrightarrow CO_2 + H_2O$	Red cells, gastric mucosa, renal tubules
Enoyl-CoA hydratase (crotonase)	α,β-Unsaturated acyl-CoA $\underset{-H_2O}{\overset{+H_2O}{\rightleftharpoons}}$ β-hydroxyacyl-CoA	Liver
(De)sulfhydrases		
Cysteine desulfhydrase	Cysteine $\xrightarrow{-H_2S}$ pyruvate + NH_3	Bacteria, liver, pancreas, kidney
Homocysteine desulfhydrase	Homocysteine $\xrightarrow{-H_2S}$ α-ketobutyrate + NH_3	Liver, kidney, pancreas
Lactoyl-glutathione lyase (formerly, glyoxalase I)	Methylglyoxal + glutathione ⟶ S-lactoylglutathione	Liver, kidney, muscle
(De)carboxylases		
Dopa decarboxylase	Dopa ⟶ dopamine + CO_2	Kidney (man); liver, intestine, pancreas (in some species)
Glutamate decarboxylase	Glutamate ⟶ γ-aminobutyrate + CO_2	Brain, bacteria
Tyrosine decarboxylase	Tyrosine ⟶ tyramine + CO_2	Kidney
Histidine decarboxylase	Histidine ⟶ histamine + CO_2	Intestine (man); liver, kidney, intestine (other species)
Hydroxytryptophan decarboxylase	5-Hydroxytryptophan ⟶ CO_2 + 5-hydroxytryptamine (serotonin)	Kidney, liver, gastrointestinal tract, lung, brain
Cysteate decarboxylase	Cysteate ⟶ taurine + CO_2	Liver
Cysteine sulfinate decarboxylase	Cysteine sulfinate ⟶ CO_2 + hypotaurine	Liver, kidney
Pyruvate decarboxylase	Pyruvate ⟶ acetaldehyde + CO_2	Yeast, plants
Oxaloacetate decarboxylase	Oxaloacetate ⟶ pyruvate + CO_2	Liver
Phosphopyruvate carboxylase	Phosphoenolpyruvate + GDP + CO_2 ⟷ oxaloacetate + GTP	Liver, kidney
Orotidine-5′-phosphate (orotidylate) decarboxylase	Or-5′-P ⟶ UMP + CO_2	Liver

TABLE 8-13. LYASES (*Continued*)

ENZYME	REACTION	OCCURRENCE
Amidine and Ammonia Lyases		
Histidine-ammonia lyase (histidase)	Histidine ⟶ urocanate + NH_3	Liver
Adenylosuccinate lyase (adenylosuccinase)	Adenylosuccinate ⟶ adenylate + fumarate	Liver
Argininosuccinate lyase (argininosuccinase)	Argininosuccinate ⟶ arginine + fumarate	Liver
Aldolases		
Aldolase (fructose diphosphate aldolase)	Fructose-1,6-diphosphate ⟷ glyceraldehyde-3-phosphate + dihydroxyacetone-phosphate	All tissues
Ketose-1-phosphate aldolase	Ketose-1-phosphate ⟷ an aldehyde + dihydroxyacetone-phosphate	Liver
Ketotetrose aldolase	Erythrulose-1-phosphate ⟷ dihydroxyacetone-phosphate + HCHO	Liver
Pentose aldolase	Ribose-5-phosphate ⟷ erythrulose-1-phosphate + HCHO	Various tissues
Threonine aldolase	Threonine ⟶ glycine + acetaldehyde	Liver, kidney
Ketoacid Lyases		
HMG-CoA synthase	Acetyl-CoA + acetoacetyl-CoA ⟶ CoA + HMG-CoA	Liver
Citrate synthase	Acetyl-CoA + oxaloacetate ⟶ CoA + citrate	All tissues
ATP-citrate lyase	ATP + citrate + CoA ⟶ ADP + P + acetyl-CoA + oxaloacetate	Wide distribution

Amidine and Ammonia Lyases

In this category may be included those enzymes which catalyze the removal, from a molecule, of ammonia, or substituted ammonia, in the free state, by means of reactions which are not of the hydrolytic, oxidative, or transfer type. The simplest example of this category is the bacterial enzyme, aspartase, which converts aspartate to fumarate and ammonia. Analogous reactions which occur in animal tissues include the conversions of histidine to urocanate and ammonia, adenylosuccinate to adenylic acid and fumarate, and argininosuccinate to arginine and fumarate.

Aldolases and Ketoacid Lyases

Fructose diphosphate aldolase derives its name from the type of reaction catalyzed, which is, superficially at least, a reversible aldol condensation. The enzyme catalyzes the reversible cleavage of hexose disphosphate into triose phosphates, a reaction of great importance in the anaerobic metabolism of carbohydrate. Other aldolases convert fructose-1-phosphate into trioses, threonine into glycine and acetaldehyde, and ketotetroses and pentoses into formaldehyde and either triose or tetrose phosphates, respectively.

The ketoacid lyases appear to be related formally to the aldolases (in that a type of aldol condensation is involved), but the reactions are made more complex by the participation of coenzyme A and, in one case, ATP.

ISOMERASES

A selection of the more important enzymes of this class is presented in Table 8-14. The two epimerases listed catalyze the rearrangement of alcoholic hydroxyl groups in monosaccharides from one steric configuration to the other. In the case of glucose ⇌ galactose, the epimerization occurs while the sugars are in the form of uridine nucleotides (see formula). The additional requirement for NAD suggests that the reaction may be an internal oxidation-reduction.

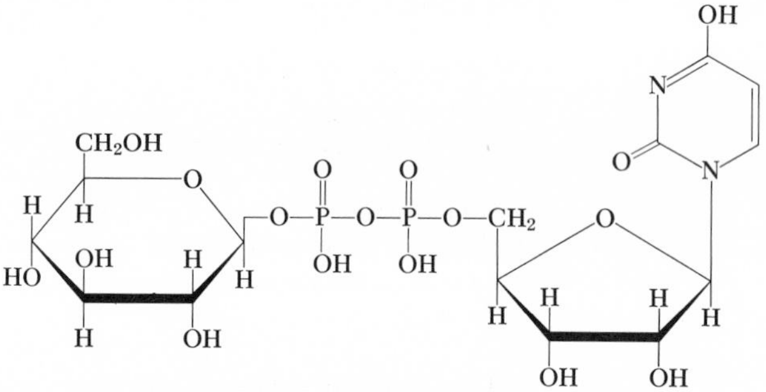

Uridine diphosphate—glucose

Maleylacetoacetate isomerase (involved in tyrosine metabolism) and retinene isomerase (concerned with visual pigments) catalyze conversions of double bonds from *trans* to *cis* configurations.

The triose-, pentose-, and hexose-phosphate isomerases catalyze the interconversions of aldose and ketose phosphates, reactions of obvious importance in the metabolism of carbohydrates.

TABLE 8-14. ISOMERASES

ENZYME	REACTION	OCCURRENCE
Ribulosephosphate 3-epimerase	D-ribulose-5-P ⇌ D-xylulose-5-P	Liver
UDPglucose epimerase	UDPglucose $\xrightleftharpoons{NAD}$ UDP galactose	Liver
Maleylacetoacetate isomerase	Maleylacetoacetate $\xrightarrow{GSH}$ fumarylacetoacetate	Liver
Retinene isomerase	All-*trans*-retinene ⇌ 11-*cis*-retinene (neo-b)	Retina
Triosephosphate isomerase	D-glyceraldehyde-3-P ⇌ dihydroxyacetone-P	Wide distribution
Ribosephosphate isomerase	D-ribose-5-P ⇌ D-ribulose-5-P	Liver
Mannosephosphate isomerase	D-mannose-6-P ⇌ D-fructose-6-P	Various tissues
Glucosephosphate isomerase	D-glucose-6-P ⇌ D-fructose-6-P	Wide distribution
Isopentenylpyrophosphate isomerase	Isopentenyl-PP ⇌ dimethylallyl-PP	Various tissues
Methylmalonyl-CoA mutase	Methylmalonyl-CoA $\xrightarrow{B_{12}}$ succinyl-CoA	Various tissues

Migration of a double bond during the synthesis of sterols is catalyzed by isopentenylpyrophosphate isomerase, whereas intramolecular migration of a carboxythioester group under the influence of methyl-malonyl-CoA mutase and a coenzyme form of vitamin B_{12} is involved in the metabolism of propionate.

LIGASES

Many ligases (Table 8-15) catalyze reactions in which a metabolite is "activated" so that it may enter important anabolic and catabolic pathways. Amino acids, for example, are converted to amino-acyl esters of "soluble" RNA in the initial step of protein synthesis.

Acetate, fatty acids, acetoacetate, and cholate are activated by forming thioesters with coenzyme A. Succinyl-CoA synthetase can activate succinate similarly, but the reac-

Table 8-15. Ligases*

ENZYME	REACTION	OCCURRENCE
Aminoacyl-sRNA synthetases	Aminoacid + ATP + sRNA $\longleftrightarrow$ aminoacyl-sRNA + AMP + PP	All tissues
Acetyl-CoA synthetase	Acetate + ATP + CoA $\longleftrightarrow$ acetyl-CoA + AMP + PP	Heart, kidney
Acyl-CoA synthetases	Fatty acid + ATP + CoA $\longleftrightarrow$ acyl-CoA + AMP + PP	Liver
Acetoacetyl-CoA synthetase	Acetoacetate + ATP + CoA $\longleftrightarrow$ acetoacetyl-CoA + AMP + PP	Kidney
Succinyl-CoA synthetase	Succinate + GTP + CoA $\longleftrightarrow$ succinyl-CoA + GDP + P	All tissues
Cholyl-CoA synthetase	Cholate + ATP + CoA $\longleftrightarrow$ cholyl-CoA + AMP + PP	Liver
Formyltetrahydrofolate synthetase	Formate + ATP + FH_4 $\longrightarrow$ 10-formyl-FH_4 + ADP + P	Liver
Glutamine synthetase	Glutamate + ATP + NH_3 $\longrightarrow$ glutamine + ADP + P	Various tissues
Phosphoribosyl-glycinamide synthetase	Glycine + ATP + ribosylamine-5-P $\longrightarrow$ ribosyl-glycinamide-5′-P + ADP + P	Liver
γ-Glutamyl-cysteine synthetase	Glutamate + ATP + cysteine $\longrightarrow$ γ-glutamyl-cysteine + ADP + P	Liver
Glutathione synthetase	γ-Glutamyl-cysteine + ATP + glycine $\longrightarrow$ GSH + ADP + P	Liver
Argininosuccinate synthetase	Citrulline + ATP + aspartate $\longrightarrow$ argininosuccinate + AMP + PP	Liver, kidney
NAD synthetase	Desamido-NAD + ATP + glutamine $\longrightarrow$ NAD + AMP + PP + glutamate	Various tissues
Pyruvate carboxylase	Pyruvate + ATP + CO_2 $\longleftrightarrow$ oxaloacetate + ADP + P	Liver, kidney, brain
Acetyl-CoA carboxylase	Acetyl-CoA + ATP + CO_2 $\longleftrightarrow$ malonyl-CoA + ADP + P	Liver
Propionyl-CoA carboxylase	Propionyl-CoA + ATP + CO_2 $\longleftrightarrow$ methylmalonyl-CoA + ADP + P	Kidney, heart, liver

* PP, pyrophosphate; P, inorganic orthophosphate; FH_4, tetrahydrofolate; GSH, glutathione.

tion is important largely in the reverse direction, in that it provides a mechanism for "substrate-level generation of a high-energy bond" in the Krebs cycle (p. 410). Formate, on the other hand, is activated by coupling with tetrahydrofolate.

Other ligases form: glutamine, a pathway of "detoxication" of ammonia; phosphoribosyl-glycinamide, a precursor of the purines; the important tripeptide, glutathione (in two steps); argininosuccinate, a precursor of urea; NAD (DPN), a coenzyme of biological oxidations.

Enzymes catalyzing carboxylations which occur with the sacrifice of a pyrophosphate bond of ATP also are classified as ligases. The three listed in the table are involved in the metabolism of carbohydrates and fatty acids. Biotin is a cofactor of all three enzymes.

BIBLIOGRAPHY

INTRODUCTORY TEXTBOOKS

Baldwin, E.: Dynamic Aspects of Biochemistry, Chapters 1, 2, 4, and 5, Cambridge, Cambridge University Press, 1963.

Gutfreund, H.: An Introduction to the Study of Enzymes, New York, John Wiley & Sons, Inc., 1965.

ANNUAL REVIEWS

Nord, F. F. (ed.): Advances in Enzymology, Volumes 1 through 27, New York, Interscience Publishers, Inc., 1941 to 1965.

GENERAL ENZYMOLOGY AND METHODS

Bergmeyer, H. U. (ed.): Methods of Enzymatic Analysis, New York, Academic Press, Inc., 1963.

Boyer, P. D., Lardy, H., and Myrbäck, K. (eds.): The Enzymes, 8 vols., New York, Academic Press, Inc., 1959 to 1963.

Colowick, S. P., and Kaplan, N. O. (eds.): Methods in Enzymology, 7 vols., New York, Academic Press, Inc., 1955 to 1964.

Dixon, M., and Webb, E. C.: Enzymes, New York, Academic Press, Inc., 1964.

Florkin, M., and Stotz, E. H. (eds.): Comprehensive Biochemistry, Vol. 12, Enzymes—General Considerations, Vol. 13, Enzyme Nomenclature, Vol. 15, Group-Transfer Reactions, Vol. 16, Hydrolytic Reactions; Cobamide and Biotin Coenzymes, Amsterdam, Elsevier Publishing Company, 1964 and 1965.

SPECIAL TOPICS

de Duve, C., Wattiaux, R., and Baudhuin, P.: Distribution of enzymes between subcellular fractions in animal tissues, Advances Enzymol. *24:*291, 1962.

Goodwin, T. W., Harris, J. I., and Hartley, B. S. (eds.): Structure and Activity of Enzymes, Symposium No. 1 of the Federation of European Biochemical Societies, New York, Academic Press, Inc., 1964.

Hochster, R. M., and Quastel, J. H. (eds.): Metabolic Inhibitors, Vols. 1 and 2, New York, Academic Press, Inc., 1963.

Koshland, D. E., Jr.: The active site and enzyme action, Advances Enzymol. *22:*45, 1960.

Litwack, G., and Kritchevsky, D. (eds.): Actions of Hormones on Molecular Processes, New York, John Wiley & Sons, Inc., 1964.

Webb, J. L.: Enzyme and Metabolic Inhibitors, Vols. 1 and 2, New York, Academic Press, Inc., 1963 and 1966.

Weber, G. (ed.): Advances in Enzyme Regulation, Vols. 1 to 3, Oxford, Pergamon Press Ltd., 1963 to 1965.

Wilson, A. C., and Pardee, A. B.: Comparative aspects of metabolic control, in Florkin, M., and Mason, H. S. (eds.): Comparative Biochemistry, Vol. 6, New York, Academic Press, Inc., 1964, p. 73.

CHAPTER 9

CHANGES IN FOODSTUFFS IN THE ALIMENTARY TRACT

DIGESTION

DIGESTION is the term applied to processes which convert relatively large organic molecules into smaller molecules capable of being absorbed by the gastrointestinal tract and utilized by the organism. With the exception of water, inorganic salts, vitamins, monosaccharides, and certain lipids, practically all common foodstuffs must undergo certain changes in the digestive tract preliminary to absorption and utilization. These digestive processes are hydrolytic in nature and are accomplished by enzymes in the various digestive fluids (salivary, gastric, pancreatic, and intestinal).

The manner in which food is prepared for ingestion influences its digestibility. Cooking causes disruption of the cellulose shell of starch granules, and softening of the connective tissue of meats, permitting more ready access to digestive enzymes. Digestibility of egg proteins is increased by their coagulation. Favorable chemical changes also occur during ripening of fruits (dextrinization) and aging of meats (hydrolysis).

Foodstuffs entering the mouth are subjected to mastication and the digestive and lubricating actions of saliva, which is secreted by the salivary and buccal glands in response to psychic, mechanical, and chemical stimuli. The bolus of food passes through the pharynx and esophagus into the stomach, where it is exposed to the digestive action of gastric juice, stimulated by psychic, gastric (nervous and hormonal), and intestinal (hormonal) factors. After an interval which varies with the nature of the ingested foodstuffs, portions of the gastric digestive mixture are periodically ejected into the duodenum, where they encounter a mixture of bile, pancreatic juice, and duodenal secretion. Secretion of pancreatic juice is stimulated by vagal impulses and by secretin and pancreozymin, hormones formed by the duodenal mucosa in response to the presence of acid in the duodenum. Secretin also stimulates the flow of bile from the liver. Relaxation of the sphincter of Oddi and simultaneous contraction and evacuation of the gallbladder result from the presence of emulsified fats in the duodenum; a hormonal influence (cholecystokinin, formed in the intestinal mucosa) may also be involved. The food mixture passes down the intestine, subjected to the digestive action of the intestinal secretions. The end-products of digestion are absorbed, chiefly in the small intestine, as are certain of the products of bacterial action on the foodstuffs. The unabsorbed residuum passes into the colon, where it is largely concentrated by reabsorption of water, to be excreted ultimately, together with intestinal bacteria and products of their activity, as the feces.

Digestive Enzymes

The enzymes secreted into the lumen of the alimentary tract, some in an inactive form, are all hydrolases concerned with fragmentation of large molecules of organic foodstuffs to smaller molecules suitable for absorption. The most important of these may be classified as follows:

(*a*) ***Peptidases*** (***proteases***). These protein-digesting enzymes include pepsin, rennin, trypsin, chymotrypsin, carboxypeptidases, aminopeptidases, and tri- and dipeptidases.

(*b*) ***Glycosidases*** (***carbohydrases***). The chief carbohydrate-splitting enzymes in the digestive secretions are salivary amylase and pancreatic amylase. Sucrase (invertase), maltase, and lactase are intestinal intracellular enzymes which hydrolyze the corresponding disaccharides during the process of absorption; similar activity within the lumen of the intestine is due to desquamation of mucosal cells.

(*c*) ***Lipases.*** These enzymes include gastric lipase and pancreatic lipase and lipases in intestinal secretions. They are esterases which act preferentially on glycerides of long-chain fatty acids.

(*d*) ***Nucleases; phosphodiesterases.*** Nucleic acids are depolymerized, i.e., certain internucleotide linkages are split, by the actions of pancreatic ribonuclease and deoxyribonuclease, with the formation of smaller polynucleotides (oligonucleotides) and certain mononucleotides. The oligonucleotides are hydrolyzed to their component mononucleotides by the action of other phosphodiesterases.

(*e*) ***Esterases*** (***carboxylesterases other than lipases***). This group of enzymes act preferentially on glycerides of short-chain fatty acids (e.g., tributyrin) and other fatty acid esters (e.g., cholesterol esters).

(*f*) ***Phosphatases.*** These include a variety of enzymes which liberate phosphoric acid from organic phosphate compounds, such as mononucleotides, lecithin (lecithinases) and other phospholipids, and phytic acid.

SALIVA

Saliva, as it occurs in the mouth, is a mixture of secretions of the three pairs of salivary glands, the parotid, submaxillary, and sublingual, and, to a lesser extent, of the buccal glands. It is a colorless, slightly opalescent, viscous fluid, the composition of which varies with the conditions of stimulation, depending chiefly upon the relative proportions of secretion from the several glands involved. The 24-hour volume varies widely, but has been calculated to average about 1500 cc. It is influenced by the water and food intake, the character of the food, and by chewing.

Under average conditions, mixed saliva is 99.42 per cent water and 0.58 per cent solid. Inorganic substances comprise about one-third of the total solids, and organic substances the remainder. The specific gravity is about 1.003 and the reaction of freshly collected saliva is usually slightly acid, pH 6.35 to 6.85, if care is taken to prevent loss of CO_2. The inorganic components include principally chloride, bicarbonate, and sodium, but also potassium and calcium, with relatively small amounts of sulfate and phosphate. There are traces of thiocyanate and, after administration of iodides, these are excreted by the salivary glands in relatively high concentration. The most important organic constituents of saliva are the amylolytic enzyme, ptyalin (salivary amylase), and mucin. Other organic components include other proteins, the exact nature of which is not known, and small amounts of such substances as urea, glucose, lactic acid, and certain enzymes, e.g., phosphatase and carbonic anhydrase (which probably enter the saliva from desquamated glandular epithelium and surface cells). The mucin, a glycoprotein, is largely responsible for the viscosity of saliva, and is secreted chiefly by the sublingual but also by the submaxillary glands. Salivary amylase is secreted principally by the parotid glands, which secrete little or no mucin.

The urea content of saliva varies directly with that of the blood plasma. The pH of saliva depends primarily on the $BHCO_3:H_2CO_3$ ratio, which varies roughly with that in the blood plasma.

Functions of Saliva

The principal functions of saliva are probably not due to its direct digestive actions, which consist chiefly of a relatively unimportant degree of digestion of starches and dextrins to maltose by the action of salivary amylase. More important, perhaps, are the facts that it serves to moisten foods and to reduce them to a consistency suitable for swallowing, and to lubricate the bolus of food for its passage through the esophagus. Its solubilizing action on dry foods aids in stimulating taste nerves which, in turn, play a role in the secretion of gastric juice.

Salivary Amylase (Ptyalin)

This carbohydrase acts on the polysaccharides, starch and glycogen, and certain of their derivatives (dextrins), hydrolyzing them to the disaccharide maltose in a manner similar to pancreatic amylase (p. 263). Since it acts only on α-1,4-glucosidic linkages (p. 244), complete hydrolysis of starch requires the presence of other enzymes, acting at the 1,6- branch points. Certain anions serve as activators, particularly Cl^- and Br^-, but also, to a lesser degree, I^-, NO_3^-, and others. Human salivary amylase requires at least 1 gram atom of calcium per mole for full activity. Its optimum pH in NaCl solution is 6.9, but varies from 5.5 to 6.5 with different substrates.

It is not stable below pH 4 to 5, and is inactivated by pepsin. Consequently, the amylolytic action of this enzyme can be exerted only during its relatively brief contact with substrate material in the mouth and before the bolus of food, mixed with saliva by chewing, has been thoroughly permeated by the acid gastric juice in the stomach (15 to 20 minutes).

Amylase acts more rapidly and vigorously on cooked than on raw starch in vitro, but this difference is not so striking in vivo. It is probable that contact of the enzyme with the starch molecule is facilitated by mechanical damage of the dense lattice structure of the starch granule. The presence of another enzyme, e.g., oligo-1,6-glucosidase, is also undoubtedly of importance in this connection. The polysaccharide is initially rapidly converted to lower molecular weight, non-fermentable, soluble dextrins (liquefaction). The latter then undergo slower hydrolysis, terminal molecules of maltose being successively split off, with gradual, more or less complete degradation of the intermediate dextrins to maltose and a small amount of glucose.

GASTRIC JUICE

Normal gastric juice is a rather watery, usually colorless liquid with a specific gravity of about 1.003, containing about 99.4 per cent water and 0.6 per cent solids. In the average young normal adult the chief inorganic constituent is HCl, with small amounts of NaCl and KCl and phosphate. The chief organic constituents are mucin, a glycoprotein, the proteolytic enzyme pepsin, and small amounts of a lipase. The gastric juice of newborn infants contains rennin, a milk-clotting enzyme, and little or no pepsin, but rather high concentrations of HCl. There is no HCl in approximately 4 per cent of otherwise apparently normal young adults (achlorhydria), the incidence of this condition increasing in older age groups.

The gastric juice is contributed to by three types of cells with different secretory functions: (1) the parietal cells of the gastric tubules secrete the HCl; (2) the chief cells secrete pepsin; (3) columnar cells of the necks of the gastric glands (mucous cells) secrete the gastric mucus. The acidity and peptic activity of the mixed gastric secretion depend upon the relative proportions of these component secretions, each of which is affected quantitatively rather specifically by certain stimuli. For example, the parietal cells are stimulated by histamine, producing a highly acid gastric juice; the peptic cells are stimulated by the vagus, producing a juice rich in pepsin.

Hydrochloric Acid

The gastric parietal cells secrete a fluid of constant composition, which is practically a pure solution of HCl, about 170 mEq./liter (0.17 N), the pH being about 0.87. This is the source of the free acid of gastric juice, which varies within wide limits, depending upon the rate (volume) of parietal cell secretion, the extent of its dilution by other gastric secretions (chief cells, mucous cells), and the buffering action of mucin. The maximum attainable acidity of gastric juice, e.g., by histamine stimulation, is consequently that of pure parietal-cell secretion. The chief function of gastric HCl is to provide a satisfactory pH for digestion of protein in the stomach (by pepsin). Other effects include: (1) slight preliminary action on proteins (swelling, denaturation, possible hydrolysis); (2) activation of pepsinogen; as is apparently true in most cases of zymogen activation, this involves removal of an inhibitory or blocking peptide moiety; (3) facilitation of absorption of iron (p. 641); (4) possibly hydrolysis of disaccharides; (5) stimulation of secretion of secretin (or activation of prosecretin) in the duodenum; (6) germicidal action restricting fermentation by microorganisms in the stomach.

Pepsin

This proteolytic enzyme, the principal digestive component of gastric juice, is secreted by the chief cells as pepsinogen (inactive). The latter is activated by H^+ ions and also, autocatalytically, by pepsin at pH 5 or lower. The process of activation consists in removal of a "blocking" peptide (p. 246). Pepsin acts optimally at pH 1.5 to 2.5, depending on the substrate. It is almost completely inactive at neutral or alkaline pH levels. Gastric juice in the infant contains but little pepsin.

Pepsin is an endopeptidase (p. 244), catalyzing hydrolysis of peptide linkages at all points in the protein molecule. There is evidence that it acts preferentially on linkages involving the amino group of tyrosine and of phenylalanine. It attacks practically all native proteins, except certain keratins, protamines, histones, and mucoproteins, but exerts a more pronounced effect on denatured proteins which possess free SH groups. Depending upon the pH, rate of gastric emptying, and nature of the protein, the latter is broken down into smaller peptide units ("proteoses," "peptones"), shorter peptide chains, and perhaps a few amino acids. Pepsin also has a milk-clotting action similar to that of rennin, converting casein by hydrolysis, first to soluble paracasein, then to insoluble paracasein in the presence of Ca^{++} ions. Milk clotting in the stomach probably involves also precipitation of isoelectric casein by HCl.

Gastric Lipase

This fat-hydrolyzing enzyme is relatively unimportant physiologically because its optimum pH, about 5.5 for lower glycerides and 7.5 for higher glycerides, is above that usually present following ingestion of a mixed meal. However, it is stable in an acid medium, and may exert a lipolytic effect in the intestine, where the pH is more favorable. The products of its action in vitro are identical with those of pancreatic lipase.

Rennin

This is a powerful milk-clotting enzyme, secreted as prorennin, which is activated by H^+ ions. It is not present in the gastric juice of human adults, but is present in infants (before pepsin formation) and, most abundantly, in the calf and other young ruminants.

$$\text{Casein} \xrightarrow[\text{Ca}^{++}]{\text{Rennin}} \text{Insoluble Paracasein (curd)}$$

In the adult, this function is assumed by pepsin and chymotrypsin. The paracasein then undergoes the digestive fate of all digestible proteins.

Gastric "Mucus"

This appears to be a mixture of substances secreted by cells of the necks of the gastric glands and the surface epithelium, containing certain glycoproteins ("mucin," "mucoprotein"), some soluble and some undissolved. Gastric mucus is not digested by pepsin. It is believed to exert an important protective influence on the mucous membrane of the stomach and to buffer the HCl secreted by the parietal cells. There is evidence that the soluble mucoprotein fraction of gastric "mucin" carries the so-called "intrinsic anti-pernicious anemia factor" (p. 202), which is essential for intestinal absorption of vitamin B_{12} (extrinsic anti-pernicious anemia factor) and, therefore, for normal erythropoiesis.

PANCREATIC JUICE

Pancreatic juice is a clear fluid, secreted by the acinar cells of the pancreas, containing about 98.7 per cent water and 1.3 per cent solids (specific gravity about 1.007). It has the highest consistent alkalinity of the normal body fluids, with a pH of about 7.5 to 8.2, owing to its relatively high bicarbonate content (Fig. 13–2, p. 322). The most important organic constituents are powerful proteolytic, lipolytic, amylolytic, and nucleolytic enzymes, which comprise virtually its entire protein content. The average daily output is about 500 cc. Vagal stimulation produces a fluid rich in enzymes, but of comparatively low volume. Secretin, a hormone produced by the duodenal mucosa by the action of acid, causes secretion of a fluid of high volume and bicarbonate content, but low enzyme concentration. Another hormone, pancreozymin, secreted by the duodenal mucosa, has an effect similar to that produced by vagal stimulation but not mediated by the vagus.

Trypsin

Trypsin, a protease, is secreted by the pancreatic acinar cells as an inactive proenzyme, trypsinogen. In the intestine, this is activated (to trypsin) by the enzyme enterokinase (optimum pH 6 to 9), subsequent activation proceeding autocatalytically (i.e., by trypsin) at pH 7 to 8, accelerated by Ca^{++} and other alkaline earth ions. This activation involves removal of an acidic peptide from the trypsinogen molecule (p. 247). Trypsin acts optimally at pH 8 to 9 as an endopeptidase (p. 244), hydrolyzing practically all types of protein, including several not attacked by pepsin. Like the latter, it digests denatured and partially digested proteins more rapidly than native proteins, breaking them down to polypeptides of various weights and some amino acids. A preferential action on peptide linkages involving the carboxyl group of either arginine or lysine has been suggested.

Extracts of the pancreas contain a trypsin inhibitor, a polypeptide, which may be identical with an inhibitor present in blood. The ovomucoid of egg white is also a potent trypsin inhibitor, as is a component of soybean.

Chymotrypsin

This is an endopeptidase (p. 244), secreted by the pancreatic acinar cells as an inactive proenzyme, chymotrypsinogen, which, in the intestine, is activated by trypsin, but not by enterokinase. Its optimum pH (8 to 9) and actions are similar to those of trypsin, but, in addition, it possesses a powerful milk-clotting action identical with that of rennin and pepsin. A preferential attack on peptide linkages involving the carboxyl group of tyrosine and phenylalanine has been suggested.

Carboxypeptidase

This is an exopeptidase (p. 244) (optimum pH 7.4), the peptide linkage attacked being that of a terminal amino acid possessing a free carboxyl group. It apparently contains —SH groups and Mg, and is inhibited by iodoacetate, cyanide, sulfide, cysteine, citrate, phosphate, and oxalate. It acts on peptide chains of various lengths, splitting off single terminal amino acids.

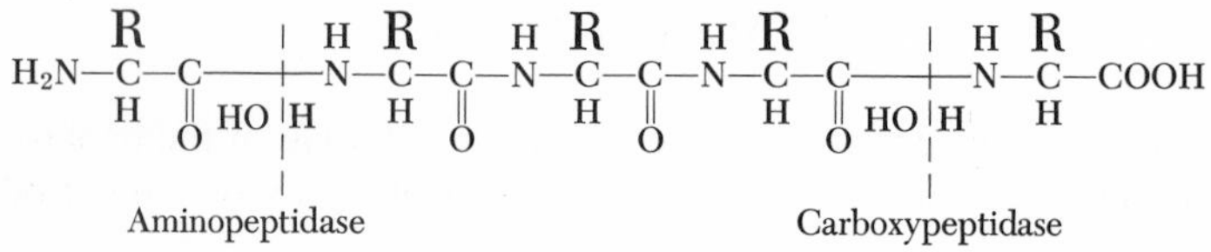

```
     R          | H R      H R      H R         | H R
H2N—C—C————————+—N—C—C—N—C—C—N—C—C————————+—N—C—COOH
     H  ‖  HO |H    H  ‖   H  ‖   H  ‖  HO |H    H
        O       |        O        O        O       |
                |                                  |
       Aminopeptidase                      Carboxypeptidase
```

Pancreatic Amylase (Diastase, Amylopsin)

The action of this carbohydrase is qualitatively identical with but more potent than that of salivary amylase. It digests cooked starch more actively than raw starch in vitro, but the latter is well digested in vivo. It requires Cl^- ions for normal activity. Its optimum pH is 6.9, but it acts well between pH 6.5 and 7.2, varying somewhat with different substrates. As in the case of salivary amylase, complete hydrolysis of starch requires the presence also of another enzyme that acts on the 1,6- branch points in the molecule. Pancreatic amylase hydrolyzes branched-chain polysaccharides such as starch or glycogen in the intestinal lumen to form maltose, higher oligosaccharides also containing the α-1,4-linkage, isomaltose (containing the α-1,6-linkage), and small amounts of glucose.

Pancreatic Lipase (Steapsin)

This is a glyceride-hydrolyzing (lipolytic) enzyme, a carboxylesterase, secreted by the pancreas in weakly active form. In the duodenum, its activity is potentiated by a number of substances, including bile acids, Ca^{++}, and certain amino acids and peptides. Its pH optimum varies (7 to 8.8), rising with increasing chain length of the fatty acids in the glyceride.

The activity of hydrolysis of glycerides by pancreatic lipase increases with (1) the molecular weight of the constituent fatty acids, (2) the extent of their unsaturation, and (3) the number of fatty acids in the glyceride molecule. Hence, triglycerides of such acids as oleic and linoleic are hydrolyzed more rapidly than diglycerides and triglycerides of short-chain acids such as butyric. Fats, in general, are attacked more actively than other esters of fatty acids.

$$\begin{array}{l} H_2C{-}O{-}C({=}O){-}R \\ \quad | \\ HC{-}O{-}C({=}O){-}R \\ \quad | \\ H_2C{-}O{-}C({=}O){-}R \\ \text{Triglyceride} \end{array} \xrightarrow[\text{Lipase}]{3H_2O} \underset{\text{Glycerol}}{C_3H_5(OH)_3} + \underset{\text{Fatty acids}}{3RCOOH}$$

Because of the insolubility of fats in aqueous media, their hydrolysis by lipase is facilitated by emulsification, which increases enormously the surface area of the substrate exposed to the enzyme. Emulsification is favored by mechanical action of the stomach and intestine but especially by the surface tension-lowering action of the bile salts, which enter the duodenum in the bile. As fatty acids are split off, the resulting monoglycerides, and perhaps also soaps (i.e., Na and K salts of the fatty acids), being surface-active substances, favor further emulsification and, consequently, digestion.

Conditions in the intestine are usually not optimal for complete hydrolysis of ingested fats to glycerol and fatty acids. The digestive mixture usually consists of undigested fats (triglycerides), diglycerides, monoglycerides and fatty acids, in varying proportions, depending upon a number of circumstances, including the quantity of fat, its nature, the pH, and the motility of the bowel.

Phospholipases; Cholesterol Esterase

Phospholipase A removes one fatty acid from lecithins and cephalins, yielding substances called lysolecithins and lysocephalins (hemolytic). These compounds are attacked by phospholipase B, which removes the second fatty acid, yielding glyceryl-phosphoryl-choline, glyceryl-phosphoryl-ethanolamine, or glyceryl-phosphoryl-serine. Glycerol is split off by the action of phosphodiesterases and the base is subsequently freed by the action of phosphatases.

Cholesterol esters are hydrolyzed by cholesterol esterase in the pancreatic juice. Bile acids are essential for activity of this enzyme. It differs in this respect from pancreatic lipase, the activity of which is enhanced by surface-active agents other than bile acids.

Nucleases

Pancreatic juice contains a ribonuclease and a deoxyribonuclease which partially hydrolyze the corresponding nucleic acids, producing oligonucleotides and, in the case of ribonuclease, certain pyrimidine nucleotides. These enzymes are endonucleases, attacking the molecule at sensitive linkages in the interior of the chain.

INTESTINAL JUICE (SUCCUS ENTERICUS)

The cells of the mucosal glands of the small intestine at different levels (duodenum, jejunum, ileum) secrete fluids of different composition, which are collectively designated "succus entericus" (intestinal juice). These secretions are apparently under nervous and hormonal (enterocrinin, secretin) control. As ordinarily collected, intestinal fluid is rather viscous and turbid, owing to the presence of mucus and of leukocytes and desquamated mucosal epithelial cells. The solid content is about 1.5 per cent, about half of which is inorganic (chiefly bicarbonate, chloride, phosphate, Na, K, Ca). The chief organic components are mucin, enzymes, and various lipids (cholesterol, phospholipids, fat), but it also contains various metabolites, such as urea.

Certain of the enzymes are undoubtedly truly extracellular, secreted into the lumen of the bowel, but others (e.g., nucleoside phosphorylases, disaccharidases) are probably intracellular, entering the bowel lumen, if at all, in disintegrating, desquamated mucosal cells. This circumstance, and functional and anatomical factors resulting in mixtures of secretions of variable constitution from different portions of the intestine, contribute to the lack of uniformity of composition of succus entericus, which is therefore not a distinct entity as are the gastric and pancreatic secretions.

The pH varies considerably at different levels of the small intestine, depending upon the acidity of the gastric contents entering the duodenum, and the volume and conditions of stimulation of pancreatic juice and bile flow. However, under average normal conditions, the pH in the duodenum in the fasting state is about 5.5 to 6.0, falling somewhat after taking food. It increases gradually at lower levels to about 6.0 to 6.5 in the terminal ileum. The pH varies within rather wide limits with variation in composition of the diet and bacterial action, e.g., with variable production of organic acids such as lactic acid (fermentation).

Carbohydrases (p. 242)

Maltase splits maltose into two molecules of glucose. Sucrase (invertase) splits sucrose into glucose and fructose. Lactase splits lactose into glucose and galactose.

These enzymes are not secreted into the intestinal lumen, their presence there resulting from desquamation of mucosal epithelium. Disaccharide hydrolysis occurs during the process of absorption of these compounds, probably in the brush-border membrane of the epithelial cells of the small intestine. There is apparently a multiplicity of disaccharidases in the human small intestine. In addition to lactase and invertase (which in some species appears to attack maltose as well as sucrose), several maltases have been described, one of which also attacks isomaltose. Various forms of disaccharide intolerance have been described, due to hereditary deficiency of intestinal lactase or invertase (and possibly other disaccharidases). In these cases, the normal increase in blood glucose fails to occur following oral administration of lactose or sucrose. These conditions are characterized by watery stools of low pH, containing acids produced by bacterial fermentation of the undigested and unabsorbed sugars.

Peptidases

Two main types are found in intestinal juices: (1) aminopeptidases, which are exopeptidases acting on the peptide linkage of terminal amino acids possessing a free amino group; (2) tripeptidases and dipeptidases, which split tri- and dipeptides in the following manner:

```
                                      Dipeptide
                              ___________________________
       R          |      H R          |      H R
NH2—C—C———+———N—C—C———+———N—C—COOH
       H  ||      |        H  ||      |        H
          O       |           O       |
            HO | H              HO | H
                  |                    |
          Tripeptidase          Dipeptidase
```

Phosphodiesterases and Phosphatases

These enzymes complete the digestion of nucleic acids. Oligonucleotides resulting from the action of the pancreatic nucleases are hydrolyzed to their component mononucleotides by the phosphodiesterases. These are exonucleases, which attack the molecule by consecutive removal of mononucleotides from ends of the chain. The mononucleotides are hydrolyzed by nonspecific phosphatases, producing nucleosides and inorganic phosphate. These are the end products of digestion of nucleic acids.

Nucleosides are absorbed as such, their subsequent degradation occurring intracellularly. They undergo phosphorolytic cleavage through the action of purine and pyrimidine nucleoside phosphorylases, yielding the free bases and pentose phosphates. Any such reactions occurring within the intestinal lumen result from desquamation of mucosal epithelium.

Enterokinase: Enteropeptidase

This enzyme, secreted by the duodenal mucosal cells, has no direct digestive action; it converts (activates) trypsinogen to trypsin by removing a "blocking" peptide from the zymogen molecule.

BILE

Human bile, as freshly secreted by the liver, is a clear, golden-yellow, slightly viscous, bitter-tasting fluid, with a pH of about 7.0 to 8.5 and a daily volume of about 500 to

700 cc. It has a solid content of about 1 to 4 per cent, approximately one-fourth of which is inorganic (chiefly HCO_3, Cl, Na, K), the remainder organic. The most distinctive organic constituents are bile acids (salts), bilirubin, and cholesterol, but there are also smaller amounts of phospholipid (lecithin), mucin, and other substances, e.g., urea, alkaline phosphatase. The inorganic substances and bilirubin are removed by the liver cells from the bloodstream for biliary excretion. The bile acids and biliary cholesterol originate in the hepatic polygonal cells; the bile phosphatase probably is formed in these cells or in the epithelial cells of the terminal bile-duct radicals. Mucin is a product of the bile-duct epithelium and gallbladder mucosa. The bile is the medium of excretion of other substances preferentially removed from the blood by the liver. These include iron and certain halogenated organic compounds, such as iodinated, chlorinated, and brominated phenolphthaleins, which are used clinically for testing liver and gallbladder function and bile duct patency.

Bile is probably secreted continually by the liver, but is prevented from entering the duodenum by the state of tonicity of the sphincter of Oddi. It accumulates and is stored in the gallbladder, where it undergoes concentration (reabsorption of water) and is periodically discharged into the bowel by relaxation of the duodenal sphincter and simultaneous contraction of the gallbladder.

Gallbladder bile is more viscous than hepatic bile, and is dark yellow, brown, or green, the color depending on the duration of its storage (oxidation of bilirubin to biliverdin) and extent of concentration. A large amount of water, and certain of the inorganic components, principally HCO_3, but also Cl and Na, are reabsorbed in the gallbladder, the solid content increasing to 4 to 17 per cent and the pH falling to as low as 5.5. The concentration of bile acids and pigment may at times reach 10 times that in hepatic bile (Table 9-1).

Bile Acids (Bile Salts) (Fig. 9-1, p. 267)

It is generally stated that the most abundant bile acids in human bile are cholic (3,7,12-trihydroxycholanic) and deoxycholic (3,12-dihydroxycholanic) acids, in the proportion of three to one. By improved techniques, there is evidence of the presence, also, of

TABLE 9-1. COMPOSITION OF HUMAN LIVER AND GALLBLADDER BILE

	LIVER BILE	BLADDER BILE
Specific gravity	1.009–1.013	1.026–1.032
pH	7.1–8.5	5.5–7.7
Total solids (%)	1–3.5	4–17
Mucin (%)	0.1–0.9	1–4
Bile acids (%)	0.2–2	1.5–10
Bile pigment (%)	0.05–0.17	0.2–1.5
Total lipid (%)	0.1–0.5	1.8–4.7
Cholesterol (%)	0.05–0.17	0.2–0.9
Phosphatide (%)	0.05–0.08	0.2–0.5
Inorganic (%)	0.2–0.9	0.5–1.1
Total base (mEq./liter)	150–180	
Chloride (mEq./liter)	75–110	15–30
Calcium (mg. %)	4–9	10–14
Iron (mg. %)	0.03–7	

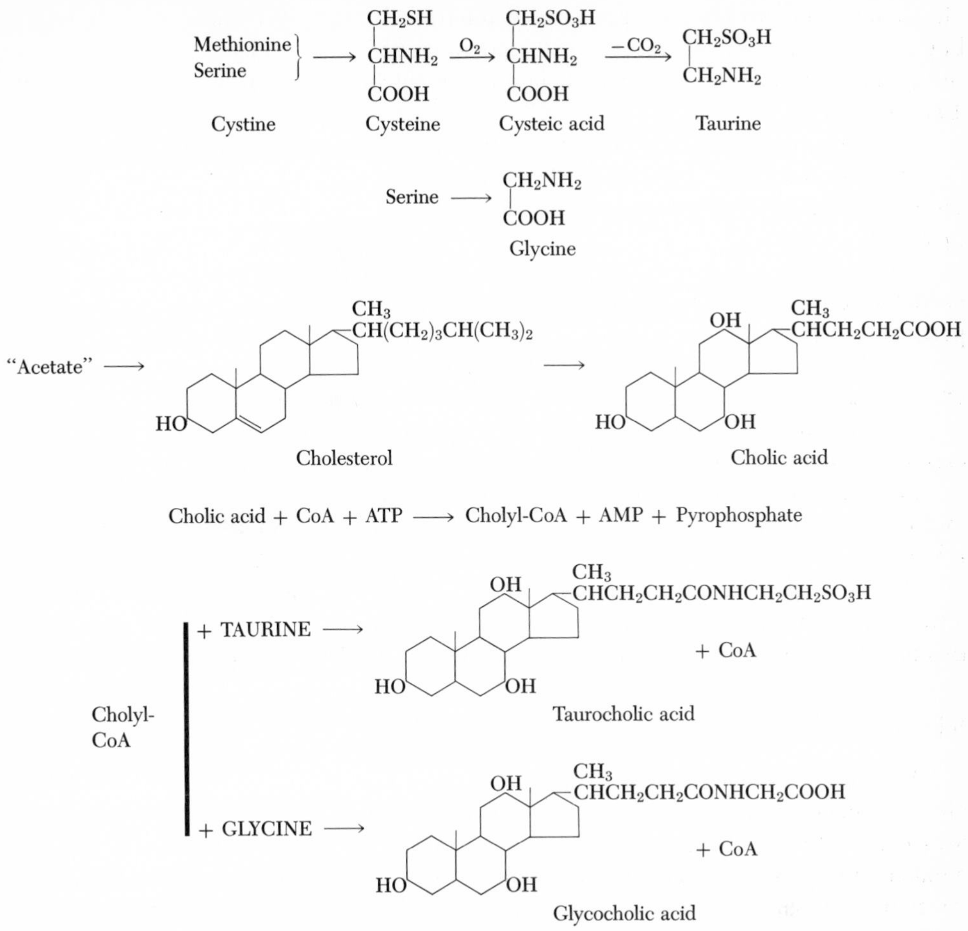

Methionine, Serine → CH_2SH–$CHNH_2$–$COOH$ (Cysteine) $\xrightarrow{O_2}$ CH_2SO_3H–$CHNH_2$–$COOH$ (Cysteic acid) $\xrightarrow{-CO_2}$ CH_2SO_3H–CH_2NH_2 (Taurine)

Cystine

Serine → CH_2NH_2–$COOH$ (Glycine)

"Acetate" → Cholesterol (HO; CH_3, $CH(CH_2)_3CH(CH_3)_2$) → Cholic acid (HO, OH, OH; CH_3, $CHCH_2CH_2COOH$)

Cholic acid + CoA + ATP ⟶ Cholyl-CoA + AMP + Pyrophosphate

Cholyl-CoA + TAURINE ⟶ Taurocholic acid (HO, OH, OH; CH_3, $CHCH_2CH_2CONHCH_2CH_2SO_3H$) + CoA

Cholyl-CoA + GLYCINE ⟶ Glycocholic acid (HO, OH, OH; CH_3, $CHCH_2CH_2CONHCH_2COOH$) + CoA

Figure 9–1. Biosynthesis of bile acids.

chenodeoxycholic (3,7-dihydroxycholanic) acid, formerly believed to occur mainly in the dog. The relative amounts of these three bile acids in human bile are approximately as follows: cholic, 25 to 60 per cent of the total; chenodeoxycholic, 30 to 50 per cent; deoxycholic, 5 to 25 per cent. These exist apparently exclusively as conjugates with glycine or taurine, i.e., glycocholic acid, taurocholic acid, etc. (Fig. 9–1), the glyco- usually predominating over the tauro- forms. The latter are apparently conjugated first, the amounts of the glyco- conjugates being determined by the excess of bile acid (i.e., cholic acid, etc.), which is usually large, except in the presence of excessive protein catabolism (i.e., excessive taurine formation).

Cholic acid is formed in the liver from cholesterol. Conjugation with glycine and taurine (from cysteine) also occurs in the liver. This reaction involves activation of cholic acid to cholyl-CoA, requiring coenzyme A, ATP, and Mg.

The quantity of bile acids formed and excreted varies within wide limits, depending presumably upon the intensity of stimulation of this function by the digestive mixture in the intestine, the capacity of the liver in this regard being very large. Their concentration in hepatic bile has been found to vary from 0.4 to 2.0 gm./100 ml. and the total daily excretion from 5 to 10 gm. In the intestine, the bile acids are absorbed into the portal circulation, from which they are largely removed by the liver and re-excreted in the bile (enterohepatic circulation). A small amount escapes removal by the liver, passing into the systemic circulation, in which cholate is present in concentrations of 0.2 to 3.0 mg./100 ml.

The most important functions of the bile acids are:

(1) They facilitate digestion of fats by their emulsifying action (lowering surface tension), thus increasing enormously the surface area of the substrate exposed to pancreatic lipase.

(2) In combination with free fatty acids and monoglycerides, they form minute particles, termed micelles, which are about 1/100 the size of the emulsified triglyceride particles entering the duodenum in the digestive mixture.

(3) They activate cholesterol esterase and pancreatic lipase, especially at an acid pH, which is usually present (after meals) in the upper small intestine.

(4) They aid in absorption of cholesterol, and the fat-soluble vitamins D and K, and of carotene, presumably by forming complexes more soluble in water ("hydrotropic" action).

(5) They are the most potent natural stimulus to hepatic bile flow, increasing severalfold the volume flow of bile (choleretic action), the output of solids being, however, not affected.

(6) They aid in keeping cholesterol in solution in the bile. When the bile acid:cholesterol concentration ratio falls below a critical level, cholesterol may precipitate; this may be a factor in the pathogenesis of biliary calculi (gallstones).

Bile Pigments

The yellow-brown color of freshly secreted human bile (hepatic) is due mainly to bilirubin glucuronide. On standing (in air or, at times, in the gallbladder) this undergoes oxidation to biliverdin (green). In certain species (e.g., rabbit), biliverdin is the chief pigment of bile. Normal bile may also contain a trace of urobilinogen, which has escaped metabolism in the liver after its absorption from the bowel. These pigments are waste products of the degradation of heme; their chemistry and metabolism are discussed in detail elsewhere (p. 614). Suffice it here to state that bilirubin, carried in the blood plasma bound to albumin (pp. 562, 616), is separated from the protein and removed from the blood by the liver cells, where it is conjugated with glucuronic acid, and excreted in the bile. A small portion of the bilirubin is formed in the Kupffer (reticuloendothelial) cells of the liver; in man, the bone marrow and spleen are the main sites of normal erythrocyte destruction and heme degradation.

The bile pigments serve no known function, but abnormalities in their formation, conjugation, excretion, and concentration in the blood plasma are of considerable clinical significance in the diagnosis of diseases of the liver and bile passages and conditions of excessive hemolysis. The quantity excreted daily in the bile (Table 9-1), normally averaging about 300 mg., is a reflection of the amount of heme undergoing degradation (about 300 mg.), the latter being derived from the approximately 7.5 gm. of hemoglobin liberated from destroyed erythrocytes.

Cholesterol

By virtue of the relatively large amounts present (Table 9-1), and its participation in the formation of gallstones, cholesterol is one of the most important constituents of bile. However, what function it serves in this fluid is conjecturable. It was formerly believed that the bile is an important medium of excretion of the cholesterol circulating in the blood plasma. It appears, however, that this is not the case. Whereas the liver cells actively remove cholesterol from the bloodstream, this is largely (at least 60 per cent in the rat) converted here to bile acids, which are excreted in the bile. Probably little of the cholesterol of the plasma is transferred as such to the bile, and its concentration in the latter medium bears no consistent relation to that in the former. The biliary cholesterol is largely synthesized in the liver, as is the plasma cholesterol.

SUMMARY OF DIGESTION

Carbohydrates

Hydrolysis of polysaccharides (starch, glycogen, dextrins) is begun by salivary amylase in the mouth and continues for a short time in the stomach, until this salivary amylase is inactivated by the increasing acidity and pepsin. Digestion products are dextrins and maltose. The unchanged polysaccharides and the dextrins are split to maltose by pancreatic amylase. The maltose and ingested lactose and sucrose are ultimately hydrolyzed to glucose, galactose, and fructose within the intestinal epithelial cells by the enzymes, maltase, lactase, and sucrase (invertase). Ingested carbohydrates therefore enter the bloodstream from the intestine normally as monosaccharides.

Proteins

Proteins are denatured to a certain extent by the gastric HCl. Gastric pepsin and pancreatic trypsin and chymotrypsin act on native and denatured proteins to form polypeptides and simpler peptides of varying size and a small amount of amino acids. The peptides are attacked further by carboxypeptidase (pancreas), aminopeptidases (intestine), and tri- and dipeptidases (intestine), the end-products of protein digestion being largely amino acids and, probably, a small amount of short peptide chains.

Casein is converted to insoluble paracasein, in the presence of Ca^{++}, by rennin (infants), pepsin, and chymotrypsin. The paracasein is then attacked by proteolytic enzymes as indicated above. Casein is also denatured and precipitated by gastric HCl.

Nucleoproteins

The proteolytic enzymes apparently split nucleoproteins into their protein and nucleic acid components, digesting the former as outlined above. The nucleic acids are depolymerized by the hydrolytic action of pancreatic ribonuclease and deoxyribonuclease, with the production of oligonucleotides and certain pyrimidine mononucleotides. The oligonucleotides are converted to mononucleotides by intestinal phosphodiesterases. The mononucleotides are hydrolyzed by nonspecific phosphatases, yielding nucleosides and inorganic phosphate, which are the end products of the digestion of nucleic acids. The nucleosides are absorbed as such.

Lipids

Digestion of fats is facilitated by the emulsifying action of bile salts, which lower surface tension. When their digestion has begun, it is further aided by the emulsifying effect of fat-digestion products. There is little fat digestion in the stomach (gastric lipase), pancreatic lipase being the most important lipolytic enzyme in the digestive tract (there are also lipases in intestinal secretions). Hydrolysis of fats does not proceed to completion in the intestine under physiological conditions. The final products to be absorbed include the original triglycerides, di- and monoglycerides, fatty acids, and glycerol. Triglycerides of short-chain fatty acids, e.g., tributyrin, are not attacked effectively by lipase, nor are other fatty acid esters. Various carboxylesterases, phosphodiesterases and phosphatases are present in the intestine, which may hydrolyze such compounds as tributyrin, phospholipids, and cholesterol esters prior to their absorption. In certain instances, e.g., cholesterol esters and phospholipids, this process may be reversed, these substances being synthesized either in the lumen or, more probably, in the mucosal cells during the process of absorption.

ABSORPTION

Nutrient materials are not ordinarily absorbed from the mouth, although certain therapeutically administered substances may be under specialized conditions. Alcohol and relatively small amounts of water, iron, amino acids, monosaccharides, other simple organic compounds, and inorganic salts may be absorbed from the stomach. However, the small intestine is the major site of entrance of nutrient and other materials into the organism, via the intestinal lymphatics (especially lipids) and portal circulation. Substances absorbed by the former route are transported in the thoracic duct to the subclavian vein, and hence enter the systemic circulation directly; those absorbed into the portal blood pass to the liver, where many of them undergo metabolic transformations before they pass into the systemic circulation. Absorptive functions of the colon are normally restricted almost exclusively to water, although certain inorganic elements and simple organic compounds may be absorbed here.

Water, inorganic substances, end-products of digestion of carbohydrates, lipids and proteins, and other essential nutrient materials, e.g., vitamins, are generally absorbed readily from the small intestine. Individual peculiarities of absorption of various foodstuffs and digestive products are considered in the discussions of the metabolism of these substances.

The contents of the terminal ileum pass through the ileocecal valve into the colon. Here the final changes occur prior to expulsion of unabsorbed material (feces) from the bowel.

ACTION OF BACTERIA

After the first few hours of life, microorganisms gain entrance to the alimentary tract and multiply, chiefly in the colon, but also to a lesser extent in the small intestine. Most of them do not survive exposure to a highly acid gastric juice, but may flourish in the presence of achlorhydria; some are attacked by digestive enzymes in the small intestine. In some species, these organisms serve important digestive functions, e.g., in cattle, rendering nutritionally available such substances as cellulose, which the host cannot digest. In man, the normal intestinal microorganisms, acting chiefly on products of enzymatic digestion of organic foodstuffs, produce substances some of which are potentially harmful (e.g., toxic amines, phenols), others beneficial (certain vitamins), others neither harmful nor beneficial (e.g., urobilinogen). These are products of metabolic activity of the bacteria, involving processes similar to many operating in animal tissues, e.g., oxidation, decarboxylation, deamination, reduction and hydrolysis, catalyzed by enzymes often similar to those encountered in mammalian cells.

The important matter of synthesis of vitamins by intestinal bacteria is considered in the discussion of individual vitamins. We are concerned here with their action on organic foodstuffs and their digestive products.

Carbohydrates and Lipids

The action of intestinal bacteria on carbohydrates is commonly referred to as intestinal fermentation. The products include chiefly (1) organic acids, such as formic, acetic, propionic, butyric, lactic, oxalic, and succinic, and (2) gases, such as methane, carbon dioxide, and hydrogen. Fats may be hydrolyzed to glycerol and fatty acids, but little is known about the action of microorganisms on lipids in the intestine.

Proteins

Bacterial enzymes act on proteins to form polypeptides (proteoses, peptones), smaller peptides, amino acids, and ammonia. Aromatic amino acids are converted to phenol, cresol, indole, and skatole. Cystine yields H_2S, mercaptans, and methane. Certain amino acids form amines (tyramine, putrescine, cadaverine, histamine). These changes are commonly included under the designation "putrefaction."

Certain of the simpler amino acids undergo (1) decarboxylation, to amines, or (2) deamination, to short-chain fatty acids, by the action of bacterial enzymes.

$$\underset{\text{Amino acid}}{R\text{—}CHNH_2\text{—}COOH} \xrightarrow{-NH_2} \underset{\text{Fatty acid}}{R\text{—}CH_2\text{—}COOH}$$

$$\underset{\text{Amino acid}}{R\text{—}CHNH_2\text{—}COOH} \xrightarrow{-CO_2} \underset{\text{Amine}}{R\text{—}CH_2\text{—}NH_2}$$

Tyrosine. Tyrosine may undergo (1) decarboxylation to tyramine, which may be converted to cresol and phenol, or (2) deamination, oxidation, and decarboxylation to cresol.

Tyramine is a "pressor base," having an action similar to but weaker than that of epinephrine and norepinephrine, to which it is closely related structurally. As indicated below, tyramine may in part be reduced in the bowel to cresol. If absorbed, it is metabolized in the liver, in part at least undergoing deamination (oxidative) to form hydroxyphenylacetic acid. Absorbed phenols are largely conjugated in the liver with sulfate and glucuronic acid, to be excreted ultimately in the urine.

Tyrosine (OH—C_6H_4—CH_2—CH(NH_2)—COOH) $\xrightarrow{-CO_2}$ Tyramine (OH—C_6H_4—CH_2—CH_2—NH_2) $\xrightarrow{+2H}$ Cresol (OH—C_6H_4—CH_3) + Methylamine (CH_3—NH_2) $\longrightarrow$ Phenol (OH—C_6H_5)

Tyrosine $\xrightarrow{-NH_2}$ p-Hydroxyphenylpropionic acid (OH—C_6H_4—CH_2—CH_2—COOH) $\longrightarrow$ p-Hydroxyphenylacetic acid (OH—C_6H_4—CH_2—COOH) $\xrightarrow{-CO_2}$ Cresol (OH—C_6H_4—CH_3) $\longrightarrow$ Phenol

Tyramine $\longrightarrow$ p-Hydroxyphenylacetic acid

Tryptophan. This may also undergo primary (1) decarboxylation to indole ethylamine (tryptamine) or (2) deamination to indolepropionic acid. The subsequent changes are indicated below, eventuating in skatole and indole, which contribute the characteristic foul odor to the feces. These substances are relatively non-toxic in quantities ordinarily produced, but may be toxic in very large amounts.

Tryptophan (indole-$CH_2 \cdot CH(NH_2) \cdot COOH$) $\xrightarrow{-NH_2,\ +H}$ Indolepropionic acid (indole-$CH_2 \cdot CH_2 \cdot COOH$) $\xrightarrow{-CO_2}$ Ethylindole (indole-$CH_2 \cdot CH_3$) $\rightarrow$ Skatole (indole-CH_3)

Indolepropionic acid $\rightarrow$ Indoleacetic acid (indole-$CH_2 \cdot COOH$) $\xrightarrow{-CO_2}$ Skatole

Tryptophan $\xrightarrow{-CO_2}$ Indole ethylamine (indole-$CH_2 \cdot CH_2 \cdot NH_2$) $\xrightarrow{-CH_3 \cdot NH_2,\ +2H}$ Skatole

Indole ethylamine $\xrightarrow{+2H}$ Indole + $C_2H_5NH_2$ (Ethylamine)

A small portion of the indole is absorbed and, in the liver, is conjugated with sulfate and excreted in the urine as indican (indoxyl sulfate). Increased amounts of indole may be absorbed and increased amounts of indican formed in constipation and lower intestinal obstruction.

Histidine. Histidine undergoes decarboxylation to histamine, a powerful vasodepressor substance with additional important actions when introduced into the organism.

Histidine (imidazole-$CH_2 \cdot CH \cdot NH_2 \cdot COOH$) $\xrightarrow{-CO_2}$ Histamine (imidazole-$CH_2 \cdot CH_2 \cdot NH_2$)

Histidine $\xrightarrow{-NH_2}$ Imidazolepropionic acid (imidazole-$CH_2 \cdot CH_2 \cdot COOH$) $\xrightarrow[O_2]{-CO_2}$ Imidazoleacetic acid (imidazole-$CH_2 \cdot COOH$) $\xrightarrow[O_2]{-CO_2}$ Imidazoleformic acid (imidazole-$COOH$)

Many tissues, including the intestines, contain histamine, and also the enzyme histaminase (diamine oxidase), which effects its oxidative degradation to innocuous metabolites.

Cystine and cysteine. Cystine undergoes primary reduction to cysteine, which may in turn be (1) deaminated or (2) decarboxylated, with the eventual production of mercaptans, H_2S and CH_4. These are largely eliminated in the feces, although mercaptans may be absorbed and excreted in the urine.

Cystine ($CH_2{-}S{-}S{-}CH_2$; $HC \cdot NH_2$, $HC \cdot NH_2$; COOH, COOH) $\xrightarrow{+2H}$ 2 Cysteine (SH; CH_2; $HC \cdot NH_2$; COOH) $\longrightarrow$ Aminoethyl mercaptan ($CH_2 \cdot SH$; $CH_2 \cdot NH_2$)

Aminoethyl mercaptan $\xrightarrow{+2H}$ $CH_3 \cdot SH$ + $CH_3 \cdot NH_2$
Methyl mercaptan, Methylamine

Methyl mercaptan $\longrightarrow$ $H_2S + CH_4$

Cysteine $\xrightarrow{-NH_2,\ +H}$ Sulfhydryl-propionic acid ($CH_2 \cdot SH$; CH_2; COOH) $\xrightarrow{-CO_2}$ C_2H_5SH (Ethyl mercaptan)

Reduction of cystine

Lysine, arginine. These amino acids may undergo decarboxylation to the diamines, cadaverine and putrescine, respectively, which are largely excreted in the feces, but are essentially non-toxic in amounts ordinarily formed.

$$NH_2 \cdot CH_2 \cdot (CH_2)_3 \cdot CH \cdot NH_2 \cdot COOH \longrightarrow NH_2 \cdot CH_2 \cdot (CH_2)_3 \cdot CH_2 \cdot NH_2$$
Lysine → Cadaverine

Arginine ($HN{=}C(NH_2){-}NH$; $(CH_2)_3$; $HC \cdot NH_2$; COOH) $\xrightarrow{H_2O}$ Urea ($O{=}C(NH_2)_2$) + Ornithine ($CH_2 \cdot NH_2$; $(CH_2)_2$; $HC \cdot NH_2$; COOH) $\xrightarrow{-CO_2}$ Putrescine ($CH_2 \cdot NH_2$; $(CH_2)_2$; $CH_2 \cdot NH_2$)

(OH, H added across the cleaved bond)

Decarboxylation of lysine and arginine

Miscellaneous

Bacteria undoubtedly act on numerous other substances in the intestine. Among these is bilirubin, which is reduced by bacterial enzymes to mesobilirubinogen and stercobilinogen (urobilinogen), these being subsequently oxidized to urobilin and stercobilin. The major, unabsorbed portion of the "bilinogens" and "bilins" is excreted by the bowel (p. 618). Fecal coprosterol is produced by bacterial reduction of cholesterol.

FORMATION AND COMPOSITION OF FECES

The contents of the terminal ileum enter the colon in a semiliquid state. The solid material includes indigestible food residues (e.g., cellulose), small amounts of undigested and unabsorbed foodstuffs, remains of desquamated mucosal cells and digestive fluids, together with bacteria and unabsorbed products of their activity. The function of the colon consists chiefly in absorption of water, converting its contents to a semisolid state. What chemical changes occur here are almost exclusively due to bacterial action. Comparatively little material is actively excreted into the colon in its mucosal secretion, which is a viscous, slightly alkaline fluid, containing a considerable amount of mucin. Large amounts of bacteria constitute the main contribution of the colon to the fecal solids.

The normal dark-brown color of feces is due chiefly to bilifuscins (p. 136), and in part to stercobilin and urobilin, produced by reduction of bilirubin by intestinal bacteria. About 40 to 280 mg. (average 200 mg.) of these pigments are excreted daily, the lower values during periods of sluggish bowel function (more urobilinogen absorbed). Bilirubin and biliverdin are present in the feces during the first few days of life, i.e., before development of an extensive intestinal bacterial flora, and in diarrheal states in adults (inadequate time for complete reduction to "urobilinogen") (p. 618). The color of feces also varies somewhat with the character of the diet, being paler on a high milk intake. Certain drugs and pigmented vegetables may influence the color, e.g., black after Fe and Bi (sulfides and oxides formed), yellowish after senna, santonin and rhubarb, etc.

The characteristic foul odor is due largely to indole and skatole, but is contributed to also by H_2S and methyl mercaptan. It is more pronounced on a high protein intake, owing to formation of large quantities of these substances by bacterial action on amino acids, and is relatively slight on high milk or high carbohydrate diets. The slightly "sour" odor of infant feces is due to organic acids resulting from bacterial fermentation of carbohydrates.

Adults on a normal mixed diet excrete 75 to 170 gm. of feces daily (average 100 gm.), about 25 to 30 per cent of which is solid (25 to 45 gm. dry weight). The quantity (total and dry weight) increases on diets rich in vegetables, especially if uncooked (indigestible cellulose). About 7 to 8 gm. of feces are excreted daily if no food is ingested, consisting largely of bacteria, remnants of desquamated mucosal cells, and residues of mucosal secretions and digestive fluids. Bacteria comprise about one-third of the dry weight of the feces under average dietary conditions. The pH, 7.0 to 7.5, is relatively uninfluenced by wide variations in composition of the diet, but may be lowered by ingestion of large amounts of lactose (fermentation acids).

The inorganic components are mainly substances poorly soluble in alkaline pH ranges, such as calcium phosphate and oxalate, iron phosphate, etc., but also small amounts of magnesium, potassium, and sodium. The organic constituents include carbohydrate (chiefly cellulose), proteins, and lipids.

Protein

On an average diet, the daily nitrogen excretion in the feces is 0.5 to 1.5 gm. (average 1.3 gm.). About half is of bacterial origin, the remainder representing nitrogenous components of (1) unabsorbed intestinal secretions and digestive fluids, (2) mucus, (3) desquamated mucosal epithelial cells, and a small amount of (4) food residues and (5) intestinal enzymes. Under normal conditions, protein digestion and amino acid absorption are so nearly complete that only small amounts of food protein nitrogen (5 to 10 per cent) escape in the feces. Enzymes are also present in very small quantities, including pancreatic amylase, trypsin, nucleases, maltase, sucrase, lipase, and lysozyme. These are increased in diarrhea. The term "metabolic N" is used to indicate the fecal N originating from sources other than bacteria and food residues. This factor is employed in quantitative studies of protein utilization and N balance.

Lipids

Lipids comprise 5 to 25 per cent (average 17) of the dry weight of normal feces. They include neutral fats, free fatty acids, soaps, and sterols. Approximately one-third of the fecal lipid is unsaponifiable, consisting mainly of phytosterols, and cholesterol and its reduction products, coprosterol and dihydrocholesterol. Cholesterol enters the bowel in the food, bile, and intestinal secretions. The only quantitatively important sterols and their derivatives absorbed by the human intestine are cholesterol and vitamin D. The remainder of the lipids are largely of endogenous origin, secreted into the bowel, and resemble the plasma lipids in their fatty acid composition. Under normal conditions, their nature and amount are altered but little by wide variations in dietary fat, which is almost completely utilized unless given in excessive amounts, causing diarrhea. The average normal distribution of saponifiable fecal lipids is as follows: (1) neutral fat, 7.3 per cent of dry weight; (2) free fatty acid, 5.6 per cent; (3) soaps, 4.6 per cent.

BIBLIOGRAPHY

Annual Review of Physiology.
Babkin, B. P.: Secretory Mechanism of the Digestive Glands, ed. 2, New York, Paul B. Hoeber, Inc., 1950.
Bockus, H. L.: Gastroenterology, ed. 2, 3 vols., Philadelphia, W. B. Saunders Company, 1963 to 1965.
Conway, E. J.: The Biochemistry of Gastric Acid Secretion, Springfield, Ill., Charles C Thomas, 1953.
Florey, H. W., Wright, R. D., and Jennings, M. A.: The secretions of the intestine, Physiol. Rev. *21*:36, 1941.
Grossman, M. I.: The physiology of secretin, Vitamins and Hormones *16*:179, 1958.
Hollander, F.: The composition and mechanism of formation of gastric acid secretion, Science *110*:57, 1949.
Hunt, R. N.: Gastric emptying and secretion in man, Physiol. Rev. *39*:491, 1959.
Sobotka, H.: Physiological Chemistry of the Bile, Baltimore, Williams & Wilkins Company, 1937.
Wilson, T. H.: Intestinal Absorption, Philadelphia, W. B. Saunders Company, 1962.
Wolf, S., and Wolff, H. G.: Human Gastric Function, London, Oxford University Press, 1944.

CHAPTER 10

DETOXICATION MECHANISMS

THE TERM "detoxication" in its broadest sense is applied to chemical changes undergone in the body by foreign organic compounds, i.e., substances not ordinarily ingested or utilized by the organism. Employed in this manner, the term is frequently inaccurate and misleading, for many of the compounds in question are originally non-toxic and, in certain instances, the chemical changes result in increased rather than reduced toxicity. In certain cases the metabolites are excreted more readily in the urine than are the original compounds. The reactions involved in these detoxication processes are (1) oxidation, (2) reduction, (3) hydrolysis, and (4) conjugation. The type of reaction depends primarily on the chemical nature of the compound, but occasionally the metabolism of a given substance follows different pathways in different species. In man, oxidation and conjugation are most widely employed in this connection, occurring almost exclusively in the liver and, to a minor extent, in the kidney.

Oxidation

Many foreign organic compounds undergo oxidation in the body. The most important types of these may be classified as follows:

(*a*) ***Primary alcohols.*** Aliphatic (e.g., methyl) and aromatic (e.g., benzyl) primary alcohols are oxidized to the corresponding acids, perhaps via aldehydes as intermediates.

$$\underset{\text{Methanol}}{CH_3OH} \longrightarrow \underset{\text{Formic acid}}{HCOOH}$$

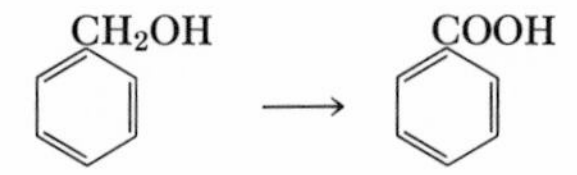

$$\underset{\text{Benzyl alcohol}}{C_6H_5CH_2OH} \longrightarrow \underset{\text{Benzoic acid}}{C_6H_5COOH}$$

(*b*) ***Aromatic hydrocarbons.*** Mono- or polycyclic aromatic hydrocarbons (e.g., benzene) are frequently oxidized to phenols. In rare instances the aromatic ring may open, but only to a slight extent.

Benzene ⟶ Phenol (OH) ⟶ Catechol (OH, OH) ⟶ Muconic acid (COOH, COOH)

(*c*) ***Methyl groups.*** Methyl groups are largely oxidized to carboxyl groups, via alcohols and aldehydes as intermediates.

$$-CH_3 \longrightarrow -CH_2OH \longrightarrow -CHO \longrightarrow -COOH$$

(*d*) ***Oxidation preliminary to conjugation.*** Oxidation may occur as a necessary preliminary to conjugation; e.g., benzene is oxidized to phenol, which then combines with sulfuric or glucuronic acid.

Reduction

This does not occur extensively in man as a detoxication mechanism. Certain of the reduced metabolites are more toxic than the original compounds. Illustrative examples of this mechanism are as follows:

(1) Certain aldehydes (e.g., chloral) may be reduced to the corresponding alcohol, usually as a preliminary to conjugation of the latter.

$$CCl_3CHO \xrightarrow{2H} CCl_3CH_2OH \xrightarrow[\text{acid}]{\text{Glucuronic}} CCl_3CH_2OC_6H_9O_6$$

Trichloroethyl glucuronide

(2) Aromatic nitro compounds (e.g., *p*-nitrobenzaldehyde) may be reduced to the corresponding amines.

p-Nitrobenzaldehyde (CHO, NO_2) $\xrightarrow[2H]{O}$ (COOH, NHOH) $\xrightarrow{2H}$ *p*-Aminobenzoic acid (COOH, NH_2)

In this instance, reduction of the nitro group is accompanied by oxidation of the aldehyde group.

Hydrolysis

Certain compounds which are used for therapeutic purposes undergo hydrolysis in the body. Acetylsalicylic acid is hydrolyzed to salicylic and acetic acids; many glucosides, e.g., digitalis, are hydrolyzed to sugars and aglucones.

Conjugation

This term, as applied specifically to detoxication processes, refers to the coupling of the foreign substance or one of its metabolites (see Oxidation and Reduction) with a compound occurring normally in the body. The latter is referred to as the conjugating agent. In man, this important type of reaction occurs virtually only in the liver; the kidney participates to only a minor extent in certain instances, although it plays a more important role in this connection in other species.

In man, eight types of conjugation have been established, the conjugating agents being as follows: (1) glucuronic acid, (2) sulfuric acid, (3) glycine, (4) cysteine, (5) glutamine, (6) acetic acid, (7) methyl groups, and (8) thiosulfate. In most, and perhaps in all instances, these reactions involve preliminary activation of one member of the conjugating pair, forming a compound which serves as the immediate donor of the conjugating agent.

In birds, ornithine (forming ornithinuric acid) also is employed as a conjugating agent (for benzoic acid). As is true of oxidation, reduction, and hydrolysis, these conjugation reactions occur also in the metabolism of compounds produced normally in the body; e.g., bilirubin (p. 616), androgens (p. 686), estrogens (p. 691), and adrenocortical hormones (p. 708) undergo conjugation with glucuronic acid and sulfate. Formation of these conjugates of steroid hormones aids in controlling the level of biologically active hormones in the blood and facilitates their excretion in the urine. Conjugation with glucuronic acid is essential for excretion of bilirubin in the bile and for its proper removal from the blood by the liver. Under experimental conditions, administration of excessive amounts of foreign substances may result in the diversion of excessive quantities of conjugating agent from normal metabolic reactions to "detoxication" processes, to the possible detriment of the organism. Variation in susceptibility to certain drugs has been found to be related to variations in the rate of their inactivation by conjugation, e.g., acetylation of isoniazid and sulfonamides.

(*a*) ***Glucuronic acid.*** Glucuronic acid, formed in the body from carbohydrate (p. 421), is the conjugating agent most commonly involved in this type of detoxication process in man. Two varieties of compounds may be formed: (1) an ether (glucosidic) linkage (e.g., phenyl glucosiduronide); (2) an ester linkage (e.g., benzoyl glucuronide). In both cases the active donor is uridine diphosphoglucuronic acid (p. 233), the transferring enzyme varying with different recipient substrates. Glucuronic acid is conjugated commonly with the following types of compounds:

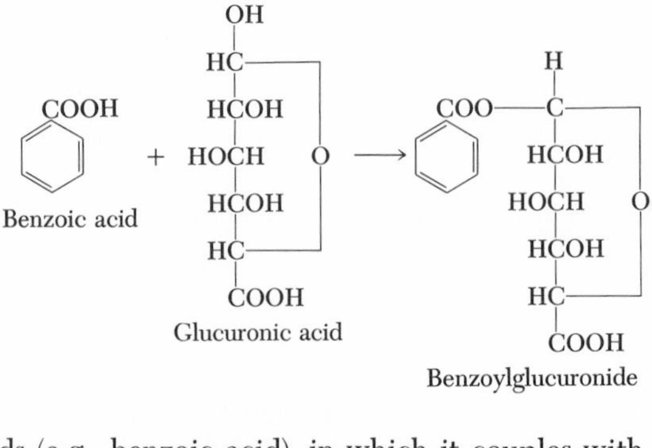

```
                   OH
                   |
                   HC——————┐                      H
                   |       |                      |
   COOH            HCOH    |          COO————C————┐
   |               |       |          |      |    |
 (C6H5)     +      HOCH    O  ——→   (C6H5)   HCOH |
                   |       |                 |    |
Benzoic acid       HCOH    |               HOCH   O
                   |       |                 |    |
                   HC——————┘                 HCOH |
                   |                         |    |
                   COOH                      HC———┘
              Glucuronic acid                |
                                             COOH
                                      Benzoylglucuronide
```

(1) Aromatic acids (e.g., benzoic acid), in which it couples with the carboxyl group.

(2) Phenols, and secondary and tertiary aliphatic alcohols, in which coupling occurs with the hydroxyl group.

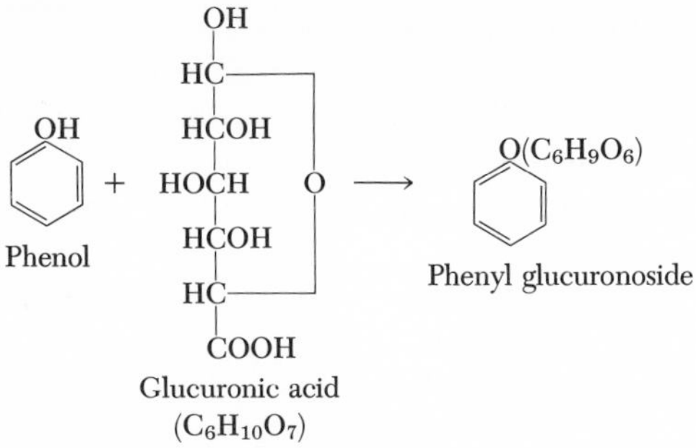

OH | HC— | HCOH | HOCH O | HCOH | HC— | COOH

Phenol + Glucuronic acid ($C_6H_{10}O_7$) ⟶ Phenyl glucuronoside ($O(C_6H_9O_6)$)

(*b*) ***Sulfuric acid.*** Phenolic hydroxyl groups (e.g., phenol, indoxyl) combine with sulfuric acid to form esters, referred to as ethereal sulfates (p. 588). This reaction involves transformation of inorganic sulfate, in the presence of ATP and Mg^{++}, to 3′-phosphoadenosine-5′-phosphosulfate, the active sulfate donor in the sulfatation reaction (p. 587).

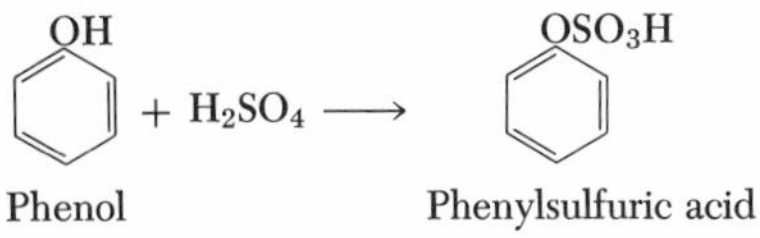

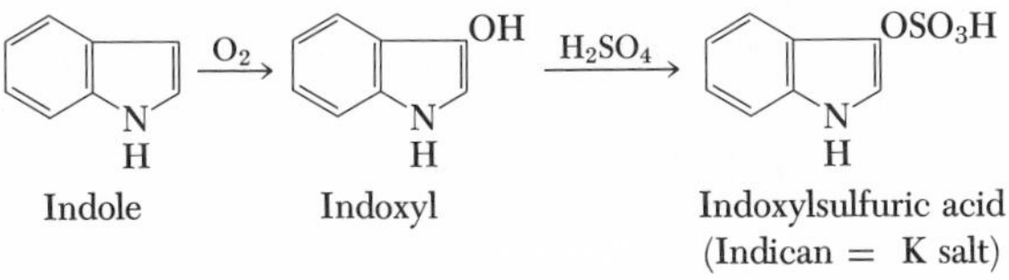

Phenol (OH) + H_2SO_4 ⟶ Phenylsulfuric acid (OSO_3H)

Indole $\xrightarrow{O_2}$ Indoxyl (OH) $\xrightarrow{H_2SO_4}$ Indoxylsulfuric acid (OSO_3H)
(Indican = K salt)

(*c*) ***Glycine.*** In man, this amino acid couples chiefly with certain aromatic acids to form aroylglycine compounds. Although aliphatic carboxyl groups as a rule do not combine with glycine, those of cholic and deoxycholic acids do so, glycine conjugates of these bile acids being important normal constituents of bile. The following types of carboxyl groups undergo this reaction:

(1) Nuclear carboxyl groups in benzene (e.g., benzoic acid), pyridine (e.g., nicotinic acid), naphthalene, thiophene, and furan rings. In man, benzoic acid, when given in relatively small doses, is excreted as hippuric acid. This reaction involves activation of benzoic acid to the form of benzoyl CoA (p. 473). When large amounts are given, a portion is excreted also as the glucuronide.

(2) Carboxyl groups separated from an aromatic ring by a vinyl group (e.g., cinnamic acid).

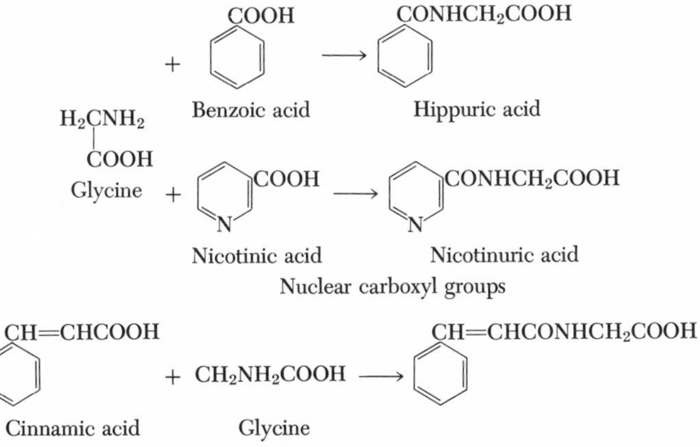

Glycine (H_2CNH_2–COOH) + Benzoic acid (COOH) ⟶ Hippuric acid ($CONHCH_2COOH$)

Glycine + Nicotinic acid (COOH) ⟶ Nicotinuric acid ($CONHCH_2COOH$)

Nuclear carboxyl groups

Cinnamic acid (CH=CHCOOH) + Glycine (CH_2NH_2COOH) ⟶ $CH{=}CHCONHCH_2COOH$

Carboxyl groups

(*d*) ***Cysteine.*** This amino acid is involved in detoxication reactions to a limited extent in man. It couples with certain aromatic compounds, which then undergo acetylation to form mercapturic acids (p. 586). These include benzene, polycyclic hydrocarbons (e.g., naphthalene), and ring-halogenated hydrocarbons (e.g., bromobenzene). In this type of conjugation the —S of the cysteine is usually linked to a nuclear carbon atom.

C_6H_5Br + $HSCH_2CH(NH_2)COOH$ + CH_3COOH ⟶ $BrC_6H_4SCH_2CH(NHCOCH_3)COOH$

Bromobenzene, Cysteine, Acetic acid ⟶ Bromophenylmercapturic acid

Naphthalene + Cysteine + Acetic acid ⟶ $C_{10}H_7SCH_2CH(NHCOCH_3)COOH$

Naphthalene ⟶ Naphthylmercapturic acid

(*e*) ***Acetic acid.*** As a "detoxication" reaction, acetylation apparently involves only the amino group, although acetylation of hydroxyl groups occurs commonly in the course of metabolism of physiological compounds (e.g., formation of acetylcholine). Aromatic amino groups are involved most commonly (e.g., sulfanilamide; *p*-aminobenzoic acid), but not exclusively. Acetylation of cysteine in the synthesis of mercapturic acid was referred to above. All of these reactions involve activation of the acetate to the form of acetyl CoA (p. 472).

$H_2NC_6H_4SO_2NH_2$ + CH_3COOH ⟶ $CH_3CONHC_6H_4SO_2NH_2$

Sulfanilamide (*p*-Aminobenzenesulfonamide) ⟶ Acetylated sulfanilamide (*p*-N-acetylaminobenzenesulfonamide)

(*f*) ***Glutamine.*** In man (and the chimpanzee), glutamine is conjugated with phenylacetic acid, forming phenylacetylglutamine. It is interesting that certain species conjugate phenylacetic acid only with glycine (e.g., dog), forming phenaceturic acid, and others only with ornithine (fowl).

$C_6H_5CH_2COOH$ + $HOOC\text{-}CH(NH_2)\text{-}CH_2\text{-}CH_2\text{-}CONH_2$ ⟶ $C_6H_5CH_2C(=O)\text{-}NH\text{-}CH(COOH)\text{-}CH_2\text{-}CH_2\text{-}CONH_2$

Phenylacetic acid, Glutamine ⟶ Phenylacetylglutamine

(*g*) ***Methylation.*** The methyl donor in these reactions is S-adenosylmethionine (p. 590). This occurs as a normal metabolic process as follows:

(1) Methylation of the heterocyclic N atom of compounds of the pyridine and quinoline types, e.g., nicotinamide (p. 185). This occurs also with other heterocyclic aromatic compounds, e.g., histamine.

(2) Methylation of *p*-monomethylaminoazobenzene to *p*-dimethylaminoazobenzene (butter yellow), a potent hepatic carcinogen.

(3) O-methylation of the phenolic hydroxyl group of certain naturally occurring amines, e.g., epinephrine, norepinephrine and their metabolites (p. 700).

(4) O-methylation of natural estrogens (p. 691).

$CONH_2$ + CH_3 ⟶ $CONH_2$ N^+ CH_3

Nicotinamide N[1]-Methylnicotinamide

(*h*) ***Thiocyanate formation.*** The highly toxic cyanides react with thiosulfate to form relatively non-toxic thiocyanates. This reaction, catalyzed by the enzyme thiosulfate : cyanide sulfurtransferase, can effectively dispose of small amounts of cyanide.

$$HCN + Na_2S_2O_3 \longrightarrow HCNS + Na_2SO_3$$

BIBLIOGRAPHY

Annual Review of Biochemistry.
Annual Review of Physiology.
Williams, R. T.: Detoxication Mechanisms, ed. 2, New York, John Wiley & Sons, Inc., 1959.

CHAPTER 11

RESPIRATION

THE MAINTENANCE of cell functions and of life is dependent upon the continual supply of adequate amounts of oxygen to the tissues. In the course of metabolic activities of the cells, large quantities of CO_2 are produced, the bulk of which must be removed from the body. Both substances being gases, these exchanges of O_2 and CO_2 between the organism and the environment are accomplished by way of the lungs, comprising the beginning and end, respectively, of the process of respiration. Proper understanding of some of the fundamental aspects of these exchanges requires an understanding of certain of the so-called "gas laws."

(1) At the same pressure and temperature, equal volumes of all gases contain the same number of moles.

(2) In the absence of chemical reaction between gas and solvent, the amount of a gas which dissolves in a liquid is directly proportional to the pressure of the gas.

(3) The pressure exerted by a gas at a given temperature depends upon the number of moles of gas in a given volume (molar concentration). This is referred to as the "partial pressure" or "tension" (P) of the gas, e.g., P_{O_2}, P_{CO_2}, P_{N_2}.

(4) The total pressure of a mixture of gases is equal to the sum of their partial pressures. Thus, the atmospheric (barometric) pressure (BP) is represented by $P_{O_2} + P_{CO_2} + P_{N_2}$. This applies only to dry atmospheric air. The partial pressure of water vapor is a function only of temperature and is independent of the presence of other gases. Consequently, in calculating P_{O_2} and P_{CO_2}, the following equation is applicable:

$$BP - P_{H_2O}\text{ vapor} = P_{O_2} + P_{CO_2} + P_{N_2}$$

Inasmuch as the pressure exerted by a gas is determined by the number of moles of gas, and since the same number of moles of gases, under the same pressure, occupy equal volumes, it follows that the partial pressure of each component of a mixture of gases will be determined by the fraction which it occupies of the total volume of the mixture. In air, therefore,

$$P_{O_2} = \frac{(BP - P_{H_2O}\text{ vapor}) \times \%\ O_2}{100}$$

$$P_{CO_2} = \frac{(BP - P_{H_2O}\text{ vapor}) \times \%\ CO_2}{100}$$

$$P_{N_2} = \frac{(BP - P_{H_2O}\text{ vapor}) \times \%\ N_2}{100}$$

TABLE 11-1. PERCENTAGE COMPOSITION OF, AND P_{O_2} AND P_{CO_2} IN, INSPIRED, EXPIRED, AND ALVEOLAR AIR IN NORMAL SUBJECT AT REST

	BAROMETRIC PRESSURE (mm. Hg)	H_2O VAPOR (mm. Hg)	OXYGEN		CARBON DIOXIDE	
			CONTENT (vol. %)	P_{O_2} (mm. Hg)	CONTENT (vol. %)	P_{CO_2} (mm. Hg)
Inspired air (dry)	760	0	20.9	158	0.04	0.3
Expired air	760	48	16.1	115	4.4	31
Alveolar air	760	48	14.2	101	5.6	40

In dry atmospheric air at a barometric pressure of 760 mm. Hg, the partial pressures of the constituent gases would be: P_{O_2} = 20.9 per cent of 760, or 158 mm.; P_{CO_2} = 0.04 per cent of 760, or 0.3 mm.; P_{N_2} = 79 per cent of 760, or 600 mm. (Table 11-1).

The air in the pulmonary alveoli similarly contains O_2, CO_2, and N_2, but is also saturated with water vapor, which evaporates from the surface of the lining membranes at body temperature, exerting a partial pressure of about 48 mm. Hg. Inasmuch as the total gas pressure in alveolar air is the same as in the inspired (atmospheric) air, the partial pressure of each of the dry gases is exerted in a total of 760 minus 48 mm., or 712 mm. Hg. The same is true of the expired air. The percentage composition of alveolar and expired air in a normal subject at rest and the P_{O_2} and P_{CO_2} are indicated in Table 11-1.

In the lungs the blood gases come into approximate equilibrium with those of alveolar air. The separating membrane is very thin (1 to 2 μ), permitting ready diffusion of gases, and its surface area is very large (50 to 100 sq. m.). Blood passes through the lungs in about 0.75 second in a resting subject and in about 0.3 second during severe exercise, gas equilibrium being approximated more closely in the former state, which provides longer exposure of the blood to alveolar air. Under normal resting conditions, therefore, the blood leaving the lungs (arterial blood) has a P_{O_2} of about 100 mm. Hg and a P_{CO_2} of about 40 mm. Hg.

In the tissue cells, where oxygen is being utilized and carbon dioxide produced, the P_{O_2} is relatively low (< 30 mm. Hg) and the P_{CO_2} high (50 to 70 mm. Hg).

Inasmuch as a gas flows from a higher to a lower pressure (diffusion gradient), O_2 passes from the arterial blood to the tissue cells and CO_2 passes in the opposite direction. Under ordinary conditions of blood flow in a normal resting subject, the P_{O_2} of the blood leaving the tissues (venous blood) is thereby lowered to about 40 mm. Hg and the P_{CO_2} increased to about 46 mm. Hg. The venous blood is then returned to the lungs, where it is arterialized, drawing O_2 from and losing CO_2 to the alveolar air, with which it comes into approximate equilibrium. These pressure relationships are illustrated in Figure 11–1.

At rest, a normal man absorbs about 250 cc. O_2 and eliminates about 200 cc. CO_2 per minute. During severe exercise, the volume exchange of these gases may increase more than ten-fold. The mechanisms of control of pulmonary ventilation are discussed in detail in texts on physiology, and the chemical aspects are summarized here only briefly.

CHEMICAL CONTROL OF RESPIRATION

The respiratory movements and pulmonary ventilation are controlled by nerve impulses arising in the respiratory center in the medulla. The activity of the latter is influenced, directly or indirectly, by changes in: (1) P_{CO_2}, (2) pH, (3) P_{O_2}, (4) blood flow,

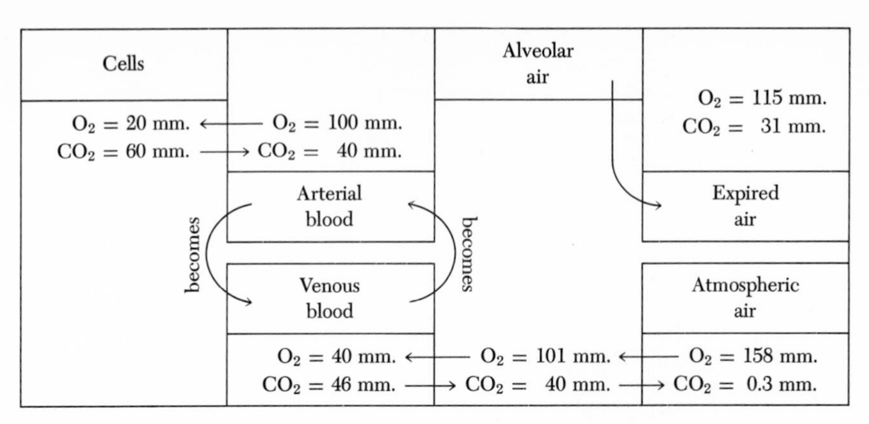

Figure 11-1. Pressure relationships and direction of flow of oxygen and carbon dioxide between tissue cells, blood, lungs, and atmosphere.

and (5) temperature. The indirect influences are mediated through chemoreceptors in the carotid and aortic bodies, which are stimulated chiefly by a decrease in P_{O_2} but also by an increase in P_{CO_2} and in H^+ ion concentration. Activity of the respiratory center is stimulated directly by an increase in P_{CO_2}, and in H^+ ion concentration, the P_{CO_2} being the most important chemical factor in the regulation of respiration.

Influence of CO_2 Tension and pH

Increase in the P_{CO_2} or acidity, either in the blood or locally in the respiratory center or aortic and carotid body chemoreceptors, results in stimulation of respiration and increased pulmonary ventilation. The reverse occurs with decrease in P_{CO_2} and H^+ ion concentration. The P_{CO_2} apparently exerts an influence in this connection beyond that which can be accounted for by the associated change in pH alone.

Under normal conditions, the extreme sensitivity of the respiratory center to minute changes in P_{CO_2} in the blood serves to maintain the latter within very narrow limits. The increased ventilation which accompanies any tendency toward a rise in P_{CO_2} (or H^+ ion concentration) results in prompt elimination of the excess CO_2. Similarly, the slowed and shallower breathing, with diminished ventilation, which accompanies any tendency toward a drop in P_{CO_2} (or H^+ ion concentration) results in decreased excretion of CO_2. This constitutes an important part of the mechanism of acid-base regulation (p. 316).

Influence of O_2 Tension

Reduction in the P_{O_2} of arterial blood causes depression of the respiratory center, but stimulation of the carotid and aortic chemoreceptors. The latter effect exceeds the former, the predominant consequence being stimulation of respiration and increased ventilation. This is of importance in physiological adjustment to diminished atmospheric O_2 tensions during ascent to high altitudes. The stimulating effects of decrease in P_{O_2} are usually not manifest in the resting subject until P_{O_2} has fallen to rather low levels, but are more pronounced at higher levels during exercise.

TRANSPORT OF OXYGEN

The tissue cells of a normal man utilize about 250 ml. of oxygen per minute in the resting state and may consume over ten times that amount during strenuous exercise. At the P_{O_2} of alveolar air, a liter of blood is able to take up in physical solution only about 2 ml. O_2. Inasmuch as the maximum attainable blood flow is about 25 liters per minute, the maximum amount of O_2 that can be supplied to the tissue cells in this form is about 50 ml. per minute, less than 2 per cent of the maximum requirement. Obviously, the oxygen must be transported in the blood chiefly in some form other than physical solution. This is accomplished by its combination with hemoglobin, the nature of which is considered in detail elsewhere (pp. 123, 128).

Under conditions of complete saturation, the blood of a normal man (15 grams Hb/100 ml.) holds a little more than 20 ml. of O_2 per 100 ml., only about 0.3 ml. of which is in physical solution. Although of small magnitude the latter factor is of considerable significance because, being a reflection of the P_{O_2}, it comes into equilibrium in the lungs with the alveolar air O_2, and in the tissues with the interstitial fluid O_2. It is therefore one of the determinants of the amount of O_2 taken up and liberated by Hb, according to the equation

$$O_2 + Hb \rightleftharpoons HbO_2$$

One mole of oxygen combines with 16,500 gm. of Hb. Inasmuch as a mole of O_2 (at 0° C. and 760 mm. Hg) occupies 22,400 ml., 1 gm. of Hb can combine with 22,400/16,500 or 1.36 ml. of O_2 (Hüfner factor). Consequently, the 15 gm. of Hb in 100 ml. of blood, when fully saturated can carry 20.4 ml. of O_2. However, under the conditions existing in the circulating blood, the Hb is not completely saturated with O_2, the amounts present in normal arterial and venous blood being indicated in Table 11-2. The degree of saturation depends upon the P_{O_2}, this relationship being expressed in the dissociation curve of oxyhemoglobin (Fig. 11–2).

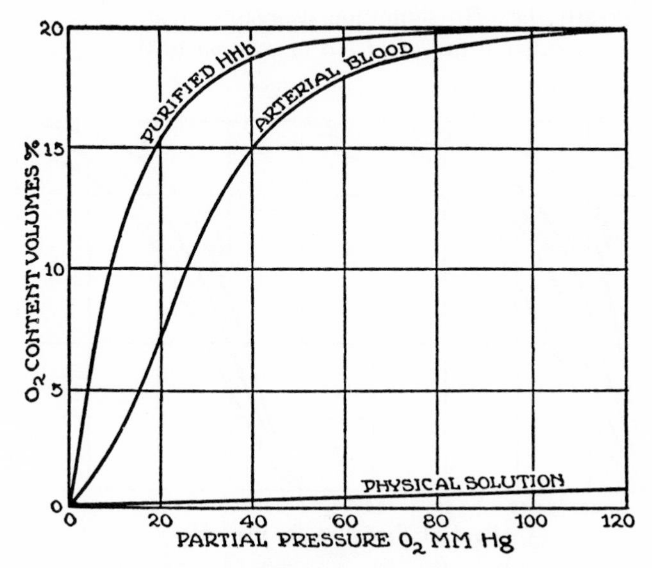

Figure 11–2. Dissociation curve of oxyhemoglobin. The O_2 contents of arterial blood and plasma (physical solution) and a solution of purified HHb at various partial pressures of O_2. (After Barcroft. From Ruch and Patton: Physiology and Biophysics, ed. 19, W. B. Saunders Co., 1965.)

TABLE 11-2. OXYGEN AND CARBON DIOXIDE CONTENTS AND PRESSURES IN BLOOD

	OXYGEN		CARBON DIOXIDE	
	CONTENT (ml./100 ml.)	P_{O_2} (mm. Hg)	CONTENT (ml./100 ml.)	P_{CO_2} (mm. Hg)
Arterial blood	17–22 (20)*	(100)	44–50 (48)	(40)
Venous blood	11–16 (13)	(40)	51–58 (55)	(46)
A-V difference	4–8 (6.5)		4–8 (6.5)	

* Mean values indicated in parentheses.

Dissociation of Oxyhemoglobin

The equation $O_2 + Hb \rightleftharpoons HbO_2$ is shifted to the right or left as the P_{O_2} increases or decreases, with corresponding increasing saturation of Hb with oxygen (HbO_2) and increasing dissociation of HbO_2, respectively. However, the degree of saturation (or dissociation) is not directly proportional to the P_{O_2}. If blood is equilibrated with air containing O_2 at different partial pressures, and the quantity of O_2 (or HbO_2) in the blood is plotted against the P_{O_2}, an S-shaped curve is obtained (Fig. 11–2). This is referred to as the dissociation curve of oxyhemoglobin and indicates the relative amounts of oxyhemoglobin (HbO_2) and reduced hemoglobin (Hb) present at different levels of oxygen tension.

Certain features of this curve are of great physiological significance.

(*a*) ***Influence of P_{O_2}.*** At a P_{O_2} of 100 mm. Hg, as in arterial blood (at P_{CO_2} 40 mm. Hg and pH 7.4), Hb is 95 to 98 per cent saturated with O_2, i.e., 95 to 98 per cent is in the form of HbO_2 and 2 to 5 per cent in the reduced form. At a P_{O_2} of 70 mm. Hg, Hb is still 90 per cent saturated. The ability of the blood to carry oxygen therefore varies relatively slightly with variations in P_{O_2} above 70 mm. Hg. In fact, there is comparatively little reduction in Hb saturation, i.e., comparatively little dissociation of HbO_2, until the P_{O_2} falls below 50 mm. Hg. As the P_{O_2} falls below this level, dissociation of HbO_2 increases greatly, i.e., Hb saturation decreases greatly (Fig. 11–3; Table 11-3).

Because of this peculiar behavior of Hb in relation to the P_{O_2}, adequate uptake of

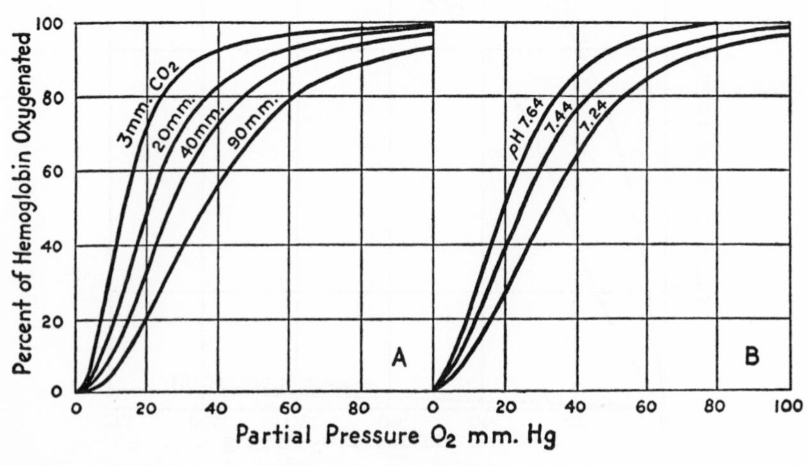

Figure 11-3. The effects of increased P_{CO_2} and decreased pH upon the dissociation of oxyhemoglobin. Increased temperature also shifts the curve in the same direction as increased P_{CO_2}. (*A* after Barcroft, *B* after Peters and Van Slyke. From Ruch and Patton.)

TABLE 11-3. EFFECT OF OXYGEN AND CARBON DIOXIDE TENSIONS ON OXYGENATION OF HEMOGLOBIN*

O_2 TENSION	PROPORTION OF HEMOGLOBIN COMBINING WITH OXYGEN AT FOLLOWING CO_2 TENSIONS			
mm.	CO_2 = 3 mm.	CO_2 = 20 mm.	CO_2 = 40 mm.	CO_2 = 80 mm.
	(%)	(%)	(%)	(%)
0	0	0	0	0
5	13.5	6.8	5.5	3.0
10	38.0	19.5	15.0	8.0
20	77.6	50.0	39.0	26.0
30	92.0	72.2	60.6	49.8
40	96.7	87.0	76.0	63.5
50	98.5	93.3	85.5	76.9
60	100	96.3	90.5	85.0
70	100	98.0	94.0	90.3
80	100	99.0	96.0	93.7
90	100	100	97.5	95.7
100	100	100	98.6	97.1

* Henderson, Bock, Field, and Stoddard: J Biol. Chem. 59:379, 1924.

oxygen by the blood in the lungs is assured as long as the alveolar air P_{O_2} is above 80 mm. Hg. Adequate liberation of oxygen from the blood is assured in the tissues, where the P_{O_2} is usually below 30 mm. Hg.

(*b*) ***Influence of P_{CO_2} and pH.*** With increasing CO_2 tension in the blood the affinity of Hb for O_2 decreases (i.e., increasing dissociation of HbO_2 or decreasing saturation of Hb), the equation, $O_2 + Hb \rightleftharpoons HbO_2$, being shifted to the left. This effect is more pronounced at relatively low than at high levels of P_{O_2}, because of the shape of the dissociation curve (Fig. 11–3, Table 11-3). Thus, at 90 to 100 mm. Hg P_{O_2} (alveolar air), variations in P_{CO_2} from 20 to 80 mm. Hg have comparatively little effect on HbO_2 dissociation (95 to 100 per cent saturation of Hb). On the other hand, at a P_{O_2} of 20 mm. Hg (tissues), increasing the P_{CO_2} from 20 mm. to 80 mm. Hg causes the percentage saturation of Hb to fall from about 40 to less than 20.

Acids other than H_2CO_3, e.g., lactic acid, exert a similar effect, i.e., increase in the H^+ ion concentration of the blood increases dissociation of HbO_2. As in the case of the P_{CO_2}, this influence is more pronounced at relatively low than at high P_{O_2} levels (Fig. 11–3).

Rise in temperature also increases dissociation of HbO_2, shifting the curve in the same direction as do increases in P_{CO_2} and acidity.

As a result of these phenomena, adequate uptake of oxygen from the alveolar air is assured, despite the presence of CO_2. Its delivery to the tissue cells, facilitated primarily by the relatively high P_{O_2}, is enhanced by the relatively high P_{CO_2}, acidity, and temperature in the actively metabolizing tissues.

TRANSPORT OF CARBON DIOXIDE

In the resting state, about 200 ml. of CO_2 are produced per minute in the tissues, and are carried in the blood to the lungs, where they are excreted. During strenuous exercise, the quantity produced and transported increases enormously. The manner in which this relatively large amount of acid ($CO_2 + H_2O \rightleftharpoons H_2CO_3$) is carried in the blood with only slight change in pH is discussed elsewhere (p. 290). Attention will be directed here chiefly to the various forms in which CO_2 exists in the blood and their quantitative distribution.

The direction of flow of CO_2 is determined by the P_{CO_2}, which is 50 to 70 mm. Hg in the tissues, about 40 mm. in the arterial blood, rises to 46 mm. during passage of blood through the tissues (venous), and is 40 mm. in the alveolar air. The diffusion constant for CO_2 is much higher than for O_2 because of its greater solubility in body fluids; consequently it diffuses readily from the venous blood into the pulmonary alveoli despite the rather low pressure gradient (Fig. 11–1, p. 284). The efficiency of transport of CO_2 in the blood depends to a large extent upon the buffer action of hemoglobin.

Buffer Action of Hemoglobin

The buffering capacity of Hb, as of any protein, depends upon the number of dissociated buffering groups, acidic (carboxyl) or basic (amino, guanidino, and imidazole), which varies with the pH of the medium (p. 74). Within the pH range 7.0 to 7.8, most of the physiological buffering action of Hb is due to the imidazole groups of histidine (Fig. 11–4).

The degree of dissociation of a buffering group in a protein, which determines its buffering capacity, is influenced by adjacent groups in the molecule. In the case of the imidazole group of histidine, which is intimately associated with the iron of hemoglobin, its strength as a buffer is affected by changes in the degree of oxygenation of hemoglobin. When oxygen is removed, the imidazole group is rendered less acidic, consequently less dissociated, removing a hydrogen ion from solution and becoming electrically positive. This effect is reversed with increasing oxygenation of the hemoglobin molecule. This reaction, illustrated in Figure 11–4, indicates that not only is the buffering capacity of Hb related to the degree of its oxygenation, but also that its ability to accept or liberate oxygen is influenced by the acidity of the medium. A decrease in acidity facilitates oxygenation of Hb and an increase in acidity facilitates liberation of oxygen, producing characteristic changes in the oxygen dissociation curve of Hb.

The implications arising from these considerations may be summarized as follows:

(1) Oxygenation of Hb increases its acidity, causing it to give up hydrogen ions to the medium; i.e., oxyhemoglobin is a stronger acid than reduced hemoglobin.

(2) Reduction of oxyhemoglobin (i.e., deoxygenated Hb) decreases its acidity, removing hydrogen ions from the medium.

(3) Introduction of an acid, e.g., H_2CO_3, into a medium containing oxyhemoglobin facilitates loss of oxygen, i.e., formation of reduced hemoglobin. This reduced hemoglobin,

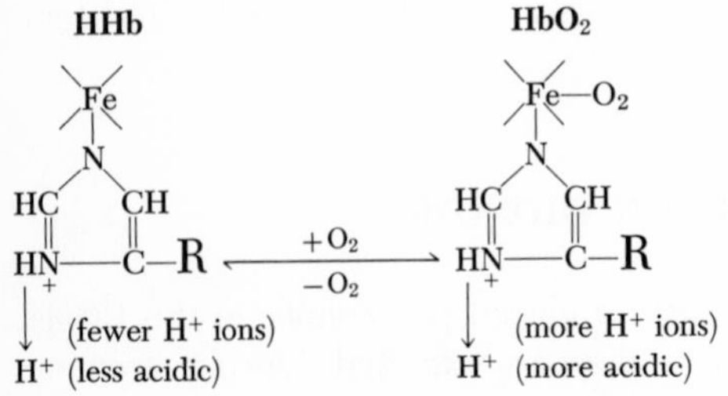

HHb — Fe, N, HC, CH, HN, C—R; H^+ (fewer H^+ ions) (less acidic)

$+O_2$ / $-O_2$

HbO_2 — Fe—O_2, N, HC, CH, HN, C—R; H^+ (more H^+ ions) (more acidic)

Figure 11-4. Effect of oxygenation and reduction on the buffering action of the imidazole group (histidine) of hemoglobin.

being less acid (i.e., more basic) than oxyhemoglobin, is better able to counteract the effect of the added acid (p. 290).

(4) Addition to the blood of CO_2 (in the tissues) or O_2 (in the lungs), in the course of normal metabolism and respiration, results in release of significant amounts of H^+ ion, in the case of CO_2 from H_2CO_3, and in the case of O_2 from hemoglobin. Under physiological conditions, hemoglobin serves as a H^+ acceptor when H_2CO_3 acts as a H^+ donor and, conversely, the HCO_3^- serves as a H^+ acceptor when hemoglobin is a H^+ donor.

CO_2 in Arterial Blood (Table 11-4)

At rest, 100 ml. of arterial blood contains 45 to 55 ml. of CO_2 (volumes per cent), about 75 per cent of which is in the plasma and 25 per cent in the erythrocytes.

The 35.6 ml. (average) in the plasma is present in three forms: (1) physical solution (1.6 ml.); (2) HCO_3^- ions (34 ml.); (3) carbamino compounds of plasma proteins (R-NHCOOH), in very small amounts (less than 0.7 ml.) because the plasma proteins contain relatively few NH_2 groups capable of combining with CO_2 under conditions existing in the blood. The 12.6 ml. (average) in the erythrocytes is present in the same forms: (1) physical solution (0.8 ml.); (2) HCO_3^- ions (9.6 ml.); carbamino compounds of Hb (2.2 ml.). About 90 per cent of the CO_2 in arterial blood is in the form of HCO_3^- ions (bicarbonate).

Entrance of CO_2 in Tissues (Table 11-4)

At rest, 3.5 to 4.5 ml. (average 3.7) of CO_2 enters each 100 ml. of blood in the tissues, diffusing across the capillary walls in consequence of the tissue : blood CO_2 diffusion gradient. It enters the blood plasma in physical solution and diffuses readily from the plasma into the erythrocytes.

Carbon dioxide reacts with water as follows:

$$CO_2 + H_2O \rightleftharpoons H_2CO_3 \rightleftharpoons H^+ + HCO_3^-$$

In the plasma, this reaction proceeds slowly, the equilibrium being far to the left. Consequently, the increment in CO_2 occurring in passing through the tissues drives the reaction to the right only slightly, the added H^+ ions being buffered by the relatively weak plasma buffer systems (viz., proteins). The pH falls slightly.

TABLE 11-4. AVERAGE DISTRIBUTION OF CARBON DIOXIDE IN 100 ML. NORMAL BLOOD

	ARTERIAL		VENOUS		DIFFERENCE	
CARBON DIOXIDE	ml.	% of total	ml.	% of total	ml.	% of total
Total	48.2		51.9		3.7	
Total in plasma (60 ml.)	35.6	74	38.0	73	2.4	65
as dissolved CO_2	1.6	3	1.8	3	0.2	5
as HCO_3^-	34.0	71	36.2	70	2.2	60
Total in erythrocytes (40 ml.)	12.6	26	13.9	27	1.3	35
as dissolved CO_2	0.8	1.5	0.9	1	0.1	3
as carbamino-CO_2	2.2	4.5	3.1	6	0.9	24
as HCO_3^-	9.6	20	9.9	20	0.3	8

Within the erythrocytes, the reaction,

$$CO_2 + H_2O \longrightarrow H_2CO_3 \longrightarrow H^+ + HCO_3^-$$

proceeds rapidly, owing to the presence of carbonic anhydrase, an enzyme which catalyzes this reaction. Because of prompt removal of the ion endproducts (H^+ and HCO_3^-), the fraction of the added CO_2 which diffuses into the erythrocytes is much larger than that which remains in the plasma (Table 11-4). This reaction is facilitated by the simultaneous liberation of oxygen, with an increment in reduced Hb, which is a weaker acid than oxyhemoglobin.

Buffering of CO_2 by Hb. Reduced Hb, being a considerably weaker acid than oxyhemoglobin, has a higher H^+-binding capacity than the latter. At the erythrocyte pH (7.25), 1 mmole of HbO_2 yields 1.88 mEq. of H^+ ion, whereas 1 mmole of Hb yields only 1.28 mEq. Consequently, in the tissue capillaries, the liberation of each millimole of O_2 (22.4 ml.) permits binding of 0.6 mEq. more of H^+ ion, permitting the formation of 0.6 mmole of $BHCO_3$ from 0.6 mmole of CO_2 (13.4 ml.) with no change in pH (isohydric transport of CO_2). At a respiratory quotient of 0.6, i.e., $\frac{0.6 \text{ mmole } CO_2 \text{ produced}}{1.0 \text{ mmole } O_2 \text{ consumed}}$ (p. 327), 0.6 mmole of H^+ ions will be formed (from 0.6 mmole H_2CO_3), which will be completely buffered as a result of reduction of Hb. At the usual respiratory quotient of 0.82, therefore, only 0.82 minus 0.6, or 0.22 mmole of H^+ ions per mmole of O_2 consumed must be buffered by other means. Under average conditions of hemoglobin content and saturation and CO_2 transport, over 73 per cent of the total amount of CO_2 entering the blood in the tissues is handled in this manner.

Transformation of oxygenated Hb to reduced Hb (less acid) involves a decrease in the net negative charge, i.e., less dissociation. Consequently, K^+ ions, previously required to balance the HbO_2^- ions, are "released" to this extent to balance the increment in HCO_3^- ions.

$$K^+ + HbO_2^- + H^+ \cdot HCO_3^- \rightleftharpoons K^+ + HCO_3^- + HHb + O_2$$

The increase in buffering capacity of hemoglobin incident to its change from the oxygenated to the reduced form is the factor chiefly responsible for the ability of the blood to take on the required additional amount of CO_2 in its passage through the tissues. Of the 3.7 ml. of CO_2 per 100 ml. of blood added (Table 11-4), about 68 per cent is transported as HCO_3^- ions. One H^+ ion must be released for every HCO_3^- ion formed and, therefore, more than 1 mmole of H^+ ion is added to each liter of blood by this reaction. The importance of the buffering action of hemoglobin is indicated by the fact that the pH of the blood falls only about 0.03 unit although the amount of H^+ ion added (1 mmole per liter) would lower the pH of water from 7.0 to 3.0. The rapid removal of H^+ ions by the reduced hemoglobin makes possible also the conversion of over 90 per cent of the added CO_2 to HCO_3^- ion (Table 11-4). If this reaction were blocked as a result of accumulation of H^+ ions, the required amount of CO_2 could not be transported from the tissues to the lungs.

Chloride-bicarbonate shift. Because of the great rapidity with which hydration of CO_2 (transformation to H_2CO_3) occurs in the erythrocytes as compared with the plasma, the concentration of HCO_3^- rises in the former faster than in the latter. Inasmuch as the erythrocyte wall is permeable to HCO_3^-, this ion diffuses from the erythrocytes into the

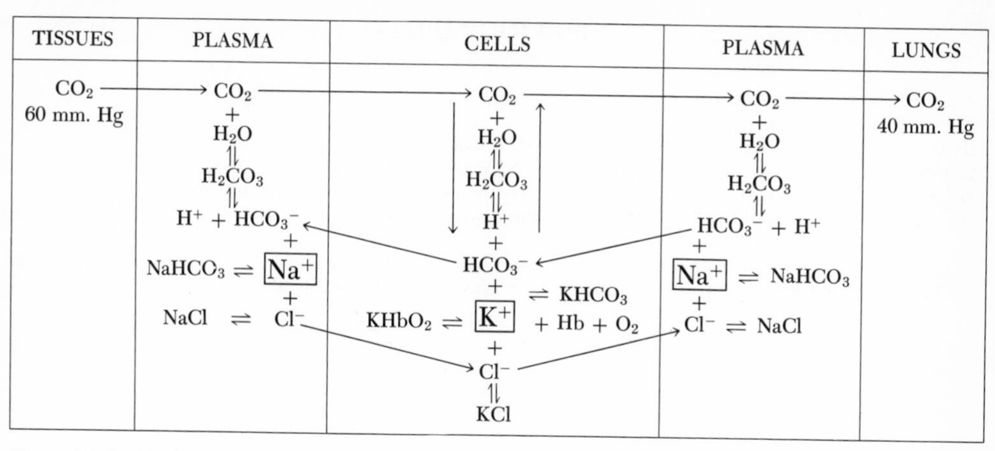

Figure 11-5. Exchange of HCO_3^- and Cl^- between the red blood cells and the plasma in the tissues and the lungs (chloride shift). The heavy arrows indicate the direction of the changes in these situations.

plasma. According to the laws of membrane equilibrium, the ratios of the concentration of individual diffusible monovalent ions in the cells and plasma must be equal, i.e.,

$$\frac{[HCO_3^-]\ \text{cells}}{[HCO_3^-]\ \text{plasma}} = \frac{[Cl^-]\ \text{cells}}{[Cl^-]\ \text{plasma}}$$

Consequently, as HCO_3^- passes from the erythrocytes into the plasma, Cl^- passes in the opposite direction. In order to preserve electrical neutrality of the cell and plasma fluids, the numbers of negative ions (i.e., Cl^- and HCO_3^-) exchanged must be identical. The Cl^- ions passing into the erythrocytes are balanced electrically by the K^+ ions previously balanced by the HCO_3^-, while the latter ions entering the plasma are balanced by the Na^+ ions previously balanced by the diffused Cl^-.

All of the above reactions are reversed in the lungs, the quantity of CO_2 entering the blood in the tissues passing into the alveoli and the quantity of oxygen lost in the tissues being restored from the alveolar air.

About 70 per cent of the added CO_2 is carried in the blood as bicarbonate (HCO_3^-), about 60 per cent in the plasma, the remainder in the erythrocytes. However, about 90 per cent of the increment in plasma HCO_3^- originates within the erythrocytes, as indicated above.

Carbamino-CO_2. The relatively small capacity of plasma proteins for forming carbamino compounds is not influenced significantly by changes which occur in the blood during its passage through the tissues. Consequently, virtually none of the added CO_2 is transported in this manner (i.e., plasma carbamino-CO_2 is unaltered). Within the erythrocytes, however, a considerable fraction of the added CO_2 is held in this form because of the fact that the capacity of reduced hemoglobin for forming carbamino compounds is more than three times that of oxyhemoglobin. Moreover, this capacity increases with increasing levels of P_{CO_2}. In consequence, therefore, of the liberation of O_2 and addition of CO_2 in the tissues, about 20 to 25 per cent of the increment in blood CO_2 is transported by hemoglobin as carbamino-CO_2.

BIBLIOGRAPHY

Annual Review of Biochemistry.
Annual Review of Physiology.
Barcroft, J.: The Respiratory Function of the Blood, London, Cambridge University Press, 1928.
Christensen, H. N.: Diagnostic Biochemistry, New York, Oxford University Press, 1959.
Davenport, H. W.: The ABC of Acid-Base Chemistry, ed. 4, Chicago, University of Chicago Press, 1958.
Gamble, J. L.: Chemical Anatomy, Physiology and Pathology of Extracellular Fluid, Cambridge, Harvard University Press, 1950.
Gray, J. S.: Pulmonary Ventilation and Its Physiological Regulation, Springfield, Ill., Charles C Thomas, 1949.
Haldane, J. S., and Priestley, J. G.: Respiration, New Haven, Yale University Press, 1935.

CHAPTER 12

WATER BALANCE

In the normal adult organism, not undergoing changes in weight, the quantity of water supplied daily is balanced by that eliminated, a state of equilibrium being maintained.

WATER INTAKE

Water is supplied to the body from the following sources: (1) dietary liquids; (2) solid food; (3) oxidation of organic foodstuffs. It comprises 70 to 90 per cent of the weight of the average diet of adults, even apparently very solid foods consisting largely of water. Moreover, it is one of the chief products of combustion of protein, fat, and carbohydrate in the body, the quantities produced by oxidation of 1 gm. of each of these substances being as follows: protein, 0.34 ml.; fat, 1.07 ml.; carbohydrate, 0.56 ml. It may be calculated that 10 to 15 ml. of water are formed per 100 Cal. of energy produced. An ordinary 3000-Cal. diet therefore contains about 450 ml. of water in the solid food and may provide an additional 300 to 450 ml. of water of oxidation. The remainder of the water intake is supplied by dietary liquids (Fig. 12–1).

WATER OUTPUT

Water leaves the body in the (1) urine, (2) feces, (3) perspiration, and (4) so-called insensible perspiration (evaporation from skin and lungs) (Fig. 12–1).

Feces

Under normal conditions, the 3000 to 8300 ml. of digestive fluids entering the alimentary tract are almost completely reabsorbed in the intestine. On an ordinary mixed diet, about 80 to 150 ml. of water are excreted daily in the feces of normal adults. This may be increased considerably on a high vegetable diet and particularly in the presence of diarrhea.

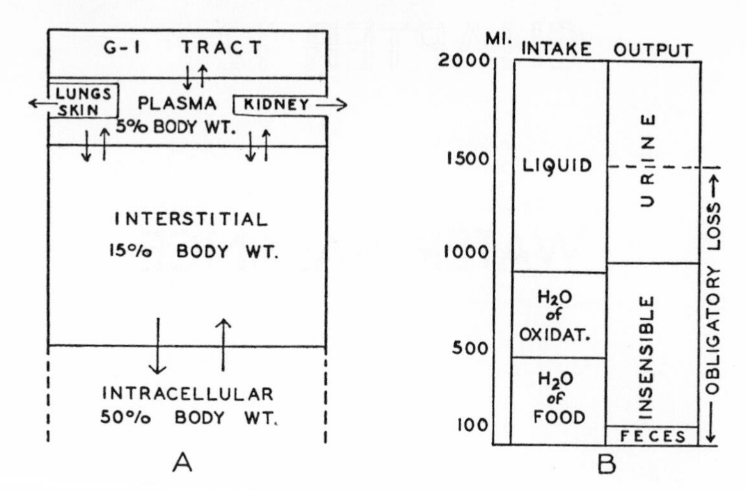

Figure 12-1. *A,* Body water compartments. *B,* Sources of water to the organism, and water excretion in a 70-kg. man on an average adequate diet. (After Gamble: Chemical Anatomy, Physiology and Pathology of Extracellular Fluid, Harvard University Press, 1950.)

Insensible Perspiration

In the absence of active perspiration, the body is continually losing water vapor from the skin surface and lungs in inverse proportion to the relative humidity of the atmosphere. Inasmuch as 0.58 Cal. is absorbed in the vaporization of 1 ml. of water, the heat lost by this process, termed "insensible perspiration," at ordinary room temperatures amounts to about 25 per cent of the total heat loss. The latter is proportional to the quantity of heat produced, which is a function of metabolism. The quantity of water lost by insensible perspiration is therefore an obligatory loss, determined by metabolic activity and, in a normal adult, may be calculated as 500 ml. per square meter of body surface area per day. This amounts to about 850 ml. for a 70-kg. man (1.73 sq. meters).

Perspiration

When the environmental temperature or humidity rise to excessively high levels, the sweat glands become active. Obviously, the quantity of water lost by this route varies enormously. Moreover, in contrast to insensible perspiration, which consists solely of water, sweat contains 30 to 90 mEq./liter of Na and of Cl (Fig. 13-2, p. 322). It is a hypotonic solution, plasma containing about 140 mEq./liter of Na. Sweating therefore removes from the body relatively more water than electrolytes.

Urine

The urine is the important medium of elimination of water provided to the body in excess of its requirement. The kidneys have a remarkable capacity for regulating renal excretion of water within wide limits, regardless of the simultaneous requirement for excretion of solids (p. 839). However, their ability to concentrate is not unlimited, a certain minimal quantity of water being required for excretion of a given amount of solute. On an average adequate diet (70-kg. adult), providing about 50 gm. of solids for daily urinary excretion, a minimum of approximately 500 ml. of water (300 ml./sq. meter body surface) is required for their solution. Failure to meet this obligatory urine volume requirement will result in retention of certain urinary constituents, mainly urea, in the body fluids.

Equilibrium Requirements

As indicated above, in addition to the small amount excreted in the feces (80 to 150 ml.), the minimal daily water requirement (70-kg. adult) is fixed by certain metabolic requirements: (1) loss of heat by insensible perspiration (normally about 850 ml.); (2) renal excretion of excess solid material, mainly urea and NaCl, and therefore determined largely by the protein and salt intake (normally about 500 ml. of water). Consequently on an average normal diet, approximately 1500 ml. of water must be available for elimination by these routes if the body temperature and blood urea N are to be maintained within normal limits. The "solid" portion of such a diet contributes about 800 ml. of water, approximately one-half of which is pre-formed, the remainder being produced in the course of oxidation of the organic foodstuffs in the body. The balance of the water requirement must be supplied by intake of liquids if the body fluids are to be maintained at normal levels.

VOLUME OF BODY FLUID COMPARTMENTS

Water comprises 60 to 70 per cent of the adult body weight, values expressed in this manner being somewhat lower in women than in men, and decreasing with advancing age. These age and sex differences after puberty are probably due to differences in the amount of body fat, which has a low water content (Table 12-1). Classically, the body water has been regarded as existing in two main compartments, (1) intracellular (approximately 50 per cent body weight), and (2) extracellular (approximately 20 per cent), the latter being further subdivided into (a) blood plasma water (about 5 per cent body weight) and (b) interstitial fluid (about 15 per cent). Although segregation into these anatomical compartments is useful from many standpoints, it cannot be applied strictly to physiological considerations. This is particularly important in relation to the distribution and exchanges of electrolytes between the various body fluids (p. 303). From the standpoint of volume alone it seems desirable to regard the extracellular water as existing in four main subdivisions: (1) blood plasma (about 4.5 per cent body weight); (2) interstitial fluid and lymph (about 12 per cent); (3) dense connective tissue, cartilage, and bone (about 9 per cent); (4) transcellular fluids (about 1.5 per cent). The latter term is applied to extracellular

TABLE 12-1. AVERAGE WATER CONTENT OF TISSUES

TISSUE	WATER (per cent)
Muscle	75–80
Connective tissue	60
Adipose tissue	20
Bone	25
Nervous tissue	
White matter	70
Gray matter	85
Erythrocytes	60

fluids that are not simple ultrafiltrates of the blood plasma and which are formed by the transport activity of cells (e.g., secretions of the gastrointestinal tract, liver, and skin; fluids in the kidneys, eyes, and subarachnoid space).

The anatomical fluid compartments are illustrated in Figure 12–1. Water entering the organism, i.e., from the gastrointestinal tract, passes into the bloodstream, an equivalent amount leaving the latter by way of the urine, lungs, skin, and feces. The water of the plasma is in equilibrium with that of the interstitial fluid, and the latter with the intracellular water, across the boundaries between these compartments, i.e., the capillary walls and the cell membranes, respectively. The interstitial fluid, serving as a sort of middleman for the other two fluids, acts also as a buffer which prevents rather sudden changes in composition of the plasma, resulting from absorption from the intestine, from being reflected directly in the intracellular fluid. Moreover, being a rather elastic compartment, it can expand or contract considerably, in conditions of excessive retention (edema) or loss (dehydration) of fluid, without comparable alterations in the volume of plasma or intracellular fluid, which must be maintained rather rigidly in the interests of normal circulation and cell function.

The volume of (1) the circulating blood, (2) the plasma, (3) total extracellular fluid, and (4) total body water could be measured by introduction of a substance into the body if that substance would fulfill the following requirements: (a) be retained exclusively in the fluid compartment in question; (b) not leave that compartment during the test period; (c) distribute itself uniformly throughout that compartment; (d) be capable of precise quantitative determination in the blood or plasma. A number of methods have been proposed, none of which is entirely satisfactory; certain of them, however, have proved useful.

Blood and Plasma Volume

(*a*) ***Carbon monoxide method.*** Carbon monoxide displaces oxygen from hemoglobin, volume for volume, and can be measured accurately in blood, either as CO or as HbCO. The subject breathes a known amount of CO and the concentration of HbCO in the blood is determined after allowing sufficient time for mixing. If the total hemoglobin concentration is known, one can calculate how much CO would be required to saturate the Hb to its full capacity and can arrive at the total blood volume. By determining the hematocrit value (relative volumes of packed cells and of plasma), the plasma volume can be derived.

(*b*) ***Radioactive iron method.*** Fe^{59} is administered to a normal or anemic subject; it becomes incorporated in the Hb of the circulating erythrocytes. A predetermined amount of the labeled red cells is injected intravenously in the test subject (compatible blood). Measurement of radioactivity in blood samples withdrawn after allowing time for mixing indicates the extent of dilution of the injected cells and permits calculation of the volumes of blood and plasma (from hematocrit value).

(*c*) ***Dye methods.*** The dye employed most commonly is Evans blue (T-1824), which is adsorbed by plasma proteins. A known amount is injected intravenously and, after allowing time for distribution throughout the blood plasma, a sample of oxalated blood is withdrawn, centrifuged, and the concentration of dye in the plasma determined colorimetrically. The extent of dilution of the quantity injected can be calculated (plasma volume) and, the hematocrit value being known, the total blood volume can be determined.

(*d*) ***I^{131}-labeled proteins.*** Serum proteins, labeled with I^{131}, are injected intravenously and the extent of dilution of the injected protein is determined by measurement of the radioactivity of withdrawn blood samples.

The CO method requires cooperation of the subject, which cannot always be secured under clinical conditions. Moreover, other technical difficulties introduce the possibility of serious errors. Furthermore, the accuracy of this procedure, as well as of the Fe^{59} method, depends upon uniformity of distribution of all of the "labeled" erythrocytes in the circulation. This cannot always be assured, especially in disease states (e.g., shock), in which variable and undeterminable numbers of cells may be "segregated" in such organs as the spleen or in the splanchnic bed. In addition, calculations of total blood volume on the basis of factors measured in either cells or plasma are subject to inaccuracies arising out of variations in the ratio of cells to plasma in different portions of the circulation.

One source of inaccuracy with the use of dyes and isotope-tagged serum proteins is the fact that these proteins normally cross the capillary wall in amounts which vary in different tissues; they are removed from the interstitial fluid mainly by the lymphatic circulation. Approximately 50 per cent of the plasma protein pool is in the interstitial fluid-lymph compartment and, following intravenous injection of tagged protein, the latter is evenly distributed throughout the entire extracellular space in about 24 hours. Although under normal conditions loss of protein from the intravascular compartment under the test conditions is not so rapid as to vitiate the usefulness of these procedures, it may become so in many disease states in which capillary permeability is increased.

Generally acceptable average values for blood and plasma volume in normal subjects are as follows: whole blood, 2500 to 3200 ml./sq. meter body surface, or 63 to 80 ml./kg.; plasma, 1300 to 1800 ml./sq. meter, or 35 to 45 ml./kg. Values for whole blood are about 7 per cent higher for men than for women, but the plasma values are approximately the same.

Total Extracellular Fluid Volume

Application of the dilution technique to the measurement of the total volume of extracellular fluids theoretically requires the use of a substance which, when injected intravenously, crosses the capillary walls readily and distributes itself rapidly and uniformly throughout all extracellular fluids, does not enter the cells, is not destroyed in the body, and is not excreted rapidly. Substances that have been used for this purpose include certain non-metabolizable carbohydrates (sucrose, mannitol, inulin) and electrolytes (thiocyanate, radioactive sodium, radioactive chloride, sulfate, bromide). There are two major sources of inaccuracy of results obtained with these procedures: (1) the heterogeneous character of the extracellular fluids with respect to composition (p. 300); (2) certain of the substances employed, particularly electrolytes, are not absolutely excluded from the intracellular compartment, but penetrate different cells to different degrees under normal conditions and particularly in pathological states.

There are marked differences in the rates of equilibration of extracellular fluids in muscle, skin, loose and dense connective tissue, cartilage, and bone. In certain of these extracellular fluids equilibrate rapidly; in others e.g., dense connective tissue and cartilage and certain regions in bones, they equilibrate very slowly. Furthermore, some of the tracer substances employed (e.g., inulin, mannitol) do not enter the transcellular fluids, the volumes of which may vary enormously in certain disease states.

The major electrolytes of extracellular fluid, Na and Cl, are present in only low concentrations in intracellular fluid generally under physiological conditions. However, both Na and Cl enter different cells to a variable degree, and not always to the same extent, the Na : Cl ratio in certain tissues (bone, cartilage, muscle) being higher and in others (erythrocytes, connective tissue, gastrointestinal mucosa) lower than in an ultrafiltrate of blood plasma. Moreover, there are marked differences in the rates at which equilibrium is established between different phases of the extracellular pool of Na. For example, in bone, which contains 35 to 40 per cent of the total body Na, only about 30 per cent is rapidly exchangeable, 10 per cent slowly exchangeable (adsorbed to the surface of bone crystals), and 60 per cent non-exchangeable (incorporated in the bone crystal, p. 636).

Values obtained by the use of electrolytes tend to be too high, and those with saccharides too low. For the reasons indicated, it is preferable to use the designations, "sodium space," "chloride space," "thiocyanate space," and "inulin space," etc., rather than "extracellular fluid volume." The inulin space seems to correspond most closely to the extracellular fluid volume in most cases. Employing these procedures, values have been obtained for total extracellular fluid volume (adults) approximating about 20 per cent of the body weight. Of this, about one-fourth is blood plasma and three-fourths is interstitial fluid and lymph (5 and 15 per cent, respectively, of body weight).

Total Body Water

There is no accurate method for determining total body water, inasmuch as no measurable substance has yet been found which, on injection, is distributed uniformly throughout the entire body water and undergoes no metabolic change during the test period. Heavy water and antipyrine are most satisfactory for clinical purposes.

The water content of several tissues (Table 12-1) has been determined by direct measurement (animals and human biopsy or autopsy material).

COMPOSITION OF BODY FLUID COMPARTMENTS

Inasmuch as water serves chiefly as a relatively inert medium in which are conducted the chemical reactions constituting living processes, its significance must be considered in relation to the other components of the body fluids which, in fact, largely determine its volume and distribution in the organism. The marked differences in composition of the intracellular and interstitial fluids and the less striking differences between the latter and the blood plasma are due to differences in permeability of the membranes separating these compartments to the solutes which these fluids contain.

Milliequivalents (mEq.)

Elements which combine chemically with one another do so in fixed ratios, which are functions of their atomic weights and valences. Thus, 1.008 gm. of hydrogen (at. wt. 1.008) combines with 8 gm. of oxygen (at. wt. 16) to form water, and with 35.457 gm. of Cl (at. wt. 35.457) to form HCl. Similarly, 35.457 gm. of Cl combine with 22.997 gm. of Na, 39.096 gm. of K, and 20.04 gm. of Ca (at. wt. 40.08). These numerical values are designated "equivalent weights," because they are equivalent in their combining power. An "equivalent weight" may be defined as the weight of a molecule, or of an atom or radical (group of atoms reacting chemically as a unit), divided by its valence. A "milliequivalent" (i.e., milligram equivalent) is 1/1000 of the gram equivalent weight.

The concentrations of the solid constituents of the body fluids may be expressed in terms of weight per unit volume (e.g., milligrams per 100 ml.) or in terms of chemical

TABLE 12-2. RADICULAR AND EQUIVALENT WEIGHTS OF IMPORTANT BODY FLUID ELECTROLYTES

ELEMENT OR ION	VALENCE	ATOMIC OR RADICULAR WEIGHT	EQUIVALENT WEIGHT
H	1	1.008	1.008
Na	1	22.997	22.997
K	1	39.096	39.096
Cl	1	35.457	35.457
Ca	2	40.08	20.04
Mg	2	24.32	12.16
HCO_3	1	61.018	61.018
HPO_4	2	95.988	47.994
H_2PO_4	1	96.996	96.996
SO_4	2	96.066	48.033

combining power (e.g., milliequivalents per liter) (mEq./liter). The former may be converted to the latter according to the following formula:

$$\text{mEq./liter} = \frac{\text{mg./liter } (= \text{mg./100 ml.} \times 10) \times \text{valence}}{\text{atomic or radicular weight}}$$

Osmolar Concentration

Although absolute osmotic equilibrium is probably never attained in living tissues, all internal body fluids, extracellular and intracellular, tend to have an equal osmotic pressure. Osmotic pressure is a function of the concentration of active chemical components in a solution, i.e., the number of ions and moles (undissociated compounds). The designation "osmole" is applied to one chemically active mole or ion. Although all solutions of identical osmolarity do not necessarily have the same osmotic pressure (e.g., solutions of electrolytes vs. non-electrolytes), under conditions existing in the body fluids osmolarity may be regarded as a satisfactory equivalent for osmotic pressure.

A solution containing 1 osmole (expressed in grams) of solute per liter of water depresses the freezing point of the water by 1.86° C. The freezing point of blood plasma is −0.56° C. It must, therefore, contain osmotically active solutes in a total concentration of 0.56/1.86 or 0.30 osmoles (300 milliosmoles) per liter of water. The other body fluids with equal osmotic pressures also have the same osmolar concentration of solutes (300 milliosmoles/liter of water), of which non-electrolytes contribute about 10 milliosmoles.

In this connection, the components of the body fluids may be classified conveniently as follows:

(1) Compounds of very large molecular size, e.g., proteins, lipids, glycogen, to which all but a few capillary and cell membranes are almost completely impervious. Inasmuch as osmotic pressure is proportional to the number of active chemical components per unit of water, these compounds, because of their large molecular size, exert relatively little effect on osmotic pressure in proportion to their concentration on a weight basis. For example, the concentration of plasma proteins, about 7 gm. per 100 ml. of plasma, with molecular weights of about 70,000 to over 1,000,000, represents only about 2 milliosmoles per liter. Moreover, since these large compounds displace a large volume of water and the osmolar concentration is expressed in terms of units per liter of water, correction must be made for this displacement. In the case of plasma, this correction

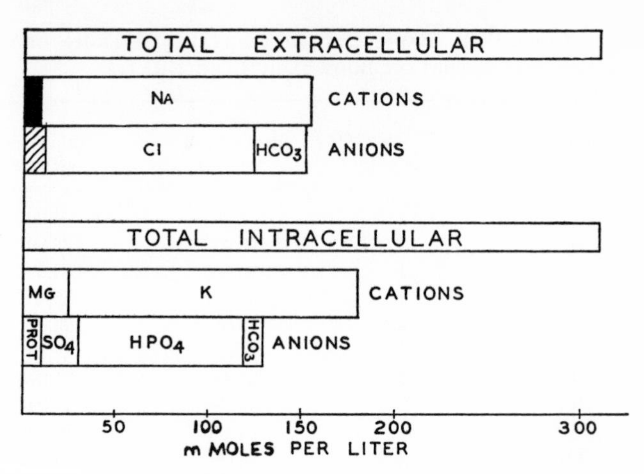

Figure 12-2. Osmolar equality of the extracellular and intracellular fluids. (After Gamble.)

factor is 0.94, the total osmolar concentration being 282 milliosmoles per liter of plasma (300 milliosmoles per liter of plasma water), 10 contributed by non-electrolytes.

(2) Electrolytes, which cross capillary walls freely, but to certain of which various cell membranes exhibit a variable degree of impermeability under different conditions. Electrolytes dissociate into ions and therefore exert an osmotic pressure greater than their molar concentrations because the ions behave as units. The osmolar concentration of NaCl is practically twice its molar concentration because it dissociates almost completely into Na^+ and Cl^-. One millimole of $CaCl_2$ represents 3 milliosmoles, dissociating into $Ca^{++} + 2Cl^-$. In the presence of large amounts of protein, certain elements, e.g., Ca and K, may exist as relatively poorly dissociated salts of protein, being osmotically active only to the extent of the degree of dissociation.

(3) Organic compounds of a molecular size which permits their free diffusion across capillary walls, e.g., urea, glucose, amino acids. Some cell membranes may be relatively impermeable to certain of these, as to certain electrolytes.

EXTRACELLULAR FLUID

All body cells exist in an environment of fluids collectively designated "extracellular fluid." These include the blood plasma, interstitial fluid, lymph, and peritoneal, pericardial, pleural, and joint fluids. Transcellular fluids also belong in this category, i.e., fluids formed by the gastrointestinal mucosa and other digestive glands, liver, kidneys, etc. These differ from other extracellular fluids in that they are formed by active cellular mechanisms and therefore do not resemble ultrafiltrates of the blood plasma. The heterogeneous character of the interstitial fluid is referred to elsewhere (p. 297); from a physiological standpoint, there are distinct differences in this respect between muscle, skin, dense connective tissue and cartilage, and bone. With these exceptions and reservations, most of the extracellular fluids may be regarded as having an essentially uniform qualitative composition. What quantitative differences exist are due chiefly to differences in the concentrations of proteins, which range from about 7 per cent in plasma and but slightly less in hepatic lymph, to about 0.1 per cent in the subcutaneous interstitial fluid. They are solutions chiefly of NaCl and $NaHCO_3$, with small amounts of Ca, Mg, K, H, phosphate, sulfate and organic acid ions, variable amounts of protein, some non-electrolytes (glucose, urea, lipids, etc.), and with pH values ranging from 7.35 to 7.45 under normal conditions.

The total concentration of the ionic constituents is about 310 mEq. per liter of plasma (about 335 mEq. per liter of plasma water). That in interstitial fluid is about 310 mEq. per liter of water. The difference is due mainly to the relatively high protein content of the plasma. In accordance with the laws of electrical neutrality, cations and anions each comprise half of the total concentration, expressed in terms of chemical equivalence.

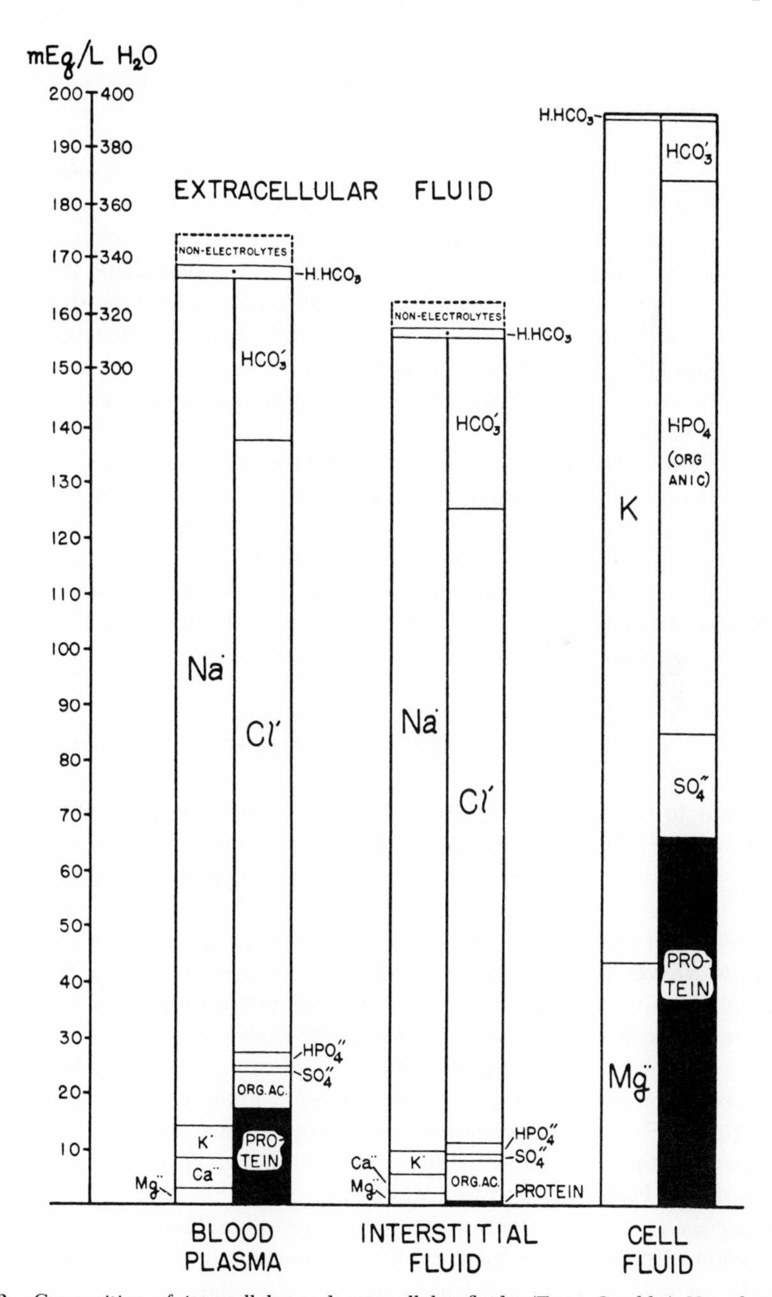

Figure 12-3. Composition of intracellular and extracellular fluids. (From Gamble.) Non-electrolytes are expressed as millimoles on the milliequivalent scale.

Proteins, being amphoteric (p. 69 ff.), act as anions in these slightly alkaline fluids, the chemical composition of which is indicated in Figure 12–3. Attention should be drawn to the distinction between this anionic function of these proteins and their buffering capacity. The former is a reflection of the net overall charge on the entire molecule at the existing pH of the solution, whereas the latter is a function almost exclusively of the imidazole groups of their histidine component (p. 74 ff.).

The milliequivalent value for protein is obtained by multiplying grams of protein per liter by 0.243 (Van Slyke factor). Each millimole (mmole) of protein represents about 8 milliequivalents (mEq.), which accounts chiefly for the discrepancy between the ionic osmolar and equivalent values for plasma. At the pH of extracellular fluid, 80 per cent of the phosphate radical carries two equivalents (B_2HPO_4) and 20 per cent one equivalent of cation (BH_2PO_4). The valence of phosphate is therefore calculated as 1.8. The commonly used designations of carbonic acid and bicarbonate values in terms of "volumes per cent CO_2" (p. 320) may be converted to milliequivalents per liter by dividing by 2.22.

The relative importance of the several components of the extracellular fluids in preserving osmotic, anion-cation, and acid-base balance is indicated by their osmolar and equivalent concentrations, respectively (Fig. 12–2; Fig. 12–3). However, those components, particularly cations, which are present in comparatively low concentrations, viz., K^+, Ca^{++}, Mg^{++}, and H^+, exert profound influences upon a variety of physiological processes. Therefore, relatively slight deviations from their normal concentrations produce significant biological effects.

As illustrated in Figure 12–3, the chief general structural difference between the two main compartments of extracellular fluid, i.e., blood plasma and interstitial fluid, is the relatively large amount of protein in the former. The presence of this nondiffusible component results in certain readjustments of the diffusible ions in order to maintain anion-cation equivalence (Donnan equilibrium, p. 304). Consequently, the interstitial fluid contains a somewhat higher total concentration of diffusible anion and a lower concentration of cation than does the plasma.

INTRACELLULAR FLUID

In contrast to the rather complete and precise information available regarding the composition of extracellular fluids, knowledge of the chemical structure of intracellular fluids is fragmentary and incomplete. It seems obvious that differences in structure and function of cells of various tissues might be reflected in differences in their chemical constitution, in contradistinction to the comparatively uniform composition of most extracellular fluids. Moreover, the previous concept of an intracellular compartment separated from extracellular fluids by a cell membrane must be revised in the light of present knowledge that various cell constituents may be distributed unequally between the soluble phase of the cytoplasm and the particulate components (nucleus, mitochondria, endoplasmic reticulum, microsomes), each of which has a limiting membrane. Nevertheless, it is useful to describe the major differences between typical extracellular fluids and the most abundant of the intracellular fluids, i.e., that of skeletal muscle which may, with certain exceptions, be regarded as typical of most cells.

Whereas Na is the major cation in the extracellular fluid (142 mEq./liter), much smaller amounts are present in the intracellular fluids (0 to 40 mEq./liter), which also contain little or no Ca. The chief cations of the latter fluids are K, about 140 mEq./liter in muscle, and Mg, about 40 mEq./liter in muscle (5 and 3 mEq./liter respectively in plasma). As regards anions, the intracellular fluids contain much more phosphate and sulfate ions and protein than do the extracellular fluids. Cl, the major anion of the extracellular fluids, is practically absent from the intracellular fluids, except in the case of erythrocytes (Fig. 12–3), and cells of the kidney, stomach, and intestines. Cells of the latter organs contain Na and Cl, since they are engaged in reabsorption or secretion of these elements. However, in these situations, Na and Cl are apparently not in diffusion equilibrium with the extracellular fluid. HCO_3^- is the only ion which exists in both fluids in concentrations of even approximately comparable magnitude. Because of the large volume of intracellular fluid, intracellular Na and Cl, despite their low concentrations, comprise about one-third of the total exchangeable Na and Cl of the body.

The marked differences in concentrations of Na and K in the extra- and intracellular fluids indicate a certain degree of impermeability of the cell membranes to these ions. This impermeability is, however, not absolute nor fixed, both ions being able to cross the membrane more freely under certain physiological and pathological conditions (p. 308). It would appear that as K leaves the cell in increased amounts, Na and H enter, the total cationic concentration being thereby maintained approximately.

The bulk of the phosphate is in organic combination and the extent of dissociation of these compounds is not known. Similarly, much of the Mg and perhaps of the K is undoubtedly present as undissociated salts of protein and organic phosphate and, therefore, is not in ionic form. Furthermore, the concentration of protein ions has not been established accurately and the estimated HCO_3^- concentration is subject to correction for carbamino-CO_2 (p. 291). These factual deficiencies contribute to the present uncertainty regarding the constitution of the intracellular fluids on an osmolar and equivalent basis.

EXCHANGES BETWEEN FLUID COMPARTMENTS

The continual entrance into the body of substances from without (oxygen, water, organic and inorganic foodstuffs, etc.) and production by the cells of a great variety of metabolites, many of which must be distributed to other tissues or be excreted, imply a continual movement of various components of the body fluid compartments across the boundary membranes (capillaries and cell walls). The most important of these exchange systems may be outlined as follows:

(1) *Alveolar air : blood plasma* (p. 283). This system provides for entrance of oxygen into and loss of CO_2 and water from the body.

(2) *Plasma : erythrocyte* (p. 289). This system provides for ready exchange of oxygen, CO_2, water, and certain anions (particularly Cl^- and HCO_3^-) in both directions. Cations are exchanged very slowly.

(3) *Plasma : interstitial fluid.* These two media are separated by the capillary walls, which are perfectly permeable to water, inorganic ions, and small organic molecules (e.g., glucose, amino acids, urea, etc.) but not to large organic molecules, such as proteins.

(4) *Interstitial fluid : intracellular fluid.* These two compartments are separated by the cell membranes, across which gases, water, and small, uncharged molecules can diffuse readily, but across which certain electrolytes, under normal conditions, cannot, at least not freely. These membranes are also relatively impermeable to large molecules, such as proteins, except in special situations, viz., the liver.

The first two of these systems are discussed in the section on respiration (pp. 282 to 291), since they are intimately concerned with the transport and exchanges of oxygen and CO_2.

Gibbs-Donnan Equilibrium

If two solutions are separated by a membrane which is freely permeable to the solvent and solutes, the concentrations of the latter will be identical when equilibrium is established. Thus, both the chemical composition and the osmotic pressures of the two solutions will be the same.

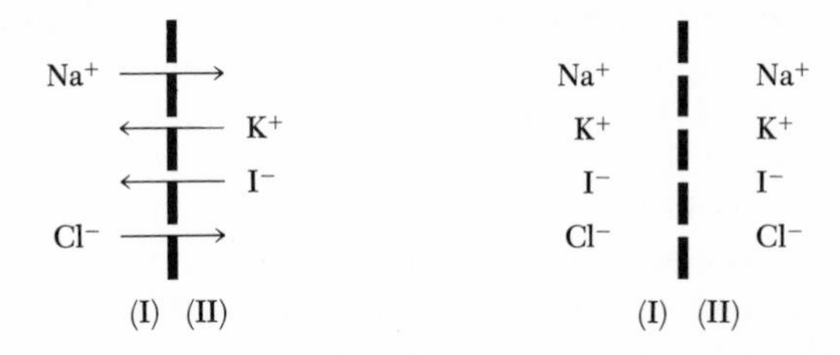

If, on the other hand, one of the solutions contains an electrolyte, e.g., NaCl, to which the membrane is permeable, and the other contains one, e.g., Na proteinate (NaR) in which R is a monovalent anion too large to pass through the membrane, the distribution of Na^+ and Cl^- at equilibrium will be unequal on opposite sides of the membrane. If both electrolytes are completely dissociated, the situation of equilibrium may be represented as follows:

Na^+ and Cl^- ions diffuse in pairs, preserving electrical neutrality, from solution (II), into solution (I), and subsequently in the reverse direction, until equilibrium is established, the net result being loss of Na^+ and Cl^- from solution (II) and their addition to solution (I). These changes in distribution can be expressed quantitatively if one assumes that there are no volume changes, i.e., that only ions are transferred, and not water.

Let x represent the number of Na^+ and Cl^- ions lost from (II) and added to (I), a the original number of Na^+ and R^- ions in (I), and b the original number of Na^+ and Cl^- ions in (II). The ionic distribution at equilibrium may be represented quantitatively as follows:

(I)	(II)
$(a + x)Na^+$	$Na^+(b - x)$
$(a)R^-$	
$(x)Cl^-$	$Cl^-(b - x)$

Inasmuch as the total number of positive and negative charges must be equal on a given side of the membrane, a Na^+ ion cannot move in either direction without a Cl^- ion. The probability of these two ions reaching and passing through the membrane at the same instant is proportional to the product of their concentrations on that side of the membrane. At equilibrium, therefore, when equal amounts of diffusible electrolyte pass in opposite directions, these concentration products must be equal.

$$Na^+_{(I)} \cdot Cl^-_{(I)} = Na^+_{(II)} \cdot Cl^-_{(II)}$$

or $$(a + x)x = (b - x)(b - x) \text{ or } (b - x)^2$$

This is the fundamental Donnan equation, expressing the quantitative aspects of this situation, referred to as the Gibbs-Donnan equilibrium. This equation may also be written:

$$ax + x^2 = b^2 - 2bx + x^2$$

or $$ax = b^2 - 2bx$$

or $$ax + 2bx = b^2$$

or $$(a + 2b)x = b^2$$

or $$x = \frac{b^2}{a + 2b}$$

Since in solution (I) the cation Na^+ must balance two anions, R^- and Cl^-, the concentration of Na^+ will exceed that of Cl^-, whereas they will be equal in solution (II). Therefore, the product of the concentrations of Na^+ and Cl^- in solution (II) represents a square, but not in solution (I). It follows, too, that whereas Na^+ in solution (I) exceeds Na^+ in solution (II), Cl^- in solution (II) exceeds Cl^- in solution (I).

The quantitative ionic relations for the Gibbs-Donnan equilibrium may be stated as follows: The concentration of a diffusible positive ion (cation) is higher and that of a diffusible negative ion (anion) lower on the side of the membrane containing a nondiffusible negative ion (e.g., protein), i.e.,

$$Na^+_{(I)} > Na^+_{(II)} \text{ and } Cl^-_{(I)} < Cl^-_{(II)}$$

It must be understood that these considerations apply only when the volumes of the solutions on the two sides of the membranes remain constant and only ion transfer occurs.

It can also be shown that, in the presence of several different diffusible ions, their distribution ratios will be as follows:

$$\frac{Na^+_{(I)}}{Na^+_{(II)}} = \frac{K^+_{(I)}}{K^+_{(II)}} = \frac{\sqrt{Ca^{++}_{(I)}}}{\sqrt{Ca^{++}_{(II)}}} = \frac{Cl^-_{(II)}}{Cl^-_{(I)}} = \frac{HCO_3^-{}_{(II)}}{HCO_3^-{}_{(I)}} = \frac{\sqrt{SO_4^={}_{(II)}}}{\sqrt{SO_4^={}_{(I)}}}$$

Gibbs-Donnan Effect and Osmotic Pressure

Certain additional facts arise out of the mathematical considerations outlined above, incident to the presence of a nondiffusible ion on one side of the membrane.

(1) At equilibrium, if the volume of the solvent is kept constant, the sum of the concentrations of diffusible ions in solution (I) (containing the nondiffusible ion) exceeds the sum of the concentrations of the same ions in solution II, the sum of the factors in a square being less than the sum of the factors in the same product which is not a square. If the value for *a* and for *b* is represented as 1 mole, the value for *x*, according to the Donnan equation $\left(x = \frac{b^2}{a + 2b}\right)$, will be 0.33 mole, and the quantitative distribution of Na^+, Cl^- and protein (R^-) will be as follows:

(I)	(II)
$Na^+(a + x) = 1.33$	$Na^+(b - x) = 0.66$
$Cl^-(x) = 0.33$	$Cl^-(b - x) = 0.66$
$R^-(a) = 1.0$	

(2) The total ionic concentration in solution (I) exceeds that in solution (II). Consequently, the former will have a higher osmotic pressure than the latter, determined not only by the concentration of the nondiffusible ion, but also by the higher concentration of diffusible ions.

The Gibbs-Donnan effect is of physiological significance in biological systems involving ion exchanges across permeable membranes, especially when the fluid on one side of the membrane contains a nondiffusible component, e.g., protein, in high concentration. It finds particular application in exchanges of Cl^- and HCO_3^- between the blood plasma and erythrocyte and in water and ion exchanges between the blood plasma and interstitial fluid (i.e., across the capillary wall).

Plasma: Interstitial Fluid Exchange

Exchanges between the blood plasma and interstitial fluid occur across the endothelial lining of the capillaries, which act as semipermeable membranes, allowing free passage of water and crystalloid solutes, inorganic and organic, but not of colloids of large molecular size, viz., proteins. This impermeability to proteins is not absolute nor uniform, the concentration of protein in interstitial fluids varying from 0.05 to 0.5 per cent in subcutaneous tissues and serous cavities to 4 to 6 per cent in liver. The concentrations of diffusible electrolytes on the two sides of the capillary will vary, their distribution depending upon the difference in protein concentration in the two fluids (Gibbs-Donnan effect). The osmotic pressure will be greater in the plasma than in the interstitial fluid, owing both to the higher protein concentration (colloid osmotic pressure; C.O.P.) and to the consequent higher concentration of diffusible ions. Such freely diffusible organic solutes as urea, glucose, creatinine, etc., being non-ionized, are not subject to the Donnan effect and are distributed equally throughout the body water. Their diffusion across semipermeable membranes is therefore determined by their concentration gradients.

In the absence of opposing forces, water and crystalloid solutes will tend to pass from the interstitial fluid to the plasma, which contains protein in higher concentration, thereby producing an osmotic pressure gradient. This tendency is counterbalanced by the opposing force of the capillary blood pressure and is also modified by the concentration gradients of the individual solutes.

The colloid osmotic pressure (C.O.P.) of the proteins of normal plasma is about 22 mm. Hg (30 cm. H_2O). The capillary blood pressure varies considerably in different tissues, but is higher than the C.O.P. at the arterial end of the capillary and lower than the C.O.P. at the venous end. Consequently, filtration from the plasma occurs at the arterial end and reabsorption into it at the venous end of the capillary. Moreover, the increasing concentration of nondiffusible colloids (viz., proteins) which results from loss of plasma water, creates a relatively small but actual gradient of C.O.P., which further favors reabsorption as the blood pressure falls in the distal end of the capillary. This mechanism (Starling hypothesis) provides for a continual circulation of fluid between the capillaries and the tissue spaces, a balance being maintained between the quantity of water filtered and that reabsorbed. Exchanges of diffusible solutes between these two fluids depend upon these circumstances and also, independently of them, upon their individual concentration gradients. The factors concerned with the transfer of materials across the capillary wall are therefore those of diffusion, osmosis, and hydrostatic pressure.

Filtration from the capillaries is opposed by the tissue tension, which varies considerably in different situations, being relatively low in loose areolar tissues (e.g., eyelids, external genitalia) and high in dense tissues (e.g., muscle, liver, etc). Fluid leaves the tissue spaces not only by direct reabsorption into the blood plasma but also by filtration across the lymph capillaries, ultimately reaching the venous blood by way of the lymphatic circulation.

Interstitial Fluid: Intracellular Fluid Exchange

Exchanges between these two compartments occur across cell membranes, which are generally freely permeable to gases, water, and small uncharged molecules (urea, glucose, etc.) but not to large colloidal molecules, such as proteins. The enormously higher concentration of proteins and other colloids in the intracellular than in the interstitial fluids would cause a much greater osmotic pressure within the cells (Gibbs-Donnan effect) were it not for the fact that the cell membranes are generally not freely permeable to inorganic ions, especially certain cations. Consequently, the electrolyte composition of cells is quite as distinctive as their organic constitution (Fig. 12–3, p. 301). Because of this limited permeability to inorganic ions, adjustment to deviations of osmotic pressure is usually accomplished largely by transfers of water, not by exchanges of electrolytes, the freely diffusible organic solutes (urea, creatinine) moving with the water.

Inasmuch as the concentrations of protein in the body fluids are more stable than the concentrations of inorganic ions, the latter constitute the dominant factor in determining the total osmotic pressure and the exchanges of water between the body fluid compartments. The milliequivalent value of the extracellular fluids (310 mEq./liter) approximates their milliosmolar value (Fig. 12–2) because of the enormous preponderance of univalent ions. This is not true, however, of the intracellular fluids, the total milliosmolar value of which approximates that of extracellular fluids, but the milliequivalent value of which is considerably higher (about 390), because of the relatively high concentrations of multivalent ions (Mg^{++}, $SO_4^{=}$, $HPO_4^{=}$, protein).

It is probable that exchanges of water across the outer cell membrane proceed passively, in relation to changes in osmotic pressure, diffusion of various metabolites, and active transport of other substances, which occur continually in actively metabolizing tissues. However, it is probable, too, that under these circumstances a state of absolute osmotic equilibrium, although constantly approached, is never reached.

The much higher concentrations of Na^+ and Cl^- in interstitial fluid and of K^+ in intracellular fluid are accompanied by a difference in electrical potential, that of resting skeletal muscle cells being about 90 millivolts negative to the interstitial fluid. It is believed that the lipid-protein membrane plays an important role in determining and maintaining these differences in concentration and potential. K^+ ions tend to diffuse out of and Cl^- ions into the cell because of their concentration gradients, but this is almost exactly counterbalanced by a tendency to diffuse in the opposite direction due to the difference in electrical potential, i.e., the relative negativity on the inside of the cell tends to keep Cl^- out and K^+ in. In the case of Na^+, however, diffusion into the cells is favored by both concentration gradient and electrical potential. Under normal conditions, there must be some mechanism for removing Na^+ from the cell virtually as rapidly as it enters. Since this is accomplished in opposition to forces of concentration and electrical potential, it involves expenditure of energy, derived from cellular metabolism. This process of active transport of Na^+ out of the cell is referred to as the "sodium pump," which effectively excludes Na^+ from the intracellular fluid (resting muscle). The extrusion of Na^+ from the cell is associated with splitting of ATP by ATPase at the inner surface of the cell membrane. The energy of hydrolysis of ATP is used by the transport mechanism for the coupled exchange of Na^+ for K^+ ions between the intracellular and extracellular fluids.

It has been suggested that pyridoxal phosphate (p. 189), due to its capacity for forming metal chelates, may serve as the carrier of cations across the cell membrane. This is based on observations that passage of K^+ into the cell is accompanied by diminution in intracellular concentration of amino acids, whereas increased concentration of amino acids is accompanied by loss of K^+ and increase of Na^+ in the cell. Phosphatides, too, have been proposed as important components of the transport system. The dependence of this function of the cell membrane upon metabolic processes in the cell is illustrated by the fact that if cells are incubated in a glucose-free medium, Na^+ enters and K^+ leaves the cell. These changes are reversed upon addition of glucose to the medium.

The relative impermeability of cell membranes to inorganic ions is not uniform or constant. HCO_3^- ions are generally freely diffusible; Cl^- ions pass freely into and out of erythrocytes (p. 291) and the acid-secreting cells of the gastric mucosa. Although permeability to Na^+ is restricted, it may enter cells in increased amounts when they lose K^+ and the passage of K^+ across cell membranes appears to be related to metabolic activities of the cells. For example, there is acceleration of the entrance of K^+ into cells during periods of administration of glucose or insulin (p. 441). Changes in the distribution of Na^+ and K^+ occur during excitation of nerve and muscle cells, and can be produced by adrenocortical hormones (p. 710), and by dehydration, anoxia, and changes in pH (p. 319), due to alterations in the properties of the cell membrane. Loss of K^+ from the cell, e.g., following administration of aldosterone, is accompanied by entrance of Na^+ and H^+ from the interstitial fluid, with consequent fall in intracellular pH and rise in extracellular pH (p. 319).

When Na is introduced into the blood plasma, it is distributed rapidly throughout the extracellular fluids, but penetrates the cells only very slowly. Consequently, an increase in Na concentration in the extracellular fluids causes water to pass out of the cells, equalizing the osmotic pressure in the two fluid compartments. Withdrawal of Na from the extracellular fluids causes passage of water in the opposite direction, i.e., into the cells.

Shifts of water are also caused by changes in pH of the body fluids. The explanation frequently given is that acids remove cations from the weakly dissociated proteins, forming more completely dissociated salts and thereby increasing the number of osmotically active components. Inasmuch as the protein content of intracellular fluids is greater than that of extracellular fluids, acidification, according to this view, results in greater increase in osmotic pressure within the cells than in the extracellular fluids. Consequently, water passes into the cells under such circumstances. This explanation is not entirely satisfactory.

Phosphate is present within cells in much larger amounts than in extracellular fluids. Much of this is in organic combination, e.g., as hexose and triose phosphates, ATP and ADP, nucleic acids, phosphocreatine (muscles), etc. However, the concentration of inorganic phosphate, too, is higher than in the extracellular fluids and fluctuates continually in relation to the latter at different levels of cell metabolic activity involving formation and splitting of phosphorylated metabolites. In contrast to the case of K^+, the rate of entrance of phosphate into muscle cells is not altered significantly by muscular activity but is increased markedly during the recovery period. It is increased also by administration of glucose and insulin.

The concentrations of K, Na, Mg, and phosphate in the cell can vary, within limits, in accordance with the metabolic activity of the cell, without influencing exchanges of water, because, presumably, considerable fractions of these substances form undissociated or poorly dissociated combinations with cell proteins, nucleic acids, polysaccharides, etc., and are therefore osmotically inactive.

REGULATORY MECHANISMS

In health, the volume and composition of the various body fluid compartments are maintained within physiological limits even in the face of wide variations in intake of water and solutes. Isotope-labeled water becomes distributed throughout the body fluids in two to three hours after administration; in the absence of increase in volume, this implies continual exchanges of water across compartment boundaries. Fluid exchanges across the cell wall are conducted in a state of osmotic equilibrium. Assuming a "steady state" of cellular metabolic activity, the osmolarity of intracellular fluids is determined mainly by their K concentration, while that of extracellular fluids is determined by their Na concentration. If constancy of osmolarity is to be maintained, the volume of intracellular fluid must be proportional to its total K content, and that of extracellular fluid to its total Na content. Consequently, if the volumes of these compartments are to be maintained at constant levels, a mechanism must be provided for adjustments in excretion not only of water but also of Na and K in response to variations in amounts of each supplied to the organism.

These adjustments are accomplished mainly by the kidney. Normal renal function provides a steady state with respect to: (1) the amount of water in the body; (2) the amounts of Na and K, which determine the volume of extracellular and intracellular fluids; (3) the osmolar concentrations of these fluids, determined largely by the concentrations of Na and K, respectively. The kidney responds promptly to deviations in osmolarity or individual ion concentrations in extracellular fluid, e.g., produced by administration of excessive quantities of water or Na, by augmented excretion of these substances in amounts required for preservation of osmotic equilibrium. However, isosmotic expansion of extracellular fluid volume, e.g., by intravenous infusion of isotonic solutions of salt or serum albumin, is followed promptly by increased urinary excretion of water and salt. Homeostasis of body fluids therefore involves a mechanism that responds to fluctuations in volume as well as mechanisms responsive to changes in concentrations of total solute or of individual ions. Urinary excretion of water and salt is conditioned by a number of variations in body fluids. These include such factors as: the volume of plasma and interstitial fluid; cellular hydration; intracranial volume or blood flow; cardiac output; pressure changes in various portions of the circulation; renal blood flow; concentrations of total or individual solutes in extracellular fluid. Certain of these variables, which involve significant alterations in renal blood flow or pressure, or in solute concentrations in the blood plasma, may produce their effects by direct action on the kidney. Others, however, can produce their effects in the absence of significant changes in renal hemodynamics or in solute concentrations in the plasma. These effects on kidney function must therefore be mediated by extrarenal factors.

Current concepts of the nature of these regulatory mechanisms include the existence of receptors sensitive to variations in osmolar (osmoreceptors) or individual ion (chemoreceptors) concentrations in extracellular fluids, and to local or general variations in intravascular pressure (baroreceptors) and plasma or extracellular fluid volume (volume receptors, stretch receptors). The intrarenal mechanisms concerned with excretion of water and solutes may be influenced by stimuli initiated in these receptors either by direct neural connections or through the medium of humoral factors, i.e., alterations in production or release of certain hormones. There is evidence that there are pathways in the nervous system capable of mediating such influences, but more precise information is available concerning the role of certain hormones in this connection. Those involved most fundamentally are the antidiuretic hormone (ADH) and aldosterone, the former regulating the excretion of water, the latter of Na and K. Adrenal glucocorticoids also exert an influence that is not as well defined. Details are presented elsewhere of the actions of these hormones in promoting renal tubular reabsorption of water (pp. 710, 825) and Na (pp. 710, 825), and excretion of K (pp. 711, 827). The mechanisms of regulation of production and release of these hormones are also considered elsewhere (pp. 706, 707). It will suffice here to consider the manner in which these two independently controlled systems may be coordinated in the interests of body fluid homeostasis.

The complexity of this regulatory system is indicated (1) by the great variety of conditions to which it makes adjustments (e.g., water and salt intake; extracellular fluid composition and volume; emotional states; blood flow and pressure, general or in certain specific regions) and (2) by the great diversity of its components (e.g., various types of receptors; diencephalic centers; nervous pathways; neurohypophysis; adrenal cortex; renal glomeruli and tubules), many of which have independent controlling mechanisms. Perhaps the simplest concept, applicable to many circumstances but certainly not to all, is that the end-effects of the action of one hormone, e.g., ADH, influence the rate of production or discharge of another, e.g., aldosterone. In addition, since adjustments may be made in either direction, the receptors of the initiating stimuli must be in a state of tonic activity, capable therefore of either excitation or depression.

Adjustment to increasing osmolarity of extracellular fluid may occur as follows: (1) stimulation of osmoreceptors, presumably in the diencephalon; (2) perhaps through neuronal connections, this causes increased production (in paraventricular and supraoptic nuclei) and discharge (from neurohypophysis) of ADH; (3) this hormone, reaching the kidney in the systemic circulation, causes increased reabsorption of water in the distal nephron; (4) normal osmolarity of the extracellular fluid is restored but its volume is increased; (5) this, directly or indirectly, depresses the activity of stretch receptors (volume receptors; baroreceptors), perhaps in various locations; (6) by some as yet undetermined mechanism, aldosterone production decreases; (7) renal tubular reabsorption of Na diminishes and it is excreted, with water, in the urine in amounts required to restore normal extracellular fluid volume and osmolarity.

The converse occurs in response to decreased osmolarity. Other relationships are superimposed upon this basic pattern. Secretion of ADH is influenced by changes not only in osmolarity but also in volume of extracellular fluids; secretion of aldosterone is influenced by variations not only in volume of extracellular fluid but also in the amount and concentrations of Na and K (chemoreceptors), in some cases at least operating independently of changes in volume.

The thirst mechanism plays an important role in fluid homeostasis, regulating water intake. It is activated by increasing osmolar concentration of extracellular fluid (osmoreceptors), resulting either from a deficit in water or an excess of solute. It also has a sensory component, mediated by the glossopharyngeal and vagus nerves, stimulated by dryness of the mouth and throat.

The intracellular and extracellular fluids are in osmotic equilibrium. Consequently, the volume of the former is determined largely by the osmolarity of the latter. Ultimately, therefore, the kidneys regulate the intracellular fluid volume by adjusting excretion of water in response to changes in osmolarity of the extracellular fluid. The volume of circulating blood plasma is of much greater concern to the welfare of the organism than is the volume of other extracellular fluids. It tends to be maintained within normal limits, largely through the operation of cardiovascular mechanisms, even in the presence of marked expansion or contraction of interstitial and transcellular fluids. However, since the plasma proteins do not cross most normal capillary walls readily, an increase in plasma volume may follow intravenous infusion of hypertonic albumin solutions. Conversely, reduction in plasma volume may occur in conditions of severe plasma protein depletion.

BIBLIOGRAPHY

Annual Review of Physiology.

Bland, J. H. (ed.): Clinical Metabolism of Body Water and Electrolytes, Philadelphia, W. B. Saunders Company, 1963.

Darrow, D. C., and Hellerstein, S.: Interpretation of certain changes in body water and electrolytes, Physiol. Rev. *38:*114, 1958.

Edelman, I. S., and Leibman, J.: Anatomy of body water and electrolytes, Am. J. Med. *27:*256, 1959.

Elkinton, J. R.: Regulation of water and electrolytes, Circulation *21:*1184, 1960.

Elkinton, J. R., and Danowski, T. S.: The Body Fluids, Baltimore, Williams & Wilkins Company, 1955.

Farrell, G.: Regulation of aldosterone secretion, Physiol. Rev. *38:*709, 1958.

Gamble, J. L.: Chemical Anatomy, Physiology and Pathology of Extracellular Fluid, Cambridge, Harvard University Press, 1950.

Gamble, J. L.: Companionship of water and electrolytes in the organization of body fluids (Lane Medical Lectures), Stanford, Calif., Stanford University Press, 1951.

Gaunt, R., and Chart, J. J.: Endocrine regulation of water and electrolyte metabolism, in Homeostatic Mechanisms, Brookhaven Symposia in Biology, No. 10, 1957, p. 162.

Josephson, B.: Chemistry and Therapy of Electrolyte Disorders, Springfield, Ill., Charles C Thomas, 1961.

Manery, J. F.: Water and electrolyte metabolism, Physiol. Rev. *34:*334, 1954.

Pinson, E. A.: Water exchanges and barriers as studied by the use of hydrogen isotopes, Physiol. Rev. *32:*123, 1952.

Pitts, R. F.: Physiology of the Kidney and Body Fluids, Chicago, Year Book Medical Publishers, 1963.

Robinson, J. R.: Metabolism of intracellular water, Physiol. Rev. *40:*112, 1960.

Robinson, J. R.: Body fluid dynamics, in Bonner, F., and Comar, C. L. (eds.): Mineral Metabolism, Vol. 1, New York, Academic Press, Inc., 1960, p. 205.

Smith, H. W.: The Kidney: Structure and Function in Health and Disease, New York, Oxford University Press, 1951.

Stehle, R. L.: The actions of the hormones of the posterior lobe of the pituitary gland, Vitamins and Hormones *7:*390, 1949.

Welt, L. G.: Water balance in health and disease, in Duncan, G. G. (ed.): Diseases of Metabolism, (ed. 5), Philadelphia, W. B. Saunders Company, 1964, p. 449.

CHAPTER 13

NEUTRALITY REGULATION ("ACID-BASE" BALANCE)

UNDER normal conditions the pH of extracellular fluids usually does not vary beyond the range 7.35 to 7.5, and is maintained approximately at 7.4. Inasmuch as large amounts of H^+ are continually contributed to these fluids from intracellular metabolic reactions, preservation of this degree of constancy requires that they be removed from the fluids effectively and promptly. The mechanisms of neutrality regulation are concerned, therefore, with maintaining a state of equilibrium between production (and introduction) and removal of H^+ ions.

Virtually all precise information concerning mechanisms of regulation of the H^+ ion concentration in body fluids is derived from studies of the blood. In view of the ready diffusibility across the capillary wall of most of the important factors concerned, relevant aspects of the structure of the blood plasma may be regarded as reflecting quite accurately the status in this connection of the other major extracellular fluids. However, the pH of interstitial fluid is probably somewhat lower than that of blood plasma, since it occupies a position intermediate between the latter and the site of production of acids within the cells. There is very little precise information concerning the intracellular pH. This undoubtedly differs considerably in different tissues. Although it may be higher than that of blood plasma in a few types of cell, e.g., 8.0 or higher in osteoblasts, it is generally lower in most cells, 7.0 or less, values below 5.0 having been reported in the prostate.

Acids and Bases

According to the modern concept (Brønsted), an acid is defined as a substance (ion, molecule, particle) that yields H^+ ions (protons) in solution and a base is anything that combines with H^+ ions. Accordingly, whereas H_2CO_3 is an acid, dissociating into H^+ and HCO_3^- ions, its anionic component, HCO_3^- is a base. Other examples are:

$$\begin{array}{rcl} \textit{Acid} & & \textit{Base} \\ HSO_4^- & \rightleftharpoons & H^+ + SO_4^= \\ CH_3COOH & \rightleftharpoons & H^+ + CH_3COO^- \\ H_2PO_4^- & \rightleftharpoons & H^+ + HPO_4^= \end{array}$$

$NaHCO_3$ acts as a base because it yields HCO_3^- ions, which can combine with H^+ ions.

HCl is a strong acid by virtue of its extensive dissociation into H^+ and Cl^- ions; accordingly, Cl^- is an extremely weak base, because it has very little capacity for combining firmly with H^+ ions. On the other hand, such anions as HCO_3^-, $HPO_4^=$, $H_2PO_4^-$, and protein$^-$ are comparatively strong bases because they have a relatively strong affinity for H^+ ions, therefore forming weak acids (i.e., relatively slight dissociation).

Failure to apply this concept of acids and bases to clinical considerations of acid-base balance has resulted in considerable confusion, mainly in terminology. Clinically, the term "base" (also "basic radicals," and "alkali") is commonly applied to the cations (Na^+, K^+, Mg^{++}, Ca^{++}) of the body fluids, and the term "acid" (or "acid radicals") to the anions (e.g., HCO_3^-, Cl^-, etc.). The designation "total base" is commonly applied to the sum of the cations. This terminology is clearly incorrect. Its widespread clinical usage depends chiefly on the fact that the concentration of buffer anions, the effective bases of the extracellular fluids, is represented by the difference between the concentrations of total cations and of nonbuffer (fixed) anions. There should be little difficulty, however, in reconciling these inaccuracies of clinical terminology with correct chemical concepts.

The term, "alkali reserve," has been applied by clinicians to the plasma bicarbonate concentration. This was based on the fact that introduction of acids other than carbonic to the extracellular fluids results in decrease in bicarbonate, the major extracellular buffer anion for these acids, in an amount roughly proportional to the amount of acid added. However, the implication that bicarbonate is the only available defense against the introduction of additional acid is, of course, erroneous. Hemoglobin is the most important buffer for carbonic acid. The defenses of the organism against acidosis include also phosphate and protein anions, as well as bicarbonate. Nevertheless, since in the case of accumulation of acids other than carbonic the bicarbonate buffer system is in equilibrium with the other buffer systems, changes in the plasma bicarbonate concentration may be regarded as reflecting changes in the capacity of the organism to resist further additions of these acids. This is not true of conditions of primary increase or decrease in carbonic acid (respiratory acidosis and alkalosis [p. 321]). The "total base," "alkali reserve," or "buffer base" of the plasma may be calculated as approximately equal to the sum of the concentrations of the cations (Na^+, K^+, Mg^{++}, Ca^{++}) minus the concentration of Cl^-, which is so weak a base that it can be disregarded for practical purposes. Its cationic equivalence must be subtracted from the sum total of the cations if the latter is to be used for calculation of the effective "buffer base" or "alkali reserve."

H_2CO_3 is the chief acid formed in the course of cellular oxidations, about 10 to 20 or more moles being produced daily. Sulfuric (oxidation of S of protein) and other acids, e.g., lactic and β-hydroxybutyric, are produced in quantities of about 80 to 120 millimoles daily under ordinary conditions. Although foodstuffs provide a certain amount of potentially "basic" substances, this is far exceeded by their potential acid content. Both the H^+ ions and the anions produced by these acids must be disposed of, i.e., ultimately excreted from the body, in such manner that their temporary sojourn in the extracellular fluids does not unduly affect the pH under normal circumstances. The means whereby these ends are accomplished comprise the mechanism of regulation of "acid-base" balance. These may be outlined as follows:

(1) Dilution: The acids introduced into and formed in the body are distributed throughout the extracellular fluid volume. Although this may not properly be regarded as a regulatory mechanism, entrance of a given amount of acid into a smaller volume of fluid, as in conditions of severe dehydration, results in relatively greater rise in H^+ concentration and decrease in effective buffer base.

(2) Buffer systems: restriction of pH change in body fluids.

(3) Respiration: regulation of excretion of CO_2 and, therefore, regulation of the H_2CO_3 concentration in extracellular fluids.

(4) Renal mechanism: ultimate excretion of excess "acid" or "base"; ultimate regulation, therefore, of the concentration of H^+ and HCO_3^- ions in the extracellular fluids.

PHYSIOLOGICAL BUFFER SYSTEMS

The capacity of the extracellular fluids for transporting acids from the site of their formation (cells) to the site of their excretion (e.g., lungs, kidneys) without undue change in pH is dependent chiefly upon the presence of efficient buffer systems in these fluids and in the erythrocytes. Each buffer system consists of a mixture of a weak acid, HA, and its salt, BA (p. 67). The most important of these are as follows:

$$\textit{Plasma:}\ \frac{H_2CO_3}{BHCO_3},\ \frac{H\cdot \text{protein}}{B\cdot \text{protein}},\ \frac{BH_2PO_4}{B_2HPO_4},\ \frac{H\cdot \text{organic acid}}{B\cdot \text{organic acid}}$$

$$\textit{Erythrocytes:}\ \frac{H_2CO_3}{BHCO_3},\ \frac{HHb}{BHb},\ \frac{HHbO_2}{BHbO_2},\ \frac{BH_2PO_4}{B_2HPO_4},\ \frac{H\cdot \text{organic acid}}{B\cdot \text{organic acid}}$$

The buffer systems in the interstitial fluids and lymph are much the same as in the blood plasma, except that proteins are generally present in much smaller quantities. The buffer systems in intracellular fluids are also qualitatively much the same as in the plasma, but the cell fluids contain much higher concentrations of protein.

Although all of these buffer systems are operative to a certain extent within the physiological range of pH values, only a few of them exist in sufficiently high concentrations to be of distinct quantitative significance in the regulation of acid-base balance. In the blood plasma, the bicarbonate and plasma protein systems, and in the erythrocytes, the bicarbonate and hemoglobin systems play the most important roles in this connection.

The buffer mechanisms involved in the case of H_2CO_3, the anhydride of which (CO_2) is volatile, differ from those for the stronger, non-volatile, fixed acids (sulfuric, phosphoric, lactic, etc.).

Buffer Systems for H_2CO_3 (CO_2)

H_2CO_3 is buffered chiefly by the imidazole groups of Hb in the erythrocytes and proteins in the plasma (p. 288; Fig. 11–4). Hb exerts by far the greater effect in this connection because its capacity for combination with H^+ ions greatly exceeds that of the plasma proteins. The overall reactions may be indicated as follows:

(Plasma)

$$CO_2 + H_2O \rightleftharpoons H_2CO_3$$

$$H_2CO_3 + \text{protein} \rightleftharpoons HCO_3^- + H^+\cdot\text{protein}$$

(Erythrocytes)

$$CO_2 + H_2O \underset{\text{anhydrase}}{\overset{\text{carbonic}}{\rightleftharpoons}} H_2CO_3$$

$$H_2CO_3 + Hb \rightleftharpoons HCO_3^- + H^+\cdot Hb$$

$$H_2CO_3 + HbO_2 \rightleftharpoons HCO_3^- + H^+\cdot HbO_2$$

The effect of addition of CO_2 is to increase both H_2CO_3 and $BHCO_3$, the latter owing to removal of additional H^+ ions by Hb and, to a minor extent, by the plasma proteins. The liberation of oxygen by Hb in the tissues, which occurs simultaneously with the addition of CO_2, increases the buffering capacity of the Hb, as indicated elsewhere (p. 290). The reciprocal exchanges of Cl^- and HCO_3^- ions between the plasma and erythrocytes (chloride shift) constitute an additional important phase of the extremely efficient mechanism for buffering and transport of H_2CO_3 (p. 290; Fig. 11–5). The addition of CO_2 to the blood (3.7 ml./100 ml.) in its passage through the tissues results in an increment in H^+ ions ($CO_2 + H_2O \rightleftharpoons H^+ + HCO_3^-$). Over 70 per cent of these are removed by Hb incidentally to its transformation from the oxygenated to the reduced state. As a result, there is a fall of only about 0.03 in pH. In the lungs this process is reversed. In essence, in the tissues reduced Hb serves as a H^+ acceptor and H_2CO_3 as a H^+ donor; conversely, in the lungs HCO_3^- serves as a H^+ acceptor and oxyHb as a H^+ donor. The H^+ and CO_2 added in the tissues are removed in the lungs and balance is restored.

Buffer Systems for Non-volatile Acids

Neutralization of non-volatile acids entering the extracellular fluids is accomplished chiefly by the $H_2CO_3/BHCO_3$ buffer system. Such acids (e.g., HCl, H_2SO_4, lactic, etc.) react with $BHCO_3$ as follows:

$$HCO_3^- \text{ (from } NaHCO_3) + H^+ \text{ (from HCl)} \rightleftharpoons H_2CO_3$$

Protein and phosphate buffer systems may also be involved, but to a relatively minor extent.

$$\text{Protein} + H^+ \rightleftharpoons H^+ \cdot \text{Protein}$$

$$HPO_4^{=} + H^+ \rightleftharpoons H_2PO_4^-$$

Bicarbonate is particularly efficient in this connection because (1) it is present in higher concentration than the other buffer salts, and (2) the acid product of the reaction, H_2CO_3, is effectively buffered (p. 290) and is readily disposed of by the lungs (p. 316) by virtue of the volatility of its anhydride, CO_2, rendering the reaction irreversible.

$$H_2CO_3 \rightleftharpoons H_2O + CO_2 \nearrow \text{ (expired air)}$$

If an alkaline substance (e.g., NaOH) enters the extracellular fluid, it reacts with the acid components of these buffer systems, chiefly H_2CO_3:

$$H_2CO_3 + OH^- \text{ (from NaOH)} \rightleftharpoons Na^+HCO_3^- + H_2O$$

$$H^+ \cdot \text{Protein} + OH^- \rightleftharpoons \text{Protein} + H_2O$$

$$H_2PO_4^- + OH^- \rightleftharpoons HPO_4^{=} + H_2O$$

Net Effect of Buffer Mechanisms

Because of the relative abundance of bicarbonate in extracellular fluids, the chief effect of the entrance of metabolic acids, both carbonic and other acids, is to increase the concentration of H_2CO_3. In the case of the nonvolatile acids, this is done at the expense of $BHCO_3$. In either case, the ratio, $H_2CO_3/BHCO_3$, which largely determines the pH of these fluids, is increased, with a consequent increase in H^+ ion concentration. Under normal conditions this increase is but slight because (1) H_2CO_3, a weak acid (i.e., weakly dissociated), forms relatively few H^+ ions, (2) it is effectively buffered (p. 290), and (3) it is readily eliminated by the lungs as CO_2, the increase in concentration of both H_2CO_3 and H^+ being thereby minimized.

$$\nwarrow CO_2 + H_2O \longleftarrow H_2CO_3 \rightleftharpoons H^+ + HCO_3^-$$

The carbonic acid produced in the course of oxidative metabolic processes is thus effectively disposed of, chiefly by the hemoglobin mechanism, with very little change in pH (p. 290). The non-volatile acids can be buffered efficiently by bicarbonate as long as adequate amounts of the latter are present in the extracellular fluids.

Respiratory Regulation of Acid-Base Balance

Participation of the respiratory mechanism in the regulation of acid-base balance is dependent upon (1) the sensitivity of the respiratory center (medulla) to very slight changes in pH and in P_{CO_2}, and (2) the ready diffusibility of CO_2 from the blood, across the pulmonary alveolar membrane, into the alveolar air (p. 288).

An increase in blood P_{CO_2} of only 1.5 mm. Hg (0.2 per cent increase in CO_2) results in a 100 per cent increase in pulmonary ventilation (stimulation of respiratory center), which increases also with slight increases in H^+ ion concentration of the blood. The excess CO_2 is thereby promptly removed from the extracellular fluids in the expired air. Decrease in blood P_{CO_2} or H^+ ion concentration causes depression of activity of the respiratory center, with consequent slow, shallow respiration, hypoventilation, and retention of CO_2 in the blood until the normal P_{CO_2} and pH are restored. This respiratory mechanism therefore tends to maintain the normal $H_2CO_3/BHCO_3$ ratio in the extracellular fluids in the face of the continual addition of H_2CO_3 as a result of the metabolic production of both CO_2 and non-volatile acids. According to the Henderson-Hasselbalch equation (p. 67), at pH 7.4, the $H_2CO_3/BHCO_3$ ratio is 1:20, which conforms to the observed concentration ratios of these substances in normal plasma, viz., 1.35 mEq. H_2CO_3/27 mEq. $BHCO_3$ per liter (3 vol. % H_2CO_3/60 vol. % $BHCO_3$).

Although the respiratory mechanism minimizes the pH change incident to the entrance of non-volatile acids, this is only a temporary expedient. It has been accomplished at the expense of an equivalent amount of HCO_3^- and, the concentration of this important buffer being decreased, the capacity of the extracellular fluids to resist additional increments of such acids is reduced.

Renal Regulation of Acid-Base Balance

Under ordinary dietary conditions, the amount of non-volatile acid produced daily exceeds the intake of available neutralizing substances by about 50 to 100 mEq. As indicated above, these acids are effectively buffered, at the expense, however, of a decrease in HCO_3^-, the chief component of the buffer base available for this purpose (total about 1000 mEq.). This "alkali reserve" would eventually be exhausted if the increment in fixed acid anions, temporarily replacing HCO_3^- anions, were not removed from the body and the HCO_3^- restored. This is accomplished by the kidneys, which are, consequently, the ultimate regulators of the acid-base balance, providing the most important final defense of the pH of the body fluids.

In the course of urine formation, a protein-free filtrate of blood plasma passes through the glomerular capillaries, the final composition of the excreted urine resulting from subsequent changes in this filtrate in the tubule (p. 823). In normal subjects, under ordinary dietary conditions, the urinary pH is about 6.0. The difference in titratable acidity between the pH of the urine and that of plasma (7.4) represents the amount of acid removed by renal action from the plasma. Under conditions of extreme requirement for removal of excess acid or base respectively, the H^+ ion concentration of the urine can vary from pH 4.5 to 8.2 if the kidneys are functioning normally. This ability to excrete urine of variable acidity (or alkalinity) removes from the blood the quantity of excess acid or base required to preserve the normal H^+ ion concentration of the body fluids.

Renal excretion of acid. Even at the maximal attainable urinary acidity, pH 4.5, all $SO_4^=$ and Cl^- anions must be electrically balanced by B^+ cations, chiefly Na^+ and K^+, i.e., they cannot exist as free acids (sulfuric, hydrochloric). The same is true of over 90 per cent of the lactate anions. Consequently, at any urinary pH, removal of these anions from the body requires practically the same amount of B^+ as is required to balance them electrically during their transport in the blood plasma; no significant deviation from the pH of the plasma (7.4) could be effected inasmuch as no H^+ ions could be carried out by these anions ($SO_4^=$ and Cl^-) of strong acids.

Increase in urinary acidity is accomplished by excretion of increased amounts of the weakly acidic BH_2PO_4 and certain weak organic acids, e.g., β-hydroxybutyric, acetoacetic, citric. In the plasma, at pH 7.4, phosphate exists as a mixture of about 80 per cent B_2HPO_4 and 20 per cent BH_2PO_4 ($Na_2^{++}HPO_4^=/Na^+H_2PO_4^- = 4/1$). At pH 4.8, about 99 per cent is in the form of BH_2PO_4 ($Na_2^{++}HPO_4^=/Na^+H_2PO_4^- = 1/99$). According to these ratios, every five phosphate molecules circulating in the plasma and entering the glomerular filtrate carry nine negative charges, which must be balanced by nine positive charges, i.e., nine Na^+ ions. In the urine at pH 4.8, these five phosphate molecules, being virtually all in the form of $B^+H_2PO_4^-$, carry only slightly more than five negative charges and require only about five Na^+ ions for their neutralization. This degree of acidification of the urine, accomplished, as indicated below, by the addition of H^+ ions from the tubular cells, effects a saving of about four Na^+ ions for every five phosphate molecules excreted in the urine, the Na^+ being returned to the blood plasma.

A similar situation obtains with respect to weak organic acids, such as β-hydroxybutyric, acetoacetic, and citric. Anions of these acids must be transported in the plasma, at pH 7.4, completely balanced by Na^+ cations, but a considerable portion can exist as the free acids in urine at pH 4.8. For example, at pH 4.8, about 45 per cent of the β-hydroxybutyrate anion in the urine is balanced by H^+ (i.e., free acid), and, consequently, excretion of each mole of this anion at this urinary pH releases and restores to the blood 0.45 mole of the Na^+ with which it had been carried in the plasma.

Acidification of the urine is accomplished by exchange of intracellular (tubular cells) H^+ ions for intraluminar (tubule) cations, principally Na^+ (ion exchange mechanism). CO_2, formed in the cells of the distal portion of the tubule (where acidification of the urine occurs) under the influence of carbonic anhydrase is rapidly transformed to H_2CO_3, which undergoes ionization:

$$CO_2 \text{ (metabolic)} + H_2O \underset{\text{anhydrase}}{\overset{\text{carbonic}}{\rightleftharpoons}} H_2CO_3 \rightleftharpoons H^+ + HCO_3^-$$

The H^+ ions thus formed are passed into the lumen of the tubule, an equal number of Na^+ ions passing in the opposite direction into the cells (Fig. 13–1). Thus, a number of Na^+ ions, previously balancing $HPO_4^=$, citrate$^-$, β-hydroxybutyrate$^-$, etc., ions in the glomerular filtrate, are exchanged for H^+ ions:

$$Na_2^{++}HPO_4^= + H^+ \longrightarrow Na^+H_2PO_4^- + Na^+$$

$$Na^+\beta\text{-hydroxybutyrate}^- + H^+ \longrightarrow \beta\text{-hydroxybutyric acid} + Na^+$$

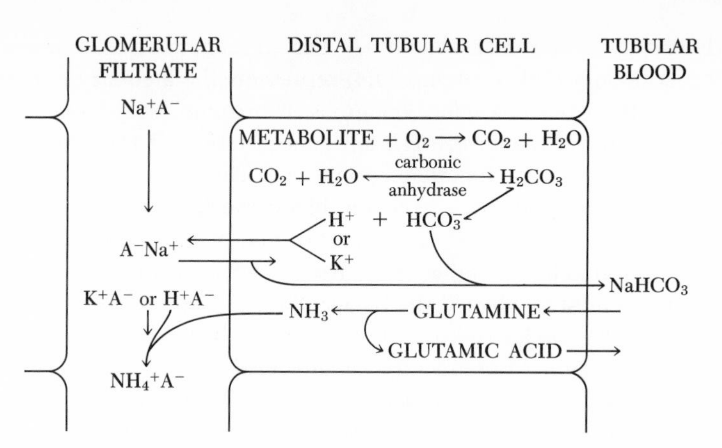

Figure 13-1. Mechanism of acidification of urine and of ammonia formation and excretion by the kidney, indicating exchange of H^+ or K^+ or both for Na^+. (After Pitts.)

The Na^+ ions, entering the cell, are absorbed into the bloodstream with HCO_3^- ions formed from the H_2CO_3, thereby supporting the bicarbonate structure of the extracellular fluids (Fig. 13–1).

The number of HCO_3^- ions originating in the renal tubular epithelial cells and restored to the bloodstream, under conditions of physiological equilibrium, equals the number of HCO_3^- ions originally displaced (and excreted by the lungs as CO_2) by the entrance of fixed acids. It is important to appreciate the fact that the return of each HCO_3^- ion to the blood is accompanied by the passage of a H^+ ion into the lumen of the tubule. Consequently, the kidney excretes one H^+ originating in the tubular epithelial cells for every H^+ ion originally contributed to the bloodstream by the fixed acids entering in the tissues. This is the final step in the maintenance of balance between H^+ production (and introduction) and excretion.

A portion of the urinary potassium enters the uriniferous tubule by active excretion by the distal tubular epithelium, in addition to the larger amount which filters through the glomeruli (p. 827). In this region (distal tubule), K^+ and H^+ ions apparently compete for some component of a common excretory mechanism, either ion being exchanged for Na^+ (Fig. 13–1). With increased concentration of K^+ in the renal tubular cells, more K^+ and fewer H^+ ions are exchanged for Na^+, the acidity of the urine falls and that of the body fluids increases. Conversely, when the tissue cells (including kidney) are depleted of K^+, more H^+ and fewer K^+ ions are exchanged for Na^+, and the urine becomes more acid even though a state of alkalosis may exist. Inhibition of renal carbonic anhydrase results not only in inability to acidify the urine but also in striking increase in excretion of potassium, another indication of the competition between these two ions for tubular excretion.

With increasing acidification of the glomerular filtrate, progressively more of the filtered HCO_3^- is converted to H_2CO_3 and, consequently, to H_2O and CO_2, the latter diffusing across the tubule into the blood, the P_{CO_2} of which is in equilibrium with that of the fluid in the uriniferous tubule (p. 827). The bicarbonate content of the urine may fall to zero as the acidity increases.

The phenomena described above occur in response to a stimulus provided the kidney by an increase in H^+ ion concentration of the plasma and glomerular filtrate (increased requirement for excretion of H^+ ions and reabsorption of bicarbonate). If the plasma pH rises (alkalosis), the renal mechanism is stimulated in the opposite direction, i.e., decreased excretion of H^+ ions, decreased reabsorption of bicarbonate. The urinary acidity falls as a result of decreased exchange of H^+ and Na^+ ions, increasing amounts of phosphate being excreted in the form of $HPO_4^=$ (requiring two Na^+ ions), instead of $H_2PO_4^-$ (requiring but one Na^+ ion). Increasing amounts of organic acid ions are also excreted, balanced by Na^+ ions (or as Na salts) instead of in the form of free acids. With increasing pH, up to 8.2, there is increased urinary excretion of HCO_3^- and of Na^+, the cation with which it is chiefly associated. Changes in the reverse direction occur in the concentrations of these substances in the blood, tending to restore the normal pH of the plasma.

Excretion of ammonia. A normal subject, under ordinary dietary conditions, excretes 30 to 50 mEq. of ammonia daily. If the plasma H^+ ion concentration rises, the urinary ammonia increases, even ten-fold in severe diabetic acidosis. A decrease occurs in alkalosis. The urinary NH_3 is formed in the cells of the distal portion of the uriniferous tubule, the site of acidification of the urine. About 60 per cent is derived from the amide group of glutamine (by the enzyme glutaminase) and the remaining 40 per cent from the α-amino group of certain amino acids (p. 570). Adrenal cortical hormones may perhaps exert a stimulating influence on this deamination process and, therefore, on NH_3 formation.

The NH_3 (gas) diffuses into the lumen of the tubule, combining with the H^+ ions in the acidified fluid to form NH_4^+ ions (Fig. 13–1). This effectively prevents undue accumulation of H^+ ions in the fluid, and therefore permits continued exchange of H^+ for Na^+ ions. The amount of Na^+ ion absorbed in the distal tubule is consequently reflected in the amount of both H^+ and NH_4^+ ions in the urine.

The urinary NH_3 begins to increase shortly after H^+ ion concentration of the blood rises, but the increase continues for some time after the blood and urine pH and bicarbonate content have reached their lowest level. The stimulus to NH_3 formation by the kidney is apparently similar to that producing acidification of the urine, i.e., decrease in pH and bicarbonate of the blood and glomerular filtrate. However, the duration of application of this stimulus influences NH_3 formation but not acidification of the urine.

INTRACELLULAR-EXTRACELLULAR pH INTERRELATIONS

Under physiological conditions, acids produced within the cells in the course of their metabolic activity, following initial buffering by intracellular systems, enter the extracellular fluids as H^+ ions and acid anions (e.g., bicarbonate, lactate, β-hydroxybutyrate) or in an uncharged state (e.g., H_2O and CO_2, H_2CO_3). Their subsequent disposition has been discussed previously.

By virtue of exchanges between H^+ and K^+ ions across the cell membrane, under certain circumstances the intracellular and extracellular fluids act in conjunction in neutrality regulation. In metabolic types of alkalosis, i.e., primary increase in plasma HCO_3^- (p. 324), H^+ passes into the extracellular fluids from the cells and K^+ passes into the cells from the extracellular fluid. An amount of HCO_3^- equivalent to that of the entering H^+ is removed from the body by the lungs as CO_2, with consequent reduction in the concentration of HCO_3^- in the extracellular fluid. Conversely, in acidosis associated with primary decrease in plasma HCO_3^-, H^+ passes into the cells from the extracellular fluid and K^+ passes in the opposite direction. The HCO_3^- concentration of the extracellular fluid is thereby increased in an amount equivalent to that of the H^+ entering the cells, now replaced in the extracellular fluid by K^+.

However, under certain other conditions, perhaps of a specialized nature, the pH changes in extracellular and intracellular fluids may occur in opposite directions. In conditions of primary K depletion, e.g., induced by aldosterone or dietary K restriction, passage of excessive amounts of K^+ from the cells into the extracellular fluid is accompanied by passage of Na^+ and H^+ in the opposite direction. Accordingly, the H^+ ion concentration increases within the cells (intracellular acidosis) and decreases in the extracellular fluid (extracellular alkalosis). Moreover, the lowered K content of the distal renal tubular cells results in an increased $Na^+ : H^+$ exchange and return of a correspondingly increased number of HCO_3^- ions to the peritubular blood. Renal functional adequacy is necessary for the development of this rather anomalous situation in states of K depletion, in which extracellular alkalosis with an increased HCO_3^- concentration is associated with intracellular acidosis and increased urinary acidity.

ABNORMALITIES OF "ACID-BASE" BALANCE

It is obvious from the preceding discussion that a number of interrelated factors and mechanisms are involved in the maintenance of the normal electrolyte pattern and pH of the body fluids, commonly referred to as "acid-base" balance. The inaccurate use of this term is indicated elsewhere (p. 313). Several of these do not lend themselves to direct quantitative study. However, factors operating in the blood can be investigated more or less readily because of accessibility of this medium. The most important of these are:

(1) *Total "base"* (B^+): the sum of the concentrations (in mEq./liter) of all cations.

(2) *H_2CO_3 content:* the concentration of H_2CO_3 (in mmoles/liter), which is in equilibrium with the P_{CO_2} (CO_2 tension) [P_{CO_2} (in mm. Hg) $\times$ 0.03 = H_2CO_3 (in mmoles/liter)].

(3) *CO_2 content:* the concentration (in mmoles/liter) of total CO_2 in solution (HCO_3^- plus H_2CO_3).

(4) *HCO_3^- content:* the concentration (in mEq./liter) of HCO_3^-, usually calculated as the difference between the CO_2 and H_2CO_3 contents (thus including the carbamino-CO_2).

(5) *CO_2 capacity or "combining power":* the HCO_3^- (or CO_2) content of blood or plasma saturated with 5.5 per cent CO_2 at 25° C.

(6) *pH:* the logarithm of the reciprocal of the H^+ ion concentration.

(7) *"Buffer base":* the "base" equivalent to the sum of the concentrations (in mEq./liter) of buffer anions (whole blood = HCO_3^- plus Hb and plasma proteins; plasma = HCO_3^- plus plasma proteins). As indicated elsewhere (p. 313), it may be calculated (in plasma) as the sum of the cations, minus Cl^-.

The important role of Hb as a buffer has been pointed out elsewhere (p. 288), as has the difference in this connection between oxyhemoglobin and reduced hemoglobin. For most precise analysis of the state of "acid-base" balance, the following factors must be determined: (1) hematocrit (relative proportions of erythrocytes and plasma); (2) pH; (3) CO_2 content; (4) buffer base; (5) H_2CO_3 content (calculated from P_{CO_2} of blood or alveolar air). However, for practical clinical purposes, certain of these may usually be dispensed with (viz., hematocrit, buffer base) inasmuch as significant abnormalities due to changes in hemoglobin are reflected in the pH and HCO_3^- content.

As indicated below, clinical aberrations of "acid-base" balance are classified conveniently as primary disturbances in either HCO_3^- (bicarbonate) or H_2CO_3, the relation of which to the pH is expressed by the Henderson-Hasselbalch equation:

$$pH = pK + \log \frac{HCO_3^-}{H_2CO_3}.$$

At pH 7.4, the $HCO_3^- : H_2CO_3$ ratio is 20:1 (27 mEq.:1.35 mEq./liter of plasma water).

TABLE 13-1. BIOCHEMICAL CHARACTERISTICS OF ACIDOSIS AND ALKALOSIS*

PLASMA	NORMAL	ACIDOSIS		ALKALOSIS	
		HCO_3^- DEFICIT	H_2CO_3 EXCESS	HCO_3^- EXCESS	H_2CO_3 DEFICIT
HCO_3^-	mmoles/liter 23–28 (26) vol. % 51–62 (53.4)	– –	+	+ +	–
CO_2 capacity	mmoles/liter 24–35 (30) vol. % 53–78 (65)	– –	+	+ +	–
H_2CO_3	mmoles/liter 1.1–1.5 (1.3) vol. % 2.4–3.3 (2.9)	–	+ +	+	– –
P_{CO_2}	mm. Hg 35–45 (40)	–	+ +	+	– –
CO_2 content	mmoles/liter 24–33 (28) vol. % 53–75 (62)	– –	+ +	+ +	– –
$\frac{HCO_3^-}{H_2CO_3}$	20	–	–	+	+
pH	7.35–7.45 (7.4)	–	–	+	+
Urinary acidity and ammonia	<27 ml./kg 0.1 N acid (+NH_3) per 24 hrs.	+	+	–	–

* Values in parentheses indicate means; +, increase; –, decrease.

Knowledge of any two of these three factors (pH, HCO_3^-, H_2CO_3) therefore permits derivation of the third. Determination of the total CO_2 content (HCO_3^- plus H_2CO_3) and any one of the three factors mentioned permits derivation of the other two. Consequently, the most widely employed approach to the investigation of clinical disturbances of "acid-base" balance centers about these factors, perhaps the most useful for practical purposes being the simultaneous determination of pH (plasma or serum) and CO_2 content (plasma, serum, or whole blood).

Primary change in HCO_3^- (metabolic acidosis and alkalosis, pp. 322, 324) is by far the most common cause of acidosis and alkalosis of clinically significant degree. For this reason, reliance is frequently placed on determination of this factor alone for the diagnosis of acidosis (decreased HCO_3^-) and alkalosis (increase). Determination of the "CO_2 combining power (CO_2 capacity)" is often employed as a substitute for the CO_2 content. This yields results of a varying degree of inaccuracy, particularly in respiratory acidosis and alkalosis, because it involves artificial equilibration of the blood at a physiological level of CO_2 tension, regardless of the status in this respect of the subject from whom the blood was obtained. It must be noted that disturbances due to primary changes in H_2CO_3 (respiratory acidosis and alkalosis) are accompanied by alterations (secondary, compensatory) in HCO_3^- and CO_2 content in directions opposite to those which occur in "metabolic" acidosis and alkalosis (p. 322 ff.; Table 13-1). Unless the true nature of the disturbance is recognized, which is often possible (e.g., diabetes mellitus, nephritis, vomiting, diarrhea, hyperventilation, etc.), an incorrect diagnosis may be made on the basis of determination of this isolated factor.

ACIDOSIS

Increase in the H^+ ion concentration of the body fluids results from the formation or absorption of acids at a rate exceeding that of their "neutralization" or elimination. It may also result from loss of excessive quantities of base from the body fluids. As indicated previously, disturbances of this nature are reflected in the bicarbonate-carbonic acid buffer system of the blood and may be investigated on the basis of the Henderson-Hasselbalch equation. Inasmuch as the pH of this system is a function of the $[BHCO_3]$: $[H_2CO_3]$ ratio, it is evident that acidosis may be caused by either a disproportionate decrease in $[BHCO_3]$ or a disproportionate increase in $[H_2CO_3]$.

Primary $BHCO_3$ (Alkali) Deficit

A variety of non-volatile acids may be produced or may accumulate in the body in excess under abnormal conditions. These include acidic ketone bodies (diabetes mellitus); phosphoric, sulfuric, and organic acids (renal insufficiency); lactic acid (anoxia, hemorrhage, ether anesthesia, prolonged strenuous exercise, etc.). These acids are buffered principally by bicarbonate (p. 315), the added H^+ ions entering into the formation of H_2CO_3 and the anion of the acid increasing in concentration at the expense of HCO_3^-. The increased plasma H_2CO_3 and H^+ ion concentrations stimulate the respiratory center (p. 316), with consequent increased pulmonary ventilation and increased excretion of CO_2, thereby dissipating the secondary increase in $[H_2CO_3]$. Similar phenomena follow administration of excessive amounts of these non-volatile acids or their ammonium salts (NH_4Cl, NH_4NO_3, etc.), the ammonia of which is converted to urea in the liver.

An excessive quantity of base ($BHCO_3$) may be lost from the body in such conditions as severe, protracted diarrhea and external pancreatic or intestinal fistulas. These result in the loss of large volumes of digestive fluids, which are more alkaline than the blood plasma, i.e., they have a higher concentration of HCO_3^- ions (Fig. 13–2). The respiratory response is identical with that indicated above, i.e., hyperventilation and decrease in plasma H_2CO_3 concentration.

Compensatory mechanisms. If functioning normally, the respiratory apparatus and the kidneys attempt to maintain the blood pH within normal limits. The action of the

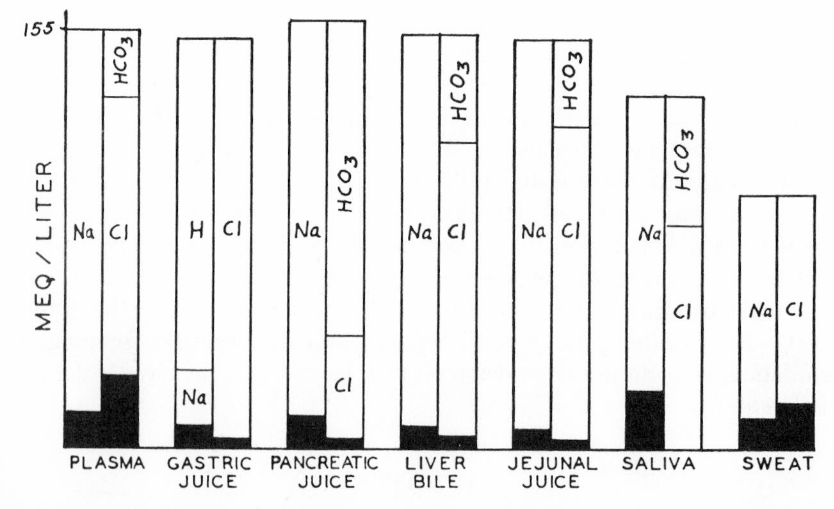

Figure 13-2. The electrolyte composition of certain important body fluids, compared with that of blood plasma. (Gamble: Chemical Anatomy, Physiology and Pathology of Extracellular Fluid, Harvard University Press, 1950.)

former is indicated above; as a result of increased pulmonary ventilation the plasma (i.e., extracellular fluid) H_2CO_3 concentration is reduced. In all but very mild cases, however, if the cause continues to operate, the decrease in $[HCO_3^-]$, being the primary event, is proportionately greater than that in $[H_2CO_3]$, the secondary event.

The kidneys (unless damaged) attempt to support the falling plasma HCO_3^- concentration by returning increased amounts of HCO_3^- to the blood in the distal renal tubules. This is accomplished by stimulation of the $H^+ : Na^+$ exchange mechanism and of NH_3 formation, as evidenced by increased urinary ammonia and titratable acidity (pp. 317, 319).

Biochemical characteristics ***(Table 13-1).*** Acidosis of this type is commonly designated "metabolic acidosis." If uncompensated, it is characterized biochemically (plasma or blood) as follows: (1) disproportionate decrease in $[HCO_3^-]$; (2) decrease in $[H_2CO_3]$ (P_{CO_2}); (3) decrease in CO_2 content ($[HCO_3^-]$ plus $[H_2CO_3]$); (4) decrease in $[HCO_3^-] : [H_2CO_3]$ ratio; (5) decrease in pH. If fully compensated, the CO_2 content is low, but the decrease in $[HCO_3^-]$ and $[H_2CO_3]$ is proportionate, the $[HCO_3^-] : [H_2CO_3]$ ratio and pH remaining within normal limits. The urinary ammonia and titratable acidity are increased (if kidneys are functioning normally).

Primary H_2CO_3 (CO_2) Excess

The respiratory center is so sensitive to an increased H_2CO_3 or H^+ ion concentration, and pulmonary alveoli so highly permeable to CO_2, that accumulation of excessive amounts of H_2CO_3 in the plasma is virtually impossible if these structures are functioning normally, unless the CO_2 content of the inspired air is excessively high. This condition can occur under the following circumstances: (1) depression of the respiratory center (morphine, barbiturates, brain lesions); (2) extensive pulmonary lesions (pneumonia,

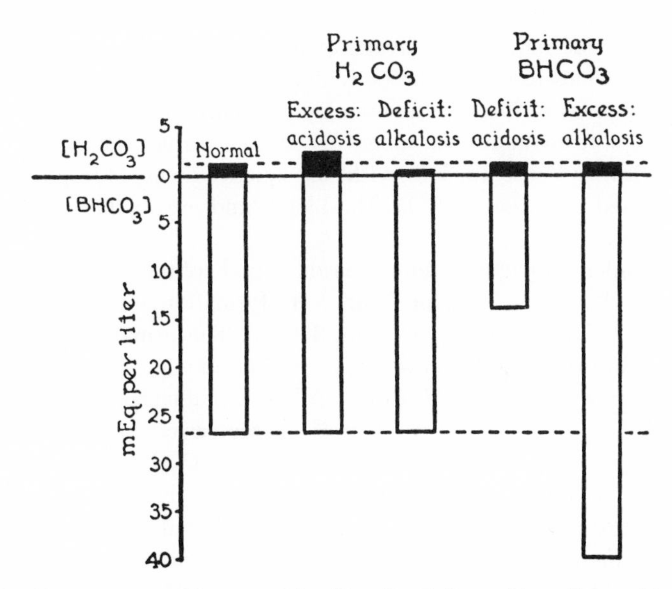

Figure 13-3. The four primary mechanisms of "acid-base" imbalance. (From Fulton: Howell's Textbook of Physiology, ed. 17, W. B. Saunders Company, 1955; modified from Gamble.)

emphysema, fibrosis, congestion); (3) mechanical obstruction of air passages; (4) rebreathing or breathing air with high (5 to 7 per cent) CO_2 content.

Compensatory mechanisms. Inasmuch as the fundamental cause of this type of acidosis is inability of the respiratory apparatus to remove CO_2 from the body efficiently, the brunt of the task of compensating for this defect falls on the kidneys. These organs respond as in the case of primary HCO_3^- deficit (q.v.), by increasing urinary acidity and ammonia and returning increased amounts of HCO_3^- to the blood (p. 316 ff.).

Biochemical characteristics (Table 13-1). Acidosis of this type is commonly designated "respiratory acidosis," for obvious reasons. If uncompensated, it is characterized biochemically (plasma or blood) as follows: (1) disproportionate increase in $[H_2CO_3]$ (P_{CO_2}); (2) increase in $[HCO_3^-]$; (3) increase in CO_2 content; (4) decrease in $[HCO_3^-]:[H_2CO_3]$ ratio; (5) decrease in pH. If fully compensated, the CO_2 content is high, but the increase in $[H_2CO_3]$ and $[HCO_3^-]$ is proportionate, the $[HCO_3^-]:[H_2CO_3]$ ratio and pH remaining within normal limits. The urinary ammonia and titratable acidity are increased (if kidneys are functioning normally).

ALKALOSIS

Decrease in the H^+ ion concentration of the body fluids results from excessive loss of acids from the body without comparable loss of base, or the formation or supply of base at a rate exceeding that of its "neutralization" or elimination. In terms of the bicarbonate buffer system, alkalosis may be caused by either a disproportionate increase in $[BHCO_3]$ or a disproportionate decrease in $[H_2CO_3]$.

Primary $BHCO_3$ (Alkali) Excess

This may be produced by administration of excessive amounts of alkali (e.g., $NaHCO_3$) and by protracted vomiting (or removal) of gastric juice with a high HCl content (duodenal or pyloric obstruction; gastric lavage or drainage). In the latter instance, HCO_3^- ions replace the Cl^- ions lost from the body fluids.

Compensatory mechanisms. If functioning normally, the respiratory apparatus and the kidneys attempt to maintain the blood pH within normal limits. The increased pH depresses the respiratory center (p. 316), with consequent slowing of respiration, hypoventilation, and decreased excretion of CO_2. The blood (and extracellular fluid) H_2CO_3 concentration increases.

The kidneys (unless damaged) attempt to rid the body of the excess HCO_3^- by decreasing the extent of $H^+ - Na^+$ exchange and NH_3 formation in the distal tubules, thus returning less HCO_3^- to the bloodstream (p. 316 ff.). The urinary acidity and ammonia are decreased; in severe cases the urine may become alkaline and contain bicarbonate.

Biochemical characteristics (Table 13-1). Alkalosis of this type is commonly designated "metabolic alkalosis." If uncompensated, it is characterized biochemically (plasma or blood) as follows: (1) disproportionate increase in $[HCO_3^-]$; (2) increase in $[H_2CO_3]$ (P_{CO_2}); (3) increase in CO_2 content; (4) increase in $[HCO_3^-]:[H_2CO_3]$ ratio; (5) increase in pH. If fully compensated, the CO_2 content is high, but the increase in $[HCO_3^-]$ and $[H_2CO_3]$ is proportionate, the $[HCO_3^-]:[H_2CO_3]$ ratio and pH remaining within normal limits. The urinary ammonia and titratable acidity are decreased (if kidneys are functioning normally).

Primary H_2CO_3 (CO_2) Deficit

Excessive quantities of CO_2 may be removed from the blood by prolonged pulmonary hyperventilation (excessively rapid, deep respiration). This may occur in hysteria, fever, anoxia (high altitudes), high external temperature (e.g., hot baths), certain cases of encephalitis (brain lesion), and after administration of certain drugs which stimulate the respiratory center (e.g., sodium salicylate in large doses).

Compensatory mechanisms. In view of the pathogenesis of this condition, the task of compensating for this defect falls on the kidneys. These organs (unless damaged) respond, as in the case of primary HCO_3^- excess, by decreasing the $H^+ - Na^+$ exchange and NH_3 formation, returning less HCO_3^- to the bloodstream.

Biochemical characteristics (Table 13-1). Alkalosis of this type is commonly designated "respiratory alkalosis." If uncompensated, it is characterized biochemically (plasma or blood) as follows: (1) disproportionate decrease in $[H_2CO_3]$ (P_{CO_2}); (2) decrease in $[HCO_3^-]$; (3) decrease in CO_2 content; (4) increase in $[HCO_3^-]:[H_2CO_3]$ ratio; (5) increase in pH. If fully compensated, the CO_2 content is low but the decrease in $[HCO_3^-]$ and $[H_2CO_3]$ is proportionate, the $[HCO_3^-]:[H_2CO_3]$ ratio and pH remaining within normal limits. The urinary ammonia and titratable acidity are decreased (if kidneys are functioning normally).

BIBLIOGRAPHY

Berliner, R. W.: Relationship between acidification of the urine and potassium metabolism, Am. J. Med. *11*:274, 1951.

Bland, J. H. (ed.): Clinical Metabolism of Body Water and Electrolytes, Philadelphia, W. B. Saunders Company, 1963.

Blumentals, A. S. (ed.): Symposium on acid-base balance, Arch. Int. Med. *116*:647, 1965.

Christensen, H. N.: Diagnostic Biochemistry, New York, Oxford University Press, 1959.

Christensen, H. N.: Body Fluids and the Acid-Base Balance, Philadelphia, W. B. Saunders Company, 1964.

Darrow, D. C., and Hellerstein, S.: Interpretation of certain changes in body water and electrolytes, Physiol. Rev. *38*:114, 1958.

Davenport, H. W.: The ABC of Acid-Base Chemistry, ed. 3, Chicago, University of Chicago Press, 1950.

Elkinton, J. R., and Danowski, T. S.: The Body Fluids, Baltimore, Williams & Wilkins Company, 1955.

Gamble, J. L.: Chemical Anatomy, Physiology and Pathology of Extracellular Fluid, Cambridge, Harvard University Press, 1950.

Gamble, J. L.: Companionship of water and electrolytes in the organization of body fluids (Lane Medical Lectures) Stanford, Calif., Stanford University Press, 1951.

Ogston, A. G.: The definition and meaning of pH, Physiol. Rev. *27*:228, 1947.

Pitts, R. F.: Renal excretion of acid, Federation Proc. *7*:418, 1948.

Welt, L. G.: Water balance in health and disease, in Duncan, G. G. (ed.): Diseases of Metabolism, ed. 5, Philadelphia, W. B. Saunders Company, 1964, p. 449.

CHAPTER 14

ENERGY METABOLISM

THROUGHOUT the discussions of the metabolism of organic foodstuffs, attention has been focused particularly on the mechanisms and nature of their chemical transformation. Various components of the tissues are undergoing degradation (catabolism) and resynthesis (anabolism) continually. Certain of the chemical reactions involved in these metabolic processes are exergonic, i.e., they are accompanied by liberation of energy, whereas others are endergonic, i.e., they require the introduction of energy. The manner in which energy is produced, stored, transferred, and utilized is considered elsewhere (p. 369).

Obviously, even under resting conditions, the maintenance of life and normal function requires the constant performance of work by a variety of tissues. This implies the utilization of energy, which must be supplied from external sources if the body stores of energy are to be preserved at a constant level. We shall concern ourselves here with the magnitude of the energy requirement under normal conditions and the factors that may influence it.

Caloric Value of Foods (Table 14-1)

Following the demonstration by early investigators in this field that production of heat in the body is dependent primarily on oxidative processes, attempts were made to relate the quantity of heat produced to the amounts of foodstuffs metabolized. This was feasible because the heat produced by burning (oxidizing) these substances outside the body can be determined readily in a combustion calorimeter, the average values (in Calories) obtained per gram being: glucose, 3.96; starch, 4.2; animal fats, 9.5; animal proteins, 5.6 (vegetable proteins lower). A "Calorie" (kilocalorie) is the amount of heat required to raise the temperature of 1 kg. of water 1° C. (i.e., from 15° to 16° C.). In the body, protein does not undergo complete oxidation, a portion of its amino groups being converted to and excreted as ammonia and urea; this involves a loss of about 1.3 Cal. per gm., leaving 4.3 Cal. produced per gm. of protein metabolized. Taking into consideration the variations in caloric value of individual carbohydrates, fats, and proteins, their average energy value when metabolized may be represented as follows (Calories per gram): fat, 9.3; carbohydrate, 4.1; protein, 4.1. When these corrected figures are applied, it is

TABLE 14-1. CALORIC, O_2, AND CO_2 EQUIVALENTS OF CARBOHYDRATE, FAT, AND PROTEIN

	CARBOHYDRATE	FAT	PROTEIN
Calories per gram	3.7–4.3	9.5	4.3
Liters CO_2 per gram	0.75–0.83	1.43	0.78
Liters O_2 per gram	0.75–0.83	2.03	0.97
Respiratory quotient	1.0	0.707	0.801
Caloric value per liter O_2	5.0 Cal.	4.7 Cal.	4.5 Cal.

found that the amount of energy (Calories) produced by a given quantity of these foodstuffs in the body is the same as that (heat) produced by their combustion outside the body, within the limits of experimental error. Inasmuch as ingested foods are not completely assimilated, the caloric values of the fats, carbohydrates, and proteins of the diet are usually calculated as 9, 4, and 4 Cal./gm., respectively.

Heat Production

In living tissues, the bulk of the energy derived from the metabolism of organic compounds is liberated, not as a single burst of heat, as occurs in their combustion outside the body, but rather in a stepwise fashion through a series of integrated enzymatic reactions (p. 372 ff.). Therefore, although in the complete oxidation of these compounds (e.g., glucose to CO_2 and H_2O) their full potential energy value is ultimately realized, relatively small fractions of the total are made available at each stage of their degradation. Presented in small parcels, energy is utilized much more efficiently than if it had been liberated explosively.

The energy thus produced is disposed of as follows: (1) A portion is primarily converted to heat for the maintenance of body temperature. (2) A portion is utilized for the performance of work, e.g., mechanical (muscle contraction), electrical (nerve impulse), secretory (glandular, intestinal, renal tubular cells, etc.), chemical (endergonic metabolic reactions). Such work is ultimately reflected largely in heat production. (3) A portion may be stored very temporarily in "energy-rich" phosphate bonds (p. 379), or for longer periods in the form of substances (e.g., fat, glycogen) that may be called upon to provide energy at some future date. The overall body composition and weight of normal adults do not vary appreciably from day to day; i.e., there is little or no accretion or loss of tissue, new components being formed only in amounts required for replacement (metabolic turnover, "dynamic state," p. 541). On an adequate diet, the organism is therefore in a state of equilibrium with its environment; this applies to its intake of energy as well as of H_2O, N, and inorganic elements. Consequently, an amount of heat must be lost, either actual (radiation, conduction, vaporization of water) or potential (constituents of urine and feces), that is equal to the caloric value of ingested proteins, fats, and carbohydrates (i.e., caloric equilibrium). This has been demonstrated to be the case by direct measurement of heat loss (direct calorimetry).

RESPIRATORY QUOTIENT

In the process of oxidation, carbohydrates, fats, and proteins react with definite amounts of oxygen, and definite amounts of carbon dioxide and water are formed. The designation "respiratory quotient" or "R.Q." is applied to the ratio of the volume of CO_2 produced to that of O_2 utilized in this process (R.Q. = Vol. CO_2/Vol. O_2).

Carbohydrate R.Q. Complete oxidation of glucose may be represented as follows:

$$C_6H_{12}O_6 + 6O_2 \longrightarrow 6CO_2 + 6H_2O$$
$$(1 \text{ mole}) + (6 \text{ moles}) \longrightarrow (6 \text{ moles}) + (6 \text{ moles})$$
$$(180 \text{ gm.}) + (192 \text{ gm.}) \longrightarrow (264 \text{ gm.}) + (108 \text{ gm.})$$

The glucose R.Q. is therefore 6/6, or 1.0. Inasmuch as 1 mole of gas occupies a volume of 22.4 liters, the volume of O_2 and of CO_2 involved in this reaction is 22.4 × 6, or 134.4 liters. Consequently, 1 gm. of glucose reacts with 134.4/180, or 0.75 liter of oxygen, forming 0.75 liter of CO_2. Since oxidation of 1 gm. of glucose liberates 3.74 Cal., 1 liter of O_2 is the equivalent of 3.74/0.75, or 5.0 Cal. when glucose is oxidized. This (5.0 Cal.) is the caloric value of 1 liter of oxygen for glucose oxidation in the body.

Fat R.Q. Complete oxidation of tripalmitin may be represented as follows:

$$2(C_{51}H_{98}O_6) + 145O_2 \longrightarrow 102CO_2 + 98H_2O$$
$$(2 \text{ moles}) + (145 \text{ moles}) \longrightarrow (102 \text{ moles}) + (98 \text{ moles})$$
$$(1612 \text{ gm.}) + (4640 \text{ gm.}) \longrightarrow (4488 \text{ gm.}) + (1764 \text{ gm.})$$

The R.Q. for tripalmitin is therefore 102/145, or 0.704. That for triolein is 0.712. The R.Q. for mixed fats in the body is regarded as 0.707. The volumes of O_2 and CO_2 involved in this reaction are 3248 liters (145 × 22.4) and 2284.8 liters (102 × 22.4), respectively. Consequently, 1 gm. of tripalmitin reacts with 3248/1612, or 2.01 liters of O_2. Since oxidation of 1 gm. of this fat liberates 9.5 Cal., 1 liter of O_2 is the equivalent of 9.5/2.01, or 4.7 Cal. when tripalmitin is oxidized. Essentially the same value applies to other animal fats and, therefore, 4.7 is the caloric value of 1 liter of oxygen for fat oxidation in the body.

Protein R.Q. Amino acids do not undergo complete oxidation in the body and, therefore, the type of equation written for carbohydrates and fats is not applicable to proteins. However, the approximate quantitative relationships between O_2 and CO_2 in the metabolic oxidation of amino acids may be calculated from data on the average composition and metabolism of meat protein. These are indicated in Table 14-2.

In its oxidation to CO_2, 12 gm. of C combine with 32 gm. of O_2; in forming H_2O, 2 gm. of H combine with 16 gm. of O_2. Consequently, 41.5 gm. of C require 110.66 gm. of O_2 and will produce 152.17 gm. (3.46 moles) of CO_2, while 3.4 gm. of H require 27.52 gm. of O_2 [total O_2 utilized is 138.18 gm. (4.32 moles)]. The R.Q. for protein oxidation is therefore 3.46/4.32, or 0.801. The volumes of O_2 and CO_2 involved were 96.7 liters (4.32 × 22.4) and 77.46 liters (3.46 × 22.4) respectively (per 100 gm. protein). Since oxidation of 1 gm. of protein liberates 4.3 Cal., 1 liter of O_2 is the equivalent of 4.3/0.967, or 4.5 Cal., which represents, therefore, the caloric value of 1 liter of O_2 for protein oxidation in the body.

TABLE 14-2. AVERAGE ELEMENTAL COMPOSITION AND METABOLISM OF MEAT PROTEIN (LOEWY)

	GM. IN 100 GM. MEAT PROTEIN	GM. EXCRETED IN FECES AND URINE	GM. IN INTRAMOLECULAR WATER	GM. REMAINING FOR OXIDATION
C	52.38	10.877		41.5
H	7.27	2.87	0.96	3.4
O	22.68	14.99	7.69	
N	16.65	16.65 (16.28 urine)		
S	1.02	1.02		

TABLE 14-3. RESPIRATORY QUOTIENT AND CALORIC EQUIVALENT OF OXYGEN FOR DIFFERENT MIXTURES OF FAT AND CARBOHYDRATE

	PERCENTAGE OF TOTAL O_2 CONSUMED BY		PERCENTAGE OF HEAT PRODUCED BY		CALORIES PER LITER O_2
R.Q.	Carbohydrate	Fat	Carbohydrate	Fat	
0.707	0	100	0	100	4.686
0.75	14.7	85.3	15.6	84.4	4.739
0.80	31.7	68.3	33.4	66.6	4.801
0.82	38.6	61.4	40.3	59.7	4.825
0.85	48.8	51.2	50.7	49.3	4.862
0.90	65.9	34.2	67.5	32.5	4.924
0.95	82.9	17.1	84.0	16.0	4.985
1.00	100	0	100	0	5.047

As indicated in Table 14-2, the metabolism of 100 gm. of protein gave rise to urinary excretion of 16.28 gm. of nitrogen. Each gram of urinary N therefore represented the metabolism of: 100/16.28, or 6.15 gm. of meat protein; 96.7/16.28, or 5.94 liters of O_2; 77.46/16.28, or 4.76 liters of CO_2. On the basis of analytical data for the average protein, it is generally estimated that 1 gm. of urinary N represents: (1) the metabolism of 6.25 gm. of protein; (2) utilization of 5.91 liters of O_2; (3) production of 4.76 liters of CO_2; (4) liberation of 26.51 Cal.

Example. The following data were obtained under basal conditions (overnight fast): (1) urinary N, 0.18 gm./hour; (2) O_2 consumption, 12.2 liters/hour; (3) CO_2 production, 9.2 liters/hour. Information desired: (1) heat (Calories) production; (2) quantities of protein, carbohydrate, and fat metabolized; (3) percentages of total heat produced by oxidation of protein, carbohydrate, and fat, respectively.

0.18 gram of urinary N represents:

$0.18 \times 6.25 = 1.125$ gm. of protein metabolized
$0.18 \times 5.91 = 1.06$ liters of oxygen
$0.18 \times 4.76 = 0.85$ liter of carbon dioxide
$0.18 \times 26.51 = 4.77$ Cal.

Total O_2 (12.2 liters) minus protein O_2 (1.06 liters) = non-protein O_2 (11.14 liters)
Total CO_2 (9.2 liters) minus protein CO_2 (0.85 liter) = non-protein CO_2 (8.35 liters)
Non-protein R.Q. = 8.35/11.14 = 0.75

As indicated in Table 14-3, a non-protein R.Q. of 0.75 represents the liberation of 4.739 Cal. per liter O_2, 15.6 per cent of which comes from carbohydrate and 84.4 per cent from fat oxidation.

11.14 liters $O_2 \times 4.739 = 52.79$ Cal. (non-protein)
15.6 per cent of 52.79 = 8.24 Cal. from carbohydrate (2.01 grams)
84.4 per cent of 52.79 = 44.55 Cal. from fat (4.79 grams)
52.79 + 4.77 (protein Cal.) = 57.56 total Cal./hour, of which
1.125 gm. protein provided 4.77/57.56, or 8.3 per cent,
2.01 gm. carbohydrate provided 8.24/57.56, or 14.3 per cent,
4.79 gm. fat provided 44.55/57.56, or 77.4 per cent.

Significance of R.Q. The chief practical value of the calculations discussed above lies in the fact that they permit estimation of the amounts of protein, fat, and carbohydrate metabolized during a given period, from knowledge of (1) the urinary N excretion, (2) the O_2 consumption, and (3) the CO_2 production.

If the organism (or isolated tissue, in vitro) were utilizing carbohydrate exclusively the R.Q. would be 1.0, if utilizing fats exclusively it would be 0.7, and if utilizing proteins exclusively it would be 0.8. Conversion of carbohydrate to fat results in R.Q. values greater than 1.0, because some of the oxygen of the carbohydrate, which contains relatively more of this element in proportion to carbon than do fats, becomes available for oxidative processes, decreasing the quantity of O_2 required from the inspired air. On the same basis, theoretically, conversion of fat to carbohydrate would produce R.Q. values below 0.7. Such values have been observed (e.g., in diabetes mellitus), but fatty acids have not been shown to produce a net increase in carbohydrate (p. 448). The R.Q. for conversion of protein to glucose has been estimated as 0.632 to 0.706.

It has been found that in the average normal adult, studied under "basal" conditions, i.e., at complete mental and physical rest, 14 to 18 hours after taking food, the R.Q. is approximately 0.82. At this level, the caloric value of oxygen is 4.825 Cal./liter (Table 14-3). Progressive decrease in the proportion of carbohydrate being oxidized in the "metabolic mixture" (i.e., carbohydrate deprivation, diabetes mellitus) is reflected in progressive lowering of the R.Q., approaching 0.7 and occasionally falling below this value (excessive gluconeogenesis from protein).

Calorimetry

On the basis of what has been stated concerning heat production, it is evident that measurement of the amount of heat lost over any given period of time affords an approach to the estimation of the energy production (oxidative metabolism) of the body during that period. This may be accomplished either directly (direct calorimetry) or indirectly (indirect calorimetry).

Direct Calorimetry

The subject is placed in an insulated chamber (calorimeter) so constructed as to permit direct and precise measurement of heat loss from the body. Water is circulated through tubes within the chamber; the rate of flow is recorded automatically, as is the temperature of the water entering and leaving the chamber. Air is circulated through the calorimeter and measurements are made of the rate of flow, and of changes in temperature and water vapor. On the basis of these data, one may calculate the actual heat loss very accurately. Determinations may be made simultaneously of the consumption of oxygen and excretion of carbon dioxide by analyses of the air entering and leaving the chamber, permitting calculation of the respiratory quotient.

This procedure requires elaborate and expensive apparatus and is now chiefly of historical interest. It was early found that calculation of heat production from data on O_2 consumption and CO_2 production gave results which approximated very closely those obtained by direct calorimetry. This observation formed the basis for the application of the widely employed procedure of indirect calorimetry.

Indirect Calorimetry

As illustrated by the example cited on page 329, the amount of heat lost during an experimental period can be calculated accurately from the following data: (1) urinary N excretion during that period; (2) O_2 consumption: (3) CO_2 excretion. The validity of this calculation rests upon the following facts: (1) 1 gm. of urinary N represents the metabolism of 6.25 gm. of protein, the consumption of 5.91 liters of O_2, the production of 4.76

liters of CO_2, and the liberation of 26.51 Cal.; (2) oxygen has a known fixed caloric value per liter at any given R.Q. level.

For usual clinical purposes, determination of urinary N may be dispensed with, inasmuch as 90 to 95 per cent of the heat produced is derived from oxidation of carbohydrate and fat. Two general types of apparatus may be employed: (1) the open-circuit system; (2) the closed-circuit system. The former is the more accurate; the latter is much more convenient, is sufficiently accurate for clinical purposes, and is used most widely.

Open-circuit system. The subject breathes atmospheric air of determined composition, the expired air being collected in a rubber bag or a spirometer. Determination of the volume, and the O_2 and CO_2 contents of the expired air permits calculation of the volumes of O_2 absorbed and CO_2 produced and also, therefore, the R.Q. From the R.Q. one can ascertain the caloric value of 1 liter of oxygen, and, therefore, the heat production during the test period.

Closed-circuit system. Several types of apparatus are available, all of which are based on essentially the same principle. The subject breathes from and into a system filled with pure oxygen, the expired CO_2 and H_2O being trapped by soda lime. Decrease in the total volume of gas in the closed system is therefore due to and is a direct measure of oxygen consumption. The test period usually occupies six or eight minutes.

Inasmuch as CO_2 production is not measured, the R.Q. cannot be determined. However, the assumption that the R.Q. is approximately 0.82 under basal conditions is quite satisfactory for most clinical purposes. The caloric value per liter of O_2 is known to be 4.825 at this R.Q. Consequently, determination of the amount of O_2 consumed permits calculation of the approximate heat production during the test period.

Basal Metabolism

The terms "basal metabolism" and "basal metabolic rate" (BMR) are applied to the heat produced per unit time under "basal" conditions, i.e., at complete physical and mental rest, and in the postabsorptive state (14 to 18 hours after taking food). It was indicated previously that energy is derived by the organism from the metabolism (mainly oxidation) of exogenous (dietary) and endogenous proteins, carbohydrates, and lipids. This energy is dissipated in the form of heat and work, or is stored in the body. Under the specified "basal" conditions, the exogenous source of energy is removed and loss of energy in the form of work by voluntary muscles is virtually abolished. Under these conditions energy is expended in the maintenance of respiration, circulation, muscle tonus, gastrointestinal contractions, and body temperature, and the functional activities of various organs (e.g., kidneys, liver, endocrine glands, etc.). Although the respiratory, heart, and other involuntary muscles continue to function, their activity does not result in permanent increase in the potential or kinetic energy of the materials on which they act, viz., the blood, respiratory air, lungs, etc. Consequently, the organism, under these conditions, is deriving its energy solely from stored sources and is dissipating it almost exclusively in the form of heat. Inasmuch as the amount of energy lost must be equal to that produced, measurement of the heat loss over a given period of time is an index of the rate of energy production, i.e., metabolism. As indicated previously, this is usually done clinically by the indirect procedure, using a closed system.

Physiological variations in BMR. Basal metabolism varies with body size, age, and sex (Table 14-4). As would be anticipated, the magnitude of energy exchange increases with body size, but more directly in relation to surface area than to either height or weight. Tables are available for derivation of surface area from the latter two factors. The BMR is therefore commonly expressed in one of three ways: (1) kilocalories/sq. meter body

TABLE 14-4. CALORIES LIBERATED PER SQUARE METER PER HOUR*

AGE	MALES	FEMALES	AGE	MALES	FEMALES
5	(53.0)	(51.6)	20–24	41.0	36.9
6	52.7	50.7	25–29	40.3	36.6
7	52.0	49.3	30–34	39.8	36.2
8	51.2	48.1	35–39	39.2	35.8
9	50.4	46.9	40–44	38.3	35.3
10	49.5	45.8	45–49	37.8	35.0
11	48.6	44.6	50–54	37.2	34.5
12	47.8	43.4	55–59	36.6	34.1
13	47.1	42.0			
14	46.2	41.0	60–64	36.0	33.8
15	45.3	39.6	65–69	35.3	33.4
16	44.7	38.5			
17	43.7	37.4	70–74	34.8	32.8
18	42.9	37.3			
19	42.1	37.2	75–79	34.2	32.3

* DuBois standards, modified by Boothby and Sandiford: Am. J. Physiol. *90*:290, 1929.

surface/hour; (2) liters of oxygen consumed/sq. meter/hour; (3) percentage above or below the mean normal for the subject in question. The last mode of expression is the one used most widely clinically, but it may occasionally obscure certain important facts, e.g., in obesity.

The average normal BMR for young adult men (20 to 30 years old) is about 40 Cal./sq. meter/hour (8.3 liters O_2/sq. meter/hour), increasing progressively below this age level (to 5 years) and diminishing progressively with increasing age. Normal values for females are about 6 to 10 per cent lower than for males (Table 14-4). For average individuals (e.g., 70 kg. man, 1.73 sq. meters), this would amount to about 1300 to 1600 Cal. daily. As indicated above, deviations from the average normal may be expressed for clinical purposes in terms of percentage increase or decrease. Inasmuch as the BMR falls between ± 10 per cent of the mean in almost 90 per cent of normal subjects, plus 10 to minus 10 are usually regarded as acceptable normal limits, although certain normal subjects yield values beyond this range (to ± 15 per cent).

During sleep the BMR falls by about 10 per cent. It is below normal in undernourished individuals (caloric restriction) and tends to be lower in hot than in cold climates. Acclimatization to a cold environment apparently involves an increase in thyroid activity, which is responsible for this change in oxygen consumption. Reported racial variations may be dependent largely on differences in nutrition and climate. The BMR increases about 13 per cent for each 1° C. rise in body temperature (7.2 per cent per 1° F.), except in the presence of severe undernutrition, e.g., in tuberculosis.

Approximately 40 per cent of the basal oxygen consumption (heat production; oxidative metabolism) is due to the action of the thyroid hormone (p. 717), the BMR falling to minus 35 to 40 in athyroid subjects. In such individuals, administration of 1 mg. of thyroxine results in an increase in BMR of about 2.8 per cent. Abnormal increase in thyroid function (hyperthyroidism) is accompanied by an increase in BMR, roughly in proportion to the degree of hyperactivity. Consequently, determination of the BMR is of great value in the diagnosis of hypo- and hyperthyroidism, this being its chief clinical application.

Increased values are obtained during pregnancy and lactation, and in certain disease states (e.g., hyperfunction of adrenals or anterior pituitary). A decrease occurs in pathological conditions other than hypothyroidism (e.g., adrenal and anterior pituitary hypofunction, malnutrition, shock).

Other factors. In interpreting BMR values, other factors must be considered that produce a state which is not exactly "basal." Anxiety, apprehension, fear, and pain or other discomfort causes an increase in metabolism. A number of drugs also produce an increase, including epinephrine, dinitrophenol, benzedrine, caffeine, and nicotine (smoking). The usual sedatives lower the metabolic rate of normal subjects only slightly, even in hypnotic doses.

Specific Dynamic Action (SDA) of Foods

Ingestion of food by subjects in an otherwise "basal" state results in an increase in heat production. This phenomenon is referred to as the specific dynamic action (SDA), or calorigenic action of foods. The extent of this increase above the basal level depends on the nature and quantity of the food. It is greatest for protein, less for carbohydrate, and least for fat. It is usually stated that ingestion of protein (25 gm.) equivalent to 100 Cal. gives rise to 130 Cal., and that ingestion of equicaloric amounts of carbohydrate and of fat gives rise to 106 and 104 Cal., respectively. The increments must be derived from body tissue sources and is "waste heat," not available for work.

The SDA of foodstuffs, therefore, is an expression of the "cost" of their metabolism, and adequate provision must be made to meet this expenditure if energy equilibrium is to be maintained. The values indicated above are of academic rather than practical importance, inasmuch as these foodstuffs administered together do not exert their SDA in an additive manner, the observed values being invariably lower than the calculated values. In calculating the dietary caloric requirement (mixed diet), it is recommended that the SDA be provided for as follows: 5 to 6 per cent of the total food calories should be added for a maintenance diet and 6 to 8 per cent for a liberal diet. More should be added (about 15 per cent) if the diet is very high in protein. On this basis, a subject with a BMR of 1600 Cal./day must be given an average mixed diet providing at least 1680 to 1696 Cal. in order to preserve caloric equilibrium.

The nature of the specific dynamic action of foods is not clear. It is not a reflection of the energy expended in digestive and absorptive processes, since it manifests itself after intravenous injection of amino acids. Amino acids vary in the magnitude of their SDA, which is apparently related to the metabolism of the non-nitrogenous moiety. For example, oxidative deamination, with transformation to urea, is accompanied by a larger heat increment than transamination. Phenylalanine, glycine, and alanine exert a particularly marked effect in this connection. There is evidence also that the increment is greater during the process of lipogenesis from glucose than during its oxidation to CO_2 and H_2O.

Total Metabolism (Caloric Requirement)

If a normal subject is to remain in energy (caloric) equilibrium, the daily diet must provide at least as much energy as is expended each day. The daily expenditure may be classified in the following categories: (1) basal metabolism (BMR), which is quite constant for any given individual, and is influenced, as indicated elsewhere (p. 331), by age (growth), sex, body size, environmental temperature (and barometric pressure), and such physiological states as pregnancy and lactation; (2) specific dynamic action of food; (3) muscular activity, the most important variable under normal conditions.

TABLE 14-5. APPROXIMATE INCREMENTS IN HOURLY CALORIC REQUIREMENTS (ABOVE BASAL) FOR DIFFERENT ACTIVITIES

ACTIVITY	INCREASED REQUIREMENT CAL./HOUR
Sitting quietly	35
Reading aloud	40
Standing quietly	40
Tailoring	70
Typing	75
Housework	110
Painting	145
Carpentry	150
Walking (moderate)	235
Sawing wood	380
Walking (fast)	550
Walking up stairs	1000

Extremely strenuous exercise may increase the energy expenditure more than ten-fold above the "basal" level (Table 14-5), or, for very brief periods (swimming race), as much as one hundred-fold. In the case of a painter (1.7 sq. meters body surface) the daily caloric requirement might be calculated as follows:

8 hours sleep, at 65 Cal./hour	=	520 Cal.
8 hours work, at 210 Cal./hour	=	1680 Cal.
2 hours light exercise, at 170 Cal./hour	=	340 Cal.
6 hours sitting quietly, at 100 Cal./hour	=	600 Cal.
		3140 Cal.
Specific dynamic action (6 per cent)	=	188 Cal.
Daily caloric requirement	=	3328 Cal.

TABLE 14-6. RECOMMENDED DAILY CALORIC REQUIREMENTS

	CALORIES PER DAY	
	MALE	FEMALE
Adults*		
Sedentary	2400	2000
Moderately active	3000	2400
Strenuously active	4500	3000
Pregnancy (latter half)		2400
Lactation		3000
Children		
16–20 years	3800	2400
13–15 years	3200	2600
10–12 years	2500	2500
7–9 years	2000	2000
4–6 years	1600	1600
1–3 years	1200	1200
Under 1 year	110/kg.	110/kg.

* Men 70 kg., women 56 kg.

In Table 14-6 are indicated the recommendations of the Food and Nutrition Board of the National Research Council with regard to the average caloric requirements at various ages and levels of activity.

BIBLIOGRAPHY

Annual Review of Physiology.

DuBois, E. F.: Basal Metabolism in Health and Disease, ed. 3, Philadelphia, Lea & Febiger, 1936.

Keys, A.: Energy requirements of adults, in Handbook of Nutrition, American Medical Association, Philadelphia, Blakiston Company, 1951, p. 259.

Keys, A.: Undernutrition, in Duncan, G. G. (ed.): Diseases of Metabolism, ed. 5, Philadelphia, W. B. Saunders Company, 1964, p. 664.

Lusk, G.: Science of Nutrition, ed. 4, Philadelphia, W. B. Saunders Company, 1928.

CHAPTER 15

METHODS OF INVESTIGATING INTERMEDIARY METABOLISM

INTERMEDIARY metabolism, in a broad sense, refers to the chemical events which take place between the ingestion of a foodstuff and the excretion of its metabolic end-products. In certain cases the processes of digestion and absorption are excluded from the definition of intermediary metabolism, presumably on the grounds that the gastrointestinal tract is continuous with the outer surface of the body, so that foodstuffs are not within the body until they have entered the bloodstream or the lymphatics.

The problems for investigation in intermediary metabolism are presented in Figure 15-1. A foodstuff, "A," is shown entering the body, and a waste product, "Z," is excreted. One problem which immediately presents itself concerns the identity of intermediary metabolites, since the breakdown of any organic foodstuff to waste products is a step-wise process. Assuming the existence of these intermediates, a second problem is the mechanism of conversion of one compound into the next in the metabolic sequence. Also, from the quantitative standpoint, the kinetics of the overall conversion of the foodstuff to the waste product, as well as of the intervening steps, is of interest. A final problem concerns the influence of regulatory factors (e.g., hormones) on the particular series of reactions under investigation.

GENERAL METHODS

In Vivo

The two major subdivisions of methods for investigating intermediary metabolism are known as "in vivo" and "in vitro," meaning in the living organism and in the glass vessel,

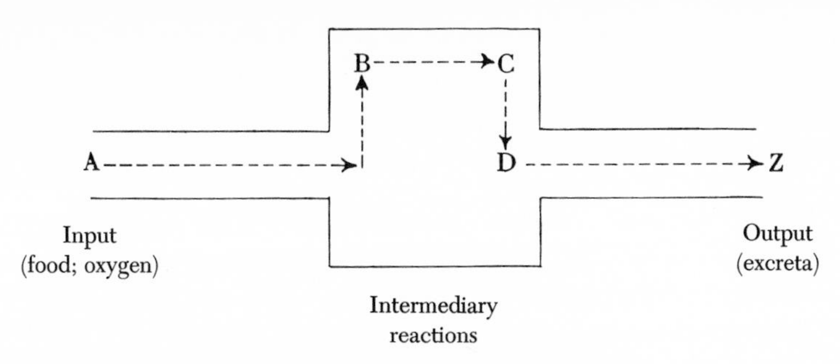

Figure 15-1. Intermediary metabolism.

respectively. One of the oldest of the in vivo methods makes use of the normal animal and "normal" foodstuffs, and depends upon the fact that the feeding or injection of a chemical compound is frequently followed by a demonstrable increase in one or more metabolites of that compound in the excreta or tissues. Suspected intermediates in the metabolic sequence can then be tested to ascertain whether they produce the same results. Often rather massive doses of the precursors are administered, in the hope that accumulation of an intermediate may occur as a result of a slow step in the series of reactions.

Although methods of this sort produced many of the data accumulated in the early years of biochemistry, it soon became evident that these procedures were of limited use and that the data were not always susceptible to unambiguous interpretation. Many foodstuffs, for example, are very smoothly metabolized to such undistinguished end-products as CO_2 and H_2O, and the difficulty in inducing accumulation of intermediates is matched by the absence of an identifiable excretory product. Furthermore, the mere fact that administration of compound A results in increased amounts of compound Z in the tissues or excreta does not prove that a direct conversion has occurred; the "precursor" may be stimulating a reaction in which some other compound produces Z. Objections of this type made it evident that "labeled" compounds were required. These substances would result in identifiable end-products or intermediates, and simultaneously would prove the direct conversion of one compound into another. In the days before the advent of isotopes the labeling was purely chemical; fatty acids, for example, were "tagged" with terminal benzene rings or were halogenated at double bonds. Such compounds differed considerably from "normal" metabolites in their physical and chemical properties, so that, despite the fact that interesting data were obtained by their use, the question always remained whether they were being metabolized by normal pathways. In the case of the isotopic labels which are being used currently, this question can generally be answered in the affirmative.

The problem of inducing an accumulation of a metabolic intermediate is neatly solved in a few cases by the occurrence of spontaneous abnormalities in human beings or experimental animals. Diabetes mellitus, with its accumulation of glucose and ketone bodies, falls into this category, as does a series of genetic abnormalities known as "inborn errors of metabolism" (p. 766). In all of these abnormalities one or more intermediary metabolites accumulate in the organism to such an extent that they may be easily demonstrated in the tissues or urine. Such accumulations are due to the inhibition, overloading, or actual deficiency of one or more enzymes.

Since many aspects of metabolism are not covered by abnormalities occurring as such in nature, the biochemist creates desired pathological states in experimental animals. The administration of certain enzyme inhibitors, for example, can cause the accumulation of compounds normally metabolized by the enzymes being inhibited. Surgical removal of an organ such as the liver is sometimes resorted to in order to demonstrate the participation of that organ in the metabolism of a given compound. Excision of an endocrine gland often yields information regarding the hormonal control of metabolic processes, as does the converse procedure of overdosage with the hormone itself.

Although restricted at present to certain lower forms of life, the technique of inducing genetic variants by irradiation, chemicals, and other means places at the disposal of the investigator mutant strains of organisms, many of which suffer from metabolic blockages similar to those which occur naturally in the "inborn errors of metabolism."

Many otherwise hidden metabolic relationships are exposed by the imposition of dietary deficiencies. For example, the omission of a certain substance from the diet may result in the retardation of a particular metabolic reaction, indicating that the missing factor plays some essential role therein. A more sophisticated approach at the present time involves the inclusion, in a complete diet, of a metabolic antagonist (p. 659) of the compound in question.

In Vitro

It is difficult, and in certain cases impossible, to probe into the finer details of intermediary metabolism in so complex and highly integrated a system as the complete animal. The biochemist has consequently fragmented the organism, working his way down into systems of decreasing complexity, from a single organ to a single enzyme. Each step in the process of simplification, although it facilitates the investigation of basic mechanisms, nevertheless removes the system one step farther from the intact organism. It is always possible in these cases, therefore, that the investigator may find himself pursuing an artifact. By and large, however, the results of in vitro investigations have fitted in quite well with the known metabolic behavior of the intact organism.

The oldest of the in vitro techniques is the perfusion of organs. The organ in question has pumped through it blood, or, more commonly, an artificial salt mixture, to which has been added the compound under investigation. After an appropriate length of time the perfusion fluid is examined for products of the metabolism of the original compound. In this way the metabolism of amino acids, for example, can be examined in the isolated liver, without interference by the kidneys or other tissues. It may be noted that this venerable technique has taken on new life of late, with particular reference to liver and brain.

Tissue culture is an in vitro method of relatively recent vintage. In this technique explants of animal tissues are grown under aseptic conditions in nutrient media. Since it is now possible to obtain growth of these tissues in completely synthetic media, one may now proceed to study the individual nutritional requirements of isolated tissues, which, after all, are the component parts of the overall nutritional requirements of the organism.

Perhaps the greatest technical advance in the field of in vitro biochemistry was the adaptation by Otto Warburg of certain types of existing manometric apparatus to the measurement of the gas exchanges of tissue slices. Slices of tissue, cut thin enough to allow adequate diffusion of oxygen (from the gas phase) into the interior of the slice, are shaken in a medium containing the required buffers and substrates. Alkali in a center well of the flask absorbs any metabolic CO_2 that is produced, so that the only gas exchange remaining is the utilization of O_2 by the tissue. This is measured by the fall in pressure observed in a manometer attached to the flask. At the end of the experiment, changes in the concentrations of substances in the medium or the slices can be determined and correlated with the uptake of oxygen.

With the aid of the Warburg technique it is possible to investigate the metabolism of many foodstuffs and intermediates in tissues which, although removed from their native environments in the body, nevertheless seem to maintain their normal metabolic patterns for periods of an hour or more. Much pioneer work on the finer details of intermediary metabolism has been and is being conducted with tissue slices. However, the very fact that cellular integrity is maintained in the slices has necessitated the adoption of even simpler systems. For example, the accumulation of intermediates is frequently difficult to observe in the intact slice. Moreover, the cell walls impose barriers to the entrance into the cell of many substrates, particularly of the ionized type. Finally, unless the animal has previously been depleted in some way, the slices will have a full complement of natural substrates and cofactors, rendering difficult the observation of the effect of the addition of such supplements to the Warburg vessels.

The first type of simpler system to be used was the mince or "brei," made by grinding the tissue with sand or in a relatively crude mechanical grinder. The resulting preparation was heterogeneous, being composed of many intact cells, cellular debris (membranes, walls, etc.), nuclei and other intracellular particles, as well as the soluble part of the cytoplasm. Minces of this type were used in place of slices in the standard Warburg technique.

In order to attain a more definite state of organization (or disorganization!), cell-free homogenates are used at the present time. These preparations can be made with a mechanical "blendor," or more satisfactorily in a motor-driven mortar and pestle device in which the tissue (in suitable buffer) is subjected to considerable shearing force while passing between the stationary and rotating components. Such homogenates consist of nuclei, mitochondria, the microsomal fraction, and the soluble phase of the cytoplasm, together with certain unavoidable amounts of debris. The virtual absence of intact cells solves, on one level at least, the problem of permeability. Dilution of the tissue, either during or after homogenization, makes feasible the demonstration of the effects of added substrates and cofactors, since endogenous materials are then present in low concentrations.

A further refinement makes use of differential centrifugation to separate the individual particulate fractions of the homogenate (p. 225). By the judicious use of these fractions, singly, combined, and with added cofactors, it has been possible to theorize, at least, concerning the probable intracellular localization of certain metabolic processes.

Enzymes occurring in the soluble phase of the cytoplasm can be fractionated by the standard procedures of protein chemistry to yield, in many cases, preparations containing a single enzyme. In favorable instances the enzyme can be obtained in a crystalline state. The availability of purified enzymes makes possible the detailed physicochemical investigation of the mechanism, kinetics, and equilibrium of a unit metabolic process.

The enzymes which reside in the particulate matter of the cell offer considerable resistance to extraction and purification, owing partly to the organized nature of the particles and partly to the lability of many of the enzyme systems involved. Nevertheless, considerable success has been achieved in the liberation of certain enzymes from particles. Especially effective has been treatment with butanol, digitonin, bile salts, and ultrasound (sonication).

Enzymes of a rather stalwart nature can withstand the action of organic solvents, particularly at low temperatures. Simultaneous dehydration and delipidation of tissues with acetone in the cold results in so-called "acetone powders." Many of these preparations are stable on storage, and can be extracted with buffers to yield active enzyme mixtures which can be fractionated. Owing to the destruction of particulate organization by the acetone, it is probable that extracts of acetone powders contain enzymes in addition to those originally found in the soluble phase of the cytoplasm.

The progress of many metabolic reactions, particularly those of an oxidative nature, is frequently followed in the spectrophotometer rather than the Warburg apparatus. This technique utilizes the fact that most cofactors of biological oxidation have different absorption spectra in the reduced and oxidized state, a difference which may be observed (with appropriate equipment) even in rather turbid preparations. Oxygen consumption can be measured in such systems electrometrically rather than manometrically.

Microorganisms

Owing to the essential unity of life, many metabolic processes are widely distributed among living organisms. Microorganisms have many advantages as experimental material, and not a few of the metabolic pathways known to occur in mammalian tissues were originally discovered in bacteria, fungi, and yeasts. Glycolysis in muscle and alcoholic fermentation in yeast, for example, correspond closely up to the terminal stages, a fact which was of considerable assistance in the development of certain aspects of mammalian biochemistry.

ISOTOPE METHODS

Introduction

The widespread use of isotopes in modern investigations of intermediary metabolism justifies separate treatment of this subject. For the sake of brevity, no mention will be made of the use of isotopes in strictly physiological investigations, or of their medical applications in diagnosis and treatment.

Isotopes may be defined as atoms having the same atomic number but different atomic weights. In other words, isotopes are varieties or subspecies of the same chemical element, and occupy the same position in the periodic table, but have somewhat different physical properties. The atomic constitution of three isotopes of hydrogen is illustrated below. Superscripts are used to indicate atomic weights.

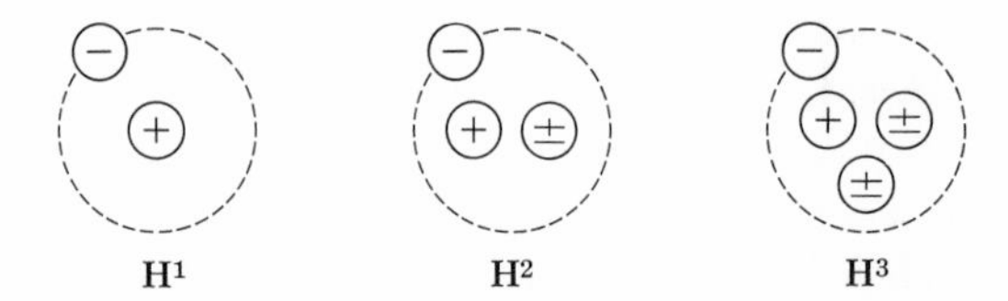

H^1, or ordinary hydrogen, consists of a nucleus containing a proton (charge: +1, mass: 1), around which revolves an electron (charge: −1, mass: 1/1850). H^2, "heavy hydrogen," also known as deuterium, contains an additional nuclear particle, a neutron (charge: 0, mass: 1). Tritium, or H^3, contains two neutrons. Since the atomic number (which determines the chemical character of the element) is given by the net nuclear charge, these three atoms are evidently varieties of the same element. Deuterium has twice the weight of ordinary hydrogen, whereas tritium has three times the weight, and is radioactive in addition.

There are two general classes of isotopes. The so-called "stable" isotopes, which have no distinguishing characteristics other than their mass, are concentrated for use from natural sources by means of fractionation procedures. Radioactive isotopes not only differ in mass from their stable brothers, but are also characterized by the possession of unstable nuclei. This causes them to decompose spontaneously, emitting radiation which may be particulate or in the form of waves (e.g., electrons and gamma radiation). Radioactive isotopes occur in traces in nature, but are prepared for experimental use by bombardment in the cyclotron or the atomic pile.

The abundance of stable isotopes in nature is expressed in "atoms per cent," meaning the number of atoms of the particular isotope present per hundred atoms of all isotopes of the element in question. In experimental materials the concentration of a stable isotope is frequently given in terms of "atoms per cent excess," i.e., the excess of the concentration of the isotope in question, in units of atoms per cent, over its concentration in nature or in a standard sample.

Concentrations of radioactive isotopes are conveniently expressed in terms of intensities of radiation emitted. The applicability of a given radioisotope to biological problems depends in part on the rate at which it decomposes, since this determines whether a measurable amount of isotope will be present at the end of the experiment. The instability of these isotopes is commonly expressed as their "half-life," which is the time required for the concentration of isotope in any given sample to decrease to half its initial value. The rate of decomposition of a given radioisotope is a fixed characteristic of the particular nucleus involved, and is not altered by changes in its physical or chemical environment. The amount of radiation emitted and measurable from any given sample containing a radioactive isotope is therefore proportional to the number of radioactive atoms of that isotope instantaneously present at that time. It will be noted that this statement is analogous to that made in connection with the concentration of substrate at any given time in a first-order reaction (p. 218). As a matter of fact, an expression can be derived for the "half-life" of a radioactive isotope by substituting the number of radioactive atoms, N, for the substrate concentration, (S), in the integrated equation for a first-order reaction:

$$\log N = \log N_0 - \frac{kt}{2.303}$$

If the number of isotopic atoms, N, is set equal to one-half that of the number present initially, N_0, then

$$t_{\frac{1}{2}} = \frac{2.303 \log 2}{k} = \frac{0.693}{k}$$

where k is the decay constant of the particular radioactive isotope in units of reciprocal time.

Table 15-1 lists certain of the more commonly used isotopes and indicates their major fields of application in biochemistry. The abundance in nature is given for the stable isotopes; half-lives are indicated in the case of the radioactive elements. More detailed examples of the employment of the various isotopes will be found in the chapters on intermediary metabolism.

The use of isotopically labeled compounds has several advantages in certain types of investigations. For one thing, such labeling enables one to distinguish newly administered molecules or atoms from those already in the body. By this means it is possible to follow the uptake of an element or compound in various tissues or tissue fractions, and, once labeled, the course of loss of the label can also be traced. The conversion of one compound into another can be proved by isotopic labeling, even in those cases in which no net increase occurs in the concentration of the product (it may even decrease!). The molecular mechanism of such conversions can also be investigated, which is difficult or impossible with the older techniques. Finally, certain special isotopic procedures permit the demonstration of the existence of metabolic intermediates which are so labile that they cannot be isolated by the usual techniques.

TABLE 15-1. BIOCHEMICALLY USEFUL ISOTOPES

ISOTOPE	ABUNDANCE IN NATURE (ATOMS %)	HALF-LIFE	MAJOR FIELDS OF APPLICATION
H^2	0.02		Body water, auxiliary label to trace C chains, mechanism of dehydrogenations
H^3		12.5 years	Body water, auxiliary label to trace C chains, mechanism of dehydrogenations
C^{13}	1.1		Metabolism of all classes of organic compounds
C^{14}		5760 years	Metabolism of all classes of organic compounds
N^{15}	0.37		Metabolism of protein, nucleic acids, phospholipids
O^{18}	0.20		Mechanisms of hydrolysis, photosynthesis, biological oxidation
P^{32}		14.3 days	Transphosphorylation, bioenergetics, phospholipids, nucleic acids, carbohydrates, inorganic P metabolism, calcification
S^{35}		87.1 days	Protein metabolism, sulfate conjugations
Fe^{55}		4 years	Iron metab. in general, hemoglobin metabolism
Fe^{59}		45.1 days	Iron metab. in general, hemoglobin metabolism
I^{131}		8.1 days	Thyroid hormone synthesis, function, and metabolism
Ca^{45}		152 days	Calcification
Na^{24}		15.1 hours	Permeability, water partition, electrolyte balance
K^{42}		12.4 hours	Permeability, water partition, electrolyte balance
Cl^{36}		4.4×10^5 years	Permeability, water partition, electrolyte balance
Cl^{38}		37 minutes	Permeability, water partition, electrolyte balance

Techniques

(*a*) ***Preparation of labeled material.*** In the case of investigations in inorganic metabolism, no complicated procedures are required. Labeled salts are used as purchased or after simple exchange reactions. Many labeled organic compounds are available commercially, but for special purposes a complicated synthesis may be required. A simple example of a procedure for labeling a fatty acid in the carboxyl group involves the Grignard reaction and labeled CO_2:

$$R{-}CH_2{-}Mg{-}Br \xrightarrow[\text{then acidify}]{C^{14}O_2,} R{-}CH_2{-}C^{14}OOH$$

(*b*) ***Introduction into biological system.*** The biological system used may range from the intact animal to a purified enzyme, employing essentially the various techniques covered earlier under "General Methods." The basic assumption underlying the isotopic method is that the organism (or its enzymes) cannot differentiate a labeled compound from the normal molecule which it usually encounters, so that the metabolic fate of the former is truly representative of that of the latter. There have been few instances in which the validity of this basic assumption has been questioned.

(*c*) ***Isolation and degradation of metabolites.*** In order to assay the isotope content of a metabolic product, it is advisable (and frequently essential) to isolate it in a pure state. When the metabolite is present in amounts too small to be handled conveniently, it is isolated by the "carrier" technique. In this procedure an appropriate amount of unlabeled metabolite is added to the mixture; the molecules of labeled and unlabeled metabolite mix and are isolated together. Of course, sufficient isotope must be present in the labeled metabolite to permit the degree of dilution caused by the carrier, otherwise there would not be enough left to assay in the compound as isolated.

The purification of isolated metabolites is sometimes difficult, for mere chemical purity is not synonymous with isotopic purity. Removal of isotopic contaminants is frequently effected by passing the isolated compound through one or more chemical derivatives, in addition to physical procedures such as chromatography. If the identity of the possible contaminants is known (and one such is always the starting material used in the experiment), a "washing-out" technique is used. This consists of adding to the isolated metabolite an excess of an unlabeled specimen of the suspected contaminant, then removing it and re-isolating the metabolite by standard procedures. Any isotope in the isolated metabolite due to the suspected contaminant will then be diluted to a negligible concentration.

In certain cases the isolated metabolite can be used as such in the isotopic assay. More frequently it is necessary to convert the isotope to some convenient form for purposes of assay, e.g., CO_2 or $BaCO_3$ for carbon, N_2 for nitrogen, $BaSO_4$ for sulfur, H_2O for hydrogen.

When questions of the molecular mechanism of metabolic reactions arise, it is necessary to determine the isotope concentration in individual parts of the metabolite molecule. This calls for special procedures of degradation, specific enough so that it is certain, for example, that the CO_2 evolved in a given degradation reaction comes from a carboxyl group and no other part of the molecule in question.

(*d*) ***Methods of assay.*** The assay of stable isotopes is based upon the difference in atomic weight between the normal element and the isotope used. In the case of deuterium (H^2), the density of D_2O is so much greater than that of H_2O that a method of assay has been developed which measures this density in a "falling drop" apparatus. This involves determination of the rate of descent of a drop of the sample "water" through a column of organic solvents of the appropriate density.

Most assays of stable isotopes are performed in the mass spectrometer. The sample, in a gaseous state (CO_2, N_2, low molecular weight hydrocarbons), is ionized by an electron beam into electrons and heavy positive ions. Regulation of the electrical or magnetic field permits the collection of ions of any desired mass at a collecting plate. The ion current resulting from this process is a measure of the quantity of ion being collected.

Radioactive isotopes are frequently determined by means of the Geiger-Müller counter. Particles or rays from the decay of the isotope enter an ionization chamber, interacting with the gas contained therein to form ions which cause a discharge of current between a highly positive central wire and a grounded cathode plate. The current from this discharge is amplified and registered automatically in a counting device, which registers the total number of counts for any desired period of time. Isotope concentrations can then by expressed as counts per unit time per unit weight of sample.

Scintillation counters are being used increasingly for the assay of radioisotopes. In the solid phosphor type, the sample is placed in juxtaposition to the phosphor, which may be an inorganic crystal or an organic phosphor incorporated within a plastic which can be machined to the desired shape. In liquid scintillation counters, the sample is dissolved in a solvent which also contains a soluble organic phosphor. In either case, the function of the phosphor is to transform the radiation emitted by the sample into flashes of light. These are picked up by a photomultiplier tube, which converts the light flashes into electrical pulses which are amplified within the tube, then passed on for further amplification and registration in a counter.

For certain purposes it is desirable to locate a radioactive isotope (in a qualitative way, at least) within a tissue or cell. In this case two adjacent sections of the tissue are used. One is stained and mounted by the usual histological methods, whereas the other is left in contact with a photographic plate or film for an appropriate length of time, after which the image is developed. Comparison of the "radioautograph" with the stained section then permits the determination of areas of high isotope concentration. The same general procedure may be used to locate radioactive compounds on paper chromatograms.

BIBLIOGRAPHY

Chase, G. D., and Rabinowitz, J. L.: Principles of Radioisotope Methodology, Minneapolis, Burgess Publishing Company, 1962.

Colowick, S. P., and Kaplan, N. O. (eds.): Methods in Enzymology, Vol. 1, Preparation and Assay of Enzymes, Section 1, General Preparative Procedures; Vol. 4, Special Techniques for the Enzymologist, Section 2, Techniques for Metabolic Studies, and Section 3, Techniques for Isotope Studies; supplement Vol. 5, Preparation and Assay of Enzymes, Section 1, General Preparative Procedures; and supplement Vol. 6, pp. 819–979, Special Techniques; New York, Academic Press, Inc., 1955 to 1963.

Cowgill, R. W., and Pardee, A. B.: Experiments in Biochemical Research Techniques, New York, John Wiley & Sons, Inc., 1957.

Hsia, D. Y.: Inborn Errors of Metabolism, Part 1, Chicago, Year Book Medical Publishers, 1966.

Umbreit, W. W., Burris, R. H., and Stauffer, J. F.: Manometric Techniques, Minneapolis, Burgess Publishing Company, 1964.

White, P. R.: The Cultivation of Animal and Plant Cells, New York, Ronald Press, 1963.

CHAPTER 16

BIOLOGICAL OXIDATIONS

INTRODUCTION

Definition and Nomenclature

The term "oxidation" has meant a number of things during the history of chemistry, such as the incorporation of oxygen into a compound, the positive increase of valence of an atom or ion, and the removal of hydrogen from an organic compound. What all of these processes have in common is the removal of electrons from the substances being oxidized, although this basic phenomenon is obscured by other factors in some cases.

$$Fe^{++} \longrightarrow Fe^{+++} + e^{-}$$

$$\begin{array}{c} COOH \\ | \\ CH_2 \\ | \\ CH_2 \\ | \\ COOH \end{array} \longrightarrow \begin{array}{c} COOH \\ | \\ CH \\ \| \\ CH \\ | \\ COOH \end{array} + 2H\ (H = H^{+} + e^{-})$$

$$Cu + O \longrightarrow [Cu^{++}O^{=}]$$

$$2H\bullet + \ddot{\underset{\circ\circ}{O}}\!: \longrightarrow H\!:\!\ddot{\underset{\circ\circ}{O}}\!:\!H$$

Referring to the above reactions, the oxidation of ferrous to ferric ion is a clear-cut example of the removal of electrons, achieved by any one of various means which will be discussed later. In the dehydrogenation of succinic to fumaric acid, the hydrogen atom may be taken as equivalent to a hydrogen ion plus an electron, both being removed from the succinic acid simultaneously. The combination of copper with oxygen to form cupric oxide would seem to involve no removal of electrons. However, such a compound, although usually written CuO, is actually an ionic crystal resulting from a transfer of electrons from the copper to the oxygen. Combinations with oxygen to form covalent compounds are somewhat more difficult to fit into the general scheme. In the case of the formation of water from hydrogen and oxygen, the electron which originally was possessed solely by the hydrogen is shared between the hydrogen and the oxygen in the water molecule. However, the H—O bond in water is partly ionic in character, the oxygen being so much more electrophilic (electron-attracting) in character than the hydrogen atom that the "shared" pair of electrons between the two atoms is actually held more closely by the oxygen than by the hydrogen. This removal of a partial share of an electron from the hydrogen may be considered an oxidation. From the standpoint of the oxygen, the acquisition of extra electrons brought in by the hydrogen atoms is certainly a reduction. For our purposes, oxidation will be defined as the removal of, and reduction the addition of, electrons.

Inasmuch as electrons are not stable in the free state, their removal from one substance implies their acceptance by another. In other words, every oxidation is accompanied by a reduction. The proper name for all such reactions is then "oxidation-reduction," although the term "oxidation" will usually be used hereafter for the sake of simplicity. The electron donor is called the "reductant," the acceptor the "oxidant."

Although some biological oxidations proceed by the transfer of single electrons, e.g., valence changes undergone by copper or iron, in most cases pairs of electrons or hydrogen atoms are involved. There is evidence that the latter reactions occur stepwise, with the formation of radicals as intermediates. For purposes of simplification, all two-electron transfers will be considered unitary reactions in the following discussions.

Significance of Biological Oxidations

The importance of oxidations in biochemistry resides in the fact that they comprise practically all of the known energy-yielding reactions which living organisms have at their disposal. As compared to all other reactions which can occur in a physiological environment (hydrolysis, simple decarboxylation, aldol condensation, etc.), oxidations by and large furnish the most energy per mole of compound. Perhaps this is why organisms at all levels of complexity, from the lowly bacterium oxidizing elementary sulfur to the gourmet with his varied intake of combustible foodstuffs, have retained oxidations as sources of energy during the long evolutionary struggle.

Fundamental Reaction of Biological Oxidations

The student will recall the lecture demonstration in which water is decomposed into its elements by the passage of a direct electric current (electrolysis). Decomposition of water into its constituent hydrogen and oxygen requires the input of energy, provided in this case by the electric current. The student will also recall the experiment in which a mixture of hydrogen and oxygen gas is ignited to form water. In this case, the reaction proceeds with the liberation of energy; in fact, the liberation of energy is so rapid that the reaction is explosive. According to the laws of thermodynamics, just as much energy may be obtained from the second reaction, ideally, as was put into the first reaction from an outside source. These simple chemical reactions are actually analogous to the fundamental reactions which provide energy in living organisms. The reaction of electrolysis is analogous to the reaction of photosynthesis which occurs in green plants, the major difference being that, in the latter, the hydrogen atoms which are stripped from the water molecule are not liberated in the free state, but are instead used to reduce carbon dioxide to the level of carbohydrate. The union of hydrogen with oxygen to form water and liberate energy is analogous to the major reactions of biological oxidation in all living organisms. The chief differences are that the hydrogen atoms are oxidized not from the free state but from various linkages to carbon, oxygen, and other elements in organic compounds, and that the reaction does not proceed with the explosive violence of the hydrogen-oxygen combustion reaction. Instead, the hydrogen and oxygen are brought together in gradual, discrete steps, a small fraction of the total energy being liberated in a useful form in each step. The study of biological oxidation is largely a study of the individual steps by which hydrogen is brought together with oxygen for the final purpose of forming water.

Thus, biological oxidation essentially reverses the process of photosynthesis as seen in the formula:

$$6CO_2 + 6H_2O \underset{\text{Biological oxidation}}{\overset{\text{Photosynthesis}}{\rightleftarrows}} C_6H_{12}O_6 + 6O_2$$

Earlier views of biological oxidation assumed that the respiratory CO_2 was formed by a direct combination of respiratory oxygen with the carbon of the substrate, while the water resulting from oxidations was abstracted from the hydrogen and oxygen atoms contained in the substrate (taking carbohydrate as the example). Actually, as shown by experiments with isotopic oxygen and by other means, the situation is quite the opposite. The inspired oxygen is used primarily to form water with the hydrogen atoms of the substrates, and the oxygen contained in the CO_2 is largely derived from the substrate itself, or from the body water (by an indirect route).

The remainder of this chapter, then, will concern itself with the mechanisms by which hydrogen atoms (to be regarded as combinations of hydrogen ions and electrons) of substrates unite with oxygen to form water.

OXIDATION POTENTIAL

Electron Affinity

In order to present a coherent picture of biological oxidations, it is necessary to digress briefly and discuss the general physical concepts involved in electron-transfer systems.

It is a matter of common experience that substances or systems differ in their affinity for electrons. The ordinary dry cell, for instance, sends a current of electricity (a stream of electrons) through an external circuit because the system on one side of the cell (+) has a much greater affinity for electrons than the system on the other side (−). By setting up standard conditions, it is possible to construct a table of all oxidation-reduction systems in order of electron affinity. The electron affinity can even be given a definite numerical value, called the "oxidation potential."

If a metal electrode is immersed in a solution containing one of its ions, there will be, on the one hand, some tendency for atoms of the metal to leave the electrode and enter the solution as metallic cations, leaving their electrons behind on the electrode. On the other hand, there will be a tendency for metallic cations in the solution to enter the electrode, picking up electrons and becoming uncharged metallic atoms in the process. If the former tendency is stronger, the electrode will tend to become more negative, being left with a surplus of electrons. If, however, the second process predominates, then the electrode will tend to be more positive. Although the concentration of metallic atoms in the electrode is ordinarily not susceptible to modification, it is clearly possible to influence the equilibrium in one direction or the other by altering the concentration of metallic cations in the solution:

$$M^0 \rightleftharpoons M^+ + e^-$$

The electrical potential (electromotive force, E.M.F., voltage) between the electrode and the solution can be shown to vary with the concentration of metallic cations according to the following equation:

$$E = E_0 + \frac{0.06}{n} \log (M^+)$$

where E is the potential difference mentioned, E_0 is a physical constant, characteristic of the system, n is the valence change or number of electrons involved in the electrode reaction, and 0.06 is a numerical expression consolidating a number of physical constants, including a temperature of 30° C. It will be noted that E_0 is the potential of this system measured when the metallic cation in solution is present in unit concentration (more strictly, unit activity). In reality, it turns out that it is impossible to measure absolute electrical potentials of single electrode systems. Therefore, an arbitrary standard has been set up, and all electrode potentials are measured, directly or indirectly, against this standard. This standard is the hydrogen electrode, which consists of a platinum electrode coated with platinum black, on which is adsorbed gaseous hydrogen under a pressure of one atmosphere, this electrode being immersed in a solution containing hydrogen ions at unit activity (pH = 0). By definition, this hydrogen electrode is assigned an arbitrary potential of zero volts at all temperatures. All electrode systems having greater electron affinity than the hydrogen electrode are positive to it, whereas the opposite may be said of systems having less electron affinity.

Most electrode systems which are of biochemical interest do not consist of a metallic electrode in a solution of its ions, but consist rather of a mixture in solution of the oxidized and reduced forms of a single compound. Designating these forms the oxidant and reductant, respectively, it can be shown that the electrical potential of such a mixture (in the presence of an inert electrode, e.g., gold) relative to the hydrogen electrode, is a function of the ratio of oxidant to reductant concentrations:

$$E = E_0 + \frac{0.06}{n} \log \frac{(Ox)}{(Red)}$$

It will be noted here that E_0 is the measured potential when the ratio of oxidant to reductant is 1, that is, when the substance is half in the oxidized, half in the reduced state.

All values designated as E_0 refer to substances in solution at pH = 0. Since it is of greater importance to calculate relationships of oxidation-reduction systems at pH's approxi-

TABLE 16-1. OXIDATION POTENTIALS (E_0' IN VOLTS)

Oxygen	0.82	Malate-oxaloacetate	−0.102
Ferricyanide	0.360	Lactate-pyruvate	−0.18
Cytochrome *a*	0.290	FMN	−0.185
Cytochrome *c*	0.26	Ethanol-acetaldehyde	−0.20
Cytochrome c_1	0.22	FAD	−0.226
2,6-Dichlorophenolindophenol	0.217	Glutathione	−0.24
Coenzyme Q	0.089	Glyceraldehyde-3-phosphate-1,3-diphosphoglycerate	−0.28
Phenazine methosulfate	0.080	α-Lipoic acid	−0.29
Ascorbate-dehydroascorbate	0.06	β-Hydroxybutyrate-acetoacetate	−0.293
Cytochrome *b*	0.04	Isocitrate-oxalosuccinate	−0.30
Cytochrome b_5	0.02	NAD, NADP	−0.32
Methylene blue	0.011	Hydrogen electrode (pH 7)	−0.42
Succinate-fumarate	0.03	Glucose-gluconate	−0.45
NAD-cytochrome reductase	0.00	Acetaldehyde-acetate	−0.468
Butyryl-CoA-crotonyl-CoA	−0.021	Ketoglutarate-succinate	−0.600
Triphenyltetrazolium chloride	−0.08		

mating the physiological, it is common practice (and will be followed in this book) to tabulate "standard" potentials of oxidation-reduction systems in terms of values measured at pH = 7, such values being designated E_0'. It is of interest, that, when a non-standard hydrogen electrode is made up at a pH of 7, its E_0' against the standard electrode is −0.42 volt.

Table 16-1 lists, in the order of decreasing electron affinity (E_0' at pH 7), a number of oxidation-reduction systems to be discussed later in this chapter.

Oxidation Potential and Electron Transfer

Biochemically speaking, oxygen has the highest oxidation potential (i.e., electron affinity) of all systems in the living cell, while the lowest values are assigned to the hydrogen atoms attached to the various substrates. Any other substances discussed in this chapter have potentials intermediate between these two extremes.

As might be expected, electrons are transferred from systems of lower potential to systems of high potential. A "coupled" oxidation-reduction reaction can thus occur between two systems:

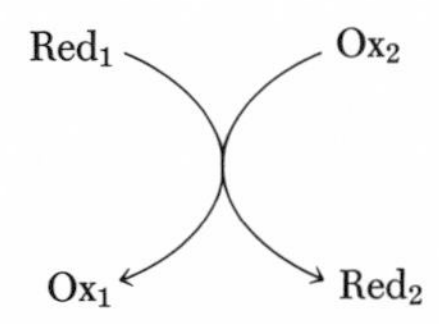

System 2 has a greater potential than System 1, hence can accept electrons from it. The reductant of System 1 provides these electrons by changing to its oxidant form, while the oxidant of System 2 accepts the electrons, and in so doing changes to its reductant form. It should be noted that the effective oxidation potential of a given system may be higher or lower than its standard potential, due to variation in the oxidant/reductant ratio. Thus, if conditions within a cell maintain a high ratio of NAD/NADH, then this system may well act as an electron acceptor (oxidant) toward systems having somewhat higher *standard* potentials. In addition, it is possible that certain oxidation-reduction systems exhibit altered potentials when bound within the mitochondria as compared with the free state.

The movement of electrons up the oxidation potential scale is an energy-yielding process, the details of which are discussed in the following chapter. The amount of energy liberated in transferring electrons from one system to another is determined by the difference in oxidation potential between the two systems.

From the foregoing one might expect that electrons could be transferred directly from substrates to oxygen, for that is certainly the direction of transfer. However, the oxidation potential gap or span between the two systems seems to be too great. Possibly, if such a large burst of energy were to be liberated all at once, most of it would be wasted, for the reaction in essence would be the direct combination of hydrogen and oxygen, a rather explosive phenomenon. Whatever the reason, the cell transfers its electrons (or hydrogen pairs) stepwise to oxygen, and the energy is liberated in correspondingly small packets. In order to effect this stepwise process the cell makes use of electron "carrier" systems, intermediate in oxidation potential between substrates and oxygen. Electrons (or hydrogen pairs) are passed along a veritable "bucket brigade" of increasing potential. The links in this chain are discussed in the next section.

OXIDATION-REDUCTION CHAINS IN NATURE

Types of Oxidative Enzyme Systems

(*a*) ***I.U.B. classification.*** The Enzyme Commission of the International Union of Biochemistry classifies the oxidizing enzymes (oxidoreductases), first according to the chemical nature of the oxidizable group (electron donor) of the substrate, and second according to the electron acceptor. Although satisfactory for purposes of classification, this system unfortunately separates enzymes which are biologically associated by sharing common chains of electron acceptors, and in addition does not consider flavins and flavoproteins as major acceptors. For didactic purposes, it will be more satisfactory to classify the oxidoreductases primarily on the basis of the type and number of electron acceptors.

(*b*) ***Classification by electron acceptors (Fig. 16–1).*** According to current usage, the term "oxidase" refers to an enzyme catalyzing electron (or hydrogen) transfer from a substrate, via one intermediate electron (or hydrogen) carrier (prosthetic group), to oxygen to form water or hydrogen peroxide. This family of enzymes may be subdivided in two ways, the criteria being (a) replaceability of oxygen by artificial electron acceptors, and (b) extent of reduction of the oxygen, i.e., formation of hydrogen peroxide or water. Although the second criterion would appear to be more fundamental, the first was usually chosen in the past. Accordingly, enzymes of this family with an obligatory requirement for oxygen were called "oxidases," whereas those which could utilize either oxygen or an artificial electron acceptor (e.g., a reducible dyestuff) were called "aerobic dehydrogenases." Despite this systematic differentiation, there has always been a tendency to name individual "aerobic dehydrogenases" as oxidases (e.g., "D-amino acid oxidase"). The term "aerobic dehydrogenase" is now obsolescent; the term "oxidase" is recommended for all of the enzymes of this type by the International Union of Biochemistry.

The water-forming oxidase enzyme in Figure 16–1 is shown catalyzing the transfer of a pair of hydrogen atoms (hydrogen ions plus electrons) from a substrate to a carrier, which in turn passes them on to oxygen to form water. The oxidized form of the carrier is thus regenerated, enabling it to operate in a cyclical manner. As found in nature, the carrier is a coenzyme or a prosthetic group which may be attached to the oxidase protein. The peroxide-forming oxidase is constructed similarly, and again the carrier is a coenzyme or a prosthetic group of the oxidase protein. In this case, however, the transfer of hydrogen to oxygen results in the formation of hydrogen peroxide. The electron carrier can be artificially coupled to a reducible dyestuff in the case of some of these oxidases.

It should be noted that, in the reactions catalyzed by the oxidases, the oxygen involved does not appear in the oxidized substrate. If a new oxygen-containing group is formed in the substrate as a result of the reaction, it arises from the oxygen of the medium (water). In contrast to this, two new classes of oxidizing enzymes have been found which, on the basis of experiments with isotopically labeled oxygen, catalyze the incorporation of this element directly into the substrate. The oxygenases (originally, "oxygen transferases") introduce both atoms of the oxygen molecule into the substrate, whereas the hydroxylases (originally "mixed-function oxidases") introduce one atom of oxygen into the substrate while reducing the other to water, requiring the participation of an auxiliary electron (hydrogen) donor.

A large class of oxidoreductases was formerly called "anaerobic dehydrogenases," the term "anaerobic" meaning that, in contrast to the former "aerobic dehydrogenases," the coenzymes or prosthetic groups (first electron carriers) are not directly oxidizable by oxygen. Instead, certain accessory carriers are required to complete the chain to oxygen.

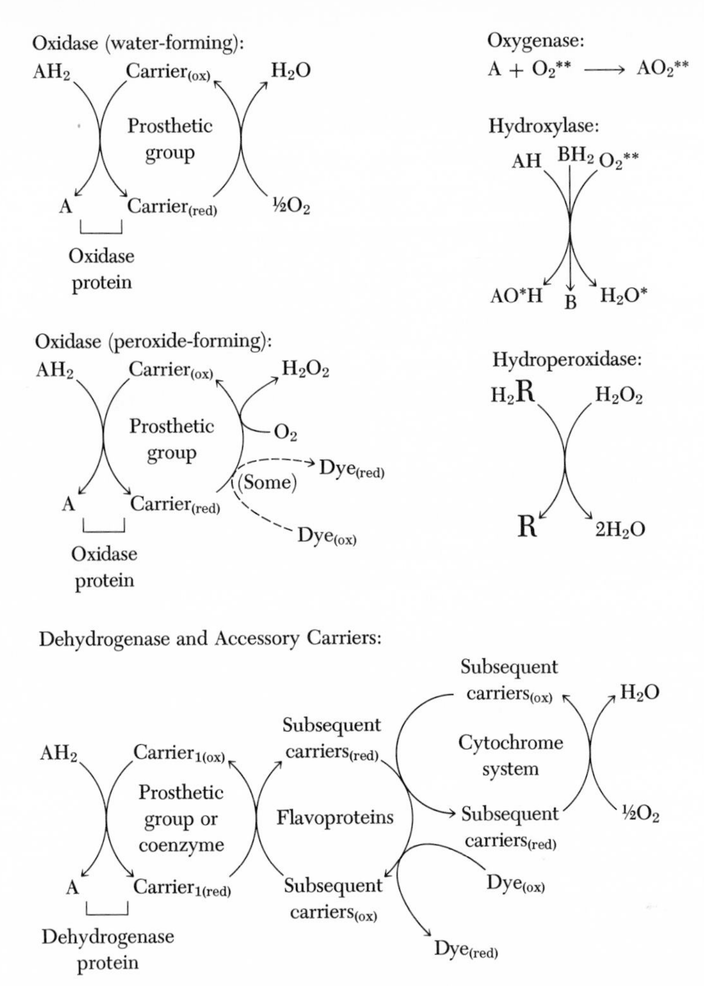

Figure 16-1. Types of oxidative enzymes.

In terms of the current nomenclature, the qualifier "anaerobic" is no longer necessary.

In the case of the dehydrogenases, the first carrier is a coenzyme or prosthetic group belonging to the dehydrogenase protein. All secondary or tertiary carriers beyond this are independent proteins bearing their own reducible prosthetic groups. Water is the final product of the reaction with oxygen. A reducible dyestuff can be used as a final electron acceptor. As discussed in a later section, the dehydrogenases may be further subclassified according to the nature of the coenzyme or prosthetic group involved.

In contrast to all of the other oxidoreductases, the hydroperoxidases (catalases and peroxidases) utilize hydrogen peroxide as substrate (actually, electron acceptor) which they reduce with the aid of an auxiliary hydrogen (electron) donor.

Coenzymes and Prosthetic Groups of Oxidation-Reduction Systems

In order to understand how the transfer of electrons or hydrogen atoms from substrate to oxygen is effected, it is necessary to examine the structures of the coenzymes and prosthetic groups involved, since they are the actual carriers. Figure 16–2 illustrates the structural formulas of the most important substances of this group.

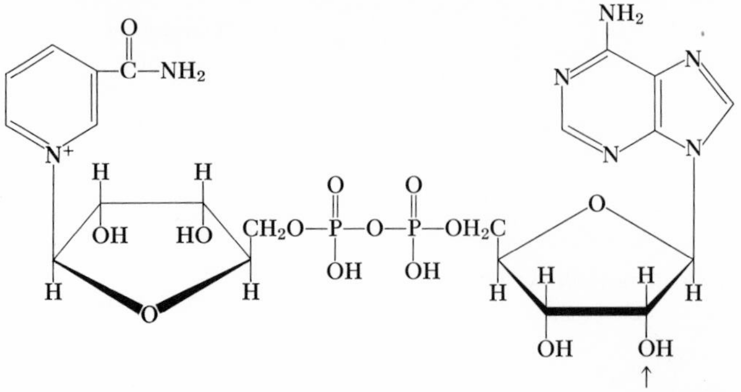

NAD

NADP has 3rd H_3PO_4 here

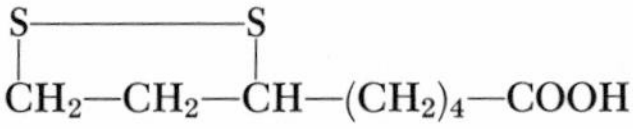

$CH_2—CH_2—CH—(CH_2)_4—COOH$

Lipoic acid

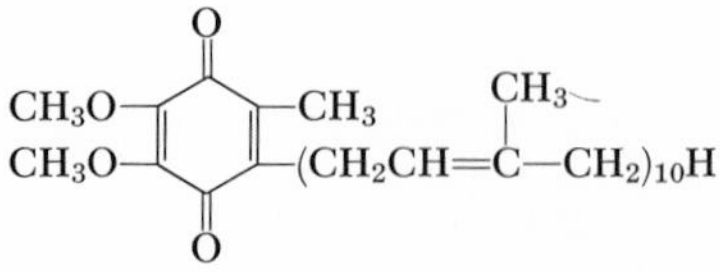

Coenzyme Q

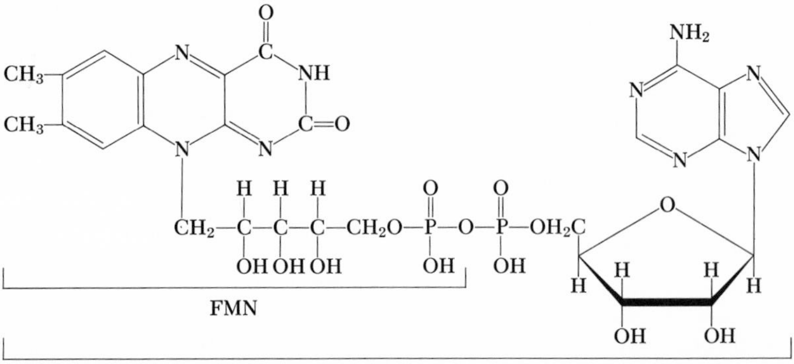

FMN

FAD

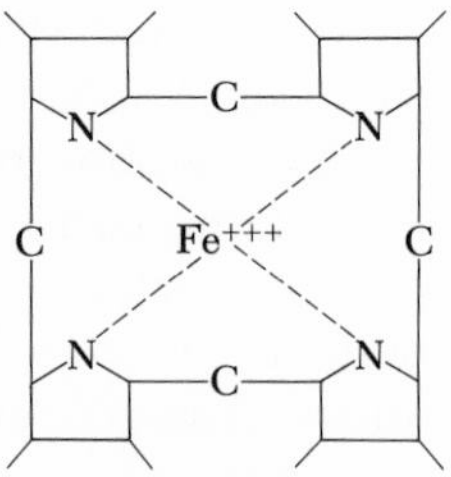

Iron porphyrin skeleton structure (ferric form)

Figure 16-2. Coenzymes and prosthetic groups of oxidation-reduction systems.

Nicotinamide-adenine dinucleotide (NAD), formerly called "diphosphopyridine nucleotide" (DPN), "cozymase," or "coenzyme 1," and the related nicotinamide-adenine dinucleotide phosphate (NADP), formerly called "triphosphopyridine nucleotide" (TPN) or "coenzyme 2," are both commonly occurring coenzymes for many dehydrogenases. Nicotinamide, it should be noted, is one of the B vitamins. Riboflavin, another B vitamin, forms part of flavin mononucleotide (FMN) and flavin-adenine dinucleotide (FAD) (alloxazine-adenine dinucleotide), which act as coenzymes or prosthetic groups for some of the dehydrogenases, and also for some of the intermediate carriers which operate in conjunction with them. Although non-oxidative decarboxylations of α-keto acids require thiamine pyrophosphate (TPP) as coenzyme, oxidative decarboxylations of certain of these compounds involve in addition lipoic acid (thioctic acid, protogen, pyruvate oxidation factor), which contains a disulfide group capable of participating in oxidative reactions. The iron-porphyrin skeleton structure will be recognized as occurring in heme, the prosthetic group of hemoglobin. Similar prosthetic groups are found in catalase and peroxidase (to be discussed later), in the cytochromes, which are intermediate electron carriers, and in cytochrome oxidase, the most important terminal link in biological oxidations. Coenzyme Q is the most recent of the oxidation cofactors to be discovered. It will be noted that it is a quinone in structure, having a poly-isoprenoid side chain. Although its function and site of action are not entirely settled, coenzyme Q appears to be closely allied to the cytochromes in the chain of biological oxidation. Vitamins E and K, both of which, chemically, can undergo reversible oxidation-reduction, have been suggested as cofactors in the oxidative chain, in the area near the postulated location for coenzyme Q.

The mechanisms of action of the compounds and groups just mentioned are indicated in Figure 16–3.

The nicotinamide, flavin, quinone, and lipoic compounds reversibly add on pairs of hydrogen atoms in the positions shown.* Although the reactions under discussion are shown as two-electron reductions, it is probable that some of them proceed stepwise, the one-electron reduction stage being a free radical. Such free radicals are most apt to be stable in the case of quinones and flavins. Evidence has been obtained, using the technique of electron paramagnetic resonance spectroscopy, for the actual occurrence of free radicals in the course of operation of the oxidative chain, specifically in the case of flavins. Certain flavin-containing enzymes have been found to contain metalloflavin prosthetic groups. These presumably act by a combination of hydrogen- and electron-transfer. On the other hand, the iron-porphyrin systems act strictly as electron carriers, the mechanism being a reversible change in the valence of the iron. A number of oxidases of the plant world, and a few found in animal tissues, contain copper. In terms of mechanism, it is probable that copper undergoes a valence change as does iron during the transfer of electrons. So-called "non-heme iron" (iron not combined in a porphyrin ring) is found in mitochondria and certain submitochondrial particles which catalyze the reactions of the oxidative chains of dehydrogenases (discussed subsequently). It may participate in electron transport.

An interesting example of steric specificity exists in the case of the nicotinamide

---

*In designating the oxidized and reduced forms of the nicotinamide coenzymes in the text proper, NAD-NADH and NADP-NADPH will be used as a simplification. On the other hand, in order to show the electrical charge on the nitrogen atom in the pyridine ring and the fact that one of the two hydrogen atoms involved in the reduction of these coenzymes immediately ionizes, balanced equations will contain the symbols NAD^+-($NADH + H^+$) and $NADP^+$-($NADPH + H^+$). This convention is in common use, despite the fact that these coenzymes are anionic at physiological pH.

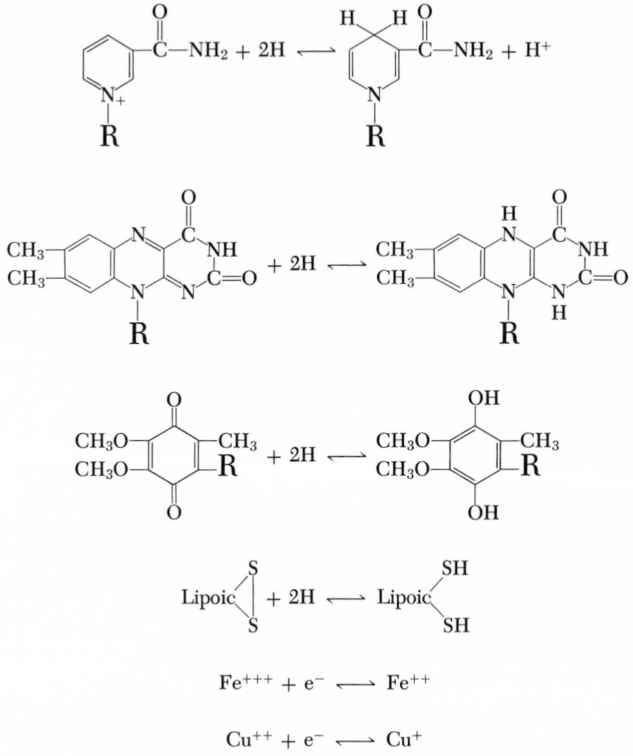

$$Fe^{+++} + e^{-} \rightleftharpoons Fe^{++}$$

$$Cu^{++} + e^{-} \rightleftharpoons Cu^{+}$$

Figure 16-3. Oxidized and reduced forms of coenzymes and prosthetic groups.

nucleotides. In the reduced form, the hydrogen atoms at position 4 project on opposite sides of the plane of the pyridine ring. Using deuterium as a tracer, it has been shown that certain dehydrogenases transfer hydrogen atoms from their substrates to one side of the pyridine ring of the coenzyme, other dehydrogenases are specific for the opposite side of the ring, and non-enzymatic reduction using ordinary chemical reagents is not stereospecific.

Oxidases

As seen in Table 16-2, there are few oxidases which form water. Ascorbate oxidase and most of the catechol oxidases occur only in plants or microorganisms. However, a catechol oxidase of somewhat greater specificity, commonly called "tyrosinase," is found in certain animal tissues (skin, retina), where it participates in the formation of the brown-black pigment, melanin. Catechol oxidases (including "tyrosinase") catalyze two types of reactions: (a) oxidation of *o*-diphenols by a normal oxidase mechanism; (b) oxidation of mono- to diphenols by a "hydroxylase" mechanism. For this reason "tyrosinase" is listed again in Table 16-3 with the hydroxylases.

Cytochrome oxidase contains an iron-porphyrin prosthetic group as well as copper. The importance of this enzyme in biological oxidations is indicated by the fact that cyanide, which inhibits this oxidase, produces an almost total block in cellular respiration. Another protein, cytochrome *c*, which itself contains an iron-porphyrin prosthetic group,

TABLE 16-2. OXIDASES

ENZYME	COENZYME OR PROSTHETIC GROUP	REACTION
Cytochrome oxidase	Heme, Cu	2 Ferrocyto *c* + $2H^+$ + $\frac{1}{2}O_2$ ⟶ 2 ferricyto *c* + H_2O
Ascorbate oxidase	Cu	Ascorbate + $\frac{1}{2}O_2$ ⟶ dehydroascorbate + H_2O
Catechol oxidase	Cu	*o*-Diphenols + $\frac{1}{2}O_2$ ⟶ *o*-quinones + H_2O
"Tyrosinase"	Cu	Dihydroxyphenylalanine ("dopa") + $\frac{1}{2}O_2$ ⟶ dopaquinone + H_2O
Urate oxidase (uricase)	Cu	Urate + O_2 + $2H_2O$ ⟶ allantoin + CO_2 + H_2O_2
Monoamine oxidase Diamine oxidase	Cu, pyridoxal-phosphate	Amines + O_2 + H_2O ⟶ aldehydes + NH_3 + H_2O_2
D-Amino acid oxidase	FAD	D-Amino acid + O_2 + H_2O ⟶ keto acid + NH_3 + H_2O_2
L-Amino acid oxidase	FMN	L-Amino acid + O_2 + H_2O ⟶ keto acid + NH_3 + H_2O_2
Xanthine oxidase	FAD, Mo, Fe	Hypoxanthine + O_2 + H_2O ⟶ xanthine + H_2O_2 Xanthine + O_2 + H_2O ⟶ urate + H_2O_2 Aldehydes + O_2 + H_2O ⟶ acids + H_2O_2
Aldehyde oxidase	FAD, Mo, (heme?)	Aldehydes + O_2 + H_2O ⟶ acids + H_2O_2

constitutes the substrate for cytochrome oxidase. This relationship is discussed more fully under the dehydrogenases.

The carriers of the preceding group of oxidases react directly with oxygen by means of valence changes in the metals. Since the metals can act only as carriers of electrons, the hydrogen atoms of the substrates dissociate into hydrogen ions and electrons, the former going into solution, the latter being transferred by the metal to oxygen. The negatively charged oxygen ion (possibly $O^=$, which may have a transient existence while attached to the oxidase prosthetic group) then picks up hydrogen ions from the solution to form H_2O. In order to simplify the situation, this additional complication was omitted previously. It will be considered again in the case of the dehydrogenases, since they are all indirectly coupled with a metalloprotein terminal link in the oxidative chain (cytochrome oxidase).

Uricase, or urate oxidase, is found in those mammals excreting allantoin as the end-product of purine metabolism; it is not present in the tissues of man and the higher apes.

There are enzymes which can oxidase monoamines, such as epinephrine, and diamines, such as histamine. These reactions may be of importance in "detoxication."

As indicated in the lower part of Table 16-2, a number of oxidases contain prosthetic groups which have been identified as flavin nucleotides. Enzymes with such prosthetic groups are called "flavoproteins" or "yellow enzymes" (from the color which the flavin group imparts to the protein). The xanthine and aldehyde enzymes are metalloflavoproteins. The enzymes in this group catalyze the direct transfer of substrate hydrogen atoms

TABLE 16-3. OXYGENASES AND HYDROXYLASES

ENZYME	COENZYME OR PROSTHETIC GROUP	COSUBSTRATE (REDUCING AGENT)	REACTION
Oxygenases			
Homogentisate oxygenase	Fe^{++}	—	Homogentisate ⟶ maleyl-acetoacetate
3-Hydroxyanthranilate oxygenase	Fe^{++}	—	3-Hydroxyanthranilate ⟶ ⟶ ⟶ nicotinate
Tryptophan oxygenase	Heme	—	Tryptophan ⟶ formylkynurenine
Hydroxylases			
Tyrosinase	Cu	Dopa	Tyrosine ⟶ dopa ⟶ melanin
Tyrosine hydroxylase	Fe^{++} ?	Reduced pteridine	Tyrosine ⟶ dopa
Tryptophan 5-hydroxylase			Tryptophan ⟶ 5-hydroxytryptophan
Dopamine hydroxylase		Ascorbate	Dopamine ⟶ norepinephrine
Aryl hydroxylase	Fe^{++}	NADPH	Ar ⟶ ArOH
Phenylalanine hydroxylase	Fe^{++}	Reduced pteridine	Phenylalanine ⟶ tyrosine
p-Hydroxyphenylpyruvate hydroxylase	Cu	Substrate itself	*p*-Hydroxyphenylpyruvate ⟶ homogentisate + CO_2
Steroid hydroxylases		NADPH	Steroid ⟶ hydroxysteroid
Squalene cyclohydroxylase		NADPH	Squalene ⟶ lanosterol
Kynurenine-3-hydroxylase		NADPH	Kynurenine ⟶ 3-hydroxykynurenine

via the flavin carriers to oxygen, forming peroxide. Evidently the reduced form of the flavin (or metalloflavin) is spontaneously autoxidizable in air. These enzymes will also reduce dyes in place of oxygen.

The metabolic significance of the D-amino acid oxidase is uncertain, since D-amino acids do not occur in animal tissues, in which the enzyme is found in considerable quantities. On the other hand, the L-amino acid oxidase, which might be expected to play a more important metabolic role, is not widely distributed and, moreover, has very low activity. This problem is discussed in more detail elsewhere (p. 566). There is some evidence that the "glycine oxidase" activity which has been described in animal tissues may be due to the D-amino acid oxidase, since these activities cannot be separated.

Xanthine oxidase is quite unusual in that it has two series of substrates. The available evidence indicates that this enzyme oxidizes aldehydes, in addition to its action on xanthine and hypoxanthine. Aldehydes are also oxidized by a specific aldehyde oxidase as well as by an aldehyde dehydrogenase.

It may be noted that, although many oxidases form hydrogen peroxide, this very reactive and cytotoxic substance ordinarily is disposed of in short order by catalase (p. 365), which is widely distributed in nature.

Oxygenases

As might be expected when both atoms of the oxygen molecule are incorporated at the site of attack, the action of oxygenases on cyclic substrates results in ring cleavage. Homogentisate oxygenase (Table 16-3) catalyzes such a reaction in the degradation of a metabolite of phenylalanine and tyrosine. 3-Hydroxyanthranilate oxygenase is a ring-cleaving enzyme important in the degradation of tryptophan, converting 3-hydroxyanthranilic acid to an unstable intermediate, which rearranges to nicotinic acid. Tryptophan oxygenase (formerly "pyrrolase") converts tryptophan to formylkynurenine.

Hydroxylases

Tyrosinase, discussed earlier as a type of catechol oxidase, also functions as a hydroxylase (Table 16-3). Dihydroxyphenylalanine (dopa), the first product of oxidation of this enzyme, also acts as the reducing agent or "cosubstrate," so that the reaction exhibits a type of autocatalysis. This enzyme is important in the synthesis of melanin. Curiously, the dihydroxyphenylalanine which is required as an intermediate in the synthesis of catecholamines (in the adrenal medulla and nervous system) is formed by a true tyrosine hydroxylase which is not identical with "tyrosinase." An aryl-hydroxylating enzyme located in liver microsomes seems to specialize in detoxications, in that it hydroxylates foreign compounds but not normal metabolites having an aromatic ring structure, particularly if these compounds are relatively fat-soluble. NADPH serves as the reducing agent for this enzyme.

Phenylalanine and *p*-hydroxyphenylpyruvate hydroxylases are of importance in the metabolism of phenylalanine and tyrosine, respectively. The latter enzyme catalyzes an extraordinary reaction involving a simultaneous decarboxylation and shift of the side chain on the ring (p. 599). A number of hydroxylases are known which catalyze oxidations of various steroids (including cholesterol) in various positions on the ring and side chain. NADPH appears to be the reducing agent in the few cases which have been well characterized.

Squalene cyclohydroxylase is involved in the synthesis of lanosterol, an intermediate in the synthesis of cholesterol. Kynurenine-3-hydroxylase is involved in the major pathway of catabolism of tryptophan, whereas tryptophan 5-hydroxylase forms a precursor of serotonin.

Flavin-Linked Dehydrogenases

As pointed out previously, the term "dehydrogenase" now means that the prosthetic group or coenzyme does not react directly with oxygen (in contrast to the oxidases). Instead, a "chain" of hydrogen- or electron-carriers is interposed. The former term, "anaerobic," which applied to these systems is misleading. All oxidative chains under physiological conditions operate aerobically, for, if the terminal member of the chain does not react with oxygen, all preceding dehydrogenase systems become inoperative.

Three groups of dehydrogenases are indicated in Table 16-4. They are differentiated by the chemical nature of their coenzymes or prosthetic groups. The first group of enzymes was called "cytochrome-linked," before the chemical nature of their prosthetic groups was known. The designation "flavin-linked" seems more reasonable at this time. The succinate, L-α-glycerophosphate, and choline dehydrogenases appear to be linked to their accessory carriers, the cytochrome system, by means of a single flavin or metalloflavin group, bound to the dehydrogenase protein proper as a prosthetic group. The aldehyde "oxidase" mentioned previously (p. 355) may also belong to this category, since there is some evidence that this enzyme, as it occurs in its natural intra-mitochondrial environment, may couple to the oxidative chain rather than directly to oxygen. The fatty acyl-coenzyme A dehydrogenases also contain flavin prosthetic groups, but differ from the previously described dehydrogenases in that the various enzymes, each specific for a particular range of fatty acid chain lengths, all transfer their pairs of hydrogens to another flavoprotein, the so-called "electron-transferring flavoprotein" (ETF), which in turn appears to couple to the cytochrome system. The same situation obtains in the case of the sarcosine and dimethyl-glycine dehydrogenases.

TABLE 16-4. DEHYDROGENASES

ENZYME	COENZYME OR PROSTHETIC GROUP	REACTION
Flavin-linked		
Succinate dehydrogenase	Fe, FAD	Succinate ⟷ fumarate
L-α-Glycerophosphate dehydrogenase	FAD	Glycerophosphate ⟷ dihydroxyacetone phosphate
Choline dehydrogenase	FAD	Choline ⟶ betaine aldehyde
Dimethylglycine dehydrogenase	Fe, flavin (+ETF)	Dimethylglycine ⟶ sarcosine + HCHO
Sarcosine dehydrogenase	Fe, flavin (+ETF)	Sarcosine ⟶ glycine + HCHO
Acyl-CoA dehydrogenases	FAD (+ETF)	Acyl-CoA ⟶ α,β-dehydroacyl-CoA
Nicotinamide nucleotide-linked		
L-α-Glycerophosphate dehydrogenase	NAD	Glycerophosphate ⟷ dihydroxyacetone phosphate
Lactate dehydrogenase	NAD (NADP)	Lactate ⟷ pyruvate
Malate dehydrogenase	NAD (NADP)	Malate ⟷ oxaloacetate
β-Hydroxybutyrate dehydrogenase	NAD	Hydroxybutyrate ⟷ acetoacetate
Alcohol dehydrogenase	NAD, Zn	Alcohols ⟷ aldehydes
Glucose dehydrogenase	NAD (NADP)	Glucose ⟶ gluconate
L-Glutamate dehydrogenase	NAD, NADP, Zn	Glutamate ⟷ ketoglutarate + NH_3
Glyceraldehyde-3-phosphate dehydrogenase	NAD, -SH	Glyceraldehyde-3-phosphate + phosphate ⟷ diphosphoglycerate
Aldehyde dehydrogenase	NAD	Aldehydes ⟶ acids
β-Hydroxyacyl-CoA dehydrogenase	NAD	β-Hydroxyacyl-CoA ⟷ β-ketoacyl-CoA
Glucose-6-phosphate dehydrogenase	NADP	Glucose-6-phosphate ⟶ gluconate-6-phosphate
Gluconate-6-phosphate dehydrogenase	NADP	Gluconate-6-phosphate ⟶ ribulose-5-phosphate + CO_2
Isocitrate dehydrogenase	NADP	Isocitrate ⟷ (oxalosuccinate) ⟶ ketoglutarate + CO_2
Isocitrate dehydrogenase	NAD	Isocitrate ⟶ ketoglutarate + CO_2
Hydroxysteroid dehydrogenases	NAD, NADP	Hydroxysteroid ⟷ ketosteroid
Malate dehydrogenase (decarboxylating)	NADP, Mg^{++} (Mn^{++})	Malate ⟷ pyruvate + CO_2
Lipoate-linked		
Pyruvate dehydrogenase system	Lipoate, TPP, Mg^{++}	Pyruvate ⟶ acetyl-lipoate + CO_2
Ketoglutarate dehydrogenase system	Lipoate, TPP, Mg^{++}	Ketoglutarate ⟶ succinyl-lipoate + CO_2

A diagram of the function of the flavin-linked dehydrogenases and their accessory carriers is shown in Figure 16–4. Under the catalytic influence of the dehydrogenase protein, two hydrogen atoms are transferred initially from the substrate to the flavin (or metalloflavin) prosthetic group. In the case of some flavin-linked dehydrogenases, the reduced prosthetic group passes its hydrogen atoms to an intermediate "electron-transferring flavoprotein" (ETF), the flavin prosthetic group of which undergoes a similar cycle of reduction and oxidation. Other flavin-linked dehydrogenases omit this intermediate step. In either case, the hydrogen atoms are transferred next to the beginning of an oxidative chain which the flavin-linked dehydrogenases share with other types of dehydrogenases.

Non-heme iron may play a role in the area of the flavin components of these oxidative chains as well as in an area near cytochrome *b*.

Figure 16–4 shows coenzyme Q (ubiquinone) as the next hydrogen carrier. This must be regarded as tentative since the exact position (and indeed the participation) of this cofactor in the oxidative chain is still under investigation. Coenzyme Q undergoes cycles of reduction to the corresponding hydroquinone and reoxidation to the quinonoid form.

The next group of carriers in the chain, the cytochromes, act as transelectronases, hence coenzyme Q sends its hydrogen ions into solution and its electrons to the cytochromes.

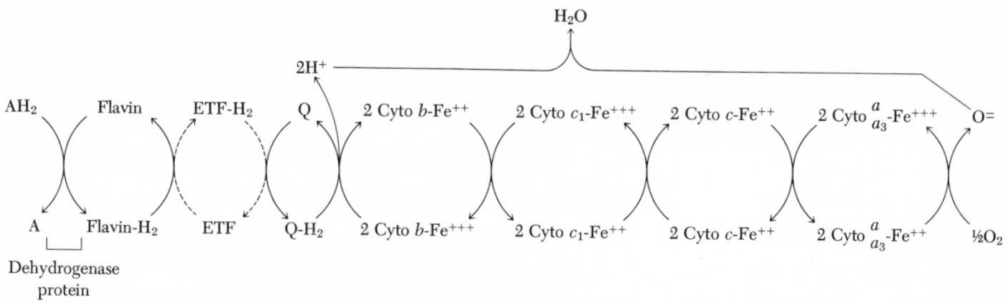

H2O
2H+
AH2
Flavin
ETF-H2
Q
2 Cyto b-Fe++
2 Cyto c1-Fe+++
2 Cyto c-Fe++
2 Cyto a a3-Fe+++
O=
A
Flavin-H2
ETF
Q-H2
2 Cyto b-Fe+++
2 Cyto c1-Fe++
2 Cyto c-Fe++
2 Cyto a a3-Fe++
½O2
Dehydrogenase protein

Figure 16-4. Flavin-linked dehydrogenases and accessory carriers.

As pointed out earlier, the cytochromes are iron-porphyrin proteins. Several different proteins of this type are found in the cell, most of them rather firmly attached to the mitochondria. Their chemical and physical properties are discussed elsewhere (p. 134). Each cytochrome accepts a pair of electrons (two moles of cytochrome required) from the preceding carrier, converting the cytochrome into its ferrous form. Regeneration of the ferric form is accomplished by electron transfer from one cytochrome to the next, and eventually to cytochrome oxidase.

It is believed that electrons are passed to cytochrome *b*, thence to cytochrome c_1, cytochrome *c*, and cytochrome oxidase, successively. The properties of cytochrome oxidase and the controversy concerning the possible identity of cytochromes *a* and a_3 are discussed elsewhere (p. 135). Cytochrome oxidase will be regarded provisionally as the complex $(a + a_3)$ until the conflict is resolved. Cytochrome oxidase accepts electrons from cytochrome *c* and passes them on to oxygen, which in its negatively charged state then combines to form water with the hydrogen ions released at an earlier stage.

Nicotinamide Nucleotide-Linked Dehydrogenases

This larger group of dehydrogenases (Table 16-4) is sometimes designated "coenzyme-linked," since the nicotinamide nucleotide cofactors (NAD, NADP) of this group are so much more easily dissociable from the enzyme proteins, in contrast to the flavoproteins mentioned in the previous section, that they are virtually always called coenzymes rather than prosthetic groups. Most of these enzymes utilize NAD as coenzyme, a few can substitute NADP but at an inferior reaction rate (indicated by parentheses), while some require NADP specifically. The glutamate enzyme can use either coenzyme quite well. The general course of hydrogen and electron transfer in these systems is illustrated in Figure 16–5.

H2O
2H+
AH2
NAD+
Fe-Flavin-H2
Q
2 Cyto b-Fe++
2 Cyto c1-Fe+++
2 Cyto c-Fe++
2 Cyto a a3-Fe+++
O=
fpD
A
NADH + H+
Fe-Flavin
Q-H2
2 Cyto b-Fe+++
2 Cyto c1-Fe++
2 Cyto c-Fe+++
2 Cyto a a3-Fe++
½O2
Dehydrogenase protein

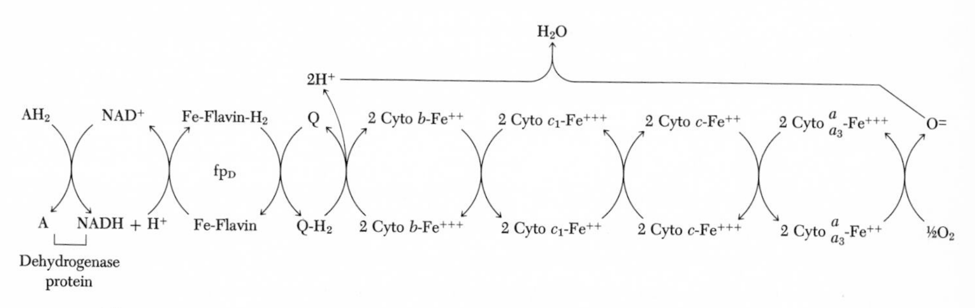

Figure 16-5. Nicotinamide nucleotide-linked dehydrogenases and accessory carriers.

Under the influence of the dehydrogenase enzyme, hydrogen atoms from the substrate are transferred to the nicotinamide nucleotide coenzyme as the first step in the series.

The secondary hydrogen carriers in these oxidative chains are metalloflavoproteins ("fp_D"). Individual metalloflavoproteins seem to be linked specifically to the different coenzymes, although the chief pathway in mitochondria appears to be via NADH and its specific flavoprotein. As a consequence, NADPH in mitochondria is largely oxidized indirectly, by first transferring hydrogen atoms to NAD (see "transhydrogenases" below). Since these flavoproteins were believed to reduce the cytochromes, they have been called "cytochrome reductases." With the discovery of coenzyme Q and its probable location in the chain, a more suitable name might be "coenzyme Q reductases." The term "NADH dehydrogenases" has also been used. In any case, the reduced forms of the metalloflavoproteins transfer hydrogen atoms to coenzyme Q. From this point on, the oxidative chain resembles that which was described for the first group of dehydrogenases.

It has been suggested that the "non-heme iron" of the mitochondria, referred to previously, may play a role in electron transport in the flavoprotein and cytochrome *b* areas of the oxidative chain.

Prior to the discovery of the cytochrome reductases, flavoproteins known as "diaphorases" were shown to couple the nicotinamide nucleotide-linked dehydrogenases to the artificial hydrogen acceptor, methylene blue. However, they did not couple to the cytochrome system, and their physiological role remained something of a mystery until the discovery that a diaphorase preparation can act as a lipoate dehydrogenase in the oxidative decarboxylation of α-keto acids (see next section).

This group of dehydrogenases includes enzymes which participate in many phases of intermediary metabolism. Lactate dehydrogenase is involved in the anaerobic metabolism of carbohydrate, as is the glyceraldehyde-3-phosphate dehydrogenase. The latter enzyme is unusual, in that a molecule of phosphoric acid *apparently* is added to the aldehyde group of the substrate before it is oxidized, thus accounting for the two phosphate groups attached to the glyceric acid which results. The actual mechanism of this reaction is somewhat more complex; it is discussed in detail elsewhere (p. 403). Glutamate dehydrogenase is of considerable importance in amino acid metabolism. The β-hydroxyacyl-CoA dehydrogenase is involved in the metabolism of lipids. Oxidations of glucose-6-phosphate and gluconate-6-phosphate are the initial steps in the synthesis of pentoses. Malate and isocitrate dehydrogenases are parts of the tricarboxylic acid cycle. There are actually two isocitrate dehydrogenases, differing in coenzyme specificity, reactivity toward oxalosuccinate, and (probably) intracellular location (p. 411). The "malate dehydrogenase (decarboxylating)," formerly "malic enzyme," is most unusual, since it seems to catalyze a one-step, simultaneous dehydrogenation and decarboxylation of malic acid without going through the stage of oxaloacetic acid. Steroids which are hydroxylated in certain positions (and with the hydroxyl group in appropriate steric configuration), viz., 3α, 11β, 17β and 21, are oxidized to the corresponding carbonyl compounds by dehydrogenases, most of which are non-specific toward coenzymes NAD and NADP.

Lipoate-Linked Dehydrogenases

The last small group of enzymes in Table 16-4 is much more complex than the rest. Both of the members of this group are distinguished by the appellation "system," since each occurs in nature as part of a multi-enzyme complex. Only the initial phase of the reaction is indicated in the table; the overall conversion and relationship to the oxidative chain is shown in Figure 16–6.

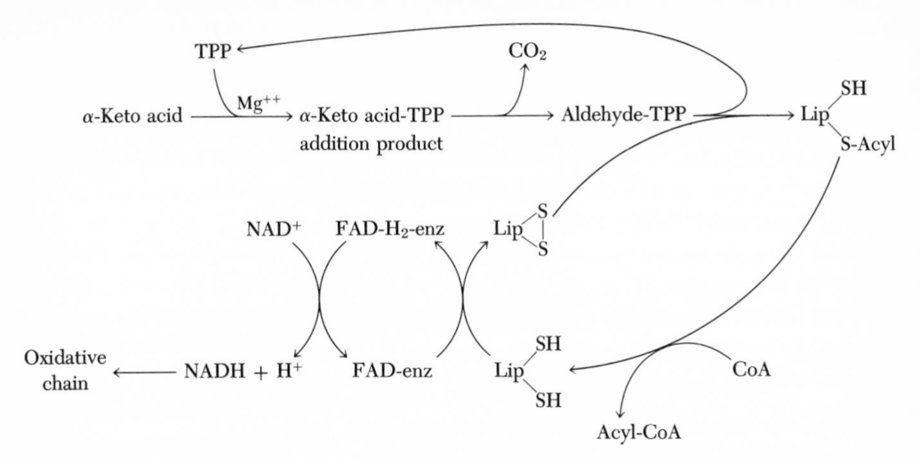

Figure 16-6. Lipoate-linked dehydrogenase systems.

The α-keto acid first forms an addition product with thiamine pyrophosphate, which is decarboxylated to an addition product of the next lower aldehyde. In the oxidation step proper, enzyme-bound lipoic acid (in its oxidized, disulfide form) is reduced, and the aldehyde residue is oxidized to form an acyl-lipoate thioester, regenerating the thiamine pyrophosphate. The acyl group is then transferred to coenzyme A, forming another thioester which may be further metabolized. Regeneration of oxidized lipoic acid is effected by a flavin-containing lipoate dehydrogenase (formerly "diaphorase"), the prosthetic group of which is reoxidized by NAD, from which point the hydrogen atoms enter the oxidative chain by the pathway utilized by the nicotinamide nucleotide-linked dehydrogenases. The role of these complex systems in the metabolism of pyruvate and ketoglutarate is discussed in greater detail elsewhere (pp. 409, 411).

Transhydrogenases

Although, as indicated previously, pathways certainly exist for the coupling of NADP-linked dehydrogenases to the cytochromes via the cytochrome reductases, it has been found that pathways also exist whereby NADPH may dispose of its hydrogen atoms via NADH oxidizing systems. These pathways are mediated by the transhydrogenases, which catalyze the reaction:

$$\text{NADPH} + \text{NAD} \longrightarrow \text{NADP} + \text{NADH}$$

It is of interest that some preparations of transhydrogenases are activated by estrogen. In addition to this "simple" transhydrogenase reaction, an energy-requiring reduction of NADP by NADH occurs which appears to be driven by the energy-yielding reactions of the mitochondrial oxidative chain.

Metabolic Roles of NAD and NADP

The role of NAD is quite obvious from the foregoing discussions. Although a few instances exist in which NADH plays the part of a special reductant, generally the reduced form of NAD simply passes on the hydrogen atoms of the substrate to the remainder of the mitochondrial oxidative chain for eventual union with oxygen. As discussed in the next chapter, the drop in oxidation potential undergone by the pair of hydrogen atoms (or electrons) from the level of substrate to that of water liberates utilizable energy.

Despite the possibility of oxidizing a certain amount of NADPH directly through the cytochrome chain and indirectly via the transhydrogenase reaction, it appears probable that the cell chiefly reserves quite a different role for this coenzyme. This is suggested, for example, by the fact that NAD is largely present in the oxidized form in the cell, as befits an oxidant, whereas NADP exists mostly in the reduced form. It appears that NADPH represents a store of hydrogen atoms or reductive energy in the cell, available for certain hydroxylase systems (p. 357), synthesis of fatty acids (p. 458) and steroids (p. 474), and reduction of glutathione in the erythrocyte (p. 804), to name a few of its pathways of utilization. It is interesting to note that most of the reactions mentioned occur in the extra-mitochondrial area of the cell, which also happens to be the locus of operation of the pentose shunt pathway (p. 416), a major source of NADPH.

General Scheme and Relationships of Oxidative Chain Systems

Figure 16–7 summarizes much of the information presented thus far, along with data on inhibitors and artificial electron donors and acceptors to be discussed in the following sections. It should be noted that, for the sake of simplicity, this figure limits itself to oxidative chains occurring in the mitochondria.

Artificial Electron Acceptors and Donors

Much of the success in arriving at our present state of understanding of biological oxidations, as well as purification and isolation of the component parts of oxidative chains, may be ascribed to the availability of various artificial electron acceptors, which may be

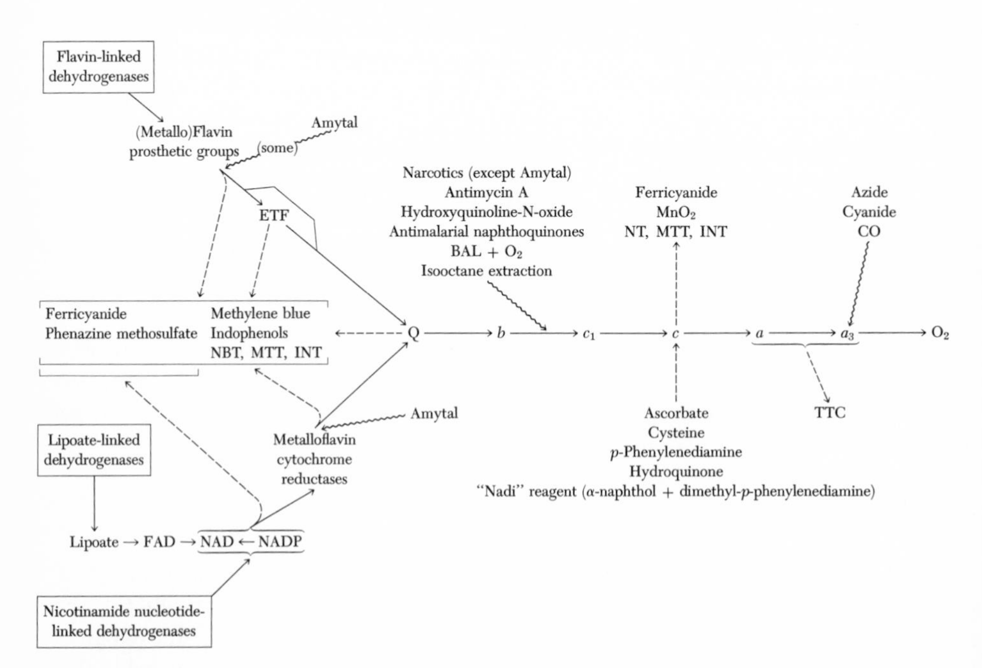

Figure 16–7. Oxidative chain used by dehydrogenases. Broken lines: artificial electron donors and acceptors. Wavy lines: inhibitors. *INT,* iodonitro tetrazolium. *MTT,* methylthiazole tetrazolium. *NBT,* nitroblue tetrazolium. *NT,* neotetrazolium. *TTC,* triphenyltetrazolium chloride.

substituted for natural acceptors in various parts of the oxidative chain. Certain of these substances, upon reduction, liberate acid or alkali, thus enabling the reaction to be followed by titrimetry or by the Warburg technique (p. 338) by performing the reaction in a medium containing bicarbonate. All undergo changes in oxidation potential, which may be measured against a standard electrode by immersing an inert metal electrode (e.g., gold) in the system to be tested. Many of these acceptors are dyes, which exhibit different colors, or are colorless in one state and colored in the other, changes which may be readily followed visually or in a simple photometer. In recent years, this technique has been extended to the use of natural electron acceptors (e.g., cytochrome *c*) which exhibit specific changes in their ultraviolet absorption spectra upon reduction. The sites where the artificial electron acceptors are thought to operate are indicated in Figure 16–7. Although its oxidation potential is a major determinant in deciding the location in which a given electron acceptor may function in the oxidative chain, other factors, such as chemical structure, accessibility of the site to the acceptor, and possibly other steric relationships are also involved.

NADH and NADPH are readily oxidized non-enzymatically by ferricyanide and phenazine methosulfate; the latter two compounds, therefore, are excellent reagents for testing the activity of dehydrogenases of the nicotinamide nucleotide-linked type. These acceptors are also reduced by the metalloflavin prosthetic group of succinate dehydrogenase, the electron-transferring flavoprotein which acts as a secondary carrier for the fatty acyl-coenzyme A, sarcosine, and dimethylglycine dehydrogenases, and by the "cytochrome reductase" metalloflavoproteins.

If it is desired to test the operations of the nicotinamide nucleotide-linked dehydrogenases and auxiliary carriers up to the point of junction with coenzyme Q, then the acceptors of choice are methylene blue and the indophenol dyes. These substances do not directly oxidize the reduced nicotinamide nucleotides, but require the intervention of flavoproteins, the "cytochrome reductases." In the case of methylene blue, its reduced form (the colorless leucomethylene blue) is spontaneously autoxidizable in air, so that reactions involving this acceptor must be performed in an evacuated (Thunberg) tube, or under a layer of mineral oil. The indophenol dyes are much less autoxidizable, hence the reaction can be run in an open tube. This group of electron acceptors is also reducible by reduced flavoproteins other than the cytochrome reductases, such as the flavin-containing oxidases, which are not shown in Figure 16–7, and the electron-transferring flavoprotein which is concerned in fatty acid oxidations. It was formerly believed that the iron-flavin prosthetic group of succinate dehydrogenase could transfer hydrogen atoms to this group of acceptors, but the current belief is that this reaction from succinate must be mediated by a carrier farther along in the chain, possibly coenzyme Q. It is of interest that the autoxidizability of methylene blue (the reduced form reacts with oxygen to produce hydrogen peroxide) makes it possible to follow the action of any dehydrogenase system in the Warburg apparatus, providing the necessary flavoproteins are intact, even in laboratory experiments in which the terminal member of the cytochrome system, cytochrome oxidase, is completely inhibited from reacting with oxygen by being poisoned with cyanide.

Since manganese dioxide (and certain other acceptors) readily oxidizes reduced cytochrome *c*, it may be used to test the function of any dehydrogenase plus intervening flavoproteins and the cytochrome chain through the stage of cytochrome *c*. Conversely, the operations of the cytochrome chain from cytochrome *c* through oxygen may be tested by studying the oxygen uptake of the system in the absence of substrates for the dehydrogenases, but in the presence of substances which readily reduce cytochrome *c* (Fig. 16–7). This system may be used to assay "cytochrome oxidase" activity ($a + a_3$), by performing the reaction in the presence of excess cytochrome *c* so that the terminal members of the chain are limiting.

The tetrazolium salts, a group of widely used, colorless electron acceptors, are reduced to the colored formazans, which are non-autoxidizable and so insoluble that they are used for the intracellular localization of reducing systems in cytochemistry. The individual tetrazolium salts differ widely in oxidation potential and in their sites of action along the oxidative chain, although there is no discernible correlation between these two characteristics. As shown in Figure 16–7, some tetrazoliums are reduced by coenzyme Q or by flavoproteins reducing Q, others by cytochrome *c*, while still others compete with oxygen for the electrons of reduced cytochrome oxidase. Furthermore, certain tetrazolium salts, although reduced chiefly at the sites mentioned, may accept electrons with lessened efficiency from other donors along the chain.

Inhibitors of the Oxidative Chain

The general subject of inhibition of enzyme action is covered elsewhere (p. 222). Here we are concerned with those inhibitors which specifically block the reactions of the oxidative chain (Fig. 16–7). It may be noted that knowledge of the sites of action of specific inhibitors has been as useful in the elucidation of the operation of the oxidative chain as has the availability of artificial electron acceptors; in fact, inhibitors are often used in conjunction with artificial electron acceptors in the study of biological oxidations. Malonate specifically inhibits succinate dehydrogenase. This inhibition is discussed in more detail in connection with metabolic antagonism (p. 666).

Amytal, alone among narcotics, inhibits the interaction between the cytochrome reductases and coenzyme Q. Amytal also is said to block the action of certain flavin-linked dehydrogenases prior to the junction point with coenzyme Q.

Narcotics other than Amytal inhibit the oxidative chain between cytochromes *b* and c_1. The same site appears to be inhibited by the antibiotic, antimycin A, antimalarial naphthoquinones, BAL (p. 223) in air, and extraction with certain organic solvents such as isooctane. Other solvents appear to extract coenzyme Q, which may be replaced from external sources. Certain authorities have claimed that other lipid-soluble factors are also extracted by organic solvents and are replaceable. Vitamins E and K have been suggested, but no conclusive evidence is available on the role of these vitamins in the oxidative chain of animal organisms. They may be involved in "oxidative chain phosphorylation" (p. 382).

Cytochrome oxidase combines in its ferric form with azide and cyanide, in its ferrous form with carbon monoxide. The combination with carbon monoxide is reversible by light. Inhibition of the oxidase in any form prevents the transmission of electrons from the preceding members of the oxidative chain to oxygen; hence, in the presence of substrates to provide the electrons, all preceding members of the oxidative chain will exist in their reduced forms, a fact most easily demonstrable by examination of the absorption spectrum of cytochrome *c*. As mentioned previously, in vitro tissue preparations poisoned in this way, in the presence of substrates, will still reduce methylene blue anaerobically, or take up oxygen in the presence of methylene blue aerobically, since this dye replaces the cytochrome system in the second instance, and the cytochrome system and oxygen as terminal acceptor in the first instance. That inhibition due to cyanide occurs late in the oxidative chain may be shown by the fact that such preparations will not take up oxygen when provided with artificial electron donors to cytochrome *c*.

Intra-mitochondrial Organization of Oxidative Chains

As indicated in connection with the discussion of the chemistry of the cytochromes, most of the components of the oxidative chain probably exist in their native states as lipoproteins or combined with lipoproteins. It has been postulated for some time that the extremely efficient transfer of electrons through the oxidative chain and the efficient recovery of the energy thus liberated (oxidative phosphorylation, p. 382) could best be accounted for by some structural arrangement in which the various components of the chain would be held in proximity, in the sequence in which they act physiologically. The evidence that most of the components of the chain are held in some type of lipoprotein matrix supports this view, as does the discovery that submitochondrial fractions may be prepared, which contain varying sequences of the oxidative chain, as though a linear array of objects had been neatly cut at one or two points. It is of interest, in connection with the intra-mitochondrial organization of the oxidative chain, that the concentrations of most of the components of the chain in the intact mitochondrion and in submitochondrial fractions are of the same order of magnitude. Most of the cytochromes, for instance, are present in approximately equimolecular proportions.

MISCELLANEOUS OXIDATION-REDUCTION SYSTEMS

Hydroperoxidases

In addition to the well-organized group of oxidizing enzymes already discussed, living tissues contain several other systems that do not readily lend themselves to easy classification with the former groups. One such class of enzymes is designated the "hydroperoxidases," and includes the catalases and peroxidases.

Formerly it was customary to emphasize the differences, or more properly the supposed differences, between the catalases and the peroxidases. With the advent of newer techniques of investigation, it has been possible to demonstrate a common reaction pattern for both types of enzymes.

All catalases and peroxidases are iron-porphyrin proteins, the iron apparently remaining in the ferric state and not undergoing changes of valence during the reaction. The hydroperoxidases are inhibited by cyanide, azide, sulfide, and hydroxylamine. Although there are exceptions to the generalization, peroxidases are more prevalent in plant tissues, and catalases in animals.

The reactions catalyzed by the hydroperoxidases are presented below:

General Reaction:

$$\underset{\text{Substrate}}{H_2O_2} + \underset{\text{Donor}}{H_2R} \xrightarrow{\text{hydroperoxidase}} 2H_2O + R$$

Special *Catalatic* Reaction $(R = \text{—O—O—})$:

$$\underset{\text{Substrate}}{H_2O_2} + \underset{\text{Donor}}{H_2O_2} \xrightarrow{\text{catalase}} 2H_2O + O_2$$

Hydrogen peroxide or the closely related alkyl hydrogen peroxides are considered the substrates. The general reaction involves reduction of the substrate by means of hydrogen atoms contributed by a donor molecule, the end-products being the reduced substrate and an oxidized donor. The special reaction whereby catalase differs from peroxidase

TABLE 16-5. TYPICAL SUBSTRATES AND DONORS FOR HYDROPEROXIDASES

	SUBSTRATES	DONORS
Catalases:	HOOH	HOOH
	CH_3OOH	$H_2C(OH)_2$ (hydrated formaldehyde)
	C_2H_5OOH	CH_3OH
		C_2H_5OH
		HNO_2
		HCOOH
Peroxidases:	HOOH	Aminophenols
	CH_3OOH	Diamines
	C_2H_5OOH	Diphenols
		Leuco dyes
		Enediols
		Uric acid
		NADH

(the "catalatic" reaction) simply utilizes one molecule of hydrogen peroxide as substrate and a second as donor; the resulting evolution of oxygen gas gave rise in the past to the idea that there was some essential difference in the mechanism of reaction of the two groups of enzymes.

Table 16-5 lists some typical substrates and donors for the hydroperoxidases. Both catalases and peroxidases can utilize alkyl hydrogen peroxides as substrates, but the substituted peroxides are less effective for the catalases than for the peroxidases. Unsubstituted hydrogen peroxide is the best substrate for all of these enzymes. Among the donors, there are significant differences in specificity between the two groups of enzymes. Catalases can use hydrogen peroxide itself, formaldehyde, certain alcohols, and nitrous and formic acids, whereas aromatic organic compounds of the types listed in the table are the best donors for the peroxidases. Ascorbic acid is one of the enediols which is oxidized.

Little can be said of the physiological importance of the hydroperoxidases. It has been thought for many years that catalase serves a protective function in the cell, by disposing of the hydrogen peroxide resulting from the action of enzymes such as the flavin-containing oxidases. It is noteworthy that liver catalase is localized intracellularly in the same particle as these oxidases. Although catalase is found in all animal cells including the erythrocytes, its importance in metabolism has been rendered doubtful by the discovery of "acatalasemic" individuals (p. 765) whose only biological disadvantage appears to be an increased susceptibility to oral infections. True peroxidases are said to occur in the thyroid gland, salivary gland, erythrocytes, leukocytes, milk, liver, and intestine. A specific glutathione peroxidase, which may be a flavo- rather than a hemoprotein, is said to protect the hemoglobin of the erythrocyte from oxidation by utilizing hydrogen peroxide to oxidize glutathione, which in turn is reduced by glucose-6-phosphate dehydrogenase, via NADPH and a glutathione reductase. A peroxidase found in thyroid gland mitochondria oxidizes iodide to iodine, which can then be used to iodinate tyrosine.

Non-enzymatic "pseudoperoxidatic" reactions are catalyzed by high concentrations of heme compounds. The common medicolegal tests for blood (guaiac, etc.) depend upon such reactions, which can be differentiated from enzymatic reactions by their stability toward heat.

Glutathione and Ascorbic Acid

The reduced and oxidized forms of glutathione and ascorbic acid form reversible oxidation-reduction systems.

$$2\text{GSH} \underset{+2\text{H}}{\overset{-2\text{H}}{\rightleftharpoons}} \text{G—S—S—G}$$

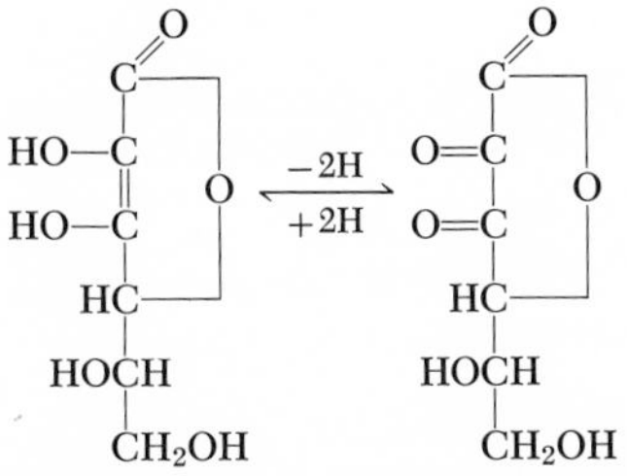

```
          O                        O
        //                       //
       C----+                   C----+
       |    |                   |    |
   HO—C     |      -2H       O=C     |
      ||    O   <=======>       |    O
   HO—C     |      +2H       O=C     |
       |    |                   |    |
      HC----+                  HC----+
       |                        |
    HOCH                     HOCH
       |                        |
      CH2OH                    CH2OH
```

It has been assumed for many years that these compounds must be involved in biological oxidations, but attempts to correlate their oxidation-reduction properties with their over-all physiological functions or distribution in tissues have had little success.

Glutathione is oxidized by the system of cytochrome *c* and cytochrome oxidase, as well as by the glutathione peroxidase of red cells. The disulfide form is reduced by NADPH and glutathione reductase. Glutathione is a coenzyme of the enzyme pair formerly known as "glyoxalases I and II," maleyl-acetoacetate isomerase, formaldehyde dehydrogenase, and indolepyruvate keto-enol tautomerase, none of which functions suggests a very important role in biological oxidations. (It may be noted that the formerly assumed participation of glutathione as cofactor of glyceraldehyde-3-phosphate dehydrogenase (p. 403) is no longer acceptable. A sulfhydryl group of protein-bound cysteine is involved, but this is not derived from a glutathione peptide.) Some investigators have concluded that glutathione also functions as a "sulfhydryl-preserver," i.e., that it helps to maintain certain proteins (as the sulfhydryl-containing enzymes) in the reduced state which is essential for their activity. It may also prevent inactivation of the sulfhydryl groups by heavy metals. Aside from biological oxidations, glutathione is involved in a detoxication process, the formation of mercapturic acids.

Ascorbic acid is a vitamin, and may have a non-specific function in the metabolism of tyrosine (p. 600). The somatic symptoms resulting from a lack of this compound, however, seem to have little relation to the metabolism of the aromatic amino acids. Ascorbic acid has been implicated in the conversion of proline to hydroxyproline during collagen synthesis, a role which may be more closely related to its physiological function. It also appears to act as hydrogen donor in the formation of norepinephrine by dopamine hydroxylase.

BIBLIOGRAPHY

INTRODUCTORY AND GENERAL TEXTBOOKS

Baldwin, E.: Dynamic Aspects of Biochemistry, London, Cambridge University Press, 1963, Chapters 6 and 7.
Lehninger, A. L.: The Mitochondrion, New York, W. A. Benjamin, Inc., 1964.

ADVANCED TREATISES AND MONOGRAPHS

Boyer, P. D., Lardy, H., and Myrbäck, K. (eds.): The Enzymes, Vols. 7 and 8, New York, Academic Press, Inc., 1963.

Falk, J. E., Lemberg, R., and Morton, R. K.: Haematin Enzymes, 2 parts, Oxford, Pergamon Press Ltd., 1961.

Florkin, M., and Stotz, E. H. (eds.): Comprehensive Biochemistry, Vol. 14, Biological Oxidations, Amsterdam, Elsevier Publishing Company, 1966.

Hayaishi, O. (ed.): Oxygenases, New York, Academic Press, Inc., 1962.

Keilin, D.: The History of Cell Respiration and Cytochrome, Cambridge, Cambridge University Press, 1966.

King, T. E., Mason, H. S., and Morrison, M. (eds.): Oxidases and Related Redox Systems, 2 vols., New York, John Wiley & Sons, Inc., 1965.

New York Heart Association Symposium: Oxygen, Boston, Little, Brown & Company, 1965.

San Pietro, A. (ed.): Non-Heme Iron Proteins, Yellow Springs, The Antioch Press, 1965.

Saunders, B. C., Holmes-Siedle, A. G., and Stark, B. P.: Peroxidase, Washington, Butterworths, 1964.

REVIEWS OF SPECIAL TOPICS

Conn, E. E.: Comparative biochemistry of electron transport and oxidative phosphorylation, Chapter 10 in Florkin, M., and Mason, H. S. (eds.): Comparative Biochemistry, Vol. 1, New York, Academic Press, Inc., 1960.

Green, D. E., and Fleischer, S.: Mitochondrial system of enzymes, Chapter 2 in Greenberg, D. M. (ed.): Metabolic Pathways, Vol. 1, New York, Academic Press, Inc., 1960.

Hatefi, Y.: Coenzyme Q (ubiquinone), Advances Enzymol. *25:*275, 1963.

Lemberg, R.: Cytochromes of group *a* and their prosthetic groups, Advances Enzymol. *23:*265, 1961.

Sund, H., Diekmann, H., and Wallenfels, K.: Die Wasserstoffübertragung mit Pyridinnucleotiden, Advances Enzymol. *26:*115, 1964.

CHAPTER 17

BIOENERGETICS

INTRODUCTION

Fundamental Concepts

All processes in the universe tend to go spontaneously toward a position of equilibrium. In general, this direction of change leads from more highly organized or complex arrangements of matter to less organized or more randomized, simpler arrangements. From another (but related) point of view, spontaneous processes convert less probable to more probable arrangements. Processes or reactions which, as written, would run in the direction opposite to the foregoing, are impossible as such. However, these latter processes can occur if they are coupled to other processes which are so spontaneous that the overall or combined reaction represents a change toward equilibrium.

The living cell is a highly organized (and improbable) arrangement of matter. The synthesis and maintenance of the structures and other complex molecules of the cell would be impossible processes, if not for the availability of certain spontaneous reactions which can be coupled to these seemingly "impossible" reactions. The spontaneous reactions so used are those involving the degradation of complex molecules of foodstuffs to simpler molecules of waste products.

Spontaneous reactions produce useful energy (defined subsequently). "Impossible" reactions require for their performance the input of energy from coupled, spontaneous reactions. The raw materials used by the organism as sources of energy and as building blocks for its tissues were described in the first few chapters, while the catalytic machinery for the breakdown of these substances (and, in some cases, for their resynthesis into more useful forms) was discussed in the chapters on enzymes and biological oxidations. We must consider now the manner in which the organism secures the energy liberated during the catabolism of foodstuffs and utilizes it for the maintenance of life.

Energy is defined as the capacity to do work. The various types of energy are generally interconvertible, except that heat (thermal) energy is only partly convertible to other types of energy in some thermodynamic systems, and not at all in others. On the other hand, all other forms of energy are completely convertible to heat. For living organisms, which remain at a relatively constant temperature (in thermodynamics, "isothermal systems"), two types of energy come under consideration: (1) heat energy, which can serve to maintain the body temperature, but is of no use for any other purpose; (2) free energy, which is available for work. Energy of both types may be expressed numerically in calories, one small calorie being defined as the amount of heat required to raise the temperature of one gram of water by one degree centigrade (a large calorie or kilocalorie equals 1000 small calories, and may be abbreviated as Cal. or kcal.). We will be concerned largely with the number of calories of free energy taken up or liberated in a chemical reaction, usually on the basis of one mole of the compound in question.

Work may be defined as the application of a force for the reversal of an ordinarily spontaneous process or the disturbance of a naturally occurring state of equilibrium. The types of work which are of special biological significance include mechanical, chemical, osmotic, and electrical work, all of which will be discussed in greater detail in later sections.

Free Energy and Spontaneity

In thermodynamics, the change in free energy occurring in a chemical reaction is symbolized by ΔF (sometimes ΔG). Since this quantity varies with the concentrations (more accurately, "activities") of the reacting substances, it is customary to tabulate *standard* free energy changes for reactions, symbolized by ΔF°, defined as the free energy change in the reaction when all reactants are in their standard states, meaning unit activity (as an approximation, 1 M concentration, except for water, which is defined as having unit activity in its ordinary liquid state, in which its actual concentration is 55.5 M). If hydrogen ion appears in the reaction, the foregoing convention results in ΔF° calculated at pH = 0 (1 M H^+ activity). Since this condition is scarcely physiological, tabulated values usually are recalculated to pH 7.0 or 7.5 and symbolized by $\Delta F^{\circ\prime}$.

By convention, negative energies are considered as being liberated from a system; positive energies, absorbed. A reaction which proceeds with the liberation of free energy is said to be *exergonic*, whereas a reaction requiring an input of free energy is *endergonic*.

The spontaneity (or lack thereof!) and related free energy change of a chemical reaction are determined by two factors: (a) the "intrinsic" chemical reactivity of the compounds (or more strictly, of the participating bonds of the compounds) which are involved; (b) the extent to which the system differs from the equilibrium state when the reaction is initiated. The first of these factors expresses itself in the equilibrium constant of the reaction, K. The second factor is reflected in the quotient of the product of the initial concentrations (activities) of the products of the reaction, divided by the product of the initial concentrations of the reactants. Thus, the free energy change in a reaction (which, as will be seen shortly, is directly related to spontaneity) is given by

$$\Delta F = -2.3RT \log K + 2.3RT \log \frac{(PRO)(DUC)(TS)}{(REA)(CTA)(NTS)}$$

where 2.3 is the factor for conversion of natural to decimal logarithms, R is the gas constant, and T is the absolute temperature.

A number of interesting and important relationships can be derived from this equation. If all products and reactants are at unit activity, the second term on the right disappears, and the free energy change, which under these conditions has already been defined as the "standard free energy change" or ΔF°, becomes related to the equilibrium constant as follows:

$$\Delta F^\circ = -2.3RT \log K$$

Hence, tabulated values of ΔF° may be used to calculate equilibrium constants, and vice versa. These values, together with a knowledge of the initial concentrations of products and reactants in a biological system, permit the calculation of the actual free energy change of the reaction under the specified conditions, using the first equation.

If the first equation is simplified by designating the product/reactant quotient as Q and evaluating numerical constants in terms of calories and a temperature of 25° C., then

$$\Delta F = -1360 \log K + 1360 \log Q \text{ calories}$$

Should the reaction "begin" with the products and reactants already at equilibrium concentrations, then the quotient Q will be equal to the quotient defining the equilibrium constant K. In that case, the two terms on the right will cancel and we arrive at the important conclusion, that at equilibrium, $\Delta F = 0$. Thus, in a reaction under conditions of equilibrium, no energy useful for work can be obtained.

Most easily reversible reactions have equilibrium constants within an order of magnitude of unity ($10 > K > 0.1$), hence the term containing K in the preceding equation either disappears or contributes but a few hundred calories (positive or negative) to the ΔF of the reaction. The reaction will proceed in either direction, depending on the initial concentrations of reactants and products as reflected in Q, usually with the evolution of only a few hundred calories of free energy.

Although all chemical reactions are reversible in theory, the term "irreversible" is used in thermodynamics (and biochemistry) to designate those reactions which proceed spontaneously toward the right as written, the reactants being virtually completely converted to the products. As might be anticipated, such reactions are usually characterized by very large equilibrium constants, so that, unless Q is of the same order of magnitude (which is unlikely and seldom encountered), ΔF becomes a large negative number. In many biological situations, as a matter of fact, Q is of the order of magnitude of unity or less, thus cancelling the last term in the equation or making it a negative number. Hence, "irreversible" or spontaneous reactions are highly exergonic, usually liberating several thousand calories of free energy at the least.

Thermodynamically "impossible" reactions have characteristics opposite to those just discussed. One might anticipate very small values of K, perhaps accompanied by large values of Q, resulting in large positive values for ΔF, on the order of several thousand calories or more, Hence, such reactions are endergonic and cannot occur spontaneously. In fact, the reverse reactions will have the characteristics required of spontaneous reactions. All of the apparently "impossible" reactions which seem nevertheless to occur in biological systems have turned out, on further examination, to be coupled to highly exergonic reactions, so that the overall processes are thermodynamically spontaneous.

A precaution must be noted in connection with the use of the term "spontaneity." Thermodynamic calculations give only the potential tendency of a system to change from one state to another. Thermodynamics says nothing concerning the time required. In the absence of an appropriate catalyst, a thermodynamically "spontaneous" reaction may not proceed at all.

The chief biological significance of the determination of the free energy change of a reaction lies in the fact that the (negative) ΔF of an exergonic reaction provides a measure of the maximum amount of work obtainable from this reaction, and the (positive) ΔF of an endergonic reaction provides an analogous estimate of the minimum amount of work which must be expended in order to "drive" this type of reaction.

Ultimate Origin of Energy

Although nitrogenous and sulfur-containing compounds may be degraded by the animal body to products such as urea and sulfate, the greatest fraction of catabolic reactions concerns the breakdown of combined forms of carbon and hydrogen to CO_2 and H_2O. This discussion, therefore, will be restricted mainly to compounds of this type.

Animals obtain their food by consuming other animals or plants. The animals which serve as food for larger animals are themselves dependent on still smaller animals or plants for nutriment, and if the food chain is traced back far enough, it becomes evident that the green plants are the major source of food for the remainder of organisms inhabiting this planet. The question then revolves around the source of the rather complex organic compounds (such as carbohydrates) produced by the plants. In a word, the answer to the question is photosynthesis, the production of complex compounds from simpler compounds by the use of radiant energy from the sun, mediated in some as yet unknown fashion by chlorophyll (a magnesium-porphyrin).

The overall reaction of the photosynthesis of carbohydrate-like compounds is indicated by the equation:

$$\underbrace{6CO_2 + 6H_2O}_{\text{Low energy level}} + \underbrace{688{,}500 \text{ cal.}}_{\text{Free energy from sun}} \longrightarrow \underbrace{C_6H_{12}O_6 + 6O_2}_{\text{High energy level}}$$

Compounds of low potential energy (CO_2 and H_2O) are built up into compounds of high potential energy (hexose), an endergonic reaction, per se, the 688,500 cal. of free energy required per mole of hexose (calculated for physiological conditions; 686,500 cal. for standard state) being supplied in the form of solar radiation. The hexose then has built into it, so to speak, 688,500 cal. of free energy available to any system which can reverse the photosynthetic reaction. The animal organism, for instance, is potentially capable of securing this amount of free energy in oxidizing glucose to CO_2 and H_2O (an exergonic reaction). In reality, no machine is 100 per cent efficient, so that we find that some 50 per cent of the total energy is actually obtained by the cells as free energy, the remainder being lost in side reactions as heat.

From another point of view (cf. p. 346), the photosynthetic reaction may be regarded as utilizing solar energy for the purpose of stripping hydrogen atoms away from the oxygen in the water molecule. Conversely, the reactions of biological oxidation reunite the hydrogen and oxygen, liberating the evolved energy in a series of gradual steps, in the course of which the energy is collected in a usable form.

It should be mentioned at this point that, although some organisms do emit light (photonic work), the free energy obtained in "reversing" the photosynthetic reaction is unrestricted, since, as will be seen, it is converted into a common currency which is utilizable for work of all types.

BIOENERGETIC SYSTEMS

Basic Requirements

The first requirement of a bioenergetic system is for a source of energy, i.e., a compound capable of being degraded to products of lower potential energy. Since most energy-yielding reactions are oxidative, the requirement more specifically calls for oxidizable foodstuffs.

Secondly, a mechanism is needed which will degrade the foodstuffs. As indicated in previous chapters, this mechanism is enzymatic. Also, it is step-wise (e.g., the oxidative chains), allowing the fractional packet of energy liberated at each step to be handled easily.

Mechanisms must be available for the collection and storage of the liberated free energy, which otherwise would go to waste. It will be seen shortly that these mechanisms involve unusual types of phosphorylated compounds.

A final, obvious requirement is for mechanisms of utilization of the stored energy. These mechanisms, most of which are discussed separately in various sections, convert free energy into such types of work as muscle contraction (mechanical); secretion, absorption, and kidney function (osmotic); synthetic, anabolic reactions (chemical); and nervous impulses (electrical).

Overall Scheme of Bioenergetics

A picture of the workings of the systems which have been under discussion is presented in diagrammatic fashion in Figure 17-1. This scheme holds not only for the general workings of bioenergetics in the total metabolism of the organism, but also for the individual reaction sequences which make up this totality.

The degradation of foodstuffs of high potential energy to products of low energy (an energy-yielding process) is shown coupled to a mechanism for collection and storage of energy. This mechanism, in brief, consists of the conversion of inorganic phosphate into "high-energy phosphate" compounds (defined in a later section), a process which requires energy and obtains it from the coupled degradation reaction already mentioned. These high-energy phosphate compounds can in turn be degraded back to inorganic phosphate, a reaction which yields energy. Another coupling mechanism insures that this energy is turned into useful work. The rest of this chapter will be devoted to a consideration of the individual phases of this overall scheme.

Energy Levels of Foodstuffs, Common Intermediates, and Waste Products

The general relationship between the energy levels of the various foodstuffs and their degradation products is shown in Figure 17-2.

It has been suggested that the catabolism of foodstuffs may be divided into three phases. In the first, foodstuffs of high molecular weight (polysaccharides, proteins) or poor solubility (fats) are digested to products more easily absorbed from the gastrointestinal tract. Analogous reactions may occur intracellularly to stored, endogenous nutrients. These reactions are all hydrolytic. The small amount of free energy liberated is not recover-

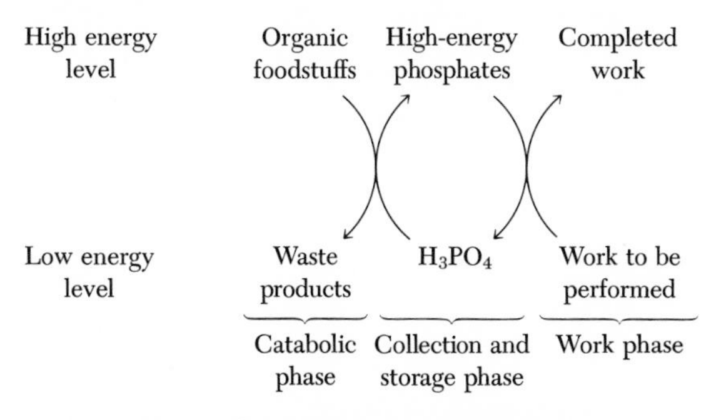

Figure 17-1. Scheme of bioenergetics.

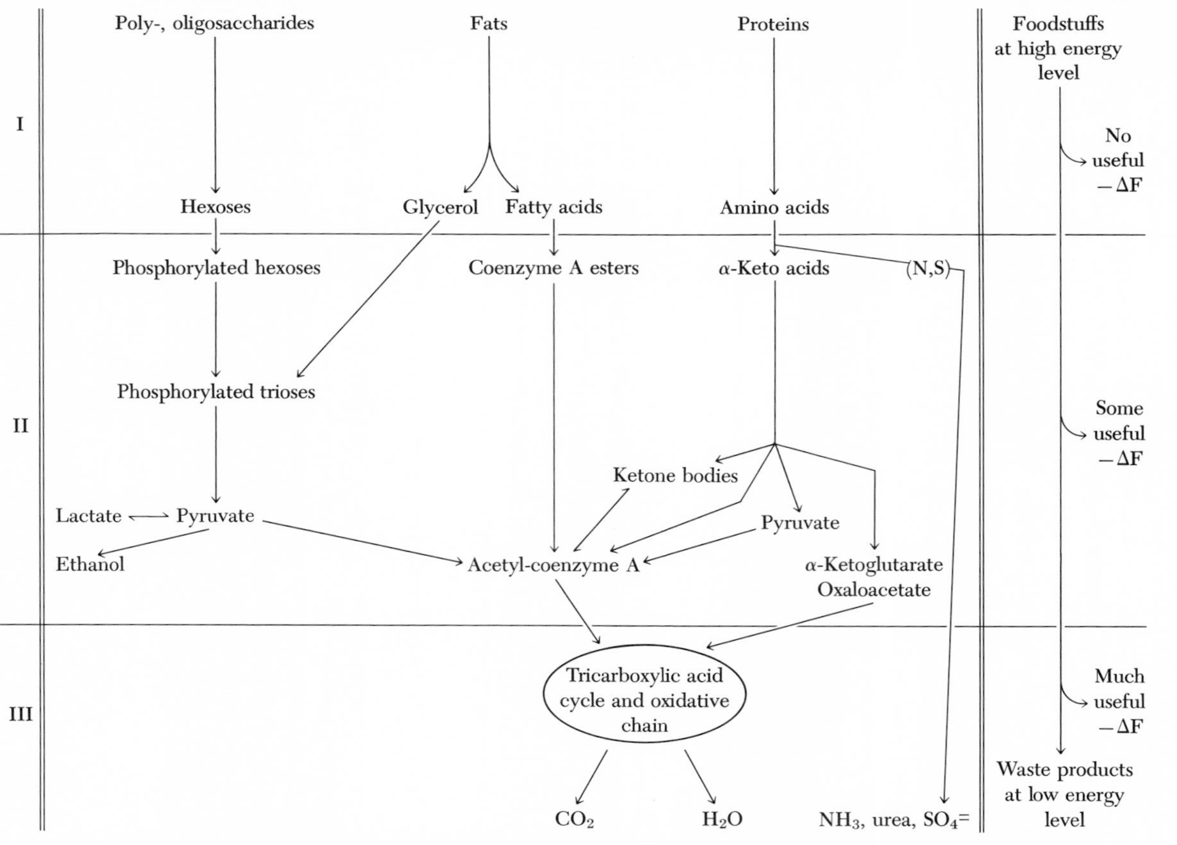

Figure 17-2. Energy levels of foodstuffs, common intermediates, and waste products. (Adapted from Krebs, H. A., and Kornberg, H. L.: Energy Transformations in Living Matter, Berlin, Springer Verlag, 1957, Table 1.)

able, but is lost as heat. Products of this phase of catabolism include chiefly two or three common hexoses, glycerol, some half dozen common fatty acids, and about 20 amino acids, together with smaller amounts of less common substances.

The second phase of catabolism converts this diverse collection of compounds into a remarkably small number of intermediates for final oxidation in the third phase. Hexoses and fatty acids are first activated by the formation of esters with phosphate and coenzyme A, respectively, reactions which consume some free energy, although more than enough additional free energy is liberated during the rest of phase II to compensate for this. Amino acids need not undergo activation for catabolism.

Hexoses (e.g., glucose) may be catabolized only partially under anaerobic conditions, producing lactate or alcohol, depending on the organism involved. Lactate formation (glycolysis) makes available about 50,000 cal., and alcohol formation (fermentation) about 62,000 cal., so that only a small fraction of the 688,500 cal. in glucose is available in organisms which must halt their carbohydrate catabolism at these points (and further corrections must be made for less than 100 per cent efficiency). Higher animals in general can oxidize glucose completely to CO_2 and H_2O, obtaining from this substance as much of its free energy as their efficiencies will allow. Under aerobic conditions, pyruvate rather than lactate is the main product, and this is further oxidized to acetyl-coenzyme A as a part of phase II.

Acetyl-coenzyme A is produced also from fatty acids. The glycerol of fat joins the carbohydrate pathway at the triose stage. Ketone bodies, which normally form in small amounts from acetate in a side reaction, may accumulate in excessive quantities under certain abnormal conditions.

Although certain amino acids are catabolized via special pathways, most are initially deaminated to form the corresponding α-keto acids. The nitrogen of the amino groups follows its own pathways to eventually appear in the urine as urea and ammonia, whereas the sulfur contained in the amino acids methionine and cysteine is oxidized to inorganic sulfate. The carbon skeletons (α-keto acids) of a few amino acids are converted to ketone bodies or acetyl-coenzyme A, whereas many amino acids either yield pyruvate, α-ketoglutarate, or oxaloacetate directly on deamination or form products readily convertible to these α-keto acids. Pyruvate as before, forms acetyl-coenzyme A.

As a result of the foregoing reactions, phase II terminates with most of the major foodstuffs having been converted to acetyl-coenzyme A and a pair of α-keto acids. A small but significant amount of recoverable free energy is liberated during this phase.

In phase III an even greater economy of metabolic pathways is evident. All of the products of phase II are channeled into a single mechanism known as the tricarboxylic acid (or Krebs) cycle, a sequence of reactions which releases as CO_2 the carbon atoms of the entering metabolites, while it feeds pairs of their hydrogen atoms into the oxidative chain to form water. Although certain oxidative reactions of phase II also involve the oxidative chain, the major fraction of biological oxidations occurs in phase III, which, in fact, is the chief source of the usable free energy of the cell.

Since chemical compounds, as has been seen, can be regarded as being on different and characteristic energy levels, it would be convenient to have some quantitative measure of this. Using as a base line the elements in their standard states, the free energy change in forming the desired compound in its standard state is defined as the "free energy of formation." The free energy liberated or consumed in any reaction is the difference between the free energies of formation of the products and reactants in the reaction. Reference works on biochemical thermodynamics tabulate free energies of formation of many compounds of biochemical interest; others must be calculated by indirect means. Employing these data, it has been possible to calculate the free energy change associated with many biochemically important reactions. It turns out that the most highly exergonic reactions are oxidations, so that one must look to these as the source of most of the free energy utilized by the cell.

It is not possible, by mere inspection of the equation, to determine how much free energy is liberated in a biological oxidation. However, as will be seen subsequently, a knowledge of the type and number of "coupling" systems involved permits an estimate of the amount of free energy recoverable by the cell from a given oxidation.

Energy Levels of Hydrolyzable Linkages

Many compounds of biochemical interest consist of two or more components united by "anhydrosynthesis," i.e., by abstraction of the elements of water from between the two participants in a linkage. Such compounds are at a higher free energy level than are their products of hydrolysis. For certain purposes it is helpful to know the free energy liberated during the hydrolysis of one mole of such compounds, rather than the free energy change attendant upon their complete catabolism to metabolic end-products.

Table 17-1 lists certain hydrolyzable linkages and examples of biochemically important compounds containing them.

All hydrolytic reactions which occur in aqueous systems are thermodynamically spontaneous and practically irreversible toward the direction of the formation of products. In addition to any special lability of a hydrolyzable linkage conferred upon it by structural factors, a general driving force in all hydrolyses must be the concentration of water, which in ordinary solutions approximates 55.5 M. This factor alone contributes about -2.4 kcal. to the free energy of hydrolysis.

It was formerly thought that hydrolyzable compounds were sharply divided into two groups, those liberating about 10 kcal. of free energy per mole and those liberating about 2 or 3 kcal. per mole upon hydrolysis. However, the accumulation of newer and more complete data makes it appear that hydrolyzable compounds form a continuous series with respect to their free energies of hydrolysis. Nevertheless, if certain compounds having free energies of hydrolysis of 5 kcal. (e.g., certain hexose-1-phosphates) are regarded as somewhat exceptional, borderline compounds, then most of the compounds listed as having low-energy hydrolyzable linkages still remain in the 2 to 4 kcal. range. It is among the high-energy compounds that a wider range of free energies of hydrolysis seems to occur. Thus, among the phosphorylated compounds, phosphoenolpyruvate has the highest free energy of hydrolysis, followed in turn by carboxyl phosphates, guanidine phosphates, and, finally, pyrophosphates.

It must be pointed out that, although it is common biochemical usage to speak of high-energy and low-energy bonds or linkages, this is merely biochemical slang, since the ΔF of hydrolysis is not a *bond* energy, but rather a thermodynamic function of the equilibrium constant of the hydrolysis reaction. It has been suggested that free energies of hydrolysis be regarded as group-transfer potentials, measuring the tendency for transfer of the groups involved to water as an acceptor. Thus, with water as the common denominator, free energies of hydrolysis may also be used to measure the tendency for a group to be transferred from one linkage to another other than water. It is customary to ascribe the high energy of a compound to the hydrolyzable linkage, and to write the high-energy bond as $\sim$ instead of the ordinary dash.

Much effort has been expended in attempts to explain the "extra" free energy of hydrolysis of the high-energy linkages over that due simply to the concentration of water mentioned previously (ca. -2.4 kcal.). Since the same reaction, hydrolysis, is involved in

TABLE 17-1. ENERGY LEVELS OF HYDROLYZABLE COMPOUNDS

LINKAGE	FORMULA	OCCURRENCE
Low energy type:		
Carboxyl ester	$R{-}C({=}O){\vdots}O{-}R'$	Glycerides
Phosphoric ester	$R{-}O{\vdots}PO_3H_2$	Hexose phosphates
Glycoside	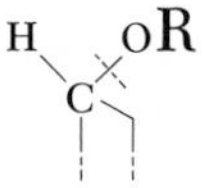 $H{\diagdown}C{\times}OR$ (ring)	Polysaccharides
Peptide	$R{-}C({=}O){\vdots}NH{-}R'$	Proteins
High energy type:		
β-Keto acid	$R{-}C({=}O){\vdots}CH_2COOH$	Acetoacetate
Thioester	$R{-}C({=}O){\vdots}SR'$	Acetyl-CoA, fatty acyl-CoA's
Pyrophosphate	$R{-}O{-}P({=}O)(OH){-}O{\vdots}P({=}O)(OH){-}O{-}R'$	ATP
Guanidine phosphate	$R{-}NH{-}C({=}NH){-}NH{\vdots}PO_3H_2$	Phosphocreatine
Enol phosphate	$R_1{-}C(R_2){=}C(R_3){-}O{\vdots}PO_3H_2$	Phosphoenol-pyruvate
Carboxyl phosphate	$R{-}C({=}O){-}O{\vdots}PO_3H_2$	No. 1 phosphate in diphosphoglycerate, carboxyl adenylates
Acyl thiazole	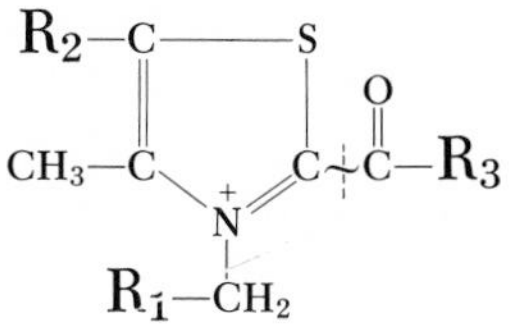 $R_2{-}C{=}C(CH_3){-}\overset{+}{N}(CH_2{-}R_1){=}C(S){\vdots}C({=}O){-}R_3$ (thiazole ring: $R_2{-}C$—S, $CH_3{-}C$, $\overset{+}{N}$, C)	Intermediates in oxidative decarboxylations requiring thiamine pyrophosphate

Probable additional high-energy types:

Acyl imidazoles, amino acid esters of sRNA, diester phosphate linkages in RNA and DNA.

all cases, one must look to structural factors as the underlying cause. Also, since the energy under discussion is not a true bond energy, but an energy of reaction, it must concern structural differences between reactants and their products of hydrolysis, such that the latter are stabilized in comparison with the former. From this viewpoint, four structural factors have been implicated.

(*1*) ***Opposing or hindered resonance.*** It is a well-known principle of electronic organic chemistry that, the larger the number of resonant structures which can be formulated for a given compound (particularly those structures which may be expected to make major contributions), the more stable the "hybrid" molecule which actually exists. In many high-energy compounds, of which the pyrophosphates are excellent examples, the hydrolyzed products can possess many more resonant forms than can be formulated when the two groups concerned are bound together. Since the amount of stabilizing "resonance energy" varies greatly from one type of compound to another, no general statement can be made concerning the average $-\Delta F$ contributed by this factor.

(*2*) ***Electrostatic repulsion.*** In some compounds, electrical charges of the same sign are located near each other across the hydrolyzable bond. Since these mutually repulsive groups would be separated upon hydrolysis, electrostatic repulsion can be considered one of the factors tending to stabilize products vs. reactants. This, again, is easily seen in the case of the pyrophosphate linkage. The effect has been estimated as contributing -3 to -6 kcal. to the free energy of hydrolysis.

(*3*) ***Ionization.*** One or both of the component groups in a high-energy linkage frequently are acids with pK's which enable them to ionize if liberated in an environment of neutral pH. This effect, which may contribute ca. -3 kcal. per acid group at pH 7, may be considered a type of mass-action influence, in that the product (un-ionized acid) of one reaction is immediately removed by participation in a second reaction having an equilibrium position far toward the right. Being of relatively low magnitude, ionization energy of a single acid group is never the sole factor concerned in a high-energy linkage.

(*4*) ***Isomerization.*** This factor resembles the ionization factor in being a mass-action effect. In this case, at least one product of hydrolysis undergoes a subsequent isomerization which is virtually complete. A good example is phosphoenolpyruvate, the enolpyruvate which results from hydrolysis spontaneously tautomerizing to the keto form. Enol-keto tautomerization may contribute some -5.5 to -9 kcal. to the free energy of hydrolysis.

Among the non-phosphorylated compounds listed, "low-energy" hydrolyzable linkages (several kcal.) occur in simple esters, glycosides, and peptides. "High-energy" bonds (ca. 7 to 13 kcal.) are found in thioesters of coenzyme A and related compounds, acyl thiazoles, acyl imidazoles, as well as in β-keto acids. The significance of these facts will become apparent in the discussions of intermediary metabolism.

Phosphorylated compounds include low-energy phosphates, mainly esters of phosphoric acid with alcohol groups, and high-energy phosphates, such as compounds of phosphoric acid with itself, and with guanidine, enolic, and carboxyl groups. The low-energy phosphates have a free energy of hydrolysis of 2000 to 4000 cal. per mole, whereas the high-energy compounds liberate 7000 to 13,000 cal.

Recent calculations suggest that the linkages of amino acids to "soluble RNA" (p. 105) and the phosphodiester linkages in the nucleic acids themselves should be placed in the high-energy category.

Some of the above compounds have been encountered previously. ADP and ATP, it will be recalled, were mentioned in connection with the enzymes catalyzing transphosphorylations. Adenylic acid (AMP), the parent compound, contains only a low-energy phosphate bond (ester type). The di- and triphosphates, on the other hand, contain respectively one and two high-energy bonds of the pyrophosphate type. ADP and ATP are important in the collection and utilization of free energy. ATP, in fact, is the "common currency" of energy which was mentioned earlier. ATP is formed in most energy-yielding (exergonic) reactions, and utilized in all energy-requiring (endergonic) reactions, directly or indirectly. It is rather unstable and is found in tissues in only small quantities, so that it is not quite so important for the storage of energy. Phosphocreatine is the major storage form of high-energy phosphate, especially in muscle and liver (in most invertebrates its place is taken by phosphoarginine). Any surplus high-energy phosphate is transferred from ATP to creatine (transphosphorylation) for storage as phosphocreatine. When the need arises, this high-energy phosphate is transferred to ADP, re-forming ATP.

Phosphoenolpyruvate and diphosphoglycerate are compounds which arise during the anaerobic catabolism of glucose. They contain high-energy phosphate groups which can be transferred to the adenylic system. Acetyl phosphate is also a high-energy compound, but is of importance only in bacteria.

As can be seen from the formulas, the low-energy phosphate compounds are all esters. They include the hexose phosphates, pentose phosphates, triose phosphates, and those glycerate phosphates which do not involve the carboxyl group.

Transphosphorylations

In order to understand the nature of the coupling mechanisms involved in the collection of energy and its utilization, a short digression on transphosphorylation is necessary. This reaction is defined as the transfer of phosphate groups from one compound to another without going through the stage of inorganic phosphate.

The chapter on enzymes listed the various transphosphorylases. It was indicated that some of the reactions were reversible, while others were not. The explanation for this can now be given. Reversible transphosphorylation can occur if the two compounds involved belong to the same energy level of phosphate. Thus, transfers on either the high level or the low level proceed with very little liberation or absorption of energy, hence they can easily be reversed in direction. This group of transphorylations includes the phosphomutases and the reversible kinases. Two examples follow:

$$\text{ATP} + \text{creatine} \rightleftharpoons \text{ADP} + \text{phosphocreatine}$$
$$\text{Glucose-6-phosphate} \rightleftharpoons \text{glucose-1-phosphate}$$

The first of these two reactions, catalyzed by creatine kinase, is reversible because the free energy of hydrolysis of the bond broken, namely the terminal pyrophosphate linkage of ATP, is of the same order of magnitude as the free energy of hydrolysis of the bond formed, the phosphoguanidine linkage in phosphocreatine. The actual numerical value of the latter bond is sufficiently higher than that of the former so that the equilibrium position actually favors the reaction to the left. Any increase in the concentration of ATP, however, favors the synthesis of phosphocreatine. The second reaction illustrated (catalyzed by phosphoglucomutase) is considered reversible, again, because the free energy of hydrolysis of the bond broken, the 6-phosphate ester, is of the same order of magnitude as that of the bond formed, the 1-phosphate ester. Again, however, an examination of the numerical values for the free energy of hydrolysis of these two bonds indicates that the energy level of the phosphorylated glycosidic hydroxyl (the 1-phosphate) is sufficiently higher than that of the other bond so that the equilibrium of this reaction also lies toward the left.

The transfer of a phosphate group from a high-energy level to a low level, or from a low level to zero level (inorganic phosphate), liberates so much energy that, for all practical purposes, these reactions must be considered irreversible. (Any apparent reversals which occur in living systems actually proceed by indirect pathways and with the aid of outside sources of energy.) This group of reactions includes the irreversible kinases and any simple hydrolytic breakdown of phosphorylated compounds, such as that catalyzed by the various phosphatases. Two examples of practically irreversible reactions follow:

$$\text{ATP} + \text{glucose} \longrightarrow \text{ADP} + \text{glucose-6-phosphate}$$
$$\text{Glucose-6-phosphate} + H_2O \longrightarrow \text{glucose} + \text{inorganic phosphate}$$

The first of these reactions, catalyzed by hexokinase, is practically irreversible because the free energy of hydrolysis of the bond broken, the pyrophosphate linkage of ATP, is much greater than the free energy of hydrolysis of the bond formed, the ester-phosphate bond. As a result, the difference between the energy levels of these two bonds, approximately 4 kcal., is liberated during the reaction. In like manner, the second reaction, catalyzed by a phosphatase, proceeds to completion because the entire free energy of hydrolysis of the ester-phosphate linkage is liberated in the course of this reaction. If either reaction were written in the reverse direction, it would be classified as an "impossible" reaction (as written).

The hydrolytic splitting of phosphate compounds and the various mutase reactions do not require the participation of the adenylic system. Most other transphosphorylations use ADP and ATP as transmitters. The following diagram indicates how various compounds of the high-energy phosphate type act as donors to the adenylic system, which in turn transfers phosphate groups to other compounds to form both high- and low-level phosphates.

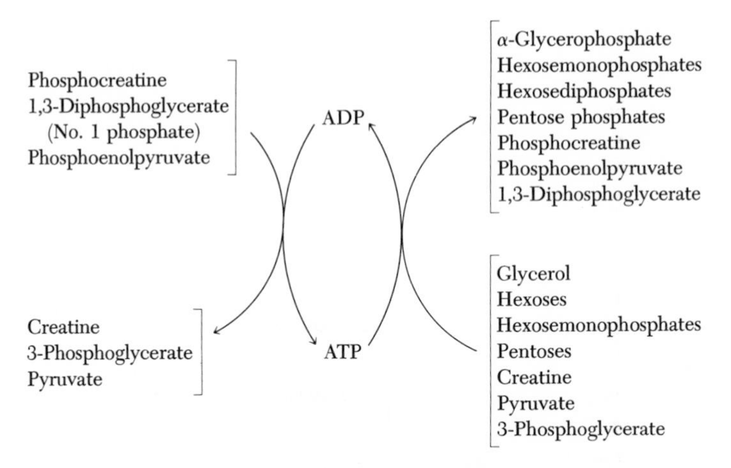

Coupling Mechanisms: Substrate Level Phosphorylation

One of the important discoveries concerning bioenergetics has been that the coupling of high-energy phosphate formation with energy-yielding (exergonic) reactions can occur at two levels of metabolism, one at the point where a substrate is oxidized and passes its hydrogen atoms over to a primary carrier, and the second along the oxidative chain, where the hydrogen atoms or electrons are transferred over various carriers to oxygen. Somewhat more information is available concerning the first of these two types of phosphorylation, often called "substrate level phosphorylation." It is important to note that this usage of the term "phosphorylation" implies *generation* of high-energy phosphate, not simply attachment of a phosphate group, although the latter reaction may very well accompany or be an integral part of the energy-generating process.

An example of definite substrate level phosphorylation occurs during the anaerobic breakdown of glucose (glycolysis), in which phosphoglyceraldehyde (containing a low-energy ester phosphate) is oxidized to diphosphoglycerate (p. 403), one of the phosphates of which is attached to the carboxyl group, making it a high-energy type. The ordinary oxidation of an aldehyde to an acid, such as occurs in many enzymatic reactions, may be depicted as follows:

$$\mathrm{R{-}\overset{H}{C}{=}O + H_2O \rightleftharpoons R{-}\underset{OH}{\overset{H}{C}}{-}OH}$$

$$\mathrm{R{-}\underset{OH}{\overset{(H)}{C}}{-}O(H) + NAD^+ \xrightarrow{\text{Dehydrogenase}} R{-}\overset{O}{\overset{\|}{C}}{-}OH + NADH + H^+}$$

An initial hydration of the aldehyde group is followed by a dehydrogenation, the pair of hydrogen atoms being passed to NAD under the influence of the dehydrogenase enzyme. Without inquiring further into the fate of the reduced NAD at this time, it will be noted that no energy has been trapped at this point in the reaction. Since an aldehyde group is at a higher energy level than a carboxyl group (by ca. 50 to 60 kcal.) the transformation of the former to the latter liberates energy, but in the example shown at least a part of this energy is lost as heat on the substrate level (trapping of energy formed during the subsequent oxidation of the NADH will be discussed in the next section).

In the glyceraldehyde-phosphate dehydrogenation, the initial reaction involves the formation of an addition product of the carbonyl group of the substrate and a sulfhydryl group of the enzyme protein. Oxidation of this product to a thioester (by hydrogen transfer to NAD) is followed by phosphorolysis, or transacylation to phosphate. Transfer of the carboxyl phosphate from the diphosphoglycerate to ADP to form ATP is catalyzed by a kinase.

$$\mathrm{R{-}\overset{H}{C}{=}O + Enz\text{-}SH \rightleftharpoons R{-}\underset{S{-}Enz}{\overset{H}{C}}{-}OH}$$

$$\mathrm{R{-}\underset{S{-}Enz}{\overset{(H)}{C}}{-}O(H) + NAD^+ \rightleftharpoons R{-}\overset{O}{\overset{\|}{C}}\sim SEnz + NADH + H^+}$$

$$\mathrm{R{-}\overset{O}{\overset{\|}{C}}\sim SEnz + H_3PO_4 \rightleftharpoons R{-}\overset{O}{\overset{\|}{C}}{-}O\sim PO_3H_2 + Enz\text{-}SH}$$

Formation of a carboxyl phosphate preserves a portion of the energy liberated by the oxidation, and also renders the reaction reversible.

The substrate level phosphorylations which occur in the oxidation of pyruvate and ketoglutarate to acetate and succinate, respectively, require coenzyme A, in addition to NAD as hydrogen carrier and lipoic acid and thiamine pyrophosphate as cofactors for the decarboxylations. It is quite probable that in these cases the sulfhydryl and disulfide groups of coenzyme A and lipoic acid participate in a series of reactions much like those just described (pp. 409, 411).

Coupling Mechanisms: Oxidative Chain Phosphorylation

Those specialized oxidations which are catalyzed by oxidases, oxygenases, and hydroxylases appear to have no mechanism for conservation of the liberated free energy. Such mechanisms do exist, however, in the case of oxidations catalyzed by many dehydrogenases. Most such reactions begin with a transfer of pairs of hydrogen atoms to the nicotinamide nucleotides. At this point in the oxidative chain, the hydrogen atoms or electrons are at an energy level not very different from that of the substrate. However, in traversing the pathway over the flavoproteins, the cytochromes, and cytochrome oxidase, the energy levels become progressively lower until, with the formation of water, all of the potential energy (from a biochemical standpoint) is drained from the hydrogen atoms. At each stage in electron transfer, therefore, a certain amount of free energy is liberated. By means of mechanisms which are largely unknown at the present time, this energy is captured and transformed into high-energy phosphate bonds.

Whereas only one high-energy bond can be generated per mole of substrate *at the substrate level* (see preceding section), it has been found that approximately three moles of high-energy phosphate are formed during the passage of each mole of hydrogen from the nicotinamide nucleotides to oxygen. In those few cases which are known also to involve substrate level phosphorylation (phosphoglyceraldehyde, pyruvate, and ketoglutarate), a total of four high-energy bonds can therefore be produced per mole of substrate oxidized. (In the case of pyruvate, one of these bonds is used to "drive" the synthesis of citrate [p. 410].) Most other oxidations form only three such bonds. The succinate and other flavin-linked dehydrogenase systems, because they bypass some of the oxidative chain, yield only two high-energy bonds per mole of substrate.

The efficiency of oxidative phosphorylation of a given system may be expressed in terms of the P/O ratio, i.e., the ratio of the number of moles of inorganic phosphate raised to the high-energy level to the number of atoms of oxygen utilized by the system. In these terms, oxidative phosphorylation proceeding along the usual oxidative chain from the nicotinamide nucleotide-linked dehydrogenases will approach an ideal P/O ratio of 3.0; the corresponding figure for the flavin-linked systems would be 2.0. These ideal ratios are not always attained in practice, because of the operation of degradative reactions on the newly formed ATP or its high-energy precursors.

The efficiency of recovery of energy in the average oxidative phosphorylation system may be calculated as follows. When two oxidant-reductant pairs interact so that hydrogen atoms or electrons are passed from that of lower potential to that of higher potential, the relationship between the free energy evolved in the process and the difference in potential of the two systems is given by

$$\Delta F \text{ (kcal.)} = -23.1n \, \Delta E_0'$$

where $\Delta E_0'$ is the difference between the oxidation potentials of the two systems, n is the number of hydrogen atoms or electrons involved in the interaction of the two systems, and the numerical constant is the Faraday in kilocalories. If we consider the overall process of oxidizing a pair of hydrogen atoms from reduced NAD, taking into consideration the difference between the potentials of the nicotinamide nucleotide system and the oxygen electrode (Table 16-1, p. 348), it develops from the above equation that complete oxidation of a pair of hydrogen atoms would result in the liberation of 52.2 kcal. of free energy. Assuming the current values for the free energy of hydrolysis of the terminal phosphate of ATP to be 7 to 8 kcal., a P/O ratio of 3.0 will conserve 21 to 24 kcal. of free energy in the form of terminal pyrophosphate linkages in ATP, thus exhibiting an efficiency of 40 to 46 per cent of the total free energy made available in the oxidation.

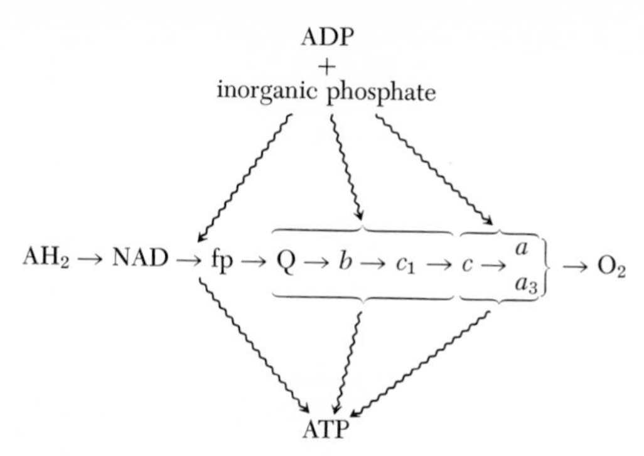

Figure 17–3. Sites of oxidative phosphorylation. *fp*, flavoprotein (cytochrome reductase). *Q*, coenzyme Q.

The exact sites along the oxidative chain where oxidative phosphorylation occurs have not been identified with certainty, but evidence is accumulating in support of the scheme shown in Figure 17–3. It will be observed that the first phosphorylation site is believed to occur between NAD and the flavoprotein cytochrome reductases. It was formerly stated that a second phosphorylating site existed between cytochromes *b* and *c*. However, the discoveries of cytochrome c_1 and coenzyme Q have added complications to this picture, since it is not certain at exactly which point the high-energy bond is generated. The third phosphorylation site is even more controversial; it has been suggested that it occurs between cytochromes *c* and *a*, or between *a* and a_3, the latter suggestion being complicated somewhat by the possibility that *a* and a_3 are not distinct entities. In any case, it is obvious why nicotinamide nucleotide-linked dehydrogenase systems should produce three high-energy bonds per mole, whereas only two should be expected from the flavin-linked systems, such as succinate dehydrogenase.

Although the exact mechanism whereby formation of a high-energy bond is coupled to certain oxidative steps is not known, the following equations illustrate a working hypothesis which is in use at the present time:

(1) $\text{Carrier}_{\text{red}} + \text{CF} + \text{2nd Carrier}_{\text{ox}} \rightleftharpoons \text{Carrier}_{\text{ox}} \sim \text{CF} + \text{2nd Carrier}_{\text{red}}$

(2) $\text{Carrier}_{\text{ox}} \sim \text{CF} + \text{PO}_4 \rightleftharpoons \text{Carrier}_{\text{ox}} + \text{CF} \sim \text{PO}_4$

(3) $\text{CF} \sim \text{PO}_4 + \text{ADP} \rightleftharpoons \text{ATP} + \text{CF}.$

The first equation depicts one step in the oxidative chain, in which one hydrogen- or electron-carrier interacts with a second carrier system, reducing the second and being itself oxidized, in the course of which the first carrier forms a high-energy bond with a coupling factor, CF. In the second reaction, this high-energy bond undergoes phosphorolysis with inorganic phosphate to re-form the oxidized form of the carrier and a high-energy phosphorylated derivative of the agent, CF. A kinase reaction then transfers this high-energy phosphate bond to ADP, forming ATP.

It should be pointed out that the actual reactions occurring in nature may be considerably more complicated than in the scheme depicted. In particular, it seems possible that there may be more than one intermediate of the type CF, interposed between the oxidative reaction and the final formation of an ATP bond at each site. The coupling factors appear to be proteins. A specific factor is required at each site of oxidative phosphorylation. Although a protein-bound histidine residue has been shown to undergo phosphorylation during oxidative chain operation, and is capable of transferring its phosphate to ADP, it is not yet established that this intermediate is the one actually involved in reactions (2) and (3) above.

Uncoupling of Phosphorylations

Inhibitors of electron transport (p. 364) also obviously inhibit oxidative chain phosphorylation, since the latter process cannot occur without the former. The converse, however, is quite possible, although a different species of inhibitor is required to elicit the effect. Many years ago, compounds such as 2,4-dinitrophenol were used in the treatment of obesity, since they had the faculty of increasing oxidative reactions in the body (increased caloric output) without stimulating anabolic processes (which might cause increases in weight). Although the medical use of these compounds has been abandoned because of their toxicity, there now exists much interest in their in vitro effects.

As was indicated previously, most high-energy phosphate bonds are generated by mechanisms which operate to couple the oxidative chain to the phosphorylative process. This coupling is very labile, in the sense that many conditions and agents disturb the phosphorylative side of the couple much more than the purely oxidative. Dinitrophenol and certain other reagents, in appropriate concentrations, are able to suppress the generation of high-energy phosphate at the hydrogen- (or electron-) transfer level in respiring mitochondria without disturbing the respiration. In fact, under certain circumstances an actual stimulation of respiration occurs. Evidently these reagents "uncouple" oxidation from phosphorylation, and convert the catabolism of substrates into a profitless undertaking.

True uncoupling agents, such as dinitrophenol (and other nitro and halo phenols), Dicumarol, gramicidin, tyrocidine, certain nitriles, long-chain fatty acids, and arsenate, are believed to cause the breakdown of a high-energy intermediate in the energy-transfer sequence and to liberate its components in an active state. Hence there is little interference with (and may be actual acceleration of) electron-transfer and respiration. Certain uncoupling agents, such as dinitrophenol, Dicumarol, and gramicidin, are believed to accelerate the hydrolytic breakdown of $\text{Carrier}_{ox} \sim \text{CF}$, thus tending to reverse equation (2), which in turn causes a reversal of equation (3). In addition to uncoupling, another result of the action of these compounds is a net hydrolysis of ATP to ADP and inorganic phosphate. This type of effect probably accounts for the so-called "ATP-ase" action manifesting itself in mitochondria under certain conditions. Arsenate competes with inorganic phosphate in reaction (2), forming an unstable CF-arsenate compound, the decomposition of which also results in a net breakdown of carrier $\sim$ CF.

The effectiveness of artificial uncoupling agents raises the question whether natural uncoupling agents also exist and aid in the regulation of energy production. Although thyroxine was a promising candidate in this regard, recent evidence has tended to be against it. In vitro, thyroxine indeed acts as an uncoupling agent, but in concentrations which are probably unphysiological. In contrast to the chemically related dinitrophenol, thyroxine appears to uncouple by altering the mitochondrial membranes. The results of thyroxine administration in vivo appear to be mediated largely by its effect in selectively inducing synthesis of certain oxidative enzymes, an action which can be blocked by specific inhibitors of protein synthesis. The well-known "time lag" involved in the appearance of the effects of in vivo administration of thyroxine is in accord with this interpretation of its action.

In addition to the true uncoupling agents, there also exists a group of "inhibitors of phosphorylating oxidation," compounds which combine with an intermediate in the energy-transfer sequence and prevent it from re-entering its usual cycle of reactions. Hence, under conditions of "tight coupling," both energy- and electron-transfer are inhibited. The respiration of uncoupled particles is not affected by this group of agents, which includes the antibiotics oligomycin, aurovertin, and valinomycin, certain guanidines, atractylate (a plant glycoside), triethyltin, and azide.

Although *most* of the agents discussed in this section have no effect on substrate level phosphorylation, arsenate uncouples the phosphorylation associated with the anaerobic oxidation of glyceraldehyde-3-phosphate, and both arsenate and atractylate appear to inhibit the substrate level phosphorylation in the oxidation of α-ketoglutarate.

Reversal of Oxidative Chain Phosphorylation

The fact that, in several of the steps in the oxidative chain, the free energy liberated in the oxidation is conserved to a considerable degree in a coupled energy-transfer reaction, suggests the theoretical possibility of reversing the operation of the oxidative chain, if the system is provided with a source of reducing power and a source of energy. This possibility was realized by the discovery that succinate could bring about the reduction of intra-mitochondrial NAD (or of substrates linked by their dehydrogenases to NAD) in the presence of ATP. The use of various inhibitors demonstrated that the pathway traversed by the reducing equivalents (2H or 2 e^-) involved only those factors in the oxidative chain concerned with the flavin- and NAD-linked dehydrogenase systems up to and including the common junction point (coenzyme Q-cytochrome *b* area). ATP as such was not an absolute requirement. It could be omitted if the mitochondria were "pre-charged" with non-phosphorylated high-energy intermediates, presumably of the type, carrier $\sim$ CF, formed in the course of previous oxidative phosphorylations. These phenomena evidently represent a true reversal of the oxidative phosphorylation occurring at the NAD-cytochrome reductase site.

Further investigation has demonstrated similar reversibility at the remaining two sites of oxidative chain phosphorylation. In addition, it appears that reversal of oxidation at one site can utilize high energy generated at another site. The mechanism of this transfer of energy is unknown, since ATP is not an obligatory additive and the non-phosphorylated high-energy intermediates are thought to be specific for each site. It is possible that energy exchange may occur between pairs of these intermediates.

In sum, the entire process of oxidative chain phosphorylation appears to be reversible, a finding directly applicable to the problem of control of mitochondrial metabolism, as discussed in the following section.

Self-Regulation of Energy Production

The organism would operate at maximum efficiency if the rate of production of high-energy phosphate equaled its rate of utilization. It appears that, to a large extent, this can be done in the case of oxidative phosphorylation by means of a self-regulating mechanism existing in the mitochondria. As pointed out previously, "coupling" mechanisms exist between electron-transport along the oxidative chain and the generation of high-energy phosphate bonds, as exemplified in the equations (1) to (3) (p. 383). In the absence of uncoupling agents, this coupling appears to be obligative, not permissive, in the sense that, inhibition (not uncoupling) of the phosphorylation mechanisms blocks electron transport. A major controlling factor in this regard appears to be the intramitochondrial ratio, $\frac{(\mathrm{ATP})}{(\mathrm{ADP})(\mathrm{PO_4})}$, sometimes called the "phosphate potential."

Thus, if the rate of oxidation of substrates along the oxidative chain proceeds at a greater rate than that of utilization of ATP for work, then the concentration of ATP will be built up to a high level, and that of ADP and inorganic phosphate to correspondingly low levels. Considering the matter from the viewpoint of the individual reactions, the lack of acceptor ADP and phosphate molecules inhibits reactions (2) and (3) (p. 383), which in turn inhibit the preceding reaction, leading to inhibition of the electron transport chain. Consequently, the oxidation of substrates will slow down or cease, and the generation of high-energy phosphate as well, until such time as the utilization of ATP for work will liberate sufficient ADP and phosphate to allow further substrate oxidation and formation of high-energy phosphate. From the standpoint of a reversible equilibrium (see previous section), a high ratio of $\frac{(ATP)}{(ADP)(PO_4)}$ will tend to drive the coupled reactions of the oxidative chain backward in the reductive direction, thus suppressing mitochondrial oxidation of substrates until the "phosphate potential" falls. Thus, the entire integrated system of oxidative chain and energy-conserving reactions may be considered a "feedback" mechanism, a type of metabolic regulation which is discussed in greater detail elsewhere (p. 769).

Oxidative Phosphorylation from Extra-mitochondrial Metabolites

Intact mitochondria are impermeable to many substrates and cofactors, such as the intermediates of the tricarboxylic acid cycle, adenine nucleotides, inorganic phosphate (which is absorbed only with the expenditure of energy), NADH, NADPH, and usually the oxidized forms of the nicotinamide nucleotides as well. Although exposure to hypotonic solutions makes available a number of intra-mitochondrial dehydrogenase systems to extra-mitochondrial substrates, it is obvious that a different sort of mechanism must be employed physiologically in order to permit the cell to secure oxidative chain energy from substrates dissolved in the cytoplasm.

One such mechanism appears to be the glycerophosphate "shuttle." A number of extra-mitochondrial dehydrogenases, such as the glyceraldehyde-3-phosphate enzyme of the glycolytic sequence, are NAD-linked. The NADH resulting from these reactions can be used by an extra-mitochondrial α-glycerophosphate dehydrogenase, acting "in reverse," to reduce dihydroxyacetone-phosphate (an intermediate in glycolysis). The resulting α-glycerophosphate is able to penetrate the mitochondrion, where it is oxidized by a flavin-linked dehydrogenase to dihydroxyacetone-phosphate, which leaves the mitochondrion to continue the cycle. Two high-energy bonds are produced per molecule of substrate through oxidative chain phosphorylation by passage of hydrogen or electron-pairs from the intra-mitochondrial dehydrogenase through the remainder of the oxidative chain. Thus, any reducing power in the soluble phase of the cytoplasm which can be transformed into NADH, eventually can also be transformed into reducing equivalents for energy generation via the intra-mitochondrial oxidative chain. (A similar "shuttle" mechanism has been proposed for the acetoacetate-D-β-hydroxybutyrate pair, but the evidence is not yet conclusive.) It is of interest, from the standpoint of regulation of biological oxidations, that the activity of the intra-mitochondrial glycerophosphate dehydrogenase in certain tissues appears to be under the control of thyroid hormones.

Ion and Water Transport in Mitochondria

Uptake of K^+ by mitochondria is an energy-dependent process, favored by conditions appropriate for oxidative chain phosphorylation, inhibited by aging, certain uncoupling agents, respiratory poisons, and agents causing mitochondrial swelling. Divalent cations (Ca^{++}, Mg^{++}, Mn^{++}) probably are absorbed passively but concomitantly with the active transport of inorganic phosphate. Uptake of phosphate, which is inhibited by oxidative chain inhibitors and uncoupling agents, may be "driven" either by energy derived from the oxidative chain or by ATP itself. Since oligomycin inhibits the ATP- but not the respiration-driven process, it has been suggested that ion transport involves nonphosphorylated high-energy intermediates of oxidative chain "phosphorylation," rather than ATP per se. After absorption, inorganic phosphate may follow either of two routes, one being incorporation into ATP, the other being formation of inorganic salts with Ca^{++} or other divalent cations.

In contrast to the situation as regards the cell membrane, the physiological function of active ion transport across the mitochondrial membrane remains to be established. Roles which have been suggested include: (1) maintenance of the composition of the intramitochondrial environment, and (2): assistance to cell membranes in transcellular ion transport (e.g., in kidney tubule cells), by establishing and maintaining ion gradients vs. the soluble cytoplasm.

Although mitochondria can behave as passive osmometers in response to changes in the tonicity of the suspending medium, greater interest attaches to "active" swelling and contraction, since these latter processes appear to be related to mitochondrial bioenergetic systems. It is noteworthy (and rather unexpected) that active changes in the size and shape of mitochondria seem not to be directly dependent on absorption or extrusion of inorganic ions.

Active swelling of mitochondria is, in general, promoted by conditions favoring oxidative chain phosphorylation, and repressed by oxidation inhibitors and certain uncoupling agents. The situation is complicated, however, by the fact that other uncoupling agents act as "swelling agents," as do a number of chemical substances having little in common with each other. Much current investigation concerns swelling caused by Ca^{++} or thyroxine.

Most investigations of mitochondrial contractions have used mitochondria "preswollen" by Ca^{++} or thyroxine. The long-chain fatty acids liberated during swelling are incorporated into phosphatidic acids during contraction. This and certain other evidence points to a possible role of phospholipids in mitochondrial water transport. Intramitochondrial catalase and glutathione peroxidase also may be involved in some as yet unknown fashion. Contraction is readily induced by ATP (which is hydrolyzed in the process), an effect which is counteracted by "inhibitors of phosphorylating oxidation" (e.g., oligomycin). However, the uncoupler, dinitrophenol, has no effect on ATP-induced contraction.

Mitochondrial swelling and contraction may assist transcellular water transport. Or, these alterations in mitochondrial size and shape, which reflect structural changes in the mitochondrial membranes, could have the function of regulating mitochondrial (and extra-mitochondrial) metabolism by changes in permeability to metabolites.

Summary of Generation of High-Energy Phosphate

Referring back to Figure 17–1, which, as was mentioned before, applies to individual bioenergetic reactions as well as to the complete scheme, the generation of high-energy phosphate may be summarized as follows. An organic compound (or a pair of hydrogen atoms) is degraded from its initial energy level to a lower level. In the course of this degradation, inorganic phosphate is raised to the high-energy phosphate level, thus conserving a part of the energy liberated in the degradation reaction. With the aid of a kinase, this new high-energy phosphate group is transferred to ADP to form ATP. If it is to be stored, the phosphate group is again transferred, this time from ATP to creatine, forming phosphocreatine. When required, the phosphocreatine returns the group to regenerate ATP. In any case, ATP is the agent directly concerned in the generation and utilization of high-energy phosphate.

Utilization of High-Energy Phosphate

Since ATP represents the "common currency" of bioenergetics, the number of examples of its utilization is as great as the number of types of physiological work carried on by the cell. Considerable sections of this book will be devoted to these examples. It may suffice at this point to cite one instance of chemical work.

The living cell, in its synthesis of complex molecules from simpler ones, is faced with the same problem which confronts the organic chemist who wishes to unite a carboxylic acid with an alcohol or amine to form an ester or amide. These condensations require the splitting out of the elements of water, a reversal of a hydrolytic reaction, and are thermodynamically difficult or impossible in an aqueous medium. The organic chemist solves the problem either by operating in a non-aqueous medium, removing the water as it is formed, or by "activating" the carboxylic acid by forming an acid chloride or anhydride. The chemist does not obtain something for nothing, both of these methods requiring the expenditure of work; in particular, the second procedure requires the performance of work on the carboxylic acid to transform it into a more active form. Given the aqueous physiological environment, the cell is limited to the latter procedure.

The synthesis of hippuric acid (benzoyl-glycine) is endergonic, i.e., it does not proceed spontaneously as written. Stated another way, the equilibrium lies far toward the side of the products of hydrolysis of the pseudopeptide linkage:

$$\text{Benzoic acid} + \text{Glycine} \longleftarrow\!\!\!\rightarrow \text{Hippuric acid} + H_2O$$

Nevertheless, this synthesis is readily performed in the animal body by the expenditure of chemical work:

$$\text{Benzoic acid} + \text{ATP} \rightleftharpoons \text{benzoyladenylate (enzyme-bound)} + \text{pyrophosphate}$$
$$\text{Benzoyladenylate (enzyme-bound)} + \text{CoA} \rightleftharpoons \text{Benzoyl-CoA} + \text{AMP}$$

In the first reaction, the carboxyl group of benzoic acid is activated by conversion to a mixed anhydride (an enzyme-bound carboxyl phosphate), at the expense of a pyrophosphate linkage of ATP. Since the bond formed and the bond broken are energetically equivalent, this reaction is freely reversible. The second reaction is also reversible and for the same reason; the carboxyl phosphate linkage is exchanged for a thioester linkage with coenzyme A, a common carrier of acyl groups.

Once the benzoyl radical is attached via a high-energy thioester linkage to coenzyme A, it is readily coupled to the amino group of glycine to form the desired product:

$$\text{Benzoyl-CoA} + \text{Glycine} \longrightarrow \text{Benzoyl-glycine} + \text{CoA}$$

Since the energy level of the thioester linkage is considerably above that of a peptide or amide, the final condensation is exergonic, thus going to completion and helping to shift the preceding two reactions toward the right.

Other examples of ATP utilization follow the same general pattern; a direct reaction occurs between ATP and some member of the system, work is performed, and inorganic phosphate or pyrophosphate is produced from the original high-energy bond. Although the mechanisms of the utilization of ATP have been worked out in most detail for chemical work, it is believed that much the same mechanisms occur also in mechanical, osmotic, and electrical work.

BIBLIOGRAPHY

INTRODUCTORY AND GENERAL TEXTBOOKS

Baldwin, E.: Dynamic Aspects of Biochemistry, Chapter 3, London, Cambridge University Press, 1963.
Lehninger, A. L.: The Mitochondrion, New York, W. A. Benjamin, Inc., 1964.
Lehninger, A. L.: Bioenergetics, New York, W. A. Benjamin, Inc., 1965.
Racker, E.: Mechanisms in Bioenergetics, New York, Academic Press, Inc., 1965.

ADVANCED TREATISES AND REVIEWS

Atkinson, M. R., and Morton, R. K.: Free energy and the biosynthesis of phosphates, Chapter 1 in Florkin, M., and Mason, H. S. (eds.): Comparative Biochemistry, Vol. 2, New York, Academic Press, Inc., 1960.
Conn, E. C.: Comparative biochemistry of electron transport and oxidative phosphorylation, Chapter 10 in Florkin, M., and Mason, H. S. (eds.): Comparative Biochemistry, Vol. 1, New York, Academic Press, Inc., 1960.
Ernster, L., and Luft, R.: Mitochondrial respiratory control: Biochemical, physiological, and pathological aspects, Advances in Metab. Disorders *1*:95, 1964.
Huennekens, F. M., and Whiteley, H. R.: Phosphoric acid anhydrides and other energy-rich compounds, Chapter 4 in Florkin, M., and Mason, H. S. (eds.): Comparative Biochemistry, Vol. 1, New York, Academic Press, Inc., 1960.
Johnson, M. J.: Enzymic equilibria and thermodynamics, Chapter 21 in Boyer, P. D., Lardy, H., and Myrbäck, K. (eds.): The Enzymes, Vol. 3, New York Academic Press, Inc., 1960.
Krebs, H. A., and Kornberg, H. L.: Energy Transformations in Living Matter, Berlin, Springer Verlag, 1957.
Pardee, A. B., and Ingraham, L. L.: Free energy and entropy in metabolism, Chapter 1 in Greenberg, D. M. (ed.): Metabolic Pathways, Vol. 1, New York, Academic Press, Inc., 1960.
Racker, E.: Mechanisms of synthesis of adenosine triphosphate, Advances Enzymol. *23*:323, 1961.
Slater, E. C.: Uncouplers and inhibitors of oxidative phosphorylation, Chapter 32 in Hochster, R. M., and Quastel, J. H. (eds.): Metabolic Inhibitors, Vol. 2, New York, Academic Press, Inc., 1963.
Slater, E. C.: Oxidative phosphorylation, Chapter 7 in Florkin, M., and Stotz, E. H. (eds.): Comprehensive Biochemistry, Vol. 14, Amsterdam, Elsevier Publishing Company, 1966.

CHAPTER 18

METABOLISM OF CARBOHYDRATE

INTRODUCTION

WHETHER from the standpoint of synthesis within the organism, or of absorption from the diet, glucose is quantitatively the most important carbohydrate available to the body for various purposes. To a considerable extent, therefore, the discussion of the metabolism of carbohydrates resolves itself into a consideration of the metabolism of glucose and its closely related derivatives. The metabolism of other carbohydrates will be considered insofar as warranted by their biological importance.

The sections immediately following will be devoted to the general metabolism of glucose, considering first the sources of glucose to the organism, and then the several routes available for its utilization. Later parts of this chapter will present in greater detail the reactions underlying these general metabolic pathways.

SOURCES OF GLUCOSE TO THE ORGANISM

Exogenous

Although certain non-carbohydrate constituents of the diet (e.g., protein) are potential sources of carbohydrate in the body, the conversion of these substances to carbohydrate is identical with that undergone by endogenous compounds of the same type; hence consideration of this topic will be deferred (p. 423). The direct exogenous source of carbohydrate is obviously the carbohydrate of the diet, and a consideration of the mechanisms whereby it becomes available to the organism involves a description of the processes of digestion and absorption.

Digestion and absorption. The indigestible carbohydrates of foodstuffs (celluloses, pentosans) are not utilizable by man and pass out of the bowel in the feces. (In ruminants, cellulose is fermented by bacteria in the rumen to various acids which are absorbed and enter the metabolic pathways of lipids [acetate and butyrate] or carbohydrate [propionate and lactate].) Digestible polysaccharides and disaccharides are hydrolyzed, either in the intestinal lumen (polysaccharides) or within the epithelial cells (disaccharides) (p. 263 ff.), to their monosaccharide components: viz., starch, glycogen, and maltose to glucose; lactose to glucose and galactose; sucrose to glucose and fructose. In addition to these sugars, foodstuffs contain small amounts of pentose and mannose.

All monosaccharides are practically completely absorbed, almost entirely in the small intestine. The rate of absorption diminishes from above downward, that in the proximal jejunum being three times that in the distal ileum. In the dog, glucose is absorbed at an average rate of approximately 1 gm./kg. body weight/hour. Although a portion enters the thoracic lymph, by far the major portion passes into the portal blood, by which it is carried directly to the liver.

That some process other than simple diffusion must be involved is indicated by the following facts:

(1) The comparative rate of absorption of the monosaccharides is as follows: galactose > glucose > fructose > mannose > xylose > arabinose.

(2) All of these monosaccharides are absorbed from the peritoneal space at the same slow rate, i.e., that of pentoses.

(3) The amounts and concentrations of these monosaccharides entering the intestine have comparatively little effect on the rate of absorption, which, in experimental animals, is relatively constant for each sugar and for each segment of the bowel.

(4) The rate of absorption of certain sugars is modified by simultaneous administration of others; e.g., that of galactose diminishes when it is given with glucose.

At least two mechanisms are involved: (1) simple diffusion, dependent on the sugar concentration gradients between the intestinal lumen, mucosal cells, and blood plasma; (2) a transport system, independent of concentration gradient. Because of the extensive absorptive surface area and the large volume of blood plasma to which it is exposed, large amounts of monosaccharides can be absorbed by simple diffusion under proper conditions. An active transport mechanism is involved in absorption of glucose and galactose but apparently not in that of other common sugars, which are absorbed either by some other type of carrier mechanism or by passive diffusion. The nature of the transport mechanisms is not known, but is believed not to involve formation or cleavage of covalent bonds. The former view that phosphorylation was involved is now contradicted by compelling evidence. On the basis of a direct correlation between sodium concentration and sugar transport, it has been suggested that the latter may be coupled directly with the sodium transport system.

In common with other substances, the rate of absorption of sugars from the bowel is influenced by such general factors as the state and area of the absorptive surface (i.e., condition of intestinal mucosa) and the intestinal motility (i.e., duration of contact with areas of optimal absorption). Thyroxine accelerates absorption of hexoses (which is increased in hyperthyroidism, decreased in hypothyroidism). Diminished absorption in adrenocortical insufficiency is due mainly to the decreased concentration of sodium in the body fluids. There is evidence, too, that the active transport of sugars, as well as of other substances, is linked in some manner with cation transport. Absorption is decreased in states of deficiency of certain B vitamins, such as thiamine, pyridoxine, and pantothenic acid.

Certain of the monosaccharides may undergo metabolic transformation in the course of their passage through the intestinal epithelial cells. Pentoses and galactose apparently enter the portal blood as such, unchanged. The same applies to glucose, except for conversion of a relatively small quantity to lactate (glycolysis). However, fructose absorbed from the intestinal lumen appears in the portal blood as a mixture of fructose, glucose and lactic acid, the proportions varying in different species.

Fate of absorbed carbohydrates. After absorption into the portal blood, carbohydrates must pass through the liver before entering the systemic circulation, a fact of considerable physiological significance. Certain hepatic mechanisms contribute to the withdrawal of carbohydrates from the blood: (1) uptake of hexoses such as fructose and galactose for conversion to glucose by the liver cells; (2) conversion of glucose to glycogen for storage in the liver (glycogenesis); (3) utilization of glucose, by oxidation, for energy production; (4) utilization of glucose for the synthesis of other compounds, such as fatty acids and certain amino acids. Opposed to these mechanisms are others which lead to the release of glucose by the liver to the blood: (1) formation of blood sugar from hexoses other than glucose by the liver; (2) conversion of liver glycogen to blood glucose (glycogenolysis*); (3) formation of blood glucose by the liver from non-carbohydrate sources, such as certain amino acids (gluconeogenesis). The amount of glucose reaching the systemic circulation at any instant is consequently the resultant of the operations of these two groups of opposing processes.

Once it is in the systemic circulation, blood glucose becomes available for utilization by the extrahepatic tissues. From what has been said about portal absorption, it is evident that these tissues are presented with carbohydrate which has already been "picked over" by the liver in a selective manner. It is to be expected, therefore, that the functional state of the liver will have a profound influence on the carbohydrate metabolism of the entire organism, an expectation abundantly fulfilled in practice.

Although glucose is taken up by intestinal mucosal and kidney tubule cells through a process of active transport, hepatic cells are freely permeable to glucose. Insulin increases the uptake of glucose in a number of tissues, including skeletal muscle, heart muscle, diaphragm, adipose tissue, and lactating mammary gland.

Endogenous

Among the minor carbohydrate sources of body glucose may be listed the small quantities of endogenous galactose, mannose, and, possibly, pentoses which may be converted to glucose under certain circumstances. The major endogenous carbohydrate source is liver glycogen. The glycogen of muscle is not directly convertible to blood glucose; however, the lactic acid formed during glycolysis of muscle glycogen can be converted to glucose and glycogen in the liver.

Certain non-carbohydrate sources are available to the organism for production of glucose. Although fatty acids cannot undergo net conversion to carbohydrate, the glycerol moiety of lipids can serve as a source of glucose (from which it can also be derived). However, the amino acids are the major raw material for the synthesis of carbohydrate from non-carbohydrate sources (gluconeogenesis). It has been estimated that over half of the average animal protein is potentially capable of conversion to carbohydrate. Those amino acids which are carbohydrate-formers are called "glucogenic." The major site of gluconeogenesis is the liver.

---

*The term "glycogenolysis" is used by some to mean any breakdown of glycogen, whether it leads to blood glucose (liver), or via the glycolytic sequence of reactions to pyruvic and lactic acids (liver, muscle).

UTILIZATION OF GLUCOSE

Storage

When a molecule of glucose is introduced into the body or synthesized de novo therein, several metabolic pathways are open to it. In the absence of urgent physiological demands for oxidative energy or conversion to special products, excess glucose may be deposited as glycogen in the liver and other tissues (glycogenesis). Inasmuch as the amount of glycogen which can be stored in the body is limited, quantities of glucose in excess of this upper limit are converted to fatty acids and stored as triglycerides in the fat depots. There seems to be no fixed limit to this process, as may be seen from everyday observations on human beings.

Oxidation

In response to physiological demands for energy, glucose may be completely converted to CO_2 and H_2O (via pyruvate), a process which occurs in all tissues. In certain tissues, such as liver and adipose, glucose also may be degraded stepwise to CO_2 via a sequence of reactions involving pentoses, rather than pyruvate and lactate, as intermediates. At certain times, special circumstances in muscle may result in only partial degradation of glucose (glycolysis). The product, lactic acid, is then largely disposed of by other tissues, notably liver.

Conversion to Fat

As indicated above, a net conversion of glucose to fatty acids occurs when accommodations for storage as glycogen are exceeded. However, since one of the major metabolites of glucose is in rapid equilibrium with fatty acids, a constant interconversion occurs between certain molecules common to the carbohydrate and fatty acid pathways. This interconversion is rapid, and investigations with isotopes have led to the conclusion that a large proportion of glucose that is metabolized forms fatty acids before final degradation to CO_2 and H_2O. It must be noted that the overall conversion of glucose to fatty acids is irreversible, for reasons which will be pointed out subsequently. In contrast, the transformation of glucose to the glycerol moiety of the lipids is readily reversible.

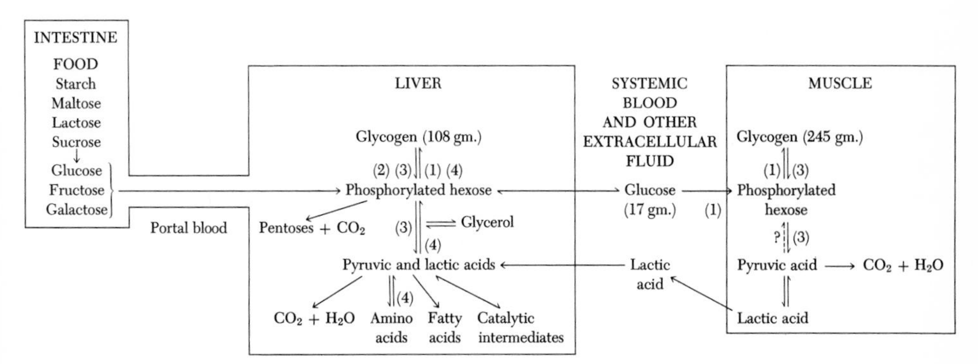

Figure 18-1. Sources and major routes of utilization of carbohydrate. Numerical data for 70-kg. man. (1), Glycogenesis; (2), glycogenolysis; (3), glycolysis; (4), gluconeogenesis.

Conversion to Other Carbohydrates

Small amounts of glucose are used, directly or indirectly, in the synthesis of certain other carbohydrates which play important roles in the economy of the organism. These include (1) ribose and deoxyribose, required for the synthesis of nucleic acids, (2) mannose, fucose, glucosamine, galactosamine, and neuraminic acid, which form parts of mucopolysaccharides and glycoproteins, (3) glucuronic acid, also involved in mucopolysaccharides and in "detoxication" reactions, and (4) galactose, which is a component of glycolipids as well as of the disaccharide, lactose, secreted in milk.

Conversion to Amino Acids

Certain amino acids are not required in the diet, although they occur in tissue proteins. It may be concluded, therefore, that they are synthesized by the body. Evidence at hand indicates that this group of amino acids, commonly designated "dispensable" or "nonessential," derives its carbon skeletons from glucose or its metabolites. Although all amino acids which are formed from glucose are also "glucogenic," the converse generalization does not hold.

Miscellaneous Pathways

As will be indicated in detail elsewhere, a large proportion of the catabolic sequences of reactions is of a cyclic nature, and, as such, requires the presence of adequate amounts of certain compounds which perform a catalytic function. These compounds are derived, more or less directly, from glucose.

The ingestion of sufficient glucose, or compounds rapidly converted to glucose, to cause significant hyperglycemia may result in the excretion of glucose in the urine. This is not, however, a normal pathway of disposal.

THE INTERMEDIARY METABOLISM OF CARBOHYDRATE: INTRODUCTION

The major sequence of catabolic reactions whereby glucose is degraded in most tissues to CO_2 and H_2O may be divided, for didactic convenience, into anaerobic and aerobic phases. It is currently believed that these phases do not involve separate pathways, but that an initial, anaerobic series of reactions takes place, continuing directly in an aerobic series in the presence of oxygen. The anaerobic phase of glucose metabolism occurs whether oxygen is present or not, its anaerobic character deriving from the fact that participation of oxygen is not required in any of its reactions. "Glycolysis" is the term commonly applied to the production of lactic acid from glucose or glycogen, a phenomenon which is rare under physiological conditions, being largely restricted to circumstances of muscle contraction in which the rate of metabolism of carbohydrate outstrips the oxygen supply to the tissue (relative anaerobiosis). In the subsequent discussions, the term "glycolysis" or the "glycolytic pathway" will be more broadly interpreted to mean the conversion of glucose or glycogen to either lactate or pyruvate. "Fermentation" refers to the analogous pathway in microorganisms, which, however, terminates in formation of ethanol and carbon dioxide. Certain microorganisms convert carbohydrate to lactate, a process which may be referred to as either glycolysis or "lactic acid fermentation."

Under the usual aerobic conditions, lactic acid is either not produced at all, or, if formed, is immediately reoxidized, in situ, to pyruvic acid. In any event, the aerobic phase of glucose metabolism begins with the end-products of the anaerobic phase, lactic or pyruvic acid, which, by means of an ingenious mechanism (Krebs cycle), are degraded stepwise to CO_2 and H_2O. The efficiencies of the anaerobic and aerobic phases are similar, insofar as recovery of liberated free energy is concerned. However, if calculated in terms of energy obtained per molecule of glucose degraded, the aerobic is superior to the anaerobic by a factor of about 15 to 20.

The important role of pentoses in the formation of nucleic acids and other biologically active compounds warrants consideration of our current knowledge in this field. Pentoses are derived from hexoses or products of hexose metabolism. The pathway involved bypasses the glycolytic sequence of reactions, differs from it in being aerobic, and in addition provides an alternate pathway for the complete oxidation of hexose to carbon dioxide.

The major portion of the discussion of carbohydrate metabolism in this chapter is devoted to those general features of the processes which are known to occur in practically all tissues. However, certain peculiarities or deviations from the general pattern are exhibited in particular tissues or organs. The individuality in carbohydrate metabolism shown by liver and muscle, for example, has a sufficiently significant influence on the metabolism of the entire organism to justify separate consideration.

The metabolic pathways of the several major foodstuffs are so intimately related that a true picture of the metabolism of carbohydrate cannot be drawn by assuming that it occurs in biochemical isolation. It is necessary, therefore, to introduce a discussion of the metabolic interrelations between carbohydrates, fats, and proteins even before the latter two groups are considered formally in detail.

ANAEROBIC METABOLISM OF GLUCOSE (GLYCOLYSIS, FERMENTATION)

The anaerobic metabolism of glucose can be subdivided into the phases of initial phosphorylation, glycogen metabolism, conversion to trioses, the oxidative step, and the formation of lactate (or ethanol). Figure 18–2 presents the complete picture of the anaerobic metabolism of glucose, sometimes called the "Embden-Meyerhof" pathway.

Initial Phosphorylation (Reaction 1, Fig. 18–2)

Entrance of glucose into the cell is facilitated by a mechanism of active transport in certain tissues (intestinal mucosa, kidney tubule), involving expenditure of work by the cell, whereas in other tissues, transport involves some type of carrier, but not expenditure of energy. Insulin facilitates the uptake of glucose in skeletal muscle, diaphragm, heart, adipose tissue, and lactating mammary gland. Liver cells appear to be freely permeable to glucose.

Within the cell, glucose (and other sugars) undergoes an obligatory phosphorylation as its initial step in metabolism. This phosphorylation is catalyzed by one subclass of a group of enzymes, the "irreversible kinases." In liver, two enzymes are involved in the phosphorylation of glucose. The first is a typical animal hexokinase, which occurs in fetal as well as adult liver, and undergoes no significant change in quantity in fasting or carbohydrate feeding, and is not influenced by the diabetic state or by insulin. Its low K_m for glucose insures full saturation even at hypoglycemic levels; hence the concentration of blood glucose exerts no significant effect upon the rate of the reaction. The enzyme is

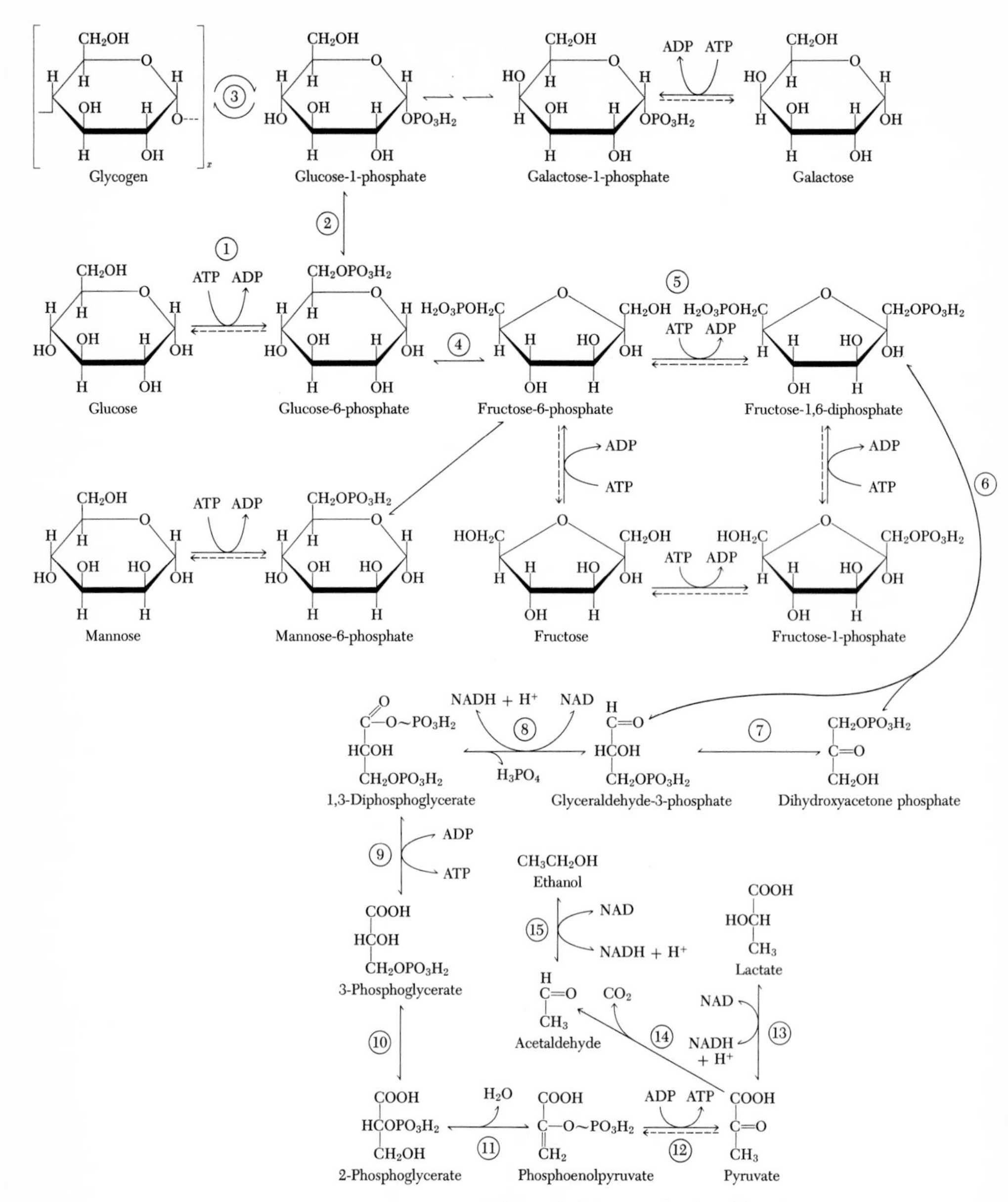

Figure 18-2. Anaerobic metabolism of glucose and related hexoses.

inhibited by the product, glucose-6-phosphate, in a feedback type of reaction, which, however, has not been shown to have physiological significance in the liver.

Liver cells also contain a glucokinase, which is physiologically labile compared to the enzyme just described. The glucokinase appears only in adult liver, is not inhibited by glucose-6-phosphate, and is characterized by a K_m of the order of magnitude of portal blood and hepatic cell glucose concentration, so that the rate of reaction of this enzyme system is markedly dependent upon glucose concentration. The level of the enzyme is depressed in diabetes and fasting, and increased by feeding glucose after fasting. Its synthesis is induced by insulin. The reported depression of glucose phosphorylation in liver upon administration of glucocorticoids and STH may be mediated through this glucokinase. Since liver possesses no control mechanisms with respect to permeability to glucose, initiation of the metabolism of exogenous glucose by the liver is controlled by factors influencing phosphorylation. Possession of the special glucokinase provides the liver with a control mechanism which is responsive to blood glucose concentration, nutritional status, and endocrine control.

In contrast, muscle contains only the hexokinase type of enzyme. Since the phosphorylation mechanism is usually present in excess, control of exogenous glucose metabolism is largely mediated through the permeability mechanism, which, as has been mentioned previously, is controlled by insulin. The hexokinase of muscle is characterized by a low K_m; hence glucose concentration has no significant effect upon the rate of the reaction. However, the enzyme is inhibited by glucose-6-phosphate (feedback), an inhibition which is counteracted by ATP. Hence, the efficiency of disposal of glucose-6-phosphate by the cell exerts a controlling effect upon the rate of phosphorylation. Phosphorylation of glucose in cardiac muscle is depressed by administration of somatotropic hormone and glucocorticoids.

The product of the reaction of ATP and glucose in the presence of the appropriate kinase and Mg^{++} is glucose-6-phosphate. Formation of an ester phosphate at the expense of a high-energy phosphate bond explains the practical irreversibility of this reaction. Other sugars are brought into the glucose pathway at the points shown in Figure 18–2. It will be noted that all of these compounds are capable of conversion to glucose-6-phosphate, which means, as will be shown later, that they are potential sources of blood glucose and liver glycogen.

Certain tissues (e.g., liver, kidney) contain a specific glucose-6-phosphatase, thus enabling them to convert the ester to free glucose. The hepatic phosphatase, which is directly involved in the formation of blood glucose from other forms of carbohydrate and carbohydrate precursors, is increased in activity by administration of glucocorticoids (or ACTH), somatotropic hormone, and thyroid hormones, and decreased in activity by insulin.

Controlling factors in the phosphorylation and dephosphorylation of glucose in liver and extrahepatic tissues are summarized in Figure 18–3.

Synthesis of Glycogen (Fig. 18–4 and Reactions 2 and 3, Fig. 18–2)

Glucose-6-phosphate, in the presence of Mg^{++} and an enzyme called "phosphoglucomutase," is reversibly transformed to glucose-1-phosphate. The mechanism of this reaction, involving glucose-1,6-diphosphate as coenzyme, is presented elsewhere (p. 235).

Under the influence of a pyrophosphorylase, glucose-1-phosphate reacts with uridine triphosphate to form uridinediphosphate-glucose (UDPG), an intermediate which is important also in the pathways leading to galactose, glucuronic acid, and mucopolysaccharides. UDPG-glycogen glucosyl-transferase (commonly called "glycogen synthetase") transfers the glucose moieties of UDPG to the free carbon 4 positions at the non-reducing termini of pre-existing polysaccharidic chains. A "primer" of branched polysaccharide, the main linkages of which are α-1,4, is essential for the reaction. The equilibrium constant of this reaction favors the synthesis of glycogen. UDP, by interaction with ATP, is converted to UTP, so that the uridine nucleotides can participate in the pyrophosphorylase and transferase reactions in a cyclic manner. In the absence of other enzymes, linear, α-1,4-linked polysaccharides are synthesized, similar to the amylose fraction of starch. A branching enzyme (amylo-(1,4 $\rightarrow$ 1,6)-transglucosidase) is required for the formation of the highly ramified glycogen molecule, which contains 1,6-linkages at the branching points.

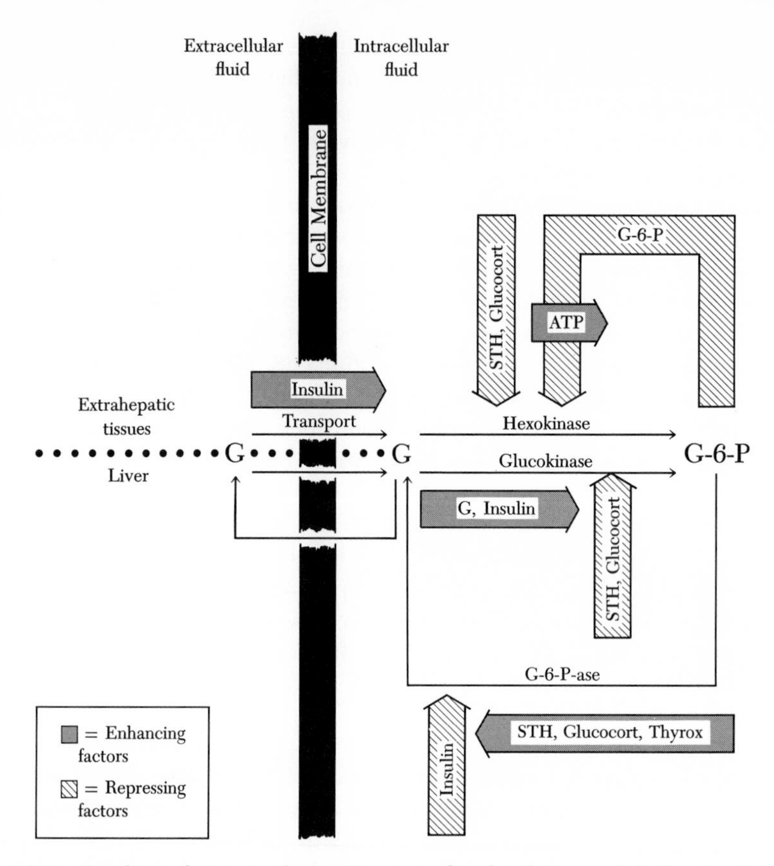

Figure 18–3. Regulatory factors in glucose transport, phosphorylation, and dephosphorylation. *G*, Glucose; *G-6-P*, glucose-6-phosphate; *Glucocort*, glucocorticoid hormones; *STH*, somatotropic hormone; *Thyrox*, thyroid hormones.

The glycogen synthetase reaction is subject to a number of controls (Fig. 18–4). Two forms of the synthetase exist, one dependent upon the presence of glucose-6-phosphate for its activity (D-form), the other independent (I-form, the more active in glycogen synthesis). Glucose-6-phosphate also induces de novo synthesis of the enzyme. Conversion of the D- to the I-form involves cleavage of a phosphate group from the enzyme; the specific phosphatase involved is activated by insulin. Transformation in the opposite direction is accomplished by ATP and a specific kinase, which exists in both active and inactive forms. Activation of the kinase appears to involve a reaction with ATP and Mg^{++} which is accelerated by cyclic 3′,5′-AMP. Production of this accelerator is influenced by hormones, which are discussed later in connection with glycogen phosphorylase, with which this compound is also involved. The I $\rightarrow$ D conversion is said to be facilitated also by Ca^{++} (cf. phosphorylase interconversions). Glucocorticoids accelerate the glycogen synthetase reaction indirectly, by raising the concentration of glucose-6-phosphate. Finally, in some

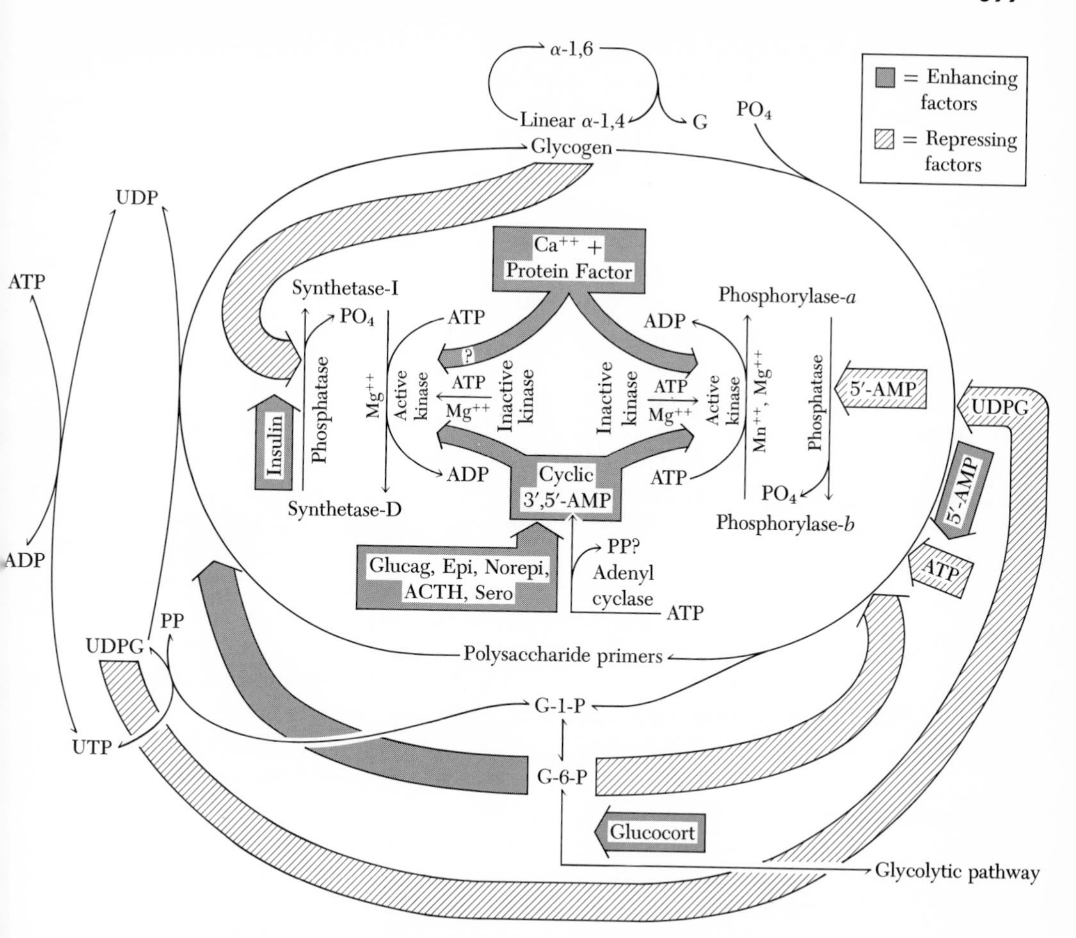

Figure 18-4. Pathways and regulatory factors in glycogen metabolism. *ACTH*, Adrenocorticotropic hormone; *Epi*, epinephrine; *G*, glucose; *G-1-P* and *G-6-P*, glucose-1- and glucose-6-phosphate; *Glucag*, glucagon; *Glucocort*, glucocorticoid hormones; *Norepi*, norepinephrine; *PO_4*, phosphate; *PP*, pyrophosphate; *Sero*, serotonin; *UDP* and *UTP*, uridine di- and triphosphate.

unknown fashion, the fraction of the synthetase in the I-form is negatively influenced by the tissue level of glycogen, so that a form of self-regulation of glycogen synthesis results.

The fine structure of glycogen seems to be somewhat variable, depending in part on the type of carbohydrate given and the route of administration. Glycogen from both liver and muscle contains fractions of different solubility and different biological lability. As might be expected, in all cases the inner tiers of glycogen are more inert metabolically than the outer.

In the direction of breakdown of glycogen to glucose-1-phosphate, splitting of the 1,6-linkages (branching points) is due to amylo-1,6-glucosidase, a purely hydrolytic enzyme. This reaction is obviously not a simple reversal of the synthesis of 1,6-linkages by the branching enzyme, which is a transglycosidase. Muscle also contains an oligo-1,4 → 1,4-glucan transferase, which catalyzes transfer of maltotriose (and to a lesser extent, maltose) units from one oligosaccharide backbone to another, either in the same or a different molecule. Since the products of phosphorylase action frequently contain two maltotetraose chains linked at a branching point, the transferase can move a chain of three glucose units from one branch to the other, leaving a 1,6-linked glucose unit at the branching point. Hydrolysis of this residual glucose by the 1,6-glucosidase then allows phosphorylase to continue its action on the entire chain.

Cleavage of the 1,4-linkages of glycogen is due to phosphorylase, an enzyme which catalyzes the transfer of glucose residues from their glucosidic linkages in the polysaccharide chain to inorganic phosphate as an acceptor, forming glucose-1-phosphate. This reaction is readily reversible in vitro, and was formerly believed to be responsible for the synthesis as well as the breakdown of glycogen. In vivo, however, the relative concentrations of inorganic phosphate and glucose-1-phosphate are such that the reaction in the catabolic direction is strongly favored.

In the case of phosphorylase, regulatory influences present a picture which is almost a mirror image of that discussed in connection with glycogen synthetase, since many factors exert opposite effects on the two enzymes (Fig. 18–4). Phosphorylase exists in two forms in all tissues investigated. One, called the "*a*" form in muscle, although activated somewhat by 5′-AMP, has no absolute requirement for this nucleotide. The other, called the "*b*" form in muscle, has an absolute requirement for 5′-AMP. The activation of phosphorylase *b* by 5′-AMP is antagonized by ATP and glucose-6-phosphate. In liver, the form corresponding to "*b*" in muscle is activated only slightly by 5′-AMP. In any case, the relatively low concentrations of 5′-AMP which obtain in most tissues suggest that the "*a*-like" forms are the more active physiologically. Muscle phosphorylase, but not the liver enzyme, contains pyridoxal-phosphate as prosthetic group. Although muscle phosphorylase *a* is a dimer of *b*, this is not true of liver phosphorylases. In all cases, *b*-like phosphorylases differ from the corresponding *a* forms in having lost hydrolyzable phosphate.

Conversion of phosphorylases type *a* to type *b* is effected by phosphorylase phosphatases, which are inhibited by 5′-AMP. Phosphorylation of phosphorylases type *b* to type *a* is catalyzed by phosphorylase kinases in the presence of ATP and Mn^{++} or Mg^{++}. These kinases exist in both active and inactive forms, the activation evidently involving interaction with ATP and Mg^{++}. Cyclic 3′,5′-AMP accelerates this activation, thus facilitating the $b \rightarrow a$ conversion and operating in a sense opposite to its behavior in the glycogen synthetase system, where it promotes formation of a *less* active form of the synthetase.

Production of cyclic 3′,5′-AMP from ATP (adenyl cyclase reaction) is accelerated in the liver by glucagon, epinephrine, and serotonin; in muscle by epinephrine; in the adrenal cortex by ACTH; in adipose tissue by ACTH, epinephrine, norepinephrine, glucagon, and serotonin. It is evident that the net glycogenolytic effect of these hormones is the result of concomitant depression of glycogen synthetase activity and augmentation of phosphorylase activity.

In muscle an additional mechanism exists for activation of phosphorylase kinase, involving Ca^{++} and a protein factor; these agents become operational in contraction (p. 429).

Conditions leading to net glycogen synthesis in muscle are aided by the fact that UDPG, the immediate reactant in the synthetase reaction, is itself an inhibitor of the muscle phosphorylase reaction.

A rapid conversion of phosphorylase *b* to *a* occurs in muscle during contraction, chiefly due to the large excess of kinase over phosphatase activity, resulting from activation of the kinase by Ca^{++}. In relaxation, phosphatase activity exceeds kinase activity. In the resting, aerobic muscle, glycogen breakdown is slow, due to the following circumstances: (a) most of the phosphorylase is in the *b* form; (b) inorganic phosphate concentration is low; (c) concentrations of ATP and glucose-6-phosphate are increased, thus inhibiting the 5′-AMP activation of phosphorylase *b*. Rapid glycogen breakdown in the anoxic muscle is accounted for only partly by the conversion of some phosphorylase *b* to *a*. More significant causes appear to be: (a) increased concentration of inorganic phosphate; (b) decreased concentrations of ATP and glucose-6-phosphate, thus allowing 5′-AMP (which is elevated in concentration) to activate phosphorylase *b*. Anoxia causes more rapid glycogen breakdown than treatment with hormones, even though the latter agents convert more phosphorylase *b* to *a*.

It may be noted that the synthesis of glycogen described above is limited to the addition of glucose units to the ends of pre-existing polysaccharide chains. Such reactions cannot increase the total number of individual glycogen molecules. Although hepatic amylase is assigned no significant role in most discussions of carbohydrate metabolism, it is possible that it may serve the purpose of fragmenting glycogen to form more molecules of primer oligosaccharide or polysaccharide. (Hepatic amylase may be the principal, if not the sole, source of serum amylase in normal circumstances.) Perhaps a similar role may be assigned to a trans-(α-1,4)-glucosylase occurring in liver, brain, and serum, which catalyzes the transfer of glucosyl residues from maltose, amylose, dextrins, and glycogen to acceptors such as maltose, forming oligosaccharides.

Genetically caused deficiency of certain enzymes results in the "glycogenoses" or glycogen storage diseases and at least one type of glycogen storage deficiency disease (Table 18-1). Thus, absence of glucose-6-phosphatase results in the classical hepatorenal

Table 18-1. Glycogen Storage Diseases

TYPE	DEFECTIVE ENZYME	GLYCOGEN STRUCTURE	ORGANS INVOLVED	CLINICAL MANIFESTATIONS
I (von Gierke's)	Glucose-6-phosphatase	Normal	Liver, kidney	Hepatomegaly, hypoglycemia, acidosis, ketonuria, blood lactate elevated and increased further by glucagon, no increase in blood glucose after epinephrine or glucagon
II	α-1,4-Glucosidase (Acid maltase)	Normal	Generalized	Cardiomegaly, cardiorespiratory failure, death
III (Limit dextrinosis)	Amylo-1,6-glucosidase (debranching enzyme)	Short outer branches	Liver, heart, erythrocytes	Hepatomegaly, moderate hypoglycemia, acidosis
IV (Amylopectinosis)	Amylo-(1,4→1,6)-trans-glucosidase (branching enzyme)	Few branch points	Liver, kidney, heart, erythrocytes, R.E. system	Liver cirrhosis, progressive hepatic failure, death
V	Phosphorylase	Normal	Skeletal muscle	Muscle cramps and depressed blood lactate during exercise
VI	Phosphorylase	Normal	Liver, leukocytes	Hepatomegaly, moderate hypoglycemia, mild acidosis
Glycogen storage deficiency	Glycogen synthetase	Normal	Liver	Fasting hypoglycemia (convulsions), mental retardation, reduced glucose tolerance, normal blood glucose response to epinephrine, subnormal response to glucagon in fasting state

glycogen storage disease of von Gierke (Type I). The most severe form of glycogenosis (Type II) is due to the absence of a lysosomal glucosidase, deficiency of which permits progressive deposition of glycogen to disrupt muscle fibers. In contrast to the majority of glycogenoses, two types (III and IV) are characterized by glycogen of abnormal structure. Two genetically distinct phosphorylase deficiencies exist, one in muscle (V), the other in liver (VI). As might be expected, deficiency of hepatic glycogen synthetase results in inability of the liver to accumulate glycogen and hence to support normal fasting blood glucose levels.

Conversion to Trioses (Reactions 4 to 7, Fig. 18–2)

As may be seen in Figure 18–2, glucose-6-phosphate is at the crossroads of carbohydrate metabolism. It is formed from glucose, glycogen, and substances in the process of forming glucose or glycogen. Conversely, glucose-6-phosphate is convertible to glucose (by means of a specific phosphatase of limited distribution), glycogen, and compounds on the pathway to lactic acid. Although not indicated on the diagram, glucose-6-phosphate is also the initial compound in the "oxidative shunt" pathway (p. 416).

The formation of lactic acid, the end-product of anaerobic glucose metabolism (glycolysis) in animals, is preceded by cleavage of the hexose skeleton into trioses. The first reaction undergone by glucose-6-phosphate on this metabolic route is its conversion to fructose-6-phosphate, catalyzed by phosphohexose isomerase (glucose phosphate isomerase). An enediol is the probable intermediate.

Fructose-6-phosphate is phosphorylated by ATP in the presence of Mg^{++} and phosphofructokinase, forming fructose-1,6-diphosphate. In this reaction, as in the hexokinase reaction discussed previously, an ester phosphate is formed at the expense of a high-energy phosphate bond. Consequently, the reaction is practically irreversible, its apparent biological reversibility being due to the action of a specific phosphatase which liberates inorganic phosphate, and does not regenerate the pyrophosphate linkage in ATP. An analogous situation obtains with regard to the formation of glucose from glucose-6-phosphate.

Phosphofructokinase activity is subject to a number of stimulatory and inhibitory influences (Fig. 18–5): ATP and citrate inhibit, whereas inorganic phosphate, AMP, ADP, cyclic AMP, NH_4^+, fructose-6-phosphate, and fructose-1,6-diphosphate activate. The enzyme, which is increased in activity in anoxia, contains thiol groups which are sensitive to oxidants. This property, in fact, has been cited as one possible mechanism of the Pasteur effect (p. 416), although the inverse relationship between kinase activity and the degree of aerobiosis might well be explained by feedback inhibition due to increased ATP under increased aerobiosis.

Inhibition of phosphofructokinase by citrate suggests another possible control mechanism of the negative feedback type; increased formation of citrate (from pyruvate entering the Krebs cycle, p. 410) could provide self-limiting regulation of the overall rate of carbohydrate catabolism. Citrate inhibition may be significant also in connection with cardiac muscle. Factors leading to increased mobilization and oxidation of fatty acids and increased production and oxidation of ketone bodies (starvation, alloxan diabetes, administration of somatotropic hormone) are known to cause elevation of cardiac citrate concentration. (Contradictory reports have appeared regarding the concentration of citrate in liver under these conditions). This, in turn, could inhibit the phosphofructokinase reaction and contribute to the depression of carbohydrate utilization observed in the conditions mentioned. Such non-utilization of carbohydrate beyond the fructose-6-phosphate stage could be a contributing factor to the "glycostatic" action of STH in heart and, probably, other muscles (p. 437).

Fructose-1,6-diphosphatase, since it catalyzes a hydrolytic "bypass" of the otherwise impossible reversal of the phosphofructokinase reaction, is important in the process of gluconeogenesis. It is present in skeletal muscle, diaphragm, liver, and kidney, but absent from heart and adipose tissue. In contrast to phosphofructokinase, the phosphatase is inhibited by AMP and fructose-1,6-diphosphate (Fig. 18–5). A more important regulatory action on the phosphatase may be the effect of glucocorticoid hormones, which have both a rapid activating influence and a slower inducing action on synthesis of the enzyme, either or both of which may contribute to the stimulation of gluconeogenesis by these hormones. The activity of the enzyme is reported to be increased also in diabetes and fasting, probably because of the absence of insulin, which normally has a repressing influence on the phosphatase.

In addition to the more obvious regulatory mechanisms which are brought to bear upon the interconversion of the fructose phosphates, it should be noted that this strategic control site also may be involved in less direct interrelations. For example, the balance between phosphofructokinase and fructose diphosphatase activities determines, in part, the steady-state level of glucose-6-phosphate (which exists in easily reversible equilibrium with fructose-6-phosphate). Since the level of glucose-6-phosphate adversely influences hexokinase activity, the rate of initial phosphorylation of glucose will be controlled indirectly by the same factors which affect the interconversion of the fructose phosphate esters.

Fructose-1,6-diphosphate is split into two molecules of triose phosphate by fructose-diphosphate aldolase, an enzyme catalyzing a reversible reaction somewhat resembling the aldol condensation of organic chemistry. No coenzymes or activators are required by animal aldolase. The product of the reaction is an equimolecular mixture of D-glyceraldehyde-3-phosphate and dihydroxyacetone-phosphate. (A specific fructose-1-phosphate aldolase is said to convert its substrate to glyceraldehyde and dihydroxyacetone phosphate.)

Triose phosphate isomerase catalyzes the interconversion of the two triose phosphates. It is of interest that the equilibrium constant of the isomerization favors the ketotriose, although glyceraldehyde-3-phosphate is the compound which undergoes the subsequent reactions of the glycolytic pathway. At any rate, the presence of the isomerase insures the eventual complete utilization of both triose moieties formed from the hexose diphosphate. It may be noted that an alternate pathway is available for dihydroxyacetone phosphate. With the aid of NADH, produced in the step to be discussed next, glycerolphosphate dehydrogenase reduces dihydroxyacetone phosphate to α-glycerolphosphate. This pathway is a major source of glycerol for the synthesis of lipids.

Oxidative Step (Reaction 8, Fig. 18–2)

The conversion of D-glyceraldehyde-3-phosphate to D-1,3-diphosphoglycerate is the first of two reactions in glycolysis in which high-energy phosphate bonds are generated. Since the oxidative chain is not available under anaerobic conditions, all of the high-energy phosphate produced in anaerobic glycolysis is due to "substrate level phosphorylation."

Glyceraldehyde-3-phosphate dehydrogenase (also called "triose phosphate dehydrogenase") differs from most nicotinamide nucleotide-coupled dehydrogenases in that its coenzyme, NAD, is rather firmly bound. Thiol groups, originally thought to reside on glutathione molecules attached to the protein, are now known to be provided by the side chains of cysteine residues in the protein; these groups are integral participants in the reaction. Owing to its sulfhydryl groups, the enzyme is inhibited by sulfhydryl-blocking reagents and oxidants in general. The mechanism of action of this dehydrogenase consists of the following steps:

$$R\text{—}\overset{H}{\overset{|}{C}}\text{=O} + HS\text{—Enz} \rightleftharpoons R\text{—}\overset{H}{\overset{|}{\underset{OH}{\underset{|}{C}}}}\text{—S—Enz}$$

$$R\text{—}\overset{H}{\overset{|}{\underset{OH}{\underset{|}{C}}}}\text{—S—Enz} + NAD^+ \rightleftharpoons R\text{—}\overset{O}{\overset{\|}{C}} \sim S\text{—Enz} + NADH + H^+$$

$$R\text{—}\overset{O}{\overset{\|}{C}} \sim S\text{—Enz} + H_3PO_4 \rightleftharpoons R\text{—}\overset{O}{\overset{\|}{C}}\text{—O} \sim PO_3H_2 + HS\text{—Enz}$$

The aldehyde group of glyceraldehyde-3-phosphate first condenses with the sulfhydryl group of the enzyme. The condensation product is then dehydrogenated to an acyl mercaptide or thioester type of compound, the pair of hydrogen atoms being accepted by NAD (the fate of the reduced NAD is discussed below). Although it contains no phosphate, the thioester linkage is energetically equivalent to a high-energy phosphate bond. Consequently, in the subsequent exchange reaction with inorganic phosphate (a phosphorolysis, or transacylation to phosphate), a high-energy carboxyl phosphate is produced. Much of the energy liberated in the oxidation of the aldehyde group to a carboxyl group is therefore conserved. Another physiologically important consequence is that the reaction becomes reversible.

The high-energy phosphate bond produced in the oxidative step is converted into ATP, the "common currency" of bioenergetics, by means of phosphoglycerate kinase, one of the reversible kinases. In the presence of Mg^{++}, the kinase transfers the carboxyl phosphate of the diphosphoglycerate to ADP, forming ATP and 3-phosphoglycerate. (A kinase has been found in skeletal muscle which transfers the high-energy phosphate of the diphosphoglycerate directly to creatine, forming phosphocreatine and bypassing the ATP system.) Since each mole of hexose metabolized results in the formation of two moles of triose, two high-energy phosphates are produced in this reaction.

It may be noted that, as a result of the requirement for inorganic phosphate in the oxidative step and for ADP in the subsequent kinase reaction, these areas have been suggested as possible control points in the metabolic regulatory mechanism known as the Pasteur effect (p. 416). In addition, NADH has been found to be a potent allosteric (p. 769) inhibitor of glyceraldehyde-3-phosphate dehydrogenase, thus providing a mechanism whereby the rate of glycolysis is dependent upon the rate of reoxidation of NADH, which in turn depends upon the availability of pyruvate under anaerobic conditions (see below) or of the oxidative chain under aerobic conditions (Fig. 18–5).

Formation of Lactate (or Ethanol) (Reactions 10 to 13, 10 to 15, Fig. 18–2)

3-Phosphoglycerate is reversibly converted to 2-phosphoglycerate by phosphoglyceromutase, utilizing 2,3-diphosphoglycerate as a coenzyme.

2-Phosphoglycerate undergoes a reversible dehydration to phosphoenolpyruvate under the influence of enolase. Mg^{++} is required for the action of this enzyme, which is inhibited by fluoride in the presence of phosphate. The phosphate linkage in phosphoenolpyruvate is of the high-energy type, although little free energy is liberated in the dehydration reaction. The largest part of the extra energy in this linkage, over that present in the ordinary phosphate ester, is due to the fact that the product of hydrolysis, enolpyruvate, is unstable and reverts spontaneously to the more stable keto tautomer, so that the free energy liberated in the spontaneous tautomerization is added to that due strictly to the hydrolysis of the phosphate linkage. In any event, the high-energy phosphate in phosphoenolpyruvate is transferred to ADP by pyruvate kinase in the presence of Mg^{++} and K^{+}. Two moles of high-energy phosphate are produced per mole of hexose metabolized. Insulin administration is reported to increase the activity of the pyruvate kinase reaction (Fig. 18–5).

Although the pyruvate kinase reaction can be reversed, the equilibrium constant is markedly unfavorable in the direction of formation of phosphoenolpyruvate. This circumstance has led to a search for pathways which circumvent this reaction. These are discussed in greater detail in connection with CO_2 assimilation in liver, a tissue in which reversal of glycolysis is of quantitative importance. One such bypass is formed of two energy-requiring reactions, pyruvate carboxylase (converting pyruvate to oxaloacetate) and phosphopyruvate carboxylase (phosphoenolpyruvate carboxykinase) (converting oxaloacetate to phosphoenolpyruvate), neither of which is present in skeletal muscle. Activity of both enzymes is depressed by insulin and increased by administration of glucocorticoid hormones, thus providing another control point where the latter compounds may act to facilitate gluconeogenesis. In addition, pyruvate carboxylase is activated by acetyl-coenzyme A, suggesting a mechanism whereby conditions leading to increased fatty acid mobilization and oxidation and ketone body formation and oxidation (and hence to increased availability of acetyl-coenzyme A) may also result in increased gluconeogenesis.

Figure 18–5 summarizes glycolytic regulatory mechanisms beyond the glucose-6-phosphate stage.

At the stage of pyruvate, there is a bifurcation in the metabolic pathway, the route taken depending on the organism involved.

The reactions described up to this point take place in yeast as well as animals. There is an anaerobic pyruvate decarboxylase ("carboxylase") in the yeast cell which converts pyruvate to CO_2 and acetaldehyde. Thiamine pyrophosphate ("cocarboxylase") and Mg^{++} are required. Acetaldehyde is reduced to ethanol, the end-product of alcoholic fermentation, by means of alcohol dehydrogenase working "in reverse." The NADH required for this reduction comes from the oxidative step discussed previously. The regenerated NAD can again act as coenzyme for the triose oxidation; thus, it shuttles back and forth between the two reactions in a cycle of its own.

In animal tissues, the decarboxylation of pyruvate is oxidative (p. 409). Under anaerobic conditions, pyruvate is reduced to L-lactate by lactate dehydrogenase and NADH, the reduced coenzyme coming from a catalytic cycle analogous to that described above. It may be mentioned parenthetically that lactate dehydrogenase is one of a number of enzymes which can exist in multiple electrophoretically distinct forms in the same tissue ("isozymes" [p. 216]).

Reversibility

All of the interconversions from glycogen to lactate are potentially reversible, at least with respect to the organic molecules involved. Any phosphorylations of the "irreversible kinase" type are reversed only in the sense that the phosphate ester may be hydrolyzed by a phosphatase. For example, fructose-1,6-diphosphate can be converted to fructose-6-phosphate by hydrolysis, not by transfer of the phosphate to ADP, which would be impossible energetically. Similarly, glucose can be formed from glucose-6-phosphate in the liver (not in muscle) by a specific phosphatase, not by reversal of the hexokinase reac-

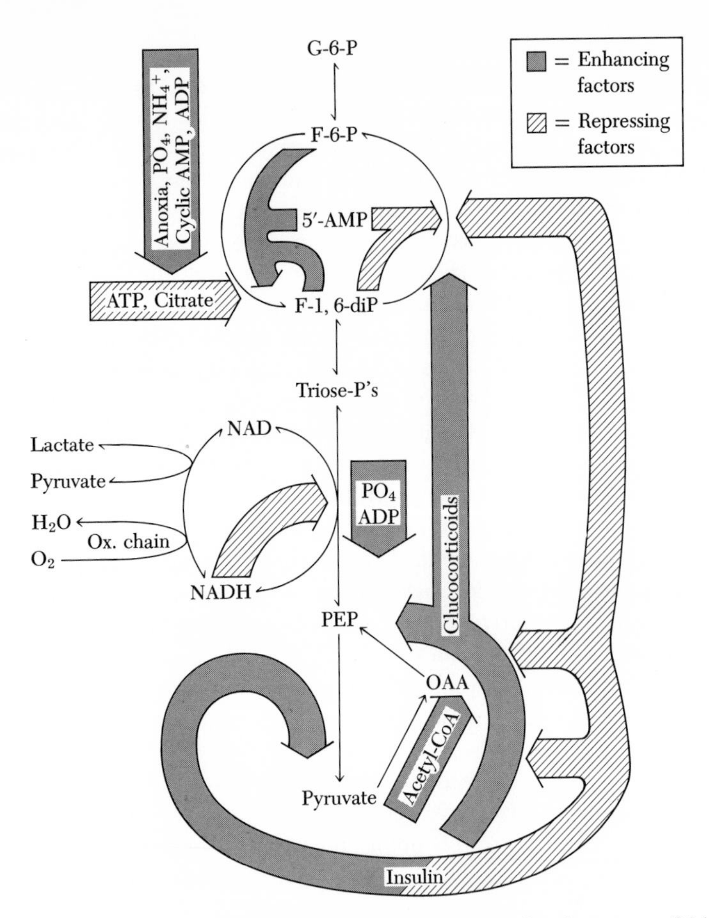

Figure 18-5. Glycolytic regulatory mechanisms beyond the glucose-6-phosphate stage. *OAA*, Oxaloacetate; *PEP*, phosphoenolpyruvate; other symbols as in previous figures.

tion. The reversal of glycolysis therefore entails a loss of energy, but the reversal of any exergonic process must necessarily be endergonic. The difficulty of reversing the pyruvate kinase reaction has been discussed previously. What little reversal of glycolysis occurs in muscle is believed to utilize this reaction, whereas the quantitatively much more significant reversal of the glycolytic pathway in liver is believed to make use of energy-requiring pathways which bypass the pyruvate kinase step (p. 414). Gluconeogenesis (in the sense of forming hexose phosphates and glycogen, not blood glucose) can occur in skeletal muscle from the triose phosphate level, since this tissue possesses the fructose diphosphatase while lacking glucose-6-phosphatase and the pyruvate kinase bypass reactions. Lipid glycerol may be significant as a precursor in this respect, by way of conversion to α-glycerolphosphate and dihydroxyacetone phosphate.

Other Hexoses

As indicated previously, a number of hexoses are known to form and be synthesized from glucose (and glycogen). Since these interconversions proceed largely by way of the glycolytic path, it is appropriate to consider them at this point.

The hexokinase of brain (and certain other tissues) forms the 6-phosphate esters from glucose, fructose, and mannose. In muscle and liver, separate glucokinases and fructokinases exist, producing glucose-6-phosphate and fructose-1-phosphate, respectively. In liver and brain there is also a kinase which phosphorylates galactose in the 1-position. In all cases, ATP is the source of the phosphate group.

Fructose-6-phosphate is on the main glycolytic pathway. Fructose-1-phosphate may be taken into this pathway by conversion to fructose-1,6-diphosphate by means of ATP and a phosphofructokinase different from that which acts on fructose-6-phosphate. The most important pathway of metabolism of fructose-1-phosphate in liver involves cleavage (catalyzed by a specific F-1-P aldolase) to dihydroxyacetone phosphate and glyceraldehyde, phosphorylation of the latter by a specific kinase, and either aldolase condensation of the triose phosphates to fructose-1,6-diphosphate or utilization as such. The fact that fructose can bypass glucose formation for catabolic purposes is indicated by the utilization of the former under conditions in which glucose phosphorylation is inhibited.

Enzymes in the seminal vesicle catalyze the interconversion of glucose and fructose by way of the sugar alcohol, sorbitol.

"Fructose intolerance" is an inborn error of metabolism, probably caused by a defect in hepatic fructose-1-phosphate aldolase. Poor utilization of fructose is explained by the accumulation of fructose-1-phosphate, a known inhibitor of hepatic fructokinase.

Mannose-6-phosphate is reversibly converted to glucose-6-phosphate by an isomerase, probably via fructose-6-phosphate. Guanosinediphosphate-mannose is converted to the analogous fucose derivative in a number of tissues.

Galactose-1-phosphate is transformed to glucose-1-phosphate in two steps, in the presence of the coenzyme uridinediphosphate-glucose.

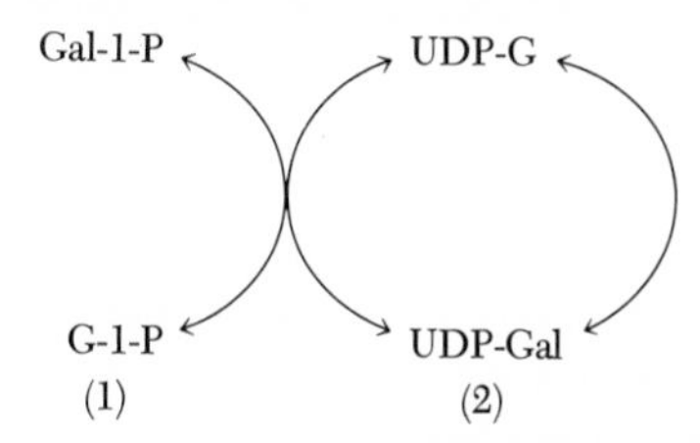

The first reaction involves an exchange of hexose moieties between substrate and coenzyme, followed by the inversion of C-4 of the hexose within the molecule of the coenzyme. The hexose exchange is catalyzed by galactose-1-phosphate-uridyl transferase. UDP-galactose-4-epimerase (galactowaldenase) catalyzes the inversion reaction. Since NAD has been implicated in this process, it is possible that the isomerization is an internal oxidation-reduction and not a true Walden inversion.

The lack of galactose-1-phosphate-uridyl transferase in congenital galactosemia accounts for the observed inability to metabolize galactose normally. Since galactokinase is present, dietary galactose forms galactose-1-phosphate as usual, the accumulation of this compound apparently being the cause of the cellular injury which occurs in many tissues. (At least part of the toxicity of Gal-1-P is due to its inhibition of phosphoglucomutase.) Early diagnosis of this condition in infants and avoidance of milk in the diet can prevent many of these ill effects. Older galactosemics apparently develop an increased tolerance to galactose, probably due to the activity of a pyrophosphorylase which is known to increase with age, and which catalyzes the reaction:

$$\text{Gal-1-P} + \text{UTP} \rightleftharpoons \text{UDP-Gal} + \text{PP}$$

There is evidence that some of the excess galactose in the galactosemic may be reduced to galactitol, a possible agent in the production of cataracts (p. 420).

Galactose, in the form of its derivative, galactosamine, is found in certain mucopolysaccharides, occurs as such in the glycolipids and, with glucose, forms the disaccharide, lactose, secreted in milk. In this last synthesis, UDP-Gal, synthesized as described above, condenses in the mammary gland with glucose-1-phosphate to form lactose-1-phosphate, which is hydrolyzed by a phosphatase to form free lactose. A similar pathway has been reported which utilizes free glucose and dispenses with the need for a phosphatase.

Energetics of Fermentation and Glycolysis

The fermenting yeast cell degrades glucose, a compound of relatively high potential energy, to CO_2 and ethanol, compounds of low potential energy. The free energy liberated in this process amounts to 62,200 cal. Examination of Figure 18–2 reveals that two high-energy phosphate bonds of ATP are expended in the course of transforming glucose to these catabolic products, one at the hexokinase step, and one in the formation of fructose diphosphate. On the other hand, four new high-energy phosphate bonds are generated, two in the oxidative step, and two as a result of the enolase reaction (in each case, *two* moles of triose must be considered per mole of hexose metabolized). Consequently, a net synthesis of two high-energy phosphate bonds occurs. Taking the free energy of formation of an ATP pyrophosphate bond to be 7500 cal., then 15,000 cal., or 24 per cent of the free energy liberated in fermentation, is captured and available to the organism for various purposes.

The free energy liberated in glycolysis from glucose is about 49,700 cal. Since the phosphorylation reactions are essentially the same as in fermentation, it follows that 30 per cent of the liberated free energy is recovered. Superficially, it would appear that a greater yield of high-energy phosphate could be obtained if the glycolytic process began with glycogen instead of glucose, since the loss of one high-energy bond in the hexokinase reaction would be avoided. As a matter of fact, the energy level of glycogen is sufficiently above that of glucose to practically nullify the apparent gain. Furthermore, in order to derive net energy from glycogen, it must be synthesized from glucose or other hexoses via the kinase reactions and UDPG pathway, both of which require the expenditure of energy. Glycogen is formed from non-carbohydrate sources only by means of a reversal of the entire glycolytic sequence, a process which consumes more energy than the glycogen can again produce.

Intracellular Localization

The enzymes and cofactors necessary for glycolysis are found in the particle-free supernatant fraction of the cytoplasm, as prepared by differential centrifugation. (Brain mitochondria may be exceptional in containing the glycolytic system.) This fact may be of importance in the regulation of the balance between the anaerobic and aerobic metabolism of carbohydrate (p. 416).

AEROBIC METABOLISM OF CARBOHYDRATE

Although special pathways for aerobic metabolism of carbohydrate exist in certain tissues, in most tissues the major route of aerobic metabolism in animals is identical with the anaerobic through the stage of pyruvate. Aerobically, pyruvate is oxidized to CO_2 and H_2O, instead of being reduced to lactate. Part of the explanation for this change lies in the oxidation of NADH (from the oxidative step of glycolysis) via the respiratory chain of catalysts under aerobic conditions; it is therefore not available for the reduction of pyruvate to lactate by lactate dehydrogenase. If a period of anaerobiosis is followed by one of aerobiosis, accumulated lactate is oxidized to pyruvate by lactate dehydrogenase, NAD being the hydrogen acceptor. Therefore, in any case, pyruvate is the initial compound to be considered in the strictly aerobic metabolism of carbohydrate.

Initial Oxidation of Pyruvate

The pyruvate dehydrogenase system is rather complex; its details are still in the process of being elucidated. At present, it is believed that the system is an aggregate of three species of enzymes, pyruvate decarboxylase, lipoate reductase-transacetylase, and dihydrolipoate dehydrogenase, functioning in that order. The probable sequence of events is illustrated in Figure 18–6.

In the first step, pyruvate reacts with enzyme-bound thiamine pyrophosphate in the presence of magnesium, the α carbon of the keto acid attaching to C-2 of the thiazole ring of the vitamin, forming "active pyruvate" or enzyme-bound lactyl-TPP. This intermediate loses CO_2, producing "active acetaldehyde" or enzyme-bound hydroxyethyl-TPP. (It is of interest that the non-oxidative decarboxylation of pyruvate which occurs in alcoholic fermentation shares the sequence of reactions up to this point.) The last intermediate is oxidized from the aldehyde to the carboxylate level by interaction with enzyme-bound lipoate, which simultaneously accepts the acetyl group in the form of an acyl thioester. Formation of this high-energy bond conserves part of the free energy liberated in the oxidation.

Reaction of the acetylated lipoate with the sulfhydryl group of coenzyme A in a "thioacyl exchange" produces acetyl-CoA and the disulfhydryl form of lipoate, which is recon-

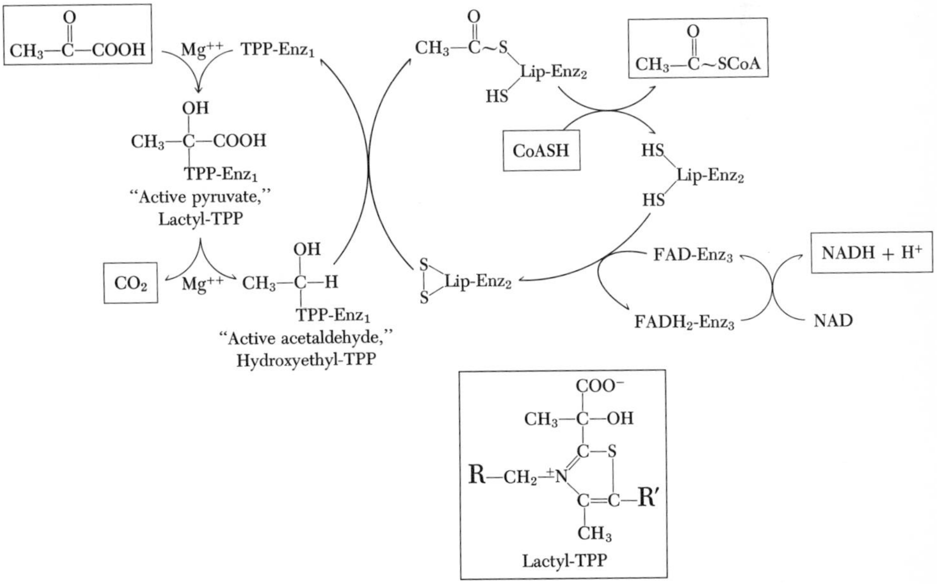

Figure 18-6. Probable steps in oxidative decarboxylation of pyruvate. *CoA*, Coenzyme A; *Enz*$_1$, pyruvate decarboxylase; *Enz*$_2$, lipoate reductase-transacetylase; *Enz*$_3$, dihydrolipoate dehydrogenase; *Lip*, lipoate; *TPP*, thiamine pyrophosphate.

verted to the disulfide form by transfer of hydrogen atoms to the flavin prosthetic group of a specific dehydrogenase (formerly called "diaphorase"), which in turn transfers the hydrogen atoms to NAD. Reoxidation of NADH proceeds via the usual aerobic oxidative chain of catalysts.

Acetyl-CoA is a very versatile intermediary metabolite. In addition to its participation in carbohydrate oxidation, it is formed in the course of the catabolism of fatty acids and certain amino acids. Although the concern at this point is with the oxidation of this substance, it has many anabolic uses in the body (p. 472).

Tricarboxylic Acid Cycle

The complete oxidation of the acetyl moiety of acetyl-CoA is effected by means of a cyclic metabolic mechanism known variously as the "citric acid," "tricarboxylic acid," or "Krebs" cycle (this last referring to the investigator largely responsible for its formulation). Figure 18–7 illustrates the reactions involved.

The initial reaction in this cycle (Reaction 1, Figure 18–7) is a condensation between

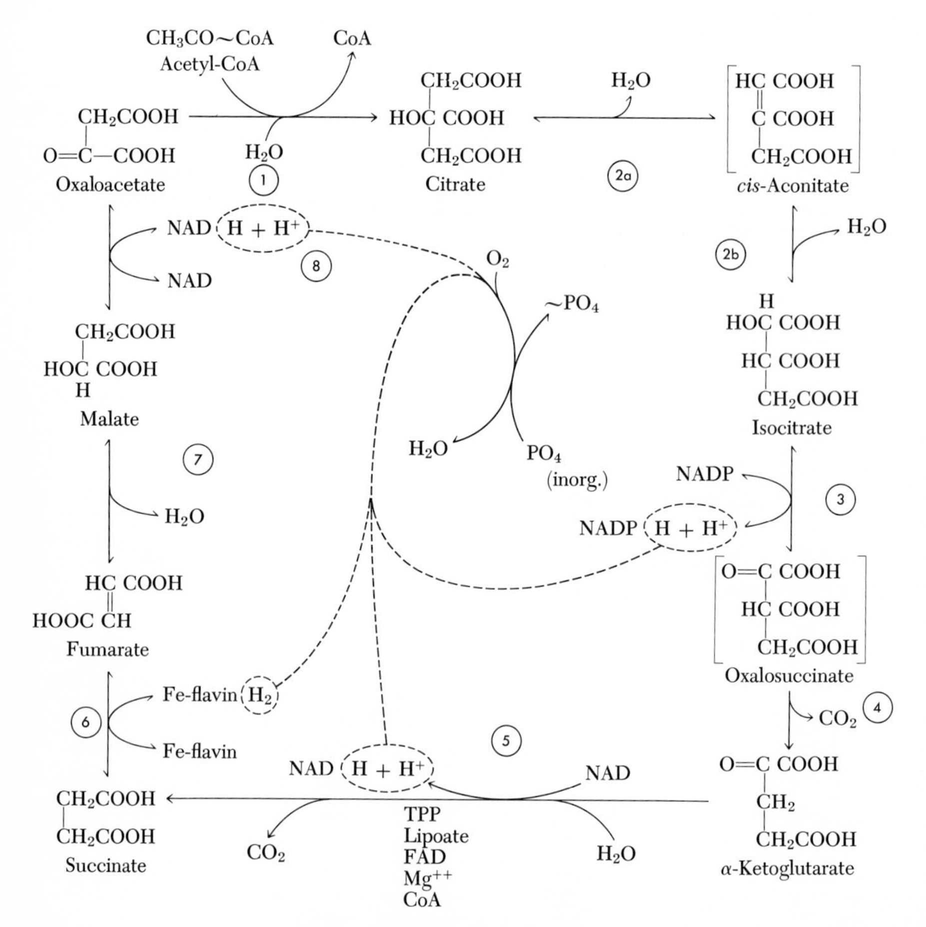

Figure 18-7. Tricarboxylic acid cycle.

oxaloacetate and acetyl-CoA, forming citrate and regenerating CoA. For practical purposes this reaction ("citrate synthase") can be considered irreversible, since it proceeds with the liberation of 7.8 kcal. of free energy. It should be noted that the oxidation of pyruvate to the acetyl level constitutes "generation of a high-energy bond at the substrate level." The energy of this thioester bond may be utilized for various anabolic purposes (p. 472). If the acetyl moiety is to be oxidized by way of the tricarboxylic acid cycle, however, the bond is sacrificed to "drive" the citrate condensation. Although the citrate synthase reaction is inhibited in vitro by physiological concentrations of long-chain fatty acyl-CoA thioesters, it is not known whether this inhibition has any metabolic significance in vivo.

A citrate-cleaving enzyme (ATP-citrate lyase) occurs in many tissues. It catalyzes the reaction: citrate + ATP + CoA → acetyl-CoA + oxaloacetate + ADP + phosphate, which constitutes an indirect reversal of the synthase reaction, but only at the expense of a mole of high-energy phosphate. It has been suggested that the citrate lyase reaction may participate in gluconeogenesis from Krebs cycle intermediates; its highly exergonic character would facilitate reversal of ordinarily irreversible reactions (e.g., α-ketoglutarate could be carboxylated and eventually form citrate by reversing part of the cycle, hence obviating the need for such compounds to traverse the entire cycle before forming oxaloacetate and then phosphoenolpyruvate). Citrate lyase activity is increased in conditions favoring fatty acid synthesis; its role in that connection will be discussed elsewhere (p. 461).

Aconitase catalyzes the second reaction of the cycle (Reaction 2*A* and *B*, Fig. 18–7), which appears to involve an equilibration between citrate, *cis*-aconitate, and isocitrate. There is evidence that aconitate is a side-product, not in the main reaction sequence. The overall isomerization may be thought of as involving removal of a molecule of water to create a double bond, then replacement in such a way as to locate the hydroxyl group in a new position. The actual reaction mechanism probably proceeds via removal and addition of a hydroxyl ion, the common intermediate being a carbonium ion which is in equilibrium with *cis*-aconitate by protonation-deprotonation. Although the equilibrium of the isolated system favors citrate, it is easily reversed if the isocitrate is removed by a subsequent reaction. Fe^{++} is a cofactor of the enzyme, which also contains essential sulfhydryl groups. The enzyme is inhibited by *trans*-aconitate (competing with *cis*-aconitate) and by fluoroacetate, after the latter compound is converted enzymatically to fluorocitrate, the actual inhibitor.

Isocitrate dehydrogenase catalyzes the overall conversion shown as Reactions 3 and 4 in Figure 18–7. The overall reaction requires a nicotinamide nucleotide and Mn^{++}. Since it is not possible to separate the dehydrogenase from the decarboxylase activity, it must be concluded that these two reactions are catalyzed by a single enzyme. It is believed by some that oxalosuccinate is not a free intermediate, but rather exists bound to the enzyme. The first phase of the reaction is readily reversible, the second only with difficulty.

In reality, there are two isocitrate dehydrogenases, one specific for NADP (much greater activity, more widely distributed), another specific for NAD (less active, absent from many tissues). In contrast to other enzymes of the tricarboxylic acid cycle, the NADP-specific isocitrate dehydrogenase of liver is located mainly in the non-particulate cytoplasm, although the activity of the NADP- exceeds considerably that of the NAD-specific enzyme within the mitochondria. The NAD-specific enzyme is limited to the mitochondria in tissues such as heart, muscle, and kidney. Peculiarly, the NAD-specific enzyme appears unable to catalyze reversal of the dehydrogenation or decarboxylation.

The oxidative decarboxylation of α-ketoglutarate (Reaction 5, Fig. 18–7) is quite similar to that of pyruvate. α-Ketoglutarate combines with enzyme-bound TPP (and Mg^{++}). This complex loses CO_2 to form bound succinic semialdehyde, which is oxidized to the succinyl level and transferred to bound lipoate as a thioester, eventually reacting with coenzyme A to form succinyl-CoA. Reoxidation of the dihydrolipoate proceeds as described previously. The major difference from pyruvate oxidation resides in the disposition of the high-energy thioester linkage, which in this case can be transformed into a high-energy phosphate linkage by the following reactions:

$$(1)\ HOOCCH_2CH_2CO \sim S\text{-}CoA + H_3PO_4 + GDP \rightleftharpoons HOOCCH_2CH_2COOH + CoA\text{-}SH + GTP$$

$$(2)\ GTP + ADP \rightleftharpoons GDP + ATP$$

A high-energy phosphate bond is formed by reaction of succinyl-CoA with inorganic phosphate and guanosine diphosphate, which is then transferred to form ATP ("substrate level phosphorylation"). In alternative reactions, succinyl-CoA may be used in the acylation of sulfonamides (p. 474), "activation" of acetoacetate (p. 467), and in the synthesis of the porphyrin ring (p. 608).

Succinate is reversibly oxidized to fumarate (Reaction 6, Fig. 18–7) by succinate dehydrogenase, a system which is coupled to the cytochromes through prosthetic groups of non-heme iron and flavin, the latter probably existing as peptide-linked FAD. The inhibition of succinate dehydrogenase by malonate is the classic example of competitive inhibition (p. 666). Oxaloacetate also is a very potent competitive inhibitor. Sulfhydryl groups are involved in the combination of the enzyme with its substrate as well as with inhibitors such as malonate.

Fumarate is reversibly hydrated to malate (Reaction 7, Fig. 18–7) by fumarase. No coenzyme is required, but phosphate is said to have an activating effect.

Malate is reversibly dehydrogenated (Reaction 8, Fig. 18–7) to oxaloacetate by malate dehydrogenase and NAD. NADP can also act as the coenzyme, but at a slower rate. The reduced coenzyme is oxidized by the aerobic oxidative chain. The cycle is thus completed with the formation of oxaloacetate, which can now react with another molecule of acetyl-CoA. Malate dehydrogenase is inhibited by the product, oxaloacetate, which, as noted previously, also inhibits succinate dehydrogenase, suggesting that these two reactions may be regulatory sites for negative feedback.

Theoretically, one molecule of oxaloacetate (being regenerated in the cycle as described) can catalyze the oxidation of an infinite number of acetyl groups. Practically speaking, quantities of oxaloacetate above the minimum are probably necessary in order that the cycle proceed at a rapid enough rate for physiological requirements. Nevertheless, relatively small amounts may suffice in many tissues. In certain tissues, however, e.g., liver, a continual loss of oxaloacetate occurs via decarboxylation and other side reactions. In such cases the supply may be maintained by synthesis from pyruvate by CO_2 assimilation (see next section), by deamination of aspartate, or by deamination of glutamate to α-ketoglutarate and operation of part of the tricarboxylic acid cycle, either in the forward direction, or in reverse with the aid of the citrate lyase reaction.

The overall oxidation of pyruvic acid is represented by:

$$CH_3COCOOH + 5\ (O) \longrightarrow 2\ H_2O + 3\ CO_2$$

As can be seen in Figures 18–6 and 18–7, the three carbon atoms of pyruvic acid are accounted for as three molecules of CO_2, one produced initially in the formation of acetyl-CoA, the others in the cycle proper. Five pairs of hydrogen atoms are combined with five atoms of oxygen to form water by way of the oxidative chain. Three molecules of water are taken up in hydration reactions, so that the final result corresponds to the above equation.

Assimilation of CO_2

Although carbon dioxide is usually considered a waste product of metabolism, ample evidence has accumulated to support the view that this substance can be an important building block in anabolic reactions. The utilization of CO_2 in the synthesis of purines and pyrimidines is discussed elsewhere (pp. 515, 520).

Most examples of CO_2 assimilation in animal tissues have been found to involve reversal of the decarboxylation of β-keto acids. The reactions which appear to account for much of the CO_2 assimilatory activity of the animal body occur readily in liver and kidney, somewhat less actively in skeletal muscle, and may be regarded as adjuncts to the reactions of the tricarboxylic acid cycle. One such reaction is the direct carboxylation of pyruvate to oxaloacetate (pyruvate carboxylase). This reaction requires Mg^{++}, ATP, and biotin. Acetyl-CoA plays an as yet unexplained catalytic role. Another reaction which achieves the same result utilizes phosphoenolpyruvate as starting material, and inosine (or guanosine) diphosphate as phosphate acceptor (phosphopyruvate carboxylase, PEP carboxykinase). A third reaction is due to the "malic enzyme" (malate dehydrogenase [decarboxylating]), which catalyzes a simultaneous reduction and carboxylation of pyruvate to malate, completely bypassing the stage of oxaloacetate.

In a sequence of reactions not involving β-keto acids, a member of the Krebs cycle, succinyl-CoA, may be synthesized from propionate, a product of the metabolism of valine and isoleucine, methionine, and those rare fatty acids having an odd number of carbon atoms. The carboxylation of propionyl-CoA requires biotin, and, as is true of other biotin-requiring carboxylases and decarboxylases, is inhibited by avidin (a basic protein found in raw egg white). Biotin probably occurs linked to ϵ-amino groups of lysine residues in the apoenzymes of which it forms the prosthetic group; CO_2 is carried on the ureide N atom on the side of the biotin ring opposite to the fatty acid side chain.

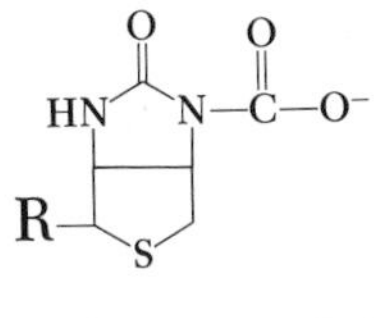

O O
HN N—C—O$^-$
R
S

(A reaction analogous to propionyl-CoA carboxylation is the conversion of acetyl- to malonyl-CoA, an early step in the synthesis of fatty acids [p. 458]). The form of methylmalonyl-CoA first produced by carboxylation of propionyl-CoA is converted by a racemase to its enantiomorph before isomerization. The isomerization of the resulting methylmalonyl-CoA to succinyl-CoA requires a coenzyme form of vitamin B_{12}, a fact which explains the greatly increased level of excretion of methylmalonate in pernicious anemia and experimental B_{12} deficiency. The isomerization involves migration of the entire thioester group (including the carbonyl carbon) from its initial position to the side-chain methyl group.

It should be noted that all of the preceding reactions leading to the synthesis of oxaloacetate are continuously opposed by the action of an active, nucleotide-independent oxaloacetate decarboxylase in liver mitochondria. A scheme of these reactions and their relationship to the tricarboxylic acid cycle is shown in Figure 18–8.

The physiological significance of these reactions would seem to be, first, that tissues in which such reactions are well developed can readily synthesize their own supply of catalytic acids for the Krebs cycle. (Of course, deamination of aspartate or glutamate accomplishes the same end.) The lack of a compensatory increase in Krebs cycle acids when fatty acid catabolism is accelerated during carbohydrate deprivation may be a

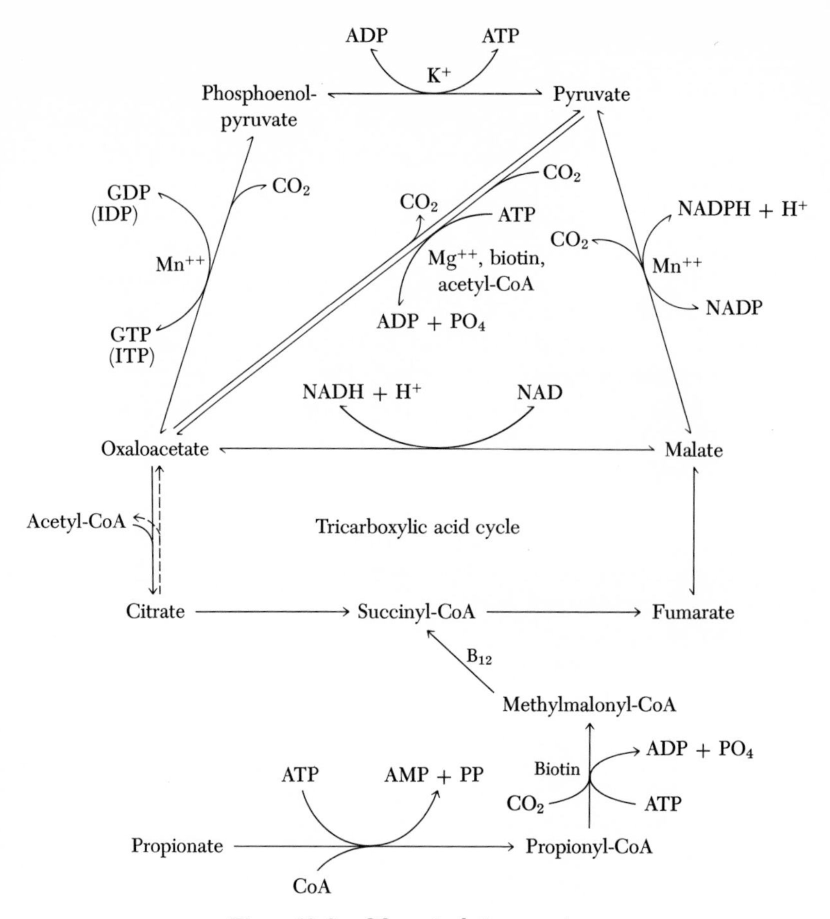

Figure 18-8. CO_2 assimilation reactions.

contributory factor in the development of ketosis. Secondly, the sequence, pyruvate $\rightarrow$ (malate) $\rightarrow$ oxaloacetate $\rightarrow$ phosphoenolpyruvate, provides an effective bypass around the pyruvate kinase reaction, an important consideration in gluconeogenesis (p. 423).

Energetics of Aerobic Oxidation of Carbohydrate

Of the 688,500 cal. of free energy liberated in the complete oxidation of glucose to CO_2 and H_2O, less than 10 per cent is produced in the anaerobic phase of the process. The tricarboxylic acid cycle is the major source of the free energy of higher organisms. An estimate of the actual amount of free energy recovered by the organism under aerobic conditions can be made as shown in Table 18-2. As calculated previously for glycolysis, two high-energy phosphate bonds are expended in phosphorylations of hexose and phosphohexose, whereas four such bonds are generated by substrate level phosphorylations (oxidative step and enolase reaction). Under aerobic conditions, the NADH produced in the oxidative reaction of glycolysis is oxidized by the respiratory chain of catalysts, the two pairs of hydrogen atoms furnishing six high-energy bonds in the process.

The oxidation of two molecules of pyruvate to acetyl-CoA produces the expected six high-energy bonds due to reoxidation of NADH. Two high-energy thioester bonds are sacrificed in the citrate condensation. In the cycle proper, the oxidation of NADPH and

TABLE 18-2. HIGH-ENERGY PHOSPHATE BALANCE IN AEROBIC DEGRADATION OF A MOLE OF GLUCOSE

REACTION	HIGH-ENERGY PHOSPHATE EXPENDED	SUBSTRATE LEVEL PHOSPHORYLATION	OXIDATIVE CHAIN LEVEL PHOSPHORYLATION	NET
Hexokinase	−1			−1
Phosphohexokinase	−1			−1
Oxidative step (×2)		+2	+6	+8
Enolase step (×2)		+2		+2
Pyruvate ⟶ citrate (×2)	−2 (thiolester, see text)	+2 (thiolester, see text)	+6	+6
Isocitrate ⟶ oxalosuccinate (×2)			+6	+6
Ketoglutarate ⟶ succinate (×2)		+2	+6	+8
Succinate ⟶ fumarate (×2)			+4	+4
Malate ⟶ oxaloacetate (×2)			+6	+6
			Total	+38

NADH accounts for six high-energy bonds in the oxidation of each two molecules of isocitrate, α-ketoglutarate, and malate. In addition, substrate level phosphorylation occurs in the case of ketoglutarate. Oxidation of succinate to fumarate, since it bypasses a part of the oxidative chain, yields only four high-energy bonds per two molecules.

As can be seen in Table 18-2, a total of 38 high-energy phosphate bonds is produced per molecule of hexose completely oxidized. Taking the average free energy of such a bond as 7500 cal., a total of 285,000 cal. is recovered by the organism from the 688,500 cal. made available in the course of the reactions, an efficiency of 41 per cent.

Under normal physiological conditions, the regulatory mechanisms of the cell maintain a certain balance between the rates of generation and utilization of high-energy phosphate. One mechanism for this purpose has been discussed in connection with the "coupling" of oxidation with generation of energy (p. 385). The close connection of Krebs cycle reactions with the oxidative chain and the normally tight coupling of the latter to mechanisms of ATP generation may be expected to result in a direct response of Krebs cycle reactions to variations in energy requirements of the cell. These relationships also may be involved in the Pasteur and Crabtree effects discussed below.

There are reports to the effect that pyruvate oxidation is impaired in experimental diabetes, starvation, and after administration of somatotropic hormone, conditions characterized by enhanced mobilization and oxidation of fatty acids and increased production of ketone bodies. Since most of the evidence indicates no significant inhibition of the oxidation of acetyl-CoA via the Krebs cycle in these circumstances (the possibility of a relative, not absolute, inadequacy of the cycle is taken up elsewhere, p. 469), the impairment of pyruvate utilization may be localized in some pre-tricarboxylic acid step, e.g., possibly competition of pyruvate with fatty acid intermediates for the available coenzyme A.

Possible self-regulation of the cycle through oxaloacetate inhibition of the succinate and malate dehydrogenases has been mentioned previously.

Intracellular Localization

The systems necessary for the initial oxidation of pyruvate, the reactions of the tricarboxylic acid cycle, and oxidative chain phosphorylation are largely (but not entirely) localized in the mitochondria. The NADP-specific isocitrate dehydrogenase appears to be exceptional. The spatial separation of these systems from those of glycolysis may have some physiological significance.

Pasteur and Crabtree Effects

When tissue slices or cell suspensions are incubated in the presence of glucose under anaerobic conditions, the glucose is converted to lactate (glycolysis) at a rate which is characteristic of the individual tissue. In the presence of oxygen, the utilization of glucose is decreased and the accumulation of lactate is largely suppressed (exceptions are noted below). This phenomenon is known as the "Pasteur effect," after its discoverer. Many conflicting explanations of this effect have been proposed, no one of which is universally accepted at this time. A number of theories are based on the dependence of both the glycolytic system and the oxidative chain upon the presence of adequate amounts of inorganic phosphate and ADP, in order that "tightly-coupled" reactions may proceed (pp. 385, 404), thus raising the possibility of competition between the glycolytic systems outside of and the respiratory systems within the mitochondria, the phosphorylative efficiency of the latter tending to deplete the glycolytic systems of ADP and inorganic phosphate. Supplementing this competitive effect would be the inhibition of phosphofructokinase due to elevation of the ratio of ATP to ADP and inorganic phosphate (p. 402), aided perhaps by additional inhibition of phosphofructokinase by increased amounts of citrate formed initially in the Krebs cycle (p. 402). The secondary inhibition of hexokinase by G-6-P arising from the inhibition of phosphofructokinase (p. 403) also would depress the rate of glycolysis. Whatever the explanation, the Pasteur effect can be regarded as a regulatory mechanism which operates to decrease the consumption of fuel under conditions in which the energy-yield per unit of fuel is increased. Since only two high-energy phosphate bonds are produced per molecule of hexose during glycolysis, whereas 38 are formed in complete oxidation, it is obvious that decreased consumption of glucose under aerobiosis would be counteracted by the higher yield of energy per molecule.

Retina, kidney medulla, intestinal mucosa, and certain tumors continue to form appreciable quantities of lactate even in the presence of oxygen (aerobic glycolysis). Intestinal mucosa, as a matter of fact, exhibits no Pasteur effect.

The converse of the Pasteur effect occurs in tissues which have a high rate of aerobic glycolysis. Addition of glucose to these tissues in vitro results in inhibition of oxygen consumption, a phenomenon known as the Crabtree effect. Explanations of the Crabtree effect rely mainly on the principle of competition, but in a direction opposite to that of the Pasteur effect, i.e., addition of substrate to a cell with highly developed ability for aerobic glycolysis results in depletion of inorganic phosphate and adenine nucleotides from the mitochondria, due to extensive utilization in the particle-free cytoplasm. As a result of "tight coupling" of respiration to phosphorylation in the mitochondria, the rate of oxidation via the cytochrome chain will fall.

ALTERNATE PATHWAYS: PENTOSE METABOLISM

It is probable that the combined anaerobic and aerobic pathways outlined in the foregoing discussions represent the major avenues of carbohydrate metabolism in the body, particularly in the preponderant muscle-mass. However, considerable evidence has accumulated to support the view that, at least in certain tissues, alternate pathways leading from glucose-6-phosphate and fructose-6-phosphate may vie with those already described. Of the several alternate pathways discovered in nature thus far, only one has been established as a possible major route in mammalian metabolism, variously designated as the "oxidative shunt," "pentose shunt," or "Warburg-Dickens-Lipmann pathway." Its quantitative importance is still a matter of controversy. Although relatively unimportant in skeletal muscle, it is of more significance in liver, adipose tissue, mammary gland, particularly during lactation, and of greater importance in fetal than adult heart. It appears to be the major pathway in the cornea and lens of the eye, but to share its functions with the Embden-Meyerhof pathway in retina.

A scheme of this pathway is presented in Figure 18–9. There are actually two aspects to this pathway, or, rather, two ways in which it may be utilized. One, the oxidative pentose pathway, begins with glucose-6-phosphate (upper left). The other, the non-oxidative pentose pathway, begins with fructose-6-phosphate (lower right). It will be noted that the sequence beginning with glucose-6-phosphate opens to this compound an aerobic alternative to the glycolytic pathway. In the presence of glucose-6-phosphate dehydrogenase ("Zwischenferment") and NADP, glucose-6-phosphate is first oxidized to gluconate-6-phosphate. (It is of interest that a hereditary defect in this enzyme in the red cells is coupled with a tendency toward hemolysis with certain antimalarials, sulfonamides, and fava beans.) (The lactone which is initially produced is hydrolyzed either spontaneously or with the aid of a lactonase.) A second dehydrogenase, also requiring NADP, then oxidizes and decarboxylates the acid, possibly via the intermediate shown in the figure. The product is ribulose-5-phosphate, which is in equilibrium with ribose-5-phosphate, presumably through an enediol, catalyzed by phosphoriboisomerase. The conversion of ribose-5-phosphate to the 1-phosphate and to phosphoribosyl-pyrophosphate is discussed in connection with the metabolism of the nucleotides (p. 515).

In addition to the formation of pentose by an oxidative route, continuation of this pathway can result in regeneration of hexose, thus forming a metabolic cycle. Under the influence of an epimerase, ribulose-5-phosphate is converted to xylulose-5-phosphate. Transketolase removes an "active glycolaldehyde" fragment or ketol grouping from xylulose-5-phosphate, leaving a residue of glyceraldehyde-3-phosphate. (Thiamine pyrophosphate and Mg^{++} are cofactors; the "active glycolaldehyde" residue exists in combination with enzyme-bound thiamine pyrophosphate, exactly analogous to the previously described "active acetaldehyde," Fig. 18–6.) Under the influence of transketolase, the ketol fragment condenses with ribose-5-phosphate to form an unusual 7-carbon sugar, sedoheptulose-7-phosphate. Transaldolase transfers the upper dihydroxyacetone moiety of the heptose to glyceraldehyde-3-phosphate, forming fructose-6-phosphate and leaving a tetrose residue, erythrose-4-phosphate. This tetrose is brought back within the fold of familiar compounds by the addition of a ketol fragment (transketolase reaction again) to form fructose-6-phosphate.

Since fructose-6-phosphate is readily converted to glucose-6-phosphate, it is evident that the elements of a cyclic mechanism are provided. Since only one molecule of CO_2 is produced in a single run, it is obvious that six runs of the cycle would be required to form enough CO_2 to account for complete degradation of a molecule of hexose. It can be shown that, if one begins with six molecules of hexose-phosphate, six molecules of CO_2 will be produced and five molecules of hexose-phosphate will be regenerated. Since such complete operation of the oxidative pentose pathway leaves no pentose as product, its physiological significance may be mainly the formation of reduced NADP, as discussed below.

A second mode of operation of the pentose pathway is non-oxidative. Fructose-6-phosphate reacts with glyceraldehyde-3-phosphate (transketolase), forming xylulose-5-

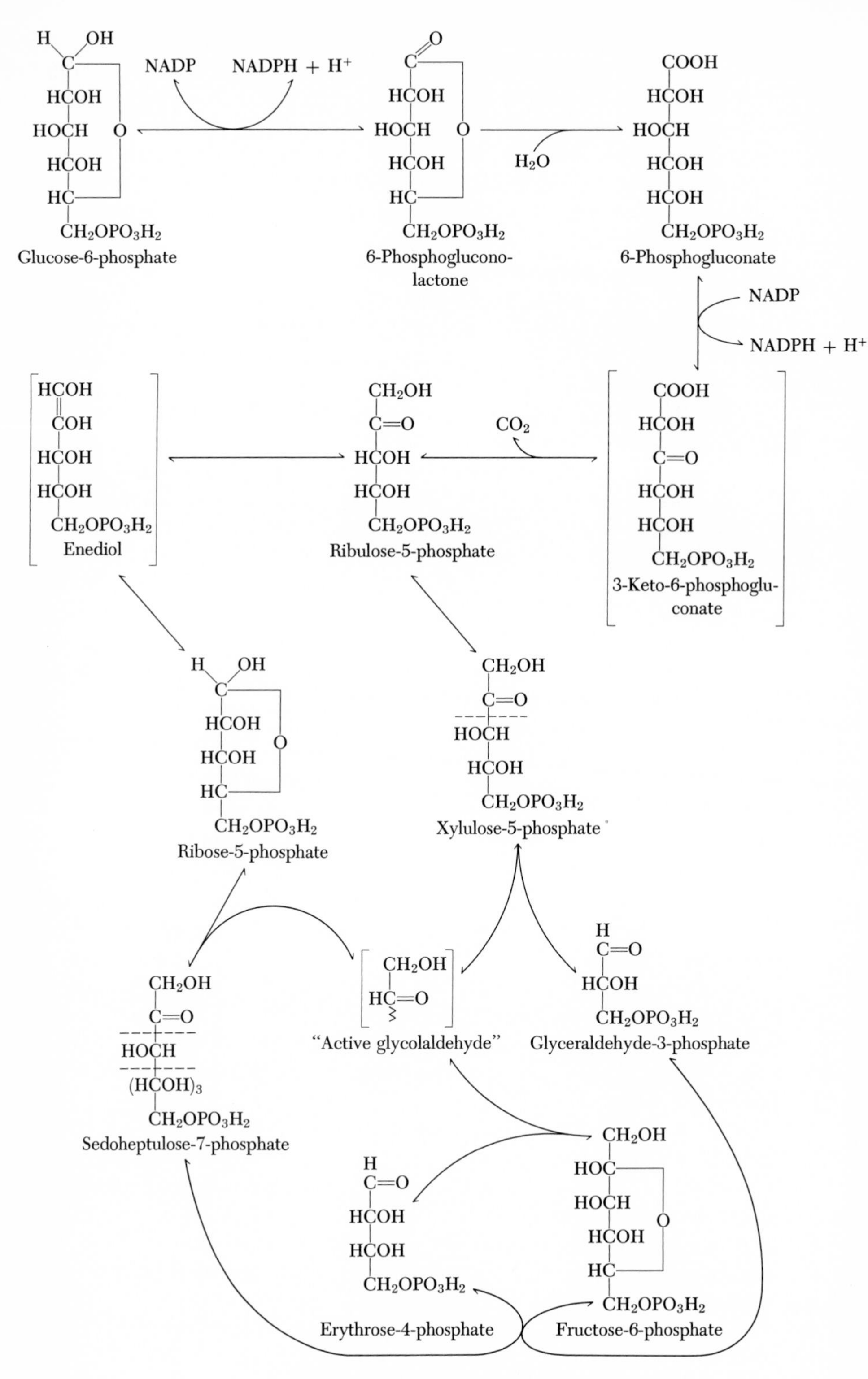

Figure 18-9. Pentose metabolism.

phosphate and erythrose-4-phosphate. The tetrose ester then reacts with another molecule of fructose-6-phosphate (transaldolase) to regenerate glyceraldehyde-3-phosphate and form sedoheptulose-7-phosphate. Interaction of this last intermediate with glyceraldehyde-3-phosphate (transketolase) produces xylulose-5-phosphate and ribose-5-phosphate. Since the pentose-phosphates are interconvertible, for each glyceraldehyde-3-phosphate and two fructose-6-phosphates entering this pathway, three ribose-phosphates are produced.

Experiments with isotopically labeled glucose have shown that most of the ribose in nucleotides and nucleic acids of mammalian cells is synthesized via the non-oxidative pentose pathway. The rest arises from the oxidative pathway operating as an incomplete cycle. The major function of the oxidative pathway appears to be the production of NADPH, which, although not well suited for energy production via the oxidative chain (p. 362), acts as a storage form of "reductive energy" or easily available hydrogen for the synthesis of reduced glutathione (p. 367), fatty acids (p. 458), and steroids (p. 474), and as a reductive cofactor for a number of hydroxylases (p. 357).

Thiamine deficiency results in a decrease in erythrocyte transketolase activity long before other signs of the deficiency can be detected. Little is known of other factors influencing the activity of the pentose pathway. Glucose-6-phosphate dehydrogenase activity is decreased in experimental diabetes, starvation, and fat feeding, in which conditions synthesis of fatty acids (and, hence, the requirement for NADPH) also is decreased. It is noteworthy that fairly low concentrations of long-chain fatty acyl-CoA thioesters (known to be increased in the tissues in the conditions mentioned) inhibit the dehydrogenase in vitro. ACTH increases the specific activity of glucose-6-phosphate dehydrogenase in the adrenal cortex, an observation in accord with the requirement for NADPH in the synthesis of steroids.

There is no evidence that deoxyribose is formed directly from a hexose. Although it can be synthesized reversibly by an aldolase type of reaction between glyceraldehyde phosphate and acetaldehyde, this reaction may not be very significant quantitatively. Most evidence points to a direct conversion of ribonucleotides to deoxyribonucleotides without preliminary liberation of the sugar (p. 515).

The rare pentose, L-xylulose, excreted in the inborn error of metabolism known as pentosuria, is derived from D-glucuronic acid.

METABOLISM OF SUBSTITUTED AND DERIVED CARBOHYDRATES

Alcohols and Cyclitols

A number of sugar alcohols are natural intermediates in metabolism. Glycerol is an important constituent of several types of lipids. It is related to the compounds of the glycolytic series by the following reactions:

$$\text{Glycerol} \underset{\text{Phosphatases}}{\overset{\text{ATP} + \alpha\text{-Glycerolkinase}}{\rightleftharpoons}} \text{L-}\alpha\text{-Glycerophosphate} \underset{}{\overset{\alpha\text{-Glycerophosphate dehydrogenase} + \text{NAD}}{\rightleftharpoons}} \text{Dihydroxyacetonephosphate}$$

In this way, depending on physiological needs, glycerol can be synthesized from glucose, or conversely can form the latter. Other sugar alcohols of much less quantitative importance are galactitol (reported to accumulate in galactosemia), sorbitol (intermediate in glucose-fructose interconversion in the seminal vesicle), xylitol (intermediate in the glucuronate pathway), ribitol (the ribose derivative in riboflavin), and erythritol (unknown function, found in urine and fetal tissues). It has been suggested that sorbitol and galactitol may be causative agents in the production of cataracts in diabetes mellitus and galactosemia, respectively.

Inositol is converted to glucose in small amounts, probably via glucuronate and the pentose pathway. The pathway of biosynthesis of inositol is not understood, although its formation from labeled glucose has been reported in the animal body.

Amino Sugars, 6-Deoxysugars, and Sugar Acids

The mucopolysaccharides and glycoproteins, and, to a lesser extent, the glycolipids, require as building blocks certain sugars, aminosugars, sugar acids, and deoxysugars. Figure 18–10 illustrates the pathways of synthesis and certain of the metabolic interrelations of many of these substances. Glucosamine is synthesized, in the form of its 6-phosphate, by the interaction of fructose-6-phosphate with glutamine, the latter contributing its amide group to form the amino group of glucosamine-6-phosphate. Glucosamine-6-phosphate is acetylated on the nitrogen by acetyl-CoA in the presence of a transacetylase in liver, followed by a mutase reaction converting it to the 1-phosphate. The derivative thus formed can undergo a pyrophosphorylase reaction with UTP to form the UDP-derivative of N-acetyl-glucosamine, in which form an epimerization can occur to yield UDP-N-acetyl-galactosamine. The UDP derivatives are the "active" forms by means of which

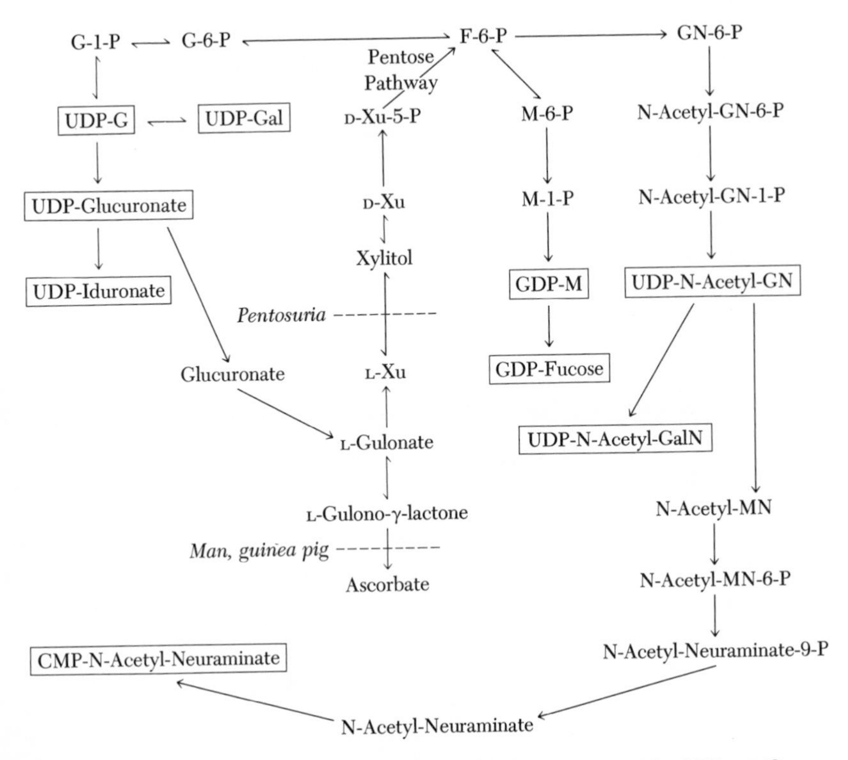

Figure 18–10. Metabolism of amino sugars, 6-deoxysugars, and sugar acids. *CMP*, cytidine monophosphate; *GalN*, galactosamine; *GDP*, guanosine diphosphate; *GN*, glucosamine; *M*, mannose; *MN*, mannosamine; *UDP*, uridine diphosphate; *Xu*, xylulose.

these amino sugars are introduced into metabolic products. UDP-N-acetyl-glucosamine can lose its UDP moiety and isomerize to form N-acetyl-mannosamine, which, after phosphorylation, can condense with phosphoenolpyruvate, yielding a phosphorylated derivative of a sialic acid. After dephosphorylation and condensation with cytidine triphosphate, the "active" form of a sialic acid is produced, namely CMP-N-acetyl-neuraminate.

The active forms of mannose and the deoxysugar, fucose, are probably the GDP-derivatives formed as shown in the figure, whereas transfer reactions involving glucose and galactose utilize the UDP-derivatives, the synthesis of which has been discussed previously.

Glucuronic acid is used by the organism for coupling or conjugation with many substances of natural and artificial origin in what have been called "detoxication reactions," as well as for the synthesis of mucopolysaccharides. Uridinediphosphate-glucose is oxidized in the liver to uridinediphosphate-glucuronate, which then supplies the glucuronate moiety in conjugation reactions. The glucuronyl transferase required for the conjugations is absent in fetal liver, which accounts for the poor ability of the newborn to conjugate bilirubin, leading to jaundice. UDP-iduronate, required for the synthesis of chondroitin sulfate B, is formed from UDP-glucuronate. After loss of the UDP moiety, glucuronate is converted to ascorbate in animals other than guinea pig and man, and to L-xylulose, which, in individuals other than pentosurics, can form D-xylulose-5-phosphate, which traverses the pentose-phosphate pathway and is reconverted to hexose in a cyclic manner.

In the case of the sulfatation reactions which form certain of the acidic sugar units of the mucopolysaccharides, it has not been decided at what stage the sulfatation occurs physiologically, since many in vitro systems equally readily transfer sulfate from phosphoadenosylphosphosulfate (PAPS, p. 587) to mono-, oligo-, and polysaccharide acceptors.

Adequate dietary vitamin A is required for normal synthesis of mucopolysaccharides in cells of the intestinal mucosa and connective tissues. Abnormal amounts of acidic mucopolysaccharides are deposited in the tissues and excreted in the urine in gargoylism (Hurler's disease), which is characterized also by abnormal deposits of gangliosides.

It is probable that most tissues synthesize their requisite mucopolysaccharides in situ. As might be expected, the site of incorporation of carbohydrate moieties into the plasma glycoproteins is liver, where it is believed that, after synthesis of peptide chains on the ribosomes (p. 552), linkage of sugars to the peptide chains then occurs on the membranes of the endoplasmic reticulum.

COMPARISON OF CARBOHYDRATE METABOLISM IN VARIOUS TISSUES

Although the picture of carbohydrate metabolism which has emerged from the foregoing discussions may be expected to hold true in its general aspects in most tissues, it might be anticipated also that the special metabolic requirements of each type of tissue would result in variations on the central theme. Figure 18–11 indicates how a number of tissues are adapted to their individual metabolic roles by differentiation in the pattern of carbohydrate metabolism.

Liver

One of the major physiological functions of liver is maintenance of the normal level of blood glucose. To this end, there exist in liver well-developed mechanisms for uptake of glucose from the blood, conversion to glycogen for storage (glycogenesis), release

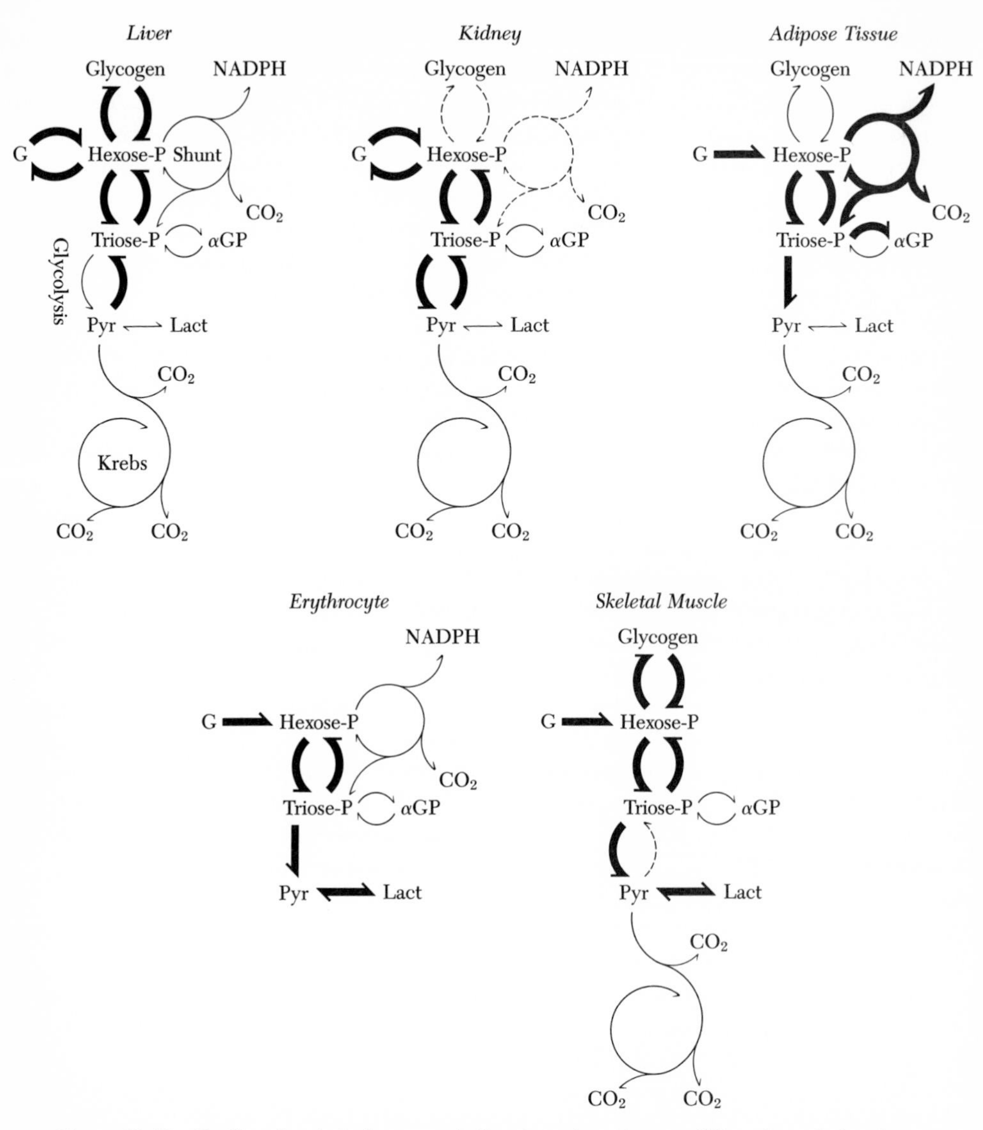

Figure 18–11. Profiles of carbohydrate metabolism in various tissues. αGP, α-glycerol-phosphate.

again as blood glucose (glycogenolysis), and de novo synthesis of glucose from non-carbohydrate precursors (gluconeogenesis) (Fig. 18–11).

Glycogenesis in liver can occur from blood glucose or from any substance capable of giving rise to pyruvate (and other intermediates in the glycolytic sequence). In the latter category are glycerol, blood lactate (from muscle), and the glucogenic amino acids.

Owing to the presence of glucose-6-phosphatase, liver glycogen can contribute directly to blood sugar (glycogenolysis) by way of glucose-1-phosphate and glucose-6-phosphate. In this connection, it is of interest that hepatic glucose-6-phosphatase activity is elevated in fasting, diabetes mellitus, and in corticoid-treated animals. It should be pointed out that glucogenic substances in liver can form blood sugar without necessarily passing through the stage of liver glycogen.

The concentration of glycogen in the liver at any time is the resultant of glycogenolysis and the various routes of glycogenesis, the influx of dietary carbohydrate being one of the most important of the latter. Human liver contains, on the average, some 5 to 6 per cent glycogen. In dogs, the concentration may rise to 10 to 15 per cent after heavy carbohydrate feeding, and falls to less than 1 per cent on fasting. Inborn errors of glycogen storage have been described previously. The level of the blood sugar itself is a major factor in determining the relative rates of glycogenesis and glycogenolysis (p. 435). Control of glycogenesis and glycogenolysis by endocrine and other regulatory influences is discussed elsewhere (pp. 398–400). In brief, glycogenesis is favored by insulin and glucocorticoids (acting via G-6-P); glycogenolysis by glucagon, epinephrine, and serotonin; and completion of glycogenolysis with the production of free glucose by STH, glucocorticoids, and thyroxine, this last series of influences being antagonized by insulin. Naturally, factors which promote gluconeogenesis (see below) will facilitate glycogenesis, at times with an efficacy which over-rides opposing effects. For example, the glucocorticoids stimulate gluconeogenesis within the liver cell so effectively that glycogenesis results, despite the fact that these hormones inhibit phosphorylation of glucose and facilitate hydrolysis of glucose-6-phosphate. In the opposite direction, however, insulin favors glycogenesis while it suppresses gluconeogenesis.

The major conversions of other types of foodstuffs into carbohydrate occur in the liver. The pathway whereby glycerol may be converted to glucose was indicated previously. This, however, is a relatively minor source of carbohydrate; the chief gluconeogenetic substances are the amino acids. The nitrogen-free carbon skeletons of certain amino acids are capable of conversion to pyruvate, from which point glucose or glycogen can be formed by reversal of the glycolytic reactions.

The reactions involved in assimilation of carbon dioxide and the adaptation of these reactions to bypass the pyruvate kinase step probably contribute to the ability of the liver to reverse the glycolytic sequence of reactions, as does the presence of fructose-1,6-diphosphatase and glucose-6-phosphatase. Regulatory influences on the "reversal of glycolysis" for gluconeogenesis have been discussed (p. 405). In general, gluconeogenesis is facilitated by glucorticoids and conditions which result in mobilization of fatty acids to the liver, and opposed by insulin.

In addition to its role in carbohydrate metabolism, liver is also an important site of synthesis of fatty acids and various glycerides. Although these pathways will be discussed in detail in the next chapter, it may be noted at this point that the α-glycerolphosphate needed for glyceride formation can be derived from triose-phosphate (or by phosphorylation of glycerol) and that a well-developed pentose shunt pathway exists in liver, thus providing reduced NADP for the synthesis of fatty acids.

Kidney

Carbohydrate metabolism in kidney resembles that in liver, except that glycogen metabolism and the pentose shunt are relatively minor pathways (Fig. 18–11). Glycolysis may be more active than in liver, whereas gluconeogenesis, although well developed, probably contributes little blood sugar.

Adipose Tissue

Since the necessary phosphatases are lacking, adipose tissue does not reverse the glycolytic sequence, perform gluconeogenesis, or form blood sugar (Fig. 18–11). Instead, the metabolic machinery is geared to one purpose: synthesis, storage, and release of fatty acids. There is some capacity for glycogenesis. Most glucose, however, is channeled down the pathways of glycolysis (providing α-glycerolphosphate at the triose stage), oxidative decarboxylation of pyruvate (forming acetyl-CoA), and the pentose shunt (providing reduced NADP). Adipose tissue lacks glycerol kinase, hence is unable to reutilize any glycerol derived from lipolysis; formation of α-glycerolphosphate by reduction of dihydroxyacetone phosphate in glycolysis is therefore an absolute requirement for glyceride synthesis in this tissue.

Adipose tissue is more sensitive than any other to the influence of insulin, the major effect of the hormone being on the mechanism for uptake of glucose. The net result of insulin action is acceleration of both the glycolytic and pentose shunt pathways and of fatty acid and triglyceride synthesis. Many of the same hormones (norepinephrine, glucagon, ACTH) promote breakdown of glycogen and release of fatty acids from adipose tissue; the connection between these two effects is obscure at present. These matters will be discussed in the next chapter.

Erythrocyte

In contrast to most other cells, the mature human erythrocyte contains no Krebs cycle. Its carbohydrate metabolism is limited to glycolysis and the pentose shunt (Fig. 18–11). The latter is important in providing reduced NADP, which is required for maintenance of glutathione in its reduced state (reduced glutathione is essential for preservation of the stability of the red cell). Glycolysis furnishes ATP, needed for various purposes by the erythrocyte (e.g., ion transport), and reduced NAD. Both reduced NAD and NADP are utilized in reduction of methemoglobin to hemoglobin. An unusual feature of carbohydrate metabolism in the erythrocyte is the high concentration of glucose-1,6-diphosphate (cofactor for phosphoglucomutase) and 2,3-diphosphoglycerate (cofactor for phosphoglycerate mutase).

Muscle

The following discussions of carbohydrate metabolism will be concerned chiefly with skeletal muscle (Fig. 18–11). Certain peculiarities of other muscle masses should be noted, however. Cardiac muscle, for example, differs from skeletal in its capacity to utilize blood lactate, and in the increase in its glycogen content during starvation. Diaphragm, in contrast to skeletal muscle, is readily able to reverse the glycolytic sequence of reactions and synthesize glycogen from pyruvate or lactate.

The formation of muscle glycogen from blood glucose follows the same path as in liver. The absence of glucose-6-phosphatase from muscle, however, makes it impossible for muscle glycogen to contribute directly to blood sugar; consequently glycogenolysis to the stage of free glucose does not occur in muscle. It should be noted that non-specific phosphatases, which might be expected to catalyze the same reaction, are also virtually absent from muscle.

The level of muscle glycogen varies with the dietary intake of carbohydrate and its precursors, but does not fluctuate as widely as liver glycogen. The average concentration in human muscle is 0.4 to 0.6 per cent. In muscle, phosphorylase kinase is activated through the cyclic 3′,5′-AMP mechanism by epinephrine (and not also by glucagon as in liver) and by a special mechanism involving Ca^{++} liberated at the onset of contraction. As discussed below, muscle glycogen is probably not formed to any significant extent by gluconeogenesis from the lactate-pyruvate level; its major source would thus seem to be blood glucose.

The glycolytic reactions in muscle follow the general course outlined previously. In muscle, however, the process seems to be reversible to only a slight extent. The reason for this has not been definitely established, although the difficulty in reversing the pyruvate kinase reaction and the absence in skeletal muscle of the dicarboxylic acid bypass of this reaction may be relevant. The presence of fructose-1,6-diphosphatase in skeletal muscle suggests the possibility of some gluconeogenesis from the triose-phosphate stage; this may be a pathway of utilization of glycerol from fats (via glycerol kinase and glycerolphosphate dehydrogenase). (It has been reported that the slight reversal of glycolysis which occurs in resting muscle is reduced to zero when the muscle is actively contracting.) Another consideration is the great permeability of muscle to lactate; any that is formed (under anaerobic conditions) is readily lost to the blood. This lactate is taken up by the liver, and may be converted to glycogen or blood glucose, the complete route of blood glucose → muscle glycogen → lactate → liver glucose-6-phosphate → blood glucose being known as the Cori cycle. Lactate may undergo direct oxidation in certain extrahepatic tissues, e.g., the myocardium, where it contributes a large portion of the energy requirement under physiological conditions.

The problem of the relative importance of the anaerobic and the aerobic catabolism of carbohydrate in muscle is discussed in connection with muscle contraction. It may be noted at this point, however, that the lactate content of the blood in the resting or moderately active organism is probably largely derived from extramuscular tissues, such as the erythrocytes and those tissues characterized by a significant rate of aerobic glycolysis.

MUSCLE CONTRACTION

Introduction

In the discussions which follow, major emphasis will be given to carbohydrate as the source of energy in muscle contraction. In vivo, skeletal muscle is known to metabolize fatty acids and ketone bodies quite readily. As a matter of fact, it has been estimated by some that as much as half of the energy produced in muscle is derived from such oxidations. In addition, as will be seen subsequently, the immediate source of energy for the contractile event proper is ATP, regardless of its manner of origin. Nevertheless, there has existed a long and venerable association between carbohydrate metabolism (particularly glycolysis) and muscle contraction in the history of these subjects, and, as a consequence of recent findings, there appears to be a common "trigger" mechanism which simultaneously activates contraction and glycolysis.

As a form of work (mechanical), it is to be expected that muscle contraction would use as its source of energy that common currency of bioenergetics, ATP. It might also be surmised that the nature of the phenomenon would be more or less as follows:

(1) Interaction of ATP and the contractile substance of muscle, producing an "activated" form of the contractile substance.

(2) Contraction of the substance, thus performing work, and liberation of inorganic phosphate at some stage in the process.

(3) Spontaneous reversion of the "deactivated" substance to a state of lower potential energy, the resting or relaxed state of muscle.

It must be confessed at this point that, whereas most current data are not in conflict with the hypothetical sequence of events outlined above, there is, on the other hand, much disagreement as to details. The problem is being actively investigated at the present time. All that can be done in this section, therefore, is to report the "current state of the art."

Model Experiments

Before describing in detail the constituents of muscle and their purported roles in contraction, it may be helpful to present certain experiments which constitute at least partial proof that the data obtained from fractionated and highly simplified systems have some physiological relevance.

If a strip of skeletal muscle is stored in 50 per cent glycerol at 0° C. for a time, the more soluble activators and cofactors are extracted, leaving behind the "structural" materials. Bundles of fibers taken from this preparation will, in the presence of salts (KCl or NaCl) and small amounts of Mg^{++}, contract when ATP is added to the suspending medium. The tension developed is the same as that pıoduced by the original muscle in vivo. If the glycerinated muscle is homogenized to a pulp in water and suspended in dilute KCl, a loose, flocculent precipitate is formed. The addition of ATP to this system causes what has been called "superprecipitation," formation of a compact, granular precipitate, which settles out readily. This phenomenon has been regarded as "contraction without architecture." The experiments with glycerinated muscle may be duplicated with myofibrils, which, when washed free of sarcoplasm, contract with ATP, and in suspension appear to "superprecipitate" when treated with ATP.

At the other end of the scale, there can be produced from muscle a substance called "actomyosin" (discussed in detail below), which, in the form of gels or flocs, also undergoes superprecipitation under the influence of ATP. Furthermore, it is possible to spin actomyosin, under proper conditions, into threads which contract in the presence of ATP.

From experiments such as these it has been concluded: (1) that the true contractile substance of muscle is actomyosin; (2) that the in vitro reactions of actomyosin are, to a considerable degree, related to the phenomena produced in the glycerinated muscle; (3) that these phenomena are basically similar to those occurring in the intact muscle; (4) that the fundamental contractile act involves some sort of interaction between actomyosin and ATP.

Proteins of Muscle

In addition to the proteins to be mentioned in this section, certain non-protein substances naturally play important roles in contraction, viz., ATP, Mg^{++}, Ca^{++}, K^{+}, and creatine. The proteins, however, claim our main attention, since a phenomenon such as contraction of a muscle on the macro scale must be a reflection of some type of "molecular" contraction on the micro scale, and contractions of significant magnitude can be undergone by few types of molecules other than proteins.

Myoglobin (which contributes to the color of muscle) aids the process of contraction indirectly by acting as a store of oxygen which may be used by the respiratory processes of the muscle during periods of relative anaerobiosis.

If minced muscle is extracted with dilute salt solutions, of a molarity corresponding to that existing in the native muscle, a mixture of albumins and globulins is obtained, derived from the sarcoplasm. Dialysis of this extract causes precipitation of a fraction known as "globulin X," a little-investigated mixture of proteins constituting 10 to 20 per cent of the total protein of muscle. A similar percentage of the total protein remains dissolved in the albumin fraction, called "myogen." Many of the enzymes of glycolysis are found in this fraction.

Although the proteins of the dilute salt extract account for about 40 per cent of the total protein of muscle, they seem to have no direct connection with the contractile event proper. This involves, rather, two proteins, actin and myosin, which are extractable only with concentrated salt solutions. Myosin and actin together account for 70 to 80 per cent of the protein of the myofibril. Tropomyosin, which constitutes a small but significant percentage of the fibrillar proteins, is believed by some to be associated with the actin filaments. Although its function is obscure at present, its exclusive occurrence in muscle suggests that it may have some role in muscle contraction.

Myosin is a fibrous protein with a molecular weight of 520,000 to 600,000, comprising about 38 per cent of the total protein of muscle and occurring mostly, if not entirely, in the A band of the muscle fibril. It has marked ability to bind ions, such as Ca^{++}, K^{+}, and Mg^{++}. As ordinarily prepared, it exists as the Mg^{++} complex. The combination of myosin with ATP or actin, and its ATP-ase activity (discussed below), depend upon intact sulfhydryl groups in the myosin.

Urea and guanidinium chloride dissociate the myosin molecule into three subunits, each of about 200,000 molecular weight and probably identical in composition. Trypsin splits myosin into characteristic subunits, the meromyosins, one "light" and one "heavy" meromyosin fragment probably originating from each of the three peptide chains of myosin. The current view of myosin structure is that of a rod, 1500 to 1600Å in overall length, 20Å in diameter, with an elongated globule of about 200Å at one end. It has been suggested that the portion of the molecule farthest from the globule consists of three α-helical polypeptide chains, wound together as a three-stranded cable, extending over 600 to 800Å and corresponding to the light meromyosin units. This is followed by a more open structure of the three peptide chains (especially amenable to tryptic digestion) for about 200 to 300Å, terminating in a globule of heavy meromyosin units.

The most striking property of myosin is its activity as an adenosinetriphosphatase (ATP-ase). Association of enzymatic action with a "structural" protein has been regarded as such an unusual occurrence that numerous attempts have been made to dissociate the enzyme activity from the myosin proper, but with no success. The ATP-ase activity is dependent upon the presence of salts, activation being exhibited by salts of K^{+}, NH_4^{+}, and Ca^{++}. Purified myosin ATP-ase is inhibited by Mg^{++}. It has been calculated that, under the conditions prevailing in muscle, myosin ATP-ase breaks down ATP at a rate only $^1/_{100}$ of that estimated to occur during contraction. Therefore, there is considerable doubt concerning the physiological importance of myosin ATP-ase (see below, however, under actomyosin ATP-ase).

Actin differs from myosin in that its most interesting characteristics are physical rather than enzymatic. It can be prepared, in the absence of salts, as a globular protein with a molecular weight of about 60,000. This form is known as G-actin, solutions of which have relatively low viscosity. Actin has high affinity for Ca^{++}. Actin and tropomyosin are believed to occur in the I band of the myofibril; actin, tropomyosin, and myosin are believed to occur together in the A band. Actin constitutes some 12 to 15 per cent of the total protein of muscle.

Solutions of G-actin undergo marked changes in the presence of salts, including the development of high viscosity and strong streaming birefringence. These changes are due to the polymerization of G-actin to F-actin, a fibrous molecule with a molecular weight of about 1.5 million. The conversion involves a native group of ATP in the G-actin, which undergoes breakdown to ADP in the course of the reaction. Intact —SH groups and Ca^{++} or Mg^{++} are required for the polymerization. It is thought that, in muscle, actin is normally present in the F-form. Both G- and F-actin combine with myosin, but only the combination involving the latter is of significance for muscle contraction (to be discussed below).

Actomyosin is formed by the combination of F-actin and myosin in the presence of Mg^{++}, in the approximate ratio of one part actin to three or four parts myosin. This combination is accompanied by a large increase in viscosity and streaming birefringence, indicative of the formation of very long molecules. The complex may be dissociated by urea, high concentrations of salts (2M KCl), and relatively small amounts of ATP. The character of the effect of ATP on actomyosin depends upon the physical state of the latter. Solutions of actomyosin decrease in viscosity and related properties on the addition of ATP; gels or flocs of actomyosin undergo "superprecipitation," whereas threads of actomyosin contract. As mentioned previously, these properties are very similar to those of the glycerol-extracted muscle fiber.

Actomyosin, as the Mg^{++} complex, is an active ATP-ase at the pH of muscle. In salt concentrations below 0.12M, both Mg^{++} and Ca^{++} enhance the ATP-ase activity. Myofibrillar ATP-ase activity (probably due to actomyosin) has been calculated to be sufficient to account for the inorganic phosphate production which occurs during muscular activity. It is thought by some that actin and myosin are present as separate entities in muscle, combining to form actomyosin only during certain phases of contraction.

Contraction

Most theories of muscle contraction agree that the contractile event proper involves some sort of reaction between actomyosin and ATP. The evidence for the participation of actomyosin (or actin + myosin) has been discussed. The choice of ATP as the direct and immediate source of energy derives from the following evidence:

(1) Muscle can contract anaerobically; therefore, aerobic pathways of metabolism are not directly concerned. Under these conditions, of course, even though oxidative chain phosphorylation is impossible, substrate level generation of energy is available through glycolysis.

(2) Muscle contracts even if glycolysis is prevented by inhibition of the oxidative step with iodoacetate. In this case, breakdown of phosphocreatine is observed, and hence remains as a possible direct source of energy.

(3) If changes in the concentrations of creatine and phosphocreatine are prevented by inhibition of creatine kinase with fluorodinitrobenzene, contraction still is possible, the only observable alterations being a decrease in ATP and increases in ADP and inorganic phosphate. The changes in the nucleotides are slightly less than expected from the increase in phosphate, due to the operation of the myokinase reaction, which reconverts some of the ADP to ATP. A linear relationship is found between the external work performed by the muscle and the extent of breakdown of high-energy bonds.

Although it cannot be pretended that the details of muscle contraction are understood at the present time, a reasonable if oversimplified picture of the chemical events of contraction and recovery can be drawn as in Figure 18–12.

Muscle contraction is initiated by a stimulus (physiologically, an electrical impulse at the myoneural junction) which depolarizes the membranes of the sarcolemma and sarcotubular system (sarcoplasmic reticulum), liberating Ca^{++} from storage sites in the latter. Ca^{++} (in addition to an effect on glycolysis discussed later) activates the myosin-actin-

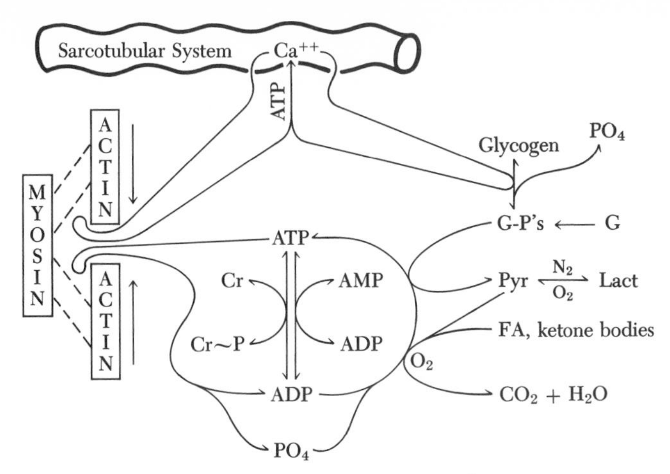

Figure 18-12. Chemical reactions in muscle contraction.

ATP system, probably causing a sliding of opposing actin filaments toward each other in the A band of the fibril, past stationary filaments of myosin. The exact mechanochemical basis of this motion, which results in overall contraction, is not yet known, but may involve making and breaking of temporary bonds between the actin and myosin, with the participation and conversion of ATP to ADP and phosphate as the source of energy.

Concomitantly with the utilization of ATP in the contractile act, there occurs the first of a series of recovery processes. Phosphocreatine, the most important storage form of high-energy phosphate in muscle, reacts with ADP to regenerate ATP, a reaction (the "Lohmann reaction") catalyzed by creatine kinase. Under certain circumstances, as when the regeneration of high-energy phosphate from other sources is inadequate and the supply of phosphocreatine is low, additional ATP may be provided by the myokinase reaction. This is a rather wasteful process, however, since it requires two moles of ADP to produce one of ATP, and since the adenylic acid (AMP) which is formed is rapidly deaminated.

More usually, the Lohmann reaction is accompanied or shortly followed by the glycolytic sequence of reactions, since the Ca^{++} liberated by the initial stimulus activates phosphorylase kinase, which in turn converts phosphorylase *b* to phosphorylase *a*, accelerating the breakdown of glycogen (p. 400). This process may be aided by any AMP formed in the myokinase reaction, since this compound inhibits phosphorylase phosphatase and is essential for the activity of any phosphorylase *b* which may be present. In emotional stress, glycogen breakdown also is accelerated by the activation of phosphorylase kinase by epinephrine, acting through cyclic 3′,5′-AMP (p. 400). It will be noted that the contractile event proper and the recovery processes mentioned thus far are essentially anaerobic, since oxygen is not involved. If the muscle fiber is in a state of relative anaerobiosis (see below), the glycolytic reactions form lactic acid as an end-product; this largely diffuses out into the blood for utilization elsewhere. Although regeneration of ATP occurs as a result of glycolysis, its rate is insufficient to cope with continuous muscular exertion for sustained periods.

Aerobic recovery processes, actually practically synonymous with the operation of the tricarboxylic acid cycle (in oxidizing not only pyruvate, but also fatty acids and ketone bodies), have a sufficiently high rate of generation of ATP to meet the requirements of sustained exertion. The question remains, to what extent muscle contraction is aerobic. A partial answer is furnished by the levels of blood lactate in various conditions, since this compound is very rapidly lost from the muscle if it is formed. At rest, the blood lactate level is probably a reflection of aerobic glycolysis in certain extramuscular tissues. In moderate exercise the blood lactate rises, but drops back to a steady level only slightly higher than that obtaining in rest. Only in violent muscular exercise does the blood lactate attain a high concentration. From these observations it may be concluded that muscular contraction, including the recovery phases, usually occurs under aerobic conditions, but that a state of relative anaerobiosis may prevail when the rate of physical activity outstrips the oxygen supply. The situation probably varies from one type of muscle to another. Some are constructed in such a way that vigorous contraction shuts off the blood supply, whereas certain physiological mechanisms actually tend to increase the circulation in others. The presence of oxygenated myoglobin probably aids in the preservation of aerobiosis for a time. Myoglobin, intermediate in oxygen-affinity between hemoglobin and cytochrome oxidase, is well suited to play the role of "oxygen buffer." To illustrate, myoglobin is 94 per cent saturated at the oxygen tension prevailing in venous blood, and 50 per cent saturated at the tension in which the cytochrome system is operative.

To sum up the changes occurring during contraction and recovery under various conditions, one may begin with the observation that the concentration of ATP in the muscle ordinarily will show no net change, owing to the rapidity of the processes of replenishment. Immediately after the reaction in which ATP is converted to ADP and inorganic phosphate, phosphocreatine, in the first of the recovery steps, reacts with the ADP to re-form ATP. In a somewhat slower sequence of reactions, glycogen is degraded to lactate (if conditions are anaerobic), resulting in a further regeneration of ATP. Anaerobically, then, the initial reaction of contraction and the very rapid recovery reaction involving phosphocreatine result in the liberation of inorganic phosphate, disappearance of phosphocreatine, and appearance of creatine. The slower reactions of glycolysis then bring about a disappearance of glycogen and inorganic phosphate, formation of lactate, and resynthesis of phosphocreatine from creatine. Aerobic contraction differs only in that lactate may never be formed, the pyruvate being oxidized immediately via the tricarboxylic acid cycle. Aerobic phosphorylations are so efficient that the concentration of phosphocreatine may remain relatively constant, the only measurable change being a loss of glycogen and other substrates.

When muscle is at rest, the usual oxidative catabolism of carbohydrate (and other substrates) produces a surplus of ATP. This excess of high-energy phosphate is stored as phosphocreatine via the Lohmann reaction, thus providing a ready reservoir of potential ATP for future contractions.

In contrast to contraction, most investigators regard relaxation as essentially passive. Some small quantity of "relaxation work" may be necessary, since the process appears to involve active "pumping" of Ca^{++} back into the sarcotubular system with the aid of Mg^{++}, ATP, and certain as yet unidentified "relaxing factors."

Fatigue and Rigor

No generally acceptable chemical interpretation of the sensation of fatigue is available at the present time. Among factors which have been implicated in this phenomenon from time to time are depletion of metabolites, accumulation of end-products (lactate), development of acidity, loss of ability to regenerate high-energy phosphate at optimum rate, etc., all of which are probably related rather than independent phenomena. The stiffness of muscle in rigor mortis is due to depletion of ATP. Accumulation of lactate, which is insufficient in itself to explain the findings in rigor mortis, nevertheless contributes to the depletion of ATP, since various ATP-ases are activated by the low pH thus produced.

POSTABSORPTIVE BLOOD SUGAR CONCENTRATION

In the resting, postabsorptive state (overnight fast), glucose is present in systemic venous blood in the following concentrations: whole blood, 60 to 100 mg./100 ml.; plasma, 65 to 110 mg./100 ml. Except for low values (30 mg./100 ml.) in the newborn, there is no clinically significant sex or age difference, although average values are somewhat higher in elderly subjects. Certain analytical procedures in common use yield higher values, i.e., 80 to 120 mg./100 ml. whole blood, because they include also non-sugar reducing substances, e.g., thioneine and glutathione, present chiefly in the erythrocytes. In the fasting state, the concentration of glucose in arterial (or capillary) blood is slightly higher (2 to 10 mg./100 ml.) than in venous blood, owing to its continued passage into and utilization by tissue cells. This "arterial-venous blood sugar difference" is increased under conditions of decreased blood flow or increased glucose utilization, e.g., following administration of carbohydrate (with rise in blood sugar) or of insulin. In man, glucose is distributed equally in the water of the plasma and erythrocytes. The lower concentration in the cells as compared to plasma, per unit volume, is due to their lower water content (because of large amount of hemoglobin). This uniform distribution of glucose between erythrocytes and plasma does not occur in other mammalian species (except anthropoids).

Owing to the operation of an efficient regulatory mechanism (p. 433), the postabsorptive blood sugar concentration is maintained within the limits indicated in normal subjects except under unusual circumstances. What deviations do occur are usually relatively slight and transitory. Pain and emotional excitement (especially apprehension, anxiety, fear, anger) produce a brief rise (10 to 20 mg./100 ml.), due to acceleration of hepatic glycogenolysis resulting from increased epinephrine secretion. As the blood sugar rises, insulin secretion is stimulated, which, together with the accelerated blood flow induced by the epinephrine, results in increased utilization (i.e., removal) of glucose by the tissue cells and, consequently, prompt fall in blood sugar. The same may occur with brief, strenuous exercise (increased hepatic glycogenolysis), but may here, too, be dependent largely on the accompanying emotional excitement. Protracted strenuous exercise (e.g., marathon race) may at times result in a fall in blood sugar as a result of depletion of hepatic glycogen. During a prolonged fast in subjects whose activity is maintained, the blood sugar falls somewhat after about two days, usually reaching a minimum at four to six days (average drop 15 to 30 mg./100 ml.), occasionally falling as low as 40 to 50 mg./100 ml. The fall is of greater degree and occurs more promptly in infants than in adults (greater utilization of glucose and faster depletion of hepatic glycogen). With continued fasting, the blood sugar rises gradually during the second week to approximately the original level. The initial drop is due to depletion of preformed hepatic glycogen, which is necessarily maintained subsequently solely by gluconeogenesis from tissue protein (small amount from lactic acid). The gradual return to normal is effected by the homeostatic mechanism; important adjustments include decreased secretion of insulin (due to hypoglycemia) and thyroxine (due to starvation), with consequent decrease in utilization of glucose, and increased adrenocortical activity (due to stress of starvation), and consequent increased gluconeogenesis.

Glucose in Body Fluids Other Than Blood

Glucose diffuses readily across blood and lymph capillary walls and, therefore, in the postabsorptive state, is equally distributed in the water of the blood plasma and interstitial fluid (also synovial fluid). Its concentration in cerebrospinal fluid removed from the ventricles is about 10 to 20 mg./100 ml. lower and that in the lumbar fluid about 20 to 30 mg./100 ml. lower than in the blood plasma obtained simultaneously (postabsorptive state). The glucose content of the aqueous humor of the eye is also somewhat lower than that of blood plasma, per unit of water. Increase in the blood sugar concentration, e.g., after ingestion of glucose, is reflected in the other extracellular fluids, the increase in the latter lagging somewhat behind that in the former.

The digestive secretions, with the exception of bile, contain virtually no glucose, even at high blood sugar concentrations. The same is true of milk and of secretions of the prostate and seminal vesicles. Unless the blood sugar is raised to unphysiological levels, viz., by intravenous injection, glucose does not appear in the urine of normal subjects except in negligible quantities. There are occasional exceptions to this statement, e.g., in pregnancy (p. 848). Although glucose diffuses perfectly through the glomerular capillaries, it undergoes practically complete reabsorption in the renal tubules under normal circumstances (p. 824).

The concentration of glucose in intracellular water varies considerably in different tissues, but is uniformly considerably lower than in the plasma, except, occasionally, in the liver. The hepatic cells differ from other cells in this connection in that they form glucose (from glycogen) in addition to receiving it from the extracellular fluids. This sugar cannot be stored, as such, to any significant extent in the cells and, consequently, is utilized at least as rapidly as it enters. Indeed, there is evidence that free glucose does not pass freely across cell membranes, except in the liver, but is largely carried in actively by a transport mechanism (p. 395). Variations in the concentration of glucose in the blood, e.g., after administration of glucose, epinephrine, or insulin, are reflected in the intracellular glucose concentration, more closely in liver and kidney, less so in muscle and brain, in which the concentration of free glucose is relatively low.

Sugars Other Than Glucose in Body Fluids

Sugars other than glucose are not present in the blood or interstitial fluid in detectable amounts under normal conditions in the postabsorptive state. In a considerable proportion of normal lactating women, a small portion of the lactose which is formed from glucose in the breast and is excreted in the milk passes into the bloodstream, and, not being utilizable by the tissues, is excreted in the urine. However, its concentration in the blood is rarely sufficiently high to permit its detection by ordinary methods. Fructose, galactose, and pentoses are readily absorbed in the intestine from dietary sources. However, under ordinary conditions of intake their removal from the circulation and their utilization proceed so rapidly that they are not detectable in the blood of normal subjects. The same is true in subjects with essential fructosuria and essential pentosuria (p. 442), in which conditions the excretion of these sugars in the urine presupposes their presence in the blood. Fructose phosphates are continually formed in all cells during the process of glycolysis, but apparently do not leave the cells. Pentoses and galactose also are formed in the organism from glucose, the former being incorporated in nucleotides and nucleic acids, the latter in galactolipids (and lactose, in lactating breast). However, they, too, are either utilized completely in situ or enter the bloodstream in amounts too small to permit their detection.

After fructose or galactose has been ingested in supertolerance quantities (e.g., 40 gm.) by normal subjects, a sufficient quantity may escape prompt conversion to glycogen in the liver to cause its transitory appearance in the systemic circulation (30 to 75 minutes) in demonstrable amounts. Fructose and galactose are also excreted in the urine under such circumstances, inasmuch as, in contrast to glucose, they do not undergo extensive reabsorption from the glomerular filtrate in the uriniferous tubules. This may occur, too, in subjects with liver damage (i.e., impaired glycogenesis) after ingestion of small amounts of fructose or galactose. An alimentary form of pentosuria is also encountered occasionally, usually without appreciable amounts in the blood.

The absence of glucose from gastrointestinal and other secretions, even in the presence of high concentrations in the blood, has been referred to (p. 432). Lactose is present in milk, being synthesized in abundance by lactating mammary tissues from glucose and galactose, both of which originate in the blood glucose, the galactose, too, being formed in situ. Insulin is apparently not involved in this process. Fructose is present in high concentration (300 to 700 mg./100 ml.) in seminal fluid. It is apparently formed by the seminal vesicular epithelium, this function, in common with others of that structure, being stimulated by androgens and decreased by castration or hypophysectomy.

REGULATION OF BLOOD GLUCOSE CONCENTRATION

The concentration of glucose in the blood is the resultant of two general factors: (1) the rate of its entrance into and (2) the rate of its removal from the bloodstream. In the normal postabsorptive state (no glucose in the intestine), it is probably contributed to the blood solely by the liver, entering the hepatic vein at the rate of approximately 115 mg. ($\pm$10%)/sq. m./min. Inasmuch as its concentration in the blood remains fairly constant under these conditions (resting, fasting), it must leave the blood, in the capillaries, at approximately the same rate. These two general processes are influenced by a number of factors under physiological conditions.

Rate of Supply of Glucose to Blood

Except for a possible minor contribution by the kidney, which probably does not occur under physiological conditions, the blood glucose may be derived directly from the following sources: (1) hepatic glycogen; (2) amino acids (gluconeogenesis, in liver); (3) other carbohydrates, e.g., lactic acid, fructose, galactose, pentose, glycerol; (4) glucose absorbed from the intestine, which may be incompletely removed from the portal blood by the liver.

Hepatic glycogenesis and glycogenolysis. In the postabsorptive state in a well-nourished person, the most important of these, quantitatively, is the liver glycogen. Under physiological conditions the following factors influence the rate of hepatic glycogenesis and glycogenolysis:

(*a*) *Blood Glucose Concentration.* A rise in blood sugar increases, and a fall in blood sugar decreases the rate of hepatic glycogenesis. This results in part perhaps from a mass-action effect (glucose $\rightleftharpoons$ glycogen), and also from the incident changes in secretion of insulin by the pancreatic islet cells. A fall in blood sugar to hypoglycemic levels stimulates secretion of epinephrine, with consequent increased hepatic glycogenolysis.

(*b*) ***Insulin.*** Increase in the amount of insulin reaching the liver increases the rate of hepatic glycogenesis and decreases that of hepatic glycogenolysis (decreased output of glucose from liver). It is particularly interesting in this connection that the blood glucose concentration is the most important if not the only factor governing secretion of insulin, which increases as the blood sugar rises and decreases as it falls.

(*c*) *Epinephrine.* Increase in the amount of epinephrine reaching the liver increases the rate of hepatic glycogenolysis. Secretion of epinephrine is stimulated by hypoglycemia, however induced, and by a variety of emotional and other factors, including fear, anxiety, apprehension, anger, pain, unusual exertion, etc.

(*d*) *Thyroxine.* Increase in the amount of thyroxine reaching the liver increases the rate of hepatic glycogenolysis. This may occur during exposure to cold.

(*e*) *Muscular Activity.* Vigorous exercise is accompanied by an increase in the rate of hepatic glycogenolysis (epinephrine?).

Gluconeogenesis. If provided in adequate amount, dietary carbohydrate is the main source of liver glycogen. In carbohydrate restriction, increasing amounts, and in starvation virtually all of the liver glycogen is derived from amino acids. This process of gluconeogenesis is accelerated by the 11-oxygenated adrenal hormones and is retarded by insulin. If adequate amounts of glycogen are present in the liver, glucose may be formed directly by gluconeogenesis and pass into the bloodstream.

Absorption from intestine. A variable portion of the glucose absorbed from the intestine is removed from the portal blood by the liver (glycogenesis, lipogenesis, oxidation). The remainder passes directly into the systemic circulation. The relative proportions taking these routes depend largely upon (1) the capacity of the liver, at the moment, for further storage of glycogen, and (2) the rate of absorption of glucose from the bowel. The latter is increased by thyroid hormone and is decreased in the presence of increased intestinal motility, the glucose being hurried through the upper intestine, the region of maximal absorption.

Rate of Removal of Glucose from Blood

Glucose leaves the blood in all tissues, being utilized by all cells for the production of energy (oxidation), and by certain cells for more specialized purposes, e.g., glycogenesis, lipogenesis, etc. Inasmuch as free glucose cannot be stored as such in cells in significant amounts, the rate of utilization of glucose in the tissues will determine the rate at which it is removed from the blood. Under physiological conditions, this is influenced by the following factors:

(*a*) ***Blood glucose concentration.*** A rise in blood sugar increases and a fall in blood sugar decreases the rate of glucose utilization. As in the case of hepatic glycogenesis, this may be due in part to a mass-action effect (glucose → end-products), and also to the incident changes in insulin secretion.

(*b*) ***Insulin (p. 723).*** Increase in the amount of insulin reaching the tissues increases the rate of utilization of glucose for all purposes (oxidation, glycogenesis, lipogenesis). Again, attention is directed to the fact that secretion of insulin increases as the blood sugar rises and decreases as it falls. One of the actions of insulin is to accelerate transfer of glucose across cell membranes, i.e., from intercellular to intracellular fluids.

(*c*) ***Adrenocortical and hypophyseal hormones (pp. 701, 736).*** Utilization of glucose is depressed by the anterior pituitary growth hormone and by the 11-oxygenated adrenocortical hormones. Increase in the latter occurs, under physiological conditions, in response to a great variety of "alarming" stimuli (alarm reaction), which include practically all unpleasant emotions (anger, fear, anxiety, etc.) and pain, as well as other types of stress (exposure to cold, physical and mental tension, etc). The mechanisms of action of these hormones are discussed elsewhere (pp. 745, 709).

Fundamental Regulatory Mechanism

The processes of hepatic glycogenesis and tissue utilization of glucose are sensitive to relatively slight deviations from the normal blood sugar concentration. As the latter rises, glycogenesis is accelerated and utilization increased, with consequent fall in blood sugar. The reverse occurs as the blood sugar concentration falls. The normal balance between production and utilization of blood sugar at a mean level of circulating (plasma) glucose of approximately 80 mg./100 ml. (65 to 110 mg.) is therefore dependent upon the sensitivity of these processes to variations above and below this concentration. This level of sensitivity is determined to a considerable extent by the balance between insulin, on the one hand, and hormones of the adrenal cortex and anterior pituitary on the other.

The overall effect of insulin is to lower the blood sugar, that of the adrenocortical and growth hormones to raise it. Inasmuch as these two sets of factors are mutually antagonistic in this respect and, indeed, in several aspects of their metabolic actions, it is the ratio between them rather than their absolute amounts that is of primary importance in this connection. With minor differences, decrease in insulin produces much the same effects on carbohydrate metabolism as does increase in adrenocortical and growth hormones. Similarly, the effects of increase in insulin resemble closely those of decrease in either of the other factors. The fundamental importance of this balance is demonstrated strikingly by the fact that diabetes induced by removal of the pancreas is ameliorated considerably by subsequent hypophysectomy (Houssay preparation) or adrenalectomy (p. 445).

The processes of hepatic glycogenesis and glycogenolysis and glucose utilization, and also the blood sugar concentration, are continually exposed to disturbing influences under physiological conditions. These include absorption of glucose from the intestine, physical and mental activity, emotional states, etc. The primary effect of the majority of these is a rise in blood sugar. As indicated previously, this automatically results in a net decrease in the delivery of glucose by the liver and acceleration of its utilization by the tissues. There is a simultaneous increase in secretion of insulin, stimulated by the elevated blood sugar concentration, with consequent increase in the ratio of insulin to adrenocortical and growth hormones. This change in hormonal balance results in increased hepatic glycogenesis, decreased gluconeogenesis, decreased output of glucose from the liver, and increased utilization of glucose. The blood sugar falls accordingly. A drop in blood sugar below the normal resting level causes decreased secretion of insulin, decrease in the ratio of insulin to the antagonistic adrenocortical and growth hormones, increased production of blood sugar, and decreased glucose utilization. Accordingly, the blood sugar rises. If the blood sugar falls to hypoglycemic levels, an additional emergency mechanism comes into operation: stimulation of epinephrine secretion (by hypoglycemia), resulting in acceleration of hepatic glycogenolysis and rise in blood sugar. The increase in epinephrine may also stimulate production of ACTH and, therefore, adrenocortical hormones, causing increased gluconeogenesis.

In the ultimate analysis, the blood sugar concentration regulates itself. Efficient operation of this autoregulation at physiological levels, however, requires a normal balance between insulin and the carbohydrate-active adrenocortical and anterior pituitary hormones, and also normal responsiveness of the pancreatic islet cells to variation in blood sugar. This constitutes the central regulatory mechanism. If it is intact, the blood sugar tends to remain within rather narrow limits in the face of periodic disturbances which may cause temporary fluctuations. On this basis it can be readily understood why conditions of abnormal functions of the islands of Langerhans, the adrenal cortex, or the anterior pituitary are accompanied by serious and fundamental disturbances in carbohydrate metabolism and blood sugar regulation. Changes in blood sugar induced by other factors,

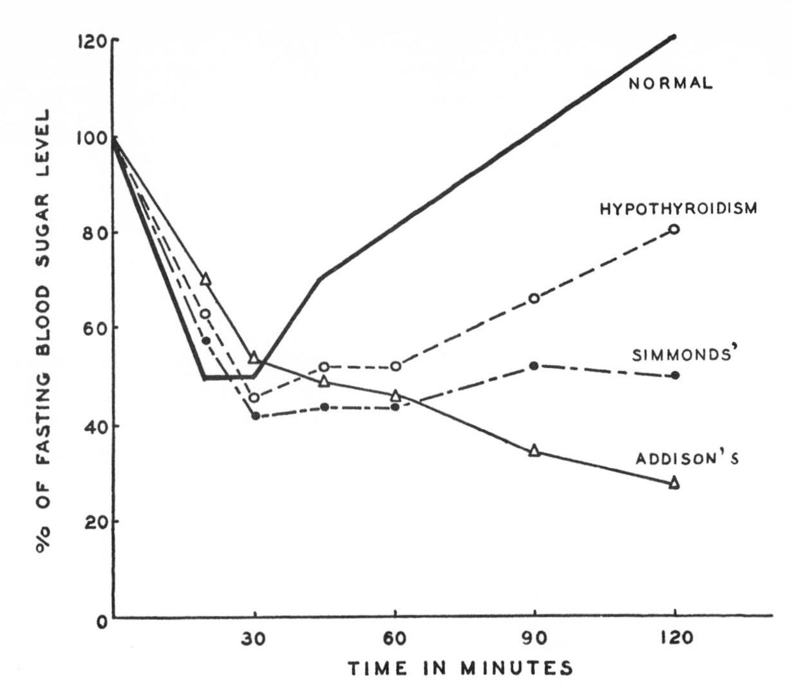

Figure 18-13. Insulin tolerance test. (From Cantarow and Trumper: Clinical Biochemistry, ed. 6, W. B. Saunders Company, 1962.)

e.g., epinephrine, thyroxine, exercise, glucose absorption from bowel, etc., are promptly and effectively counteracted by this control mechanism and are therefore usually limited in extent and of rather brief duration.

ENDOCRINE INFLUENCES IN CARBOHYDRATE METABOLISM

The several processes concerned with the supply of glucose to the blood by the liver and with its utilization in the tissues must be regulated and integrated, not only with one another, but also with certain phases of the metabolism of proteins and lipids. Endocrine organs play an important role in this homeostatic mechanism. These may be placed in two categories in this connection: (1) those which exert a fundamental regulatory influence, their normal function being essential for normal carbohydrate metabolism (viz., pancreatic islet cells, adrenal cortex, anterior pituitary); (2) those which influence carbohydrate metabolism, but are not essential for its regulation (viz., adrenal medulla, thyroid). The metabolic effects of secretions of these organs are considered in detail elsewhere (p. 677 ff.). It will suffice here merely to summarize their most important effects on carbohydrate metabolism.

Insulin (p. 723)

Administration of insulin is followed by a fall in blood sugar, to hypoglycemic levels if adequate amounts are given. This results from (1) net decrease in the rate of delivery of glucose to the systemic blood by the liver, and (2) increase in the rate of utilization of glucose by tissue cells.

The diminished supply of glucose to the blood is due to decreased hepatic glycogenolysis or increased hepatic glycogenesis. Gluconeogenesis (from protein) is decreased. The liver glycogen tends to increase, although this may be obscured by the hypoglycemia, which itself tends to accelerate hepatic glycogenolysis.

Glucose is removed from the blood more readily and is utilized more actively for (1) energy production (oxidation), (2) lipogenesis, and (3) glycogenesis. The overall effect of insulin is antagonistic to that of the adrenal 11-oxysteroids and growth hormone. Insulin is not essential for the utilization of glucose, but, at least in the presence of these adrenal and pituitary factors, it is essential for adequate utilization at normal blood sugar levels. Its primary action in extrahepatic tissues is to facilitate entrance of glucose into the cell, i.e., stimulation of the "transfer mechanism" (p. 726).

In the liver, which is freely permeable to glucose, insulin exerts a regulatory influence upon the activity of glucokinase, i.e., on the first step in the intracellular metabolism of glucose (phosphorylation). Other actions on enzyme systems are illustrated by the following changes in the liver in diabetic animals: increased glucose-6-phosphatase activity, decreased glucose-6-phosphate dehydrogenase activity, decreased activity of UDPG glycogen transferase, decreased activity of glycerol phosphate dehydrogenase.

Adrenal Cortical Hormones (p. 701)

Administration of 11-oxygenated adrenocortical hormones is followed by a rise in blood sugar and an increase in liver glycogen and total body carbohydrate. These effects result from actions of these hormones in: (1) increasing the output of glucose by the liver; (2) diminishing peripheral uptake and utilization of glucose; (3) increasing gluconeogenesis, related perhaps to stimulation of activity of certain transaminases (p. 712). The increase in liver glycogen may be attributable in part to increased activity of glycogen synthetase. The hyperglycemic effect of the glucocorticoids is contributed to by their stimulation of activity of glucose-6-phosphatase and fructose-1,6-diphosphatase, key enzymes in the reversal of glycolysis in the liver.

Adenohypophyseal Factors

The adrenocorticotropic (ACTH) and thyrotropic (TSH) hormones, by stimulating secretion by their respective target organs (adrenal cortex; thyroid), produce effects on carbohydrate metabolism identical with those produced by adrenocortical and thyroid hormones. In addition, unfractionated anterior pituitary extracts cause a rise in blood sugar and a decrease in R.Q. in adrenalectomized and thyroidectomized animals, which, therefore, cannot be due to ACTH or TSH (p. 745). There is also an increase in muscle glycogen ("glycostatic" action).

The "diabetogenic" action of such extracts (hyperglycemia, decreased R.Q.) has been attributed to somatotropin (p. 745). These effects are apparently dependent upon depression of utilization of glucose. The mechanism of action of STH has not been established with certainty. It has been suggested that its main action, in common with glucocorticoids, is to inhibit phosphorylation of glucose by glucokinase.

Epinephrine (p. 698)

Epinephrine produces an increase in blood sugar and blood lactic acid. This is due to acceleration of glycogenolysis in the liver and muscles, respectively, and is accompanied by a decrease in glycogen content of these structures. The mechanism involved is stimulation of phosphorylase activity (reactivation of inactivated phosphorylase by increased production of cyclic AMP). There is evidence, too, that epinephrine may diminish the uptake of glucose by tissue cells, thus interfering with its utilization.

Thyroid Hormone (p. 713)

Thyroxine accelerates hepatic glycogenolysis, with consequent rise in blood sugar. This may be due in part to increased sensitivity of the organism to epinephrine and in part to accelerated destruction of insulin. This effect is partially offset by simultaneously increased utilization of glucose incident in part to stimulation of glycolysis and oxidative metabolism and in part to increased blood flow (p. 431). Thyroxine may also increase the rate of absorption of hexoses from the intestine.

Glucagon (p. 728)

The physiological significance of this factor is not known. Formed in the alpha cells of the islands of Langerhans, it causes an increase in blood sugar, when injected intravenously, by accelerating hepatic glycogenolysis. This effect is produced by reactivating liver phosphorylase from an inactive form by increasing production of cyclic AMP.

BLOOD SUGAR AFTER GLUCOSE ADMINISTRATION

Ingestion of glucose, starch, and, to a lesser degree, other carbohydrates (fructose, galactose) or protein (but not fat) is followed, in normal subjects, by a rise in blood sugar. The degree of elevation depends somewhat upon the amount of glucose contained in or produced from the ingested material, but this relationship is by no means quantitative. This "alimentary reaction" forms the basis for the carbohydrate tolerance tests commonly employed for the detection of disturbances of carbohydrate metabolism. The characteristics of a normal response may be illustrated by describing the changes which follow ingestion of 100 gm. of glucose (oral glucose tolerance test). Samples of blood are obtained before, and at intervals (Fig. 18–14) after, administration of the glucose. The characteristic changes in venous blood are as follows:

(1) A sharp rise to a peak, averaging about 50 per cent above the fasting level, within 30 to 60 minutes. The extent of the rise varies considerably, but the maximum should not exceed 170 mg./100 ml. in normal subjects, regardless of the initial level. This rise is due directly to the glucose absorbed from the intestine, which temporarily exceeds the capacity of the liver and tissues for removing it. As the blood sugar concentration increases, however, the regulatory mechanism comes into play: hepatic glycogenesis is accelerated and glycogenolysis decreased, and glucose utilization increases, principally because of stimulation of insulin secretion. The peak of the curve is reached when utilization is accelerated to the point where the glucose is removed from the bloodstream as rapidly as it enters. This point is usually reached while glucose is still being absorbed from the intestine.

(2) A sharp fall to approximately the fasting level at the end of $1\frac{1}{2}$ to 2 hours. Glucose is now leaving the blood faster than it is entering. This is due to continuing stimulation of the mechanisms indicated in (1) (increased utilization and hepatic glycogenesis) and to slowing or completion of glucose absorption from the bowel.

(3) Continued fall to a slightly sub-fasting (10 to 15 mg. lower) concentration (hypo-

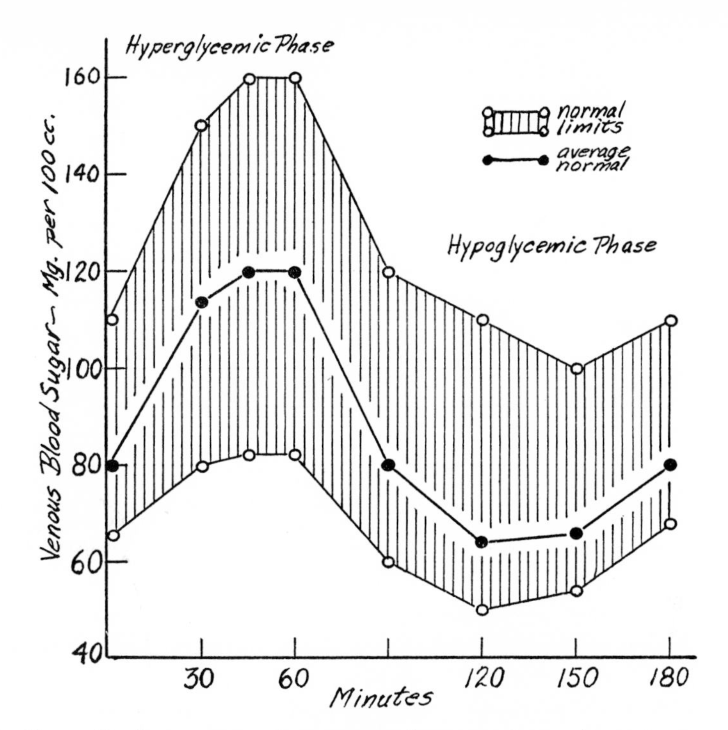

Figure 18-14. Venous blood sugar curve after ingestion of 100 gm. glucose. (From Cantarow and Trumper: Clinical Biochemistry, ed. 6, W. B. Saunders Company, 1962.)

glycemic phase) and subsequent rise to the fasting level at $2\frac{1}{2}$ to 3 hours. This hypoglycemic phase of the curve is due to the inertia of the regulatory mechanism. The decreased output of glucose by the liver and the increased utilization, induced by the rising blood sugar, are not reversed as rapidly as the blood sugar falls. The higher the initial rise, e.g., after intravenous injection of glucose, the more pronounced the hypoglycemic phase.

The changes in arterial (capillary) blood differ from those in venous blood characteristically as follows:

(1) The rise begins somewhat earlier. When the blood sugar has increased about 20 mg./100 ml., the rise in venous blood begins to lag behind that in arterial blood.

(2) At the peak, usually reached at 30 to 45 minutes, the level in arterial blood (150 to 220 mg./100 ml.) may be 20 to 70 mg. (average 30) higher than in venous blood. This arterial-venous blood sugar difference is an expression of the extent of removal of glucose from arterial blood by the tissues, i.e., of glucose utilization.

(3) The return to the fasting level (at $1\frac{1}{2}$ to 3 hours) is not as rapid as in the case of venous blood, indicating that active removal from the blood, i.e., increased utilization, continues beyond the period of hyperglycemia. The two curves converge at the resting level or slightly below in $2\frac{1}{2}$ to 3 hours.

Factors Influencing Absorptive Blood Sugar Response

In normal subjects, the height to which the blood sugar rises increases with increasing doses of glucose up to about 50 gm., which produces a curve approximating that described above. The blood sugar rises no higher (in normal subjects) following ingestion of increased amounts of glucose (to 200 gm. or more), but the fall may be somewhat

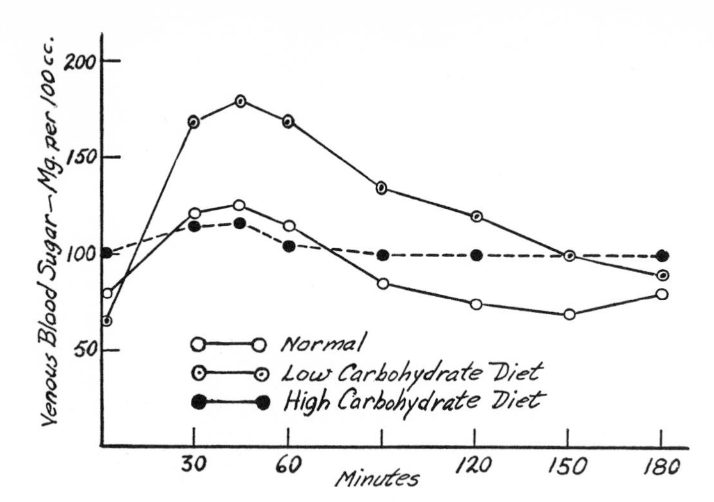

Figure 18-15. Effect of previously high and low carbohydrate diets on oral glucose tolerance curves. (From Cantarow and Trumper: Clinical Biochemistry, ed. 6, W. B. Saunders Company, 1962.)

delayed. This is due to the fact that absorption of glucose from the intestine proceeds at a relatively constant rate regardless, within wide limits, of the quantity present. As soon as the increasing rate of utilization matches the increased rate of entrance of glucose into the bloodstream, no further increment occurs in blood sugar concentration regardless of continuing absorption from the bowel. This is not the case in the presence of defects in the blood sugar regulating mechanism, e.g., in diabetes mellitus, in which the degree of elevation of blood sugar increases with increasing doses of glucose.

The antecedent diet has an important effect on the alimentary glucose response. If the subject is in a state of relative carbohydrate starvation, the rise in blood sugar following ingestion of glucose is more pronounced and its fall more delayed than under normal conditions of nutrition. A diet low in carbohydrate for a few days prior to performance of the test, especially if it is also high in fat, may result in a curve typical of carbohydrate starvation. This phenomenon is related to the amount of glycogen in the liver and to the "readiness" of the blood sugar regulating mechanism to cope with a sudden influx of exogenous glucose.

When glucose is administered repeatedly at intervals of 1 to 2 hours, each successive dose produces a smaller rise in blood sugar than the one preceding. This phenomenon, which forms the basis for a type of glucose tolerance test, the 1-hour, two-dose test, is attributable to the development of a state of increased responsiveness and efficiency of the blood sugar regulating mechanism.

The rise in blood sugar is higher and more prolonged in old age; the curve may resemble that seen in mild diabetes. Prolonged strenuous exercise before ingestion of glucose may cause an excessive rise (as in carbohydrate starvation), whereas strenuous exercise after its ingestion may produce an abnormally marked and prolonged hypoglycemic phase (stimulation of utilization and depletion of liver glycogen).

Phenomena Associated with Absorptive Response

The increased utilization of glucose which follows its absorption from the intestine in normal subjects is accompanied by other biochemical changes.

(*a*) ***Decreased serum phosphate.*** The inorganic phosphate of the blood plasma appears to be intimately related to the intermediary metabolism of glucose. Formation of hexose phosphates occurs in the process of utilization of glucose (p. 395). Consequently, during this process inorganic phosphate is withdrawn from the plasma; the phosphate content of the tissues, particularly muscle, increases and phosphate excretion decreases. These changes in phosphate occur independently of the level of blood sugar; e.g., they continue beyond the period of hyperglycemia induced by glucose administration and occur also during the hypoglycemia induced by administration of insulin. The hypophosphatemia is therefore a reflection of the increased utilization of glucose.

(*b*) ***Decreased serum potassium.*** Stimulation of glucose utilization is accompanied by a shift of potassium from extra- to intracellular fluids. This occurs most strikingly when glucose and insulin are administered after a period of carbohydrate restriction or to subjects with uncontrolled diabetes mellitus. This shift may be sufficiently pronounced to produce a fall in the serum potassium concentration. The basis for this phenomenon is not clear, but it may be related to the passage of phosphate ion in the same direction, i.e., to the increased utilization of glucose.

(*c*) ***Increased respiratory quotient.*** An increase in R.Q. above the normal resting level (0.82) is usually regarded as an indication of increased carbohydrate utilization (oxidation, lipogenesis) (p. 329). About 1 to $1\frac{1}{2}$ hours after oral administration of glucose (100 gm.) the R.Q. rises from 0.82 to 0.88 or 0.90, reaching 0.95 or 0.96 in about 2 hours and then gradually falling to the resting level in about 4 hours. The period of this increase coincides approximately with that of hypophosphatemia, discussed above.

EXCRETION OF SUGAR IN URINE (MELITURIA)

Under ordinary dietary conditions, in normal subjects, glucose is the only sugar present in the free state in the blood plasma in demonstrable amounts. Although normal urine contains virtually no sugar, under certain circumstances glucose or other sugars may be excreted in the urine. This condition is called "melituria," the terms "glycosuria," "fructosuria," "galactosuria," "lactosuria," and "pentosuria" being applied specifically to the urinary excretion of glucose, fructose, galactose, lactose, and pentose, respectively. Some employ the term "glycosuria" to indicate the presence of any sugar in the urine, and the term "glucosuria" to indicate the urinary excretion of glucose.

Mechanism of Glycosuria (Glucosuria)

Glucose is present in the glomerular filtrate in the same concentration as in the water of the blood plasma (arterial). Under normal conditions it undergoes practically complete reabsorption by the renal tubular epithelial cells and is returned to the bloodstream. In normal subjects a very small amount ($<$0.5 gm. daily) may escape reabsorption and be excreted in the urine (p. 824). Under controlled conditions, normal kidneys are capable of reabsorbing 250 to 350 mg., and perhaps as much as 450 mg. of glucose per minute. If one assumes an average glomerular filtrate volume of 125 ml., and a maximum arterial blood sugar concentration of about 200 mg./100 ml. (after glucose ingestion), the quantity of glucose delivered to the tubules seldom exceeds 250 mg./min. in normal subjects.

Excretion of abnormal amounts of glucose in the urine may be due to two types of abnormality: (1) increase in the amount entering the tubules per minute; (2) decrease in the glucose-reabsorptive capacity of the tubular epithelium.

(1) The quantity of glucose entering the tubules is the product of (a) the minute

volume of glomerular filtrate and (b) the concentration of glucose in the filtrate, i.e., in the arterial blood plasma. Inasmuch as glomerular filtration is rarely increased markedly, glycosuria of this type is due almost invariably to an increase in the blood sugar concentration above the so-called "threshold" level, i.e., 160 to 170 mg./100 ml. (venous blood). This may be designated "hyperglycemic glycosuria." It should be pointed out that the amount of glucose presented to the tubules may remain within normal limits in the face of considerably higher blood sugar concentrations if the volume of glomerular filtrate is reduced simultaneously (e.g., glomerular damage complicating diabetes).

(2) Reabsorption of glucose by the renal tubular epithelium is accomplished mainly by an active transport mechanism, presumably enzymatic. The capacity for reabsorption may be diminished by induced (phlorizin), hereditary ("renal" glycosuria), or acquired (certain types of kidney disease) defects in this mechanism, with consequent glycosuria in the presence of normal or subnormal blood glucose concentrations. These are forms of so-called "renal glycosuria" ("lowered renal threshold" for glucose) (p. 848).

Other Sugars in Urine

The renal tubular epithelial cells are apparently unable to reabsorb considerable amounts of sugars other than glucose. Consequently, when these appear in the blood (and, therefore, in the glomerular filtrate) in demonstrable concentrations, they are eliminated in the urine. Lactosuria may occur during lactation and the later months of pregnancy. Pentose (L-arabinose), fructose, and galactose may appear in the urine of normal subjects following ingestion of supertolerance quantities of these sugars, i.e., quantities in excess of the capacity of the organism (particularly liver) to remove them from the bloodstream and incorporate them in the scheme of intermediary carbohydrate metabolism. Genetically determined metabolic abnormalities due to enzyme defects may produce similar conditions (inborn errors of metabolism, p. 766). There is a form of pentosuria (L-ketoxylose) that is due probably to congenital absence of the enzyme which reduces L-xylulose (ketoxylose) to xylitol, a step in the metabolism of glucuronic acid (p. 420). "Essential" fructosuria is due to congenital absence of one of the enzymes concerned with an early step in the metabolism of fructose, i.e., before the formation of glyceraldehyde phosphate. Galactosemia, one feature of which is galactosuria, is characterized by inability to convert galactose to glucose normally, due to a genetically determined defect in phosphogalactose uridyl transferase, which is involved in the conversion of galactose-1-phosphate to glucose-1-phosphate (p. 407).

EXPERIMENTAL DIABETES MELLITUS

Metabolic counterparts of clinical diabetes mellitus can be produced experimentally by disturbing the balance between insulin, on the one hand, and adrenocortical and anterior pituitary hormones on the other (p. 435). This induced imbalance is in the direction of a decrease in the amount of insulin in relation to that of the other two types of hormones. The importance of the balance between these fundamental regulatory factors is reflected in the following facts: (1) the typical diabetic state, with minor differences, results from either (a) absolute deficiency in insulin or (b) absolute excess of anterior pituitary or adrenocortical hormones (i.e., relative deficiency in insulin); (2) the severe diabetes produced by total pancreatectomy is alleviated strikingly by subsequent removal of either the anterior hypophysis or the adrenals.

Total Pancreatectomy

Surgical removal of all pancreatic tissue is followed by characteristic manifestations of diabetes mellitus, the severity of which varies considerably in different species (e.g., severe in dog and cat; moderately severe in man; mild in monkey, goat, pig; none in duck). Removal of the source of insulin (islet β-cells) (in susceptible species) results in the following metabolic phenomena.

(1) Decreased utilization of glucose, indicated by: (a) decreased glucose tolerance (blood sugar curve); decreased R.Q.; fasting hyperglycemia; glycosuria.

(2) Decreased protein synthesis and increased gluconeogenesis (from protein), indicated by negative nitrogen balance and increasing urinary G:N ratio. This is due to relative preponderance of adrenocortical hormones.

(3) Increased mobilization of body lipids, due to relative preponderance of pituitary and adrenocortical hormones. This is reflected in loss of body fat and increase in blood plasma lipids. Lipogenesis is decreased.

(4) Increased oxidation (in liver) of the fatty acids, mobilized in excess, to active 2-carbon fragments. These cannot be utilized adequately for lipogenesis in the absence of insulin, and are present in amounts greater than can be oxidized in the liver (tricarboxylic acid cycle). They are therefore diverted in increased amounts to the formation of acetoacetate and cholesterol. This results in ketosis, ketonuria, and hypercholesterolemia.

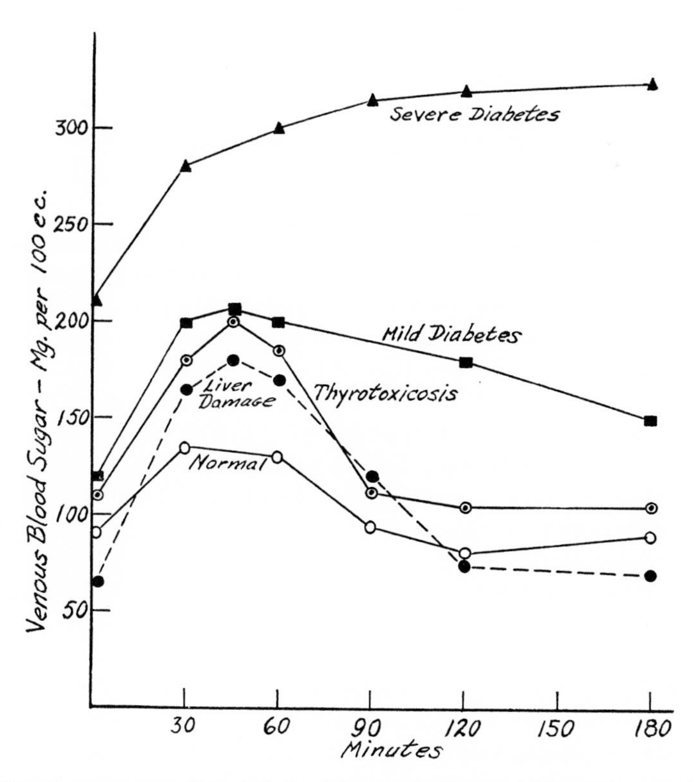

Figure 18-16. Blood sugar curves characteristic of decreased tolerance (100 gm. glucose). (From Cantarow and Trumper: Clinical Biochemistry, ed. 6, W. B. Saunders Company, 1962.)

(5) Excessive production of acetoacetic and β-hydroxybutyric acids, resulting in acidosis, with reduction in bicarbonate.

(6) Dehydration, initiated by the polyuria incident to the glycosuria. Excessive amounts of sodium and potassium are lost from the organism, in addition to water. In advanced stages, e.g., in diabetic coma, the plasma volume decreases, and shock and renal failure develop.

In man and the dog, the diabetes produced by removal of 90 to 95 per cent of the pancreas is more severe than that which follows total pancreatectomy. This has been attributed to the aggravating influence, in the former case, of the hyperglycemic factor, presumably secreted by the α-cells of the pancreatic islets. Residual β-cells undergo degeneration as a result of prolonged hyperglycemia, as indicated below.

Subtotal Pancreatectomy

In certain species, if an amount of pancreatic tissue inadequate to produce diabetes is removed and the blood sugar is maintained subsequently at a high level by various means, diabetes ensues. At first this is mild and reversible; later it is severe and irreversible. The hyperglycemia may be induced by intraperitoneal administration of glucose, administration of a high caloric diet, Bernard puncture, or anterior pituitary extracts.

The elevated blood sugar constitutes a stimulus to the remaining β-cells, which, if the hyperglycemia continues, presumably pass through phases of hyperfunction, functional exhaustion, vacuolization, and other degenerative changes eventuating in hyalinization or fibrosis, i.e., permanent destruction. The importance of hyperglycemia in inducing morphological damage of the β-cells is indicated by the fact that these lesions do not develop if the elevation of blood sugar is prevented by simultaneous administration of insulin or phlorizin.

Alloxan Administration

Injection of alloxan, a substance related to the pyrimidine bases, causes permanent diabetes, after brief transitory phases of hyper- and hypoglycemia. The diabetes is due to degeneration and resorption of the β-cells of the pancreatic islets, the α-cells and acinar tissue being unaffected. The alloxan acts directly, promptly, and specifically on the β-cells, and its effect can be prevented by administration of cysteine, glutathione, BAL (dimercaptopropanol), or thioglycolic acid immediately before or within a few minutes after injection of the alloxan. This protective action is due apparently to the —SH content of these compounds, the alloxan being perhaps reduced to an inactive substance. A similar diabetogenic effect is produced by dehydroascorbic and dehydroisoascorbic acids (p. 158), which resemble alloxan structurally.

There are interesting differences between the diabetes that follows pancreatectomy and that produced by alloxan. In alloxan diabetes, hyperglycemia and glycosuria are more severe and the insulin requirement is higher, but the animals survive longer without insulin than do depancreatized animals, show little ketonuria, and do not go into coma. If alloxan diabetic dogs are subsequently depancreatized, glycosuria and the insulin requirement diminish but ketosis and coma supervene rapidly if insulin is withheld. It has been suggested that the differences between the two diabetic states are dependent upon a hormone elaborated by the α-cells (glucagon), present in the alloxanized but not, of course, in the depancreatized animal.

Administration of Adrenocortical Hormones

The effects of 11-oxygenated adrenal hormones on carbohydrate metabolism are discussed elsewhere (p. 711). Diabetes develops in subjects with certain types of adrenocortical hyperfunction and can be induced in rats by administration of these hormones together with a high carbohydrate diet. There is a considerable species difference in this regard. A temporary diabetic state occurs in man following prolonged administration of adrenal glucocorticoids. "Adrenal diabetes" differs from "pancreatic diabetes" chiefly in the associated increased resistance to insulin and the rather consistent increase in liver glycogen.

Adenohypophyseal Extracts

The influence of hormones of the adenohypophysis on carbohydrate metabolism is described elsewhere (p. 745). Injection of crude saline anterior pituitary extracts (APE) causes hyperglycemia and, if repeated over periods of 1½ to 4 weeks, permanent diabetes in certain species, e.g., adult dog and cat. The rabbit is moderately susceptible, but the rat and mouse are highly resistant to this influence. The permanent diabetes so induced is due to destruction of the islet β-cells induced by the prolonged hyperglycemia. It does not develop if the latter is prevented by simultaneous (with APE) administration of insulin.

This "diabetogenic" action of anterior pituitary extracts is not due entirely to ACTH, for it occurs in adrenalectomized animals. It is apparently due to the pituitary growth hormone (somatotropin) (p. 744).

Thyroid Administration

Diabetes ("metathyroid diabetes") can be produced in partially pancreatectomized dogs in which hyperglycemia is maintained by administration of thyroid hormone. The islet β-cells undergo degeneration, as described above with hyperglycemia induced by other means.

Carbohydrate Metabolism in Hypophysectomized-Depancreatized Animals

Houssay demonstrated that manifestations of diabetes in depancreatized animals are prevented or alleviated by hypophysectomy. Such animals ("Houssay animals") differ from those merely depancreatized as follows:

(1) Glycosuria and polyuria are diminished and at times absent.

(2) They survive for longer periods, with less weight loss, are less susceptible to infection, and wounds tend to heal more rapidly.

(3) The blood sugar is maintained at lower levels and is occasionally subnormal.

(4) The Houssay animal is extremely sensitive to insulin, as is the simply hypophysectomized animal.

(5) There is less ketosis, and the plasma bicarbonate remains within normal limits.

(6) Hepatic and muscle glycogen may be normal and the R.Q. may exhibit an almost normal increase following ingestion of glucose.

(7) The glucose tolerance curve in some cases is less distinctly abnormal, although it usually remains of the "diabetic" type.

(8) The nitrogen balance becomes less markedly negative.

These animals are, however, far from normal. They are rather precariously balanced between hypoglycemia and hyperglycemia. The blood sugar exhibits wide fluctuations, responding unduly to abstinence from (hypoglycemia) and administration of (hyperglycemia) carbohydrate. The ameliorating influence of hypophysectomy on pancreatic diabetes is apparently due to diminished gluconeogenesis and ketogenesis, and improved utilization of glucose at a more normal blood sugar concentration. Similar improvement occurs in depancreatized animals if the adrenals are removed, and not the pituitary. These observations emphasize the physiological importance in this connection of the balance between insulin, on the one hand, and hormones of the anterior pituitary and adrenal cortex on the other.

NON-DIABETIC GLYCOSURIA

As indicated elsewhere (p. 441), glycosuria may occur whenever the quantity of glucose entering the uriniferous tubules exceeds their glucose reabsorptive capacity. This is usually due to either (1) hyperglycemia or (2) a functional defect in the tubular epithelium ("renal" glycosuria).

Hyperglycemic Glycosuria

Apart from the conditions discussed in connection with the production of diabetes mellitus, anything which causes sufficient elevation of the blood sugar for a sufficiently long period can cause glycosuria. The following may be cited as examples: pain, emotion (anger, fear, anxiety, etc.), asphyxia and anesthesia (opiates, barbiturates, ether, chloroform), Bernard ("diabetic") puncture.

Renal Glycosuria

The classic experimental prototype of this condition is the glycosuria which follows administration of phlorizin. This substance causes selective inhibition of renal tubular reabsorption of glucose, directly or indirectly, by inhibiting phosphorylation, although other factors are involved. Glucose is excreted in the urine in concentrations of 5 to 15 per cent or higher. The tissue glycogen stores are depleted and the blood sugar is normal or subnormal. The blood glucose tolerance curve is normal. Gluconeogenesis, fat mobilization, and ketogenesis are accelerated, and acetone and acetoacetic and β-hydroxybutyric acids may appear in the urine. The urinary G:N ratio (p. 573) rises to about 3.6 to 3.65 (fasting, phlorizinized dog), indicating that all of the urinary sugar is derived from protein. The metabolic picture therefore simulates that of severe diabetes mellitus, with the very important exceptions of the normal (or subnormal) blood sugar concentration and normal glucose tolerance.

A milder glycosuria of this type occurs spontaneously, as a hereditary, familial trait, persisting throughout life and due to a defect in the renal tubular enzyme mechanism responsible for reabsorption of glucose. It is referred to clinically as "renal glycosuria." As in the case of phlorizin glycosuria, there is no other abnormality of carbohydrate metabolism. Under ordinary dietary conditions, the body stores of carbohydrate are never depleted to the point where fat and protein catabolism are significantly increased, as they are in the phlorizinized animal. However, deprivation of carbohydrate may cause hypoglycemia, increased sensitivity to insulin, and ketosis more readily than in normal subjects.

Renal glycosuria may occur also in association with evidences of other renal tubular transport defects, e.g., aminoaciduria, renal tubular acidosis, hyperphosphaturia, as in the Fanconi syndrome.

INTERRELATION OF CARBOHYDRATE, PROTEIN, AND FATTY ACID METABOLISM

As has been mentioned previously in several connections, the metabolism of the three major foodstuffs exhibits many points of interaction. Metabolites of carbohydrate can form fatty acids and the carbon skeletons of certain amino acids, and many amino acids can be converted in turn to carbohydrate. Fragments from all classes of foodstuffs are eventually channeled into a common pathway of aerobic catabolism, the tricarboxylic acid cycle. Although the detailed treatment of the metabolism of amino acids and fatty acids will be left to the appropriate chapters, it may prove useful to summarize the metabolic relations between the foodstuffs at this point. The relations shown in Figure 18–17, for reasons which have been mentioned previously, apply particularly to the metabolism of liver.

Certain amino acids, such as alanine, aspartate, and glutamate, are directly interconvertible with α-keto acids, which are products and precursors of carbohydrate. Many

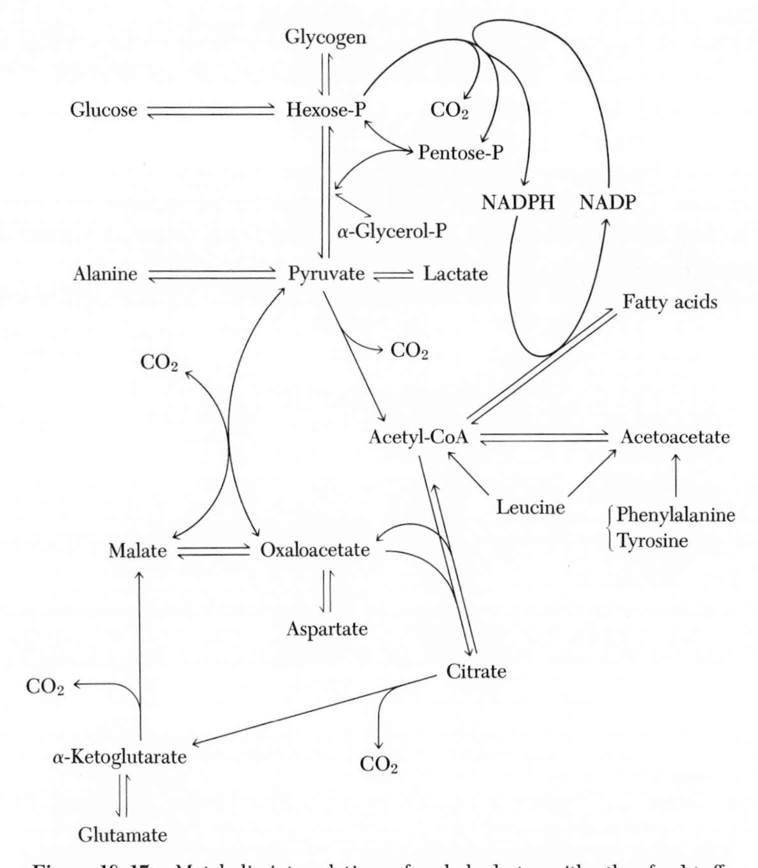

Figure 18–17. Metabolic interrelations of carbohydrates with other foodstuffs.

other amino acids follow the same pathways after preliminary transformations. A few are "ketogenic," forming acetate or acetoacetate. Metabolic fragments from both groups join in a final common route of oxidation through the tricarboxylic acid cycle. Only the first group of amino acids ("glucogenic") can produce new molecules of pyruvate, and consequently can effect a net synthesis of carbohydrate.

Oxaloacetate and other members of the Krebs cycle are readily synthesized from carbohydrate. In the absence of a normal flow of precursor material from this source, glucogenic amino acids appear to be able to make up the deficiency. However, under certain circumstances, a "relative" shortage of oxaloacetate may be said to occur.

Although fatty acids are eventually metabolized via the same acetyl fragments as carbohydrate, they cannot achieve a net synthesis of the latter, since the decarboxylation of pyruvate is irreversible in animal tissues. The glycerol moiety of lipids, on the other hand, is directly convertible to trioses and thence to hexoses. In the opposite direction, carbohydrate is the major source of acetyl-CoA for the synthesis of fatty acids. In addition, it is believed that the NADPH needed for reduction steps in the synthesis of fatty acids (p. 458) is supplied by reactions such as occur in the pentose shunt pathway of carbohydrate catabolism and by the decarboxylating malate dehydrogenase (p. 413). Consequently, failure of the organism to catabolize carbohydrate at the normal rate seriously inhibits synthesis of fatty acids and tilts the equilibrium toward breakdown of fatty acids to acetyl-CoA. Other factors which contribute to this imbalance, and the consequences of "overloading" the Krebs cycle in liver while simultaneously failing to provide a compensatory increase in oxaloacetate are discussed elsewhere (p. 469). Carbohydrate deprivation, in addition to causing an acceleration of the catabolism of fatty acids and amino acids for energy production, leads to a further breakdown of amino acids to form members of the tricarboxylic acid cycle, upon the proper functioning of which depends a major part of the metabolism of the body.

Thus, no metabolic pathway is an isolated route, although it may be so treated for didactic purposes. Each pathway and each substance traveling thereon have metabolic links with many other pathways and other substances. These concepts are developed further in connection with the discussions of the "dynamic state" and "metabolic pool" (pp. 541–543).

BIBLIOGRAPHY

GENERAL

Annual Review of Biochemistry.
Annual Review of Physiology.
Baldwin, E.: Dynamic Aspects of Biochemistry, London, Cambridge University Press, 1963, Chapters 17 to 20.

DIGESTION AND ABSORPTION

Bernfeld, P.: Polysaccharidases, Chapter 8 in Florkin, M., and Mason, H. S. (eds.): Comparative Biochemistry, Vol. 3, New York, Academic Press, Inc., 1962.
Wilson, T. H.: Intestinal Absorption, Philadelphia, W. B. Saunders Company, 1962, Chapter 4.

GLYCOGEN, GLYCOLYSIS, AND FERMENTATION

Aisenberg, A. C.: The Glycolysis and Respiration of Tumors, New York, Academic Press, Inc., 1961.
Axelrod, B.: Glycolysis, Chapter 3 in Greenberg, D. M. (ed.): Metabolic Pathways, Vol. 1, New York, Academic Press, Inc., 1960.
Bueding, E., and Farber, E.: Comparative biochemistry of glycolysis, Chapter 9 in Florkin, M., and Mason, H. S. (eds.): Comparative Biochemistry, Vol. 1, New York, Academic Press, Inc., 1960.
Hassid, W. Z.: Biosynthesis of complex saccharides, Chapter 6 in Greenberg, D. M. (ed.): Metabolic Pathways, Vol. 1, New York, Academic Press, Inc., 1960.

Hers, H. G.: Glycogen storage disease, Advances in Metab. Disorders *1:*1, 1964.
Krebs, E. G., and Fischer, E. H.: Molecular properties and transformations of glycogen phosphorylase in animal tissues, Advances Enzymol. *24:*263, 1962.
Leloir, L. F., Cardini, C. E., and Cabib, E.: Utilization of free energy for the biosynthesis of saccharides, Chapter 2 in Florkin, M., and Mason, H. S. (eds.): Comparative Biochemistry, Vol. 2, New York, Academic Press, Inc., 1960.
Manners, D. J.: Enzymic synthesis and degradation of starch and glycogen, Adv. Carb. Chem. *17:*371, 1962.
Stetten, D., Jr., and Stetten, M. R.: Glycogen metabolism, Physiol. Rev. *40:*505, 1960.
Whelan, W. J., and Cameron, M. P. (eds.): Control of Glycogen Metabolism (Ciba Foundation Symposium), Boston, Little, Brown & Company, 1964.

TRICARBOXYLIC ACID CYCLE

Krebs, H. A., and Lowenstein, J. M.: The tricarboxylic acid cycle, Chapter 4 in Greenberg, D. M., (ed.): Metabolic Pathways, Vol. 1, New York, Academic Press, Inc., 1960.
Lioret, C., and Moyse, A.: Acid metabolism: The citric acid cycle and other cycles, Chapter 3 in Florkin, M., and Mason, H. S. (eds.): Comparative Biochemistry, Vol. 5, New York, Academic Press, Inc., 1963.

MISCELLANEOUS PATHWAYS

Axelrod, B.: Other pathways of carbohydrate metabolism, Chapter 5 in Greenberg, D. M. (ed.): Metabolic Pathways, Vol. 1, New York, Academic Press, Inc., 1960.
Bernfeld, P.: The biogenesis of carbohydrates, Chapter 6 in Biogenesis of Natural Compounds, Oxford, Pergamon Press Ltd., 1963.
Burns, J. J.: Ascorbic acid, Chapter 8 in Greenberg, D. M. (ed.): Metabolic Pathways, Vol. 1, New York, Academic Press, Inc., 1960.
Cheldelin, V. H., Wang, C. H., and King, T. E.: Saccharides: Alternate routes of metabolism, Chapter 9 in Florkin, M., and Mason, H. S. (eds.): Comparative Biochemistry, Vol. 3, New York, Academic Press, Inc., 1962.
Ginsberg, V.: Sugar nucleotides and the synthesis of carbohydrates, Advances Enzymol. *26:*35, 1964.
Glaser, L.: Biosynthesis of deoxysugars, Physiol. Rev. *43:*215, 1963.
Hollmann, S. (translated by Touster, O.): Non-Glycolytic Pathways of Metabolism of Glucose, New York, Academic Press, Inc., 1964.
Kaziro, Y., and Ochoa, S.: The metabolism of propionic acid, Advances Enzymol. *26:*283, 1964.
Neufeld, E. F., and Hassid, W. Z.: Biosynthesis of saccharides from glycopyranosyl esters of nucleotides ("sugar nucleotides"), Adv. Carb. Chem. *18:*309, 1963.
Pon, N. G.: Expressions of the pentose phosphate cycle, Chapter 1 in Florkin, M., and Mason, H. S. (eds.): Comparative Biochemistry, Vol. 7, New York, Academic Press, Inc., 1964.

MUSCLE CONTRACTION

Gergely, J. (ed.): Biochemistry of Muscle Contraction, Boston, Little, Brown & Company, 1964.
Needham, D. M.: Biochemistry of muscular action, Chapter 2 in Bourne, G. H. (ed.): Structure and Function of Muscle, Vol. 2, New York, Academic Press, Inc., 1960.
Paul, W. M., Daniel, E. E., Kay, C. M., and Monckton, G. (eds.): Muscle, London, Pergamon Press Ltd., 1965.
Perry, S. V.: Muscular contraction, Chapter 5 in Florkin, M., and Mason, H. S. (eds.): Comparative Biochemistry, Vol. 2, New York, Academic Press, Inc., 1960.
Rodahl, K., and Horvath, S. M. (eds.): Muscle as a Tissue, New York, McGraw-Hill Book Company, 1962.

HORMONAL INFLUENCES

Ball, E. G., and Jungas, R. L.: Some effects of hormones on the metabolism of adipose tissue, Recent Progress in Hormone Research *20:*183, 1964.
deBodo, R. C., Steele, R., Altszuler, N., Dunn, A. and Bishop, J. S.: On the hormonal regulation of carbohydrate metabolism, Recent Progress in Hormone Research *19:*445, 1963.
Krahl, M. E. (ed.): The Action of Insulin on Cells, New York, Academic Press, Inc., 1961.
Levine, R. (ed.): Symposium on diabetes, Am. J. Med. *31:*837, 1961.
Litwack, G., and Kritchevsky, D. (eds.): Actions of Hormones on Molecular Processes, New York, John Wiley & Sons, Inc., 1964.
Rosen, F., and Nichol, C. A.: Corticosteroids and enzyme activity, Vitamins and Hormones *21:*136, 1963.
Weber, G., Singhal, R. L., and Srivastava, S. K.: Action of glucocorticoid as inducer and insulin as suppressor of biosynthesis of hepatic gluconeogenic enzymes, Advances in Enzyme Regulation *3:*43, 1965.
Winegrad, A. I.: Endocrine effects on adipose tissue metabolism, Vitamins and Hormones *20:*142, 1962.

CHAPTER 19

METABOLISM OF LIPIDS

ALTHOUGH certain structural functions are ascribed to specialized types of lipids, the body uses the simpler varieties (e.g., triglycerides) mainly as fuel. On a weight basis, the calorific value of fat is more than twice that of carbohydrate or protein, it can be stored in practically anhydrous condition and in almost unlimited quantities, and it is metabolically sufficiently labile to be readily mobilized when needed. Nevertheless, carbohydrate, and not fat, is the preferred fuel of the body, and any attempt to oxidize appreciable quantities of fat without concomitant degradation of adequate amounts of carbohydrate can lead to serious consequences.

Although the total number of compounds that must be considered in discussing the metabolism of lipids does not equal, for example, the number of proteins and amino acids, the chemical types represented are much more heterogeneous. First are the fatty acid esters of glycerol (triglycerides, neutral fats) and of other alcohols (waxes). Then there are the "glycerophosphatides," some of which contain fatty acids (as esters), phosphoric acid, and a base (ethanolamine, choline, serine), and a few of which contain fatty aldehydes. The sphingomyelin type of phospholipid and the glycolipids contain the unusual basic alcohol, sphingosine, to which fatty acids are attached in amide linkage. The carbohydrate components of the glycolipids and the presence of inositol in certain phospholipids add to their diversity. Finally, substances must be mentioned that are related to the lipids, partly by metabolic connections, largely by common solubilities, e.g., the sterols and bile acids, other steroids, and the fat-soluble vitamins and provitamins.

In considering the metabolism of the individual constituents of the lipids, it is obvious that most of them are only remotely connected with the lipids. The carbohydrates of the glycolipids and the glycerol moiety of the fats and phospholipids are synthesized and degraded via pathways common to the general metabolism of carbohydrates. Serine, ethanolamine, and choline are more directly related to amino acids than to lipids in their anabolism and catabolism. In fact, the only constituents of lipids that have a completely "lipoid" metabolism are the fatty acids. Most of the other components enter into this area of metabolism only at such points as they are incorporated into the lipid molecule in the process of its formation. Consequently, although the incorporation of all constituents into the lipids must be considered, discussion of anabolism and catabolism of the lipids consists largely of a treatment of the synthesis and degradation of the fatty acids themselves.

As a consequence of the diversity of compounds encompassed by the class of lipids, the treatment of the metabolism of these substances necessarily differs from that applicable to the carbohydrates and proteins. The individual carbohydrates are connected, more or less directly, with the glycolytic sequence of reactions, and a common thread of metabolism runs through the reactions of the proteins and even of the individual amino acids, with few exceptions. The metabolism of the individual types of lipids and their constituents, however, must be considered independently, for practically no metabolic interrelations are known among these substances of a type characteristic of the other major foodstuffs.

Another unusual feature of lipid metabolism is the importance of certain phenomena of transport and deposition. Although mobilization of carbohydrate and protein from one site in the body to another certainly occurs, as does deposition of stores of surplus (at least in the case of carbohydrate), these phenomena do not occupy the prominent position or display such aberrations under abnormal conditions as in the case of lipids.

DIGESTION AND ABSORPTION

Triglycerides

Conditions existing normally in the small intestine are not optimal for pancreatic lipase activity (e.g., pH 6.6 to 6.9 in the duodenum and jejunum). However, lipolysis does occur, inasmuch as analysis of the lipid contents of the small intestine after a fat meal reveals the presence of mono-, di-, and triglycerides, glycerol, and fatty acids, the relative proportions varying under different conditions. Interpretation of such observations in terms of completeness of hydrolysis of dietary fat is complicated by the facts that (1) resynthesis of glycerides occurs in the intestine through formation of new ester bonds; (2) exchanges may occur between the fatty acids of glycerides, phosphatides, and cholesterol esters; (3) lipids of the blood plasma may be secreted into the intestinal lumen. Because of the insolubility of fats in water, the area of their contact and, therefore, their reaction with the water-soluble enzyme, lipase, are enhanced by emulsification. This is favored by the churning action of gastric and intestinal peristalsis, but particularly by the surface tension-lowering action of bile acids entering the duodenum in the bile. A similar effect is exerted by surface-active products of fat digestion, such as monoglycerides, and soaps formed from liberated fatty acids. Bile acids also increase the activity of pancreatic lipase, especially at suboptimal pH levels. Although they certainly play an important role in normal fat digestion and absorption, complete hydrolysis of dietary fat may occur in the absence of bile, as in complete obstruction of the common duct.

Although there is still some uncertainty with respect to certain aspects of fat digestion and absorption, there is general agreement on the following points:

(1) After a fat meal, 50 per cent or more of the lipid mixture undergoing absorption from the intestinal lumen is in the form of mono- and diglycerides; complete lipolysis is therefore not essential for absorption.

(2) Long-chain fatty acids (C_{11} and longer), whether present in the intestinal lumen in the free state or in ester form, are absorbed predominantly via the intestinal lacteals, appearing in the thoracic duct lymph mainly as triglycerides with a relatively small proportion as cholesterol esters (mainly polyunsaturated fatty acids) and phosphatides.

(3) Shorter-chain fatty acids may enter the portal blood, either as esters or in the free state (e.g., butyric acid), the proportion taking this route and in the free form diminishing

with increasing chain length. Bile acids, some of which form water-soluble complexes with fatty acids, aid in their transport into the mucosal cells, where this combination is broken, the bile acids entering the portal blood and passing to the liver for subsequent re-excretion in the bile (entero-hepatic circulation).

(4) Under usual dietary conditions, it has been estimated that at least 60 per cent of the absorbed lipids enter the systemic circulation directly via the intestinal lymph, the remainder passing to the liver via the portal blood.

The processes involved in the transfer of dietary triglycerides from the lumen of the intestine to the bloodstream occur in part in the intestinal lumen and in part within the cells of the intestinal mucosa.

Intraluminar processes. The emulsified triglycerides are hydrolyzed by pancreatic lipase, which attacks the outer (α, α') ester bonds, producing a mixture of free fatty acids, β-monoglycerides and glycerol. An important consequence of this reaction is the production of minute lipid particles, termed micelles, consisting mainly of free fatty acids, monoglycerides and conjugated bile salts. The latter are absorbed actively in the ileum, subsequently undergoing enterohepatic circulation; the lipid components are absorbed mainly in the upper small intestine.

Intracellular mechanisms. The mechanism whereby the mixture of fatty acids and glycerides passes from the lumen into the intestinal epithelial cells has not been established. It is believed that a portion enters by pinocytosis and a portion by diffusion, undergoing solution in the lipids of the cell membrane.

Glycerol and fatty acids of medium and short chain lengths (up to C_{10}) may be absorbed as such into the portal blood, the fatty acids mainly as albumin-bound complexes.

Regardless of the form in which they had existed in the lumen, i.e., ester or free, long-chain fatty acids absorbed from the intestine appear in the mesenteric lymph mainly as triglycerides, and to a minor extent as cholesterol esters and phospholipids. This increment in lymph lipids is largely in the form of chylomicrons. Moreover, despite wide qualitative variations in the fatty acids of dietary lipids, the fatty acid pattern of the chylomicrons tends to remain relatively constant during alimentary lipemia.

It follows that (1) resynthesis of triglycerides occurs within the intestinal mucosal cells, and (2) the absorbed fatty acids undergo equilibration with a larger pool of tissue lipids, including those in the intestinal mucosa. There is probably also rapid recycling of fatty acids, both free and esterified.

(1) The first step in the resynthesis of triglycerides in the intestinal mucosa is the transformation of fatty acids to fatty acyl-CoA by the action of fatty acid thiokinases in the presence of ATP, Mg^{++} and CoA.

(2) Fatty acyl-CoA reacts with absorbed monoglycerides to form diglycerides, and with the latter to form triglycerides.

(3) Diglycerides are formed also by reaction of fatty acyl-CoA with α-glycerol-phosphate (p. 482), the latter being produced either from glucose (via glycolysis) or glycerol (glycerol kinase).

(4) Phospholipids may be formed from α-glycerol-phosphate, via phosphatidic acid, and from diglycerides (p. 484).

(5) Within the intestinal mucosal cell, the triglyceride-phospholipid particles acquire a coating of protein, forming very low-density lipoprotein particles termed chylomicrons. These pass into the thoracic duct lymph via the lacteals and enter the systemic circulation.

There is an increased rate of turnover of intestinal phospholipids during fat absorption, and changes in the pattern of their constituent fatty acids, depending upon the nature of the fatty acids administered. Moreover, fat absorption is enhanced by administration of lecithin, choline, or glycerol-phosphate. Such observations led to the concept that phospholipids may be involved as intermediates in the resynthesis of triglycerides in the intestine.

Chylomicrons were originally defined by microscopic observation as particles of fat contributed to the blood plasma by intestinal absorption, producing characteristic lactescence in plasma after a fat meal. The diameter of the majority of particles is less than 0.5μ, occasionally 1μ or more. Chylomicrons probably consist of a central core of triglyceride with an outer film of phospholipid, cholesterol, and a protein, which resembles that of high-density lipoproteins (p. 492). Since labeled protein, cholesterol, and phospholipid of the chylomicrons rapidly transfer or exchange with these components of other high-density lipoproteins in the plasma, it has been suggested that the surface film that coats the triglyceride core of the chylomicron may consist of intact lipoprotein molecules. The solubilizing action of this lipoprotein film may be important in the transport of triglycerides across the cell.

Sterols

A high degree of specificity is exhibited in the intestinal absorption of steroids. Cholesterol is normally absorbed readily, but certain of its isomers and reduction products are not (e.g., coprostanol, cholestanol [p. 478]). Although most phytosterols (plant sterols) are poorly absorbed, if at all, e.g., ergosterol and sitosterol, certain closely related substances, such as vitamin D and digitalis glycosides, are absorbed quite readily.

Cholesterol enters the intestine in animal foodstuffs and in the intestinal secretions and bile. Cholesterol esters in the digestive mixture are largely hydrolyzed by cholesterol esterase (pancreatic juice), bile acids being essential for the activity of this enzyme. The current view is that cholesterol, mainly in the free state, diffuses into the intestinal epithelial cell, dissolved in the lipid portion of the cell membrane. Cholesterol is absorbed virtually exclusively by the lymphatic route. Although some may enter the lymph in the free state, the bulk of the cholesterol undergoes gradual esterification within the intestinal mucosal cells and is released slowly into the lymph.

Following administration of cholesterol, there is an increase in the lymph not only of cholesterol, esterified and free, but also of triglyceride, phospholipid, and protein, i.e., of lipoproteins and chylomicrons. Conversely, during absorption of fat, there is an increase also in lymph cholesterol. This indicates that intestinal synthesis and absorption of cholesterol are related to absorption and transport of other lipids. The nature of the intracellular mechanisms involved in the transport of cholesterol across the intestine is not clear. Protein complexes may be formed and exchanges may occur between various lipoproteins and the pool of free cholesterol in the mucosa. Dihydrocholesterol and sitosterol, which are absorbed to a relatively limited extent, interfere with absorption of cholesterol; this may be due to saturation of specific lipoproteins with the foreign sterols, thereby reducing their capacity for transporting cholesterol.

Substitution in the diet of fats rich in unsaturated fatty acids (linoleic) for those rich in saturated acids (stearic, palmitic) may result in lowering of the plasma cholesterol concentration. This effect is probably due to an influence on synthesis of plasma cholesterol rather than on intestinal absorption. It is of interest in this connection that cholesterol esters contain a particularly high concentration of polyunsaturated fatty acids.

Phosphatides

Phospholipids may be absorbed as such, and may also be hydrolyzed by phospholipases present in pancreatic juice. The end-products of complete digestion by these enzymes are free fatty acids and phosphatidyl-choline in the case of lecithins, and phosphatidyl-ethanolamine or -serine in the case of cephalins. The glycero-phosphate linkage may be hydrolyzed, probably in the intestinal mucosa, by phosphodiesterases. The hydrophilic properties of phosphatides may be important in several aspects of the digestion, absorption, and transport of triglycerides and cholesterol. They, too, appear in the lymph and blood as components of lipoprotein complexes. Their relation to the absorption of other lipids is indicated in the discussions of intestinal absorption of triglycerides and cholesterol.

Fat-Soluble Vitamins

Both preformed vitamin A and carotene may be absorbed from the intestine in the absence of bile acids, but the amounts absorbed are influenced by factors which affect lipid absorption, as would be anticipated in view of the lipid solubility of these vitamins. Their absorption is diminished in various types of steatorrhea and is favored by conditions which promote emulsification in the intestinal lumen.

Bile salts are required for optimal absorption of vitamin D, which is promoted also by fat absorption. Vitamin D deficiency due to inadequate absorption may occur in various forms of steatorrhea, contributing to defective skeletal mineralization, particularly in children (p. 164).

Naturally occurring forms of vitamin K, being fat-soluble, require bile salts for optimal absorption. Vitamin K deficiency may therefore occur in obstruction of the common duct and in external bile fistula, resulting in defective prothrombin formation and a hemorrhagic tendency (p. 173).

Fecal Fat

Under ordinary conditions of dietary fat intake and normal fat digestion and absorption, the lipid content of the feces remains quite constant, usually less than 5 gm. of fatty acids being excreted daily. This is derived in part from the dietary fat, but mainly apparently from endogenous sources (intestinal secretions, bile) and, possibly, from bacterial synthesis in the lumen of the intestine (p. 275).

Increase in fecal fat (steatorrhea) may result from defective emulsification, digestion, or absorption which may occur because of absence of bile (obstructive jaundice), absence or defective formation of pancreatic juice (pancreatic duct obstruction, chronic pancreatitis), or loss of extensive areas of absorptive surface (extensive small bowel resection). In other cases of malabsorption the mechanism of production of steatorrhea is unknown, e.g., in sprue and celiac disease.

QUALITATIVE DISTRIBUTION OF LIPIDS

Normal Tissue Distribution

The occurrence of the various types of lipids was indicated in connection with the discussion of their chemistry. The salient points will be summarized here in a qualitative way. Approximate quantitative data for the major lipid deposits are indicated in Figure 19–1. It should be noted that, for the sake of simplicity in this introductory section, the binding to lipoproteins of both tissue and extracellular fluid lipids is not indicated in Figure 19–1. Quantitative aspects of blood lipids are discussed elsewhere (p. 493).

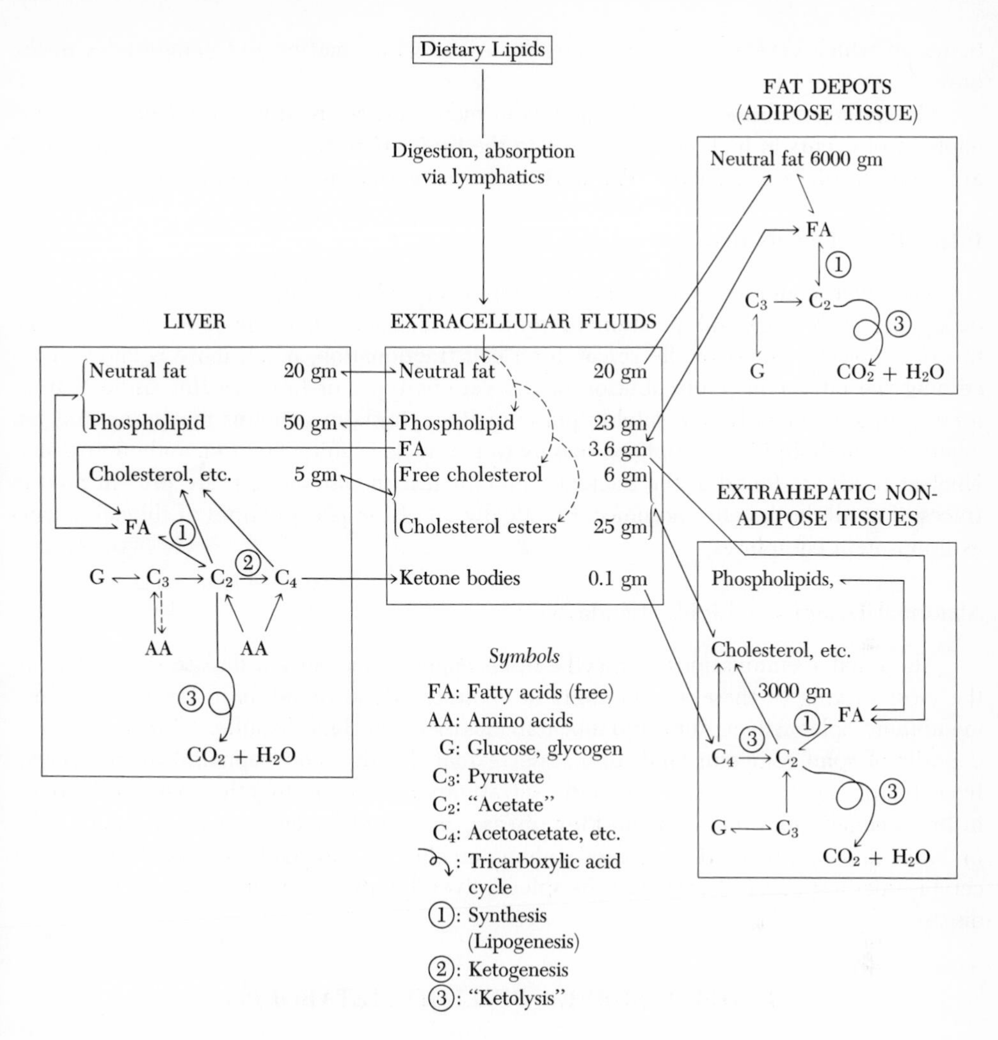

Figure 19-1. Overall metabolism and distribution of lipid in 70-kg. man. Binding of lipids in lipoproteins is not indicated.

Free (unesterified) fatty acids are found in the blood, largely bound to plasma albumin. Although low in concentration, the free fatty acids of plasma have a rapid rate of metabolic turnover and are believed to be the most important form in which lipid is mobilized from the adipose tissue depots to the liver and other tissues for oxidation.

Outside the liver, neutral fat (triglyceride) is confined normally largely to the fat depots (adipose tissue), e.g., the subcutaneous, intermuscular, perinephric, omental, and mesenteric fat. Relatively large quantities of unsaturated fatty acids are found in the liver, as compared with other tissues.

Phospholipid constitutes the dominant type of lipid in tissues other than adipose. Lecithin and the several types of cephalin are found in practically all tissues in significant concentrations. The concentration of sphingomyelin is generally low except in lung and brain. Plasmalogens are especially abundant in muscle and brain. Inositol-containing phospholipids have been isolated from liver, heart, and brain.

Glycolipids are found in many tissues, but in appreciable quantities only in nervous tissue, in which cerebrosides occur largely in the white matter and gangliosides in the gray.

Cholesterol is found in small amounts in many tissues, usually in the free state. Free cholesterol occurs in high concentration in the brain. Both free and esterified cholesterol are found in plasma and liver. The adrenal cortex is rich in cholesterol esters.

Intracellular Distribution

The liver contains representatives from every class of lipids, as befits an organ occupying such a central position in lipid metabolism. Since the liver has been the favorite subject of most of the research on cell fractionation, much more is known concerning the intracellular distribution of the various types of lipids in this tissue than in others. Stated generally, the soluble phase of the cytoplasm contains mostly neutral fat, whereas phospholipids are confined mainly to the nucleus, mitochondria, and microsomes. Nuclear lipids are found in the nucleolus and nuclear membrane, but are present only in traces, if at all, in the chromosomes. Practically all of the phospholipid of the cell occurs as lipoprotein complexes.

Abnormal Deposits of Lipids (Lipidoses)

Abnormal accumulations of specific lipids characterize certain disease states. Among the most striking of these are: deposits of cholesterol and its esters in the skin, mucous membranes, spleen, liver, dura, and subcutaneous tissues in Hand-Schüller-Christian disease; deposits of sphingomyelin (and, to a lesser extent, lecithin and cephalin) in the spleen, liver, lymph nodes, bone marrow, and central nervous system, together with an increase in brain gangliosides, in Niemann-Pick disease; increased concentrations of gangliosides in brain and spleen (and decreased sphingomyelin) in Tay-Sachs disease; deposits of cerebrosides (especially kerasin) in the spleen, liver, lymph nodes, and bones in Gaucher's disease.

GENERAL SURVEY OF LIPID METABOLISM

The major subdivisions of lipid metabolism to be considered are: (1) synthesis and degradation of the fatty acids; (2) synthesis and degradation of the simple and compound lipids and related substances; (3) phenomena of lipid transport and deposition. Related matters include the interrelations between the metabolism of lipids and that of other substrates, the special lipid metabolism of certain tissues, and the general biological role of the individual types of lipids. This section constitutes a brief summary of these topics, which are discussed in detail subsequently.

A scheme of the general metabolism of lipids is presented in Figure 19–1. The numerical values which indicate the quantitative distribution of lipids are to be taken as rough approximations, since there is little reliable information on these items for the human being, and, in any case, there are wide variations between individuals.

Fate of Dietary Lipid

The appearance of newly absorbed lipid in the plasma occurs chiefly by way of the lymphatics. Dietary lipid manifests itself largely in the neutral fat fraction of the plasma lipids, although increases occur also in other lipids during absorption. Neutral fat (chylomicrons) is taken up rapidly by fat cells in adipose tissue, by the liver, and to some extent by other tissues, the proportion going to each of these sites being determined by the physiological state of the organism. The small dietary contributions to other lipids are probably destined chiefly for the liver, since they are taken up by extrahepatic tissues relatively slowly. Cholesterol may be exceptional in this regard.

Anabolism and Catabolism of Fatty Acids

The fatty acid moieties of the lipids of a given tissue are derived from (1) the diet, (2) transfer from other tissues, or (3) synthesis in situ from carbohydrate or protein. Adipose tissue and liver are the major sites of synthesis of fatty acids. *Net* formation of fatty acids occurs as a result of an intake of carbohydrate in excess of immediate requirements, but it has been demonstrated by the use of isotopes that a "steady-state" conversion proceeds continuously, the catabolic reactions keeping pace with the anabolic. Fatty acid synthesis may be effected by any one of several pathways. Although these differ in detail, they utilize in common, as raw material, acetyl units in the form of acetyl-CoA, derived from the oxidative decarboxylation of pyruvate. Disregarding for the time being the various complexities involved, the basic mechanism for synthesis of fatty acids consists of head-to-tail condensation of these acetyl units, followed by reduction of the β-keto groups formed. Limitations to the synthesis of fatty acids are indicated by the existence of certain highly unsaturated fatty acids which are essential dietary factors.

Fatty acids are catabolized primarily by oxidation, the extent and rate varying with the physiological state of the organism. By way of reaction mechanisms, some of which are shared with those involved in the anabolic pathways, fatty acids are degraded to 2-carbon units, formerly called "active acetate," now identified as acetyl-CoA. Any such fragments formed from fatty acids in the extrahepatic tissues are immediately channeled into the tricarboxylic acid cycle for oxidation. Owing to certain circumstances, the facilities for entry of acetyl-CoA into the cycle in *liver* are rather easily overloaded. When the rate of formation of acetyl-CoA outstrips the capacity of the hepatic tricarboxylic acid cycle, condensation occurs between pairs of acetyl groups, forming acetoacetate ("ketogenesis"). In a side reaction, a significant proportion of this compound may be reduced to β-hydroxybutyrate. Liver differs from other tissues also in its inability to split acetoacetate once it is formed. Acetoacetate, acetone (formed by the spontaneous decarboxylation of acetoacetate), and β-hydroxybutyrate (collectively called "ketone bodies") therefore are sent into the bloodstream under normal circumstances ("ketonemia"). Excessive ketonemia is one aspect of "ketosis." The extrahepatic tissues have a great capacity for cleavage and oxidation of ketone bodies ("ketolysis"), which, however, may be exceeded, resulting in ketosis and excretion of detectable amounts of ketone bodies in the urine ("ketonuria").

Anabolism and Catabolism of Lipids

Within each tissue, fatty acids and other constituents of lipids are involved in a constant interchange between free and bound molecules. The rate of "turnover" of each type of lipid, as well as the general direction of net movement (synthesis or degradation), is determined by the chemical character of the lipid, its location in the body in general and in the tissue in particular, as well as by the physiological exigencies of the moment.

Lipid Transport and Deposition

Lipids synthesized or stored in one tissue may, in response to physiological demands, be transferred to another site. The mechanism of transport in the blood plasma, from liver to fat depots, appears to involve lipoproteins, a group of substances currently under intensive investigation due to a suspected relation to abnormal lipid deposits in the blood vessels (atherosclerosis). Transport of lipid from the depots to other tissues occurs in the form of unesterified fatty acids bound to plasma albumin. The level of lipid in the blood is a resultant, on the one hand, of the rate of influx from the diet, synthesis in such tissues as the liver and depots, and mobilization from the liver and fat stores of the depots and, on the other hand, of the rate of oxidation in the various tissues and deposition in the liver and depots. Excessive levels of blood lipid ("hyperlipemia") may result from an imbalance between these sets of factors.

In periods of nutritional plenty, dietary lipids as well as those synthesized from carbohydrate in the liver are sent to the depots for storage. Adipose tissue itself is responsible for much of the synthesis of lipid from carbohydrate. In "lean" times, these stored materials are mobilized from the depots to the liver (and other tissues) for oxidation. The concentration of lipid in the liver, then, is a resultant of the rates and directions of mobilization of lipid between liver and depots, as well as of the rates of synthesis and utilization within the liver. Imbalances may result in the development of "fatty liver." Agents which promote the clearance of lipid from the liver are said to be "lipotropic."

METABOLISM OF FATTY ACIDS

It has been known for some years, largely on the basis of experiments with isotopes, that fatty acids can be degraded oxidatively to 2-carbon units, "active acetate," which, depending on circumstances, either may condense to form acetoacetate or may be oxidized completely via the tricarboxylic acid cycle. Other experiments have indicated that fatty acids are synthesized by means of reductive condensations of these same acetate units. In the catabolic direction, it is not the fatty acids themselves which undergo the various dehydrogenations, hydrations, etc., but rather their thioester derivatives with coenzyme A. On the other hand, evidence has accumulated that, in the major, extra-mitochondrial pathway of synthesis of fatty acids, the intermediates are esterified to enzyme-bound sulfhydryl groups.

Synthesis

Carbohydrate is the major raw material for the synthesis of fatty acids. Pyruvate, by means of oxidative decarboxylation, forms "active acetate," acetyl-CoA:

$$CH_3COCOOH \xrightarrow[\searrow CO_2]{\text{Lipoate, Mg}^{++}\text{, TPP, NAD, CoA}} CH_3CO \sim CoA$$

Metabolic pathways are also available for the synthesis of fatty acids from amino acids. The glucogenic amino acids are convertible to pyruvate; the ketogenic amino acids form acetate or acetoacetate, both of which are lipogenic. In any case, acetyl-CoA is the immediate starting material for the formation of fatty acids.

Although the catabolism of fatty acids is restricted to the mitochondria, independent anabolic pathways are found both within and without these particles. An important extra-mitochondrial pathway is indicated in Figure 19–2. In the first step, an example of CO_2 assimilation, acetyl-CoA is converted to malonyl-CoA, ATP providing the energy

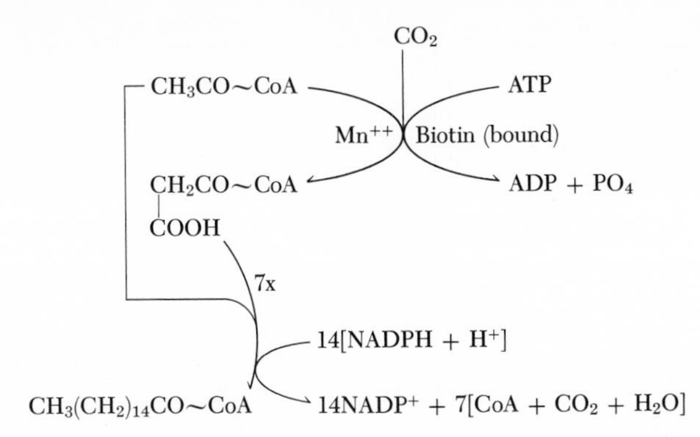

Figure 19-2. Extra-mitochondrial pathway for fatty acid synthesis.

for formation of the carbon-carbon linkage. Biotin is a cofactor for this reaction, functioning as a carrier for the CO_2. In the overall conversion, a molecule of acetyl-CoA condenses with seven molecules of malonyl-CoA in a series of reactions comprising decarboxylation, dehydration, and the equivalent of double reduction, forming (chiefly) palmityl-CoA. It may be noted that this pathway is favored by the high NADPH/NADP ratio obtaining in the cytoplasm outside the mitochondria, particularly in tissues such as liver and adipose, in which the pentose shunt, an important source of NADPH, is of quantitative significance.

Although the mechanism of carboxylation of acetyl-CoA to malonyl-CoA is well established, the subsequent steps in the synthesis of fatty acids in animal tissues have yet to be elucidated. However, since there appears to be considerable similarity among the enzyme systems catalyzing these reactions in animals, yeast, and bacteria, a probable sequence of events can be constructed, based largely upon the findings in microorganisms. Initially, malonyl-CoA undergoes a transesterification from coenzyme A to an enzyme-bound thiol group. (In E. coli, the prosthetic group is phosphopantetheine [coenzyme A minus its adenylate moiety] esterified through the phosphate to an hydroxyl group of serine.) Then acetyl-CoA, which is destined to provide the two methyl-terminal carbon atoms of the fatty acid, condenses with the malonyl-enzyme, CO_2 is lost, and acetoacetyl-enzyme is formed. The enzyme-bound intermediate is then subjected to reduction (NADPH), dehydration, and a second reduction (NADPH, with $FMNH_2$ as a possible intermediate carrier to the substrate), forming butyryl-enzyme. Condensation of the butyryl moiety with another enzyme-bound malonyl group begins another cycle. In the case of the animal system, the cycles end with the formation of palmitate as the major product.

It will be noted that the series of reactions just described is practically identical with a reversal of the intra-mitochondrial catabolic sequence (Fig. 19–5), except that the intermediates are bound to coenzyme A in the latter case. It is also of interest that odd-carbon fatty acids are formed if the acetyl-CoA "primer" is replaced by propionyl-CoA.

Since the chief source of acetyl-CoA for synthesis of fatty acids is pyruvate, which undergoes decarboxylation within the mitochondrion, whereas the chief site of synthesis of fatty acids is the particulate-free cytoplasm, questions have arisen concerning the mode of transport of acetyl-CoA from its site of origin to its site of utilization. The major possibilities are indicated in Figure 19–3. It is generally agreed that thioesters of coenzyme A do not readily traverse the mitochondrial membrane, hence egress of acetyl-CoA as such is doubtful. Two candidates have been proposed as acetyl-carriers, carnitine (the

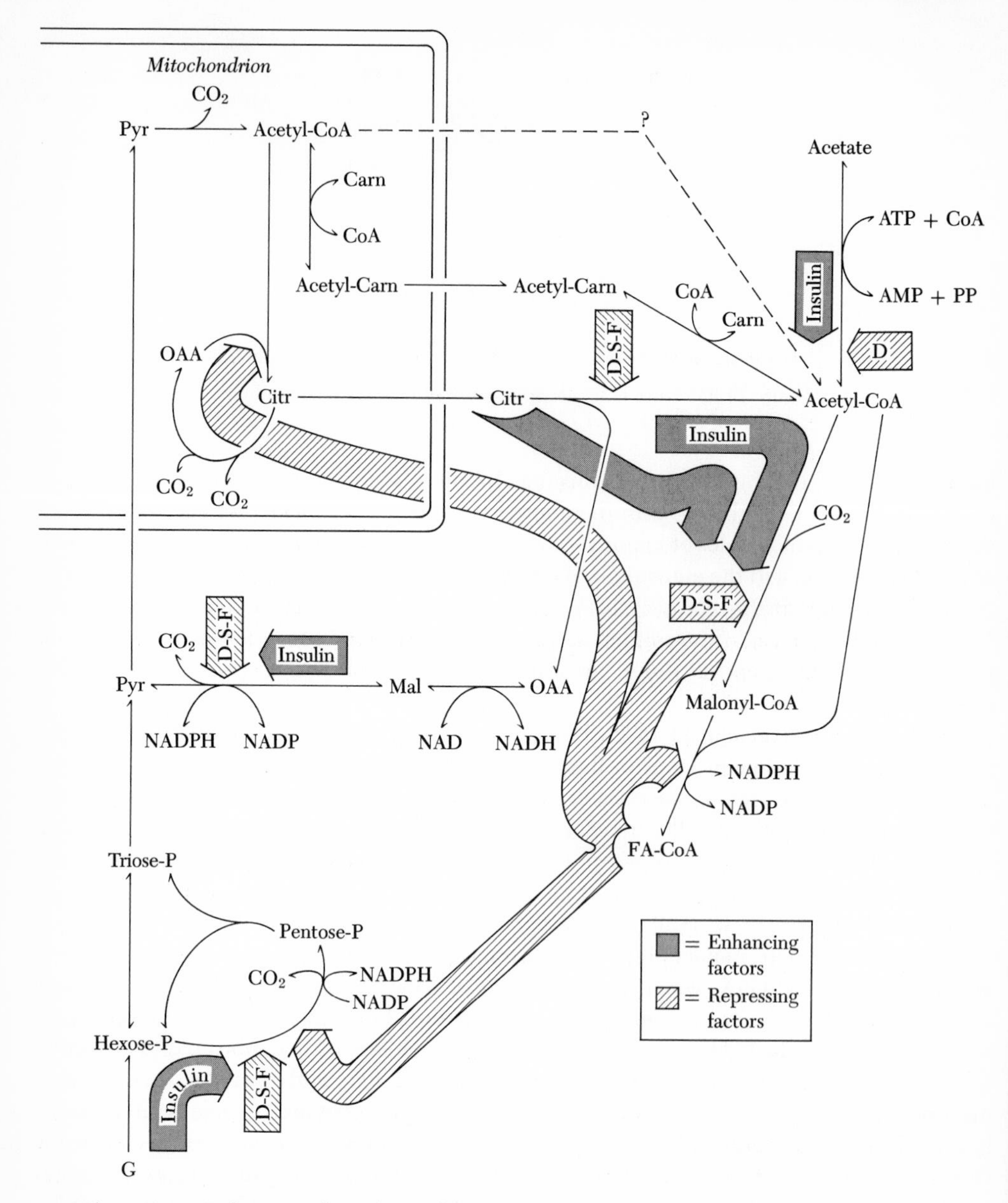

Figure 19–3. Pathways and regulatory factors in extra-mitochondrial synthesis of fatty acids. *Carn,* Carnitine; *Citr,* citrate; *D,* diabetes mellitus; *D-S-F,* diabetes, starvation, high-fat diet; *FA,* fatty acid; *G,* glucose; *Mal,* malate; *OAA,* oxaloacetate; *Pyr,* pyruvate.

trimethylbetaine of β-hydroxy, γ-aminobutyrate, also believed to be involved in the transport of fatty acids into the mitochondrion for oxidation, p. 465) and citrate, the former capable of undergoing reversible transacetylation with coenzyme A (inside and outside the mitochondrion), the latter formed by condensation of acetyl-CoA and oxaloacetate (citrate synthase, intra-mitochondrial) and cleaved to the same compounds (ATP-citrate lyase, extra-mitochondrial). As indicated in Figure 19–3, any free acetate arising in the cytoplasm from hydrolysis of acetate esters or from acetate-forming amino acids is readily "activated" to its CoA ester form by acetyl-CoA synthetase.

In addition to carboniferous raw material in the form of acetyl-CoA, the synthesis of fatty acids requires also a source of reducing power, in the extra-mitochondrial pathway specifically NADPH. As noted on several previous occasions, the "pentose shunt" pathway of carbohydrate metabolism has been recognized for some time as a major supplier of NADPH for this purpose. However, it has been suggested that this source may not suffice in conditions of very rapid lipogenesis. Supplementary NADPH may be provided by the so-called "malic enzyme," the cytoplasmic, NADP-specific, decarboxylating malate dehydrogenase, which was mentioned in connection with CO_2 assimilation (p. 413). Unlike the other enzymes discussed at that point, the malate enzyme appears not to be significantly involved in gluconeogenesis, but rather rises and falls in activity in response to the need for synthesis of fatty acids. As indicated in Figure 19–3, cytoplasmic malate is formed from oxaloacetate, which in turn arises from the cleavage of citrate or from other sources, such as deamination of aspartate.

The extra-mitochondrial pathway of fatty acid synthesis is subject to a number of regulatory influences, as shown in Figure 19–3. Insulin has a generally favorable influence on lipogenesis, since it facilitates glucose metabolism, thus providing a supply of pyruvate. The pentose shunt pathway participates in this facilitation, producing reducing equivalents in the form of NADPH. In addition, insulin exerts a beneficial influence at certain specific sites: the activities of malate dehydrogenase (decarboxylating), acetyl-CoA synthetase, ATP-citrate lyase, and acetyl-CoA carboxylase are increased in the presence of adequate amounts of insulin in the organism and decreased in experimental diabetes mellitus, and, in most cases, also by starvation or a high-fat diet. Citrate has a direct activating effect on acetyl-CoA carboxylase, so that increased concentrations of citrate not only may provide increased amounts of acetyl-CoA, but also accelerate its incorporation into fatty acids. The end-products of the entire process, fatty acyl-CoA thioesters, in a multiple example of negative feedback, inhibit glucose-6-phosphate dehydrogenase (pentose shunt), acetyl-CoA carboxylase, the condensation-reduction steps of fatty acid synthesis, and the intra-mitochondrial citrate synthase. These inhibitions, in addition to matching the rate of synthesis of fatty acids to the rate of utilization, also may be involved, along with decreased circulating insulin, in the suppression of lipogenesis in diabetes mellitus and starvation (in liver, due to mobilization of large amounts of fatty acids from the depots) and in high-fat diets (in both liver and adipose tissue due to influx of excess lipid).

Pathways for the synthesis of fatty acids also exist within the mitochondria. One of these pathways is virtually a reversal of the catabolic pathway described in Figure 19–5, differing only at the last step. Since the degradative reactions will be discussed in detail later, it will suffice at this point to summarize the anabolic path as follows: (1) condensation of acetyl-CoA on the "carboxyl end" of another acyl-CoA, splitting out one molecule of CoA, and forming a β-keto acyl-CoA (Reaction 5, Figure 19–5); (2) successive reduction, dehydration, and reduction, forming an acyl-CoA two carbon atoms greater in length (Reactions 4, 3, and special reversal mechanism of Reaction 2 in Figure 19–5). This sequence of reactions differs from that described previously in not involving malonyl-CoA, in utilization of intermediates bound to coenzyme A instead of to enzyme-sulfhydryl groups, and in requiring NADH as well as NADPH. It is believed that the second pathway for fatty acid synthesis is utilized mostly for lengthening of fatty acid chains, not for synthesis de novo. There is some evidence for the existence of a malonyl-CoA dependent pathway within the mitochondria.

The synthesis of fatty acids is an endergonic reaction. In the malonyl-CoA pathway, ATP is utilized as such. In both pathways, reduced forms of the coenzymes are required and are supplied by exergonic reactions, such as occur in the anaerobic and aerobic breakdown of carbohydrate. Since the hydrogen atoms of these reduced coenzymes do not traverse the oxidative chain, a certain amount of oxidative chain phosphorylation is sacrificed by the organism, thus also contributing to the endergonic character of fatty acid synthesis.

The rate of renewal of fatty acids (synthesis and degradation), as indicated by studies employing isotopes, is highest in the liver, adipose tissue, and intestinal mucosa, intermediate in other internal organs, lowest in muscle, skin, and nervous system. It is under the control of both hormonal and dietary factors.

Interconversion

Apart from total synthesis of fatty acids, mechanisms exist whereby interconversions can be effected between saturated fatty acids of different chain length, by addition or removal of 2-carbon units. These reactions, which undoubtedly proceed by the schemes already discussed, were originally studied with the aid of deuterium-labeled fatty acids. Some of the interconversions shown were:

$$\text{Myristate} \underset{-C_2}{\overset{+C_2}{\rightleftharpoons}} \text{Palmitate} \underset{-C_2}{\overset{+C_2}{\rightleftharpoons}} \text{Stearate}$$

More recent experiments with C^{14}-labeled fatty acids indicate that, whereas palmitate is usually synthesized de novo from acetate units, stearate is usually formed by the addition of acetate units to pre-existing palmitate molecules.

Singly unsaturated fatty acids are easily formed in the body from the saturated fatty acids of corresponding chain length:

$$\text{Palmitate} \xrightarrow{-2H} \text{Palmitoleate} \qquad \text{Stearate} \xrightarrow{-2H} \text{Oleate}$$

The enzymes catalyzing these conversions are different from those forming the α,β-unsaturated intermediates in the metabolic scheme of Figure 19–5, since the double bonds are in quite different locations. A microsomal oxidase of liver and adipose tissue desaturates fatty acyl-CoA's in the presence of oxygen and either NADH or NADPH. Its activity rises and falls concomitantly with other enzymes involved in lipogenesis.

Unsaturated acids of the oleate type are synthesized more slowly than the saturated acids. Although reduction of mono-unsaturated fatty acids can occur, the process is of minor importance in animals. Unsaturated fatty acids are readily degraded, the pathway probably being the same as that utilized by the saturated fatty acids.

By a combination of repetitive chain-elongation and desaturation, a great variety of fatty acids is synthesized in the organism, including acids of the polyunsaturated type. However, as noted in the following section, certain polyunsaturated fatty acids cannot be formed by the animal.

Polyunsaturated Fatty Acids

There are limits to the ability of the animal organism to desaturate fatty acids. Certain polyunsaturated fatty acids are considered dietary essentials, viz., linoleate, linolenate, and arachidonate. It is highly probable that man requires these fatty acids, particularly in infancy; the quantitative nature of the requirement has not been established, however. Definite symptoms have been produced in the mouse, chick, dog, and rat, maintained on diets deficient in these substances. They may be grouped conveniently as follows (rat):

(1) Cessation of growth (interpreted as possibly indicating a structural role for these fatty acids).

(2) Skin lesions, viz., acanthosis (hypertrophy of prickle cells), parakeratosis (keratin collected into globules), hyperkeratosis (hypertrophy of stratum corneum). The visible cutaneous signs bear a superficial similarity to those characteristic of pyridoxine deficiency, but differences are quite evident histologically.

(3) As a result of the skin lesions listed above, the skin becomes abnormally permeable to water. The increased loss of water increases the basal metabolic rate, and is accompanied by an increased intake of water and food.

(4) Abnormalities of pregnancy and lactation.

(5) Fatty liver (p. 504), accompanied by increased rates of fatty acid synthesis, Krebs cycle oxidations, and turnover of hepatic phospholipids.

In addition, deficiency of essential fatty acids leads to increased lability of mitochondrial structure, and, curiously, ameliorates certain of the symptoms of vitamin E deficiency.

Several families of polyunsaturated fatty acids exist, as indicated in Figure 19–4. The acids of the linoleate family (Δ_ω^6; see Fig. 19–4 for meaning of symbols), which includes arachidonate (synthesized in the animal organism from linoleate), are the principal essential fatty acids; they are fully effective in restoring growth and in curing the skin lesions of deficient animals. The acids of the linolenate (Δ_ω^3) family promote growth, but do not cure the dermal symptoms. Neither the oleate (Δ_ω^9) nor the palmitoleate (Δ_ω^7) family is effective in alleviating any of the symptoms listed. The latter two groups also differ from the former two in being readily synthesized by the animal organism from saturated fatty acids.

Certain of the metabolic interconversions which have been established for the polyunsaturated fatty acids are indicated in Figure 19–4. Thus, linoleate undergoes, successively, dehydrogenation, addition of an acetyl unit at the carboxyl end of the molecule,

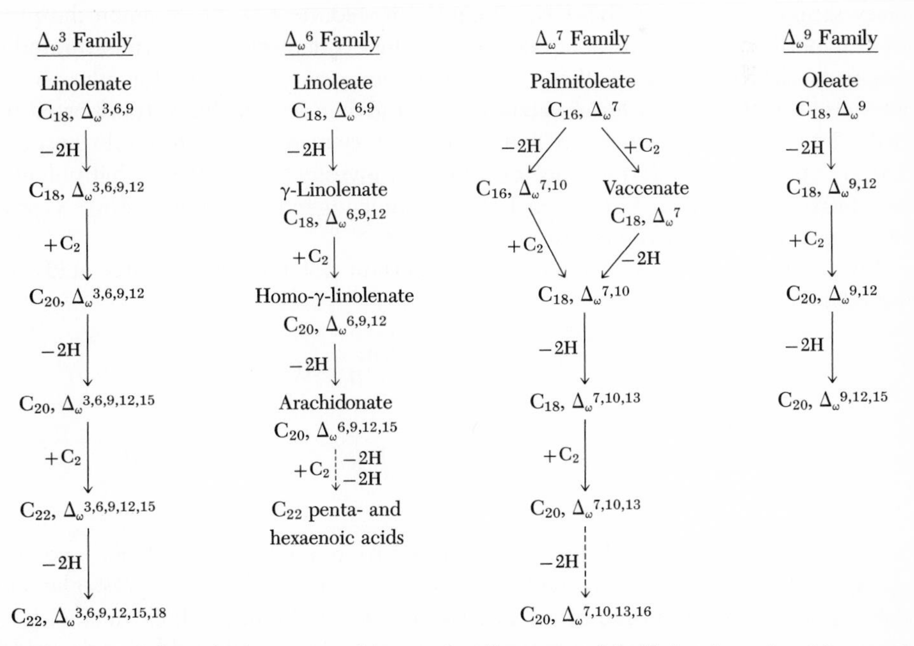

Figure 19–4. Metabolism of polyunsaturated fatty acids. All positions of double bonds numbered from methyl group (ω carbon atom) in order to show structural relationships.

and a second dehydrogenation, forming arachidonate, which can undergo further reactions of the same type to form acids of the C_{22} series, containing five and six double bonds. Linolenate undergoes a similar series of reactions, producing a C_{20} fatty acid containing five double bonds. This compound also may be converted to fatty acids of the C_{22} series, containing five and six double bonds. The conversion of linoleate and linolenate to their respective C_{20} metabolites is impaired in avitaminosis B_6, but the role of the pyridoxine derivatives appears to be indirect.

It has been shown that the animal organism is capable of totally synthesizing certain polyunsaturated fatty acids, although these do not have the biological properties of the "essential" fatty acids. As shown in Figure 19–4, palmitoleate, a major fatty acid in the fat-deficient animal, and the ubiquitous oleate, both can undergo alternating dehydrogenation and addition of an acetyl unit at the carboxyl end to form trienoic and tetraenoic acids. These products occur in significant concentrations only in the animal deficient in essential fatty acids, since the essential fatty acids appear to have a greater affinity than the non-essential for the elongation-desaturation systems.

It may be concluded that the animal organism can synthesize polyunsaturated fatty acids from the unsaturated fatty acids of the diet or those derived from the saturated fatty acids of the body by the introduction of new double bonds between the existing double bonds and the carboxyl group. The organism is evidently unable to introduce new double bonds at positions Δ_{ω}^{3} or Δ_{ω}^{6}. The new double bonds are located so as to maintain the divinyl methane spacing between themselves and the old double bonds. When the double bond system approaches within a few carbon atoms of the carboxyl group, the fatty acid chain is lengthened by the addition of an acetyl unit at the carboxyl end. It is possible that the animal organism does not synthesize linoleate and linolenate because the requisite mono-unsaturated fatty acids of proper structure are not available.

The requirement of experimental animals for essential fatty acids is increased by alloxan diabetes, hypothyroidism, hypercholesterolemic agents, dietary cholesterol, and dietary saturated fat. Since these experimental procedures have in common the production of hyperlipemia, it is possible that they produce a depletion of polyunsaturated fatty acids from the tissues, since these compounds are components of the phospholipids, cholesterol esters, and to a lesser extent of the triglycerides which are transported in the blood. The relationship between polyunsaturated fatty acids and cholesterol transport is a matter of considerable interest, since many recent investigations indicate that polyunsaturated fatty acids may act as hypocholesterolemic agents, thus suggesting a possible dietary approach to atherosclerosis.

Enzymes of the seminal vesicle convert certain polyunsaturated fatty acids to the prostaglandins, e.g.:

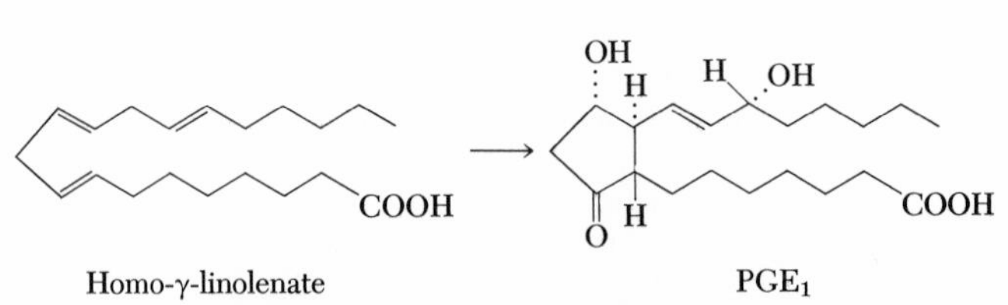

COOH → OH H H OH COOH O H

Homo-γ-linolenate PGE$_1$

Other prostaglandins of the E series are formed from arachidonate (PGE_2) and from a C_{20}, $\Delta_{\omega}^{3,6,9,12,15}$ acid probably derived from linolenate (PGE_3). In prostaglandins of the F series, the ketone group of the E series is reduced to an alcohol. Metabolic transformations undergone by the prostaglandins include reduction of double bonds, oxidation of alcohol to ketone groups, and loss of acetate fragments from the carboxyl end. Current interest in the prostaglandins stems from their physiological activity. PGE_1, for example, upon administration to experimental animals, stimulates smooth muscle, depresses the blood pressure, raises the heart rate, and counteracts equimolar amounts of catecholamines in its effect on blood pressure and on release of free fatty acids from the depots.

Degradation of Fatty Acids to Acetate

The extra-mitochondrial cytoplasm is the site where fatty acids are chiefly synthesized and where they initially arrive after hydrolysis of triglyceride transported to the cell or after uptake of free fatty acids. Since neither the long-chain fatty acids nor their esters with coenzyme A are believed to penetrate the mitochondrial membrane very readily, it has been proposed that carnitine (the trimethylbetaine of β-hydroxy, γ-aminobutyric acid),

$$CH_3-\overset{\overset{\displaystyle CH_3}{|}}{\underset{\underset{\displaystyle CH_3}{|}}{N^+}}-CH_2CHOHCH_2COOH$$

which has already been mentioned as a possible carrier for acetate out of the mitochondrion, may function similarly in the inward transport of fatty acids for intra-mitochondrial oxidation. Once fatty acids have been "activated" in the form of their CoA esters (see next paragraph), they can undergo reversible transesterification between coenzyme A and carnitine (ester linkages to the β-hydroxyl of carnitine appear to be of the high-energy type), both inside and outside the mitochondrion.

(*a*) ***Reaction 1*** (***Fig. 19–5***). The initial step in the catabolism of a fatty acid involves a reaction with ATP and CoA to form adenylic acid, inorganic pyrophosphate, and a fatty acyl thioester of CoA, enzyme-bound acyl-adenylates being the probable intermediates. A series of "activating enzymes" or acyl-CoA synthetases exists, each specific for fatty acids within a range of chain lengths. Initiation of fatty acid catabolism in isolated mitochondria requires the presence of a Krebs cycle acid as a so-called "sparking" or priming agent. This agent has two functions: one is the provision of ATP through the Krebs cycle and oxidative phosphorylation; the second is the provision of sufficient oxaloacetate so that the acetyl-CoA formed at the end of the sequence of fatty acid degradative reactions will condense, form citrate, and liberate CoA. A steady supply of ATP and CoA is required for Reaction 1. In liver mitochondria, where CoA is readily liberated from its esters by thiolesterases, the priming agent is replaceable by ATP alone.

(*b*) ***Reaction 2*** (***Fig. 19–5***). The fatty acid thioester is next dehydrogenated in the α,β-position by an acyl-CoA dehydrogenase bearing an FAD prosthetic group. Several such enzymes have been isolated, each exhibiting specificity toward a range of acyl chain lengths. All of these dehydrogenases transfer hydrogen atoms to the "electron-transferring flavoprotein" which is oxidized by the cytochromes. As a flavin-linked dehydrogenase, this system probably generates two high-energy phosphate bonds per hydrogen pair. It should be noted that this reaction, as written in the catabolic direction, is physiologically irreversible. Reduction of the α,β-unsaturated acyl-CoA is effected by a separate enzyme, an enoyl-CoA reductase, utilizing NADPH as coenzyme. As mentioned previously, this enzyme is involved in the synthesis of fatty acids via the intra-mitochondrial pathway.

(*c*) ***Reaction 3*** (***Fig. 19–5***). A molecule of water is added to the unsaturated linkage so as to form a β-hydroxy compound. This reaction is catalyzed by an enoyl-CoA hydratase.

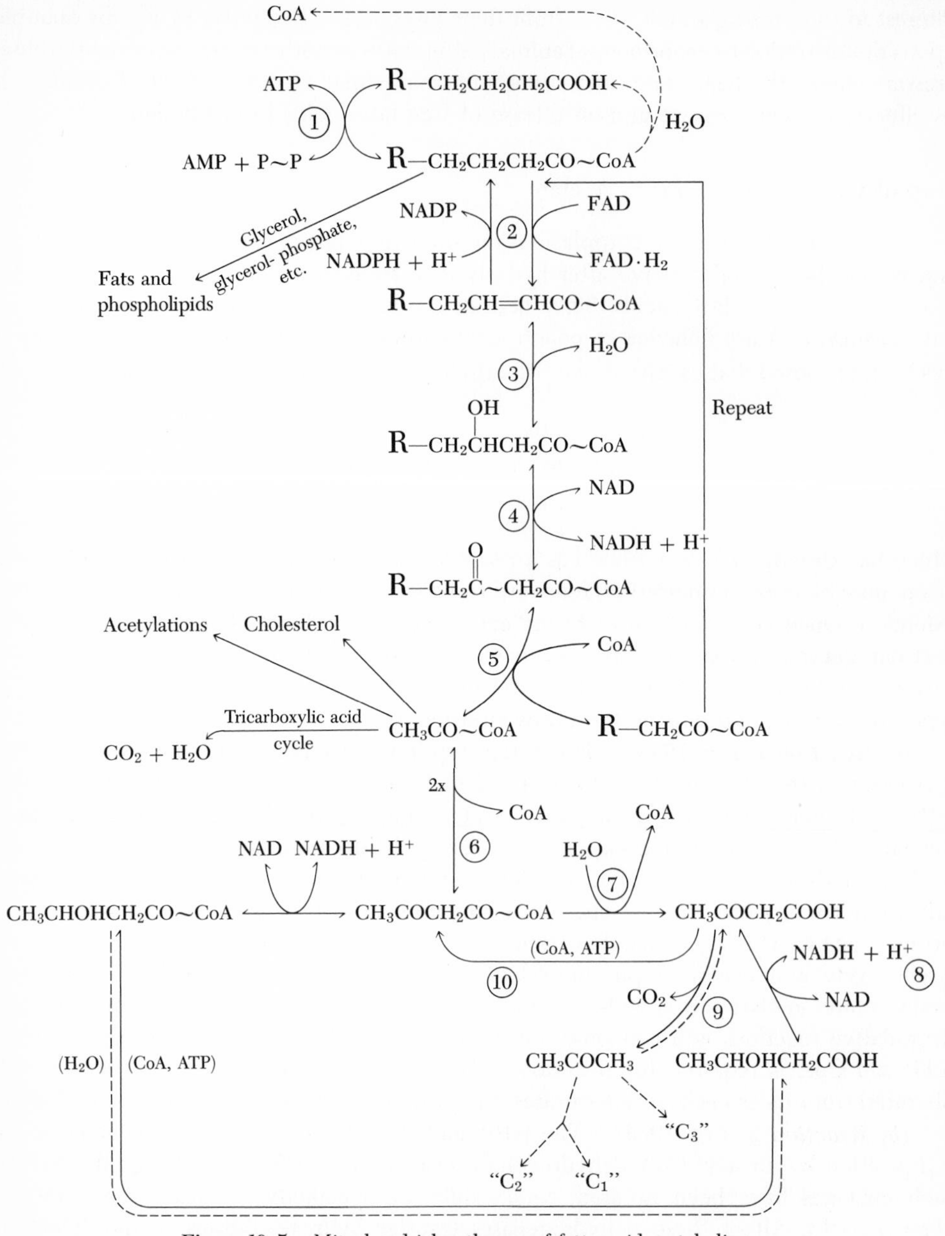

Figure 19-5. Mitochondrial pathways of fatty acid metabolism.

(*d*) ***Reaction 4*** (***Fig. 19-5***). The second dehydrogenation occurs in Reaction 4. A β-keto compound is formed under the influence of a β-hydroxyacyl-CoA dehydrogenase, NAD being the coenzyme. Since the subsequent reactions of the aerobic oxidative chain (NAD, flavoproteins, cytochromes, etc.) are known to produce high-energy phosphate, this step must account for a portion of the energy evolved in the breakdown of fatty acids.

(*e*) ***Reaction 5*** (***Fig. 19-5***). The β-keto linkage,

$$R\!-\!\overset{O}{\overset{\|}{C}}\,\vdots\,CH_2\!-\!\overset{O}{\overset{\|}{C}}\!-\!R'$$

is energetically equivalent to the thioester (and high-energy phosphate) bond. Therefore, a reaction similar to hydrolysis, but involving CoA instead of water, can take place (thiolysis catalyzed by a β-ketoacyl-CoA thiolase), splitting off a molecule of acetyl-CoA and leaving a fatty acid thioester containing two less carbon atoms than the original. This thioester can repeat the sequence of reactions just described, beginning with Reaction 2 (since it is already "activated"). Thus, fatty acids can be degraded stepwise, each overall sequence of reactions producing a molecule of acetyl-CoA.

Ketogenesis

In most extrahepatic tissues, and to a large extent in liver, the units of acetyl-CoA produced in the degradations described above are either taken up immediately by the tricarboxylic acid cycle for oxidation in order to produce energy, or are utilized for certain syntheses by means of transacetylation reactions (discussed later). Owing to accumulation of small amounts of acetyl-CoA even under normal circumstances, a side reaction occurs (Reaction 6, Fig. 19–5) in which two molecules of acetyl-CoA condense with the loss of one molecule of CoA (similar to Reaction 5 in the anabolic direction), forming acetoacetyl-CoA. Hydrolysis catalyzed by a thiolesterase (found primarily in liver) produces free acetoacetate and CoA (Reaction 7, Fig. 19–5). A major fraction (about two-thirds) of the acetoacetate thus formed is reduced in the liver by β-hydroxybutyrate dehydrogenase and NADH to β-hydroxybutyrate (Reaction 8, Fig. 19–5). A minor fraction undergoes spontaneous decarboxylation to acetone (Reaction 9, Fig. 19–5). A second source of free acetoacetate is hydroxy-methylglutaryl-CoA, an intermediate in the synthesis of cholesterol:

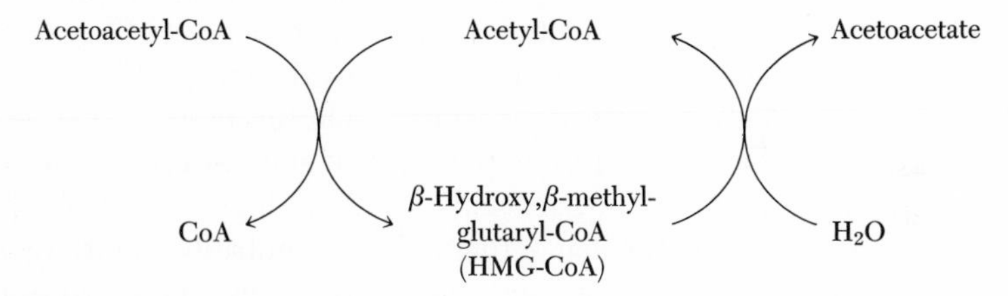

The quantitative significance of the HMG-CoA pathway in ketogenesis is controversial; according to some, it is of greater importance in the diabetic than in the normal state. Acetoacetate, β-hydroxybutyrate, and acetone are collectively designated "ketone bodies" or "acetone bodies," and the process of their formation as "ketogenesis."

Although ketogenesis occurs to some extent in extrahepatic tissues (e.g., kidney), the further metabolism of the ketone bodies in these tissues is so rapid that their formation is actually difficult to demonstrate. In liver, on the other hand, acetoacetate, once formed, is not reconverted to acetyl-CoA to any significant extent. The explanation appears to be that extrahepatic tissues contain systems for "activation" of acetoacetate which are lacking in liver. One of these is Reaction 10, Figure 19–5. Another is an exchange reaction (β-ketoacid CoA-transferase) proceeding as follows:

$$\text{Acetoacetate} + \text{Succinyl-CoA} \longleftrightarrow \text{Acetoacetyl-CoA} + \text{Succinate}$$

Thus, in extrahepatic tissues, but not in liver, any hydrolysis of acetoacetyl-CoA is balanced by its rapid resynthesis. These circumstances lead to the formation in liver, and to the entry into the bloodstream, of detectable quantities of ketone bodies under conditions of normal lipid metabolism. Although it is quite true that even under these circumstances the majority of acetyl-CoA molecules are oxidized via the tricarboxylic acid cycle in liver, only a slight acceleration in the rate of lipid metabolism suffices to overload the disposal system of the liver. These increased quantities of ketone bodies pass into the systemic circulation and are carried to the extrahepatic tissues, where they are oxidized to completion under normal circumstances.

Ketogenesis from amino acids is discussed elsewhere (p. 574).

Ketolysis

The oxidation of ketone bodies to completion is known as ketolysis. Acetoacetate and β-hydroxybutyrate, to the extent that they are formed in the liver, are carried by the bloodstream to the extrahepatic tissues, mainly kidney and muscle, where they are oxidized by way of the tricarboxylic acid cycle. The hydroxy acid undergoes preliminary oxidation to the keto acid; the latter then participates in a CoA-exchange reaction of the type mentioned above, or in a β-keto acid activation reaction (Reaction 10, Fig. 19–5). The resulting acetoacetyl-CoA then reacts with a second molecule of CoA (reversal of Reaction 6, Fig. 19–5), forming two molecules of acetyl-CoA, which then are oxidized in the usual manner. Alternatively, β-hydroxybutyrate can be converted directly to a CoA thioester by synthetases which have been found both in liver and extrahepatic tissues. Since β-hydroxybutyryl-CoA is readily oxidized to acetoacetyl-CoA, this system may account for the small amount of ketone bodies reported to be oxidized in liver itself.

The oxidation of acetyl-CoA formed from fatty acids, whether occurring directly in liver and extrahepatic tissues, or only after ketogenesis in the liver and ketolysis elsewhere, is the source of the major fraction of the energy available to the organism from the catabolism of fatty acids. It may be assumed that the number of high-energy phosphate bonds generated during the oxidation of each unit of acetyl-CoA derived from a fatty acid is the same as that produced in pyruvate oxidation (p. 414), if the energy of the oxidative decarboxylation of pyruvate is omitted. On this basis, 12 high-energy bonds are produced in the tricarboxylic acid cycle per mole of acetyl-CoA. Oxidation of NADH produced in Reaction 4, Figure 19–5, accounts for three high-energy phosphate bonds, whereas Reaction 2, being on the flavoprotein level, probably yields two. The total quantity of energy derivable from a long-chain fatty acid can be approximated by multiplying the expected number of acetyl units by 12, adding 5 times the number of acetyl units less one (the terminal acetyl unit obviously needs to undergo no dehydrogenation to become acetyl-CoA), and from this product subtracting the energy expended in the initial activation step (probably one high-energy bond, assuming that the bond in the pyrophosphate is recoverable). Palmitate (C_{16}), for example, will produce eight acetyl fragments, the oxidation of which will yield $(8 \times 12) + (5 \times 7) = 131$ high-energy bonds. Allowing for a loss of one bond in the activation reaction $(131 - 1 = 130)$, and taking 7.5 kcal. as the average energy value of a high-energy phosphate bond, the approximate quantity of free energy recoverable as high-energy phosphate from the combustion of a mole of palmitate is $130 \times 7.5 = 975$ kcal. Since the complete oxidation of palmitate releases approximately 2340 kcal. per mole (not corrected to physiological conditions), it can be calculated that the high-energy phosphate obtained by the organism in this case represents a recovery of about 42 per cent $(975/2340 \times 100)$, which is comparable to the figures obtained in the case of glucose (p. 415).

Acetone, which is formed in small quantities by the spontaneous decarboxylation of acetoacetate, can be metabolized by the organism. One pathway involves a C-2, C-1 cleavage (possibly via acetol, acetol-phosphate, and 1,2-propanediol-1-phosphate), producing fragments of the acetate and "formate" (p. 592) types, which are then disposed of in the manner normal to each of these groups. Acetone is also converted to intermediates (again possibly 1,2-propanediol-1-phosphate) which can in turn form lactic and pyruvic acids.

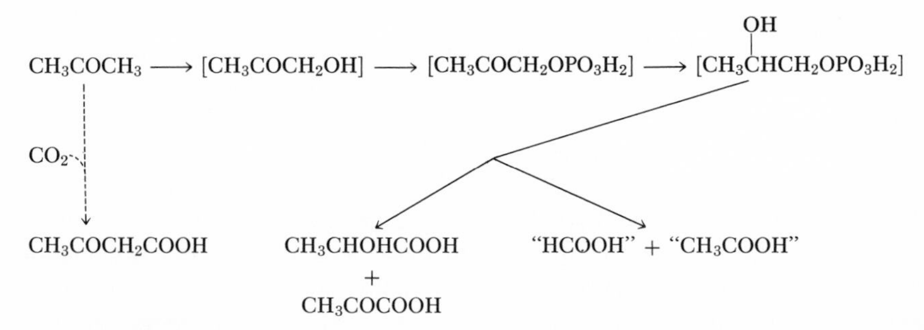

Lest it be concluded from this statement that a suitable pathway exists for the conversion of fatty acids to carbohydrate, it should be pointed out that, regardless of the findings with acetone, it has been shown that no significant quantity of acetoacetate traverses this route. Finally, it has been found, by the use of isotopic tracers, that small amounts of acetone (via unknown intermediates) can be carboxylated to acetoacetate.

Ketosis

Under certain conditions (all characterized by absolute or relative carbohydrate deprivation), the metabolism of fat is greatly accelerated. Such a state of affairs overloads the capacity of the liver to metabolize the fragments of acetyl-CoA derived from the fatty acids, causing the formation of significant quantities of ketone bodies. These substances are liberated into the blood in greater than normal concentrations. The extrahepatic tissues have a great capacity for the utilization of ketone bodies (ketolysis); however, when the rate of ketogenesis by the liver exceeds the rate of ketolysis in the periphery, the concentration of ketone bodies in the blood increases (ketonemia, hyperketonemia) and they appear in the urine (ketonuria). The overall picture of abnormally elevated concentrations of ketone bodies in tissues and fluids is termed "ketosis." If severe, ketosis may eventuate in acidosis, e.g., in uncontrolled diabetes.

Typical conditions in which ketosis is observed include fasting, clinical and experimental diabetes mellitus, and high-fat, low-carbohydrate diets, all obviously states of absolute deficiency of utilization of carbohydrate. Ketosis also occurs as a result of relative deficiency of carbohydrate, when increased metabolic demands (pregnancy, lactation) are not met by provision of adequate quantities of carbohydrate. This type of ketosis is aggravated in the bovine by the influx of short-chain fatty acids from the rumen.

Explanations of ketosis under conditions of diminished carbohydrate utilization have been offered from two opposing viewpoints. According to the "overproduction" theory, the rate of formation of acetyl-CoA is increased to the point where it can no longer be completely absorbed by the hepatic pathways of utilization, mainly fatty acid synthesis and the Krebs cycle. The surplus therefore forms acetoacetyl-CoA, which is rapidly deacylated to free acetoacetate, excessive quantities of which (together with the other ketone bodies) no longer can be handled by the catabolic mechanisms (Krebs cycle) of the peripheral tissues, which are postulated to retain their normal ketolytic capacities. According to the "underutilization" theory, the rate of formation of acetyl-CoA and ketone bodies is normal, but pathways of utilization in liver or periphery are restricted.

In the light of current knowledge, neither of these theories is wholly complete or correct.

Each of the foregoing points of view warrants closer examination. Considering first the problem of underutilization, there is no doubt that, in the experimentally diabetic animal, in fasting, or on a high-fat diet, the synthesis of fatty acids from acetyl-CoA is reduced severely. As indicated previously (p. 461), under these conditions one may anticipate decreased activity of a number of key enzymes in lipogenesis: malate dehydrogenase (decarboxylating), acetyl-CoA synthetase, ATP-citrate lyase, acetyl-CoA carboxylase, glucose-6-phosphate dehydrogenase, the condensing-reducing enzymes of fatty acid synthesis, and citrate synthase. However, available data suggest that the nonutilization of acetyl-CoA for fatty acid synthesis cannot, of itself, account for the extremely large ketone body production by the ketotic liver. At one time the explanation was offered that in conditions of underutilization of carbohydrate the provision of oxaloacetate from pyruvate might be deficient, resulting in a subnormal rate of operation of the tricarboxylic acid cycle. More recently, it has been claimed that the augmented rate of oxidation of fatty acids in the liver under these conditions results in elevated levels of NADH, forcing the equilibrium between malate and oxaloacetate toward the reductant, thus decreasing the concentration of oxaloacetate. Neither of these explanations is generally accepted. Although the concentrations of certain of the tricarboxylic acid cycle components are depressed in the diabetic liver, the concentration of oxaloacetate itself has usually been found to be normal. Whether the cycle in liver may be operating subnormally in a *relative sense* is discussed subsequently. It may be noted that citrate synthase is inhibited by the fatty acyl-CoA's which increase in concentration in the liver under the conditions specified. As regards peripheral tissues (particularly muscle), some investigators have found decreased uptake and utilization of ketone bodies in the diabetic (but not in the fasting) state, with some disagreement as to whether the operation of the Krebs cycle itself is depressed. It is interesting that high concentrations of acetoacetate in the body fluids inhibit utilization of glucose by muscle, suggesting that "positive feedback" may aggravate the situation in ketosis.

There is no doubt that, in a general sense, overproduction of acetyl-CoA and, consequently, of acetoacetate, occurs under conditions of carbohydrate deprivation. The amount of substrate for acetyl-CoA formation, in the form of fatty acids, is tremendously increased in the liver under these conditions by mobilization of fatty acids from the depots to the liver. Formation of free acetoacetate may be facilitated also by increased activity of acetoacetyl-CoA hydrolase and of the HMG-CoA pathway (concerning both of which there is disagreement). A rapid rate of production of acetyl-CoA, by itself, cannot be the complete explanation for the accumulation of acetoacetate, since the rapid oxidation of carbohydrate or pyruvate via acetyl-CoA does not cause ketosis. Interestingly, pyruvate is strongly ketogenic in isolated mitochondria under conditions in which oxaloacetate or precursors are absent and CO_2 assimilation is impossible.

Evidently there is something peculiar to pyruvate oxidation in liver which prevents pyruvate, except under artificial circumstances, from being ketogenic. The same peculiarity probably endows pyruvate with the ability, so long as carbohydrate is well utilized to provide it, to prevent concomitantly oxidized fatty acids from becoming excessively ketogenic. At the present time, the only mechanism which appears to have the proper characteristics to fit the requirements is the provision of oxaloacetate from pyruvate by CO_2 assimilation. We may postulate that a certain normal concentration of oxaloacetate exists in the liver, and that, even under conditions of carbohydrate deprivation, this normal concentration may be maintained, partly from whatever traces of carbohydrate intermediates may be available, partly by deamination of glucogenic amino acids. Influx of large amounts of carbohydrate into the metabolic systems of the liver is readily taken care of by the tricarboxylic acid cycle, since increased carbohydrate (and therefore increased pyruvate) automatically carries with it increased facilities for synthesis of whatever oxaloacetate is required to operate the tricarboxylic acid cycle at a supernormal rate. Influx of fatty acids, if accompanied by normal carbohydrate utilization, may be taken care of similarly. However, increased degradation of fatty acids in the absence of normal carbohydrate utilization results in greatly increased production of acetyl-CoA in the presence of no more than the normal amount of oxaloacetate. The tricarboxylic acid cycle therefore, although operating at normal capacity, is unable to cope with the excess acetyl units, hence excessive amounts of acetoacetate are produced. Superimposed upon this postulated "relative" defect in the Krebs cycle would be the well-established decrease in utilization of acetyl-CoA for lipogenesis, possible decreased synthesis of citrate, possible increased activity of enzymes forming free acetoacetate, and possible decreased utilization of ketone bodies in the periphery.

Although the above composite theory, combining certain aspects of both the "overproduction" and "underutilization" theories, fits most of the facts, it should be noted that attempts to alleviate ketosis in experimental animals by injection of various tricarboxylic acid cycle intermediates have had only limited success.

Omega Oxidation

The general pathway of catabolism of the fatty acids outlined previously involves, fundamentally, β-oxidation (beginning at the carboxyl end of the molecule) and cleavage of acetyl units. To some extent, certain fatty acids can undergo oxidation at the carbon atom farthest removed from the carboxyl group (the "omega" carbon), producing a dicarboxylic acid, which is then subjected to β-oxidation and cleavage to form successively smaller dicarboxylic acids. Evidence has been obtained that the oxidation proceeds stepwise, forming first an ω-hydroxy acid (requiring NADPH, molecular O_2, and a microsomal oxidase), followed by successive dehydrogenations (requiring NAD) to an ω-aldehydic acid and finally a dicarboxylic acid. Omega oxidation is at best a minor pathway of fatty acid metabolism.

Alpha Oxidation

Brain sphingolipids contain α-hydroxy acids and odd-carbon fatty acids. The former are precursors of the latter, possibly via α-keto acids as intermediates, the conversion occurring in brain microsomes.

Metabolism of Odd-Carbon and Branched-Chain Fatty Acids

Although most of the fatty acids found in nature contain an even number of carbon atoms, the metabolism of the odd members of the series has been of some interest. The acids containing an odd number of carbon atoms appear to be metabolized by the same mechanisms as the even-numbered acids, losing two carbon atoms at a time. However, when the terminal 3-carbon unit is reached, a new pathway is taken. Propionate is glucogenic rather than ketogenic; hence the odd-carbon fatty acids participate in both the lipid and the carbohydrate pathways. (Propionate itself is a metabolite of methionine.)

The pathway from propionate to glucogenic intermediates occurs via the following reactions:

$$\text{Propionate} + \text{ATP} + \text{CoA} \rightleftharpoons \text{propionyl-CoA} + \text{AMP} + \text{PP}$$
$$\text{Propionyl-CoA} + CO_2 + \text{ATP} \rightleftharpoons \text{methylmalonyl-CoA} + \text{ADP} + PO_4$$
$$\text{Methylmalonyl-CoA} \rightleftharpoons \text{succinyl-CoA}$$

The second reaction requires biotin as a cofactor; the third requires a coenzyme form of vitamin B_{12}. Other pathways suggested for propionate metabolism include conversion to acrylate, lactate, and pyruvate, or conversion via acrylyl-CoA to β-hydroxypropionyl-CoA, which may be oxidized to malonic semialdehyde, the oxidation product of which, malonyl-CoA, is an intermediate in fatty acid synthesis.

A few branched-chain fatty acids occur in nature in association with lipids. Those which are of general interest, however, arise in the course of the metabolism of certain amino acids, and will be discussed in that connection (p. 580).

Amide Formation

Microsomes of liver, kidney, and brain synthesize ethanolamides from ethanolamine and fatty acids, especially palmitate. This compound, together with small amounts of the stearate derivative, is found in brain, liver, and skeletal muscle of fasted animals. Although its physiological importance is not known, palmitic ethanolamide has potent anti-inflammatory and anti-anaphylactic properties.

Ethanol

Although ethanol is not considered part of the normal diet, its imbibition in greater or lesser quantities by human beings on festive and funereal occasions confers more than passing interest on its metabolism. Ethyl alcohol is oxidized to acetaldehyde by an alcohol dehydrogenase present mainly in liver, NAD being the coenzyme. The enzyme is sufficiently active to account for the rate of oxidation of alcohol in vivo. It is also concerned in the metabolism of rhodopsin.

Acetaldehyde is oxidized to acetate primarily by an aldehyde dehydrogenase of liver, which is inhibited by Antabuse (tetraethylthiuram disulfide), a drug used in the treatment of chronic alcoholism. The accumulation of acetaldehyde causes disagreeable symptoms. Acetate, after activation by ATP and CoA, is completely oxidized in the normal manner of acetyl-CoA. It is apparent that the oxidation of alcohol can liberate considerable energy in the body (potentially, about 312 kcal. free energy per mole or 7 kcal. per gram).

Chronic alcoholic intoxication in rats causes an initial rise in hepatic alcohol and aldehyde dehydrogenases, followed by a fall, the latter phase coinciding with fatty degeneration of the liver.

Methanol is oxidized (by alcohol dehydrogenase) to the very toxic formaldehyde, which is oxidized further to the less toxic formate. Ethanol competes with methanol for alcohol dehydrogenase, and is bound more tightly, hence the rationale of treating methanol poisoning by administration of ethanol.

GENERAL ASPECTS OF ACETYL AND ACYL METABOLISM

In addition to its role in the metabolism of lipids, the acetyl group (and several other acyl groups) is involved in a great variety of reactions of other types of compounds. Al-

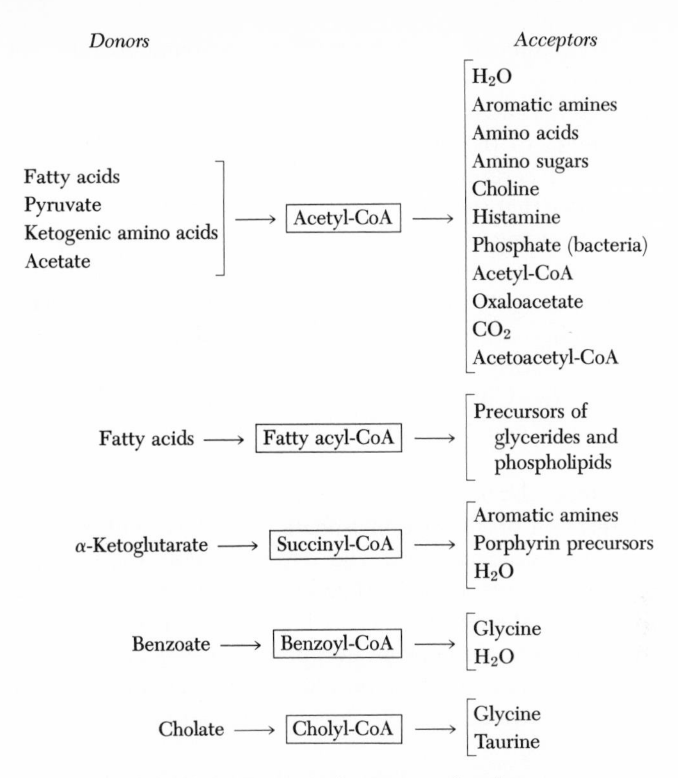

Figure 19-6. Donors and acceptors of acyl groups.

though most of these reactions are discussed in their relation to specific aspects of intermediary metabolism, the universality of the "transacylation" reaction warrants a unified presentation at this point. Typical "donor" and "acceptor" compounds for acyl groups are indicated in Figure 19-6.

Donors

All major classes of foodstuffs are sources of acetyl-CoA. Pyruvate, in the course of its oxidative decarboxylation, forms acetyl-CoA. This provides a pathway not only for carbohydrate, but also for the glucogenic amino acids (p. 573). The ketogenic amino acids can form acetyl-CoA by means of reactions which are discussed elsewhere (p. 574). Fatty acids (and ketone bodies) are sources of this compound by the routes indicated in this chapter, the reactions being, in all probability, reversible. Free acetate itself can form acetyl-CoA via an activation step similar to that undergone by the long-chain fatty acids.

Succinyl-CoA is formed in the course of the oxidative decarboxylation of α-ketoglutarate in the tricarboxylic acid cycle. Benzoyl-CoA and cholyl-CoA are synthesized by an activation reaction, involving, as usual, ATP and CoA. It is probable that many other acyl-CoA molecules are formed in a similar manner. It has also been shown that a second acyl-CoA can be synthesized at the expense of a preformed acyl-CoA by acyl exchange:

$$\text{Succinyl-CoA} + \text{Butyrate} \longleftrightarrow \text{Butyryl-CoA} + \text{Succinate}$$

Acceptors

Water may be considered an acceptor of acyl groups from all types of acyl-CoA compounds; deacylases (thiolesterases) which attack these compounds hydrolytically are of widespread occurrence.

Aromatic amines, e.g., sulfanilamide, are acetylated and succinylated. Since the aromatic amines are foreign to the body, such acylations are classified as "detoxications," although the products of certain of these reactions are more harmful than the original compounds. It is probable that the body performs its normal reactions with any compound, native or foreign, without regard to toxicity.

Several types of aliphatic amino groups are also acylated. Many amino acids can be acetylated, although the significance of the reaction is not known. The acetylation of histamine may be another instance of "detoxication." Succinyl-CoA is involved in the synthesis of porphyrins. Benzoyl-glycine (hippurate) is the form in which ingested benzoate is excreted from the body. Glucosamine and galactosamine are both acetylated on the amino group, the products doubtless being intermediates in the synthesis of mucopolysaccharides.

Alcohol groups may also be acylated, viz., the formation of various types of lipid precursors by the reaction of glycerol-phosphate with fatty acid esters of CoA, and the esterification of choline by acetyl-CoA. The latter reaction, carried out by the choline acetylase system of nervous tissue (and striated muscle), is an important preparatory step in electrical conduction, a phenomenon which involves the neurohormone, acetyl-choline.

Inorganic phosphate can serve as an acceptor of acetyl groups from acetyl-CoA in bacteria, leading to the formation of acetyl-phosphate. This reaction, which is reversible owing to the energetic equivalence of the thioester and carboxyl-phosphate linkages, does not occur in animal tissues.

In all of the reactions enumerated thus far, the carboxyl portion of the acetyl group was involved in the condensations. At least four instances are known, however, in which the methyl group of the acetyl-CoA is the reactive site. One of these is the condensation of acetyl-CoA with another acyl-CoA, forming a β-keto acyl-CoA containing two more carbon atoms than the original. Such a reaction takes place in the synthesis of fatty acids from smaller units in the intra-mitochondrial pathway, and in the formation of acetoacetate from fatty acids. Another reaction of this type is the conversion of acetyl-CoA to malonyl-CoA in the extra-mitochondrial pathway of fatty acid synthesis. The third such reaction is the condensation of acetyl-CoA and oxaloacetate to form citrate, the first step in the tricarboxylic acid cycle. The methyl group of acetate is also involved in the first of a complex sequence of reactions which utilizes acetyl and acetoacetyl units to synthesize the steroid ring system.

It is therefore apparent that transacetylation or, stated more generally, transacylation, is a reaction of widespread occurrence in the organism. It is employed in the catabolism of the major classes of foodstuffs, in the synthesis of complex compounds from simpler starting materials, and, to a certain extent, in the preservation and transfer of high-energy bonds.

METABOLISM OF STEROLS AND BILE ACIDS

Synthesis of Cholesterol

The reasons for discussing the sterols and bile acids in connection with the lipids have been presented elsewhere (p. 42). Of the many sterols in nature, cholesterol is the only one which is of any great significance in animal metabolism. (The products of ultraviolet irradiation of the plant sterol, ergosterol, are absorbed through the intestine and certain of them have vitamin D activity in animals [p. 161]. Other plant sterols are absorbed to a slight extent and their presence in the intestine hinders absorption of cholesterol.)

It has been known for some time that the animal organism can synthesize cholesterol, although the mechanism was completely obscure until quite recently. With the aid of isotopic labeling, small fragments such as acetate, acetoacetate, and the isopropyl moiety of isovalerate (p. 580) have been shown to be precursors of the sterol molecule. Recent evidence suggests that "isoprene" units, derived from these fragments, may be important building blocks in both animals and plants. In the plant, these units condense to form terpenes, carotenoids, and rubber. In animals the condensation leads to squalene, an unsaturated hydrocarbon once thought to be restricted to shark liver. Squalene has been shown to be a precursor of cholesterol.

The current schema of the formation of squalene and cholesterol from small fragments is illustrated in Figure 19–7. Acetyl-CoA and acetoacetyl-CoA condense to form β-hydroxy-β-methylglutaryl-CoA (HMG-CoA), a compound formed also by the amino acid, leucine. (An enzyme which occurs in liver splits hydroxy-methylglutaryl-CoA into acetyl-CoA and free acetoacetate, thus constituting a possible source of ketone bodies in the liver. Its contribution is controversial.) HMG-CoA is reduced by two moles of NADPH to form mevalonate, which also may be produced by the condensation of acetyl-CoA with enzyme-bound acetoacetate (an intermediate in fatty acid synthesis), forming enzyme-bound HMG, which may be the substrate for reduction to mevalonate. In either case, the product is phosphorylated three times in succession by ATP, forming first a phosphate, next a pyrophosphate, and finally a triply phosphorylated transient intermediate which simultaneously loses a mole of phosphate and is decarboxylated, producing Δ^3-isopentenyl pyrophosphate, the biological "isoprene" unit referred to earlier. This compound isomerizes by a shift of the double bond to give γ,γ-dimethylallyl pyrophosphate. One mole of each of these last two compounds condenses to form geranyl pyrophosphate, to which is added another molecule of isopentenyl pyrophosphate to form farnesyl pyrophosphate. Two moles of farnesyl pyrophosphate are reductively condensed to form the unsaturated hydrocarbon, squalene. A so-called "oxidocyclase" converts squalene to lanosterol in the presence of molecular oxygen and NADPH.

The conversion of lanosterol to cholesterol involves the following transformations: removal of three methyl groups (one at C-14, two at C-4), possible shift of a double bond from Δ^8 to Δ^7, reduction of Δ^{24} and Δ^7, and dehydrogenation to form Δ^5. The identity of the intermediates (two possible examples of which are shown in Fig. 19–7) is uncertain, since the order in which the transformations occur is not known. It is believed that the demethylations take place prior to the majority of double-bond modifications, and that the single methyl group at C-14 is removed before the geminal pair at C-4. Demethylation alone would produce zymosterol ($\Delta^{8,24}$). Blockage of Δ^{24}-reduction with the inhibitor triparanol (MER-29) causes accumulation of desmosterol ($\Delta^{5,24}$), inhibition of Δ^7-reduction by AY-9944 causes accumulation of 7-dehydrocholesterol ($\Delta^{5,7}$), whereas double inhibition using both drugs results in accumulation of a $\Delta^{5,7,24}$-trienol, suggesting this as a possible precursor of the more saturated sterols. On the other hand, some believe that lathosterol (Δ^7) is a precursor of 7-dehydrocholesterol (which is interconvertible with cholesterol). It is possible that several pathways to cholesterol are normally functioning, but that certain ones are more important in particular tissues. Whatever the pathway, cholesterol is the final product of demethylation, migration of the double bond in the ring system, and reduction of the double bond in the side chain.

In terms of total output, the liver is probably the major site of synthesis of cholesterol.

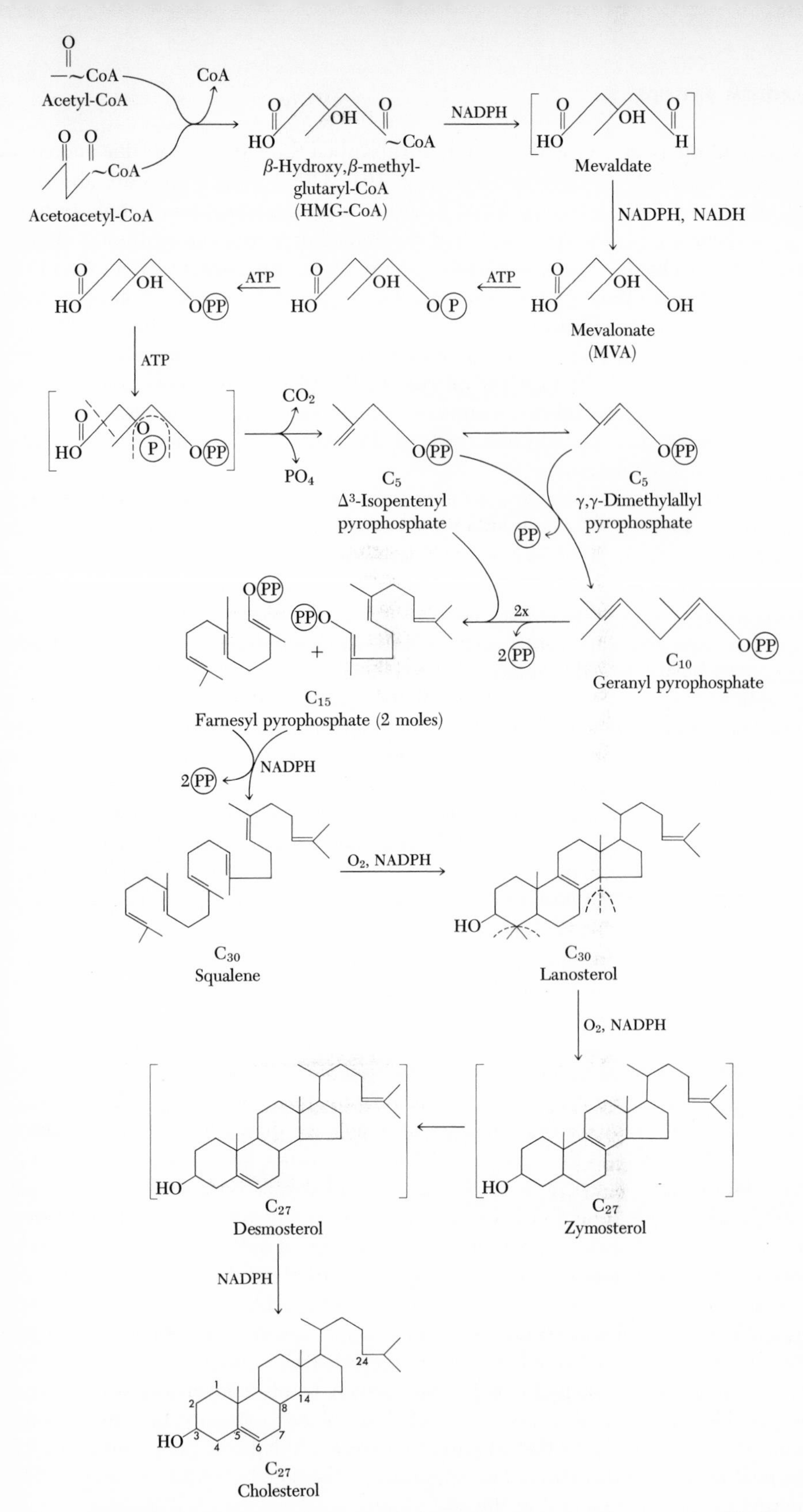

Figure 19-7. Synthesis of cholesterol. Intersections and ends of lines represent C atoms; Ⓟ, phosphate; ⓅⓅ, pyrophosphate.

Active synthesis occurs also in the adrenals, spleen, intestinal mucosa, red cell, bone, heart, omentum, muscle, skin, lungs, kidney, gonads, and perhaps in all tissues. Although cholesterol can be synthesized in the arterial wall, most of the sterol found in atheromatous lesions comes from the plasma. Brain, which has a very high concentration of cholesterol, synthesizes the sterol at a very slow rate, if at all, in the adult. From isotopic labeling studies, it has been calculated that the "half-life" (p. 542) of a serum cholesterol molecule in man is eight days.

The rate of synthesis of cholesterol by the liver is influenced by a number of factors. It is, for example, inversely related to the supply of dietary cholesterol, which may be regarded as a homeostatic mechanism. The step involved in this example of "negative feed-back" (p. 769) is the reduction of hydroxy-methylglutaryl-CoA, a reaction which is also depressed in the fasted animal. The rate is depressed in the hypophysectomized animal (probably a secondary effect due to undernutrition), in pregnancy, in the absence of androgens, and by the administration of estrogens, and is often increased in the uncontrolled diabetic. Introduction into the bloodstream of a number of surface-active agents, such as synthetic detergents as well as bile salts, results in greatly increased synthesis of cholesterol in the liver and mobilization of cholesterol and other liver lipids into the plasma. Infusion of phosphatides (e.g., lecithin) raises blood cholesterol, but only secondarily by increased synthesis; the primary effect is to increase transport out of the liver. The level of cholesterol in the plasma is influenced by the functional status of the thyroid, the hormones of which facilitate both synthesis and degradation of the sterol, but predominantly the latter. The rate of cholesterol synthesis in the animal organism appears to be generally proportional to the caloric intake, and more specifically to the fat content of the diet (in contrast to the rate of fatty acid synthesis). It is interesting that livers of diabetic animals exhibit increased activity of HMG-CoA reductase and increased cholesterol synthesis, whereas this pathway is depressed in the fasting state. It appears that acetyl fragments are channeled toward formation of ketone bodies in both diabetes and fasting, but toward formation of cholesterol only in the former condition.

Liver is the main source of plasma cholesterol, and it is also the main depository of cholesterol already present in the blood. Extrahepatic tissues largely synthesize their own supplies of cholesterol, but considerable equilibration occurs between plasma and tissue cholesterol in the human.

Esterification of cholesterol occurs in the intestinal wall, liver, and in certain other tissues (e.g., the adrenal cortex). The liver is the chief source of esterified as well as of free cholesterol.

Cholesterol as Precursor of Other Steroids

It is well established that cholesterol is the parent substance of the bile acids, as will be discussed in the following section. Isotopically labeled acetate and cholesterol are converted into progesterone (p. 696), testosterone (p. 684), estrogens (p. 690), and the adrenocortical hormones (p. 704). Doubts have been expressed whether cholesterol is a direct, obligatory precursor of these steroids.

In addition to the steroid hormones, cholesterol is related chemically and biologically to the D vitamins. In the liver and intestinal wall (and possibly in the skin), cholesterol is dehydrogenated in ring B to 7-dehydrocholesterol, which is transformed to vitamin D_3 under the influence of ultraviolet light (p. 161).

Catabolism and Excretion of Cholesterol, Conversion to Bile Acids

The general pathways of catabolism of cholesterol and the routes of excretion of the waste products are indicated in Figure 19–8. The more detailed chemical relations between the various compounds are presented in Figures 19–9 and 19–10. For convenience, the catabolism of cholesterol may be divided into two compartments, the excretory route via neutral sterols, and that involving the bile acids.

(*a*) ***Neutral sterols* (*Fig. 19–9*).** In the liver and other tissues, cholesterol is accompanied by small amounts of cholestanol (dihydrocholesterol), a compound in which rings A and B are in *trans* relationship to each other (p. 682). There is some evidence that cholesterol may be converted into cholestanol via the intermediates shown in the figure, although it has been suggested also that both are derived from a common precursor. Cholestanol also appears to be metabolized independently of cholesterol. For example, it forms bile acids differing in structure from cholate and deoxycholate. A certain amount of cholesterol and cholestanol is excreted through the intestinal wall; the quantitative importance of this pathway is controversial. Cholesterol and cholestanol are excreted also by the liver, via the bile, into the small intestine. Biliary cholesterol is largely formed in the liver. The cholesterol thus excreted mixes with dietary cholesterol and may be partially reabsorbed by way of the lymphatics, mainly after preliminary esterification in the cells of the intestinal mucosa. Unabsorbed cholesterol and cholestanol are found in the feces.

A third neutral sterol excreted in the feces is coprostanol (coprosterol), in which rings A and B bear a *cis* relation to each other (p. 682). This compound is formed by reduction of cholesterol by intestinal bacteria.

A small amount of neutral sterols is excreted from the body in the sebum of the skin. In connection with sterols of the skin, the interconversion of cholesterol and 7-dehydrocholesterol is of interest.

(*b*) ***Bile acids* (*Fig. 19–10*).** As determined by isotopic tracers, 10 to 20 per cent of exogenous cholesterol is accounted for in the neutral sterol fraction of bile and feces. The remaining 80 to 90 per cent is converted to bile acids in the liver and excreted via the bile into the intestine, from which the major fraction is reabsorbed. Unabsorbed bile acids

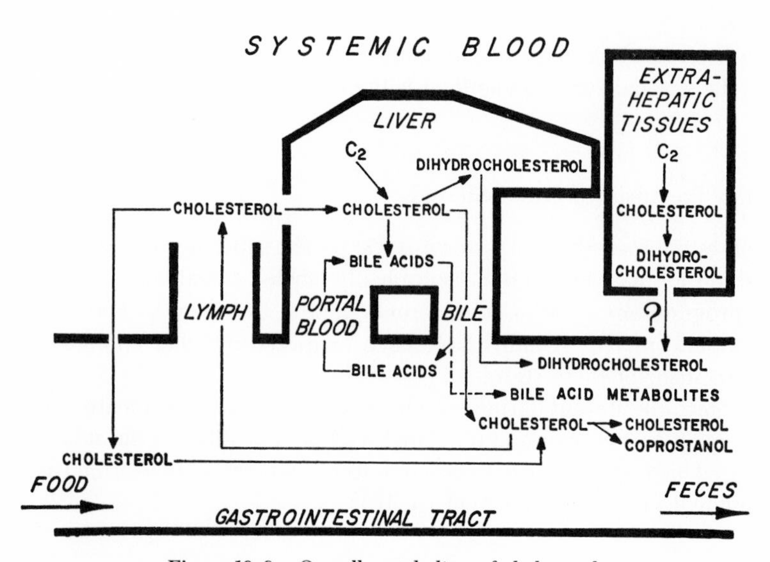

Figure 19–8. Overall metabolism of cholesterol.

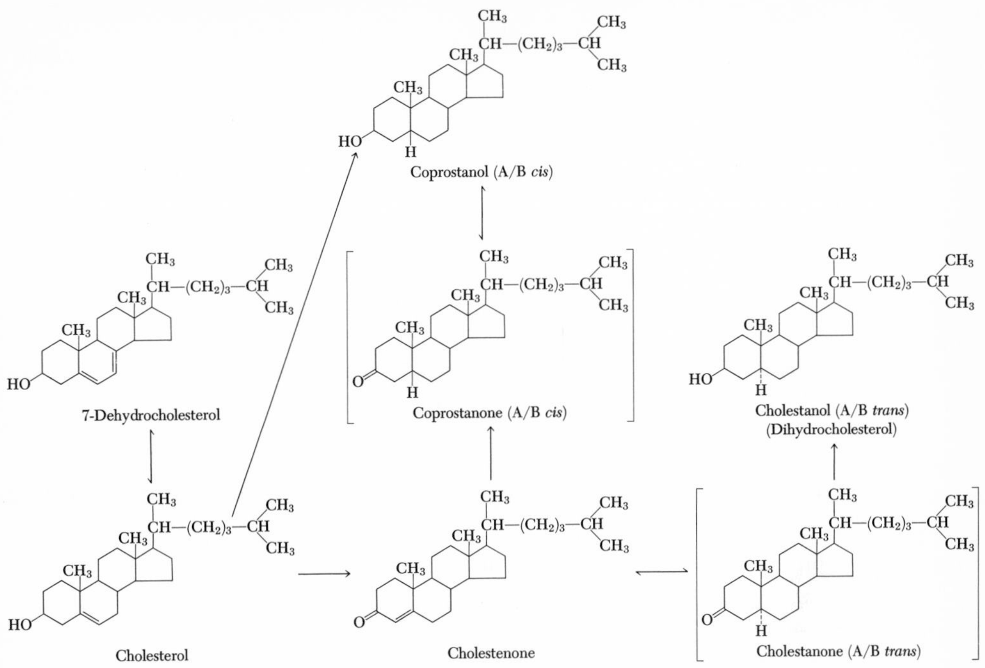

Coprostanol (A/B *cis*)

7-Dehydrocholesterol

Coprostanone (A/B *cis*)

Cholestanol (A/B *trans*)
(Dihydrocholesterol)

Cholesterol

Cholestenone

Cholestanone (A/B *trans*)

Figure 19-9. Interrelationships between cholesterol and other neutral sterols.

are attacked by intestinal bacteria, which hydrolyze the conjugated bile acids, reduce the hydroxyl group at C-7, and oxidize hydroxyl groups to ketone groups. The various products of bacterial action are excreted in the feces.

The bile acids differ chemically from cholesterol in having been reduced at C-5 (incidentally producing a *cis* relation between rings A and B) and oxidized in the side chain with the loss of three carbon atoms and the formation of a carboxyl group. In addition to the hydroxyl group at C-3, most of the bile acids are also hydroxylated at C-7, C-12, or both.

Although experiments with isotopically labeled cholesterol have demonstrated the transformation of this sterol to bile acids, the mechanism is still under investigation. Recent results indicate that ring hydroxylation precedes the complete transformation of the side chain. Thus, cholesterol is hydroxylated to form 7α-hydroxycholesterol, which undergoes inversion at the C-3 position and reduction of the double bond (producing a *cis* relation between rings A and B) to form 3α,7α-dihydroxycoprostane. Further hydroxylation produces 3α,7α,12α-trihydroxycoprostane. Oxidation at the terminal carbon in the side chain of the two preceding compounds produces the corresponding coprostanates, which, by further oxidation of the sidechains, form chenodeoxycholate and cholate, respectively. The oxidations are analogous to those of fatty acids, involving activation with ATP, formation of thioesters with coenzyme A, β-oxidation, and thiolysis to form a propionyl-CoA fragment, leaving the bile acids in the form of CoA esters. These may conjugate directly with glycine or taurine for excretion in the bile. Any free bile acids liberated by hydrolysis in the liver or absorbed after hydrolysis in the intestine may undergo conjugation after "activation," as noted subsequently. Bacterial reduction of the hydroxyl group at C-7 converts chenodeoxycholate to lithocholate and cholate to deoxycholate in the human intestine.

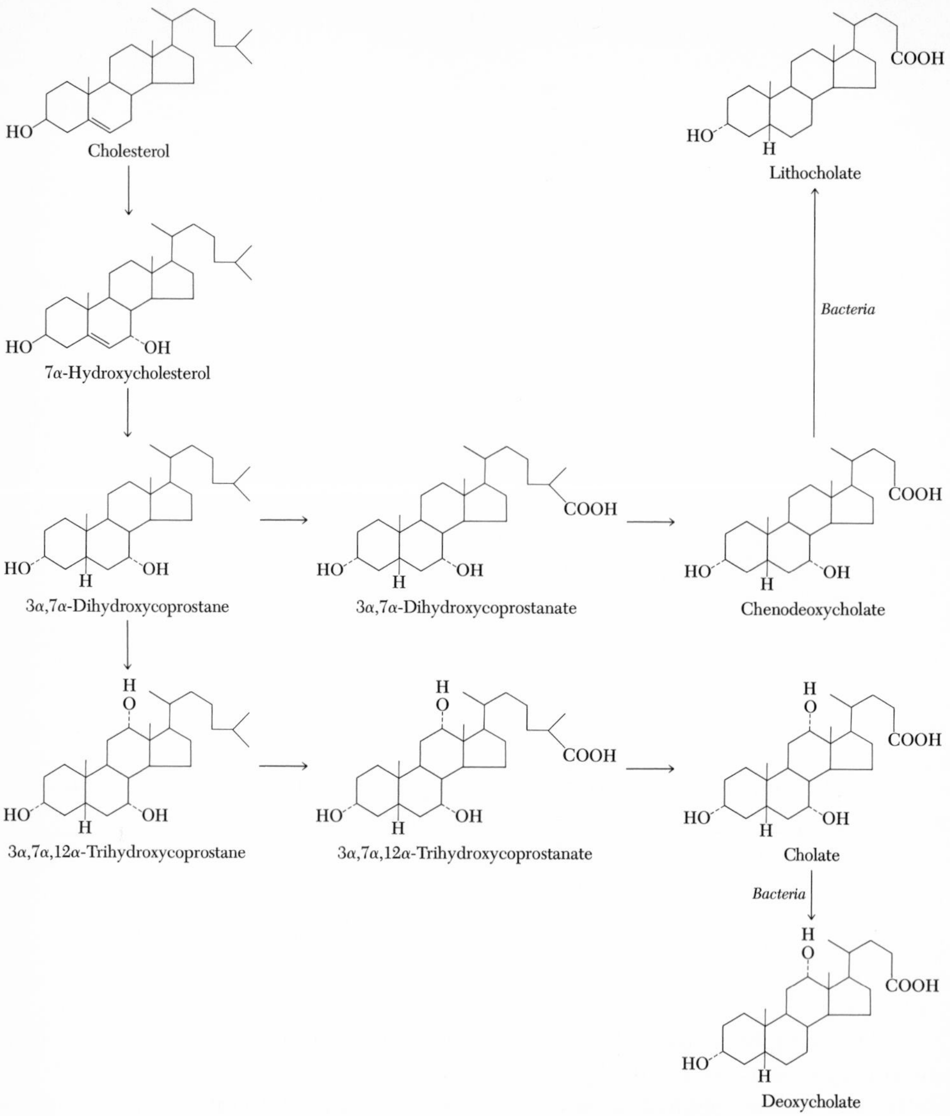

HO
Cholesterol

HO OH
7α-Hydroxycholesterol

HO OH
H
$3\alpha,7\alpha$-Dihydroxycoprostane

COOH
HO OH
H
$3\alpha,7\alpha$-Dihydroxycoprostanate

COOH
HO OH
H
Chenodeoxycholate

Bacteria

COOH
HO
H
Lithocholate

H
O
HO OH
H
$3\alpha,7\alpha,12\alpha$-Trihydroxycoprostane

H
O
COOH
HO OH
H
$3\alpha,7\alpha,12\alpha$-Trihydroxycoprostanate

H
O
COOH
HO OH
H
Cholate

Bacteria

H
O
COOH
HO
H
Deoxycholate

Figure 19-10. Synthesis and interconversion of bile acids.

The oxidation of cholesterol to bile acids is controlled by a feedback mechanism. The concentration of bile acids provided to the liver by way of the enterohepatic circulation limits the rate of synthesis of bile acids. The rate-determining step which is involved in the homeostatic control mechanism is probably 7α-hydroxylation. Cholate production varies with the thyroid state of the individual. In addition to an absolute decrease in bile acid formation, the hypothyroid also conjugates a greater proportion of bile acids with glycine instead of taurine. Thyroxine stimulates those reactions leading to cleavage of the cholesterol side chain, rather than hydroxylation of the ring.

The free bile acids are conjugated to glycine and taurine by enzymes of the liver, the reactions of cholate being typical of the group:

$$\text{Cholate} \xrightarrow[\text{Mg}^{++}]{\text{CoA, ATP}} \text{Cholyl-CoA} \xrightarrow[\text{Taurine}]{\text{Glycine,}} \begin{array}{l}\text{Glycocholate,}\\ \text{Taurocholate}\end{array}$$

The occurrence of these glycine and taurine conjugates in human bile is discussed elsewhere (p. 266).

METABOLISM OF FATS AND WAXES

Fats

Neutral fat comprises a large portion of the dietary lipid. It is also the major storage form of fatty acids in the body (fat depots), available for rapid mobilization to the extra-adipose tissues in time of need. Oxidation of its fatty acid constituents provides the major source of energy derived from the catabolism of lipids, although degradation of the glycerol of the triglycerides via carbohydrate pathways also provides energy from substances of lipid origin. The pathways of synthesis and degradation of the fatty acid component have been outlined previously. The glycerol moiety of the fats is derived from carbohydrate (glycolytic intermediates) by the following reaction:

$$\text{Dihydroxyacetone-phosphate} \xrightleftharpoons[\text{dehydrogenase, NAD}]{\text{Glycerol-phosphate}} \text{L-}\alpha\text{-Glycerol-phosphate}$$

Although L-α-glycerol-phosphate may be hydrolyzed by a phosphatase to inorganic phosphate and free glycerol, glycerol-phosphate itself is the form in which glycerol is incorporated into both fats and phospholipids. Any free glycerol which is formed by hydrolysis of glycerol-phosphate or of glycerol-containing lipids may be directed back into the pathway of carbohydrate or lipid metabolism through phosphorylation via a glycerolkinase and ATP, re-forming L-α-glycerol-phosphate. Such kinase activity has been reported in liver, kidney, lactating mammary gland, and to a slight extent in intestinal mucosa, but is virtually absent from adipose tissue.

The fats are synthesized by the series of reactions shown in Figure 19–11. In addition to the major pathway, leading from glycerol-phosphate through lysophosphatidate, phosphatidate, and diglyceride, many tissues (liver, kidney, aorta, lactating mammary gland, intestinal mucosa) contain an alternate route involving direct acylation of a monoglyceride to a di- and triglyceride. A third possibility is opened by the existence of a kinase which, like the one which phosphorylates the α,β-diglyceride to phosphatidic acid, converts monoglycerides to lysophosphatidates which then rejoin the main path.

It is of interest that the same phosphatidic acid and diglyceride intermediates are utilized in the synthesis of the glycero-phosphatides. The apparent paradox of formation of a D-glyceride from an L-phosphatidic acid is resolved as follows: The conventions of organic chemical nomenclature require that the free alcoholic group of the α,β-diglyceride be written at the top of the molecule, whereas the same hydroxyl group, when esterified with phosphoric acid in the phosphatidic acid, is placed at the bottom of the molecule. Owing to rotation of the molecule in the plane of the paper, the central, asymmetric carbon atom of the glycerol projects to the left in the case of the phosphatidic acid and to the right in the case of the diglyceride.

Nothing is known concerning the mechanisms which determine the types of fatty acid units incorporated into a given triglyceride molecule, the chronological order of the esterifications, or the location taken by each acyl radical.

The available evidence indicates that the fats must be hydrolyzed before they are oxidized. Glycerol and the fatty acids are liberated by intracellular lipases, after which they may be degraded by mechanisms already discussed.

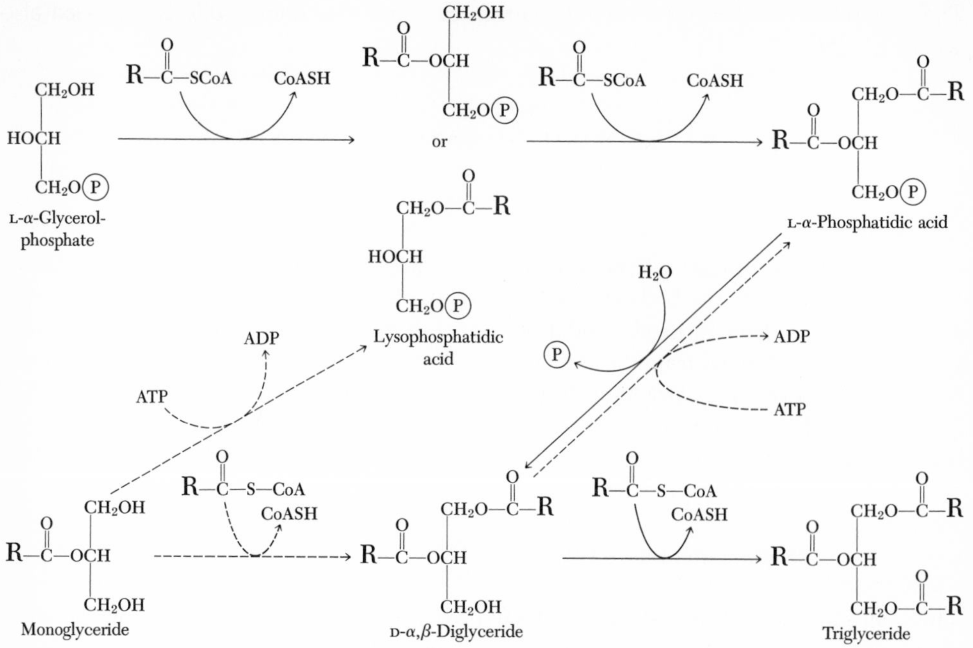

Figure 19-11. Synthesis of triglycerides. Ⓟ, phosphate.

In the animal organism, neutral fat is found normally in significant quantities only in adipose tissue (fat depots) and in liver. The types of triglycerides present in the fat depots appear to represent the resultant of two metabolic "forces." One of these is the mechanism for synthesis of fatty acids from carbohydrate, which, in the average land animal, results in a triglyceride mixture containing approximately one-third saturated fatty acids (largely palmitic) and two-thirds unsaturated (oleic and related acids). This composition is approached by the depot fat of animals on high-carbohydrate, low-fat diets. The second factor contributing to the composition of adipose tissue is the fat of the diet. The component fatty acids of the dietary lipids enter into the triglycerides of the depots to a considerable degree, especially if the quantity of fat in the diet is high. The "native" pattern of depot fat can therefore be altered by dietary means, a fact of considerable commercial importance, e.g., in the production of bacon and lard with an appropriately high melting point (high-carbohydrate diet).

The triglycerides of liver tend to contain more unsaturated fatty acids than those of the depots. This was interpreted at one time as indicating preliminary desaturation of fatty acids in the liver, preparatory to their complete oxidation. It is currently believed, however, that the liver preferentially selects the more highly unsaturated fatty acids from the mixture offered by the diet. Relations between the neutral fat of depot and liver (including the phenomenon of mobilization from the depots to the liver) will be discussed in connection with lipid transport (pp. 489, 497).

The composition of milk is considered elsewhere (Ch. 29). Largely by the use of isotopic labeling techniques, it has been demonstrated that milk fat (including the glycerol as well as the fatty acids) is mainly synthesized in the mammary gland, rather than derived from the lipids of the blood as was believed formerly. In non-ruminants, glucose is the precursor of the fatty acids; in ruminants, its place is taken by acetate, large amounts of which are absorbed from the digestive tract, where it is formed by bacteria from the cellulose of the diet. The glycerol moiety is synthesized from glucose in all cases.

Waxes

The biological significance of waxes is obscure. It is possible that the waxes of the skin aid in maintaining its pliability and rendering it waterproof, in man as in the apple. Cholesterol esters do not appear to play a quantitatively significant role in lipid transport in the blood, as believed formerly; their occurrence at sites of active cholesterol metabolism (intestinal mucosa, liver, adrenal cortex), however, suggests their importance in that respect, but their role remains undefined. The high concentration of polyunsaturated fatty acids in plasma cholesterol esters indicates the possible involvement of polyunsaturated fatty acids in cholesterol transport, or of cholesterol in polyunsaturated fatty acid transport.

Information concerning the intermediary metabolism of the waxes is less plentiful than that concerning the fats. Practically nothing is known about the synthesis and breakdown of the waxes derived from aliphatic alcohols, except that the alcohols themselves (e.g., cetyl, C_{16}) can be synthesized in the body from the fatty acids of corresponding chain length. The origin of the steroid alcohols, sterols, has been discussed previously. Cholesterol is esterified in the course of its absorption from the intestine, and also by the liver. In the intestine the esterification of cholesterol is catalyzed by the same enzyme which catalyzes the hydrolysis of cholesterol esters. Esterification of cholesterol in the liver, however, is said to proceed via a more orthodox mechanism involving the interaction of the alcohol with fatty acyl-CoA's. Other features of cholesterol ester metabolism will be mentioned in connection with lipid transport and storage.

METABOLISM OF PHOSPHOLIPIDS

Synthesis

The class of phospholipids includes a wide variety of compounds. Those containing glycerol (frequently designated "glycerophosphatides") are perhaps simplest in structure, being composed of fatty acids or aldehydes, phosphoric acid, and a base, in addition to glycerol. The sphingomyelins (sometimes included with the glycolipids in a group designated "sphingolipids") contain, in addition to phosphoric acid, fatty acid, and choline, the basic alcohol, sphingosine. Least well defined of all are the phosphoinositides, which contain, among other constituents, the cyclic alcohol, inositol. The diversity of constituents enumerated indicates the complexity which may be anticipated in the discussion of the metabolism of the phospholipids.

It seems probable that all tissues synthesize phospholipids, but at widely varying rates. In all tissues but one, these compounds are apparently synthesized, used, and degraded in situ. Liver is exceptional, in that a large proportion of the phospholipids synthesized in this organ is liberated into the plasma. As a matter of fact, liver is practically the sole source of plasma phospholipids, and is also the chief site of their further metabolism or degradation. Although there is every indication that the phospholipids play important roles in intermediary metabolism, the specific nature of these roles can scarcely be conjectured at this time.

(*a*) ***Origin of components.*** The sources of the inorganic phosphate and fatty acid moieties of the phospholipids present no problem in general, although certain of the highly unsaturated acids which seem to be selectively incorporated into phospholipids belong to the group of "essential" fatty acids, and must therefore be secured from the diet. Glycerol, which is derived from the pathways of carbohydrate metabolism, is utilized for phospholipid synthesis in the form of L-α-phosphatidic acid or D-α,β-diglyceride, as it is in the synthesis of neutral fats. As might be expected, the fatty acids are utilized in the form of their CoA thioesters. Inositol, required for the synthesis of the phosphoinositides, is sometimes regarded as one of the members of the vitamin B group (p. 204). The fatty aldehydes of the plasmalogens are formed by reduction of fatty acyl-CoA's.

Of the constituent bases of the phospholipids, serine is derived from the pathways of both carbohydrate and protein (glycine) metabolism (p. 576). Ethanolamine is formed by the decarboxylation of serine (p. 579). Stepwise methylation of ethanolamine yields choline (p. 590). Choline and ethanolamine participate in the synthesis of phospholipids in their "activated" forms, that is, as cytidine nucleotides, which are formed as follows:

$$\text{Base} \xrightarrow{\text{ATP} \quad \text{ADP}} \text{Base-phosphate} \xleftrightarrow{\text{CTP} \quad \text{PP}} \text{Cytidine-diphosphate-base}$$

The form in which serine enters into phosphatides is not understood, but it is probably different from that indicated above. Sphingosine originates partly from fatty acids and partly from serine:

$$\text{Palmityl-CoA} + \text{NADPH} + \text{H}^+ \longrightarrow \text{Palmitic aldehyde} + \text{CoA} + \text{NADP}^+$$

$$\text{Palmitic aldehyde} + \text{Serine} \xleftrightarrow[\text{Mn}^{++}]{\text{Pyridoxal-PO}_4} \text{Dihydrosphingosine} + \text{CO}_2$$

$$\text{Dihydrosphingosine} \xrightarrow{\text{Flavin}} \text{Sphingosine}$$

(*b*) ***Mechanisms of synthesis.*** As may be seen in Figure 19–12, the L-α-phosphatidic acid, and the D-α,β-diglyceride derived by hydrolysis of it, are key intermediates in the synthesis of the phospholipids, as they are in the synthesis of the triglycerides. Thus, both ethanolamine phosphatide and choline phosphatide (lecithin) are synthesized by the interaction of the diglyceride with cytidine-diphosphate-ethanolamine and -choline, respectively. The ethanolamine and choline plasmalogens are believed to be synthesized in an analogous

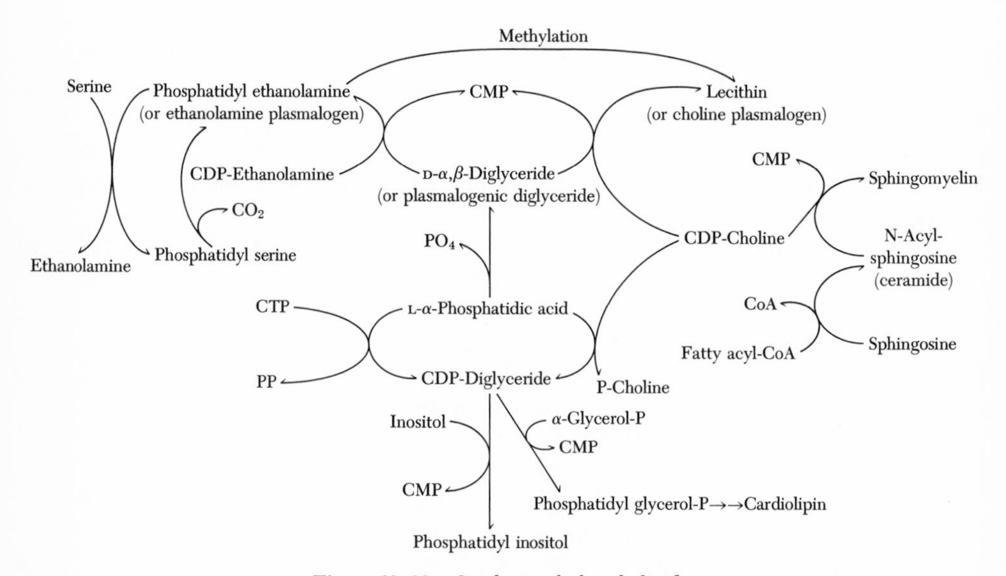

Figure 19–12. Synthesis of phospholipids.

fashion, but with the D-α,β-diglyceride replaced by a "plasmalogenic diglyceride" containing the necessary enol-ether linkage.

The synthesis of phosphatidyl serine involves an exchange reaction between serine and phosphatidyl ethanolamine. Phosphatidyl serine may be the parent compound of cephalins and lecithins by decarboxylation to phosphatidyl ethanolamine, which is methylated three times in succession to form, finally, lecithin.

Phosphatidyl inositol is synthesized somewhat differently from the other glycerophosphatides in that L-α-phosphatidic acid rather than diglyceride is the starting material. Two pathways have been described for conversion of the phosphatidic acid to a cytidine-diphosphate-diglyceride. In one, the cytidine-diphosphate group is provided by cytidine triphosphate; in the other, it is provided by cytidine-diphosphate-choline. In any case, interaction of the cytidine-diphosphate-diglyceride with inositol results in the formation of phosphatidyl inositol and cytidylic acid (cytidine monophosphate, CMP). Successive phosphorylation converts the mono- to di- and triphosphoinositides.

Interaction of CDP-diglyceride with α-glycerol-phosphate produces phosphatidyl glycerol-phosphate, which is hydrolyzed to phosphatidyl glycerol. It is probable that cardiolipin [bis (phosphatidyl) glycerol, p. 39] is synthesized by further reaction with another molecule of CDP-diglyceride.

The synthesis of sphingomyelin begins with the N-acylation of sphingosine by a fatty acyl thioester of CoA, producing an N-acylsphingosine (a ceramide). This intermediate then reacts with cytidine-diphosphate-choline to form sphingomyelin.

Turnover

By "turnover" is meant the rate at which a given type of molecule is renewed in the organism. Turnover may be a measure of the rate of total synthesis or degradation of the molecule in question, or, as is frequently the case in isotopic-labeling experiments, it may merely indicate the rate at which one segment of the molecule "exchanges" with its free brethren in the "metabolic pool" (p. 542).

Whether measured by labeling the phosphate, fatty acids, or bases, the turnover of phospholipids exhibits the same relative rates in the various tissues; liver, intestine, and kidney comprise the most active group; such organs as pancreas, adrenals, and lungs have intermediate activity; and muscle and brain are in the slowest category. The turnover of phospholipids is zero in the myelin sheath around nerve axons.

Since several components enter into the structure of the phospholipids, it might be anticipated that each would turn over at a characteristic rate. Normally, choline, phosphate, and fatty acids exhibit comparable rates of turnover in the phospholipid fraction of liver (or plasma, which is largely a reflection of events in the liver in the case of the phospholipids). However, divergent rates may be exhibited under various physiological or pathological conditions. For example, fatty acid turnover is greatly diminished in the phospholipid fraction of liver slices from fasted rats, whereas phosphate turnover is much less affected, and the turnover of glycerol and the bases remains normal.

Data obtained in experimental animals using labeled acetate indicate that, in liver and plasma, neutral fat turns over more rapidly than phospholipid, whereas the converse holds true in most other organs (including mesenteric lipid). Turnover rates are equal for fat and phospholipid in the carcass. The half-life of liver and plasma phospholipid is a matter of hours rather than days.

As might be anticipated, the turnover of phospholipids is markedly affected by dietary or metabolic influences. Fat feeding increases the turnover in liver and intestine, decreases that of the kidney, and has no effect on other organs. Deficiency of essential fatty acids greatly increases the turnover of phospholipids in liver. Experimental diabetes results in markedly increased turnover in liver and plasma, whereas other tissues are affected slightly or not at all. Administration of choline increases the rate of turnover of the lecithin fraction of liver.

Catabolism

The initial reactions of breakdown of phospholipids in the tissues are hydrolytic, similar to those taking place in the digestive tract. Various lecithinases and phosphodiesterases are found in animal tissues. As indicated in Figure 19-13, the major pathway for hydrolysis of the glycerophosphatides involves, first, loss of the unsaturated fatty acid found in the β position of the glycerol, producing compounds known as lysolecithins and lysocephalins. (Enzymes which are present in a number of tissues can re-acylate the various lysophosphatides.) Further hydrolysis removes the saturated fatty acid from the α position, followed by cleavage of the bond between the phosphoric acid and the base or alcohol. α-Glycerol-phosphate is readily hydrolyzed to glycerol and inorganic phosphate. This pathway of catabolism is well established for lecithin and phosphatidyl ethanolamine. Phosphatidyl serine probably follows the same pathway, at least as far as glycerophosphoryl-serine. Although plasmalogens undergo the usual initial hydrolysis in the series, the second step requires hydrolysis of the vinyl ether linkage by a specific enzyme which releases the aldehyde. Enzymes also have been found which hydrolyze the ether linkage in intact plasmalogens. There is some evidence that phosphatidyl inositol may be

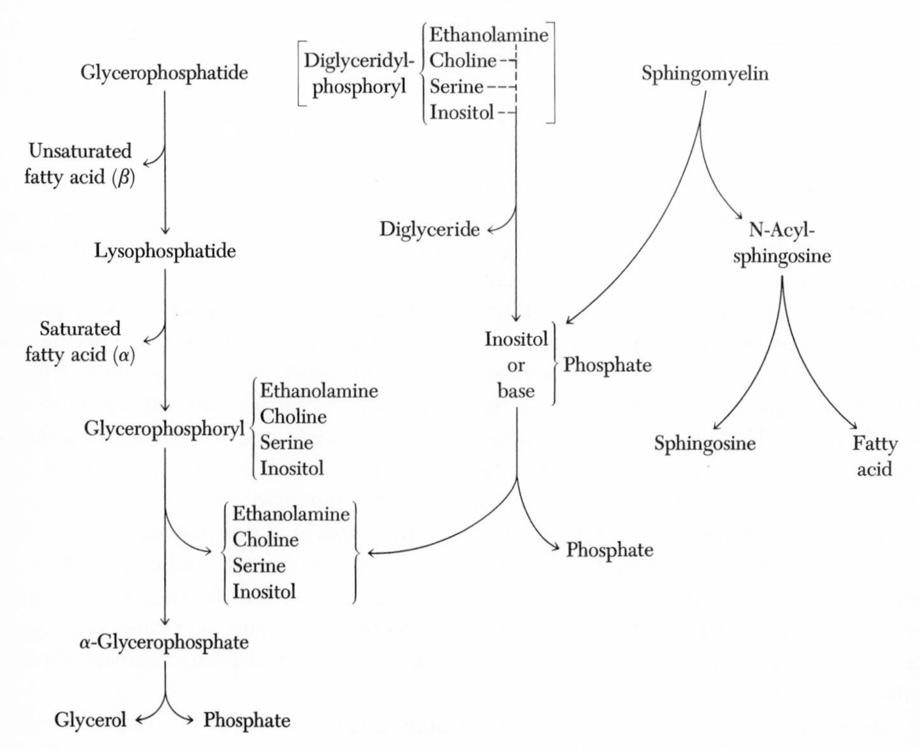

Figure 19-13. Catabolism of phospholipids.

degraded by the same pathway; however, an alternate path, shown in Figure 19–13, although probably not significant for the other glycerophosphatides, may be the major catabolic pathway for phosphatidyl inositol. This pathway involves removal of the inositol-phosphate moiety, leaving a diglyceride residue. Inositol is then liberated by a phosphatase. The same enzyme which initiates this pathway is said to attack sphingomyelin, liberating phosphorylcholine and leaving N-acylsphingosine, which is hydrolyzed to its constituents, presumably by an amidase.

Functions of the Phospholipids

(*a*) ***Structural.*** Early investigations led to the conclusion that there are two types of lipids, from the standpoint of metabolic lability: (1) a fraction undergoing relatively wide fluctuations in concentration in the tissues in response to dietary changes—the *"élément variable;"* (2) a fraction, predominantly phospholipid, characterized by constancy of concentration, even in the face of death by inanition—the *"élément constant."* Exceptions and contradictions to this point of view soon resulted from numerous investigations performed by the classical techniques; modern studies with isotopes render dubious a claim of durability of any constituent of the body.

Although the phospholipids, or any fraction thereof (with the exception of constituents of myelin), can scarcely be considered metabolically inert, this fact in itself does not prevent these compounds from serving a structural function (cf. the discussion of the dynamic state, p. 541). Indeed, it is probable that phospholipids participate in the lipoprotein complexes which are thought to constitute the matrix of cell walls and membranes, the myelin sheath, and of such structures as mitochondria and microsomes. In this role, they impart certain physical characteristics to these structures, viz., unexpectedly high permeability toward certain non-polar (hydrophobic) molecules, and lysis by surface-active agents (detergents, bile salts, etc.).

Certain enzymes appear to require tightly bound phospholipid for their action. Numerous examples of this occur in the mitochondrial enzyme system involved in the oxidative chain and oxidative chain phosphorylation. For example, a purified cytochrome oxidase preparation, solubilized by treatment with bile salts and thereby inactivated, can be reactivated by phosphatidyl serine. Whether or not the phospholipid deserves the status of a prosthetic group, the fact remains that its removal from the enzyme protein inactivates the latter. This function may be considered structural in the broad sense. Although it may not be a strictly structural function, it has been observed that phospholipid turnover is proportional to mitotic activity, as seen in growth and tissue regeneration.

(*b*) ***Blood coagulation.*** Substances having the properties of phospholipids are believed to function as parts of both "thromboplastin" and "antithromboplastin" in the mechanism of blood coagulation (p. 799). The former, a lipoprotein, contains phosphatidyl serine, phosphatidyl ethanolamine, and possibly phosphoinositides and phosphatidic acids. Purified phosphatidyl ethanolamine promotes coagulation.

(*c*) ***Lipid absorption in intestine.*** It has been thought for some time that phospholipids act as carriers of fatty acids, particularly during the absorption of fatty acids from the intestine. Although the increased turnover rate of the total phospholipids of the intestinal mucosa during fat absorption has been found to be inadequate to account for any major fraction of absorbed fatty acids, recent studies indicate very high metabolic activity in the phosphatidic acid fraction. It has been suggested that these compounds may be involved in the incorporation, into the triglycerides of the lymph, of the fatty acids freed during digestion, via the same mechanism used in triglyceride synthesis elsewhere in the body. Phospholipids (particularly lecithins) may form an important part of the stabilizing layer of the chylomicrons.

(*d*) ***Lipid transport between tissues.*** A suggested function of phospholipids has been the transport of fatty acids from one tissue or organ to another, e.g., between liver and depots. This concept has had to be abandoned. According to present information, the phospholipids of the plasma are synthesized almost exclusively in the liver, and are removed from the plasma mainly by the same organ. Other tissues synthesize their own phospholipids, liberate practically none into the plasma, and absorb very little from that source.

A possible indirect role of phospholipids in lipid transport in the blood is suggested by the participation of phospholipids in the structure of lipoproteins, which are, themselves, vehicles of lipid transport.

(*e*) ***Ion transport and secretion.*** That phospholipids are in some way implicated in the mechanism of secretion is suggested by the observation that phospholipid (especially phosphatidic acids and phosphoinositide) turnover is proportional to the rate of secretion of cells liberating such products as hormones, enzymes, mucins, and other proteins. The observation that many phospholipids are sufficiently anionic to combine with cations has led to the hypothesis that these compounds may act as carriers of inorganic ions across membranes. The phosphoinositides and phosphatidic acids have been particularly implicated.

(*f*) ***Oxidation of fatty acids.*** Since the phospholipids, on the average, contain fatty acids that are more highly unsaturated than those of the neutral fats, it has been suggested in the past that the fatty acids are desaturated, and perhaps otherwise degraded, while they form a part of the phospholipid molecule. In addition to certain direct contradictory evidence, this hypothesis has been rendered superfluous by the currently established mechanism.

The ease of autoxidation of the polyunsaturated fatty acids (which are to be found mainly in the phospholipids) has led to the theory that the phospholipids act as catalysts of biological oxidations. No good evidence supports this theory. Furthermore, certain phospholipids are effective antioxidants in vitro, and are so used commercially. As pointed out previously, however, a *structural* role in biological oxidations appears to be well established.

That phospholipids nevertheless play some role in the metabolism of fatty acids, at least in the liver, seems probable from the observations cited previously, in which the turnover of phospholipids is correlated with the intensity of fat metabolism (fat feeding and diabetes). Also, administration of choline to experimental animals increases the rate of oxidation of fatty acids in the liver, whereas the rate of oxidation is decreased in the livers of choline-deficient rats on low-protein diets. Nevertheless, the specific nature of the role played by the phospholipids in these cases remains to be elucidated.

METABOLISM OF GLYCOLIPIDS

Little can be said of the metabolism of this group of lipids, the chemistry of which is not even entirely settled. The origin of the sphingosine moiety was discussed in connection with the phospholipids. As indicated in the preceding chapter, carbohydrate building blocks of the glycolipids are introduced while coupled to "carriers:" glucose, galactose, and N-acetylgalactosamine as the UDP derivatives; sialic acid in the form of CMP-N-acetylneuraminic acid.

Cerebrosides appear to be synthesized by glycosylation of sphingosine followed by acylation with a fatty acid. Sulfate for the formation of sulfatides (cerebroside sulfates) is probably provided by phosphoadenosine phosphosulfate (PAPS, p. 587). In the catabolic direction, a cerebrosidase hydrolyzes N-acylsphingosine-galactosides to ceramides and galactose. Breakdown of ceramides is catalyzed by a ceramidase. Sulfatides are hydrolyzed by a cerebroside sulfatase, the activity of which is said to be depressed in metachromatic leucodystrophy, an inborn error of metabolism characterized by accumulation of sulfatide in the white matter of the nervous system.

In the synthesis of the more complex glycolipids, the order of addition of constituents is not known, although there is some evidence that cerebrosides do not act as precursors. Tay-Sachs disease may involve an inborn defect in the synthetic pathway of gangliosides, since the major compound which accumulates differs from a normal monosialoganglioside (for which, indeed, it may be the normal precursor) in lacking one galactose residue. The catabolism of the more complex glycolipids may normally proceed through cerebrosides. Gaucher's disease apparently results from an inherited defect (at the cerebrosidase level) in the degradation of erythrocyte globosides by reticuloendothelial cells of the spleen and other tissues, resulting in accumulation of cerebrosides.

TRANSPORT OF LIPIDS

The subjects of lipid transport, deposition, and storage cannot, at the present time, be discussed as satisfactorily as can comparable phases of the metabolism of carbohydrate and protein. Many facts are well established, but in many cases their significance is still in doubt. This state of uncertainty is reflected in the present status of knowledge concerning the blood lipids, despite the accumulation of information on this topic in recent years.

Phospholipids (chiefly lecithin), cholesterol, and neutral fat are the most abundant lipids in the plasma. There are small amounts of free (unesterified) fatty acids, glycolipids, and minute quantities of certain important hormones and vitamins of lipid nature. Normal values for the major plasma lipids are indicated in Table 19-2, p. 493. Because of the heterogeneity of this group of substances and because different components have different metabolic origins, fates, and significance, it is necessary to consider them individually from these standpoints. Before doing so, however, certain general features of their state in the plasma should be reviewed. These have to do largely with recent observations concerning the intimate relationship between the plasma lipids and certain fractions of the plasma proteins.

State of Lipids in Blood: Lipoproteins

As has been indicated previously, practically all of the lipids of plasma are present as lipoprotein complexes. These substances are described from the standpoints of lipid and of protein chemistry elsewhere (pp. 45, 560). Electrophoretic studies of plasma protein fractions precipitated by ethanol at low temperatures disclosed the presence of two groups of lipoproteins, one migrating with the α_1-globulins, the other with the β_1-globulins. (Although the union is much more labile, the complex formed between free (unesterified) fatty acids and plasma albumin may be considered another class of lipoprotein.) Ultracentrifugal analysis by the flotation technique has led to the detection of a hierarchy of lipoproteins of varying particle weight, subdivided into high- and low-density groups, corresponding generally, but not entirely, to the α and β classifications determined by electrophoresis.

The plasma lipoproteins contain cholesterol (free and esterified), phospholipids, neutral fat, free (unesterified) fatty acids, and traces of the lipid-soluble vitamins and the steroid hormones. Transport of the latter substances in a water-soluble form may be an important function of the lipoproteins. The β-lipoproteins differ from the α-group in transporting more of the total plasma cholesterol (about two-thirds), in containing a higher concentration of both free and esterified cholesterol and phospholipid, and in having a much higher cholesterol:phospholipid ratio.

It appears probable that the abnormally high cholesterol:phospholipid ratio observed clinically in certain hyperlipemic sera may be a reflection of elevated concentration of the β-lipoproteins relative to that of the α-group, which does not vary greatly in concentration. The β-lipoproteins are also of particular clinical interest, since it is claimed that the occurrence of elevated concentrations of these substances in human sera is correlated with the incidence of atherosclerosis. Significant reductions in the levels of these substances in the blood are said to follow dietary restriction of fat.

The ultracentrifugal composition of human serum is shown in Figure 19–14. The right side of the figure presents the ultracentrifugal pattern for those components of serum which sediment in a medium of density 1.200, plotted on a thirtyfold-reduced scale. The major components seen are albumin at 4 S (p. 561), globulin at 7 S, and a rapidly sedimenting component at 19 S. Between densities of 1.200 and 1.063 are the high-density lipoproteins (HDL), corresponding in general to the α_1-globulins determined electrophoretically. As indicated in the figure, the two major subgroups are HDL_2 and HDL_3. Lipoproteins having densities less than 1.063 may be separated by the process of

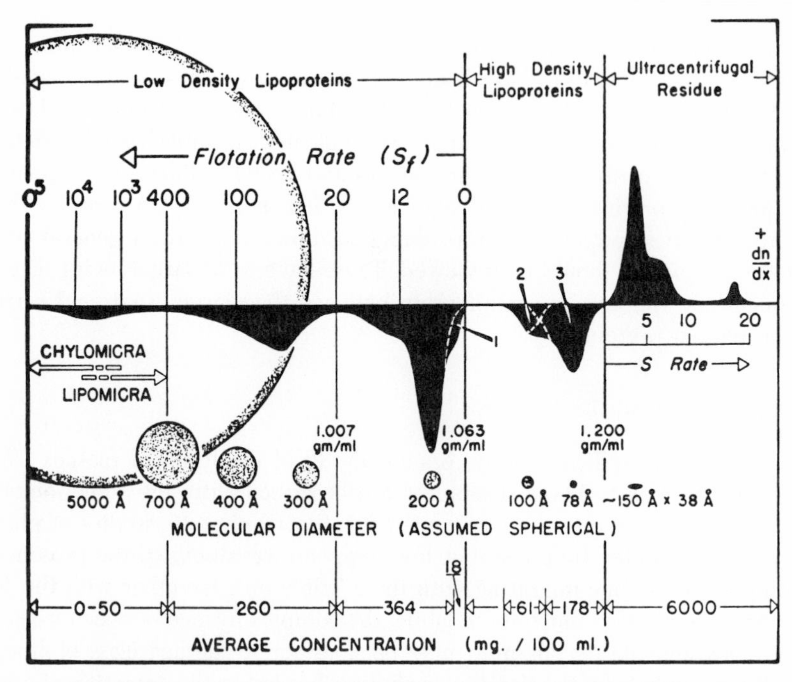

Figure 19-14. Ultracentrifugal composition of human serum. (From F. T. Lindgren and A. V. Nichols, in Putnam (ed.): The Plasma Proteins, Vol. 2, Academic Press, Inc., New York, 1960, p. 12.)

TABLE 19-1. CHEMICAL COMPOSITION OF MAJOR LIPOPROTEIN CLASSES*

CLASS	% OF TOTAL LIPID PRESENT AS					PROTEIN %
	TRI-GLYCERIDE	PHOSPHO-LIPID	CHOLESTEROL ESTERS	FREE CHO-LESTEROL	UNESTERIFIED FATTY ACIDS	
HDL_2 HDL_3	17	44	28	6	6 or less	35–60
S_f 0–20	14	25	46	14	1 or less	20–25
S_f 20–400	55	20	5	8	2	10
$S_f > 400$ (chylo-microns)	85–90	6–9	2	1	<1	2

* Tabulated from data cited by F. T. Lindgren and A. V. Nichols, in Putnam (ed.): The Plasma Proteins, Vol. 2, Academic Press, Inc., New York, 1960, Chapter 11.

ultracentrifugal flotation. Although belonging properly in the low-density class, lipoproteins of S_f (p. 561) 0 to 2 are not completely recovered when centrifuged in a medium of density 1.063. Therefore, for analytical purposes, these lipoproteins are frequently determined with the high-density group and designated HDL_1. It is clear from the figure that, among the lipoproteins which undergo flotation in a medium of density 1.063, minima in concentrations occur at S_f values of 20 and 400, so that these limits may be used arbitrarily to divide the low-density lipoproteins into subgroups. It is recognized that each subgroup is by no means homogeneous in either a chemical or a physical sense.

The serum fraction of density greater than 1.20, although containing none of the lipoproteins which are the general subject of this discussion, does include the metabolically important complexes of free fatty acids with serum albumin. Small quantities of other lipids, chiefly phospholipid, have also been reported in this fraction.

The chemical composition of the major classes of lipoproteins is given in Table 19-1. The high-density lipoproteins (average density 1.12), which with few exceptions are found in the α_1-globulin class in electrophoresis, contain more protein and less lipid than the low-density lipoproteins as a class. They also differ from the low-density lipoproteins in that phospholipids and unesterified fatty acids make up a greater percentage of the total lipid. Their molecular weights range from 100,000 to 400,000, in contrast to the low-density lipoproteins which have minimum molecular weights of about a million. The protein moiety is characterized by containing N-terminal aspartic acid and C-terminal threonine. Although the formation of chylomicrons (discussed subsequently) depends primarily on the ability of the intestinal cells to synthesize β-lipoproteins, it is a curious fact that α-lipoproteins also can be detected in the completed particles. The concentration in plasma of high-density lipoproteins is maintained at a more constant level than that of the low-density lipoproteins. Although most of the unesterified fatty acids of the plasma are transported by albumin, an appreciable, but lesser, fraction is carried by the high-density lipoproteins. The metabolic significance of this fact is not understood.

As indicated in Table 19-1, among the low-density lipoproteins, an increasing S_f value is associated with a decreasing content of protein, phospholipid, both free and combined cholesterol, and with an increasing content of triglyceride. The low-density lipoproteins of S_f classes 0 to 400 contain chiefly N-terminal glutamic acid. The S_f 0 to 20 class (average density 1.03) migrates with β_1-mobility in electrophoresis, whereas lipoproteins of classes greater than S_f 20 may be found in either the β_1 or α_2 electrophoretic classes. (Chylomicrons, S_f greater than 400, migrate with α_2-mobility.) The mobilities of S_f classes greater than 20 (density < 1.006, sometimes called "very low density lipoproteins") vary somewhat with the particular technique of electrophoresis employed. As in the case of the intestinal synthesis of chylomicrons, the formation of "very low density lipoproteins" by the liver, although requiring primarily the ability to synthesize β-lipoproteins, also involves (but does not absolutely require) incorporation of α-lipoproteins. The metabolic function of the low-density lipoproteins appears to be the transport of triglyceride from the liver to adipose tissue for storage. It has been suggested that "carrier" low-density lipoproteins of S_f range 0 to 12 are formed initially, and that an increasing burden of triglyceride, which must be transported in the plasma, results in the construction of species of lower-density lipoproteins of S_f classes 12 to 400, containing greater percentages of triglycerides. From this point of view, the cholesterol (free and esterified) and phospholipid moieties of the low-density lipoproteins may merely represent the original fabric or structural material of the "carrier" lipoprotein.

The turbidity of plasma in post-alimentary hyperlipemia is due to large particles called chylomicrons, smaller species of which are sometimes designated lipomicrons. These particles, which usually exhibit α_2 electrophoretic mobility, have S_f values greater than 400 and densities less than 0.96. As may be seen in the table, they contain very little protein, and most of the total lipid consists of triglyceride. Chylomicrons are synthesized in the intestine and have the function of transporting triglyceride to the liver, muscle, and adipose tissue. As mentioned previously, α-lipoproteins are found in the chylomicrons, although their role therein is obscure, since these particles appear to be absolutely dependent for their formation on the ability of the intestinal cells to synthesize β-lipoproteins. The lactescence of plasma in diabetes mellitus or starvation is due to lipoprotein particles (density < 1.006) which, though resembling chylomicrons, actually originate in the liver in response to mobilization of free fatty acids from the depots.

It has been observed that the injection of heparin results in marked clearing of the plasma in post-alimentary hyperlipemia. Plasma thus "activated" in vivo can exert clearing action on another hyperlipemic plasma in vitro. Clearing action, which may result in transformation of lipoproteins of S_f 20 to 400 to S_f 0 to 20 and of chylomicrons to higher-density lipoproteins, is due to an enzyme, lipoprotein lipase, which is either liberated or activated by heparin. Its inhibition by protamine (a basic protein) and heparinase suggests that the enzyme may contain as prosthetic group a heparin-like acidic mucopolysaccharide. The enzyme, which is found in adipose tissue, heart, lung, and skeletal muscle, as well as plasma, acts specifically on protein-bound lipid in much the same way as ordinary lipase acts on free triglyceride, producing di- and monoglycerides, as well as some free glycerol. Proper functioning of the enzyme requires the presence of an acceptor for the fatty acids which are liberated; this role is performed by plasma albumin. The enzyme is activated by ammonium ions or divalent cations, Ca^{++} probably being the natural activator. Intravascular clearing is probably a minor metabolic pathway. As discussed in a later section, a large part of the task appears to be accomplished by the liver. Quantitative determination of the relative importance of various pathways of disposal of chylomicrons has yielded the following decreasing series: liver $>$ carcass plus adipose tissue $>$ intravascular lipolysis. Since elevated concentration of the lower density lipoproteins may have some relationship to atherosclerosis, the mechanism involved in clearing action and possible abnormal deviations therefrom are of considerable clinical interest.

Tissue lipoprotein lipases, which are liberated into the circulation by heparin or a fatty meal, exert their primary functions in their tissues of origin. As will be discussed subsequently, the enzyme in adipose tissue decreases in activity in fasting and diabetes mellitus, in which conditions the major function of adipose tissue is not to take up, hydrolyze, and store fat coming from the circulation, but rather to mobilize fatty acids to the extra-adipose tissues. In complementary fashion, lipoprotein lipases of skeletal muscle and heart increase in activity in these conditions, thus facilitating utilization of circulating triglyceride (probably synthesized in the form of lipoprotein by liver from free fatty acids mobilized from adipose tissue).

Postabsorptive Plasma Lipid Concentration

It is apparent (Table 19-2) that the range of normal variation in the concentration of plasma lipids is unusually wide, even in the postabsorptive state. Moreover, although the three major components, i.e., triglycerides (neutral fat), phosphatides (phospholipids), and cholesterol, frequently vary in the same direction, this is not always the case. Total fatty acids and neutral fat are particularly variable, even in the same individual. The cholesterol: phospholipid ratio is more stable and uniform, although its significance is not apparent. Little is known concerning the intrinsic mechanisms which regulate the equilibrium levels of the blood lipids. It is conceivable that the cholesterol: phospholipid ratio may be influenced, if not fixed, by the hepatic mechanism for synthesis of the lipoproteins in which these molecules are found. The possibility has been mentioned previously that there is a "carrier" low-density lipoprotein of fixed composition to which may be added increasing quantities of lipid, in particular triglycerides, as requirements for transport of these substances from liver to adipose tissue are increased. Although there is no complete agreement on this point, there is evidence that "adult" patterns of blood lipid concentrations are established at an early age (first few days of life), and change but little, if at all, in later years in normal subjects. Low values for cholesterol and phospholipids have been reported in the newborn.

Cholesterol. Cholesterol exists in the plasma in two forms, (1) free and (2) esterified (combined with fatty acids), both of which are incorporated in lipoprotein molecules. Free cholesterol comprises about 20 to 40 per cent, and ester cholesterol about 60 to 80 per cent of the total of 140 to 260 mg./100 ml. This ratio is usually preserved with remarkable constancy even in the presence of wide variations in the total owing to

TABLE 19-2. MAIN PLASMA LIPIDS (POSTABSORPTIVE)*

SUBSTANCE	CONCENTRATION (mg./100 ml.)
Total lipid	385–675 (530)
Neutral fat	0–260 (140)
Unesterified fatty acids	8–31 (26)
Phospholipids	110–250 (165)
Lecithin	80–200 (110)
Cephalin	0–30 (10)
Sphingomyelin	10–50 (30)
Cholesterol	140–260 (200)
Ester	90–200 (145)
Free	40–70 (55)
Total fatty acids	110–485 (300)

* Figures in parentheses are mean values.

disease states that are not accompanied by disturbance of liver cell function. Although cholesterol is undoubtedly synthesized by a number of tissues, the liver is the main if not the only source of plasma cholesterol as well as the main site of its esterification (also intestinal mucosa, p. 453). This organ is therefore fundamentally concerned in the maintenance, not only of the level of cholesterol in the plasma (in the nonabsorptive state), but also of the ester: free cholesterol ratio. It plays an important role, too, in the removal of this substance from the blood, and in its subsequent metabolism, as indicated by the fact that the bulk of exogenous cholesterol is recoverable as bile acids in the bile.

Apart from the low values in the newborn (about 50 mg./100 ml.) and an increase during pregnancy, reaching a maximum (about 35 per cent above non-pregnant state) at about the 30th week, there are no significant variations under physiological conditions (postabsorptive). There is statistical evidence of an increased concentration in advanced years, and of higher values in men than in premenopausal women. Abnormalities in certain disease states can be explained on the basis of aberrations of known physiological mechanisms, although many cannot.

In severe impairment of liver cell function (e.g., hepatocellular jaundice) the ester cholesterol decreases, resulting in hypocholesterolemia and a decrease in the ratio of ester to free cholesterol. This is presumably due to diminished production and esterification of plasma cholesterol by the damaged liver cells. In cases of obstruction of the common bile duct (obstructive jaundice) the plasma cholesterol concentration rises, if the liver cells are not seriously damaged. The explanation for this phenomenon is not clear, but recent observations suggest that the hypercholesterolemia is associated with the increase in bile acids in the plasma which occurs under these circumstances (regurgitation as a result of biliary obstruction). These differences in plasma cholesterol in hepatocellular and obstructive types of jaundice may aid in differential diagnosis of these conditions.

Hypercholesterolemia occurs in uncontrolled diabetes mellitus. This may be due to diversion of abnormally large amounts of 2-C fragments ("acetate") to cholesterol synthesis (also ketogenesis) in the liver as a consequence of (1) increased mobilization of free (unesterified) fatty acids from the adipose tissue depots to the liver, and (2) increased catabolism of fatty acids. It may be due in part also to delayed removal from the bloodstream.

The mechanism underlying abnormalities of plasma cholesterol concentration in certain other diseases is not well understood: e.g., the increase in hypothyroidism and decrease in hyperthyroidism (the rates of both synthesis and catabolism of cholesterol are increased by thyroid hormones in the liver and other tissues; however, the catabolic effects are greater than the anabolic); the increase in glomerulonephritis and nephrosis; the decrease in certain types of anemia, infections, and inanition. Estrogens have a profound influence on lipid metabolism in certain species (e.g., producing hyperlipemia in birds; lipotropic action [p. 505] in rats). There are reports that they cause a decrease in plasma cholesterol in man and alter its distribution between the plasma lipoprotein fractions, but these effects are still uncertain. Estrogens are said to increase and androgens to decrease the ratio of α- to β-lipoproteins in man. The rate of turnover of the cholesterol pool in man may also be increased by estrogen.

Varying the cholesterol intake (man) has little influence on the plasma cholesterol concentration under normal conditions. A high cholesterol intake depresses cholesterol synthesis in the liver. It has been found, however, that rigid restriction of dietary lipids may lower abnormally high plasma cholesterol concentrations in certain disease states. Unsaturated fatty acids in experimental diets are reported to favor the absorption of cholesterol; other reports claim a reduction in plasma cholesterol concentration in man. Plant sterols in the diet apparently interfere with the absorption of cholesterol, inhibit its synthesis in the liver, and are reported to lower plasma cholesterol concentration in man.

Attention has been directed toward the possible implication of an increase in plasma cholesterol, particularly in the β-lipoprotein category, in the pathogenesis of atherosclerosis. This important subject is currently under intensive investigation.

Phospholipids. The range of normal variation in plasma phospholipids is indicated in Table 19-2. Lecithin is the main component of this fraction, which, like other lipids, occurs in the blood plasma in association with certain globulins, as lipoprotein complexes. It has been shown, by the use of isotope-labeling techniques, that the plasma phospholipids, similarly to cholesterol, not only originate in the liver but are also removed from the blood and metabolized largely by that organ. It appears, therefore, that the bulk of the plasma phospholipid undergoes its complete metabolic cycle within the liver, with a temporary sojourn in the bloodstream. The possibility cannot be excluded that the plasma phospholipids may originate in part in the intestinal mucosa, reaching the bloodstream via the intestinal lymph. This is known to occur during fat absorption from the intestine. The constancy of the cholesterol: phospholipid ratio suggests that this factor (ratio) is of physiological significance. Present evidence renders untenable the formerly prevailing view that the plasma phospholipids serve as an important medium of transport of fatty acids between the liver and extrahepatic tissues.

In common with other lipids, the concentration of phospholipids in the plasma is low in the newborn and increases during pregnancy. It varies in a number of disease states in the same direction, although not necessarily to the same extent as the cholesterol concentration, viz., hyper- and hypothyroidism, diabetes mellitus, nephritis and nephrosis, hepatocellular and obstructive jaundice.

Triglycerides (neutral fats). The variable concentration of neutral fat in the plasma in the postabsorptive state is indicated in Table 19-2. The components of this fraction, too, exist as lipoprotein complexes. During the period of absorption of fats from the intestine, they occur temporarily also in the almost purely triglyceride form of chylomicrons. In the postabsorptive state they represent mainly triglycerides from the liver, en route to the fat depots.

Free (unesterified) fatty acids. The normal concentration of free (unesterified) fatty acids is indicated in Table 19-2. In addition to "unesterified fatty acids" (UFA), this fraction of the plasma lipids has been referred to as "non-esterified fatty acids" (NEFA) or "free fatty acids" (FFA). However, these substances are not truly free, since two-thirds of the total amount is attached to albumin and one-third to the lipoproteins (chiefly the high-density fractions). Plasma albumin, which has considerable affinity for many anions, binds 7 moles of fatty acids tightly per mole of albumin, and holds perhaps 20 more in looser combination.

Free fatty acids are the form in which stored lipid is mobilized from the fat depots to liver and other tissues for oxidation. Doubts concerning their importance in this regard, based on the relatively low concentration of free fatty acids in plasma, have been allayed by the discovery of their extremely brief half-life (1 to 3 minutes in man). This rate of turnover, even allowing for considerable recycling of fatty acids leaving the plasma, still is believed to represent a significant fraction of the daily caloric output.

The concentration of free fatty acids in plasma is decreased by administration of glucose or insulin, and increased in diabetes mellitus, by fasting, or by administration of growth hormone, epinephrine, and norepinephrine, with cortisone exhibiting "permissive" action in the last three instances. Thyroid hormones also play a "permissive" role with respect to a number of factors which tend to elevate the concentration of free fatty acids in plasma. Adrenocorticotropic hormone (ACTH) may exert an influence in the same direction, although results in the intact organism have not been as clear-cut as in vitro experiments with adipose tissue (discussed later). Exercise initially decreases the plasma level of free fatty acids (uptake by muscle), which subsequently rises due to increased mobilization from the depots. Cessation of exercise is followed by increased concentration ("overshoot" due to continued mobilization in the face of diminished utilization) which eventually falls to normal levels. These phenomena underscore the importance of fatty acids as fuel for muscle (p. 425).

The detailed mechanisms by which the above-mentioned factors influence mobilization of free fatty acids from the fat depots into the plasma will be discussed in connection with the metabolism of adipose tissue. It may be noted at this point, however, that free fatty acids thus liberated are converted by the liver into low-density lipoproteins which may be returned to the plasma, resulting in hyperlipemia. It is apparent that free fatty acids enter the blood from the fat depots at an accelerated rate under a variety of conditions in which carbohydrate is either not provided in adequate amounts in the diet or cannot be utilized adequately because of hormonal or other abnormalities. Increase in blood lipid (hyperlipemia) occurs therefore in starvation (early, before depots are depleted), dietary carbohydrate restriction, and uncontrolled diabetes mellitus (insulin deficiency). It may be present also in severe anemia (deficient oxidation?) and in glomerulonephritis (starvation effect?).

Influence of Food and Nutrition

After a high-fat meal, the plasma lipids begin to rise within two hours, reach a peak in four to six hours, and then tend to drop rather rapidly toward the resting level. Most of the increment is due to neutral fat; cholesterol and phospholipids make minor contributions. This temporary absorptive hyperlipemia is due to the fact that the major portion of the dietary lipid is absorbed by the intestinal lymphatics and enters the bloodstream directly, via the thoracic duct. If large amounts of fat are ingested the plasma may become opalescent, owing to the presence of chylomicrons. So-called "normal" meals often produce no significant rise in plasma lipids.

There is no general correlation between the blood lipid levels and the amount of body fat, but chronic malnutrition and wasting diseases are often accompanied by subnormal levels of phospholipids and cholesterol. In the initial stages of starvation, or of carbohydrate deprivation, after depletion of the preformed glycogen stores (about 36 hours), hyperlipemia occurs as a result of increased mobilization of depot unesterified fatty acids and consequent increased synthesis of low-density lipoproteins by the liver. This may be accompanied by "fatty liver" (p. 503). Ketogenesis is increased, owing to the accelerated degradation of fatty acids in the liver, in conjunction with a possible relative shortage of oxaloacetate (normally derived mainly from carbohydrate). Overloading of ketolytic mechanisms of the extrahepatic tissues soon results, followed by a significant degree of ketonemia and ketonuria. If the fasting period is prolonged to the point of depletion of available fat stores, the concentrations of blood lipids and ketone bodies may fall.

Diets deficient in protein result in subnormal rates of synthesis of serum lipoproteins. With the exception of outright deprivation, the level of plasma triglycerides and S_f 12 to 400 lipoproteins generally varies inversely with the carbohydrate intake.

DEPOSITION AND STORAGE OF LIPIDS

Role of Adipose Tissue in Lipid Metabolism

Although adipose tissue has long been considered a rather inert storage depot for fat, it is apparent from more recent investigations that this tissue is by no means static. On the contrary, it carries on all the metabolic processes characteristic of any active tissue, and, in addition, performs certain specialized functions of paramount importance in the metabolism of lipids. In addition to its storage function, it is probable that adipose tissue is the major site of synthesis of fatty acids in the organism, although the liver also is important in this regard.

Adipose cells probably belong to the reticuloendothelial system and may be considered well supplied with capillaries, if the fat-free protoplasmic mass is taken into account. The tissue is under nervous control, since conditions which cause sympathetic discharge result in the liberation of free fatty acids and thus a loss of fat, whereas mobilization is inhibited by denervation, although fat deposition still may occur in this condition. Different types of adipose tissue (e.g., brown and white) and adipose tissues located in various areas of the body exhibit differences in metabolism.

The respiratory quotient (p. 327) of adipose tissue from normally fed animals is 1.0, suggesting mainly carbohydrate metabolism, whereas that from fasting animals may approach a value of 0.71, characteristic of fat metabolism. Respiratory quotients from 1.27 to perhaps 1.6 are obtained from adipose tissue under conditions in which carbohydrate is being converted into fat.

Figure 19–15 contains a simplified scheme of those aspects of carbohydrate and fat

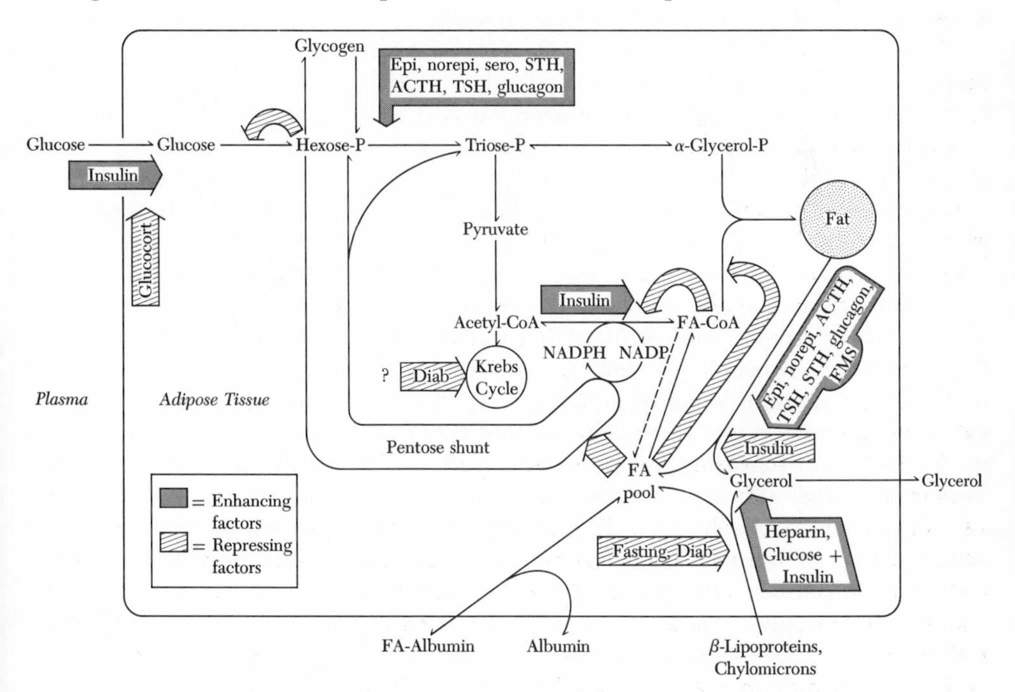

Figure 19-15. Metabolism of adipose tissue and its regulation. *ACTH,* Adrenocorticotropic hormone; *Diab,* diabetes mellitus; *Epi,* epinephrine; *FA,* fatty acids or fatty acyl; *FMS,* fat-mobilizing substance(s); *Glucocort,* adrenal glucocorticoid hormones; *Norepi,* norepinephrine; *Sero,* serotonin; *STH,* somatotropic hormone; *TSH,* thyrotropic hormone.

metabolism which are relevant to our discussion of adipose tissue, accompanied by indications of certain interchanges between adipose tissue and plasma.

Adipose tissue appears to contain the usual complement of metabolic pathways for the utilization of carbohydrate. Glucose uptake is facilitated by insulin and inhibited by adrenal glucocorticoid hormones. Phosphorylation of glucose is catalyzed by two kinases, as in liver (p. 395), a hexokinase which is not altered significantly by diet, (but is inhibited by excess glucose-6-phosphate) and a glucokinase (high K_m) which is decreased in activity by fasting and increased by refeeding. Under conditions of normal carbohydrate metabolism, glycogen is deposited, a usual prelude to the synthesis of fat in adipose tissue. Compared to liver or muscle, the store of glycogen is relatively small. Activities of the glycogen-synthesizing enzymes vary directly with the carbohydrate content of the diet. The glycogen phosphorylase reaction is facilitated by many of the same hormones which are effective in other tissues (p. 400). Both the glycolytic sequence of reactions and the pentose-shunt pathway are operative in adipose tissue. However, glycolysis is apparently irreversible and gluconeogenesis does not occur. With respect to fat synthesis, the glycolytic pathway has the task of providing the raw materials, e.g., the α-glycerol-phosphate (derived from dihydroxyacetone-phosphate) required for the glycerol backbone of the triglycerides and the acetyl-CoA fragments utilized in the synthesis of the fatty acids. The pentose pathway provides much of the NADPH required for the reductive steps in lipogenesis. Insulin facilitates all routes of carbohydrate metabolism almost equally, although in adipose tissue the pentose shunt appears to be favored slightly by the hormone. The pentose pathway is inhibited by free fatty acids (possible feedback control?) and by certain "lipolytic" hormones which may function through the free fatty acids. There are reports that the Q_{O_2} and functioning of the tricarboxylic acid cycle are depressed in adipose tissue of diabetic animals.

The system which synthesizes fatty acids in adipose tissue resembles that of liver in its facilitation by insulin and in the feedback inhibition of acetyl-CoA carboxylase by fatty acyl-CoA. Synthesis of mono-unsaturated fatty acids is decreased in diabetes and returned to normal by treatment with insulin. The rate of synthesis of fatty acids and of cholesterol in adipose tissue is related to the thyroid state (and basal metabolic rate). Formation of triglyceride, which collects in fat droplets, proceeds via the usual phosphatidic acid-diglyceride mechanism, utilizing the α-glycerol-phosphate provided by carbohydrate sources. Fat synthesis is inhibited by free fatty acids.

Adipose tissue contains a lipase which hydrolyzes stored fat to free fatty acids and glycerol. The glycerol is not reutilized, but is liberated into the plasma and metabolized by other tissues. Although glycerolkinase activity has been reported in both brown and white adipose tissue, it is not quantitatively significant. The fatty acids may be "reactivated" by the usual ATP-CoA system and thus may re-enter the pathways of fat synthesis. In addition to traversing the intracellular pathways of metabolism, the free or unesterified fatty acids also may combine with plasma albumin and be transported to liver and other tissues for utilization. The intracellular lipolytic system of adipose tissue is activated by a rather formidable list of factors, including direct sympathetic stimulation (norepinephrine), epinephrine (from the adrenals), glucagon, adrenocorticotropic hormone, thyrotropic hormone, somatotropic hormone, and various ill-defined fat-mobilizing substances (FMS) which probably originate in the anterior pituitary. Thyroid hormones and glucocorticoids also facilitate lipolysis, supposedly via a "permissive" effect on the action of the catecholamines. It is significant that the activity of this lipase is depressed by insulin (and, although of uncertain physiological importance, also by vasopressin, oxytocin, and prolactin).

In addition to the lipase concerned with hydrolysis of stored triglyceride, adipose tissue contains also a lipoprotein lipase. The location of this enzyme is controversial at present, evidence having been adduced for its association with the capillary wall on the one hand, and with the fat cell rather than stromal or vascular tissue elements on the other. In any case, this enzyme is responsible for hydrolysis of triglyceride entering adipose tissue from the circulation in the form of chylomicrons (representing fat from the diet) or low-density (β) lipoproteins (representing fat transported from the liver). In contrast to liver, in adipose tissue such fat undergoes complete hydrolysis and resynthesis before appearing in stored fat droplets. This lipoprotein lipase, similarly to that in other tissues, is liberated or activated by heparin and inhibited by protamine. Lipoprotein lipase activity (probably a reflection of quantity of enzyme) in adipose tissue is increased by administration of insulin and carbohydrate, decreased in diabetes mellitus and fasting.

Adipose tissue at any given time will be in some state of lipogenic-lipolytic balance, the equilibrium position depending on the factors previously enumerated. The influence of carbohydrate metabolism upon this balance is profound. In conditions of carbohydrate deprivation, such as starvation or diabetes mellitus, fatty acids and triglycerides are not synthesized. Decreases are observed in uptake of glucose by the tissue, provision of NADPH by the pentose pathway, synthesis of fatty acyl-CoA from carbohydrate, and provision of α-glycerolphosphate for fat formation. The lipolytic process goes on, however, (absence of usual inhibitory influence of insulin on the triglyceride lipase) converting the stored fat to free fatty acids, which are transported as albumin complexes to liver and other tissues. In these circumstances, adipose tissue is less able to take up chylomicrons and low-density lipoproteins, due to absence of the usual favorable influence of glucose and insulin on the lipoprotein lipase. The heavy influx of fatty acids into the liver results in greatly increased synthesis of low-density lipoproteins. Their liberation into the plasma, in the face of decreased uptake by adipose tissue, contributes to the resultant hyperlipemia. In contrast, adequate provision of insulin and carbohydrate to adipose tissue results in increased uptake of glucose, formation of NADPH through the pentose shunt, synthesis of fatty acyl-CoA from carbohydrate, provision of α-glycerolphosphate, and uptake and hydrolysis of fat from chylomicrons and low-density lipoproteins, accompanied by inhibition of hydrolysis of stored fat. The consequences are a diminution of the fatty acid pool, decrease of the net output of free fatty acids attached to albumin, and facilitation of fat storage.

In addition to the relatively slow-moving adjustments in the lipogenic-lipolytic balance described, there exists an emergency mechanism which is comparable to, and indeed probably functions simultaneously with, that which mobilizes glucose in "fight or flight" situations (p. 434). Stressful stimuli have a potent lipolytic influence, resulting in rapid liberation of free fatty acids from adipose tissue. (The utilization of fatty acids as fuel by muscle has been discussed previously.) Direct sympathetic stimulation and catecholamines liberated by the adrenals accelerate hydrolysis of the fat stores of adipose tissue. Glucocorticoids aid by their "permissive" action, and, indirectly, perhaps by inhibiting uptake of glucose. The physiological significance of direct stimulation by ACTH and the remaining "lipolytic" hormones in Figure 19–15 is uncertain.

Role of Liver in Lipid Metabolism

Although incidental mention has been made of the role of the liver in various aspects of lipid metabolism, it seems desirable to summarize here the pertinent information on this point.

1. The liver is an important site of synthesis of fatty acids from carbohydrate, and of cholesterol from acetate fragments.

2. The liver is probably the sole source of bile acids.

3. The phospholipids and cholesterol (free and esterified) of the plasma, and the lipoproteins in which they are incorporated, are synthesized by the liver.

4. In the other direction, the liver is the organ chiefly concerned in removal of phospholipids, cholesterol, and probably also certain species of lipoproteins from the plasma.

5. The liver is a major site of degradation of fatty acids of dietary or depot origin when the physiological state of the body calls on fat for the major provision of energy.

6. The liver is the only physiologically significant site of formation of ketone bodies.

7. The liver is one of the poles of the "liver-depot axis," along which fatty acids or fat is transported in one direction or the other in response to physiological needs. In this connection, the level of fat in the liver at a given time reflects the current status and net direction of the mobilization mechanisms.

Whereas previous discussions concerning liver have concentrated upon its role in synthesis and degradation of fatty acids and in ketone body metabolism, the following section will be devoted exclusively to phenomena of fat deposition in and mobilization from that organ.

Fatty Liver and Lipotropism

The amount of lipid in the liver at any given time is the resultant of several influences, some acting in conjunction with, some in opposition to others. (Normal total lipid about 4 per cent, three-fourths of which is phospholipid, one-fourth neutral fat.) This situation is illustrated in Figure 19–16. Factors that tend to increase the fat content of the liver are: (1) the synthesis of fatty acids in that organ from carbohydrate and protein, (2) influx of dietary lipid, and (3) mobilization of fatty acids from the depots to the liver. Decrease in liver fat results from: (1) mobilization of fat into the blood and to the depots from the liver, accompanied by cholesterol esters and phospholipids which are probably essential structural components of the lipoproteins carrying the triglyceride, and (2) degradation of the fatty acids within the liver itself. Normal levels of lipid in the liver are the result of maintenance of a proper balance between these factors. A *relative* increase or decrease in the rate of one or other of these processes can result in the accumulation of abnormal quantities of lipid in the liver, so-called "fatty liver." On this basis, five types of fatty liver can be distinguished, in theory at least, due to the following causes: (1) overfeeding of fat; (2) oversynthesis of fat from carbohydrate; (3) overmobilization from depots to liver; (4) undermobilization from liver to depots; (5) underutilization in the liver. Although it is doubtful whether all of these types have been observed in uncomplicated form, a summary of the probable general features characteristic of each is presented in Table 19-3).

Type 1. Overfeeding of fat results in the appearance of chylomicrons in the plasma. Although some are taken up by adipose and other tissues, and a small fraction may be cleared by lipoprotein lipase in the plasma, the major factor in removal of chylomicrons from the plasma is the liver, the fat content of which increases. (It is interesting to note that liver takes up chylomicrons by pinocytosis, forming cytoplasmic lipid inclusions, which may be stored as hepatic triglyceride without prior hydrolysis and resynthesis, at least initially.) In response to this increase in fat, the liver synthesizes larger quantities of low-density lipoproteins which it liberates into the plasma for transport to adipose

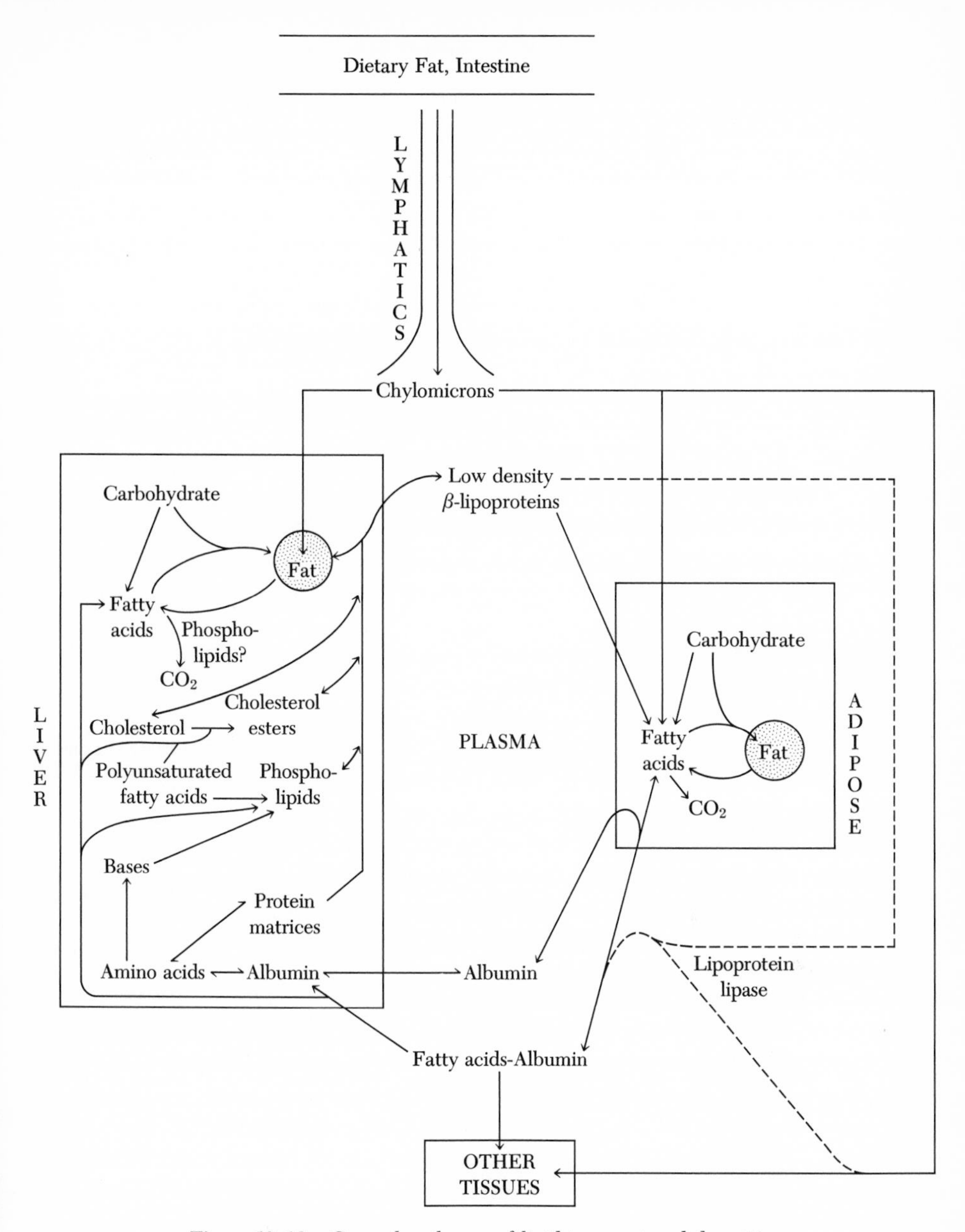

Figure 19-16. General pathways of lipid transport and deposition.

tissue, in which the stores of fat also increase. Depending upon the severity of the cause, the post-absorptive level of blood lipids may show no change or an increase in triglycerides and low-density lipoproteins. (In the unusual experimental condition in which the fat is highly unsaturated, the effects on the blood lipids are opposite to those given.) Although fatty livers of pure Type 1 can be produced in experimental animals, they are frequently deliberately aggravated by the imposition of conditions conducive to the development of Type 2 or 4. The lipids deposited in Type 1 reflect the composition of the dietary lipid, as would be expected. The "cholesterol fatty liver" may belong to this category, although it is usually considered in another context (Type 4).

TABLE 19-3. CLASSIFICATION OF FATTY LIVER

TYPE	EFFECT ON BLOOD LIPIDS (POSTABSORPTIVE)	EFFECT ON LIVER LIPIDS	EFFECT ON DEPOT LIPIDS	IMMEDIATE CAUSE	CURATIVE AGENTS* (LIPOTROPIC FACTORS)
1. Overfeeding of fat	None or increase	Increase	Increase	Excessive fat in diet	Choline and precursors or substitutes
2. Over-synthesis	None or increase	Increase	Increase	Excessive carbohydrate, cystine, B vitamins, alcohol in diet Deficiency of threonine, isoleucine Hydrazine	Choline and precursors or substitutes
3. Over-mobilization to liver	Increase, normal pattern Increase in free fatty acids	Increase, normal pattern	Decrease	Carbohydrate deprivation (dietary, hormonal) Hydrazine Fatty acid-mobilizing hormones	
4. Under-mobilization from liver	Decrease, especially in phospholipid and cholesterol	Increase in fat, cholesterol, and sometimes phospholipid (but decreased lecithin in choline deficiency)	Decrease	Deficiency of:	
				Protein	
				Essential fatty acids	
				Pyridoxine	Inositol, choline
				Pantothenic acid	Choline and precursors or substitutes
				Choline (direct or indirect)	Choline and precursors or substitutes, lipocaic
				Excess of:	
				Diet cholesterol	Choline and precursors or substitutes, plus inositol or lipocaic
				Biotin	Inositol, lipocaic, choline
				CCl_4, P, ethionine, puromycin	
5. Under-utilization	Increase in phospholipid and cholesterol Decrease later, if severe	Increase	Increase; decrease ?	Deficiency of pantothenic acid Rare earths (Ce)	Choline and precursors or substitutes

* Other than direct removal of cause.

Type 2. Ingestion of quantities of carbohydrate greatly in excess of the caloric requirement soon overloads the capacity of the cells which normally store glycogen. The surplus carbohydrate is channeled into synthesis of fatty acids and occurs very readily in liver and adipose tissue. The liver responds to the excessive amount of endogenous fat just as it does to that from the diet: increased quantities of low-density lipoproteins are synthesized and transported to the fat depots. Consequently, an increase in plasma triglyceride and low-density lipoproteins may be observed, depending again upon the severity of the condition. Oversynthesis from carbohydrate can result from forced feeding; it is more generally produced experimentally by the administration of excessive amounts of certain B vitamins (thiamine, biotin, riboflavin) or cystine, which seem to stimulate the appetite. Deficiency of threonine or isoleucine also increases fatty acid synthesis. Increased consumption of fat as well as carbohydrate sometimes lends to this type of fatty liver certain of the characteristics of Type 1. The situation is even more complex, however. The increase in general metabolic activity occasioned by the inclusion of large quantities of B vitamins or cystine in the diet results in a greater demand for certain factors, such as inositol and choline. The consequent *relative* deficit in these factors may produce fatty livers partially of Type 4.

Fatty livers produced by alcohol or hydrazine are due, in part, to increased incorporation of fatty acids into triglycerides. However, both types involve other mechanisms as well: alcohol and hydrazine both depress transport of fat out of the liver (Type 4); hydrazine stimulates mobilization of free fatty acids to the liver in addition (Type 3). The fatty liver of chronic alcoholism is probably the result of mutliple nutritional deficiency, but particularly deficiency of protein (Type 4).

Type 3. Fatty liver of this type is referred to by some as "physiological" fatty liver, because it represents merely an exaggeration of a normal process, the mobilization of fatty acids from the depots to the liver. The liver responds in characteristic fashion: larger quantities of low-density lipoproteins are synthesized and liberated into the plasma. The normal proportions among the various types of lipids in blood and liver are maintained: all are equally elevated in concentration. Fatty livers of this type develop in conditions involving greatly increased utilization of fat as fuel, which is the physiological equivalent of saying all conditions in which there is interference with the oxidation of carbohydrate. Such conditions exist in: (1) diabetes, human or experimental, of the hypoinsulin, hyperpituitary, or hyperadrenocortical type; (2) "pseudodiabetes" induced by phlorizin; (3) starvation; (4) carbohydrate deprivation. The fat which accumulates in the liver is derived from the fatty acids of the depots, the fat content of which decreases accordingly. (Owing to the non-utilization of carbohydrate, adipose tissue is unable to take up low-density lipoproteins, thus aggravating the hyperlipemia.) In addition to fatty liver and hyperlipemia, this condition is characterized by ketosis and, in advanced cases, acidosis.

As mentioned previously, the hydrazine fatty liver is partially caused by overmobilization of free fatty acids. Type 3 fatty liver may be produced also by administration of the "lipolytic" or fatty acid-mobilizing hormones (p. 498). Carbon tetrachloride mobilizes fatty acids through release of catecholamines, although this is not the major mechanism of CCl_4-fatty liver (see Type 4).

Type 4. Fatty liver of this type has been differentiated from the preceding type by being designated "pathological." It is accompanied by a decrease in plasma lipids (hypolipemia) which affects mainly the phospholipids and cholesterol esters. The pattern of liver lipids is also abnormal; fat, sometimes phospholipid, and cholesterol esters are especially increased, although lecithin is present in less than the usual proportion in the choline-deficient types. Fatty livers of this type may eventuate in cirrhosis of the liver and there may be associated hemorrhagic lesions in the kidneys. They appear to be caused by agents or conditions which produce either an absolute or a relative deficiency in certain of the ingredients used by the liver for synthesis of low-density lipoproteins, such as the protein matrix itself, or the building-blocks of its "structural" lipid moieties, such as cholesterol esters and phospholipids, viz., choline, inositol, and the polyunsaturated fatty acids. Factors interfering with the secretory mechanism for transporting β-lipoproteins into the blood would have the same effect.

Agents (e.g., choline, methionine, betaine, and inositol) which have the apparent effect of facilitating the removal of fat from the liver are said to be "lipotropic," the phenomenon itself being called "lipotropism." Antagonistic agents and the converse condition are "antilipotropic" and "antilipotropism," respectively.

Fatty livers of Type 4 may be roughly classified according to the causative agent or phenomenon:

(*a*) *Deficiency of Essential Fatty Acids.* The fatty livers due to deficiency of the essential fatty acids are cured only by the reintroduction of these substances into the diet. Since the phospholipids (and cholesterol esters) of the liver are characterized by a relatively high content of polyunsaturated fatty acids, it is surmised that a shortage of the latter substances results in impairment of synthesis or turnover of the former, thus interfering with the synthesis of the basic structure of the low-density lipoproteins.

(*b*) *Imbalance of B Vitamins.* Deficiencies of pyridoxine and pantothenic acid, and excessive amounts of biotin in the diet give rise to fatty livers, the etiologic factor of which is in dispute. It is possible that the fatty liver of pantothenic acid deficiency properly belongs to Type 5 rather than 4, since a shortage of CoA (of which pantothenic acid is a part) might be expected to result in impairment of the degradative mechanisms for fatty acids. Lack of pyridoxine and a surplus of biotin are said to elicit a greater demand upon the supply of inositol, thus supposedly interfering with the synthesis of inositol-containing phosphatides. Although the fatty livers in these conditions respond well to inositol, this explanation leaves much to be desired. It may be noted that pyridoxine deficiency interferes (although probably indirectly) with certain interconversions of polyunsaturated fatty acids, whereas the involvement of biotin in the malonyl-CoA mechanism of fatty acid synthesis suggests the possibility that excessive amounts of this vitamin may result in oversynthesis of fatty acids, thus transferring the biotin fatty liver to Type 2.

(*c*) *"Cholesterol" Fatty Livers.* Fatty livers resulting from administration of excessive amounts of cholesterol are sometimes regarded as belonging to Type 4, although they may perhaps as readily fit the requirements of Type 1. One explanation advanced for the former classification is that cholesterol may compete with phospholipids for the polyunsaturated fatty acids, since the acids found in cholesterol esters are highly unsaturated. In support of this point of view, it may be noted that elevation of the level of dietary cholesterol increases the requirement for essential fatty acids; also, in cholesterol fatty livers, phospholipid turnover is depressed.

(*d*) *Choline Deficiency.* Certain fatty livers of Type 4 are due, more or less directly, to a deficiency of choline. Since choline is synthesized by the successive methylation of ethanolamine, it is true that induced deficiencies of the methyl group produce fatty livers, solely, however, because of the resulting shortage of choline. The use of the phenomenon of lipotropism to demonstrate the reaction of transmethylation (p. 589) has to some extent obscured the essential point that choline, and not the methyl group or transmethylation per se, is the lipotropic agent. This is indicated by the observation that certain compounds, completely incapable of transmethylation, are nevertheless lipotropic, and, in some cases, are actually incorporated into the phospholipids as substitutes for choline. Such compounds are arsenocholine (arsenic in place of the choline N), sulfocholine (sulfur in place of N), and the triethyl analog of choline.

An indication of the probable importance of choline and other components of phospholipids for the synthesis of plasma lipoproteins is furnished by the observation that, in experimental animals, choline deficiency results in lowering the concentration of the high-density lipoproteins and virtual disappearance of the low-density lipoproteins. In man, lowering the dietary protein and choline, without changing dietary fat or calories, results in decreases in blood cholesterol and low-density lipoproteins.

Animals maintained on diets deficient in the usual sources of preformed methyl groups (choline, methionine, betaine), and also in the vitamins necessary for synthesis of methyl groups from appropriate precursors (folic acid, B_{12}), develop fatty livers of Type 4. These fatty livers are cured by the methyl donors mentioned above, by choline itself or its proper analogs, and are at least alleviated by folic acid and vitamin B_{12}.

A deficiency of choline can be induced also by inclusion in the diet of compounds which will compete with ethanolamine for available methyl groups. Nicotinic acid or amide and guanidoacetic acid, for example, are methylated in the body to N^1-methylnicotinamide and creatine, respectively. Administration of greatly excessive quantities of these compounds depletes the supply of methyl groups available for the synthesis of choline, and fatty liver results.

Pancreatectomized animals maintained adequately with insulin develop fatty livers, not of the overmobilization type characteristic of diabetes, but of Type 4. The condition is alleviated by the administration of raw pancreas. According to one school of thought, "lipocaic," a purported *internal* secretion of the pancreas, is the lipotropic agent responsible. The majority believe that an *external* secretion of the pancreas is involved, probably a proteolytic enzyme which specifically facilitates the liberation of methionine from the proteins of the food.

Other substances exert a lipotropic action the mechanism of which has not been explained, e.g., estrogens. Certain androgens and growth hormone are lipotropic in the case of experimental fatty liver induced by feeding ethionine.

(*e*) *Deficiency of Protein.* Lack of adequate protein (of good biological value) in the diet, such as occurs in many parts of the world (kwashiorkor), depresses the rate of synthesis of the β-lipoproteins and leads to fatty liver of Type 4. Protein deficiency of the dietary type also may be a superimposed factor in other types of fatty liver, e.g., in chronic alcoholism. Interference with the mechanism of synthesis of protein in the liver can lead to the same result; such appears to be the case after administration of the antibiotics azaserine and puromycin, ethionine (analog of methionine), pyrazolopyrimidines (analogs of adenine), orotic acid (intermediate in pyrimidine synthesis), and certain hepatotoxic agents such as phosphorus and carbon tetrachloride, although some of these compounds more directly depress cellular ATP concentrations and others are said also to affect the mechanisms of secretion of β-lipoproteins [see (*f*)]. The hepatotoxic agents represent a particularly complex situation. Their administration frequently results in an initial rise in plasma lipid, due, at least in the case of CCl_4, to a catecholamine-mediated mobilization of free fatty acids from the depots. This is followed by a hypolipemic phase, presumably reflecting interference with synthetic or secretory mechanisms of lipoprotein. As a further complexity, it may be mentioned that it is possible to counteract or mitigate with choline or methionine the fatty infiltration of the liver caused by hepatotoxic agents, if the therapeutic agent is given promptly after administration of the toxic agent, or better, prophylactically.

(*f*) *Inhibition of Secretion.* As noted in the preceding section, it is not possible to decide in all cases whether certain inhibitors act primarily on the mechanisms of synthesis or of secretion of the lipoproteins. There is some evidence that fatty liver following alcohol or hydrazine administration is partly due to interference with lipoprotein secretion.

Type 5. As suggested previously, it is possible that the fatty livers of pantothenic acid deficiency are of this type, i.e., underutilization. Poisoning by salts of the rare-earth elements (e.g., cerium) also appears to cause underutilization, by inhibition of the mitochondrial system which oxidizes fatty acids. Finally, as was noted in the discussion of functions of the phospholipids, there is some evidence that normal metabolism of phospholipids appears to be essential for proper oxidation of fatty acids, although the mechanism of this relationship is unknown. Such a phenomenon may also impart to the choline-deficient variety of Type 4 fatty liver some of the characteristics of Type 5.

ENDOCRINE INFLUENCES IN LIPID METABOLISM

Hormones play an important role in the coordination of various phases of lipid metabolism and in their integration with carbohydrate metabolism (p. 443). The most important hormones in this connection are insulin, the 11-oxygenated adrenal cortical hormones, and anterior hypophyseal factors (growth hormone, or some principle intimately associated with it; adrenocorticotropic hormone, acting via the adrenal cortex). The metabolic effects of these factors are considered in detail elsewhere (Ch. 26). It will suffice here merely to summarize their important effects on lipid metabolism.

Insulin (p. 723)

Administration of insulin is followed by increased synthesis of fatty acids from 2-C fragments (lipogenesis), representing one phase of the increased utilization of glucose induced by this agent. This is dependent, in part at least, upon stimulation of glucose-6-phosphate dehydrogenase activity, with consequent increased production of NADPH via the hexose monophosphate oxidative pathway. This cofactor is a requirement for synthesis of long-chain fatty acids. Insulin also induces synthesis of acetyl carboxylase, a rate-limiting step in the synthesis of fatty acid, and also of a microsomal oxygenase necessary for monoene synthesis from saturated fatty acids (p. 462).

Insulin increases synthesis of triglyceride in both adipose tissue and liver. It decreases the rate of release of free fatty acids from adipose tissue with consequent decrease in their concentration in the blood plasma.

Ketogenesis is depressed by insulin, another consequence of the stimulation of glucose utilization in the liver, which increases the supply of oxaloacetate for incorporation of 2-C fragments from fatty acid into the Krebs cycle.

In the absence of adequate amounts of insulin, e.g., in pancreatic diabetes, decreased lipogenesis and increased ketogenesis, referable to the insulin actions indicated above, are accompanied by acceleration of mobilization of fatty acids from the fat depots, with consequent increase in blood and liver lipids. Insulin deficiency is accompanied also by increased synthesis of cholesterol (liver) from 2-C fragments from the increased amounts of fatty acid mobilized from the fat stores; the plasma cholesterol rises.

Adrenocortical Hormones (p. 701)

The principal effects of glucocorticoids on lipid metabolism are related to their effects on carbohydrate metabolism and are therefore conditioned by such factors as the adequacy of insulin secretion and carbohydrate intake and utilization. When these are inadequate, administration of glucocorticoids produces increased lipolysis in adipose tissue and increase in the rate of release of unesterified fatty acids into the blood plasma. Under these conditions of depression of utilization of carbohydrate and increased supply of free fatty acid to the liver, the oxidative capacity of this tissue for these substances is exceeded and they consequently enter other metabolic pathways, i.e., ketogenesis, and synthesis of cholesterol, phosphatides and triglycerides, with the production of ketonemia and ketonuria, hypercholesterolemia, hyperlipemia, and increase in liver fat.

Adenohypophyseal Hormones (p. 736)

In addition to effects mediated by stimulation of the adrenal cortex, ACTH exerts a direct action on adipose tissue, increasing lipolysis and mobilization of unsaturated fatty acids into the blood plasma. As a consequence, there is increased ketogenesis and decrease in the respiratory quotient. This "adipokinetic action" requires the presence of adrenocortical hormones. Somatotropin exerts an effect on lipid metabolism similar to that of ACTH.

Epinephrine (p. 698)

Epinephrine stimulates mobilization of unesterified fatty acids from adipose tissue. The presence of adrenocortical and thyroid hormones is necessary for this action. There is an associated increase in liver lipids and in ketogenesis.

Thyroid Hormone (p. 713)

Administration of thyroid hormones is followed by a decrease in plasma cholesterol, phospholipids, and lipoproteins of the S_f 10 to 20 class, which increase following thyroidectomy. Although the precise mechanism of action is not clear, it may involve acceleration of both biosynthesis and catabolism of cholesterol in liver and extrahepatic tissues, the catabolic effect predominating over the anabolic.

The stimulation of oxidation which follows administration of thyroid hormones may include fatty acids. However, they also increase the rate of release of unesterified fatty acids from adipose tissue with consequent increase in their concentration in the blood and, in the absence of adequate amounts of carbohydrate and insulin, increased ketogenesis and ketonemia. These effects are believed to be due to the action of the thyroid hormones in increasing the sensitivity of adipose tissue to the actions of epinephrine.

METABOLIC INTERRELATIONS OF LIPIDS, CARBOHYDRATES, AND PROTEINS

Figure 19–17 illustrates the metabolic interrelations between the major types of lipids and other foodstuffs.

The lipids do not contribute significant quantities of material to the synthesis of amino acids. Glycerol is the only major raw material which may be provided for the synthesis of carbohydrate from lipid sources, although it is probable that the usual net flow of this substance is in the reverse direction. The characteristic relation of lipids to other foodstuffs involves either synthesis of the former from the latter, or some type of coupling between the rates of synthesis and degradation of the two families of compounds.

Carbohydrate is converted to lipid in various ways. Small amounts of galactose (and in some cases glucose) are undoubtedly provided for the synthesis of cerebrosides and gangliosides. The glycerol moiety of the triglycerides and glycerophosphatides is

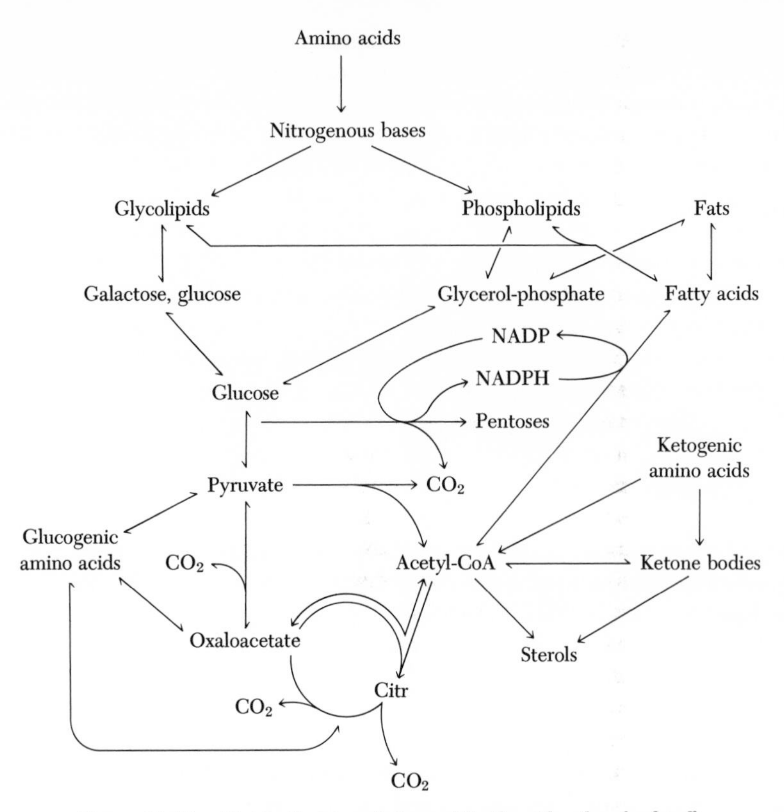

Figure 19-17. Metabolic interrelations of lipids with other foodstuffs.

formed readily from the intermediates of glycolysis. However, the major conversion in this direction, and the one usually meant by the phrase, "synthesis of fat from carbohydrate," is the formation of fatty acids from acetyl units, which are in turn derived from the oxidative decarboxylation of pyruvate. The irreversibility of this decarboxylation, incidentally, forms the basis of the current view that fatty acids cannot be converted into carbohydrate.

The concluding statement of the previous paragraph seems to be belied by many experiments with isotopes, in which labeled carbon atoms from fatty acids have been shown to be incorporated into glucose or glycogen. The contradiction is more apparent than real, however. Inspection of the reactions of the tricarboxylic acid cycle subsequent to the condensation of acetyl-CoA and oxaloacetate reveals that the two carbon atoms lost as CO_2 from the cycle are not the same atoms which entered the cycle as acetate. The carbon atoms of the acetate finally appear in the regenerated oxaloacetate, which can form pyruvate by decarboxylation. Hence a labeled atom from acetate or a fatty acid can be incorporated into glucose or glycogen. Nevertheless, the "material balance" shows that two carbon atoms have reacted with a molecule of oxaloacetate to form two molecules of CO_2 and regenerate the oxaloacetate. Since no additional molecules of oxaloacetate are formed, no net synthesis of pyruvate or carbohydrate from fatty acids has occurred, despite the transfer of carbon atoms from one to the other.

Amino acids contribute to the synthesis of lipids. Ethanolamine, choline, serine, and sphingosine, for example, components of the phospholipids, are derived from the pathways of protein metabolism. The ketogenic amino acids form acetate or acetoacetate, from which fatty acids can be derived. The glucogenic amino acids, directly or indirectly, form pyruvate, which can be used for the synthesis of either carbohydrate or fatty acids.

An intimate quantitative relationship exists between the metabolism of fatty acids and of carbohydrate. When the rate of oxidation of carbohydrate, the preferred fuel of the body, falters, fatty acids are mobilized from the depots to the liver, by a mechanism involving an altered metabolic equilibrium between lipogenesis and lipolysis within the adipose cells. The rate of degradation of fatty acids to acetyl-CoA in the liver is then increased. Simultaneously, the rate of utilization of acetyl-CoA fragments for the synthesis of fatty acids is decreased. Since the decreased rate of catabolism of carbohydrate does not permit the liver to synthesize increased quantities of oxaloacetate to keep pace with the greatly augmented production of acetyl-CoA, a larger than normal fraction of the latter molecules is unable to enter the Krebs cycle. The resulting increase in ketogenesis and its consequences have been described previously (p. 469). It would appear, then, from the foregoing remarks that, whereas carbohydrate may be considered a competing substrate to fatty acids in one sense, it is a necessary partner in their oxidation in another.

Although this discussion of the metabolism of fatty acids and carbohydrates has stressed the net flow of metabolites in one direction or another, it may be well to conclude with the reminder that, regardless of net synthesis or catabolism or steady states, all groups of molecules connected metabolically interchange material continually, as indicated by isotopic labeling. Whether the physiological situation of the moment calls for oxidation predominantly of carbohydrate or of fat, a certain amount of conversion of carbohydrate to fat always takes place. These and other aspects of the "dynamic state of the body constituents" are considered in greater detail in connection with the metabolism of protein (p. 541).

BIBLIOGRAPHY

GENERAL

Annual Review of Biochemistry
Annual Review of Physiology
Baldwin, E.: Dynamic Aspects of Biochemistry, Chapter 21, Cambridge, Cambridge University Press, 1963.
Dawson, R. M. C., and Rhodes, D. N. (eds.): Metabolism and Physiological Significance of Lipids, New York, John Wiley & Sons, Inc., 1964.
Popják, G., and Grant, J. K. (eds.): The Control of Lipid Metabolism, New York, Academic Press, Inc., 1963.
Strickland, K. P.: The biogenesis of the lipids, Chapter 3 in Bernfeld, P. (ed.): Biogenesis of Natural Compounds, New York, The Macmillan Company, 1963.

DIGESTION, ABSORPTION

Desnuelle, P.: Pancreatic lipase, Advances Enzymol. *23:*129, 1961.
Frazer, A. C. (ed.): Biochemical Problems of Lipids, Amsterdam, Elsevier Publishing Company, 1963.
Johnston, J. M.: Recent developments in the mechanism of fat absorption, Advances in Lipid Research *1:*105, 1963.
Wilson, T. H.: Intestinal Absorption, Chapters 7 and 8, Philadelphia, W. B. Saunders Company, 1962.

ADIPOSE TISSUE

Kinsell, L. W. (ed.): Adipose Tissue as an Organ, Springfield, Ill., Charles C Thomas, 1962.
Renold, A. E., and Cahill, G. F., Jr. (eds.): Handbook of Physiology, Section 5, Adipose Tissue, Washington, American Physiological Society, 1965.
Rodahl, K., and Issekutz, B. (eds.): Fat as a Tissue, New York, McGraw-Hill Book Company, 1964.

FATS, FATTY ACIDS, KETONE BODIES

Bressler, R.: The biochemistry of ketosis, Ann. New York Acad. Sci. *104:*735, 1963.
Engel, F. L., and Amatruda, T. T., Jr.: Hormonal aspects of ketosis, Ann. New York Acad. Sci., *104:*753, 1963.

Favarger, P.: Comparative evaluation of lipid biosynthesis, Advances in Lipid Research *2:*447, 1964.
Fritz, I. B.: Carnitine and its role in fatty acid metabolism, Advances in Lipid Research *1:*286, 1963.
Green, D. E.: Fatty acid oxidation, Progr. Chem. Fats and Other Lipids *6:*87, 1963.
Gibson, D. M.: Fatty acid biosynthesis, Progr. Chem. Fats and Other Lipids *6:*117, 1963.
Pascaud, M.: Chromatographic investigations in fatty acid biosynthesis, Advances in Lipid Research *1:*253, 1963.
Wolf, G. (ed.): Recent Research on Carnitine: Its Relation to Lipid Metabolism, Cambridge, Mass., M.I.T. Press, 1965.

PHOSPHOLIPIDS, GLYCOLIPIDS, STEROLS

Ansell, G. B., and Hawthorne, J. N.: Phospholipids, Amsterdam, Elsevier Publishing Company, 1964.
Danielsson, H.: Present status of research on catabolism and excretion of cholesterol, Advances in Lipid Research *1:*335, 1963.
Dawson, R. M. C.: The metabolism of phospholipids, Chapter 6 in Florkin, M., and Mason, H. S. (eds.): Comparative Biochemistry, Vol. 3, New York, Academic Press, Inc., 1962.
Grant, J. K.: Lipids: Steroid metabolism, Chapter 3 in Florkin, M., and Mason, H. S. (eds.): Comparative Biochemistry, Vol. 3, New York, Academic Press, Inc., 1962.
Hawthorne, J. N., and Kemp, P.: The brain phosphoinositides, Advances in Lipid Research *2:*127, 1963.
Staple, E.: The biosynthesis of steroids, Chapter 4 in Bernfeld, P. (ed.): Biogenesis of Natural Compounds, New York, The Macmillan Company, 1963.

LIPOPROTEINS, TRANSPORT

Dole, V. P., and Hamlin, J. T., III: Particulate fat in lymph and blood, Physiol. Rev. *42:*674, 1962.
Lindgren, F. T., and Nichols, A. V.: Structure and function of human serum lipoproteins, Chapter 11 in Putnam, F. W. (ed.): The Plasma Proteins, Vol. 2, New York, Academic Press, Inc., 1960.
Meng, H. C., Coniglio, J. G., LeQuire, V. S., Mann, G. V., and Merrill, J. M. (eds.): Proceedings of an International Symposium on Lipid Transport, Springfield, Ill., Charles C Thomas, 1964.
Robinson, D. S.: The clearing factor lipase and its action in the transport of fatty acids between blood and the tissues, Advances in Lipid Research *1:*134, 1963.
Searcy, R. L., and Bergquist, L. M.: Liprotein Chemistry in Health and Disease, Springfield, Ill., Charles C Thomas, 1962.

HORMONAL INFLUENCES

Ball, E. G. and Jungas, R. L.: Some effects of hormones on the metabolism of adipose tissue, Recent Progress in Hormone Research *20:*183, 1964.
Engel, F. L.: Extra-adrenal actions of adrenocorticotropin, Vitamins and Hormones *19:*189, 1961.
Fritz, I. B.: Factors influencing the rate of long-chain fatty acid oxidation and synthesis in mammalian systems, Physiol. Rev. *41:*52, 1961.
Jeanrenaud, B.: Dynamic aspects of adipose tissue metabolism, Metabolism *10:*535, 1961.
Krahl, M. E.: The Action of Insulin on Cells, New York, Academic Press, Inc., 1961.
Litwack, G. and Kritchevsky, D. (eds.): Actions of Hormones on Molecular Processes, New York, John Wiley & Sons, Inc., 1964.
Winegrad, A. I.: Endocrine effects on adipose tissue metabolism, Vitamins and Hormones *20:*142, 1962.

CHAPTER 20

METABOLISM OF NUCLEIC ACIDS AND RELATED SUBSTANCES

THE IMPORTANCE of the nucleic acids and their derivatives is of quite a different sort from that ascribed to the other classes of metabolites. It is doubtful whether significant quantities of energy are derived from the catabolism of nucleic acids, neither they nor their constituents are dietary essentials, and their only "structural" role appears to be in the composition of the chromosome. Rather, the chief role of nucleic acids and related compounds appears to be that of metabolic specialists, involved (1) in controlling the general pattern of metabolism and (2) in aiding the catalysis of certain particular reactions. The former category includes the genes, bacterial "transforming factors," viruses, and the cytoplasmic regulators of protein synthesis; the latter includes the adenylic system and the free nucleotides which act as coenzymes.

In the strict sense, the discussion of the compounds considered in this chapter should include the nucleoproteins, since the nucleic acids are (chemically) nothing more than prosthetic groups. However, although something is known of the identity and characteristics of a few of the nucleoproteins native to the cell, little information is available on the metabolism or biological function of these molecules. Aside from certain recent speculations on the role of histones in the function of DNA, which will be mentioned at the appropriate point, it will be assumed that the protein components of the nucleoproteins follow the general pathways of protein metabolism.

The nucleic acids are high polymers of strongly acidic character. Their monomeric components are the mononucleotides, consisting of base, sugar, and phosphoric acid. Two series of bases are involved, purines and pyrimidines, and two pentose sugars, ribose and deoxyribose. Consequently, it will be necessary to consider the metabolism of these individual building blocks of the nucleic acids, as well as that of the macromolecules themselves.

In addition to the usual summary of the digestion and absorption of the nucleic acids, brief mention will be made of their intracellular localization, a topic of considerable relevance from the standpoints of their intermediary metabolism and metabolic role. Then, in order to provide a background for the more specific discussions to follow, a general survey is presented of the overall metabolism of the nucleic acids and their constituents. This is followed by detailed discussions of the intermediary metabolism of the several constituents of the nucleic acids, i.e., pentoses, purines, and pyrimidines. Consideration of the metabolism of the macromolecules themselves (ribonucleic acid, RNA; deoxyribonucleic acid, DNA) is preceded by a section devoted to a discussion of the synthesis and degradation of the "free" nucleotides (adenylic system and nucleotide coenzymes). Following a discussion of the biological significance of the nucleic acids and related compounds, the chapter concludes with a brief consideration of interrelations between the metabolism of nucleic acids and that of other classes of foodstuffs.

DIGESTION AND ABSORPTION

The course of digestion of nucleoproteins is discussed elsewhere (pp. 264–5) and requires only brief review here. Their protein components undergo the same changes as those described for other proteins, in the progress of which the constituent nucleic acids (RNA and DNA) are liberated. These are hydrolyzed by the enzymes, ribonuclease and deoxyribonuclease, respectively, of the pancreatic juice. The products of ribonuclease action on RNA consist of pyrimidine mononucleotides and a mixture of oligonucleotides containing chains of purine nucleotides terminated by pyrimidine nucleoside-2′ or 3′-phosphates, the intermediates being pyrimidine nucleoside-2′, 3′-cyclic phosphates. Deoxyribonuclease forms from DNA a small amount of mononucleotides and a much larger amount of oligonucleoside-5′-phosphates, linkages between deoxypurine and deoxypyrimidine nucleotides being split preferentially. Completion of hydrolysis of both types of nucleic acid to the stage of mononucleotides is catalyzed by a phosphodiesterase of the intestinal mucosa.

The extent to which further degradation occurs in the lumen of the intestine is not clear. The intestinal mucosa, and also other tissues, contains non-specific phosphatases (alkaline and acid) which hydrolyze the sugar-phosphate bond of mononucleotides ("nucleotidase" action), forming nucleosides (purine and pyrimidine) and phosphoric acid. The presence of these phosphatases in the intestinal lumen probably is due to exfoliated mucosal cells, in which case the "digestion" of nucleotides occurs primarily intracellularly as part of the process of absorption. The same may be said concerning "nucleosidases," found in the intestinal fluids, which split nucleosides into their pentose and base components. There is evidence that this reaction involves phosphorolysis rather than hydrolysis (i.e., "nucleosidase" = nucleoside phosphorylase), which would localize it as an intracellular rather than a digestive process. It appears likely, therefore, that the end-products of nucleic acid digestion are largely if not entirely purine and pyrimidine nucleotides, some question existing as to participation of phosphatases and nucleosidases in the process of digestion.

The nucleotides are absorbed readily from the small intestine. As indicated above, further degradation of nucleotides may occur within the intestinal mucosal cells, i.e., to nucleosides and phosphoric acid, through the action of phosphatases. Some of the nucleosides may also be split here (nucleoside phosphorylase) to bases and pentose. In general, pyrimidine nucleoside breakdown appears to be a slow process. Some of the cytidine produced from cytidylate in the mucosa is deaminated to uridine, which is slowly converted to uracil. Adenosine is similarly converted to inosine, which then follows the usual catabolic pathway of purines (but within the mucosa) to hypoxanthine, xanthine, and urate. Some guanine forms xanthine and joins this pathway. The ribose-1-phosphate, produced as a result of nucleoside phosphorylase action, appears to be disposed of within the mucosal cells. Absorption occurs mainly via the portal circulation, the bulk of the products of digestion and intestinal metabolism of nucleic acids, as of proteins, reaching the liver before entering the systemic bloodstream.

INTRACELLULAR LOCALIZATION OF NUCLEIC ACIDS AND POLYNUCLEOTIDASES

DNA is confined to the nucleus of the cell, except for a very small amount in the mitochondria, which are thought to be self-duplicating organelles. RNA is found in both the nucleus and the cytoplasm; in the latter location it occurs in the mitochondrial, microsomal, and particle-free fractions. In the liver cell less than 4 per cent of the total RNA is found in the mitochondria, 80 per cent is found in the microsomal fraction (contained entirely within the ribosome particles), and 10 to 15 per cent is found in the soluble phase of the cytoplasm. RNA accounts for 20 per cent of the total nucleic acid content of the nucleus and is located both in the nucleolus and in the chromosomes. The bulk of nuclear DNA is located in the chromosomes, although some is associated with the nucleolus; this latter fraction represents an extension of chromosomal material. These matters are discussed in greater detail elsewhere (p. 773).

Ribonuclease with an alkaline optimum pH has a rather diffuse distribution throughout the cell; "acid" ribonuclease is found in the lysosomes. A magnesium-dependent deoxyribonuclease (alkaline-neutral pH optimum) is found in the mitochondria, whereas the "acid" deoxyribonuclease again is located in the lysosomes, along with other hydrolases having acidic pH optima.

SURVEY OF NUCLEIC ACID METABOLISM

For convenience, the metabolism of the nucleic acids may be subdivided into (1) the metabolism of components, (a) non-nitrogenous and (b) nitrogenous, and (2) the metabolism of the macromolecules. The overall picture of nucleic acid metabolism is illustrated in Figure 20–1.

Non-nitrogenous Constituents

Phosphate is readily obtained from the diet and endogenous sources. The ester phosphate groups found in nucleotides originate via kinase reactions utilizing ATP. Phosphate is excreted in the urine as inorganic phosphate at the end of its metabolic career.

Ribose and deoxyribose are derived more or less directly from glucose or its metabolites. It is doubtful whether dietary pentoses contribute significantly to the synthesis of nucleic acids. The catabolic pathways of the pentoses probably proceed via the pentose-shunt cycle.

Nitrogenous Constituents

Purines liberated by digestion of nucleic acids are largely catabolized directly to waste products, with the exception of a small amount of adenine that is incorporated into

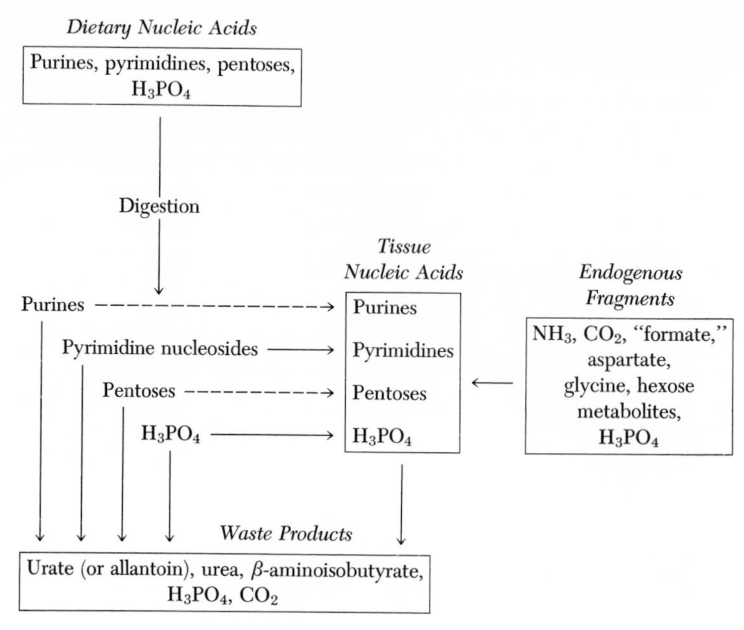

Figure 20-1. Overall metabolism of the constituents of the nucleic acids.

nucleic acids. However, there is great species variation in this respect. Pyrimidine nucleotides are probably not digested completely to the stage of the free bases; significant quantities of pyrimidine nucleosides (or nucleotides) are utilized for the synthesis of nucleic acids. Small metabolic fragments (NH_3, CO_2, "formate," glycine) are drawn upon extensively for the formation of both the purine and the pyrimidine moieties of nucleic acids, preformed bases derived from the diet playing a relatively more important role in the case of the pyrimidines than of the purines.

The unused bases of the diet, as well as those arising from the catabolism of the nucleic acids, are degraded to waste products which are excreted in the urine. Purines eventuate in urate in man and the higher apes, in allantoin in other mammals. Pyrimidines form urea, and β-aminoisobutyrate and β-alanine, both of which are largely degraded to urea.

Nucleic Acids

The mechanism of synthesis of the macromolecules is currently under intensive investigation; nucleoside triphosphates appear to be involved, polymerized by enzymes of the pyrophosphorylase type. Degradation of the nucleic acids probably involves the polynucleotidases, phosphatases or specific mononucleotidases, nucleoside phosphorylases or nucleosidases, and various deaminases and oxidoreductases which attack the bases.

RNA appears to be synthesized or "turned over" at a rate correlated (not always closely, however) with protein synthesis and growth of the cell. Synthesis of DNA apparently is limited mainly to cell multiplication.

METABOLISM OF PENTOSES

Synthesis and Degradation

Since these topics are discussed in detail elsewhere (p. 416), it will suffice here merely to summarize the available information. Ribose appears to arise from glucose partly via an aerobic pathway involving, essentially, oxidative decarboxylation of the phosphorylated hexonic acid, but mainly via a non-oxidative pathway involving the transaldolase-transketolase reactions. Ribose catabolism may proceed by continued cycling of the oxidative pentose phosphate pathway, resulting in stepwise degradation to CO_2, or via degradation (by means of the glycolytic sequence of reactions) of triose and hexose intermediates arising in the pentose pathway.

Deoxyribose is not synthesized directly from a hexose. Although it can be formed by condensation of acetaldehyde and D-glyceraldehyde phosphate under the influence of a deoxyribose aldolase, this reaction is more likely a part of the catabolic than the anabolic pathway of deoxyribose. There is now appreciable evidence of a direct conversion of ribose to deoxyribose while the pentoses are integral parts of nucleotides. The transformation appears to occur on the nucleoside diphosphate level.

Incorporation into Nucleosides, Nucleotides, and Nucleic Acids

As indicated in connection with the metabolism of the purines (below), ribose apparently is coupled to the precursors of the purine ring quite early in the sequence of reactions leading to the synthesis of the base. Ribose joins in the synthesis of pyrimidines later in the sequence; a type of pyrophosphorylase reaction is involved. Preformed purines and pyrimidines participate in nucleoside phosphorylase reactions, leading to formation of nucleosides, which may be converted to nucleotides by ATP and kinases. Nucleoside triphosphates are precursors of the nucleic acids.

METABOLISM OF PURINES

Synthesis

Considering the relatively slight anabolic utilization of preformed purines and pyrimidines by the mammalian organism, the synthesis of these compounds de novo must be regarded as one of the major preliminary processes in the formation of the nucleic acids. It has been suggested that, although liver, intestinal mucosa, and thymus are capable of synthesizing purines, most tissues are not and must rely upon external supplies. Liver is the primary source of purines to tissues in mammals. Since many of the enzymes of purine and pyrimidine catabolism are absent in hepatoma and regenerating liver, it is probable that the bases are conserved and recycled in these tissues.

The origin of the atoms comprising the purine skeleton is illustrated in the upper part of Figure 20–2; the detailed reactions involved are indicated in the lower part. It will be observed that the purine skeleton is synthesized from small fragments. N-1 is derived from the amino group of aspartate, N-3 and N-9 from the amide nitrogen of glutamine, C-2 and C-8 from "formate" (carried by a coenzyme of the tetrahydrofolate type), C-6 from CO_2, whereas the sequence C-4–C-5–N-7 is derived from glycine.

Synthesis of the purines begins with the formation of phosphoribosyl pyrophosphate,

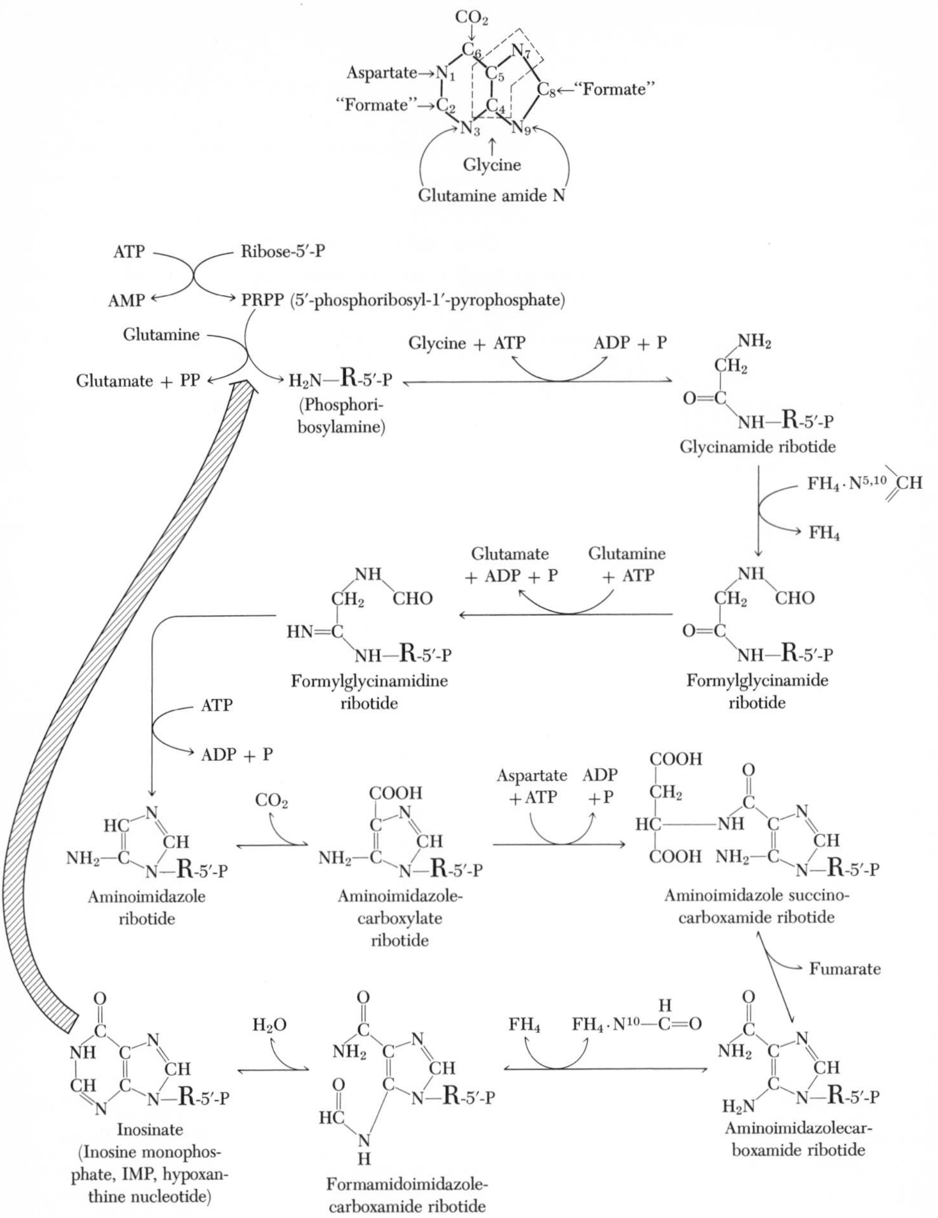

Figure 20-2. Synthesis of purines. Striated arrow indicates negative feedback inhibition. FH_4, tetrahydrofolate.

an intermediate also in pyrimidine synthesis. This is converted to an amino sugar, by reaction with glutamine, a step which is inhibited (although not as strongly as a subsequent reaction also involving glutamine) by certain compounds which act as metabolic antagonists to glutamine. The amino sugar condenses with glycine to form glycinamide ribotide, which then is formylated by anhydroformyl-tetrahydrofolate. This and other reactions of nucleic acid metabolism involving folate coenzymes may be inhibited by metabolic antagonists of folate (e.g., aminopterin, p. 673), which prevent the reduction of folate to dihydro- and tetrahydrofolate. Formylglycinamide ribotide is aminated to formylglycinamidine ribotide by reaction with glutamine, a step strongly inhibited by O-diazoacetyl-L-serine (azaserine) and 6-diazo-5-oxo-L-norleucine (DON), which are metabolic antagonists of glutamine (p. 664). Closure of the ring and reaction with a molecule of CO_2 produce aminoimidazolecarboxylate ribotide. This compound is converted to an amide by condensation with aspartate and cleavage of fumarate from the product, reactions very similar to those involved in the formation and breakdown of argininosuccinate in the ornithine cycle. Aminoimidazolecarboxamide ribotide (the free base of which accumulates in cultures of bacteria inhibited by sulfonamides [p. 665]) is next formylated to a formamido derivative, the formyl carrier in this case being formyltetrahydrofolate. Cyclization of the remaining ring forms inosinate, the parent compound of all the purines.

The amidotransferase which forms phosphoribosylamine is subject to control through end-product feedback inhibition by inosinate (and other purine nucleotides). Certain purine analogs (e.g., mercaptopurine, p. 674) exert a similar effect at this site. Thyrotropic hormone increases purine nucleotide synthesis in the thyroid gland by accelerating ribose (therefore also PRPP) formation from glucose.

Interconversions

Inosinate is converted to the adenylate and guanylate components of the nucleic acids as indicated in Figure 20–3. Adenylate can arise by amination of the keto-enol group at

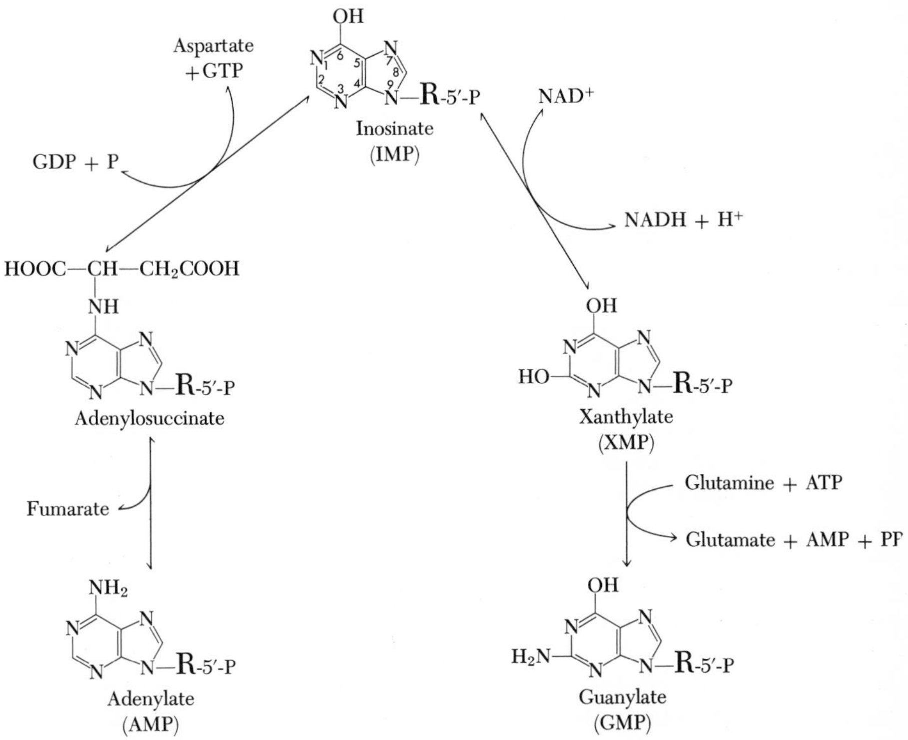

Figure 20–3. Interconversions of purines. *A*, Adenosine; *DP*, diphosphate; *G*, guanosine; *I*, inosine (hypoxanthine nucleoside); *MP*, monophosphate; *P*, phosphate; *PP*, pyrophosphate; *TP*, triphosphate; *X*, xanthosine (xanthine nucleoside).

position 6 of inosinate. The reaction involves condensation with aspartate and subsequent splitting out of fumarate, thus resembling an amination reaction occurring in the synthesis of inosinate (above). Guanylate, on the other hand, is formed by oxidation of inosinate to xanthylate, followed by amination utilizing glutamine. There is evidence for the direct conversion of adenylate to deoxyadenylate and of guanylate to deoxyguanylate without cleavage of the riboside bond, probably via the nucleoside diphosphates. 6-Mercaptopurine, a purine analog (p. 674), is converted in the organism to a nucleotide which inhibits the conversion of inosinate to both adenylate and guanylate.

Kinases are available to convert adenylate and guanylate, and their deoxy analogs to the corresponding triphosphate precursors of the nucleic acids.

Incorporation into Nucleic Acids

Administered adenine and adenylate are incorporated into the adenine and guanine moieties of DNA and RNA. Neither guanine nor guanosine is utilized in this manner to any great extent (traces of guanine are assimilated by certain species of experimental animals). Guanylate, however, is efficiently converted to nucleic acid guanine (not to adenine). Administered purines (or derivatives) which are not utilized for the synthesis of nucleic acids are catabolized to urate (man and apes) or allantoin (most mammals), which are excreted in the urine. Since the purines of the diet are probably assimilated in the free state, and since even administered adenine is diluted many-fold by endogenous adenine in the synthesis of nucleic acids, it is evident that only a fraction of the nucleic acid purines of the tissues is derived from preformed bases. Most of the nucleic acid purine component must be synthesized de novo.

Probable mechanisms of incorporation of the purines into nucleic acids are discussed later (p. 527).

Catabolism

The major catabolic pathway of the purines is illustrated in Figure 20–4. Subsequent to hydrolysis of the parent nucleic acids by polynucleotidases and other phosphodiesterases, the mononucleotides are hydrolyzed to nucleosides by phosphomonoesterases. Guanosine is attacked by a nucleoside phosphorylase, forming free guanine. Adenosine may undergo a similar phosphorolysis, but most of the available evidence indicates that the phosphorolytic reaction is preceded by a hydrolytic deamination to inosine, which is then converted to the free base, hypoxanthine. Adenylate also is directly deaminated to inosinate, although this is not believed to be the major pathway. Xanthine, an intermediate common to the catabolism of both adenine and guanine, is formed by the oxidation of hypoxanthine (xanthine oxidase) and by the hydrolytic deamination of guanine. Xanthine is oxidized further by xanthine oxidase, forming urate, the major end-product of purine metabolism in man and the higher apes. Other mammals degrade urate to allantoin with the aid of urate oxidase (uricase), an enzyme lacking in primates.

Reduced xanthine oxidase may act as a reductant for ferritin iron in the liver, converting it to the more readily liberated ferrous form. There is some evidence that the synthesis of xanthine oxidase may be induced by inosine. Xanthinuria, an inborn error of purine catabolism, probably is due to defective synthesis of xanthine oxidase.

The main site of formation of urate is probably the liver (although intestinal mucosa also contains an active xanthine oxidase) from which it is carried in the bloodstream to the kidneys, and excreted in the urine. There is suggestive evidence that most of the urate is

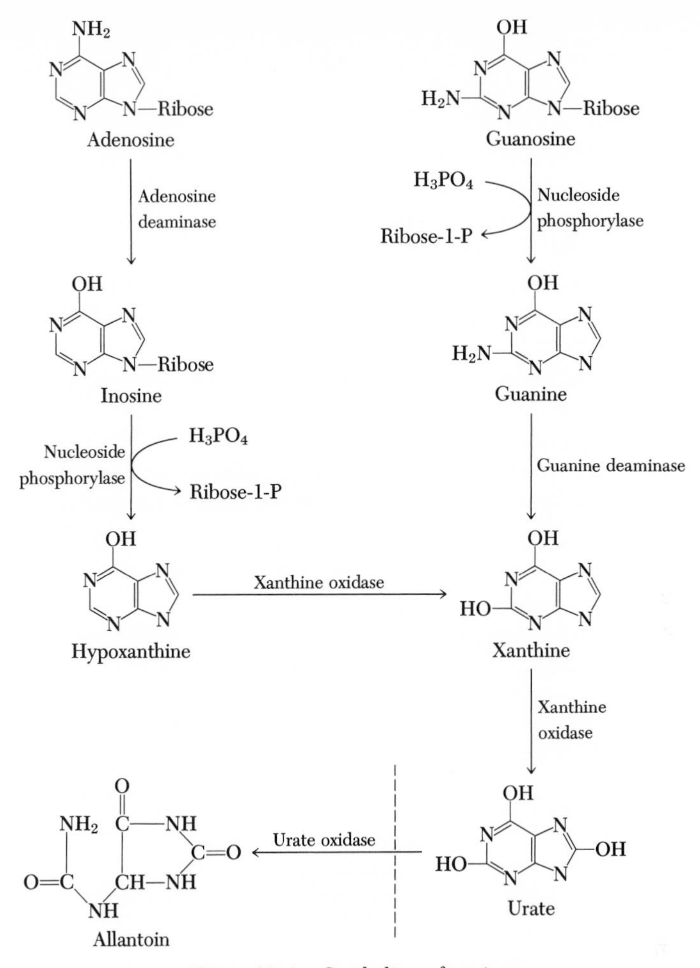

Figure 20-4. Catabolism of purines.

actively excreted by the renal tubules; the mechanism may be defective in gout, an inborn error of purine metabolism probably involving overproduction as well as underexcretion of urate. Allopurinol, an analog of xanthine and hypoxanthine, has been used to inhibit xanthine oxidase in the gouty patient. It lowers the urate level of blood and urine, replacing urate with the somewhat more soluble xanthines.

The urate pool (p. 542) amounts to about 1 gm. in normal human subjects; it may be expanded 15 to 25 times in gout. The normal half-life of urate is somewhat less than one day. From turnover data in man, obtained with the aid of isotopic labeling, it has been concluded that the urate excreted in the urine does not quite account for the total quantity formed. The disposition of the missing urate probably can be attributed to decomposition by bacteria in the intestinal tract.

The rate of purine catabolism, as reflected in the daily output of urinary urate, is influenced by the dietary intake of purines and the rate of endogenous purine catabolism. Administration of the glucocorticoid hormones of the adrenal cortex, or of ACTH, increases the urinary excretion of urate. It is not certain whether the effect of these hormones is primarily on the turnover of the purines or on the renal tubular reabsorption of urate.

METABOLISM OF PYRIMIDINES

Synthesis

The mechanism of synthesis of the pyrimidines is shown in Figure 20–5. Nitrogen 1 is derived from NH_3, carbon 2 from CO_2, both by way of carbamoyl-phosphate. The chain composed of nitrogen 3 and carbons 4, 5, and 6 is formed from aspartate. "Form*al*" (formaldehyde carried by tetrahydrofolate, which also provides hydrogen atoms for reduction of the 1-carbon fragment to methyl) is the source of the methyl group of thymine in DNA.

The sequence of reactions begins with the formation of carbamoyl-phosphate, which condenses with aspartate, forming ureidosuccinate (carbamoyl-aspartate). Ring closure and oxidation produce orotate, which forms a ribotide (pyrophosphorylase reaction) which is decarboxylated to uridylate.

Pyrimidine synthesis is subject to a number of control systems in microorganisms. A

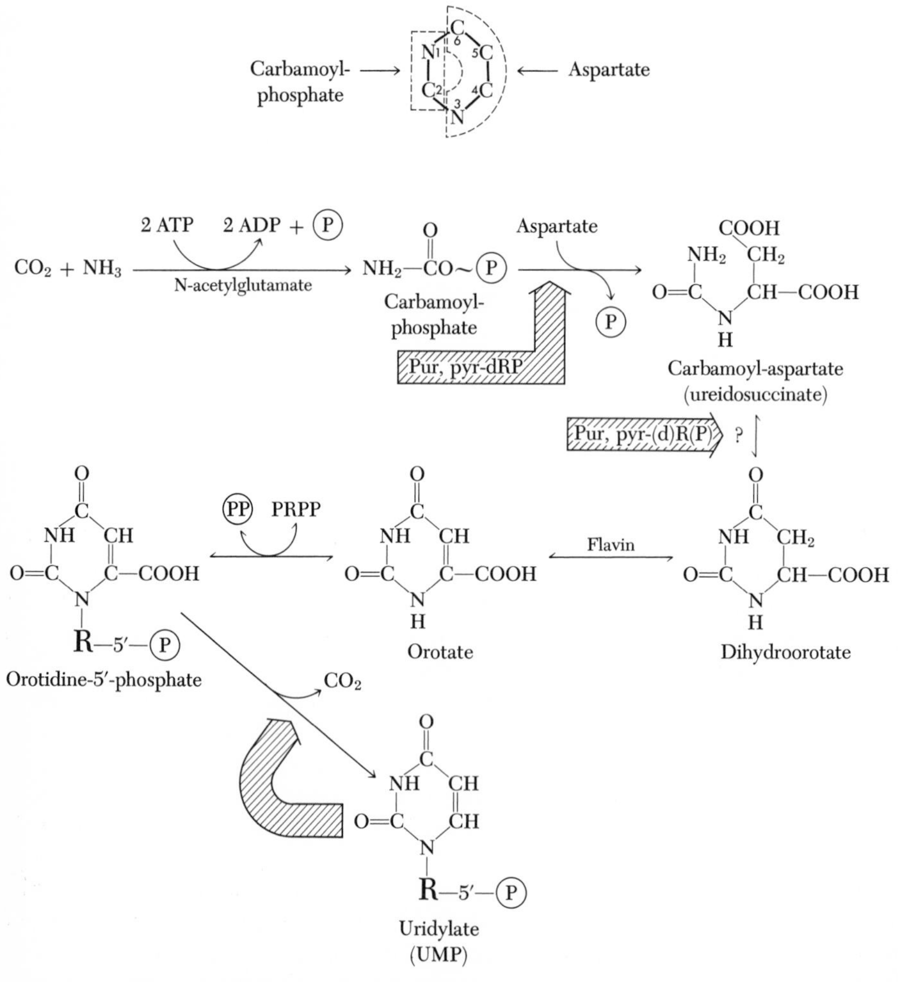

Carbamoyl-phosphate → [ring N1, C2, N3, C4, C5, C6] ← Aspartate

$CO_2 + NH_3$ —(2 ATP → 2 ADP + Ⓟ; N-acetylglutamate)→ NH_2—CO~Ⓟ Carbamoyl-phosphate —(Aspartate; → Ⓟ)→ Carbamoyl-aspartate (ureidosuccinate)

Pur, pyr-dRP

Pur, pyr-(d)R(P) ?

Dihydroorotate —(Flavin)→ Orotate —(PRPP → ⓅⓅ)→ Orotidine-5′-phosphate —(CO_2)→ Uridylate (UMP)

Figure 20–5. Synthesis of pyrimidines. *PRPP*, phosphoribosyl-pyrophosphate. Striated arrows denote inhibitory influences.

few instances of regulation are known in mammalian cells. Although in vivo evidence is lacking, purified aspartate transcarbamoylase of liver and hepatoma is inhibited by purine and pyrimidine deoxynucleotides. Formation of dihydro-orotate in ascites cells is inhibited by CMP, ATP, and a number of deoxynucleotides and deoxynucleosides. UMP is a competitive inhibitor of orotidylate decarboxylase. These observations suggest that, in the animal cell, negative feedback by end-products of both the pyrimidine and purine pathways may exert a regulatory influence on the rate of synthesis of pyrimidines. The antimetabolite, azauridine (p. 675), forms the corresponding nucleotide in the organism, this product acting as an inhibitor of the orotidylate decarboxylase.

Oroticaciduria, a probable inborn error of pyrimidine synthesis, is said to be characterized by a simultaneous defect in orotidylate pyrophosphorylase and decarboxylase. If substantiated, this double defect may be due to mutation of a regulator gene (p. 766).

Interconversions

As in the case of the purines, interconversions of pyrimidines (Fig. 20–6) involve the nucleotides or nucleosides rather than the free bases. Uridylate (UMP) is converted to the triphosphate by kinase reactions. The product is aminated to cytidine triphosphate in the presence of glutamine and ATP (guanine nucleotides also are said to favor the reaction). Reconversion of cytosine to uracil derivatives occurs in the form of the nucleosides, i.e., cytidine is deaminated to uridine. This pathway is probably largely catabolic, as discussed later. Cytidine and uridine diphosphates, formed by kinase reactions, are converted to the corresponding deoxy derivatives by a reaction in which ribose is reduced to deoxyribose without cleavage of the riboside linkage. The reaction requires ATP and either NADH or NADPH. Rapidly dividing cells contain an enzyme which deaminates deoxycytidylate to deoxyuridylate, which also can be formed by partial hydrolysis of deoxyuridine diphosphate. Conversion of deoxyuridylate to thymidylate involves the eventual appearance of a methyl group at position 5 of the thymine ring of the latter. This group is furnished by methylene ("form*al*") tetrahydrofolate. The hydrogen atoms required for the reduction of the 1-carbon unit from the oxidation level of formaldehyde to that of methyl are provided by the tetrahydrofolate itself, which is oxidized to dihydrofolate in the process. Thymidylate synthesis is inhibited by antimetabolites of folate (p. 673), and by 5-fluorouracil, the active inhibitory form of which is probably the corresponding

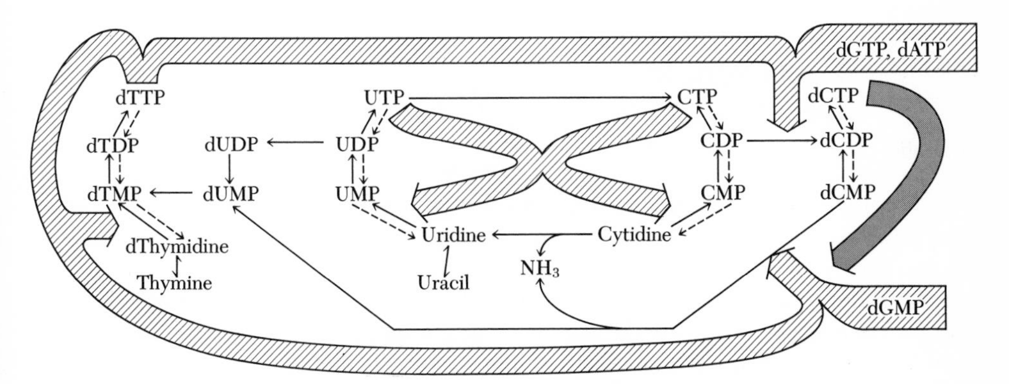

Figure 20-6. Interconversions of pyrimidines. Striated arrow indicates inhibitory influences, gray arrow enhancing influences (counteraction of inhibitory influences). *C*, Cytidine; *d*, deoxy; *T*, thymidine; *U*, uridine.

nucleotide or deoxynucleotide. On the other hand, the 5-bromo- and 5-iodo-deoxyuridine derivatives primarily act as antagonists of the further metabolism of thymine.

Regulatory influences in the area of pyrimidine interconversion include a number of end-product inhibitions of enzymes, such as the kinases acting on thymidine (by dTTP), uridine and cytidine (by UTP and CTP), the CDP reductase (by dTTP, dGTP, dATP), and the dCMP deaminase (by dTTP and dGMP, counteracted by dCTP).

Uracil is not well utilized for anabolic purposes by non-dividing cells since active catabolic pathways are present and the uridine phosphorylase and uridine kinase reactions appear to function only at high concentrations of substrate. Non-dividing cells also appear to be deficient in the kinase which converts thymidylate to thymidine triphosphate. On the other hand, rapidly dividing tissues, such as embryonic, tumor, or regenerating tissues, appear to be characteristically deficient in catabolic pathways and to contain such enzymes as thymidylate kinase and deoxycytidylate deaminase, which catalyze reactions favorable to the formation of DNA.

Limitations to the ability of certain tissues to synthesize pyrimidines and their derivatives are suggested by experiments involving brain perfusion. Maintenance of various constituents of the brain in normal concentration requires that the liver be part of the perfusion system, although the liver can be removed if cytidine and uridine are added to the perfusion fluid.

Incorporation into Nucleic Acid

Administration of isotopically labeled uracil, cytosine, or thymine to experimental animals does not result in significant labeling of the tissue nucleic acids. Uridine and uridylate are but slightly utilized. On the other hand, the nucleosides, cytidine, deoxycytidine, and thymidine, and the nucleotide, cytidylate, are incorporated into nucleic acids to a considerable extent.

It is of interest that administration of labeled cytidine results in labeling of deoxycytidine in the DNA of the tissues, in agreement with the direct conversion of ribose to deoxyribose while in glycosidic linkage, as described in the previous section. The conversion appears to be irreversible.

Since digestion of pyrimidine nucleosides apparently does not proceed to completion, it is probable that many nucleosides are absorbed as such, in which case they may be used for the synthesis of nucleic acids, as indicated by the data presented earlier. The relative importance of de novo synthesis of pyrimidines consequently may be less than in the case of the purines.

Probable mechanisms for the incorporation of pyrimidine nucleotides into the nucleic acids are presented later (p. 527).

Catabolism

The pathway of catabolism of the pyrimidines is presented in Figure 20–7. In preparation for this catabolic pathway, various pyrimidine derivatives may be interconverted by the reactions indicated in Figure 20–6, the actions of nucleotidases and nucleoside phosphorylases resulting in the formation of the free bases, uracil and thymine. These two bases are reduced to the dihydro derivatives, which, after opening of the ring, lose nitrogen 1 and carbon 2 to form β-alanine (from dihydrouracil) and β-aminoisobutyrate (from dihydrothymine). β-Alanine is readily deaminated; the ammonia thus produced, and that from the previous cleavage, form urea. The carbon skeleton, malonate semialdehyde, is decarboxylated and oxidized to form acetate, which may be metabolized via its usual

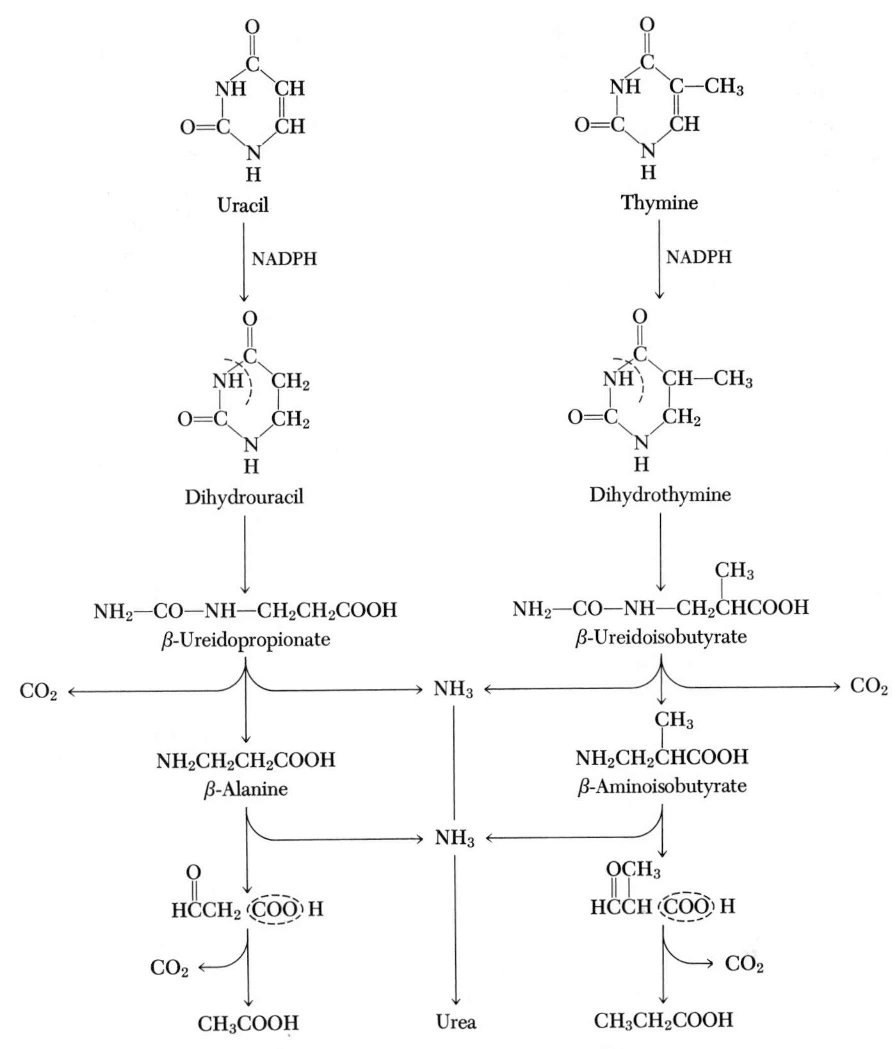

Figure 20-7. Catabolism of pyrimidines.

routes. Deamination of β-aminoisobutyrate produces methylmalonate semialdehyde (also formed in the degradation of valine), which is decarboxylated and oxidized to form propionate, a glucogenic substance. β-Aminoisobutyrate sometimes is found in the urine; there is a genetically transmitted difference in the population between low and high excretors of this compound.

In a side-path, the importance of which is uncertain at present, thymine is oxidized to hydroxymethyluracil and uracil carboxylate.

METABOLISM OF THE "FREE" NUCLEOTIDES (COENZYMES)

In addition to the nucleic acids proper, all cells contain a number of "free" nucleotides. These include the mono-, di-, and triphosphates of adenosine, guanosine, uridine, cytidine, and thymidine. It is possible that some or all of these compounds are intermediates in the synthesis or degradation of the nucleic acids. In addition, however, many of these compounds, as well as nucleotides containing bases which do not occur in the nucleic acids (e.g., hypoxanthine, flavin, nicotinamide, pantetheine), function as coenzymes in a wide variety of reactions. There is no reason to believe that the purine and pyrimidine moieties of these nucleotides are synthesized by any pathway other than that involved in the synthesis of the bases of the nucleic acids. Certain of the "bases" in the coenzymes are vitamins (e.g., riboflavin, niacin, pantothenate) and must be supplied from sources outside the animal tissues (diet, intestinal flora). Although the "free" nucleotides may be metabolized independently of the nucleic acids, their structural similarity to the "bound" nucleotides (i.e., in the nucleic acids), their common constituents (ribose, base, phosphate), and the probable common anabolic and catabolic pathways of these constituents justify their discussion here.

Table 20-1 summarizes certain pertinent information concerning those free nucleotides which are at present known to act as coenzymes.

TABLE 20-1. FREE NUCLEOTIDE COENZYMES

PARENT BASE(S)	ACTIVE FORM(S)*	FUNCTION(S)
Adenine	AMP-ADP-ATP	Transphosphorylation, energy trapping
	Fatty acyl-adenylates	Activation of fatty acids
	Amino acyl-adenylates	Activation of amino acids
	S-Adenosylmethionine	Transmethylation
	Phosphoadenosine phosphosulfate	Sulfatation
	Cyclic 3′,5′-AMP	Activation of phosphorylase
Hypoxanthine	IDP-ITP	CO_2 assimilation (oxaloacetate carboxylase), energy trapping in ketoglutarate oxidation
Guanine	GDP-GTP	Energy trapping in ketoglutarate oxidation, incorporation of amino acids into protein
	GDP-Mannose, fucose	Glycoproteins, mucopolysaccharide synthesis
Uracil	UDP-Glucose, galactose	4-Epimerase, lactose synthesis
	UDP-N-Acetyl-glucosamine, galactosamine	Mucopolysaccharide synthesis
	UDP-Glucuronate	Glucuronide conjugation, mucopolysaccharide synthesis
	UDP-Iduronate	Mucopolysaccharide synthesis
Cytosine	CMP-N-Acetyl-neuraminate	Mucopolysaccharide synthesis
	CDP-Choline, ethanolamine	Phospholipid synthesis
Nicotinamide + adenine	NAD, NADH NADP, NADPH	Oxidation-reduction
Flavin, flavin + adenine	FMN, FMN · H_2 FAD, FAD · H_2	Oxidation-reduction
Pantetheine (Pantothenylthiol-ethylamine) + adenine	Acyl-SCoA	Transacylation
Dimethylbenzimidazole (also adenine in nucleoside)	5′-Deoxyadenosyl-cobalamine	Methylmalonyl-CoA isomerase
	CH_3-cobalamine	CH_3-group synthesis

* *A*, Adenosine; *C*, cytidine; *G*, guanosine; *I*, inosine; *U*, uridine; *MP*, monophosphate; *DP*, diphosphate; *TP*, triphosphate.

Mononucleotides

The synthesis and degradation of the purine and pyrimidine nucleotide coenzymes may be assumed to proceed along the paths already delineated for the nucleotide constituents of the nucleic acids. Alternate pathways involve reactions of the type of phosphorylases, pyrophosphorylases, and kinases, by means of which the requisite nucleotide may be constructed stepwise from the free base, if necessary.

Dinucleotides

(*a*) ***Nicotinamide coenzymes.*** Formation of dinucleotides is a much more complex process than the reactions covered previously, and will be outlined in greater detail for the major members of this class of coenzymes. The synthesis of nicotinate (in the form of its mononucleotide) from tryptophan is discussed in connection with the metabolism of that amino acid (p. 596). This vitamin is provided also by the diet. It is probable that the synthesis of NAD occurs as follows:

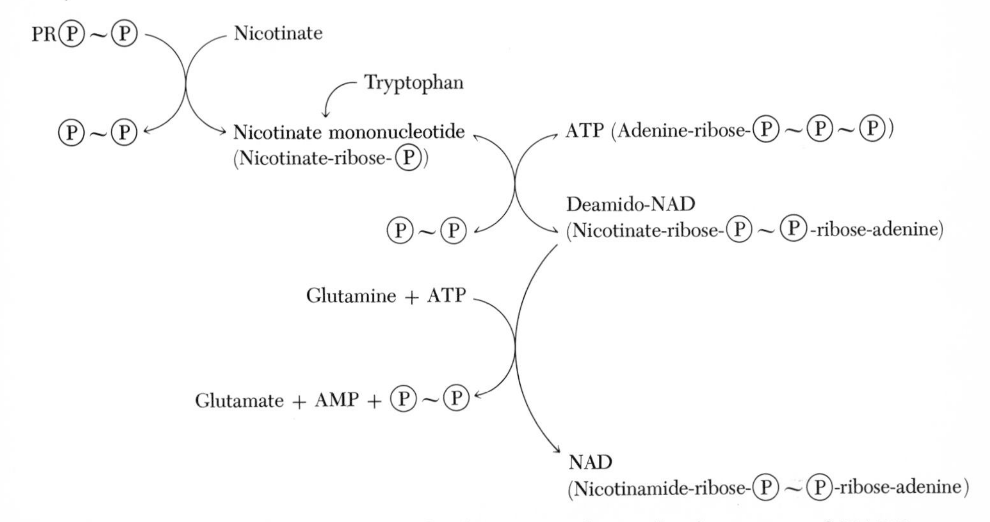

Phosphorylation of NAD by ATP and a kinase results in the formation of NADP.

NADP is reconverted to NAD by a phosphatase. The degradation of NAD may take the following pathways: (1) cleavage between nicotinamide and ribose, catalyzed by NAD glycohydrolase (NADase), (2) scission of the pyrophosphate group by a pyrophosphatase, yielding two mononucleotides (NADP is split similarly). Final degradation products include nicotinamide and a number of its metabolites (p. 185).

(*b*) ***Flavin coenzymes.*** Although the carbohydrate moiety of riboflavin is ribitol, a sugar alcohol, the vitamin is usually considered a nucleoside, and its 5′-phosphate a nucleotide (flavin mononucleotide, FMN). The nucleotide is formed under the influence of a kinase, and is converted to flavin-adenine dinucleotide (FAD) by a reaction analogous to that involved in the synthesis of deamido-NAD:

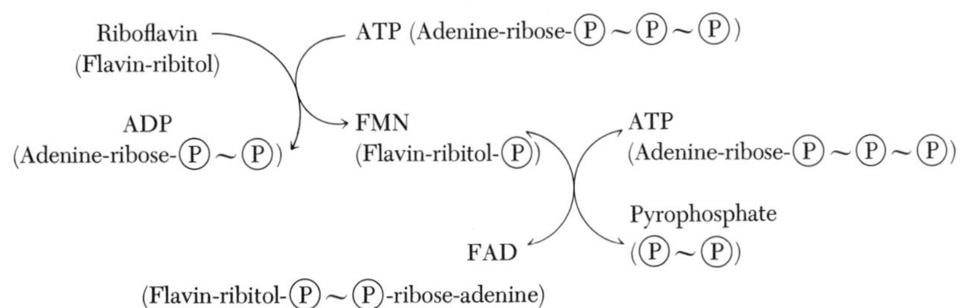

FAD is split at the pyrophosphate linkage by the same enzyme that attacks NAD and NADP. FMN is hydrolytically dephosphorylated by a phosphatase.

(*c*) ***Coenzyme A.*** This coenzyme is synthesized in much the same manner as those discussed previously. Pantothenate first is phosphorylated, then condenses with cysteine, forming a phosphopseudopeptide which is decarboxylated to yield phosphopantetheine. The phosphopantetheine acquires an adenylate component in a pyrophosphorylase reaction. CoA is finally produced by another kinase reaction.

Pantothenate $\xrightarrow{\text{ATP}}$ Phosphopantothenate $\longrightarrow$ Phosphopantothenyl cysteine
Cysteine
$\downarrow$ → CO_2
Phosphopantetheine
ATP → Pyrophosphate ((P)~(P))
"Dephospho-CoA"
(Pantetheine-(P)~(P)-ribose-adenine)
ATP → ADP
CoA
(Thiolethylamine-pantothenate-(P)~(P)
3′-(P)-ribose-adenine)

Coenzyme Forms of Vitamin B_{12}

Compounds of this type do not fit readily into the preceding classification, since, although they are no less legitimate mononucleotides than FMN, they sometimes also contain a nucleoside moiety. An example follows of conversion of cyano- or hydroxo-forms of vitamin B_{12} (p. 198) to a coenzyme form:

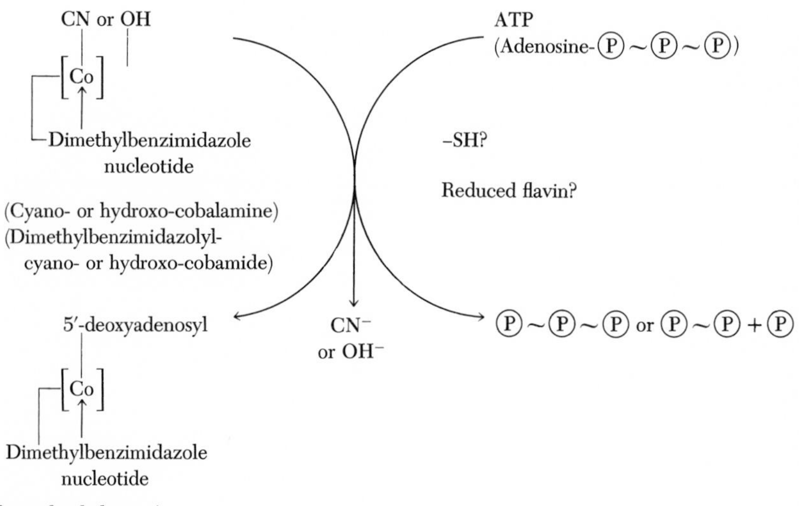

METABOLISM OF THE NUCLEIC ACIDS

Synthesis of DNA ("Replication")

The currently accepted view of DNA synthesis is illustrated in Figure 20-8. Under the influence of DNA polymerase, in the presence of Mg^{++}, the double strands of DNA (p. 113) are believed to separate, a small portion at a time, cleaving the hydrogen bonds between complementary bases. Deoxynucleoside triphosphates, all four of which are

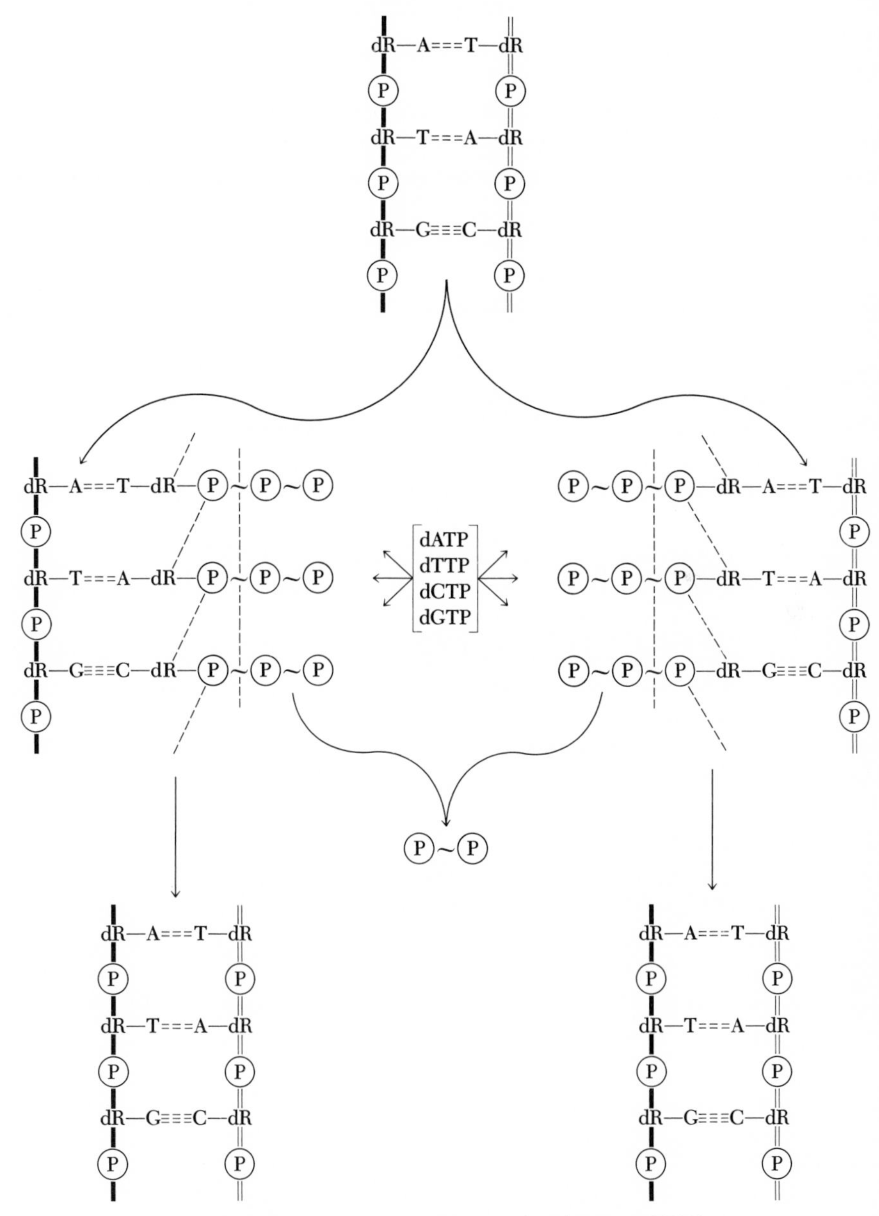

Figure 20-8. Probable mechanism of replication of DNA.

required for synthesis to proceed, are attracted from solution in the nuclear sap to form hydrogen bonds with their complementary bases on the separated strands. Each new nucleotide loses a pyrophosphate group while forming an ester linkage from its remaining phosphate to the 3′-hydroxyl group of the deoxyribose on an adjacent new nucleotide. Thus, two daughter double helices are formed, each consisting of an old strand of the parent DNA, coupled to a complementary new strand, the final composition and nucleotide sequence of each strand being identical with the corresponding strand which existed in the parent molecule. The process has been aptly named "replication." Its suitability for the duplication of genetic information is evident.

Although the parent DNA, which must be present for synthesis to occur, has been called a "primer," its function differs fundamentally from that of the priming polysaccharide in glycogen synthesis (p. 397). It would be more appropriate to use the term "template."

It is of interest that, in the case of the DNA polymerase, unnatural nucleotides containing synthetic analogs of the bases may be incorporated in place of the natural reactants, with the qualification that the unnatural base (e.g., 5-bromouracil) must have the proper structure to form hydrogen bonds in the DNA helix with the partner of the base which it replaces. It seems probable that the efficacy of purine and pyrimidine analogs in inhibiting the multiplication of cells may, in part, be explained on the basis that these analogs are incorporated into DNA, thus forming a fraudulent molecule which can no longer accomplish its normal biological functions.

DNA replication is inhibited by acridine drugs, e.g., proflavine (which also inhibit synthesis of RNA), probably by intercalation of the inhibitor between successive base pairs, thus disturbing the structure of the double helix. Antibiotics of the mitomycin type yield similar results, but in this case probably by cross-linking the two strands of DNA. In vitro, histones inhibit replication of DNA, but it is not established that this occurs in vivo.

Subsequent to replication, DNA is partly methylated by S-adenosylmethionine in the presence of a specific nuclear DNA-transmethylase, forming methylcytosine residues. (A similar enzyme in bacteria methylates the adenine residues of DNA). The histones of the nucleus are methylated and acetylated after synthesis. The biological significance of these modifications of composition in DNA and histone is not known.

As might be anticipated, the concentration of DNA in the nucleus doubles during cell division. In the average mammalian cell, newly formed during 1 hour of mitosis, a period of 10 to 20 hours occurs (G_1) during which no DNA is synthesized. This is followed by a phase of active replication of DNA (S) lasting 6 to 8 hours. Synthesis then ceases for 1 to 4 hours (G_2) until mitosis. Experiments utilizing isotopic tracers support the view that DNA is metabolically stable, except for the period of replication. The rate of turnover of DNA in various tissues is found to decrease in the order: intestine $>$ thymus $>$ spleen $>$ liver $>$ muscle $>$ kidney, with additional slow components detectable in intestine, spleen, and thymus. Increases in the content of DNA, RNA, or both, in neoplastic tissue are not observed consistently, and appear to reflect the rate of growth and degree of cellularity of the tumor more than any special neoplastic peculiarity.

Synthesis of RNA ("Transcription")

The synthesis of RNA is more complex than that of DNA. In contrast to the latter, which consists of a relatively homogeneous family of molecules with composition and nucleotide sequence fixed by the genetic history of the cell, there exist several types of

RNA, each varying in quantity (and, in certain cases, in composition and nucleotide sequence) with the physiological state of the cell, which in turn is subject to many environmental influences. Nevertheless, a general pattern of RNA synthesis is emerging from recent investigations, making it possible to sketch a probable mechanism as illustrated in Figure 20-9.

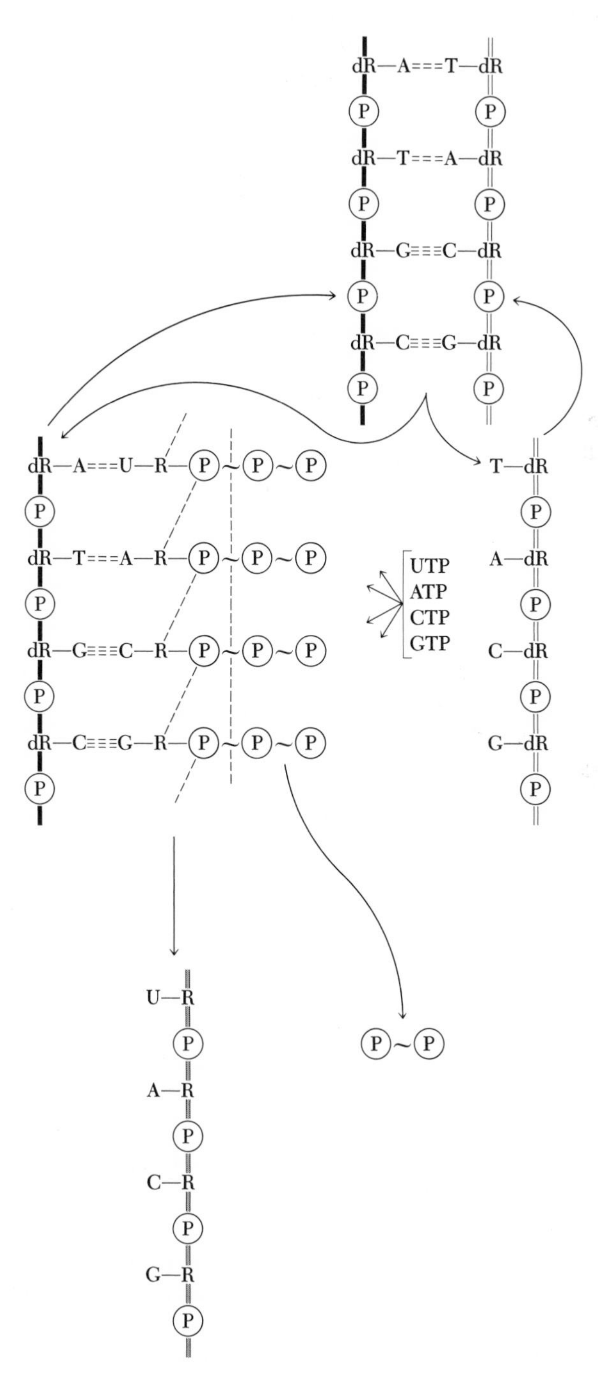

Figure 20-9. Probable mechanism of transcription of DNA to RNA.

The weight of current evidence suggests that virtually all of the RNA of the animal cell is synthesized in the nucleus, although most of it eventually finds its way into the cytoplasm. (The only exception is mitochondrial RNA, which appears to be synthesized within the mitochondria under the influence of the small amount of DNA found in these organelles). Much of this synthesis occurs in the nucleolus. In addition, recent evidence supports the view that all RNA is synthesized on a DNA template. Since this process amounts to a transfer of the information contained in the DNA over to another species of nucleic acid, it is appropriately termed "transcription."

It will be noted in Figure 20–9 that the beginning of the process resembles DNA replication, in that some degree of separation of the double strands of DNA and cleavage of hydrogen bonds must occur. Since there is evidence from bacterial genetics that much (if not all) of DNA-directed RNA synthesis is blocked by repressor substances when not in action, this separation of strands may require the services of "de-repressors" (p. 762) in addition to the enzyme, RNA polymerase. In any case, only one of the two strands of DNA is active in transcription in vivo, although it is not known how this is accomplished.

In the presence of Mg^{++} and the polymerase, ribonucleoside triphosphates (all four of which must be present) are attracted from solution, their bases forming hydrogen bonds with complementary bases on the transcribing strand of DNA. This process and the subsequent union of ribonucleotides to form RNA are analogous to DNA replication, the major differences being the type of pentose involved and the substitution, in the case of RNA, of uracil for thymine in base-pairing with adenine.

No further processing appears to be required in the synthesis of that species of RNA which specifies the sequence of amino acids during protein synthesis, messenger RNA (mRNA). In contrast, the two types of ribosomal RNA (rRNA) of different molecular weight and the many small molecules of the RNA species which carries activated amino acids (soluble RNA, sRNA; transfer RNA, tRNA) are partially methylated in the nucleus (various base-specific RNA transmethylases), and also may undergo certain rearrangements (leading to pseudouridine) or other modifications of the usual bases (forming hypoxanthine or dihydrouracil). Any molecules of sRNA deficient in the terminal sequence -cytidylic-cytidylic-adenylic, required for transport of amino acids, can acquire these terminal nucleotides by the following sequence of reactions occuring in the cytoplasm:

$$\text{sRNA} \xrightarrow[\text{Mg}^{++}]{\text{CTP} \searrow \nearrow \text{PP}} \text{sRNA-CMP} \xrightarrow[\text{Mg}^{++}]{\text{CTP} \searrow \nearrow \text{PP}} \text{sRNA-CMP-CMP} \xrightarrow[\text{Mg}^{++}]{\text{ATP} \searrow \nearrow \text{PP}} \text{sRNA-CMP-CMP-AMP}$$

The bacterial enzyme, polynucleotide phosphorylase, catalyzes the following reaction:

$$\text{n Base-R-}ⓟ\sim ⓟ + \text{Primer} \xrightleftharpoons{\text{Mg}^{++}} \text{Primer-(}ⓟ\text{-R-Base)}_n + nⓟ$$

Although of no known significance in animal cells, and probably having a catabolic function in bacteria, this enzyme is nevertheless mentioned here because of its utility as a biochemical reagent. It catalyzes the reversible interaction of ribonucleoside diphosphates with the free 3′-hydroxyl group of a poly- or oligoribonucleotide primer to form a polynucleotide and inorganic phosphate. In this case, the primer does not act as a template, since a mixture of the four ribonucleotides is not required, and the product does not reflect the composition or nucleotide sequence of the primer. Instead, polymers containing single types of monomeric units can be prepared. Mixed polymers also can be formed, the composition of the product merely reflecting the composition of the reaction mixture, with random sequence of the various constituent nucleotides. The synthetic polynucleotides synthesized by this enzyme act as "messenger RNA" when added to a ribosomal protein-synthesizing system, and have been of inestimable value in elucidation of the genetic code (p. 556). Thus, synthetic polyuridylate causes formation of polyphenylalanine in such systems, suggesting UUU as a codeword for phenylalanine.

All DNA-directed synthesis of RNA is inhibited by the antiobiotic, actinomycin D, which appears to bind to guanine residues. The acridines, which have already been mentioned as inhibitors of DNA replication, also block RNA synthesis. Histones inhibit RNA synthesis even more effectively than DNA replication, and have been proposed as natural "repressors" of gene function.

As might have been anticipated, isotopic labeling experiments have demonstrated much greater metabolic lability in RNA than in DNA. The turnover rate of RNA in various liver fractions decreases in the order: nucleus > soluble phase of cytoplasm > microsomal + mitochondrial fraction. In various tissues the turnover rate decreases in the order: intestine > testis > spleen > liver > kidney. Each tissue and fraction, of course, contains many species of RNA, the "average" turnover probably corresponding to that of ribosomal RNA, which predominates in most cases.

A decreased concentration of RNA is observed in livers of experimental animals which are fasted or fed low-protein diets. Partial hepatectomy is followed by hyperplasia of the remaining liver tissue, during which large increases occur in the concentration of RNA. Intense stimulation of nerve cells results in a decrease of RNA (and protein). Administration of many hormones results in increased activity of RNA polymerase in the target tissues, leading to increased synthesis of mRNA. In general, influences favoring increased rates of protein synthesis result in increases in cytoplasmic (largely ribosomal) RNA.

Catabolism of Nucleic Acids

It seems reasonable to assume, in the absence of evidence to the contrary, that the catabolism of nucleic acids is initiated by the tissue polynucleotidases, which, together with other phosphodiesterases, degrade the macromolecules to mononucleotides. The mononucleotides may be hydrolyzed to the nucleosides, in a few instances by specific nucleotidases, generally by phosphatases. Certain nucleosidases have been described; however, it is probable that nucleosides are split mainly by nucleoside phosphorylases. The free bases and sugars are then catabolized further along independent pathways. A number of catabolic changes (e.g., hydrolytic deamination) may be undergone by certain bases while still in the form of nucleotides and nucleosides, as indicated previously.

BIOLOGICAL SIGNIFICANCE OF NUCLEIC ACIDS

Information accumulating in recent years has stimulated intense interest in the biochemistry of nucleic acids. The association of nucleic acids with chromosomes and viruses, and evidence of their influence in protein synthesis, suggest that these substances are of great fundamental biological importance. It seems desirable here to point out certain of the directions of current studies in this field.

Involvement of Nucleic Acids in Genetics

Evidence of both circumstantial and direct type points to the nucleic acids (DNA in animal, plant, bacterial cells, and some viruses, RNA in other viruses) as the chemical repositories of genetic information. By way of circumstantial evidence, it may be noted that chromosomes, of both spermatozoa and somatic cells, consist largely of deoxyribonucleoproteins. The obvious implication is that their component genes are made up largely of these substances, which, therefore, may be regarded as the "genetic material," concerned in processes of cell reproduction. It is pertinent in this connection that the amount of DNA in spermatozoa containing the haploid number of chromosomes is one-half that of the somatic nuclei of the same species. Moreover, there is a quite striking, although not absolute, uniformity and constancy in the DNA content of the nuclei. The base composition of DNA is identical for all tissues of the same organism, but varies between species. The relative metabolic stability of DNA, except during cell division, also is consonant with its probable role as carrier of genetic information. Agents which are mutagenic are also known to affect DNA, viz., ionizing radiation, nitrogen mustards, and base analogs. The only cellular site outside of the nucleus which contains DNA is the mitochondrion, which is now regarded as a self-duplicating organelle, in which DNA probably subserves some genetic function.

Powerful support has been given to the theory that DNA is indeed the bearer of genetic information in the cell by the establishment of the Watson-Crick structure for this compound. Thus, the requirement for hydrogen bonding between complementary bases in the double helix suggests that the sequence of nucleotides in one strand is determined automatically by that of the other. Thus, if a double helix untwisted and each single strand attached to itself a new complementary strand of nucleotides, the resulting two double helices each would be duplicates of the original DNA, exactly the sort of replication to be expected of genetic material. It has been shown, in fact, that bacteria, the DNA of which is almost completely labeled with N^{15}, when allowed to reproduce in a medium containing solely N^{14} in the nitrogen source, produce a first generation of offspring containing DNA in which half of the nitrogen is N^{15}, and half is N^{14}. Second generation progeny contain half-labeled and unlabeled DNA in equal amounts. These experiments indicate that, in cell division, each DNA molecule is cleaved to two sub-units, each incorporated into a different DNA molecule in the offspring; de novo synthesis produces the complementary strand paired to each of these molecules in the progeny. Each subunit remains chemically intact, thus qualifying again as a genetic carrier.

More direct evidence of the genetic role of DNA derives from the phenomenon of bacterial transformation. Certain strains (e.g., Type 3) of pneumococcus possess capsules containing specific polysaccharides and others (e.g., Type 2) do not. This capacity for formation of a type-specific capsule is a hereditary characteristic. If one adds to an appropriate culture of a non-encapsulated strain an extract of an encapsulated strain, the former type is transformed to the latter, developing its characteristic capsular polysaccharide, as do its progeny subsequently. The active agent (transforming factor) is a deoxyribonucleic acid. It apparently endows the bacterial cell with the capacity for synthesizing an enzyme or enzyme sysystem that it did not previously possess, which, in turn, catalyzes the formation of the type-specific capsular polysaccharide. Inasmuch as this new function is subsequently transmissible, this may be regarded, in effect, as an example of induced mutation. Many different specific transforming factors have been found for pneumococci, Hemophilus influenzae, Escherichia coli, and meningococci. In addition to the factors inducing type-specific encapsulation, others confer upon bacteria the ability to resist certain drugs or antibiotics or to exhibit nutritional characteristics not possessed by the organisms before treatment. All of these factors appear to be deoxyribonucleates. It is perhaps of fundamental importance that these agents, as is true of genes and viruses, are reduplicated by the bacterial cell and, like viruses, can be recovered in large amounts from descendants of the cell into which they originally entered.

A phenomenon somewhat related to bacterial transformation is transduction. In this case, bacteriophage (bacterial virus) grown initially in bacteria having the ability to carry out a certain chemical reaction (e.g., the synthesis of thymine), when infecting organisms lacking that particular chemical reaction, can induce catalysis of the previously absent process. Evidently the phage DNA transfers from the former to the latter organisms the "genetic" information necessary for establishing an otherwise absent metabolic pathway.

Other direct evidence of the genetic role of nucleic acids are the observations that the DNA of bacteriophage suffices for phage reproduction, that the RNA of tobacco mosaic virus is the infective component of the virus, and that chemically induced mutations in tobacco mosaic virus RNA result in the expected substitutions of amino acids in the protein of the virus progeny. Finally, it has been found that, in sexual reproduction in E. coli, the sequence of transfer of genes from one cell to its conjugate is the same as the sequence of genes determined by chromosome mapping, and that both sequences correlate well with the rate of transfer of DNA between cells.

Genes resemble viruses in at least two important characteristics: (1) they are autoreproducible, their exact duplication during mitotic division endowing each daughter cell with all of the specific hereditary biochemical potentialities and mechanisms of the original cell; (2) they are capable of undergoing mutation. In determining the biochemical characteristics of the cell, dependent largely on enzymes, it appears that DNA is responsible in some way for the synthesis of these substances and that each gene directs the production of a single enzyme, the "one gene–one enzyme" hypothesis (more recently modified, for reasons which appear elsewhere, to "one gene–one polypeptide"). A current working hypothesis states that chromosomal DNA carries genetic information in the form of coded sequences of nucleotides, that this coded information is passed on, via a messenger RNA which travels from the nucleus into the cytoplasm, bearing a specific sequence of nucleotides as a "template" for arranging the sequence of amino acids in proteins (e.g., enzymes) at the ribosomal site. These matters are discussed more fully in a later section on the role of nucleic acids in protein synthesis.

Role of Nucleic Acids in Mutation and Carcinogenesis

The fact that genes and viruses, largely if not entirely nucleoprotein in nature, possess in common the highly distinctive properties of autoduplication and susceptibility to mutation, raises the fundamentally important question of the relation of nucleic acids to these phenomena. The former has been referred to previously; genes and viruses are the only two sub-cellular substances known to be capable of duplicating ("reproducing") themselves. They also can undergo mutation "spontaneously," and as a result of exposure to certain mutagenic agents. The latter include: (1) ultraviolet light, (2) ionizing radiations (e.g., X- and gamma rays and neutrons), and (3) certain chemicals (e.g., colchicine, nitrogen mustards, certain chemical carcinogens).

Many if not all of these agents are capable of altering the structure or conformation of DNA, and it is possible that this is the basis of their mutagenic action. This subject may have basic relevance to the problem of carcinogenesis, which, according to some students of this subject, is one of induced somatic mutation. This opinion is by no means unanimous. It may be significant in this connection, however, that such factors as ultraviolet light, ionizing radiations, and at least some chemicals that are mutagenic, are also carcinogenic. Moreover, certain types of malignancy are known to be due to viruses, which not only are largely if not entirely nucleoprotein in nature, but also impose upon the invaded cell their own specific nucleic acid synthesizing capacities. These observations suggest that the induction of malignancy may be related fundamentally to the development of an abnormal type of nucleic acid in the cell.

Role of Nucleic Acids in Protein Synthesis

Growth and maintenance of the organism require continuous synthesis of protein molecules, specific for each cell. The mechanism of protein synthesis involves enzymes, which are themselves protein in nature. As indicated previously, the cytoplasmic enzyme pattern is determined genetically, i.e., by the DNA in the nucleus. However, although in this sense the nuclear nucleic acids may be regarded as the ultimate determinants of all metabolic reactions, a more intimate relation to protein synthesis has been established by certain observations.

RNA is present in greatest abundance in the cytoplasm of actively growing cells (e.g., embryonic, tumor, tip of plant root) and in cells engaged in the production and secretion of proteins (e.g., pancreatic acinar cells). Increased protein synthesis, e.g., stimulation of pancreatic secretion by pilocarpine, is accompanied by an increase in RNA. Conversely, when production of protein by liver cells is inhibited by starvation, their RNA content decreases simultaneously.

Current investigations on the mechanism of protein synthesis (p. 551) indicate a three-fold function for cytoplasmic RNA. First, relatively small, soluble molecules of RNA (sRNA) bearing the proper cytidylic-cytidylic-adenylic terminal sequence act as acceptors for aminoacyl units present as aminoacyl-adenylates attached to “activating” enzymes, each sRNA being specific for an individual species of amino acid. Each sRNA then transfers its amino acid burden to the polyribosomes, in which messenger RNA acts as a template upon which sRNA’s are aligned by hydrogen bonding between purine and pyrimidine base pairs and in which the ribosomal RNA plays some as yet unspecified role. The amino acids are then coupled to form a protein, the amino acid sequence of which is determined by the sequence of nucleotides in the messenger RNA.

The nucleus apparently contains few of the important enzyme systems concerned in the metabolic activities of the cell, although nucleic acids (and, to some extent, protein) can be synthesized in this site. It would therefore appear, in view of the localization of oxidative and phosphorylating enzyme systems in the mitochondria, and of others elsewhere in the cytoplasm, that the nucleus depends on the cytoplasm for its energy supply. On the other hand, there is much evidence to indicate nuclear control over metabolic patterns in the cytoplasm. Recent data from the field of bacterial genetics suggest that, whereas the *potential* pattern of enzymes and other proteins in the cell is determined genetically, much of the genetic information is latent, in a state of repression, the *functional* pattern being varied according to the metabolic requirements of the cell. These requirements manifest themselves in a “back-flow” of information from the cytoplasm to the nucleus (“inducers”), bearing signals for the activation (derepression) of genic areas concerned with ultimate synthesis of specific proteins (cf. Chapter 27). The picture evoked is that of a continuously reciprocal relationship, the nucleus deriving energy and information from cytoplasmic mechanisms which can be maintained and controlled only through nuclear activities.

Viruses

Until comparatively recently, it was generally agreed that viruses were living organisms characterized, among other things, by: (1) small size (passage through bacterial filters),

(2) inability to grow and multiply on artificial culture media, (3) ability to multiply or reproduce within the living cells of the host, and (4) the development of mutation forms during multiplication. Several plant viruses have been shown to be crystallizable nucleoproteins, and many animal viruses are largely if not entirely nucleoprotein. Some (bacteriophage, vaccinia, rabies) contain only deoxyribonucleoproteins; others (poliomyelitis, influenza, encephalitis, and all plant viruses, such as tobacco mosaic), only ribonucleoproteins. It has been shown that if crystalline tobacco mosaic virus, non-living by usual standards, is introduced into a healthy tobacco plant, the latter develops the disease in typical form. Moreover, the virus nucleoprotein can be subsequently recovered in amounts greatly exceeding that originally introduced, i.e., it reduplicates (reproduces?) with progression of the disease.

Viruses vary widely in size and structural complexity, certain of the smaller ones exhibiting the physical and chemical behavior of molecules, whereas certain of the larger ones approach microorganisms in size and in structural and functional complexity. The observations reviewed above have led to the suggestion that viruses provide a link between molecules and "living" cells, completing the pathway from such simple structures as electrons to the highly complex structure of the mammalian organism.

The structure of the rod-shaped tobacco mosaic virus has been established as consisting of an axial core of ribonucleic acid (6 per cent), "coated" with protein (94 per cent). These two components have been artificially separated, with abolition of virus activity, and have been subsequently recombined, with restoration of activity. The nucleic acid is apparently the genetically important component. The immunological properties and host specificity of the virus are apparently determined by the protein.

The bacteriophage (bacterial virus) which attacks E. coli consists of tadpole-like particles, the hexagonal head containing a high concentration of DNA covered by a layer of protein. The phage particle attaches its tail to the cell wall of the bacterium, where the action of tail enzymes results in penetration of the wall. The phage particle then acts like a miniature syringe injecting DNA into the bacterial cell, the empty protein sheath remaining behind. The metabolism of the host cell is then altered so as to produce new virus particles which are finally liberated by lysis of the bacterium.

Viruses possess no enzyme activity (other than virus activity); nevertheless, on entering susceptible cells, they alter and direct certain metabolic sequences within the cell into new channels. Of particular significance is the fact that metabolic precursors are derived from the host cell for construction of the nucleic acid and protein molecules of the multiplying virus. These transactions between the host and the virus are apparently irreversible. Synthesis of the host cell nucleic acids may actually cease, while the specific virus nucleic acid continues to accumulate, as in the case of bacteria infected by a bacteriophage. This phenomenon may occur without demonstrable alteration in oxygen utilization, i.e., metabolic activity, of the infected cell.

All plant viruses replicate their RNA in the nucleus of the cell. Animal viruses are more varied, the synthesis of viral RNA and DNA, respectively, occurring in the cytoplasm for some viruses, in the nucleus for others. Some may be synthesized within the mitochondria. It is interesting that administered bromodeoxyuridine is incorporated in place of thymine in the DNA of herpes virus, leading to the formation of a mutated, noninfective virus.

Although viruses are often thought of as "genes looking for a home," a viewpoint supported by the interaction of bacteriophage with the genetic material of the bacterium (e.g., transduction) and by those viruses known to be oncogenic, in some respects viruses resemble messenger nucleic acids carried in a protective coat of protein. Thus, one of the first tasks of viral nucleic acid in a host cell is to initiate synthesis of the specific viral nucleic acid polymerase, probably by union with the ribosomes of the host cell in much the same manner as host mRNA. Single-stranded viruses convert themselves to double-stranded replicative forms, which in turn produce single-stranded progeny. Viral nucleic acid also carries the information for synthesis of messenger RNA for formation of viral protein.

Viral infection of an animal cell (or treatment with heterologous RNA) results in the production of "interferons," basic proteins of low molecular weight which inhibit the synthesis of viral nucleic acid but not that of the host.

Other Functions of Nucleic Acids

Since all cells of a multicellular organism contain the same genetic information, the problem of their ultimate differentiation arises. There is suggestive evidence that the embryonic organizers which lead to cell specialization may be messenger RNA's. If this should prove to be the case, an even more complex problem arises, since the orderly process of development and differentiation requires release of specific messengers at specific times. The nature of this cellular "biological clock" is unknown.

There is much current speculation concerning the possible role of RNA in memory (obviously a type of information storage). The RNA content of cortical neurons of experimental animals increases with learning, its base composition shifting toward that which is typical of messenger RNA (changes also occur in glial RNA). Direct attempts to increase memory or learning by administration of RNA and to abolish these by destruction of RNA must await further evaluation. It may be predicted that this field will have an exciting, if controversial, future.

INTERRELATIONS OF METABOLISM OF NUCLEIC ACIDS WITH OTHER FOODSTUFFS

As illustrated in Figure 20–10, the nucleic acids and their derivatives are related metabolically to a number of other foodstuffs. However, no obvious connections are found between the metabolism of lipids and that of nucleic acids, aside from the rather non-specific contribution of lipids to metabolic CO_2.

The pathways of protein metabolism provide much of the raw material for the synthesis of purines and pyrimidines, viz., glycine, formate, glutamine, aspartate, and NH_3. Carbohydrate supplies keto acid precursors of the dicarboxylic amino acids, and is also the ultimate source of the pentoses.

The "free" nucleotides, synthesized from the same raw materials as the "bound" nucleotides, exert a considerable influence on the metabolism of all classes of foodstuffs. As collecting, storing, and transferring agents for high-energy phosphate, and as cofactors for biological oxidation and certain other types of reactions, the free nucleotides of the tissues may control the rates of many reactions through variations in concentration.

The nucleic acids and nucleoproteins themselves, however, are probably much more important as agents controlling intermediary metabolism, although their exact roles are still under investigation. They control the genetic pattern of potential enzymes and metabolic pathways in the cell at the nuclear level, and regulate the final realization of that pattern in the cytoplasm in response to signalled requirements from the latter area.

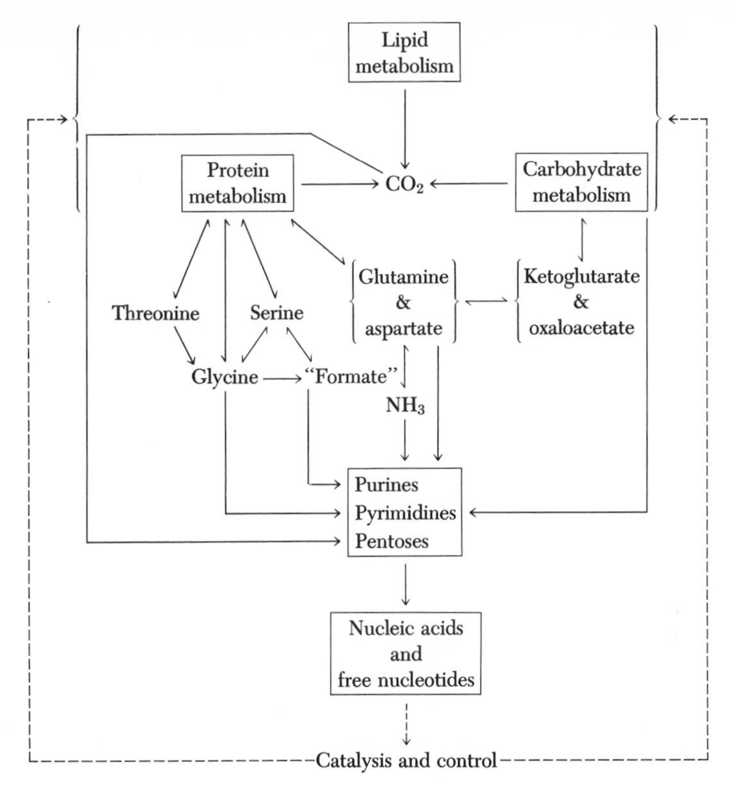

Figure 20-10. Metabolic interrelations of nucleic acids with other foodstuffs.

An abnormal variation of these functions may be seen in the mechanism of virus infections and in malignant disease.

Thus, it is seen that a reciprocal type of relation exists between the nucleic acids (and derivatives) and other classes of metabolites; the latter provide the raw materials (and probably the energy and information) for the synthesis of the nucleic acids and derivatives, which in turn exert an influence over the general pattern and rate of metabolism of the other foodstuffs.

BIBLIOGRAPHY

GENERAL

Annual Review of Biochemistry
Annual Review of Physiology
Chargaff, E., and Davidson, J. N. (eds.): The Nucleic Acids, 3 vols., New York, Academic Press, Inc., 1955 to 1960.
Davidson, J. N.: The Biochemistry of the Nucleic Acids, London, Methuen & Company, 1965.
Davidson, J. N., and Cohn, W. E. (eds.): Progress in Nucleic Acid Research (and Molecular Biology), 4 vols., New York, Academic Press, Inc., 1963 to 1965.

DIGESTION, ABSORPTION

Anfinsen, C. B., and White, F. H., Jr.: The ribonucleases, Chapter 7 in Boyer, P. D., Lardy, H., and Myrbäck, K. (eds.): The Enzymes, Vol. 5, New York, Academic Press, Inc., 1961.

Khorana, H. G.: Phosphodiesterases, Chapter 6 in Boyer, P. D., Lardy, H., and Myrbäck, K. (eds.): The Enzymes, Vol. 5, New York, Academic Press, Inc., 1961.

Laskowski, M., Sr.: Deoxyribonucleases, Chapter 8 in Boyer, P. D., Lardy, H., and Myrbäck, K. (eds.): The Enzymes, Vol. 5, New York, Academic Press, Inc., 1961.

Wilson, T. H.: Intestinal Absorption, Philadelphia, W. B. Saunders Company, 1962, Chapter 9.

PURINES, PYRIMIDINES, NUCLEOTIDES

Bresnick, E.: Regulatory control of pyrimidine biosynthesis in mammalian systems, Advances in Enzyme Regulation *2*:213, 1964.

Guarino, A. J.: The biogenesis of purine and pyrimidine nucleotides, Chapter 2 in Bernfeld, P. (ed.): Biogenesis of Natural Compounds, New York, The Macmillan Company, 1963.

Hutchinson, D. W.: Nucleotides and Coenzymes, London, Methuen & Company, 1964.

Schulman, M. P.: Purines and pyrimidines, Chapter 18 in Greenberg, D. M. (ed.): Metabolic Pathways, Vol. 2, New York, Academic Press, Inc., 1961.

Warren, L.: Nucleotides and nucleosides, Chapter 19 in Greenberg, D. M. (ed.): Metabolic Pathways, Vol. 2, New York, Academic Press, Inc., 1961.

Wyngaarden, J. B.: Gout, Advances in Metab. Disorders *2*:1, 1965.

NUCLEIC ACIDS, NUCLEOPROTEINS

Bonner, J., and Ts'o, P. (eds.): The Nucleohistones, San Francisco, Holden-Day, Inc., 1964.

Busch, H.: Histones and Other Nuclear Proteins, New York, Academic Press, Inc., 1965.

Kornberg, A.: Enzymatic Synthesis of DNA, New York, John Wiley & Sons, Inc., 1962.

Mantsavinos, R., and Zamenhof, S.: The biosynthesis of nucleic acids, Chapter 8 in Bernfeld, P. (ed.): Biogenesis of Natural Compounds, New York, The Macmillan Company, 1963.

BIOLOGICAL FUNCTIONS OF NUCLEIC ACIDS

Perutz, M. F.: Proteins and Nucleic Acids, Amsterdam, Elsevier Publishing Company, 1962.

Taylor, J. H. (ed.): Molecular Genetics, New York, Academic Press, Inc., 1963, Part I.

Vogel, H. J., Bryson, V., and Lampen, J. O. (eds.): Informational Macromolecules, New York, Academic Press, Inc., 1963.

Watson, J. D.: Molecular Biology of the Gene, New York, W. A. Benjamin, Inc., 1965.

Wiseman, A.: Organization for Protein Biosynthesis, New York, American Elsevier Publishing Company, Inc., 1965.

CHAPTER 21

METABOLISM OF PROTEINS

As INDICATED elsewhere in various connections, proteins are of primary importance in intermediary metabolism. Not only are the amino acid constituents of proteins metabolically interrelated with fat, carbohydrate, and other substances, but also the proteins themselves form the structural framework of the body and its working machinery as well. Thus proteins function in the body both statically as fibers, walls, and membranes and dynamically as the body's catalysts, the enzymes. In addition, many of the hormones, the regulators of metabolism, are proteins. Obviously, the importance of the proteins cannot be exaggerated. Because of the numerous facets of this subject which must be considered, it may be useful, for purposes of orientation, to indicate the various segments into which the discussion will be divided.

Mention has been made elsewhere concerning the concepts of the "dynamic state of body constituents" and the "metabolic pool." Although the application of these concepts is by no means restricted to the proteins, the ideas developed originally largely with reference to protein metabolism and many of the best illustrations of the concepts are to be found in that field. For these reasons the discussion of protein metabolism (after a brief review of digestion, absorption, and uptake by tissues) is initiated with a consideration of the general concept of dynamics and pools.

Since much information can be obtained concerning protein metabolism from a study of the metabolism of nitrogen, the intake, excretion, and various states of nitrogen balance are discussed. Included in this connection are the essential amino acids, nutritional aspects of the proteins, and certain interrelations with other foodstuffs.

The overall metabolism of protein, as of all foodstuffs, consists of both anabolic and catabolic phases. Of particular importance is the topic of protein synthesis, including rates, mechanisms, and illustrations of the synthesis of particular proteins.

Plasma proteins are of such central importance in protein metabolism and of such diagnostic value clinically that a separate section is devoted to them.

A consideration of hormonal influences concludes the section on general protein metabolism.

Although the amino acids are prime examples of metabolic "rugged individualism," they undergo certain chemical reactions in common. The general mechanisms are described for the separation of the nitrogenous moieties of the amino acids from their carbon skeletons, followed by a consideration of the pathways available for the disposal of each of the fragments.

The discussion of the metabolism of the individual amino acids, always a most vexing topic to treat on an introductory level, is preceded by an outline of the interrelations existing between them, thus providing at least certain threads of connection between topics otherwise virtually isolated and independent.

The chapter is concluded with a discussion of the metabolic interrelations between the proteins and other major foodstuffs.

DIGESTION AND ABSORPTION

The course of protein digestion and the factors involved are discussed in detail elsewhere (pp. 260–265); it is necessary here merely to review briefly the most important features of this process.

Mainly through the hydrolytic action of the proteinases, pepsin (stomach), trypsin (pancreas), and chymotrypsin (pancreas), the large protein molecules are broken down to polypeptides and free amino acids. Completion of digestion, i.e., complete hydrolysis of the peptides, is accomplished by the action of carboxypeptidase (pancreas), and amino-, tri-, and dipeptidases of the intestinal secretions. The process consists essentially in the production of progressively smaller peptides by cleavage of internal peptide linkages (endopeptidases) and liberation of amino acids by cleavage of terminal peptide linkages (endo- and exopeptidases).

If an intact "foreign" protein, i.e., other than human, is introduced into the organism, it acts as an antigen, i.e., it stimulates the formation of specific antibodies, "sensitizing" the organism to this protein (allergic state). Subsequent exposure to the protein results in a serious, and sometimes fatal, reaction (anaphylaxis). Obviously, if this phenomenon is to be avoided, food proteins must be so altered before absorption that they have lost their species specificity and thereby their capacity for inducing this state of sensitization. This is accomplished effectively by digestion to the stage of amino acids, which, of course, exhibit no such specificity. It is possible, too, that small peptide molecules escape complete hydrolysis and are absorbed without harmful effect.

Intestinal absorption of some intact protein molecules, e.g., antibodies of the colostrum, occurs in the newborn of certain species. However, this does not occur normally in man. When it does occur, only minute antigenic amounts are absorbed, but these may form the basis for subsequent idiosyncrasies toward proteins of milk and egg. This intestinal absorption abnormality may be due to temporary morphologic or physiologic defects, in conjunction with impaired digestion of protein owing to the low concentration of proteolytic enzymes in the digestive secretions of the newborn, and to the presence of a potent antitryptic factor in the colostrum during the first few days.

Food proteins are generally readily digested (90 to 97 per cent) under normal conditions, very little escaping in the feces. One important exception is the insoluble fibrous protein, keratin, which is not hydrolyzed by enzymes of the human digestive tract. Most proteins are profoundly altered by many procedures commonly used in the preparation of foods. Heating to coagulation temperatures causes polymerization; superheated steam, excluding air (pressure cookers), causes hydrolysis; dry heat may cause oxidation. In the majority of instances, the digestibility and biological value of these proteins are not affected by such procedures. However, proper cooking may facilitate digestion and utilization, e.g., cooked egg albumin is digested more readily than raw; heating soybeans increases their biological value by inactivating a component with antitryptic activity. The nutritional value of cereal proteins is lowered by overheating or toasting (e.g., certain breakfast cereals).

With the few exceptions indicated above, food proteins enter the organism in the form of their constituent amino acids. Certain aspects of protein digestion that have an important bearing on their nutritional value, e.g., variation in the rates of liberation of amino acids, are discussed elsewhere (p. 656). The amino acids are readily soluble in water and are promptly absorbed from the small intestine, mainly into the portal circulation (to the liver), and to a much smaller extent, via the lacteals, into the thoracic duct and thence directly into the systemic circulation. Only small amounts of free amino acid are found in the intestinal contents during the process of digestion, indicating the rapidity of their absorption. This is reflected also in the rather prompt postprandial increase in blood amino acid concentration (p. 811).

UPTAKE BY TISSUES

Both absorption of amino acids from the intestine and their uptake by the tissues from the extracellular fluids are processes of active transport. Although differences exist among transport mechanisms of intestine, kidney, and other tissues, it appears to be generally true that separate mechanisms exist for groups of structurally related amino acids, viz., cationic (basic), anionic (acidic), and neutral, with the possible addition of a special subclass of the last which includes the prolines, compounds with betaine-like structures, and perhaps glycine. Certain inborn errors of renal transport (cystinuria, Hartnup disease) are characterized also by concomitant defects in intestinal absorption of the same groups of amino acids.

Although transport of amino acids is defective in pyridoxine deficiency, the direct participation of derivatives of this vitamin (e.g., pyridoxal phosphate) in the transport mechanism proper remains to be established.

Certain hormones enhance the uptake of amino acids by specific tissues. Indeed, this effect may play a major role in the influence of these hormones on protein metabolism. Such may be the case, for example, in the endocrine regulation of the flow of amino acids between visceral organs (particularly liver) and carcass (largely the muscle mass), which will be discussed subsequently (p. 565). Among hormones which favor uptake of amino acids in specific tissues there may be mentioned STH (muscle, diaphragm, and a number of other sites), insulin (muscle, diaphragm), testosterone (skeletal muscle, kidney, uterus), estradiol (uterus), epinephrine and glucocorticoids (liver), and the various tropic hormones, which affect their respective target tissues in this manner.

METABOLIC DYNAMICS AND POOLS

Dynamic State

It was realized even for some time prior to the use of isotopes, but particularly clearly since the introduction of labeling techniques, that the constituents of the body are in a constant state of flux. All molecules, even of the "structural" variety, are constantly being broken down and rebuilt. The apparent stability of the adult organism is the result of a balance between the rates of synthesis and degradation of its constituents. In a growing organism, the rates of synthesis of many of its constituents must exceed the rates of breakdown, in order that new tissue may be constructed. Wasting diseases, starvation, and related states are characterized by rates of catabolism which are greater than the rates of anabolism.

In a given physiological (or pathological) state, the rate of synthesis or degradation of a specific compound will be characteristic of (1) the chemical nature of the compound in question, (2) its location in a particular tissue or organ, and (3) its intracellular location.

Several methods of expression are currently used to describe the rate of synthesis or breakdown of a body constituent. Most of these have been developed in connection with isotopic labeling techniques. The "half-life" is the time required for replacement of one-half of the molecules of the compound in question, the definition being analogous to that used in describing the unstable isotopes (p. 341). The "average life" of a given compound is the time required to replace the molecule of "average stability." Sometimes the rate of a synthetic or degradative process is expressed directly in terms of mass of compound transformed per unit time per unit weight of tissue or animal, e.g., "moles of urea synthesized per day per kilo body weight." On other occasions the rate of turnover of a compound is stated as the percentage of the amount present which is metabolized per unit time.

Metabolic Pool

Since the "endogenous" molecules are in a state of flux, they and their metabolites must be constantly mixing with those derived from the diet ("exogenous"). This mixture of originally endogenous and exogenous materials, which is drawn upon for both anabolic and catabolic reactions, constitutes a reservoir or "metabolic pool" of the compounds in question. For example, the alanine derived from the continuous breakdown of body protein and that obtained from dietary protein mix to form an "alanine pool." The amino group of the alanine, together with the amino groups of all other amino acids which are able to participate in nitrogen exchange reactions (e.g., transamination, p. 568), form a pool of metabolically labile nitrogen. (Lysine and threonine are exceptional in that they contribute their amino nitrogen to the general pool, but do not accept nitrogen from this source.)

Members of one pool are metabolically equilibrated with other pools. Alanine, for example, is reversibly converted by deamination to pyruvate, hence the carbon skeleton of this amino acid is involved in the pyruvate pool, which is directly connected to the carbohydrate pool.

The size of a pool is the quantity of constituent instantaneously present and available for all of the reactions leading into and from that particular pool. The pool of metabolically labile amino groups in the human being, for example, has been estimated at 2 gm. of nitrogen (70 kg. man), i.e., of the same order of magnitude as the free amino acids of the tissues.

The concepts of dynamic state and metabolic pool have been invaluable in the interpretation of data resulting from experiments with isotopic labeling. For example, consider the case of an adult experimental animal in nitrogen equilibrium (p. 545) being fed a dose of glycine labeled with N^{15}. According to the classical theories of biochemistry, the metabolic paths of endogenous and exogenous compounds are compartmentalized; hence exogenous glycine, since it is not required for tissue construction (adult animal, nitrogen equilibrium), should be degraded directly and the nitrogen excreted as urea within approximately 24 hours. What is found experimentally is that a quantity of extra urea is excreted, equivalent to the glycine administered. However, only a small fraction of the N^{15} is excreted in this urea; several days are required for the recovery of an appreciable fraction. Hence, the nitrogen output is equivalent to the intake, but the atoms excreted are mainly not those ingested. To begin with, the ingested glycine enters the glycine pool, so that the concentration of N^{15} in the average glycine molecule is lowered by dilution with all of the N^{14}-glycine molecules. Secondly, the amino group of glycine is readily equilibrated with that of most other amino acids (transamination), resulting in further dilution or spread of N^{15} throughout most of the amino acids of the body. The nitrogen pool which is drawn upon for the synthesis of urea, therefore, contains a much lower concentration of molecules labeled with N^{15} than did the sample of glycine administered. A simplified illustration of such situations follows:

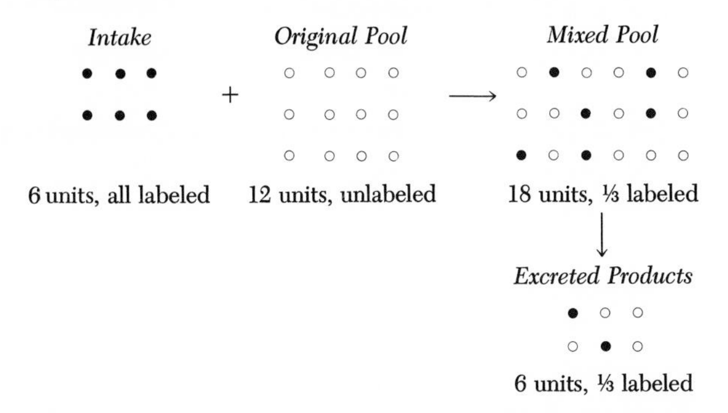

It is obvious that the classical concept of independent exogenous and endogenous metabolism is directly contradicted by such observations, and can no longer be maintained.

GENERAL PATHWAYS OF PROTEIN METABOLISM

The most important of the metabolic pathways of proteins and amino acids may be illustrated as shown in Figure 21–1.

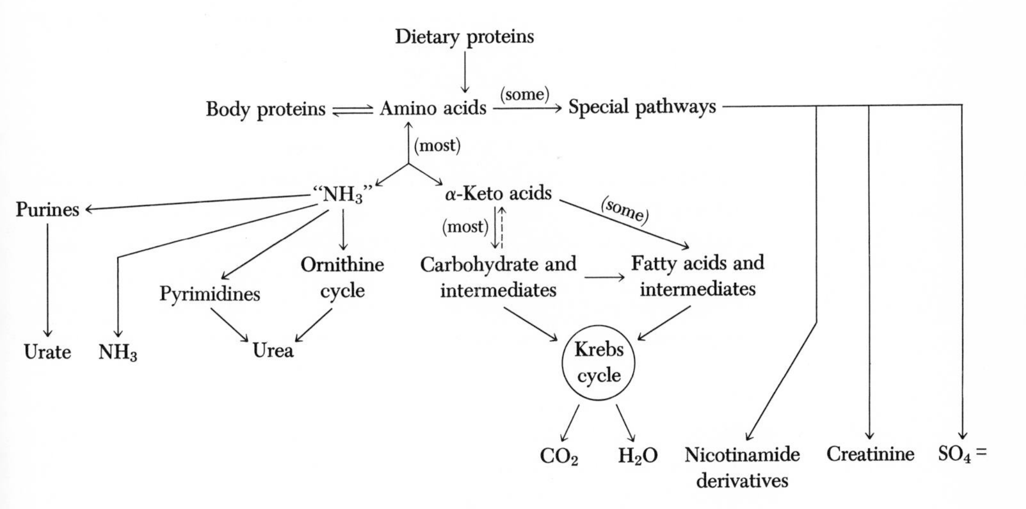

Figure 21–1. General pathways of protein and amino acid metabolism.

In accord with what was said in the preceding discussion, the proteins of the body are continuously undergoing breakdown to (and resynthesis from) their constituent free amino acids. The proteins of the diet, upon digestion and absorption, contribute their amino acids to the general pool. This amino acid pool is drawn upon, on the one hand, for anabolic purposes, such as the synthesis of protein, and, on the other, for catabolic purposes.

Most of the catabolic (and a few of the anabolic) reactions are preceded by a cleavage of the amino acid into its nitrogenous (amino group, ammonia) and non-nitrogenous (carbon skeleton, α-keto acid) moieties. These fragments then follow separate pathways. The nitrogen may be used in certain synthetic reactions, such as the synthesis of purines, the final excretory product of which is urate, or the synthesis of pyrimidines, which eventually break down to form urea (a relatively minor source of this compound). The nitrogen also may be excreted as ammonia itself, or as urea, which is the major nitrogenous excretory product of protein metabolism.

The carbon skeletons of the amino acids, present as α-keto acids, join the pathways of either carbohydrate (most) or fatty acids (a few), in either case being eventually oxidized to CO_2 via the tricarboxylic acid cycle. Certain amino acids follow special metabolic routes; among them are some leading to the final excretion of sulfate, creatinine, and nicotinamide derivatives.

OVERALL METABOLISM OF PROTEIN

Nitrogen Metabolism

(*a*) ***Importance of nitrogen.*** Much of the information on the metabolism of protein can be expressed (and is frequently measured) in terms of nitrogen, the reasons for which are readily apparent. The carbon and hydrogen atoms of the proteins form CO_2 and H_2O as end-products of metabolism, indistinguishable from the end-products of the metabolism of carbohydrates or fatty acids. Although certain proteins contain phosphoric acid, this constituent is more characteristic of the nucleic acids, phospholipids, and certain intermediates in carbohydrate metabolism. Sulfur is an almost invariable constituent of proteins, but its metabolism reflects only the reactions of cystine and methionine. In contrast to these elements, nitrogen is uniquely characteristic of proteins, from the standpoints of both its high concentration in the protein molecule (average, 16 per cent) and its specialized excretory products (ammonia, urea, etc.).

(*b*) ***Nitrogen of the food.*** Protein nitrogen outweighs all other forms of nitrogen in the diet. Traces of inorganic nitrogen are ingested in the form of nitrates and nitrites. Small amounts of organic non-protein nitrogen (NPN) are also present in the food, including nucleic acids and their derivatives, and amino acids and peptides.

(*c*) ***Nitrogen of the body.*** Many nitrogenous compounds are found in the tissues and fluids of the body. Protein itself averages about 20 per cent of the wet weight of most tissues. In the blood, in addition to protein, several types of NPN are found. Urea, the major waste product of protein catabolism, formed in the liver, passes into the bloodstream to the kidneys for excretion. Blood creatine may be en route to muscle for the synthesis of phosphocreatine, or may have leaked out of muscle. Creatinine is a waste product, formed from phosphocreatine and creatine. Urate is the end-product of purine catabolism. Free amino acids are also found in the blood; they are in transit from one organ to another for purposes of synthesis or breakdown. Other components of the blood NPN include polypeptides, glutathione, purines and pyrimidines, ATP, and ergothioneine.

(*d*) ***Excretion of nitrogen.*** Fecal nitrogen appears not to be related to the nitrogen of the ingested protein. Its quantity varies with the bulk of the diet, and does not normally represent unabsorbed dietary protein. In the adult human, it amounts to 1 to 2 gm. N/day. Perspiration, unless sweating is excessive, accounts for a loss of only 0.3 gm. N/day or less.

The urine is the major route of excretion of nitrogen. In the average, normal, human adult, the total nitrogen of the urine is about 13 gm./day, and this is normally all NPN (no significant quantities of protein are found in the urine normally). Urea (about 85 per cent of the total) and ammonia (about 3 per cent) vary directly with the level of protein in the diet. Creatinine excretion (5 per cent of the total) is related to the muscle mass and is quite constant for an individual. Creatine is not normally excreted by adult males or by most females. Only traces of amino acids are found in the urine. Urate output (1 per cent of total) fluctuates with the level of dietary purines. About 5 per cent of the total is composed of compounds not ordinarily determined. The factors which influence the urinary excretion of the various nitrogenous substances are discussed elsewhere (p. 840).

(*e*) ***Nitrogen balance.*** Since most of the nitrogen of the diet represents protein, and most of the nitrogenous excretory products are derived from protein catabolism, it is apparent that the balance between the two will reveal significant features of protein metabolism. Nitrogen balance is defined as the quantitative difference between the nitrogen intake and the nitrogen output, both expressed in the same units (such as gm. N/day). By intake is meant the nitrogen of the food. Included in output are such routes of excretion as urine, feces, milk, sweat, expectoration, vomitus, desquamation of skin, menstrual fluid, and loss of hair; in practice, however, only the first two are taken into account except under unusual circumstances.

Positive nitrogen balance exists when intake exceeds output. This condition obtains whenever new tissue is being synthesized, such as during growth of the young, in pregnancy, and in convalescence from states of negative nitrogen balance.

In negative nitrogen balance, the output exceeds the intake. This condition, which obviously cannot continue indefinitely, occurs on inadequate intake of protein (fasting, diseases of the gastrointestinal tract), in states of accelerated catabolism of tissue protein (fevers, infections, wasting diseases), and when the loss of protein from the body is accelerated in some way (lactation on inadequate diets, albuminuria). Experimentally, negative nitrogen balance occurs also in the absence from the diet of an "essential" amino acid (p. 546).

From the preceding discussion, it is evident that nitrogen equilibrium (intake = output) can be achieved only in the adult organism, and only in the absence of the abnormal conditions enumerated above. An "adequate diet" must also be specified, which means that all requirements for minerals and vitamins are fulfilled, that the protein of the diet is of high "biological value" (p. 549) and is administered at a sufficiently high level, and that the caloric needs of the body (p. 333) are met satisfactorily by the carbohydrate and fat of the diet. In these circumstances, the nitrogen output equals the intake, and an increase or decrease in the intake is followed, within a day or two, by a corresponding adjustment in the output, so that nitrogen equilibrium is established at a new level. There appears to be no marked tendency toward storage of surplus nitrogen, as there is in the case of the fats and carbohydrates.

Calorigenic Value of Protein

The fuel value of protein (p. 326) is approximately the same as that of carbohydrate, 4 kcal./gm. The "specific dynamic action" (p. 333) of protein is the highest of all the foodstuffs. A detailed discussion of these matters will be found in the pages cited.

Essential Amino Acids

It is possible to replace the protein of the diet completely with pure amino acids. The so-called "dietary requirement" for protein is, therefore, really a requirement for amino acids, and is expressed in terms of protein only because the amino acids of the available foodstuffs are found in that form.

By the elimination of single amino acids from an otherwise complete diet, it has been found that the organism can successfully dispense with certain of these compounds, but not with others. Evidently all amino acids are not synthesized with equal facility by the body. An "essential," or "indispensable," amino acid is defined as one which cannot be synthesized by the organism from substances ordinarily present in the diet at a rate commensurate with certain physiological requirements. The definition includes the phrase, "cannot be synthesized by the organism from substances ordinarily present in the diet," because certain of these amino acids may be replaced by the corresponding α-keto or α-hydroxy acids, or by their D isomers. Since such substances do not occur in diets unless placed there experimentally, the topic is of interest only to investigators of the metabolism of amino acids and will not be discussed further. The requirements specified in the most extensive series of investigations are: (1) optimal growth of the young and (2) maintenance of nitrogen equilibrium in the adult.

Although the amino acid requirement for growth has been investigated in several species, the most thorough experiments have been performed in the white rat. The ten amino acids required by this animal for optimal growth (and, in the absence of data to the contrary, the same list is assumed to apply to other mammals, including man) are the eight given in Table 21-1 plus arginine and histidine. In the case of arginine, the requirement is not absolute; the animals grow, but suboptimally, in its absence, indicating a slow and (for this physiological requirement) inadequate rate of synthesis of this amino acid.

The requirement for nitrogen equilibrium in the adult appears to be less stringent. In

TABLE 21-1. QUANTITATIVE REQUIREMENTS OF AMINO ACIDS FOR NITROGEN EQUILIBRIUM IN HUMAN ADULTS*

AMINO ACID	MINIMA FOUND (GM./DAY) MALE	FEMALE
Isoleucine	0.70	0.45
Leucine	1.1	0.62
Lysine	0.80	0.50
Methionine		
Cystine absent	1.1	
Cystine present	0.20	0.35
Phenylalanine		
Tyrosine absent	1.1	
Tyrosine present	0.30	0.22
Threonine	0.50	0.31
Tryptophan	0.25	0.16
Valine	0.80	0.65

* Adapted from National Academy of Sciences-National Research Council: Evaluation of Protein Nutrition, Publication 711, Washington, D.C., 1959.

man, only eight amino acids are required for maintenance of nitrogen equilibrium, the list differing from the preceding in the absence of histidine and arginine. It has been possible to quantitate the requirements. These are shown in Table 21-1.

The requirement for certain essential amino acids may be spared by the inclusion of specific non-essential amino acids in the diet. In each case the sparing action appears to be explicable on the basis that a significant fraction of the essential amino acid is required for synthesis of a related non-essential amino acid, a burden which may be removed by inclusion of the latter in the diet. Thus, tyrosine spares phenylalanine, cystine spares methionine, and glutamic acid and proline spare arginine (in the growing animal). In phenylketonuric individuals (p. 599), who are unable to convert phenylalanine into tyrosine, the latter becomes an essential amino acid.

A curious fact concerning the essential amino acids is that the complete group must be administered to the organism simultaneously. If a single essential amino acid is omitted from the group and fed separately several hours later, the nutritional effectiveness of the entire group is impaired. The "excess" amino acids are almost completely oxidized during the elapsed interval.

It might logically be expected that the optimal ratio of essential amino acids in the diet should approximate that found in the carcass of the animal concerned. This appears to be true. In fact, significant deviations from this ratio result in a number of adverse effects:

1. Certain amino acids are toxic to the experimental animal when fed at a high level. In some instances, the toxicity is counteracted by increasing the concentration of a structurally related amino acid in the diet. Such cases are probably genuine examples of metabolic antagonism (p. 663).

2. Vitamin deficiencies can be aggravated by addition to the diet of increased quantities of a single amino acid (or by improvement of the dietary intake of protein in general). These effects may be due to an increase in the rate of amino acid metabolism, leading to increased utilization and breakdown of vitamins.

3. True imbalance of amino acids can occur when the diet is marginal or suboptimal in one essential amino acid, whereupon increasing the dietary level of another essential amino acid sets up an imbalance and growth is decreased. This condition may be corrected by supplementation with small amounts of the limiting amino acid. The explanation appears to be that the body uses amino acids for synthesis of protein in ratios required by the carcass composition, in quantities determined by the limiting amino acid. The excess is catabolized. Furthermore, the process of catabolizing the excess may increase the rate of general amino acid catabolism, including that of the limiting amino acid, thus aggravating the condition.

From a general point of view, the negative nitrogen balance or decrease of growth resulting from omission of an essential amino acid from the diet, or its separate administration at a time appreciably different from the rest of the diet, may be considered special cases of amino acid imbalance.

The lists of essential amino acids must be taken provisionally, particularly in their application to human nutrition. In the case of the ten amino acids required for growth, there is a certain risk in transferring nutritional requirements from one species to another (glycine, for example, is essential for the chick!). Although the nitrogen equilibrium experiments in human adults seem satisfactory, they were run for periods of time which represent only small fractions of the lifetime of the individual. It is possible that additional requirements, quantitative and qualitative, exist if longer periods of time are considered, or if the individual is subjected to stress.

Isolated tissues other than the liver may exhibit requirements for amino acids in addition to those required by the entire organism, largely because of the lack of the versatile synthetic capabilities of the hepatic tissue. For example, tissue cultures of many types of mammalian cells require, in addition to the eight amino acids essential for nitrogen balance in the intact adult organism, arginine, cystine, glutamine, histidine, and tyrosine.

It had been claimed in the past that proteins contribute something to nutrition in addition to amino acids, and that experimental animals grow more rapidly on diets of protein than on mixtures of amino acids simulating the composition of the protein. The difference was attributed to small peptides resulting from incomplete digestion of the protein. One such peptide has been called "strepogenin," since it appears to stimulate the growth of certain streptococci. At present, improvements in experimental techniques have led to the conclusion that no significant difference in the growth rate of experimental animals is found whether the diet consists of intact protein or mixtures of synthetic amino acids.

Biosynthesis of Essential Amino Acids

In the animal organism, most non-essential amino acids are synthesized from keto acids derived from carbohydrate. Although the biosynthesis of essential amino acids in

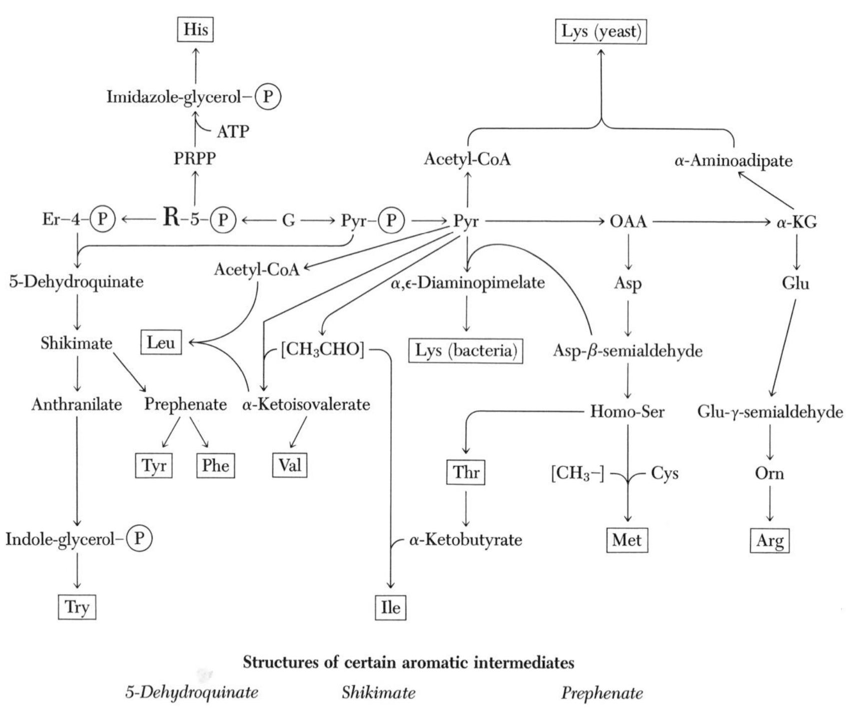

Structures of certain aromatic intermediates

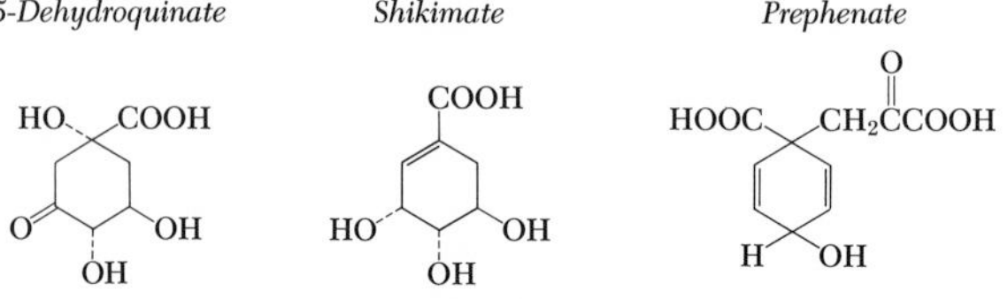

Figure 21-2. Biosynthesis of essential amino acids. *Er*, Erythrose; *KG*, ketoglutarate; *OAA*, oxaloacetate; *Pyr*, pyruvate.

plants and microorganisms has no great relevance to animal biochemistry, it is interesting that these compounds also are derived from carbohydrate and its metabolites, as illustrated in Figure 21–2. The pathway shown for arginine in the figure is believed to be followed also in the adult mammal; the synthesis of histidine in the adult mammal has yet to be elucidated. It will be noted that, in contrast to those organisms in which phenylalanine is an essential amino acid and tyrosine is not (being synthesized from phenylalanine), those forms of life which synthesize both of these amino acids do so by independent pathways which branch from a common precursor.

Biological Value of Proteins (cf. p. 654)

In order that a food protein may have value to the organism, it must be digested and absorbed. Keratins, for example, are practically immune to the action of digestive enzymes, and consequently are of no value in the diet. Even if digestible, a protein may be nutritionally inadequate owing to the absence (or presence in inadequate amount) of an essential amino acid. Gelatin (no tryptophan) and zein (no lysine, low tryptophan) are in this category (cf. Table 4-2, p. 59). In general, animal proteins are nutritionally superior to plant proteins. The latter may be satisfactory if the food contains a sufficiently wide variety, but many individual plant proteins are seriously deficient in one or more of the essential amino acids.

Dietary Protein Requirements

(*a*) ***General nutrition.*** If it is assumed that the protein of the diet is biologically adequate, the nutritional requirements can be discussed in terms of quantities of protein, rather than of amino acids. As a further assumption, sufficient fat and carbohydrate must be included in the diet to cover the caloric requirements of the individual. Under these conditions, quantitative recommendations can be made for the infant, the growing child, and the adult (p. 657). Increased requirements occur in certain situations, viz., pregnancy, lactation, and convalescence.

In connection with protein nutrition, the subject of "storage protein" is of interest. From the relatively rapid adjustment of nitrogen excretion to variations in intake in adult organisms, it appears that no significant quantity of protein is stored. It is nevertheless true that, in states of protein deprivation, certain tissues are able to contribute significant quantities of their protein for the preservation of certain vital functions. Although there is no chemically or morphologically distinct storage form of protein, corresponding to glycogen or depot fat, the more metabolically labile proteins of the tissues are available in case of need. These include the plasma proteins (however, other tissue proteins are usually sacrificed to provide plasma protein), and the proteins of the liver, gastrointestinal tract, and kidney. Only a small percentage of muscle protein appears to be labile, but the size of the muscle mass is such that it provides the greatest absolute amount of protein in conditions of deprivation.

(*b*) ***Synthesis of special proteins.*** If some of the blood is removed from an animal, centrifuged, and the cells suspended in saline and reinjected into the same animal, it is possible to lower the plasma protein level considerably ("plasmapheresis" technique). Initial bleedings of this type in dogs result in rapid regeneration of the plasma protein (from the labile protein of the tissues). Repeated plasmapheresis of dogs kept on appropriate diets eventually depresses the plasma proteins to a low, constant level. The effect can then be tested of various proteins or amino acids in the diet on the synthesis of plasma proteins.

Similar experiments in which the red cells are removed and the plasma replaced lead to an anemia type of depletion. Iron, of course, is very important in the regeneration of hemoglobin. So also is the intake of histidine, a finding to be anticipated from the concentration of this amino acid in hemoglobin (p. 59). It is of interest that, in animals suffering from a double deficiency (plasma proteins and hemoglobin), the process of regeneration favors hemoglobin over the plasma proteins.

As might be expected, dietary proteins effective in the repletion of the protein of one depleted tissue often are ineffective in the "nutrition" of another. Restoration of the protein content of the livers of animals which have been deprived of proteins for various periods of time is accomplished effectively by certain dietary proteins which are considerably less efficient in the regeneration of plasma proteins.

In an in vitro study of the synthesis of amylase by slices of pancreas, it has been found that 10 of the 16 amino acids involved in the structure of amylase are required in the medium for a maximum rate of synthesis. The list includes all of the essential amino acids present in the enzyme and one "non-essential," which is evidently essential for the tissue in question.

(*c*) ***Protein-sparing effects.*** It has been observed that the dietary requirement for protein is influenced markedly by the level in the diet of fat and carbohydrate, these latter foodstuffs appearing to have a "protein-sparing" effect. This phenomenon is best understood by consideration of the physiological functions of the major foodstuffs. Fat, although it has certain structural uses, functions primarily as a fuel. Carbohydrate also serves as a fuel, but in addition is required for the synthesis of certain catalytic compounds of metabolic cycles (e.g., oxaloacetate in the tricarboxylic acid cycle), and provides the carbon skeletons for the synthesis of the non-essential amino acids. Protein has an obvious structural role, but even more important from the dynamic point of view is its catalytic function, the enzyme proteins forming a major part of the actual working machinery of the body.

In the absence of fat and carbohydrate from the diet, protein must be degraded to provide fuel and catalytic compounds of metabolic cycles. Essential amino acids may be broken down to supply the raw materials for the synthesis of the non-essential amino acids. To provide for these increased burdens, the protein intake consequently must be increased. Conversely, addition of fat to the diet will take care of the caloric needs, a relatively small amount of carbohydrate will furnish the catalytic compounds of the cycles and carbon skeletons of the non-essential amino acids, and the protein requirement will be decreased as a result.

In addition to the overall sparing effect of carbohydrate on the requirement for protein, the former influences the distribution of the latter within the organism. Inclusion of carbohydrate in the diet tends to cause deposition of plasma amino acids in skeletal muscle in the form of labile protein, which in turn is mobilized in the form of amino acids to the liver in carbohydrate deprivation. These effects are part of a complex control system involving interaction of dietary influences with endocrine regulation (p. 565).

(*d*) ***Protein deprivation.*** As stated previously, protein forms the structural framework of the body and the active machinery as well. Liver, intestinal mucosa, and kidney are sites of very active protein metabolism. The turnover rate of protein is very high in these tissues, and they also happen to discharge functions in protein digestion or metabolism which are important to the body as a whole. Protein deprivation, therefore, is particularly harmful to the activity of these tissues. Impairment of their metabolic efficiency results in further disturbances in protein digestion and metabolism, thus aggravating the state of deprivation. A "cycle of degeneration" sets in, reversal of which becomes increasingly difficult. It is obvious, therefore, why so much emphasis has been placed by the medical profession in recent years on the state of protein nutrition of the patient.

ANABOLISM AND CATABOLISM OF PROTEINS

Protein Turnover

As discussed previously, all proteins in the body are constantly breaking down to their constituent amino acids and being resynthesized (dynamic state), the rate of this turnover varying for different proteins in different tissues. The amino acids from the body proteins and those derived from the food form a metabolic pool, the members of which are drawn upon for reactions in either the anabolic or catabolic direction.

The metabolic lability of the proteins in the various tissues can be investigated by noting the rapidity with which each tissue loses protein when the organism is depleted (i.e., on a protein-free diet) and regains protein on repletion. A more recent technique measures the rate of uptake into the proteins of each tissue of an isotopically labeled amino acid, or, in certain cases, the rate of loss of an isotope already incorporated. Whatever the method, high rates of turnover have been shown in plasma proteins, intestinal mucosa, pancreas, liver, and kidney, and low rates in muscle, skin, and brain. Certain numerical data are available (Table 21-2). It may be seen that individual proteins within a given tissue may turn over at rates quite different from the "average protein" of that tissue. Note the very rapid turnover rate of the enzyme, tryptophan pyrrolase, in comparison to total liver protein.

Protein Synthesis

A complete description of the process of protein synthesis should include explanations of:

(1) Mechanism of formation of the peptide linkage.

(2) Specification of the primary level of organization (amino acid sequence).

(3) Specification of the three-dimensional conformation of the protein (secondary, tertiary, and in some cases quaternary levels of organization).

(4) Mechanism of attachment of prosthetic groups, if any.

(5) Mechanisms of regulation.

TABLE 21-2. RATES OF TURNOVER OF PROTEIN

ANIMAL	TISSUE OR PROTEIN	HALF-LIFE IN DAYS
Man	Whole body	80
Man	Serum protein and liver	10
Man	Muscle	180
Rat	Whole body	17
Rat	Liver, plasma, internal organs	6
Rat	Muscle	24–30
Rat	Liver tryptophan pyrrolase	0.083–0.167 (2–4 hours)

Although great advances have been made in recent years in this area of biochemistry, only the first two items in the above list can be said to be understood fairly satisfactorily at this time.

Fundamental reaction. The formation of the peptide linkage is the basic reaction of protein synthesis:

$$R_1-\underset{}{\overset{NH_2}{\overset{|}{C}H}}-COOH + R_2-\overset{NH_2}{\overset{|}{C}H}-COOH \longrightarrow R_1-\overset{NH_2}{\overset{|}{C}H}-\overset{O}{\overset{\|}{C}}-NH-\overset{R_2}{\overset{|}{C}H}-COOH + H_2O$$

As in the case of most reactions involving the splitting out of water in an aqueous medium, the equilibrium is far toward the side of hydrolysis. Since the reaction in the anabolic direction is endergonic, an outside source of energy is needed. As will be shown subsequently, the condensation is preceded by "activation" reactions, and the endergonic reaction is driven to completion by coupling with a strongly exergonic reaction, namely the breakdown of ATP.

Pseudopeptide synthesis. A number of compounds are synthesized in the body which contain linkages closely related to peptide bonds. Many of these were mentioned earlier under the heading "Pseudopeptides" (p. 60). A study of the mechanism of synthesis of these model compounds sheds a certain amount of light on the synthesis of proteins. Thus, the in vitro formation of acetyl-sulfanilamide, various hippurates, and the conjugated bile acids requires the presence of ATP and CoA. The participation of CoA has not been demonstrated in other peptide syntheses. However, ATP has been implicated in the synthesis of ornithuric acid, glutamine, and the true peptide, glutathione. In many instances of pseudopeptide synthesis, formation of the pseudopeptide linkage has been shown to be preceded by activation of the carboxyl member of the linkage. In certain cases, the activated form has been found to be a carboxyl-adenylate. From the foregoing observations it may be surmised that amino acids undergo a preliminary "activation" at the expense of ATP, subsequent to which the activated forms condense exergonically to produce peptides. As indicated in Figure 21–3, this generalization is certainly valid, although the detailed process exhibits many complexities.

Early experiments. Investigations utilizing isotopically labeled amino acids in vivo or in preparations consisting of intact cells in vitro showed that the earliest incorporation of isotope occurred in the microsomal fraction (later found to be specifically in the ribosomal particles). Non-uniform labeling of a given amino acid in various positions along the peptide chain of certain proteins, particularly in brief experiments, suggested that the incorporation of amino acids was stepwise rather than simultaneous. The process, nevertheless, was found to be very rapid; it was calculated that a complete peptide chain of hemoglobin could be synthesized in about one minute, corresponding to the incorporation of two amino acid residues per second. The energy-dependence of the process of protein synthesis was shown by its inhibition by anaerobiosis and by uncoupling agents such as dinitrophenol. When cell-free preparations became available, it was possible to demonstrate inhibition by ribonuclease (implicating RNA), replacement of the energy requirement by ATP, and the involvement of GTP and enzymes from the non-particulate phase of the cytoplasm (as well as ribosomes).

Site of synthesis. Although protein synthesis occurs in nuclei and mitochondria, it is possible that these pathways are restricted to the construction of specialized proteins required by the organelles involved. At any rate, little is known of the mechanism. The discussion which follows will be limited to the cytoplasmic ribosomal system, which is responsible for the bulk of the protein synthesis in the cell, and to which most of our recently obtained information applies.

Figure 21–3 illustrates, for simplicity, the steps believed to be involved in the insertion of a single amino acid residue (phenylalanine) into the growing peptide chain.

Activation of amino acids. The non-particulate phase of the cytoplasm contains a group of enzymes which are precipitable at pH 5. This so-called "pH 5 fraction" contains activating enzymes (aminoacyl-sRNA synthetases) for the amino acids, each activating enzyme being specific for an amino acid. (Although the specificity of each enzyme is sufficient to enable it to distinguish its substrate from among the 20-odd amino acids normally present, analogs, closely related in chemical structure to the amino acids, also

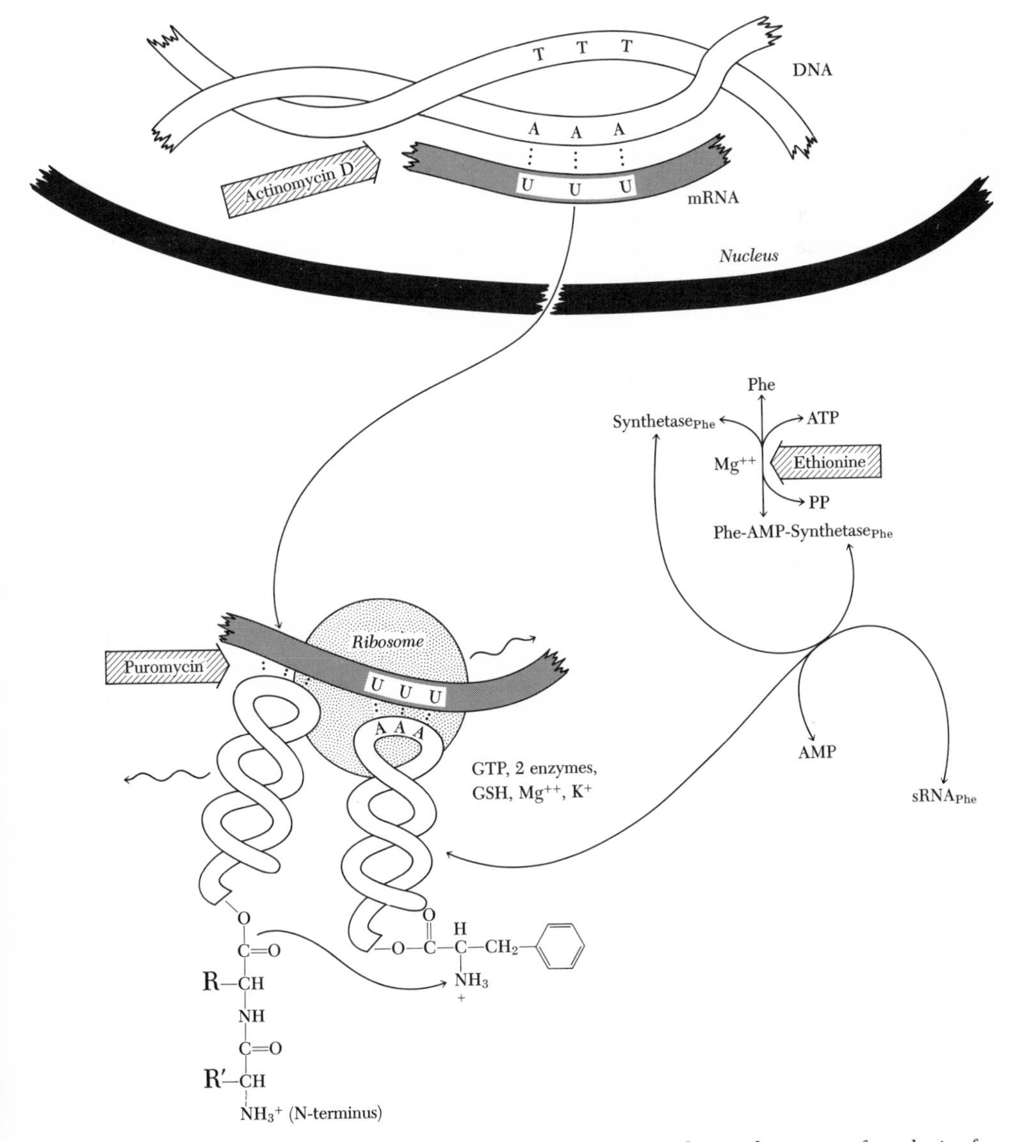

Figure 21–3. Probable mechanism for insertion of a phenylalanine residue in the course of synthesis of a protein.

may be activated, thus leading to the eventual synthesis of proteins containing abnormal amino acid residues.) As shown in Figure 21–3, the activation reaction involves the formation of aminoacyl-adenylate-enzyme complexes, accompanied by the loss of a pyrophosphate residue from ATP. Progress of this reaction toward completion is probably insured in the living cell by hydrolysis of the pyrophosphate by means of pyrophosphatases.

Ethionine, a structural analog of methionine, inhibits the activation reaction. Although ethionine is one of those analogs which can be activated and incorporated into proteins, it is believed that the inhibition of protein synthesis by this compound is largely due to its action as an "ATP trap," depleting the cellular ATP by reacting with it to form S-adenosyl-ethionine (p. 590).

Transfer of amino acids to soluble RNA. There occurs in the non-particulate phase of the cytoplasm a group of soluble (or "transfer") ribonucleic acids, symbolized by "sRNA." These molecules are of relatively low molecular weight (20,000 to 30,000), containing approximately 60 to 90 nucleotides. Although the soluble ribonucleic acids differ from each other sufficiently to be separable by various physicochemical techniques, they all contain the terminal nucleotide sequence: -cytidylic-cytidylic-adenylic. Soluble RNA contains atypical nucleotides such as 5-ribosyl-uracil-phosphate and nucleotides of methylated bases in higher proportion than the particulate RNA.

The second stage of protein synthesis consists of a transfer of aminoacyl residues from the aminoacyl-AMP-enzyme complexes produced in the preceding step to these ribonucleic acids. The amino acids are linked through their carboxyl groups to the 2′ or (more probably) 3′ hydroxyl groups of the terminal ribose of the sRNA. There is considerable evidence that several sRNA species may be able to transport each amino acid, although these several are specific for the given amino acid. It may be noted that the activating enzymes (aminoacyl-sRNA synthetases) exhibit a double specificity, since each synthetase must be able to recognize its specific amino acid for the reaction with ATP, as well as the specific sRNA's which will accept the aminoacyl residue.

The template: messenger RNA. Before continuing with the description of the process of protein synthesis, it is necessary to digress briefly, in order to set the stage for the specification of the amino acid sequence of the protein. This sequence is determined ultimately by the genetic constitution of the cell, and is in fact specified by the sequence of nucleotides in the nuclear DNA forming the "gene" for the peptide chain in question. The "codeword" for each amino acid consists of a trinucleotide sequence. (As will be noted later, several sequences serve for each amino acid.)

At the appropriate time, frequently if not always in response to a signal from the cytoplasm, one of the double strands of DNA is activated to become a template for synthesis of a species of RNA. It is believed, largely on the basis of work with microorganisms, that this function of DNA is ordinarily repressed (possibly by histones), and that activation consists of derepression, mediated by substances as yet unknown. In any event, under the influence of an RNA polymerase, a complementary strand of RNA is constructed in juxtaposition to the active strand of DNA, in a manner similar to DNA replication (p. 528), except that a ribonucleic acid is produced and the base thymine is replaced by uracil. Otherwise, the usual rules of complementarity and hydrogen bonding hold true. This reaction, called "transcription," forms a species of RNA which carries the genetic message of amino acid sequence to the cytoplasm. The product is known, therefore, as "messenger RNA" or mRNA.

Transcription is inhibited by the antibiotic, actinomycin D, probably through binding of this substance to the guanine residues of DNA. Since such inhibition blocks synthesis of mRNA, it would also be expected to result in inhibition of synthesis of the protein being specified. Many examples are known in which this is the case. In fact, susceptibility to actinomycin D inhibition is generally regarded as an indication that the phenomenon under investigation involves DNA-directed synthesis of RNA and subsequent de novo synthesis of protein. However, *increased* synthesis of protein (i.e., certain enzymes) has been reported to follow administration of actinomycin D over long periods of time. This long-term effect has been explained by postulating that a cytoplasmic repressor, operating at the ribosome level (p. 762), requires for its formation continued synthesis of RNA and protein. Hence, long-term administration of the inhibitor would eventually result in cytoplasmic "de-repression."

Although mRNA was first identified in microorganisms largely by its rapid rate of turnover, it has since been established that this type of RNA varies widely in stability. In animal cells some species of mRNA are stable for hours to days. As noted later, one of the properties of mRNA is its ability to bind to ribosomes. An additional property, widely employed in the detection of mRNA, derives from the similarity in base composition and complementarity of its nucleotide sequences to those of the DNA which served as template in its construction. This complementarity permits formation of hybrids (p. 114) between mRNA and its homologous DNA which are identifiable by density gradient centrifugation.

The polyribosome. After migration from the nucleus into the cytoplasm, the working form of the mRNA template is constructed by association (in the presence of Mg^{++}) of this strand of RNA with one or (more usually) several ribosomal particles, yielding a complex known as a polyribosome, polysome, or ergosome. It is believed that the ribosomes move along the mRNA, each ribosomal particle initially attaching itself to that end of the mRNA strand which carries the beginning of the message of amino acid sequence, corresponding specifically to the N-terminus of the peptide chain. It is believed further that the area of the mRNA in contact with the ribosome is in some manner activated to perform the next step in protein synthesis.

Incorporation of amino acids into protein. The genetic information on the sequence of amino acids in the protein to be synthesized, originally present as a series of trinucleotides in one strand of DNA, then transcribed as a series of complementary trinucleotides in mRNA (the codewords of the message, or "codons"), finally is "translated" into the actual amino acid sequence as follows. Each sRNA is believed to bear, somewhere in its structure, a trinucleotide sequence complementary to that of the mRNA codon for the amino acid transported by the sRNA, i.e., an "anti-codon." Matching of codons with anti-codons, when the various sRNA's are charged with their specific amino acids, thus results in a "lineup" of amino acids in the requisite sequence for the peptide chain to be formed.

Although it is not known exactly what role they play, GTP, glutathione (or other thiols), Mg^{++}, K^+ or NH_4^+, and two enzymes (aminoacyl-transferases) present in the soluble cytoplasm and not precipitable at pH 5, all are required for the overall process of attachment of aminoacyl-sRNA's to the polyribosomes and the formation of peptide chains. The process begins with the ribosomal particle in contact with the codon of mRNA corresponding to the N-terminus of the peptide chain. To this codon is attached, by hydrogen bonds, the complementary anti-codon area of the N-terminal aminoacyl-sRNA. Attached to the adjacent codon is the sRNA bearing the second amino acid residue of the peptide to be formed. The ammonium group of this second amino acid residue attacks the carboxyl carbon atom of the N-terminal residue to form a peptide bond, displacing the first sRNA, which then leaves the area. The peptidyl-sRNA is then attacked similarly by the third aminoacyl-sRNA, and so on. Room is available on the mRNA for several ribosomal particles to operate simultaneously. Figure 21–3 illustrates the process of addition of an amino acid residue to the growing peptide chain.

The antibiotic, puromycin, interrupts the process of peptide formation, apparently by acting as a structural analog of an aminoacyl-sRNA (p. 664), combining with the nascent chain to form compounds which cannot remain attached to the polyribosome, resulting in the release of incomplete peptides which probably terminate in puromycin. Other antibiotics have varied effects. Tetracyclines inhibit the binding of aminoacyl-sRNA's to the mRNA-ribosome complex, whereas chloramphenicol (p. 663) competes with mRNA for sites on the ribosome. Streptomycin apparently causes misreading of the code.

It is usually assumed that, in animal cells, each mRNA codes for one peptide chain. However, there is evidence in microorganisms for the formation of polygenic (polycistronic, p. 760) mRNA, which codes for several related peptide chains (e.g., the enzymes catalyzing the successive reactions of a metabolic pathway). In any case, it is not known exactly how the process of peptide chain synthesis is terminated. There is evidence that newly formed proteins may remain temporarily attached to the ribosomal particles, and that energy (ATP + Mg^{++}) may be required to detach them.

Higher levels of organization and prosthetic groups. It was assumed for many years that the characteristic three-dimensional conformations of proteins required specification (probably of a genetic type) on the part of the cell. It now appears that the amino acid sequence per se controls the higher levels of organization, through interactions among polar and non-polar groups. However, the specification of formation of covalent disulfide linkages has yet to be explained.

Addition of the prosthetic groups of glycoproteins requires the participation of the membranous fraction of the endoplasmic reticulum. Little is known of the process of attachment of other types of prosthetic groups.

The genetic code. When it became evident, through the accumulation of data from several areas of research (p. 531), that genetic information in general, and that applying to the amino acid sequence of proteins in particular, was carried in the form of nucleotide sequences in DNA (RNA in certain viruses), attention was directed to the nature of the "code" and "codewords." Since the four major bases of DNA, if taken in pairs, provide only 16 two-letter codewords (assuming a non-overlapping code), it was concluded that three-letter codewords must be involved (as a minimum) for encoding the 20 amino acids. However, 64 three-letter codons are possible; hence either many are unused, or there are many "nonsense" codewords, or else the code is "degenerate," that is, each amino acid may be encoded by several codons. The last possibility is supported by considerable evidence.

A major advance in elucidating the nature of the code came with the discovery that properly supplemented ribosomal systems could utilize synthetic "mRNA," prepared from pure nucleoside diphosphates with the aid of RNA phosphorylase (p. 530). Thus, polyuridylate caused the incorporation of phenylalanine into polyphenylalanine, suggesting UUU as a codon (on the mRNA level) for this amino acid. The use of synthetic messengers containing mixtures of bases as well as single bases has permitted identification of many probable codons, although the random nature of the nucleotide sequence in the "mixed" RNA precludes establishment of the order of bases within each codon. Much support for the codons thus determined has come from data on "amino acid replacement," in which spontaneous or induced (e.g., by nitrous acid) mutations in the

TABLE 21-3. THE GENETIC CODE: TENTATIVE ASSIGNMENT OF CODONS*

Amino acid				Amino acid			
Ala	GCA	GCG		Leu	UUA	CUA	CUG
	GCC	GCU			UUG	CUC	CUU
Arg	CGA	CGG	AGA	Lys	AAA		
	CGC	CGU	AGG		AAG		
Asp	GAC						
	GAU			Met	AUG		
AspN	AAC			Phe	UUC		
	AAU				UUU		
Cys	UGC			Pro	CCA	CCG	
	UGU				CCC	CCU	
Glu	GAA			Ser	UCA	UCG	AGC
	GAG				UCC	UCU	AGU
GluN	CAA			Thr	ACA	ACG	
	CAG				ACC	ACU	
Gly	GGA	GGG		Try	UGA		
	GGC	GGU			UGG		
His	CAC			Tyr	UAC		
	CAU				UAU		
Ile	AUC	AUA		Val	GUA	GUG	
	AUU				GUC	GUU	

* Internal phosphate linkages are 3′–5′ left to right.

genetic material are correlated with substitution of one amino acid for another in the final peptide structure.

Recently, it has been shown that aminoacyl-sRNA's are specifically bound to ribosomes by trinucleotides of known base-sequence. Codons determined in this way agree well with those previously predicted, and in addition the letter sequences are now known. Table 21-3 lists the currently accepted codewords on the mRNA level.

Several points of interest may be seen in the code. Obviously, it is extensively degenerate, agreeing with the finding of several sRNA species for each amino acid. Also, a certain pattern of degeneracy emerges: the codons of each amino acid are usually constructed of two invariant bases in the first two positions, with C equivalent to U or A equivalent to G in the third. Codons of chemically related amino acids frequently are quite similar (Asp and Glu, Phe and Tyr). Amino acid amides (glutamine and asparagine) are coded as independent amino acids, implying that they are not formed by amidation subsequent to incorporation of the parent dicarboxylic amino acids; identical conclusions have been reached in the study of amino acid requirements of cells in tissue culture. On the other hand, it will be noted that no codons exist for hydroxyproline and hydroxylysine, since these amino acids are formed after incorporation of the parent proline or lysine residues into some type of collagen precursor. Finally, it should be noted that the code apparently is universal among all forms of life, even including the viruses.

Synthesis of Intracellular and Extracellular Proteins

Each tissue synthesizes its characteristic proteins. In most cases these remain within the cell. Liver is unusual in that only approximately half of the protein which it synthesizes is liver protein proper, the other half being plasma protein. Other proteins which are synthesized intracellularly and then secreted into the body fluids include the extracellular enzymes and the protein hormones, viz., insulin from the β-cells of the pancreatic islets, the enzymes of the pancreas, the enzymes of the intestinal mucosa, and the hormones of the pituitary.

Breakdown of Protein in the Tissues

The reactions of proteins in the catabolic direction, such as must occur continuously to account for the dynamic state, are generally assumed to be catalyzed by the intracellular proteolytic enzymes, the "cathepsins." These enzymes are responsible for the autolysis of tissue after death. In life, catabolic reactions are balanced, in the adult, or overbalanced, in the growing organism, by the processes of protein synthesis. In contrast to the anabolic reactions, the catabolic may be expected to be exergonic. However, the release of certain amino acids from proteins has been shown to require a source of energy. How general this phenomenon may be and what relation it may have to the purely hydrolytic breakdown of the proteins remain to be seen.

THE PLASMA PROTEINS

Segregation of the discussion of the plasma proteins is justified by two considerations. First, owing to their intimate relation to protein metabolism in the liver, as well as to their interaction with other tissues throughout the body, the plasma proteins occupy a central position in the metabolism of protein. The second consideration is entirely practical: the plasma proteins happen to be the most conveniently obtainable sample of protein available in the body. Because of the interrelations between the proteins of plasma and the tissues, a great deal can be learned concerning the general status of protein metabolism in the individual from the examination of the plasma proteins, and the student will find much clinical information expressed in such terms.

Identity and Properties

The heterogeneity of the plasma proteins is readily demonstrated in the ultracentrifuge. In addition to fibrinogen, albumin, and a group of globulins sedimenting at a rate between these two, the ultracentrifugal analysis of plasma reveals a group of very rapidly sedimenting globulins and a lipoprotein fraction, the sedimentation of which varies markedly with the density of the medium.

The degree of resolution of the plasma proteins in the ultracentrifuge is greatly inferior to that obtainable with electrophoresis. An electrophoretic diagram of normal plasma is shown in Figure 21–4. It will be noted that, in addition to albumin and fibrinogen, this technique resolves the globulins into four groups (α_1, α_2, β, and γ).

Most of the older clinical data on the plasma proteins have been obtained by the method of salting out. Precipitates or supernatant solutions produced by the addition to the plasma of certain concentrations of salts are analyzed for protein content by the Kjeldahl or biuret method. Sodium sulfate has generally been the salt of choice. Before the advent of the electrophoretic technique, clinical analyses of plasma by salting out were performed according to the method of Howe. The Howe fractions have since been shown to disagree markedly with the results of electrophoresis. A comparison is

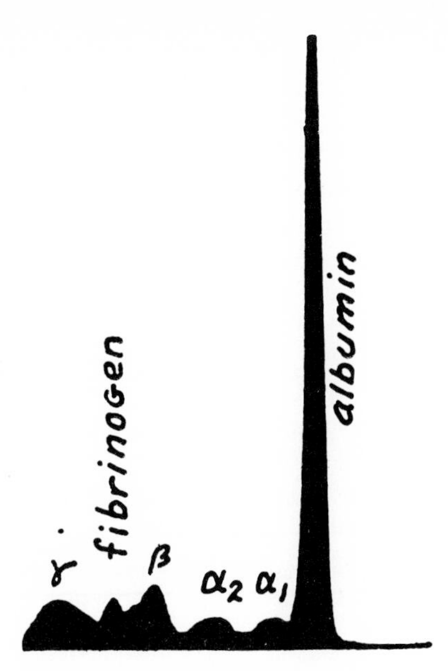

Figure 21-4. Electrophoretic pattern of normal plasma.

shown in Table 21-4 of the Howe method and a modern adaptation which yields fractions more closely related to those obtained electrophoretically. Quantitative data on the normal levels of the plasma proteins, and information on the mechanism of the various types of abnormalities, are presented elsewhere (p. 806).

The fractions of the plasma proteins obtained by ultracentrifugation, electrophoresis, or salting out are chemically heterogeneous. For scientific and other purposes, methods have been elaborated which permit fractionation of the plasma proteins to the point of isolation of relatively homogeneous chemical constituents. These methods, which have been developed mainly at Harvard University, are of interest not only in that they permit, for the first time, a closer study of the physicochemical and physiological properties of the individual proteins of the plasma, but also because they have made possible the large-scale production of plasma protein products for therapeutic use, viz., fibrin film and foam (surgery), purified albumin (shock), and γ-globulin (measles, hepatitis, poliomyelitis).

The procedure developed for use during World War II, Harvard "Method 6," is based upon the fractional precipitation of the plasma proteins with ethanol at low

TABLE 21-4. PLASMA PROTEIN FRACTIONS OBTAINED BY SALTING OUT

METHOD	% Na_2SO_4	NAME OF FRACTION	GM./100 ML. WHOLE BLOOD	ELECTROPHORETIC CONSTITUENTS
Howe	13.5	Euglobulin	0.2	*Ca.* ⅓ of γ-globulin
	21.5	Pseudoglobulin	1.8	Chiefly β-globulin, with rest of γ-globulin and some α
	Supernatant	Albumin	5.2	Albumin + α_1- + α_2-globulins
Milne	19.6	Euglobulin	1.9	β- and γ-globulins
	26.8	Pseudoglobulin	1.3	α_1- and α_2-globulins
	Supernatant	Albumin	4.0	Albumin

temperatures and low salt concentration. Proper adjustment of the concentrations of protein, salts, and ethanol, temperature, and pH, permits the isolation of six fractions, each of which can be subfractionated by appropriate procedures into relatively pure components.

Methods developed more recently in the Harvard laboratories (e.g., "Method 10") make use of protein–protein interactions to precipitate groups of proteins bearing electrical charges of opposite sign at a particular pH, and protein-metal interactions for the precipitation of certain groups of proteins by the formation of insoluble complexes with zinc, barium, lead, and mercury.

Two lipoprotein fractions, an α_1- and a β_1-globulin, have been isolated by the methods described. However, there is evidence that a larger number of such proteins may be present in plasma. By the addition of salt to plasma, its density may be elevated

TABLE 21-5. PROPERTIES OF MAJOR PLASMA PROTEINS*

ELECTROPHORETIC CLASS	ULTRACENTRIFUGAL CLASS, SVEDBERG UNITS	pI	MOLECULAR WEIGHT	SPECIAL PROPERTIES
Albumin	4.6	4.7	69,000	Osmotic pressure, fatty acid transport
α_1-Globulins				
Orosomucoid	3.1	2.7	44,100	41% carbohydrate
α_1-Glycoprotein (Schultze)	3.5		54,000	14% carbohydrate
Haptoglobin, Type 1-1	4.2	4.1	85,000	Binds hemoglobin, different genetic types, 23% carbohydrate
α_1-Lipoprotein* (HDL_3)	5.0	5.2	195,000	43% lipid
α_1-Lipoprotein* (HDL_2)	5.5		435,000	67% lipid
α_2-Globulins				
Small α_2-glycoprotein	2.6	3.85		16% carbohydrate
Plasminogen	4.28	5.6	143,000	Precursor of plasmin, a fibrinolysin
Prothrombin	4.85	4.2	62,700	Blood coagulation, 11% carbohydrate
Ceruloplasmin	7.1	4.4	151,000	Transports Cu
α_2-Macroglobulin	19.6	5.4	820,000	8% carbohydrate
β-Globulins				
β-Lipoproteins,* d. 0.98–1.002	S_f 20–100		$5–20 \times 10^6$	91% lipid } Lipid transport
β-Lipoproteins,* d. 1.03	S_f 10–12		3.2×10^6	79% lipid } Lipid transport
Lipoeuglobulin III,* d. 1.036	8.2 S, S_f 6–8	5.3	3×10^6	75% lipid } Lipid transport
Transferrin (Siderophilin)	6.1	5.9	89,000	Transports Fe, 5.5% carbohydrate
Lipid-poor euglobulin	7.10	5.5	$0.5–1 \times 10^6$	
Fibrinogen	7.63	5.8	341,000	Blood coagulation, 5% carbohydrate
γ-Globulins				
γ_1 macroglobulins (γ_{1M},β_{2M})	19	5.5–7.4	930,000	10% carbohydrate 5–10% of total γ } Antibodies
γ_{1A} (β_{2A})	6.6–13	5.8	160,000	10% carbohydrate, 5–25% of total γ } Antibodies
γ_2	7	7.3	160,000	3% carbohydrate, 70–85% of total γ } Antibodies

*Lipoproteins are presented also in Table 19-1, p. 491.

to the point where the lipoproteins (having a lower density than ordinary proteins due to their lipid content) will migrate toward the axis instead of toward the periphery in the ultracentrifuge. Whereas the rates of sedimentation of particles in conventional ultracentrifugation are expressed in Svedberg units ($S = 1 \times 10^{-13}$ sec.), those of the lipoproteins observed in the flotation method are expressed in "negative" S units, or "flotation" S units, S_f. In these terms, particles have been found distributed over a wide range of S_f values. A more detailed description of the plasma lipoproteins has been presented in connection with the discussion of lipid metabolism (p. 489). A probable relationship exists between the concentrations of certain groups of lipoproteins and the incidence of atherosclerosis.

The properties of the major plasma proteins are given in Table 21-5.

Metabolism

From isotopic and other evidence, it has been concluded that the liver is the chief, if not the sole, site of formation of albumin, fibrinogen, prothrombin, and the α- and β-globulins.

It is currently believed that the γ-globulins are synthesized in cells of the reticuloendothelial system, specifically in immature plasma cells of spleen, lymph nodes, and bone marrow. It has been suggested that antigens are taken up and digested by macrophages, which then send RNA (messenger?) to other cells (such as lymph node plasma cells) to direct the synthesis of antibody globulins.

As indicated previously, the nutritional status of the individual with respect to protein has a profound effect on the synthesis of plasma proteins, both directly, in terms of provision of raw materials of synthesis, and indirectly, due to the deleterious effect of protein deprivation on the liver. It is of interest that protein deprivation has its most marked effect on the levels of plasma albumin and γ-globulins, a sufficiently severe decrease in the former leading to edema, a decrease in the latter fraction resulting in impaired resistance to infections.

It has been estimated from studies with isotopes, that a 70-kg. man synthesizes and degrades approximately 15 to 20 gm. of plasma protein per day. Not all of the fractions turn over at the same rate, however. Albumin and γ-globulins are synthesized at slower rates than the α- and β-globulins.

The plasma proteins, among their other functions (discussed below), serve as a source of protein nutrition for the tissues. Indeed, a dynamic equilibrium exists between the proteins of the tissues and those of the plasma, each group sustaining the other when the need arises. In conditions of protein deprivation, however, the normal level of the plasma proteins is apparently guarded more zealously than that of the tissue proteins, since the latter are degraded to provide for the former. As a result, considerable loss of tissue protein may occur with minimal decrease in the concentrations of plasma proteins. It has been calculated that a decrease in total circulating plasma protein of 1 gm., in hypoproteinemia due solely to protein deprivation, represents a concomitant loss of 30 gm. of tissue protein.

Functions

The nutritive functions of the plasma proteins, discussed above, are probably attributable largely to the albumin fraction, owing to its quantitative dominance. Intravenously administered albumin has been shown in fact to be efficiently, although slowly, utilized in human beings.

The osmotic function of the plasma proteins, of great importance in the maintenance of the normal distribution of water in the various compartments of the body, is also due largely to the albumin. In addition to its high concentration in plasma, albumin exerts a greater osmotic pressure per gram than do the other plasma proteins because of its lower molecular weight (Table 21-5).

From a quantitative standpoint, the buffering ability of the plasma proteins is not very great. In whole blood, however, the combined buffering action of the hemoglobin and plasma proteins is as important as that due to the bicarbonate and other inorganic buffer systems of the blood. Over the physiological pH range, the buffering action of the blood proteins is due largely to the imidazole groups contributed by histidine.

The lipid-transporting functions of the plasma proteins have been discussed in detail previously (p. 489). In addition to the lipids, the lipoproteins transport certain lipid-soluble compounds, such as the steroid hormones, e.g., estriol, and the fat-soluble vitamins (e.g., A, D, and E). Bilirubin is transported in plasma attached chiefly to albumin, partly to α_1- and α_2-globulins. Any hemoglobin which finds its way into the plasma is bound by haptoglobins (α_2-globulins), hemoglobin-binding plasma proteins which exist in three genetically different types. A β_1-metal combining globulin (transferrin; siderophilin) is responsible for the transport of non-heme iron in the plasma. This protein can also combine with copper; however, a specific α_2-globulin glycoprotein (ceruloplasmin) also appears to be elaborated for this purpose. Approximately half of the calcium of plasma is bound to protein in a linkage which is relatively weak in comparison to the metalloproteins just mentioned. Albumin binds more calcium (and magnesium) than do the globulins. Thyroxine appears to be transported in association with an α-globulin having acidic characteristics, possibly a small α_2-glycoprotein. In this connection, it may be pointed out that three other transport proteins, haptoglobin, transferrin, and ceruloplasmin are all glycoproteins. In addition to the more or less specific transport functions already mentioned, due in most cases to the various globulins, plasma albumin has been found to exhibit considerable affinity for anions and cations having a wide variety of structures. It is probable that many drugs and dyes are transported in the plasma in combination with albumin. Albumin also acts as acceptor of the fatty acids liberated by lipoprotein lipase.

In addition to fibrinogen and prothrombin, plasma contains a number of other components which participate in the process of blood coagulation. The more important of these factors are discussed in detail elsewhere (p. 799).

Reference has been made to the immunological functions of the plasma proteins. The γ-globulins contain a large number of antibodies, among which may be mentioned those against influenza, mumps, poliomyelitis, measles, infectious hepatitis, typhoid, whooping cough, and diphtheria. The chief γ globulin type (γ_2 or 7s) is believed to consist of two pairs of peptide chains, an identical "light" pair (m.w. about 20,000) and an identical "heavy" pair (m.w. about 53,000), joined by disulfide linkages as follows:

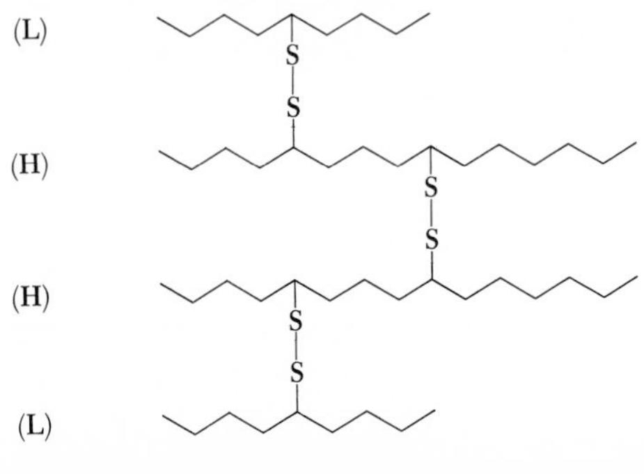

(L)
S
S
(H)
S
S
(H)
S
S
(L)

Much effort is being expended in attempts to localize the site(s) of antibody activity in this molecule, and to ascertain whether the specificity of this activity lies in the amino acid sequence or in the three-dimensional conformation.

Abnormally high concentrations of certain γ globulins occur in the plasma in macroglobulinemia (β_{2M}) and multiple myeloma (7s or β_{2A}). In both of these conditions so-called "Bence Jones" proteins appear in the urine. These "γ-microglobulins" have no antibody activity, no carbohydrate, and are of low molecular weight (about 22,000, but usually occurring as a dimer). They apparently correspond to the light (L) chains of the 7s γ-globulins.

The protein constituents of the plasma include a number of enzymes. Certain of the proteins involved in blood coagulation are undoubtedly enzymic in nature. In addition to the enzymes specifically concerned in coagulation, there are others having a wider range of activity. It is possible that many of these enzymes, which occur in rather low concentrations, are the result of leakage from the tissues or arise from the fragmentation of cells. The level of certain enzymes in plasma has diagnostic significance. Thus, an increase in acid phosphatase occurs in cancer of the prostate, whereas increases in alkaline phosphatase occur in diseases of bone and liver. Decreases in cholinesterase occur in individuals treated with or exposed to drugs or insecticides which act as anticholinesterases (p. 668). Increases in lipase and amylase generally signify disorders of the pancreas. Increases in glycolytic enzymes (aldolase and lactate dehydrogenase) occur particularly in diseases of liver and muscle. Certain transaminases are elevated following damage to cardiac and hepatic tissue.

ENDOCRINE INFLUENCES IN PROTEIN METABOLISM

Anabolism (synthesis) and catabolism (degradation) of proteins are influenced, if not indeed regulated, by certain hormones, which also influence the interrelationships between the metabolism of protein and of carbohydrate. The most important of these are the growth hormone (adenohypophysis), the adrenal 11-oxysteroids, thyroxine, androgens, and insulin. The actions of these hormones in this connection have been discussed elsewhere in detail (Ch. 26). It will suffice here merely to review them briefly.

Growth Hormone (Somatotropin) (p. 744)

This exerts a protein anabolic effect. Its administration is followed by diminished urinary excretion of nitrogen (positive N balance), with a decrease in plasma urea and amino acids and increased deposition of protein in the tissues. Somatic growth is induced in prepubertal children. This effect is essentially one of stimulation of chondrogenesis and osteogenesis, involving increased synthesis of chondroitin sulfate as well as of proteins. The protein anabolic action of STH is promoted by physiological amounts of insulin, glucocorticoids, and thyroxine.

Androgen (p. 684)

Testosterone, too, exerts a protein anabolic effect, as do androstenediol and androstenedione, but androsterone and dehydroisoandrosterone exhibit little such action. Administration of testosterone is followed by decreased urinary excretion of nitrogen, positive N balance, stimulation of somatic growth in prepubertal children (adolescent growth spurt), and increased weight (i.e., protein deposition) not only of specific target tissues (e.g., prostate, seminal vesicles), but also of other organs, particularly the kidneys (renotropic action). Castration is followed by increased urinary excretion of creatine; this is reversed by testosterone. Methyltestosterone, a synthetic androgen which also exerts a protein anabolic effect, increases urinary excretion of creatine. It is believed to stimulate synthesis as well as storage of creatine, whereas testosterone stimulates only its storage.

Adrenal 11-Oxysteroids (p. 701)

Under usual experimental and clinical conditions, the 11-oxygenated adrenocortical hormones cause increased urinary excretion of nitrogen and a negative N balance. This effect is intimately related to their action in increasing gluconeogenesis (p. 423), which is associated with increased production of certain transaminases and tryptophan pyrrolase in the liver. The negative nitrogen balance results from a decreased rate of incorporation of amino acid into protein in extrahepatic tissues (antianabolic effect). The availability of increased amounts of free amino acids in the liver results, on the other hand, in increased incorporation of amino acids into proteins in this tissue. Glucocorticoids depress growth of embryonic tissue (chick) and certain tumors. They inhibit healing of wounds, interfering with the formation of granulation tissue and sulfated mucopolysaccharides (p. 778).

Insulin (p. 723)

As has been indicated elsewhere, insulin is necessary for the protein anabolic effect of growth hormone, and antagonizes the gluconeogenic action of adrenocortical hormones. Independently of its effect on glucose utilization, it accelerates the entry of amino acids into cells and augments their incorporation into proteins. This promotion of protein synthesis probably is based on the action of insulin in increasing synthesis of messenger RNA and perhaps ribosomal RNA.

Thyroid Hormone (p. 713)

In physiological doses, thyroid hormone exerts a protein anabolic effect, as indicated by a positive N balance, especially in the growing organism. This action would be inferred from the fact that removal of the thyroid in early life results in retardation of growth, which can be corrected by administration of thyroid hormone. Similarly, thyroxine in physiological doses promotes incorporation of amino acids into protein, which is depressed following thyroidectomy. Thyroidectomy (and hypothyroidism) is followed by accumulation in the extracellular fluids of a mucoprotein, rich in hyaluronic acid and similar to fetal mucin in composition (myxedema).

In unphysiological (large) doses, thyroid hormone exerts a protein catabolic effect, with increased urinary nitrogen excretion and negative N balance. It causes also increased urinary excretion of creatine (creatinuria, p. 842), resulting from excessive catabolism of muscle tissue and also, perhaps, from a decreased capacity for prompt resynthesis of phosphocreatine during the recovery stage of muscle contraction (p. 429).

INTERRELATION OF DIETARY FACTORS, HORMONES, AND TRANSLOCATION OF NITROGEN

The levels of dietary fat and carbohydrate and of circulating hormones influence not only the balance between anabolism and catabolism of protein, but also cause shifts of nitrogen, in the form of amino acids, from one tissue to another, where they are derived from and converted to protein. In addition, various interactions occur among the dietary factors, among the hormones, and between these two groups of agents, resulting in a highly complex network of regulatory mechanisms.

Figure 21-5 presents, in greatly oversimplified form, some of the major actions of the factors mentioned. Shifts toward the right in the figure imply increased protein anabolism as well as transfer of nitrogen from visceral organs (particularly liver) to skeletal muscle. Shifts toward the left imply increased protein catabolism and gluconeogenesis as well as transfer of nitrogen from muscle to liver.

Dietary fat as a caloric source generally favors nitrogen retention by the organism. However, if the protein intake is inadequate, this generalization does not hold. On the other hand, dietary carbohydrate, acting as caloric source, raw material for synthesis of

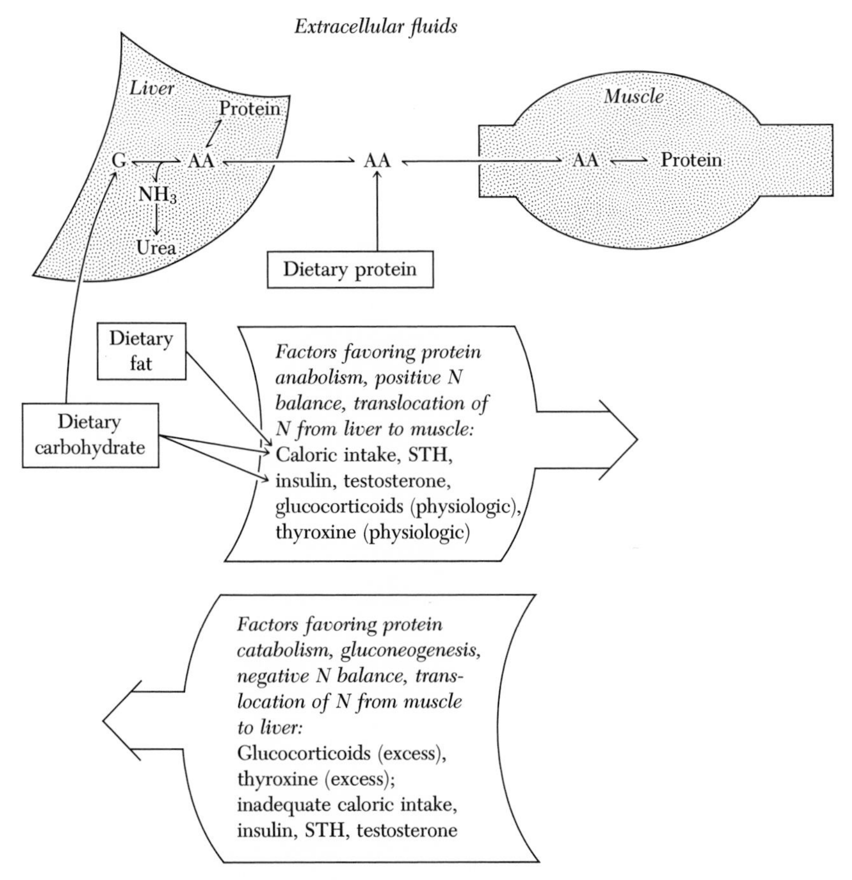

Figure 21-5. Certain interrelations of dietary factors, hormones, and translocation of nitrogen. *AA*, Amino acids; *G*, glucose; *STH*, somatotropic hormone. See text for qualifying statements.

amino acids, and stimulus for insulin secretion, favors nitrogen retention even with inadequate intake of protein. The diversion of nitrogen from liver to muscle, however, when it occurs on high-carbohydrate, low-protein diets (e.g., in kwashiorkor), may be disadvantageous, since it results in decreased synthesis of plasma proteins (especially albumin) by the liver.

On an adequate protein intake, testosterone promotes anabolism of protein in both liver and muscle (note also its "renotropic" action mentioned in the preceding section), but on low-protein diets it favors the synthesis of muscle protein at the expense of liver protein.

Inadequate intake of protein, in an action not shown in the figure, markedly depresses the output of STH and gonadotropins (but not TSH) from the anterior pituitary gland, with resultant protein-catabolic effects.

Although traces (physiological concentrations) of glucocorticoids and thyroxine favor anabolism of protein, excessive amounts of these hormones can cause loss of protein from muscle, increased gluconeogenesis, and negative nitrogen balance, accompanied by a paradoxical increase in liver protein (probably due primarily to flooding with amino acids, although direct action of these hormones on hepatic synthesis of protein is not excluded). Shifts in the catabolic direction obviously occur also in the case of inadequate provision of factors that favor anabolism of protein.

GENERAL METABOLIC REACTIONS OF AMINO ACIDS

Although many amino acids pursue individual metabolic pathways, there are a few general reactions common to almost all of them. With few exceptions, the catabolic pathway of amino acids begins with the separation of the amino group from the carbon skeleton of the molecule (which becomes an α-keto acid). The ammonia, whether free or combined, joins the ammonia pool, and participates in the anabolic and catabolic reactions characteristic of that area of metabolism. Being a more specialized structure, the carbon skeleton cannot be assigned to a single pool of keto acids. The majority of the α-keto acids produced from amino acids join the carbohydrate pool more or less directly; a minority are more closely related to the ketone bodies and fatty acids. Many amino acids, although they have special functions of their own, also participate in group activities such as those just enumerated. A few, however, are completely individualistic, and enter into none of the common metabolic pools. They will be discussed separately.

Removal of Nitrogen from the Carbon Skeleton

(*a*) ***Oxidative deamination.*** The removal of nitrogen is accomplished in mammalian tissues primarily by two known methods, oxidative deamination and transamination. Setting aside, for the time being, certain specialized enzyme systems, there are three enzymes concerned with oxidative deamination which have potential general functions in the metabolism of the amino acids. One of these, the D-amino acid oxidase, is a flavoprotein (containing FAD), quite active, and widespread in animal tissues. Much effort has been expended in attempts to determine the physiological function of this enzyme, since its substrates, the D-amino acids, do not occur in mammalian tissues. Recent data suggest the identity of D-amino acid oxidase with glycine oxidase, although the affinity of the enzyme for glycine is much less than for D-amino acids. L-Amino acid oxidase, which attacks most of the L-amino acids, is also a flavoprotein (containing FMN), but has remarkably low activity and a rather restricted distribution. It catalyzes reactions of the following type:

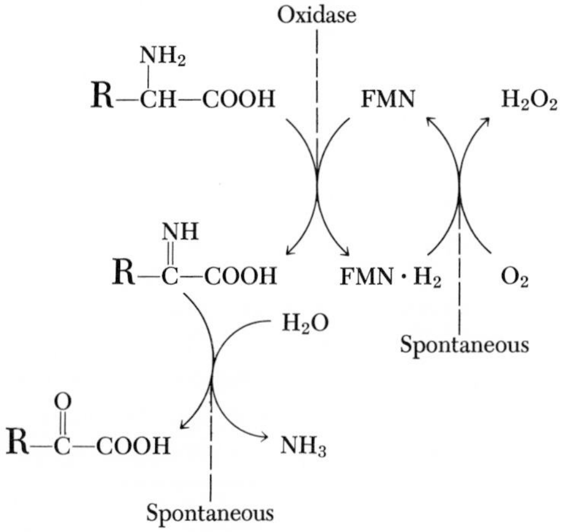

Oxidase

$R{-}CH(NH_2){-}COOH$ FMN H_2O_2

$R{-}C({=}NH){-}COOH$ $FMN \cdot H_2$ O_2

H_2O Spontaneous

$R{-}C({=}O){-}COOH$ NH_3

Spontaneous

The imino acid which is first formed is unstable and spontaneously undergoes hydrolysis to ammonia and the α-keto acid. Since this enzyme is an oxidase, its prosthetic group, after reduction, is reoxidized spontaneously by oxygen. The hydrogen peroxide is decomposed by the catalase present in all cells. It is doubtful whether this L-amino acid oxidase plays more than a very minor role in the general process of deamination of amino acids.

The third of the enzymes catalyzing oxidative deaminations is L-glutamate dehydrogenase. This enzyme, although it specifically attacks one L-amino acid, probably has certain general functions which are discussed later. It is widely distributed in nature, very active, and catalyzes a reversible reaction:

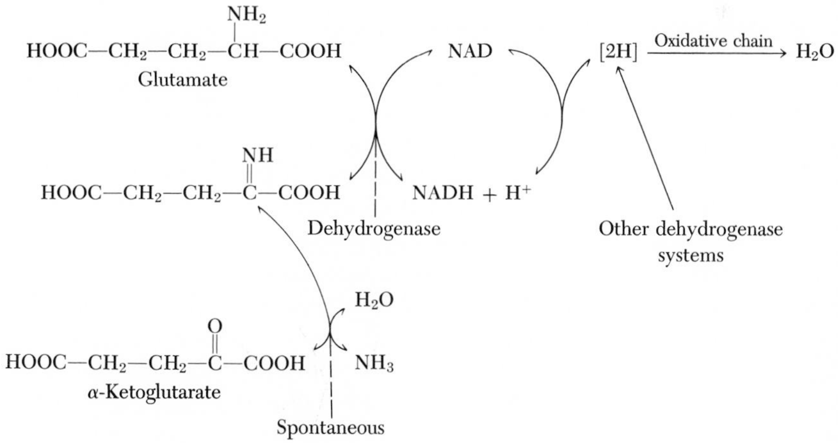

$HOOC{-}CH_2{-}CH_2{-}CH(NH_2){-}COOH$ NAD $[2H] \xrightarrow{\text{Oxidative chain}} H_2O$

Glutamate

$HOOC{-}CH_2{-}CH_2{-}C({=}NH){-}COOH$ $NADH + H^+$

Dehydrogenase

Other dehydrogenase systems

H_2O

$HOOC{-}CH_2{-}CH_2{-}C({=}O){-}COOH$ NH_3

α-Ketoglutarate

Spontaneous

The first part of the reaction is similar to that discussed above. However, the reduced coenzyme in this case is oxidized by the flavoproteins, cytochromes, etc., of the oxidative chain. In the presence of ammonia and a source of reduced coenzyme (easily formed by the dehydrogenation of another substrate in a system using the same coenzyme), α-ketoglutarate can be reductively aminated to L-glutamate.

Glutamate dehydrogenase of liver has a molecular weight of about one million. A number of agents dissociate the enzyme into sub-units (probably four), concomitantly inhibiting its activity as a glutamate dehydrogenase and, in most cases, enhancing its activity as an alanine dehydrogenase (although the correlation of this last effect with depolymerization is disputed by some). Agents acting in this way include (in the presence of NADH) ATP and GTP, estrogens, androgens, progesterone, and thyroxine. ADP, NAD, and NADP act in the opposite direction. Glutamate dehydrogenase activity is decreased in the livers of animals treated with estrogen or adrenalectomized. As a result of all of these findings, it is suggested, but not proved, that this enzyme may be a site of metabolic regulation.

(*b*) ***Transamination.*** The transfer of an amino group from an amino acid to what is originally an α-keto acid, forming a new amino acid and keto acid, without the appearance of ammonia in the free state, is known as "transamination." Pyridoxal phosphate is the coenzyme of the transaminases. It is believed that the coenzyme functions in the following manner, where the aldehyde group only of the coenzyme is fully written out:

$$R_1{-}CH(NH_2){-}COOH \quad\quad Pyr{-}CH{=}O \text{ (Pyridoxal phosphate)} \quad\quad R_2{-}CH(NH_2){-}COOH$$

$$R_1{-}C(=O){-}COOH \quad\quad Pyr{-}CH_2NH_2 \text{ (Pyridoxamine phosphate)} \quad\quad R_2{-}C(=O){-}COOH$$

As indicated, the reaction is freely reversible. Two of the most active transaminases of animal tissues are those catalyzing the interconversions:

(1) L-glutamate + oxaloacetate $\longleftrightarrow$ α-ketoglutarate + L-aspartate, and

(2) L-glutamate + pyruvate $\longleftrightarrow$ α-ketoglutarate + L-alanine.

However, many other transaminases also exist (p. 234). Although most of the transaminations which have been described appear to involve a dicarboxylic amino or keto acid, in particular glutamate (ketoglutarate), transaminations also occur between pairs of monocarboxylic acids. Furthermore, transaminations have been described which involve β-, γ-, or δ-amino acids, aldehydo-acids, and even D-amino acids (in bacteria). Finally, enzymes exist which catalyze transaminations between glutamine and a wide variety of keto acids, forming α-ketoglutaramate, which is immediately hydrolyzed to ammonia and α-ketoglutarate by an ω-amidase. This second reaction is irreversible. Asparagine undergoes an analogous sequence of reactions.

The glutamate-pyruvate transaminase of liver appears to function mainly in protein catabolism. Its activity increases after administration of adrenal glucocorticoids (as does that of tyrosine-ketoglutarate transaminase) and in alloxan diabetes, conditions characterized by increased gluconeogenesis from protein.

Elevated levels of glutamate-oxaloacetate and glutamate-pyruvate transaminases occur in the serum of individuals suffering from certain types of damage to the hepatic and cardiac tissues.

It should be emphasized at this point, particularly in view of the subsequent discussion, that transamination per se involves neither uptake nor release of free ammonia.

(*c*) ***Transdeamination.*** Experiments in vivo with isotopes have shown that the transfer of amino groups from one amino acid to another (and equilibration of these amino groups with a pool of free ammonia) is a rapid, reversible, widely occurring, and continuous reaction, in which few amino acids fail to participate. (Lysine and threonine, however, contribute their amino groups irreversibly to the general pool.) Deaminations, in the general sense, are found to have similar characteristics. From what is known of the properties of the L-amino acid oxidase, it seems unlikely that the physiological phenomenon of rapid and reversible deamination could involve this enzyme to any great extent. In order to reconcile the requirements of the physiological system with the properties of known enzymes in vitro, a combination of transamination and oxidative deamination (of glutamate) called "transdeamination" has been suggested as a possible mechanism:

$$R{-}CH(NH_2){-}COOH + \alpha\text{-Ketoglutarate} \xrightarrow{\text{Transaminase}} R{-}C(=O){-}COOH + \text{L-Glutamate}$$

$$\text{L-Glutamate} \xrightarrow{\text{Glutamate dehydrogenase}} \alpha\text{-Ketoglutarate} + NH_3 + [2H]$$

The amino group is first removed from a given amino acid by transamination with α-ketoglutarate. The resulting glutamate is then deaminated by the specific L-glutamate dehydrogenase. There is every reason to expect that such a system would be widely distributed in animal tissues, very active metabolically, and readily reversible. It provides a pathway for the removal of ammonia from amino acids for catabolic purposes, and also a convenient sequence of reactions by means of which amino acids may be readily synthesized from ammonia and α-keto acids.

Disposal of the Nitrogen

(*a*) ***Synthetic pathways.*** Although deamination is ordinarily thought of as essentially catabolic, the liberated ammonia which enters the general ammonia pool of the body may be drawn upon for either anabolic or catabolic purposes. It may be used, for example, in the reductive amination of α-keto acids (derived from carbohydrate) to form new amino acids, by reversal of the transdeamination reactions. The synthesis of purines, pyrimidines, and porphyrins also requires the participation of ammonia, although this is usually utilized in the form of a "carrier," rather than in the free state (viz., glutamine, aspartate, carbamoyl-phosphate, and glycine).

(*b*) ***Glutamine pathway.*** Ammonia is a toxic substance, and large concentrations are not permitted to accumulate in cells. One of the possible mechanisms of "detoxication" of ammonia is the synthesis of glutamine. This reaction, which occurs in extrarenal tissues, resembles somewhat the synthesis of a peptide linkage, and similarly requires a source of energy. Although the exact mechanism is not known, ATP has been shown to participate:

$$HOOC{-}CH_2{-}CH_2{-}CH(NH_2){-}COOH + NH_3 + ATP \longrightarrow NH_2{-}C(=O){-}CH_2{-}CH_2{-}CH(NH_2){-}COOH + ADP + H_3PO_4$$

Enzyme-bound γ-glutamyl-phosphate has been suggested as an intermediate. The glutamine then travels from the various tissues through the blood to the kidneys, where it is hydrolyzed by glutaminase:

$$NH_2-\overset{\overset{O}{\|}}{C}-CH_2-CH_2-\overset{\overset{NH_2}{|}}{CH}-COOH \xrightarrow{H_2O} HOOC-CH_2-CH_2-\overset{\overset{NH_2}{|}}{CH}-COOH + NH_3$$

The ammonia which is thus liberated accounts for about 60 per cent of that found in the urine.

Certain types of hepatic disease are accompanied by increases in blood ammonia, due to failure of the liver to take up from the portal blood and detoxify completely the normal influx of ammonia (arising largely through bacterial action in the intestine). It has been suggested that the coma observed in these cases results from the synthesis of glutamine in the detoxication of ammonia by the brain. There follows a deficit in glutamate and, consequently, in the pool of α-ketoglutarate required for the function of the Krebs cycle. Due to the limited capacity of cerebral tissue to form its own Krebs cycle acids, the rate of operation of the cycle (a major source of energy in the brain) diminishes, eventuating in coma.

(*c*) ***Direct excretion.*** It has been assumed in the foregoing discussion either that the deamination of amino acids occurs in extrarenal tissues, or that the ammonia is immediately channeled into certain metabolic pathways which bind it. If, however, the deamination occurs in the kidney, in the absence of immediate physiological requirements for synthetic purposes in that organ, the liberated ammonia may be excreted directly into the urine. This source of urinary ammonia amounts to some 40 per cent of the total. The importance of the production of ammonia from glutamine and amino acids to acid-base balance is discussed elsewhere (p. 319). It should be noted that ammonia does not normally appear in the systemic blood as such; it is transported from other tissues to the kidneys in the form of glutamine or amino acids.

(*d*) ***Formation of urea.*** If the deamination occurs in the liver (as most of it does), the ammonia may enter the "ornithine cycle" to form urea. The development of the current view of the mechanism of urea synthesis provides an appropriate example of the application of a wide range of techniques, from the classical to the most modern, over a considerable period of time, culminating in a metabolic scheme which correlates very well the known physiological facts in the whole animal with the properties of enzyme systems in vitro.

In the normal animal, an increase in dietary protein is followed by an increase in the concentration of amino acids in the blood (which are taken up largely by the liver), and by an increase in urinary urea. When liver function is severely impaired, e.g., in acute hepatic necrosis, there is a rise in the blood amino acids and a fall in the urea concentration of blood and urine. Similarly, removal of the liver in an experimental animal is followed by a rise in the concentration of amino acids and ammonia in the blood, and a fall in blood and urinary urea. If the kidneys are removed and the liver left intact, the blood urea rises. Removal of both liver and kidneys results in a constant level of blood urea. From all of these data, it may be concluded that the liver is the chief, if not the sole site of urea synthesis, the precursors of which are amino acids and ammonia. These conclusions are confirmed by perfusion experiments. The bulk of the amino acids (NH_2 groups) not utilized in the organism is thus transformed to urea, which is excreted in the urine as a terminal (waste) metabolite.

The actual mechanism of formation of urea began to be investigated when suitable in vitro methods became available. Using liver slices and the Warburg technique, conditions were found in which urea was produced from various amino acids or ammonium salts. It was known that arginine could be hydrolyzed by the enzyme arginase of liver to ornithine and urea. When arginine, ornithine, or citrulline (a compound structurally intermediate between ornithine and arginine) were incubated with liver slices, in contrast to the results with other amino acids, the yield of urea was greater than stoichiometric, indicating a catalytic role for these three compounds. Since ornithine, citrulline, and arginine differ structurally only by the simple addition (on paper) of CO_2 and NH_3, the following catalytic cycle was proposed for the synthesis of urea:

CO_2
Ornithine
NH_3
Urea
Arginase
Citrulline
Arginine
NH_3

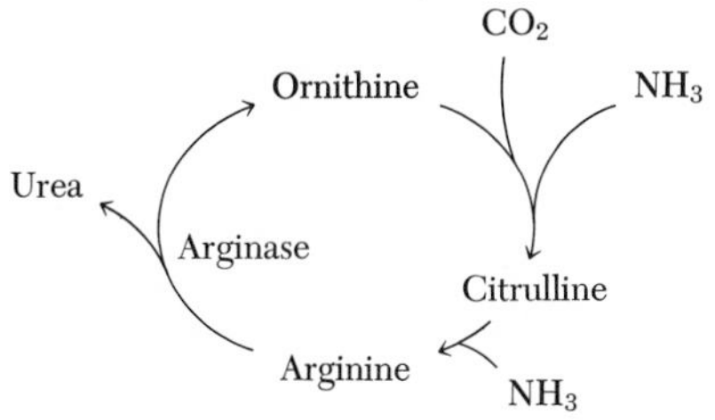

Although the accumulation of additional information has expanded the ornithine cycle and considerably increased its complexity, the basic formulation still stands. Experiments with isotopes have completely confirmed the in vivo and in vitro work.

From the standpoint of energetics it is obvious that this formulation of the ornithine cycle is incomplete. The synthesis of urea entails the formation of two amide linkages, an endergonic process, and yet the cycle makes no provision for the input of energy. This defect has been remedied by studies with cell-free homogenates and partially purified enzyme systems. It has been found that CO_2 and NH_3 enter the cycle in "carrier" molecules, and that the condensations involve ATP.

The current status of the ornithine cycle can be formulated as shown in Figure 21–6.

Ammonia, derived from the deamination of amino acids, and carbon dioxide, derived from decarboxylations such as occur in the Krebs cycle, combine, with the aid of ATP, to form carbamoyl-phosphate. Since two molecules of ATP are required, it has been suggested that the synthesis occurs in two steps. N-acetylglutamate or other N-acylglutamates act as cofactors of the reaction, possibly by having an allosteric effect on the enzyme. In addition to its role in the ornithine cycle, carbamoyl-phosphate is utilized also in the synthesis of pyrimidines (p. 520).

The ornithine cycle proper begins with the transcarbamoylation from carbamoyl-phosphate to ornithine, forming citrulline. The second molecule of ammonia required for the synthesis of urea is provided by the amino group of aspartate which, with the aid of ATP, condenses reversibly with citrulline to form argininosuccinate. Under physiological conditions, this reaction may be less reversible, since pyrophosphate, one of the products, is readily hydrolyzed by pyrophosphatases. Since the amino group of aspartate may derive from the amino group of glutamate by transamination, and since the latter may arise via transaminations between α-ketoglutarate and practically any amino acid, it is apparent that a number of readily accessible pathways are open for the conversion of amino acid nitrogen to urea. Argininosuccinate is cleaved reversibly to fumarate and arginine. Hydrolysis of the latter by arginase completes the cycle.

Argininosuccinate is found in the urine (argininosuccinuria), plasma, and cerebrospinal fluid in an inborn error of metabolism associated with mental deficiency; hence it is a

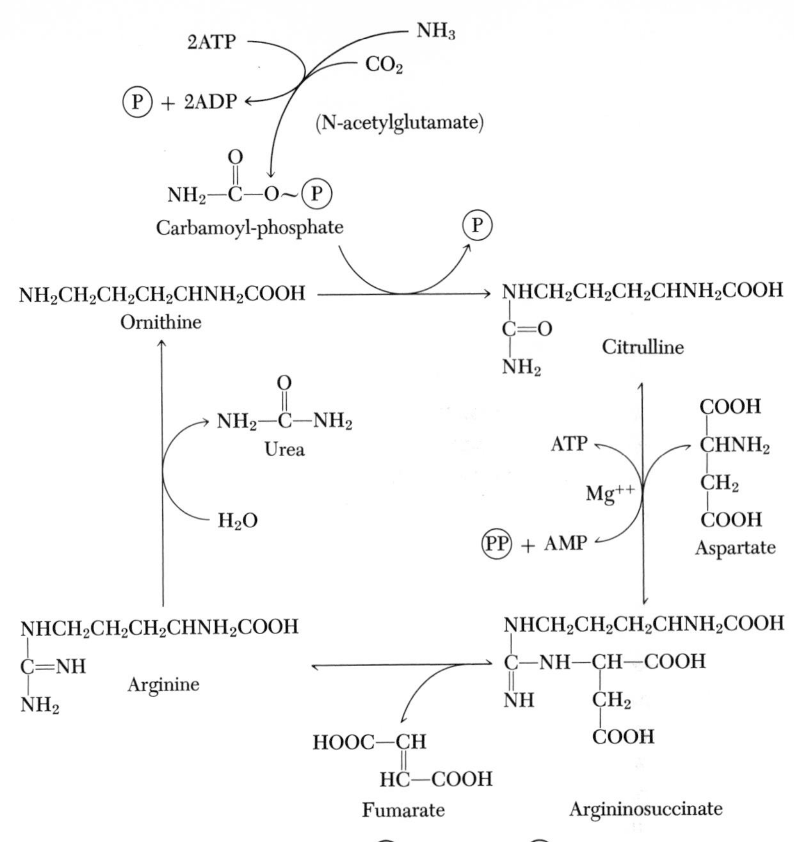

Figure 21-6. Ornithine cycle. (P), phosphate; (PP), pyrophosphate.

matter of considerable interest that small amounts of urea are known to be synthesized in the brain. A defect in the cleavage of argininosuccinate in brain is suggested in this disorder. Other genetic defects of the ornithine cycle are citrullinuria (probably a partial block in argininosuccinate formation) and hyperammonemia (probably defective carbamoylation of ornithine).

The importance of the ornithine cycle in the detoxication of ammonia is indicated by the ability of arginine and other members of the cycle, when administered concomitantly, to prevent the rise in blood ammonia to toxic levels during the intravenous administration of amino acids in experimental animals. Intravenous injection of arginine may reduce the high blood ammonia concentration resulting from certain hepatic disorders.

The enzymes of the hepatic ornithine cycle, as catalysts of the major catabolic pathway for protein nitrogen, respond adaptively to conditions calling for heightened activity, viz., increased intake of dietary protein, starvation, and administration of glucocorticoids.

(*e*) ***Creatine and creatinine.*** Creatinine, derived from creatine, is a significant excretory form of amino acid nitrogen. However, since its formation involves the special metabolism of only three, rather than the entire group of amino acids, it is logically discussed elsewhere (p. 578).

Disposal of the Carbon Skeleton

(*a*) ***Synthetic pathways.*** The α-keto acids resulting from deamination may be reductively aminated by reversal of the transdeamination mechanism, re-forming the original amino acids. This process is continuous, as is the deamination, the net change being determined by physiological requirements. Certain fragments of the carbon skeletons are used for special syntheses, which are discussed in connection with the metabolism of the individual amino acids.

(*b*) ***Glucogenic pathway*** (*Fig. 21-7*). Most of the amino acids are convertible to carbohydrate ("gluconeogenesis from protein"). The routes vary with the compound concerned, but all converge at pyruvate. The pathways of three glucogenic amino acids to pyruvate are particularly direct:

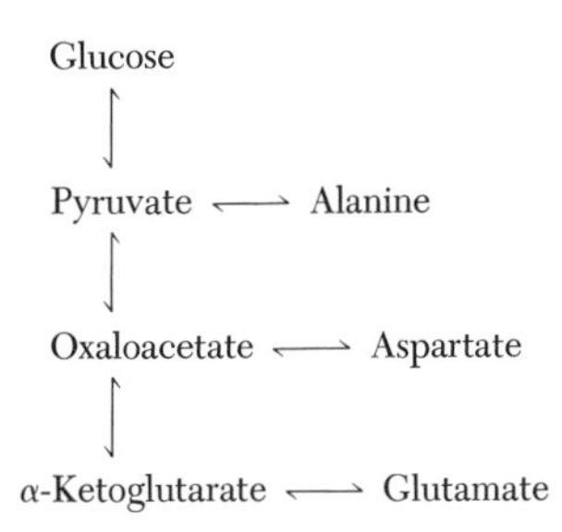

α-Ketoglutarate, oxaloacetate, and pyruvate are interconvertible by means of the tricarboxylic acid cycle and the decarboxylating side-reactions to it which occur in liver. (In the central nervous system, glutamate is converted to succinate via γ-aminobutyrate [p. 582].) Pyruvate and glucose are connected by the glycolytic series of reactions.

It will be noted that the reactions listed above are reversible. This is generally true for the non-essential, glucogenic amino acids, which can be synthesized by the body from ammonia and the α-keto acids provided by carbohydrate. Many amino acids in addition to those shown are glucogenic. Their pathways to pyruvate are more devious, however, and will be discussed in the section on metabolism of the individual amino acids.

Transamination plays a major role in gluconeogenesis from amino acids. The process requires pyridoxal phosphate as a cofactor and is facilitated by adrenal glucocorticoids.

It has been estimated that over half of the amino acid constituents of the average animal protein are glucogenic. If a state of total diabetes or phlorizin-diabetes is induced in an experimental animal, it becomes virtually unable to utilize glucose. Preformed carbohydrate or any which may be synthesized from protein is lost practically quantitatively in the urine. If such an animal is fasted, its preformed glycogen is consumed in short order, followed by depletion of its fat stores, at which time the body attempts to support itself by the degradation of tissue protein. All of the protein which is degraded gives rise to urinary nitrogen (urea, NH_3, creatinine, urate), which can be determined by a Kjeldahl analysis. Since the animal is in a diabetic state, the glucose derived from the glucogenic amino acids of the degraded protein is excreted, unused, in the urine also. This can be determined by any of the standard methods for reducing sugars. The ratio of glucose to nitrogen in the urine is known as the "G/N ratio" (sometimes D/N, where D = dextrose). This varies with the severity of the diabetes, reaching a maximum value of about 3.65 in the phlorizinized animal. This means that each gram of nitrogen resulting from the degradation of tissue protein has been accompanied by the formation of 3.65 gm. of glucose. Since nitrogen constitutes 16 per cent of the average animal protein (protein $= N \times 1/0.16$), each gram of *protein* has produced $3.65 \times 0.16 = 0.58$ gm. of glucose. Hence, 58 per cent by weight of the protein is glucogenic. Actually, there are a number of objections to this simple interpretation of the G/N ratio, and it is no longer regarded as an accurate index of the severity of the diabetes or the degree of gluconeogenesis from amino acids or proteins. However, other techniques have confirmed the general finding that a large proportion of the amino acids in the average protein is glucogenic.

(*c*) ***Ketogenic pathway (Fig. 21-7).*** The α-keto acids derived from a few amino acids are more closely allied to the fats than to the carbohydrates. In contrast to the glucogenic amino acids, the ketogenic group in various test systems produce ketone bodies instead of glucose. The pathways are rather specialized and complex, and will be discussed in connection with the metabolism of the individual amino acids concerned. In comparison to the glucogenic group, the ketogenic amino acids are a minority, comprising only phenylalanine, tyrosine, leucine, and isoleucine. Furthermore, all of these amino acids but leucine are metabolized along pathways which are glucogenic as well as ketogenic.

(*d*) ***Branched-chain amino acids.*** The α-keto acids resulting from deamination of two ketogenic (leucine, isoleucine) and one glucogenic (valine) amino acid, after oxidative decarboxylation, undergo a sequence of reactions which closely parallels that undergone by the fatty acids. The pathway cuts across the usual glucogenic-ketogenic classification, for the remarkably similar reactions (p. 580) of these three amino acids eventuate in both propionate derivatives (glucogenic, from isoleucine and valine) and ketone bodies (from isoleucine and leucine).

(*e*) ***Miscellaneous pathways (Fig. 21-7).*** Certain amino acids traverse metabolic pathways which do not correspond to any that have been described thus far. These routes are highly individual, and are discussed in the appropriate sections of this chapter. It may be pointed out, however, that in many cases the entire amino acid undergoes the specified transformations, which are not preceded by a deamination. One such case is the conversion of tryptophan to nicotinate (p. 596).

ENERGETICS OF AMINO ACID OXIDATION

Due to the multiplicity of the amino acids, the diversity of their catabolic pathways, and the simple lack of thermodynamic data in many instances, it is difficult to form broad generalizations concerning the energetics of the process. However, if it is assumed that most of the nitrogen derived from catabolism of amino acids is excreted in the form of urea, and that most of the carbon-hydrogen skeletons, after deamination, are oxidized to CO_2 (HCO_3^- at physiological pH) and H_2O through the Krebs cycle, then it is possible to discuss the energetics of oxidation of a typical amino acid. Glutamate will be used as the example, since its catabolic pathway is in accord with the foregoing assumptions, reasonably accurate thermodynamic data are available, and the compound is very widely distributed in proteins.

The overall oxidation of one mole of glutamate to bicarbonate, water, and half a mole of urea at physiological pH can be estimated to yield about −490 kcal. of free energy. The extent of conservation of this energy in the form of ATP can be calculated as follows:

(1) Deamination of glutamate by glutamate dehydrogenase forms α-ketoglutarate, ammonia, and reduced NAD (or NADP). Oxidation of the reduced coenzyme via the cytochrome chain yields 3 moles of high-energy phosphate per mole of glutamate (p. 382).

(2) Leaving aside for the moment the fate of the ammonia, the oxidation of ketoglutarate may be traced through the Krebs cycle. Oxidations of ketoglutarate to succinate (yielding 4 moles of high-energy phosphate), succinate to fumarate (yielding 2), and

malate to oxaloacetate (yielding 3), provide a total of 9 moles of high energy phosphate from this part of the cycle (p. 414). Pyruvate, formed by decarboxylation of the oxaloacetate, then undergoes its usual complete oxidation to produce an additional 15 moles of high-energy phosphate, bringing the total to 24 from the carbon skeleton, or 27 when step (1) is included.

(3) Conversion of ammonia to urea is an endergonic process, requiring the expenditure of 3 moles of high-energy phosphate per mole of urea (p. 571). However, only half a mole of urea is formed from one mole of glutamate, hence the amount to be debited in this calculation is 1.5 moles of high-energy phosphate. The net yield is then 25.5 moles.

Assuming an average free energy of hydrolysis of -7.5 kcal. per mole of pyrophosphate in the terminal bond of ATP, it is seen that 191 kcal. of free energy are conserved in the complete oxidation of glutamate. Of the total 490 kcal. liberated, then, 39 per cent is recovered, which compares favorably with other areas of metabolism (pp. 414, 468).

METABOLISM OF INDIVIDUAL AMINO ACIDS

Metabolic Interrelations

In contrast to the carbohydrates and lipids, there is no one chain or cycle of metabolic reactions followed by all of the individual amino acids. Certain common pathways have been described for the nitrogenous portions of these molecules; brief mention has also been made of the various alternative metabolic routes available to the carbon skeletons of the deaminated amino acids. It is possible to organize these latter reactions, as well as certain direct interconversions between amino acids, into a metabolic scheme which illustrates the major areas or metabolic pools which are shared by two or more amino acids. Such a scheme is shown in Figure 21–7, from which several conclusions may be drawn. First of all, it is obvious that most of the amino acids are more closely related to carbohydrate than to lipid (or ketone bodies). As a matter of fact, leucine is the only amino acid which is solely ketogenic. Phenylalanine, tyrosine, and isoleucine are both ketogenic and glucogenic, depending upon the particular test system employed. No satisfactory evidence has been obtained of the *net* conversion of lysine, methionine, or tryptophan to glucose or ketone bodies, although isotopic data indicate that such products can be formed from carbon atoms derived from these amino acids.

It will be noted in Figure 21–7 that most of the glucogenic amino acids can be arranged in two groups, one clustered about pyruvate, the other in close relation to α-ketoglutarate. These groups are interconnected by means of several members of the tricarboxylic acid cycle, with aspartate occupying a position between the two groups.

The individual pathways of metabolism of certain amino acids will be presented in some detail in the following pages, where this appears justified by the general physiological importance of the amino acid or its metabolic products. In this group are included glycine, cyst(e)ine, methionine, tryptophan, phenylalanine, and tyrosine. Other amino acids, the metabolism of which possesses no unusual features or has been discussed elsewhere in the text, generally will be dismissed with a brief statement and cross-references. However, certain metabolic pathways which may be of interest will be summarized by flow diagrams.

Alanine

This non-essential amino acid is readily formed from carbohydrate by its reversible conversion to pyruvate (Fig. 21–7).

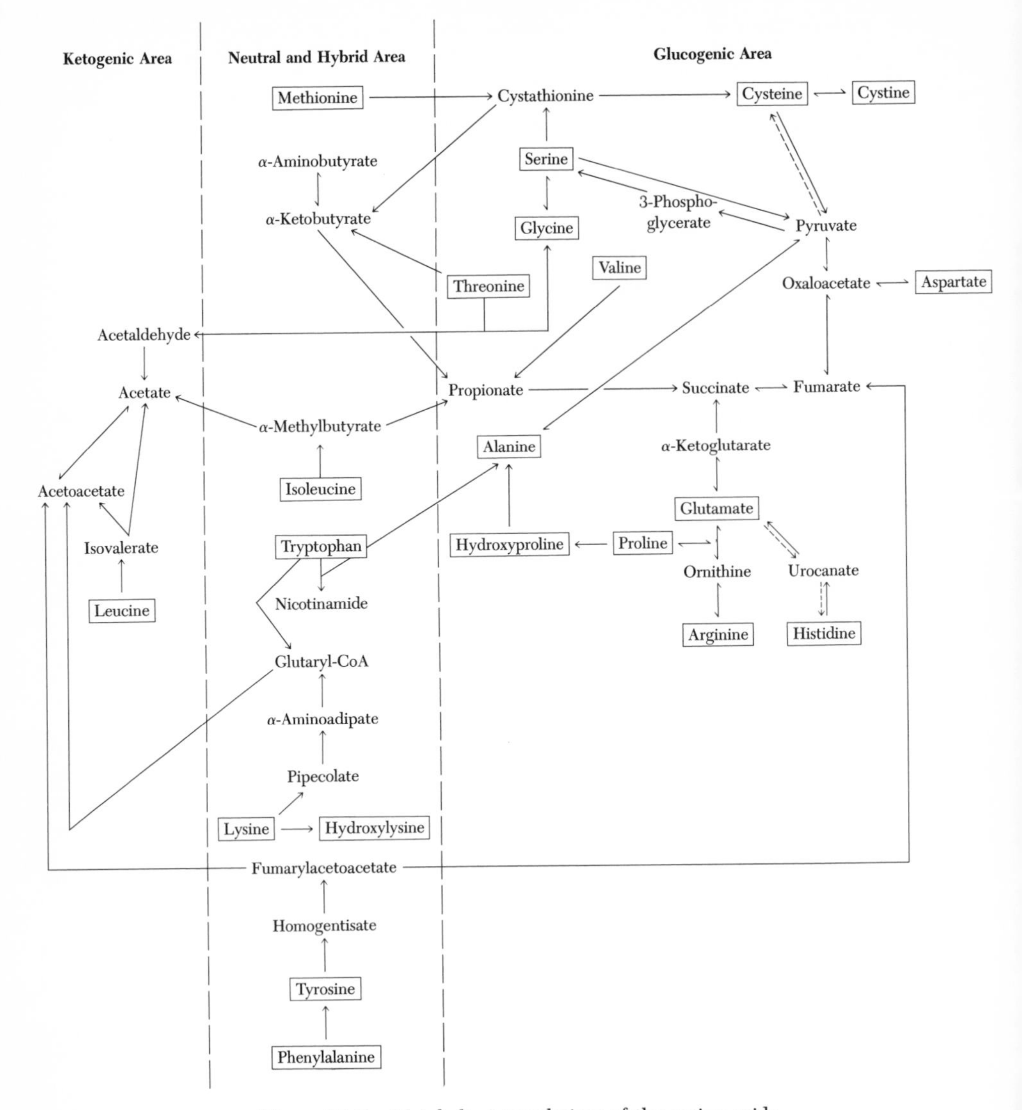

Figure 21–7. Metabolic interrelations of the amino acids.

Glycine

The major pathways of glycine metabolism are indicated in Figure 21–8. Glycine is glucogenic, non-essential, and can be synthesized from threonine (Figs. 21–7 and 21–8), and from serine by the following reaction:

$$HOCH_2 \vdots CHNH_2{-}COOH \longleftarrow \begin{cases} NH_2CH_2COOH \\ \text{"Formaldehyde"} \end{cases}$$

Serine is reversibly cleaved between the α and β carbon atoms to yield glycine and a 1-carbon fragment ("formaldehyde"), which will be discussed later (p. 592). The interconversion involves pyridoxal phosphate and tetrahydrofolate.

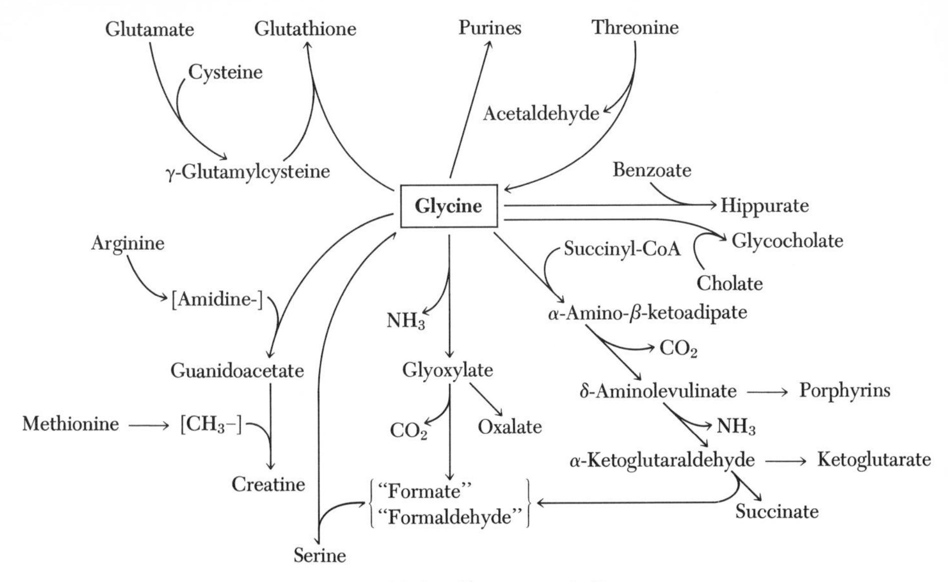

Figure 21-8. Glycine metabolism.

The degradation of glycine may take several pathways. One is merely the reverse of the synthetic pathway indicated above, followed by the usual catabolic reactions of serine. Another involves deamination of glycine, chiefly by transamination, to a lesser extent by glycine oxidase (probably = D-amino acid oxidase), the glyoxylate thus produced being split into CO_2 and a "formate" fragment, the further metabolism of which is discussed elsewhere (p. 592). Glyoxylate may form oxalate in a reaction which normally is of minor importance. Glycine may also be degraded in a side-reaction along the "succinate-glycine cycle," which is involved in the synthesis of porphyrins. Another cycle which has been suggested involves the condensation of glycine with acetyl-CoA to form aminoacetone, which loses ammonia to yield methylglyoxal, from which compound metabolic pathways are known which can lead to pyruvate and eventually to the regeneration of acetyl-CoA.

Glycine participates in the synthesis of certain heterocyclic ring systems, such as purines and porphyrins.

Glycine forms "pseudopeptides" with the bile acids and the benzoic acids (e.g., *p*-amino-benzoic). These reactions occur in the liver. The mechanism of synthesis of hippurates from the latter acids has been discussed previously (p. 388). The formation of hippurates is an example of "detoxication," and probably has no great physiological significance. The importance of the conjugated bile acids is discussed elsewhere (p. 266).

Glutathione is a true peptide, in the formation of which glycine participates. The first step in the synthesis is the combination of glutamate and cysteine to form the "γ" peptide, γ-glutamyl-cysteine, which is then condensed with glycine, yielding glutathione. Both steps (which occur in the liver) require ATP:

$$\left.\begin{array}{l}\mathrm{HSCH_2CHNH_2COOH}\\ \mathrm{HOOCCH_2CH_2CHNH_2COOH}\end{array}\right\}\xrightarrow{\text{ATP}}\mathrm{HOOCCHNH_2CH_2CH_2{-}\overset{\overset{\displaystyle O}{\|}}{C}{-}NH{-}\underset{}{\overset{\overset{\displaystyle CH_2SH}{|}}{C}H}{-}COOH}$$

$$\mathrm{HOOCCHNH_2CH_2CH_2{-}\overset{\overset{\displaystyle O}{\|}}{C}{-}NH{-}\overset{\overset{\displaystyle CH_2SH}{|}}{C}H{-}\overset{\overset{\displaystyle O}{\|}}{C}{-}NHCH_2COOH}\xleftarrow{\text{ATP}}\mathrm{NH_2CH_2COOH}$$

It is probable that each step is a composite of several, presumably including an activation reaction preceding each condensation. Analogous reactions lead to the formation of ophthalmic acid and related peptides of the lens (p. 60). Glutathione is hydrolyzed via intermediates which differ from those involved in its synthesis. The first step in the hydrolysis produces glutamate and cysteinyl-glycine; the latter is then hydrolyzed by a second enzyme system. There is now substantial evidence against the metabolic role of glutathione as a prosthetic group of glyceraldehyde-3-phosphate dehydrogenase. Glutathione has a number of functions in the erythrocyte. It protects hemoglobin against oxidation by hydrogen peroxide. It is normally maintained in its reduced form in the red cell by a reductase which utilizes NADPH. Lack of this latter cofactor in conditions of congenital deficiency of glucose-6-phosphate dehydrogenase results in a diminution of reduced glutathione in the red cell and a consequently increased susceptibility of the cell to hemolysis by various agents. Glutathione may have a general role in maintenance of the essential sulfhydryl groups of many enzymes in the reduced form. Glutathione is the source of the cysteine in the synthesis of mercapturic acids (p. 586). The insulin-inactivating action of liver is due to an insulin-glutathione transhydrogenase, which catalyzes the reductive cleavage of insulin to its constituent (and physiologically inactive) A and B chains. Glutathione is a cofactor of maleylacetoacetate isomerase (p. 600) and glyoxalase (p. 252).

Glycine is one of the building blocks in the synthesis of creatine (Fig. 21–9), which takes place in two steps, the first occurring in the kidney, pancreas, and liver, the second in the liver and kidney, although there are species differences, particularly with respect

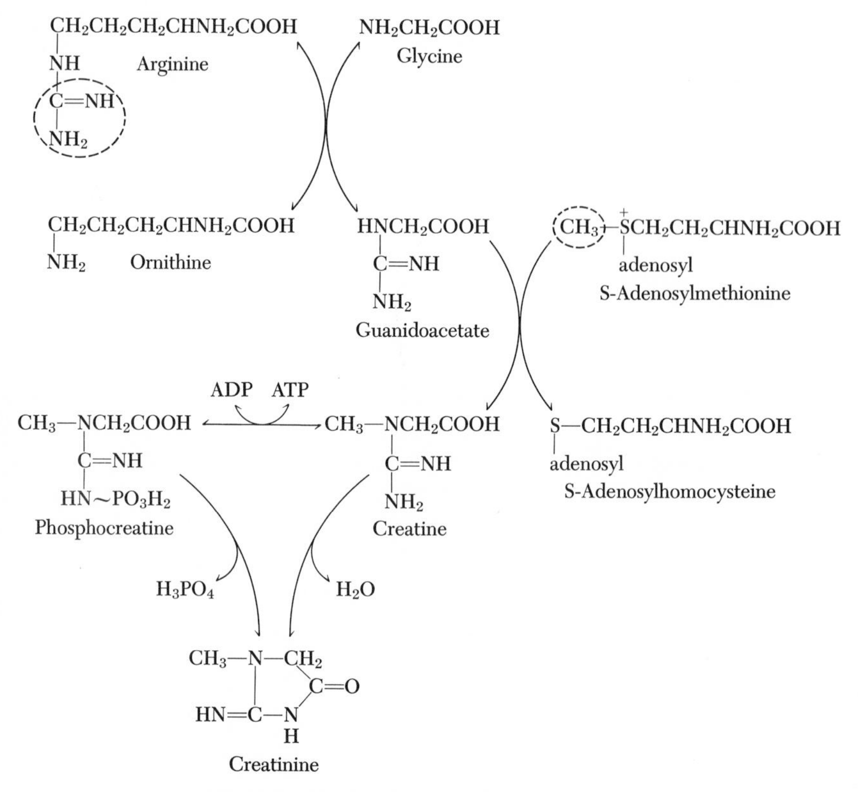

Figure 21-9. Synthesis of creatine and phosphocreatine and formation of creatinine.

to the first reaction. In the first reaction, the amidine group of arginine is transferred to glycine, forming guanidoacetate (glycocyamine) and ornithine. Guanidoacetate is then methylated by "activated" methionine, producing creatine. The first reaction is reversible; no cofactors are required. The second reaction is an example of transmethylation (p. 588). Phosphocreatine is an important storage form of high-energy phosphate, especially in muscle. Phosphocreatine, under physiological conditions of pH, temperature, etc., spontaneously loses the elements of phosphoric acid in a ring-closure reaction, yielding creatinine. Creatine itself loses water to form the same product, but at a slower rate. These two reactions result in the steady production of an amount of creatinine which is proportional to the total amount of creatine + phosphocreatine in the body, and also to the muscle mass of the organism. Consequently, creatinine (which cannot be reutilized for any purpose) is excreted in the urine in quantities which are independent of the diet, a circumstance which gave rise at one time to the theory that there is an endogenous phase of nitrogen metabolism, uninfluenced by nitrogen from exogenous sources. Transamidinase activity is subject to feedback inhibition by dietary creatine.

Inborn errors of glycine metabolism include glycinuria (a defect in renal reabsorption of glycine), glycinemia (unknown cause), and hyperoxaluria (possible defect in oxidation of glyoxylate to CO_2 and formate, channeling catabolism into oxalate).

Serine

An outline of the major metabolic paths of this glucogenic, non-essential amino acid is shown in Figure 21-10. The deamination of serine to pyruvate is noteworthy, being a dehydration, requiring pyridoxal phosphate as coenzyme, and catalyzed by the same enzyme which is responsible for the cystathionine condensation (p. 584).

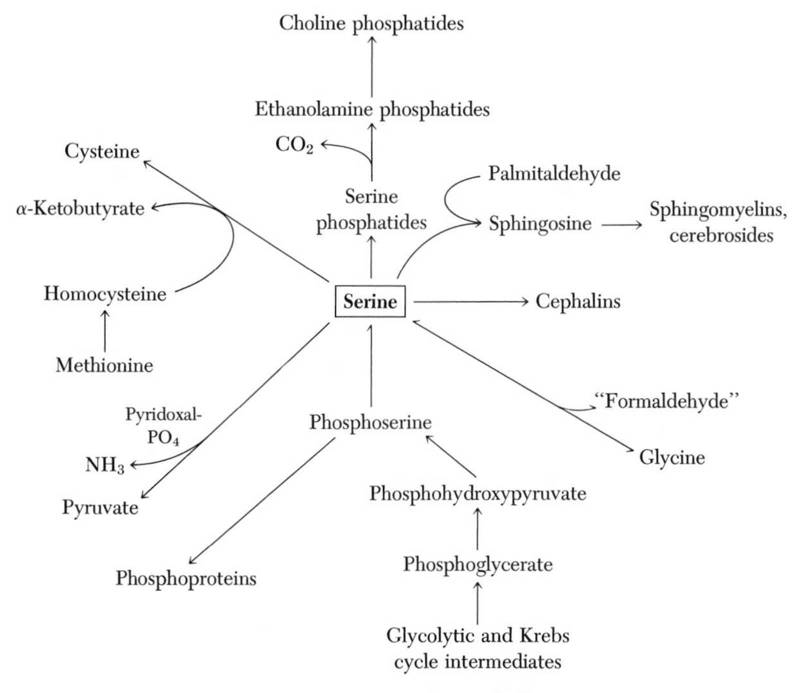

Figure 21-10. Serine metabolism.

Threonine

The major pathways of metabolism of this amino acid, which is essential for growth in the young and maintenance of nitrogen equilibrium in the adult, are indicated in Figure 21–7. Threonine is one of the few amino acids which do not take up nitrogen from the metabolic pool.

Valine, Leucine, Isoleucine

The explanation of the ability of these essential amino acids to form carbohydrate (valine), ketone bodies (leucine), or both (isoleucine) is indicated in Figure 21–11, which also emphasizes the parallelism between the catabolic reactions of these amino acids and the fatty acids. A metabolic block occurs in the metabolism of these three amino acids in the inborn error of metabolism, maple syrup urine disease. This condition, which derives its name from the unusual odor of the urine, is characterized by increased concentration

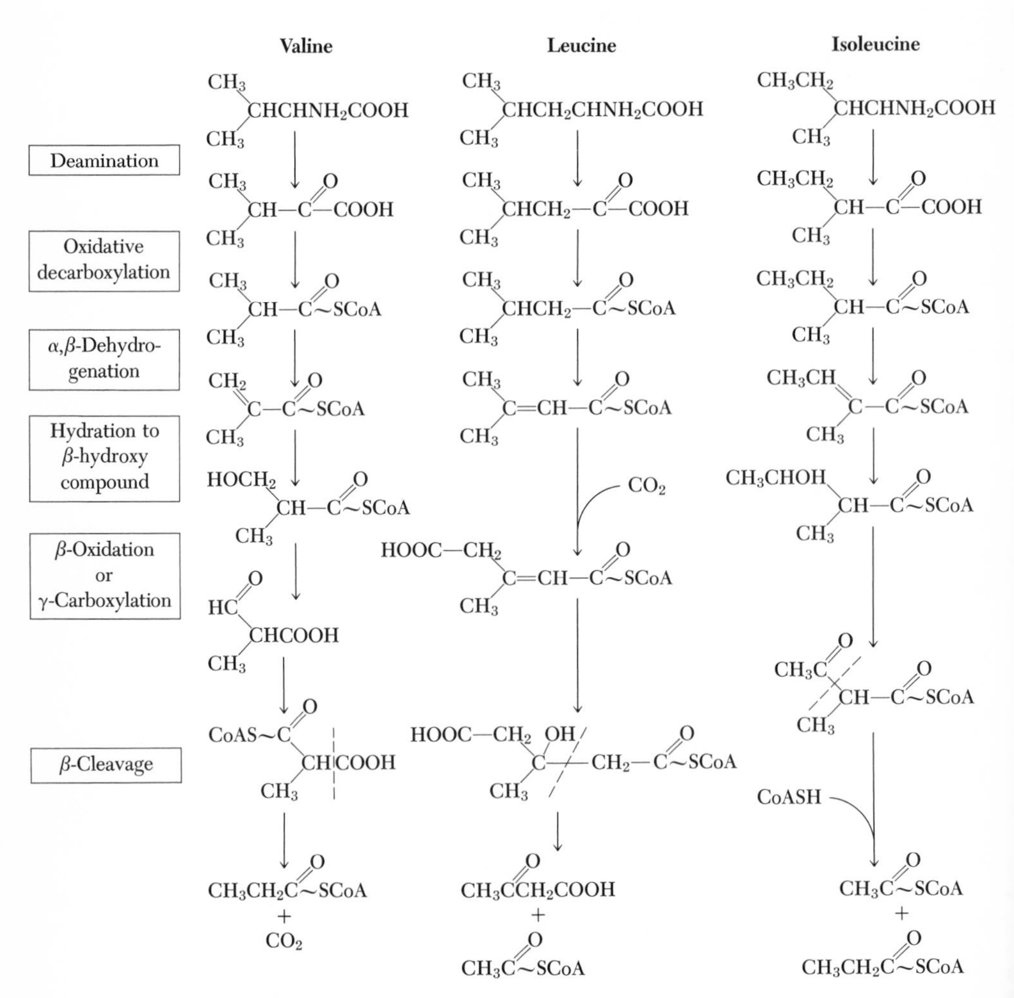

Figure 21-11. Metabolism of branched-chain amino acids.

in the blood and urine of the branched-chain amino acids and the corresponding α-keto and α-hydroxy acids; decomposition products are probably responsible for the odor of the urine. The basic enzymatic defect appears to be the inability to oxidatively decarboxylate the α-keto acids. It may be noted that one of the products of leucine catabolism, β-hydroxy-β-methyl-glutaryl-CoA, also occurs as an intermediate in the synthesis of the steroid ring (p. 475).

Aspartate

This non-essential, glucogenic amino acid is involved in transamination reactions, the ornithine cycle, and the formation of carnosine and anserine (p. 583), purines, and pyrimidines. N-acetylaspartate occurs in mammalian brain in relatively high concentration; its function is unknown.

Glutamate, Arginine, and the Prolines

An outline of the metabolism of these amino acids is presented in Figure 21-12. Glutamate is non-essential, being readily synthesized from (and converted to) carbohydrate by way of α-ketoglutarate. The interconversion of the amino acid and keto acid may occur by either oxidative deamination (glutamate dehydrogenase) or transamination. The importance of these reactions in the general deamination-reamination reactions of the amino acids was indicated previously. Aspartate and glutamate are the most active amino acids in transamination.

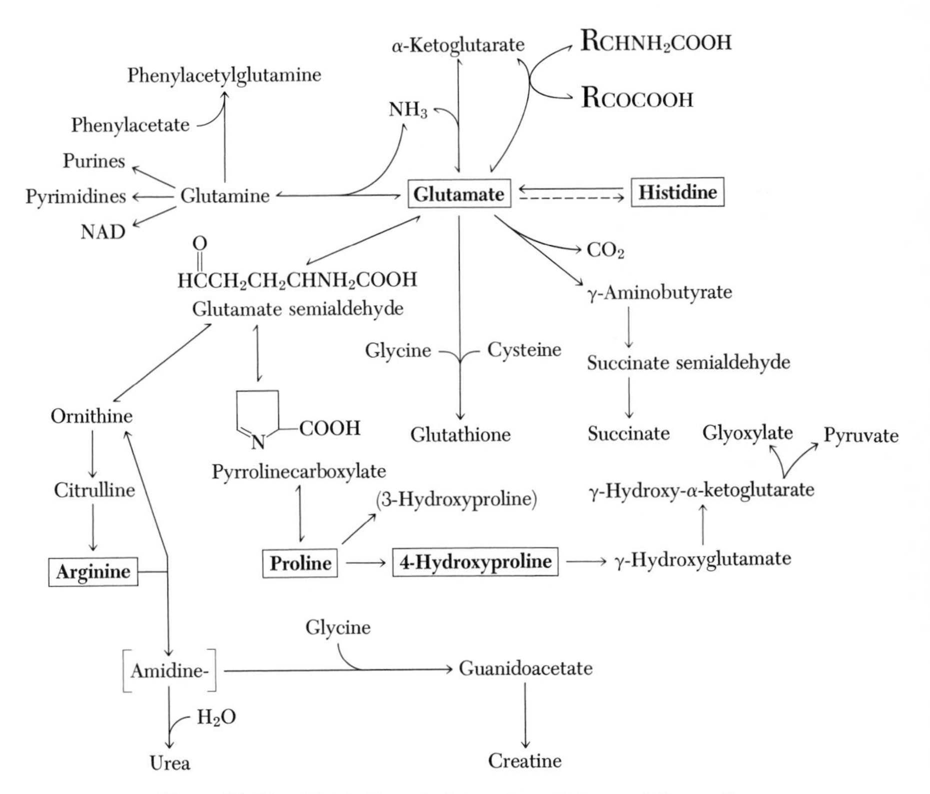

Figure 21-12. Metabolism of glutamate, arginine, and the prolines.

Glutamate is involved in the synthesis of certain special products, viz., glutathione and glutamine. In addition to its function in the general storage and transport of ammonia (playing a specific role in the regulation of acid-base balance), glutamine participates in the synthesis of purines, pyrimidines, NAD, aminosugars, and in the "detoxication" of phenylacetate in man and the higher apes, forming phenylacetylglutamine. Almost all of the reactions of glutamine which involve transfer of the amide nitrogen are inhibited by the antibiotic analogs, azaserine and diazo-oxo-norleucine (p. 664). In tissue cultures of certain types of mammalian cells, a requirement exists for glutamine which cannot be satisfied by glutamate, thus indicating that glutamine is not synthesized from glutamate in these cases.

Glutamate is one of the few compounds in addition to glucose which is used as a substrate by brain tissue. A decarboxylase has been found which converts glutamate to γ-aminobutyrate, the further metabolism of which involves transamination to succinate semialdehyde, oxidation to succinate, and final oxidation through the Krebs cycle. Although both the decarboxylation and the subsequent transamination require pyridoxal phosphate, this cofactor appears to be more loosely bound to the decarboxylase enzyme. Since γ-aminobutyrate is believed to act as an inhibitor of synaptic transmission in the central nervous system, the convulsions seen in pyridoxine deficiency may be ascribed to decreased synthesis of γ-aminobutyrate by the decarboxylase reaction. Convulsions are produced in experimental animals by injection of hydrazides which combine with the aldehyde group of pyridoxal, and by injection of anti-metabolites (p. 666) of B_6 vitamins, such as methoxypyridoxine. Since γ-aminobutyrate may be a naturally-occurring "tranquilizer," efforts are being made to find means of increasing its concentration in the central nervous system, perhaps by inhibition of the transaminase which destroys it. One such experimental inhibitor is aminooxyacetate, administration of which leads to general sedation and relaxation of muscles.

Glutamate is a constituent of the vitamin, folate (pteroylglutamate).

Arginine and the prolines are related to glutamate through the intermediate, glutamate semialdehyde. The prolines and arginine are glucogenic, but, although the former are non-essential in the young as well as the adult, arginine is not synthesized in the young animal at a rate sufficient to support optimal growth (which proceeds, nevertheless, at a suboptimal rate). Arginine is dispensable for nitrogen equilibrium in the adult. Its major metabolic roles include the synthesis of urea and creatine.

Proline and hydroxyproline are both important amino acid constituents of collagen (see composition of gelatin, p. 59), which also contains small amounts of the 3-hydroxy isomer of the ordinary hydroxyproline (hydroxyl on position 4). It is a curious fact that free hydroxyproline is not incorporated into collagen, suggesting that the synthesis of protein-bound hydroxyproline utilizes either protein-bound proline or some activated form of hydroxyproline which can be formed from free or protein-bound proline but not from free hydroxyproline. Ascorbate is involved in the conversion of proline to hydroxyproline.

In Marfan's syndrome, abnormal quantities of hydroxyproline peptides are excreted in the urine, reflecting a breakdown of body collagen. Inborn errors of this area of metabolism include hydroxyprolinemia (probable block in the initial step of hydroxyproline catabolism) and prolinemias, one type of which involves a defect in oxidation of proline to pyrrolinecarboxylate, another a defect in the further oxidation of the latter compound.

Histidine

As was stated previously, histidine is essential for growth of the young, but apparently can be synthesized at an adequate rate in the adult human being. Whether the route of synthesis is the exact reversal of the route of catabolism via glutamate (Fig. 21–13) is not certain.

Although a specific histidine decarboxylase forms histamine in mast cells, the same reaction is catalyzed in many tissues by a non-specific aromatic amino acid decarboxylase which also attacks tyrosine, dihydroxyphenylalanine, and 5-hydroxytryptophan. Histamine formation occurs at a significant rate in fetal and regenerating liver and in healing skin wounds. Owing to its pharmacological potency, it is necessary for the body to have methods of disposing of histamine. It may be excreted in the urine as such, as its acetyl derivative, or may be oxidized by diamine oxidase and aldehyde dehydrogenases to imidazoleacetate, which is excreted in the urine as such, as a ribotide, or as a methylated derivative (major metabolite in man).

Histidine and β-alanine (from aspartate) combine to form the pseudopeptide, carnosine. This compound and its methylated derivative, anserine, are found in the muscle of vertebrates, but not invertebrates.

The betaine of thiolhistidine, ergothioneine, occurs in the blood, where, as a reducing substance, it interferes with certain methods for the determination of glucose and urate. This compound is probably strictly exogenous.

The major catabolic pathway of histidine results in the formation of glutamate, and accounts for the reported glucogenicity of the former amino acid. Under the influence of a series of enzymes in liver, histidine is converted to open-chain compounds, liberating a "formimino" fragment (p. 593) in the process. Formiminoglutamate, an intermediate in the catabolic pathway, is excreted by rats deficient in folate or vitamin B_{12}.

A normally minor pathway of histidine catabolism, involving formation and excretion

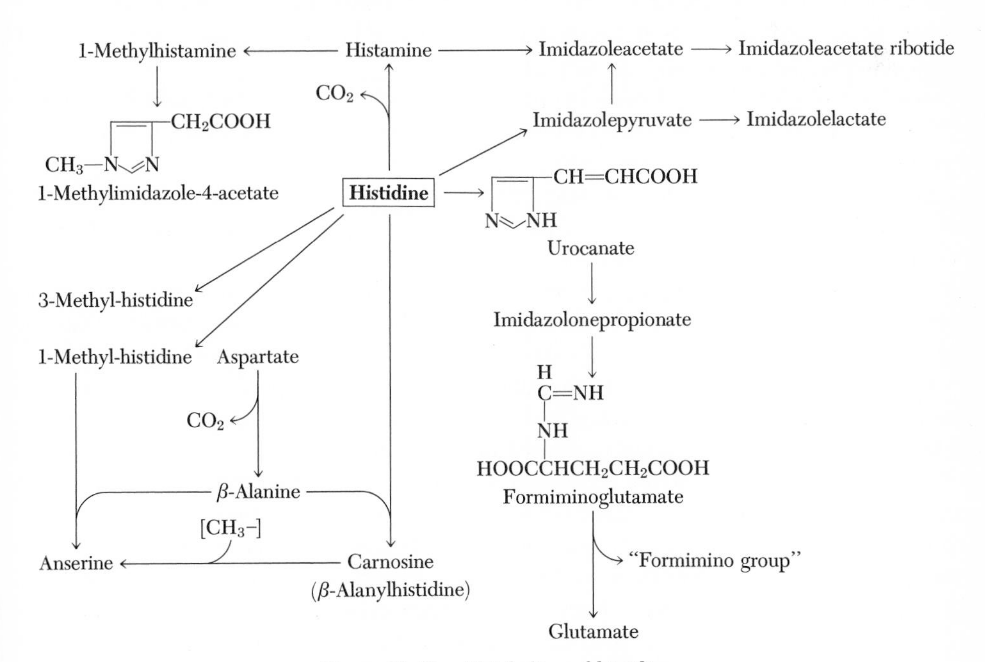

Figure 21–13. Metabolism of histidine.

of imidazole-pyruvate, -lactate, and -acetate, is a major pathway in the inborn error, histidinemia. The ferric chloride test sometimes used on urine samples for the detection of phenylpyruvate in phenylketonuria (p. 599) also is positive with imidazolepyruvate; a definitive differential finding is the elevated level of histidine, but not of phenylalanine, in the blood and urine in histidinemia. The metabolic cause of histidinemia is the lack of histidase (histidine ammonia-lyase), which normally deaminates histidine to urocanate. Patients frequently exhibit retardation of normal speech development.

Cysteine and Cystine

Separation of the discussion of methionine from that of cysteine and cystine may appear somewhat artificial from the standpoint of general sulfur metabolism. However, there are sufficient areas of metabolism in which no appreciable overlapping occurs between the two groups to justify the arbitrary division. The metabolic pathways of cysteine and cystine are outlined in Figure 21–14, in which methionine is included solely as a source of sulfur in the synthesis of cysteine.

Before entering into a detailed discussion of the metabolism of cysteine and cystine (glucogenic, non-essential), it may be helpful first to consider their interconvertibility:

$$2\begin{array}{c} COOH \\ | \\ HCNH_2 \\ | \\ CH_2SH \end{array} \underset{+2H}{\overset{-2H}{\rightleftharpoons}} \begin{array}{ccc} COOH & & COOH \\ | & & | \\ HCNH_2 & & HCNH_2 \\ | & & | \\ CH_2{-}S & {-} & S{-}CH_2 \end{array}$$

Cysteine Cystine

From the formulas, it would appear that these two amino acids constitute a typical oxidation-reduction system, each half of the system differing from the other by two hydrogen atoms (equivalent to 2 hydrogen ions + 2 electrons). There is considerable evidence that cysteine and cystine are in fact easily interconvertible in the intact organism. The oxidation of cysteine to cystine is catalyzed by cytochrome *c* and cytochrome oxidase; the reaction in the reverse direction can be effected by a number of reducing agents in the tissues, including the sulfhydryl groups of certain enzymes, hydrogen sulfide, and the reduced form of glutathione. Certain apparent discrepancies in the metabolic behavior of cysteine and cystine actually may be due to differences in rates of absorption from the intestine, and in "renal threshold."

In the case of most of the non-essential amino acids, sources must be found for the nitrogenous moiety and for the carbon skeleton. Cysteine poses the additional problem of a source of sulfur of the proper valence. As the result of investigations over a period of years, involving many techniques, it has been found that the amino group and carbon skeleton of cysteine are provided by serine, whereas the sulfur is derived from methionine (Fig. 21–15).

It was originally assumed that methionine simply gives up its methyl group in a transmethylation to some appropriate acceptor, leaving homocysteine. From what is known now concerning transmethylations from methionine (p. 590), it appears that the provision of homocysteine is not so simple. In order to transmethylate, methionine first must be "activated," forming S-adenosylmethionine. After transmethylation, the S-adenosylhomocysteine residue is cleaved to adenosine and free homocysteine. Cysteine synthesis is then initiated by condensation of homocysteine with serine to form the thioether, cystathionine. (This compound is found in very high concentration in human brain.) In animal tissues, the thioether is split specifically on the side of the sulfur which yields cysteine and α-ketobutyrate. Pyridoxal phosphate is the coenzyme of the condensation as

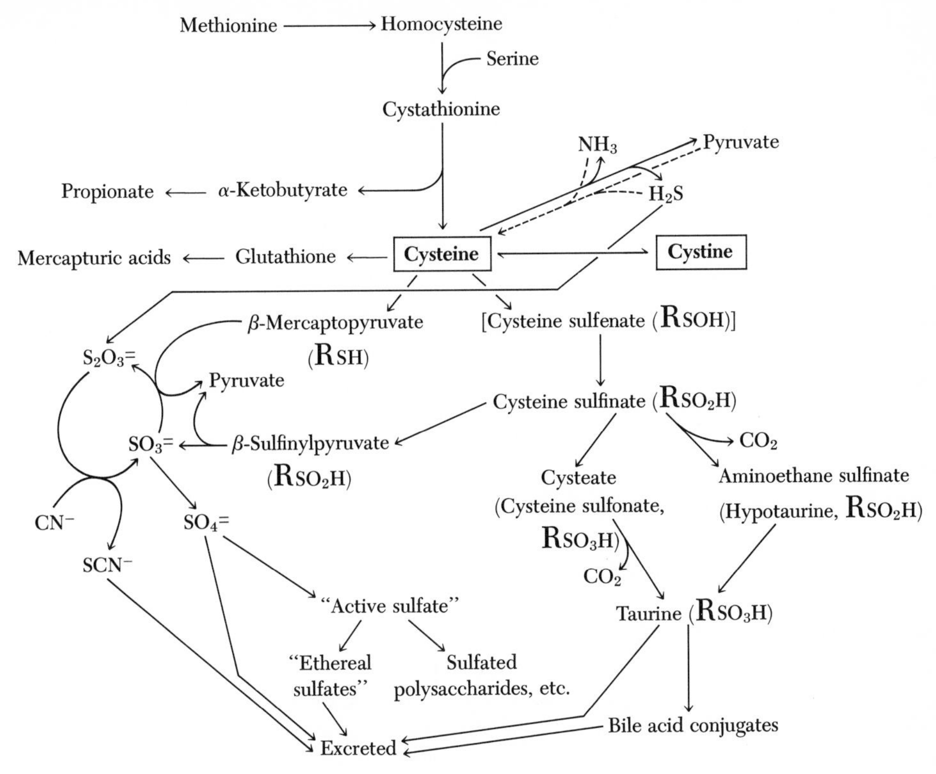

Figure 21-14. Cysteine metabolism.

well as of the "cystathionase" system. The α-aminobutyrate which is excreted in the urine in certain circumstances is probably derived from α-ketobutyrate, which may be produced from threonine as well as methionine. The synthesis of cysteine from methionine is irreversible.

Two inborn errors have been found in the area of cysteine synthesis, cystathioninuria

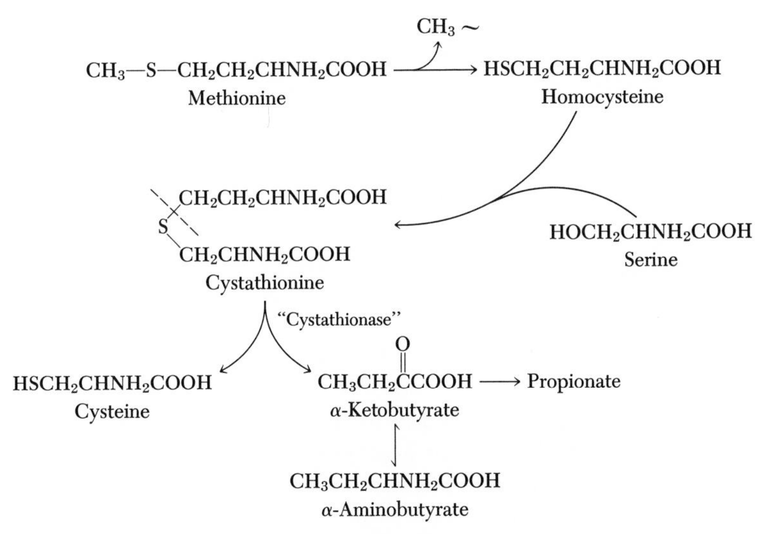

Figure 21-15. Synthesis of cysteine.

(possible absence of cystathionase) and homocystinuria (absence of the synthetase which couples homocysteine and serine).

Although there is no unanimity concerning cystine, most investigations have shown cysteine to be glucogenic. Since these amino acids are interconvertible, it is probable that both should be considered glucogenic. The conversion of cysteine to pyruvate bears a resemblance to the serine dehydratase reaction, being, however, a desulfhydration rather than a dehydration. It is apparently catalyzed by "cystathionase." The cofactor here again is pyridoxal phosphate. Although the liberation of H_2S from cysteine *can* be reversed, as shown with radioactive sulfur in vitro, this has not been found to occur to any appreciable extent in the intact organism. The H_2S evolved in this and other reactions is oxidized to sulfate in the body. (The general metabolism and excretion of sulfur are discussed on page 588.)

The sulfur of cysteine may undergo oxidation while still attached to the organic molecule (Fig. 21–14). Taurine, one of the products of this metabolic route, is involved in conjugation of the bile acids. Thiosulfate, another product of sulfur oxidation, is used in the detoxication of cyanide by formation of thiocyanate.

Cysteine is utilized in the synthesis of glutathione and coenzyme A. Cysteine also participates in a novel form of "detoxication," the formation of mercapturic acids. Aromatic hydrocarbons, certain of their halogenated or nitrated derivatives, benzyl and alkyl halides, and certain nitroparaffins are conjugated with cysteine in the body, and the cysteine moiety is then acetylated. Recent experiments indicate that cysteine participates in the conjugation initially in the form of glutathione, rather than in the free state. It has been known for some time that, in the case of those compounds in which the cysteine sulfur is directly attached to a nuclear carbon atom of an aromatic ring, the derivatives actually excreted in the urine are "premercapturic" acids, which are readily converted by acid to the mercapturic acids themselves. It has been established that the premercapturic acids are dihydro derivatives of the aromatic rings. Since those aromatic compounds which form mercapturic acids also form phenols and catechols, it has been suggested that an epoxide type of intermediate may be the common precursor of all of these derivatives. The following reactions incorporate these concepts into a tentative scheme for the formation of the mercapturic acid derived from bromobenzene:

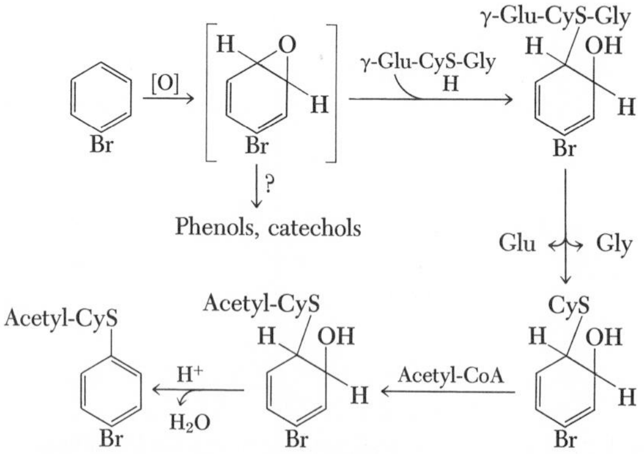

Br → [O] → [H, O, H, Br] → (γ-Glu-CyS-Gly H) → γ-Glu-CyS-Gly, H, OH, H, Br

[H, O, H, Br] → ? → Phenols, catechols

γ-Glu-CyS-Gly, H, OH, H, Br → (Glu, Gly) → CyS, H, OH, H, Br

CyS, H, OH, H, Br → Acetyl-CoA → Acetyl-CyS, H, OH, H, Br → (H^+, H_2O) → Acetyl-CyS, Br

The sulfur-containing amino acids are involved in an inborn error of metabolism known as cystinuria. In this condition, as in other inborn errors, a genetically transmitted deficiency in one enzyme causes the accumulation of an ordinarily metabolized compound, which is consequently excreted in sufficient quantities to be detected. These metabolic anomalies in themselves are not always harmful to the individual, although serious consequences sometimes result from quite accidental features of the condition. In the case of cystinuria, for example, an individual may go through life unaware of his daily excretion of cystine in the urine. On the other hand, the insolubility of cystine can lead to the crystallization of this substance in the urine, which sometimes results in the formation of cystine calculi requiring surgical intervention.

Modern investigations have resulted in a satisfactory explanation of the mechanism of cystinuria. It is known that the quantity of cystine excreted by a cystinuric varies with the level of protein in the diet. Administration of methionine or cysteine to a cystinuric results in increased excretion of cystine, whereas cystine itself is easily and completely oxidized to sulfate. In the past, these curious findings have been explained on the basis that the interconversion of cystine and cysteine is interfered with in cystinuria, and that cystine has a metabolic pathway completely independent of cysteine, an explanation which poses more problems than it solves. A more satisfactory solution is suggested by earlier work on the excretion of amino acids other than cystine in the urine of cystinurics, recently confirmed and refined by the application of paper and column partition chromatography. It appears that cystinurics excrete, in addition to cystine, abnormally large quantities of lysine, arginine, and ornithine. The formulas of these amino acids and cystine are shown below:

$NH_2CH_2CH_2CH_2CH_2CHNH_2COOH$ Lysine

$$\begin{array}{l} NHCH_2CH_2CH_2CHNH_2COOH \\ | \\ C{=}NH \\ | \\ NH_2 \end{array}$$ Arginine

$NH_2CH_2CH_2CH_2CHNH_2COOH$ Ornithine

$$\begin{array}{l} NH_2CHCH_2{-}S{-}S{-}CH_2CHNH_2COOH \\ \quad\ | \\ \quad COOH \end{array}$$ Cystine

It is suggested that the cystinuric inherits a defect in an enzyme system of the kidney involved in the tubular reabsorption of compounds possessing diamine structures of the type indicated above. Cystine itself, when fed, is absorbed only slowly from the intestine and cannot result in high levels of cystine in the blood. It is metabolized or otherwise utilized as rapidly as it enters the body and does not appear in the urine. Methionine and cysteine, on the other hand, are rapidly absorbed and rapidly converted to cystine, presumably at a rate sufficient to elevate the level of blood cystine beyond the point of complete tubular reabsorption in the kidney, resulting in cystinuria.

The genetics of cystinuria is rather complex; several variants of the disorder have been described. It is interesting that cystinurics exhibit defective absorption of diamino acids from the intestine.

Cystinosis is an inborn error of metabolism unrelated to cystinuria. This condition is characterized by deposits of cystine crystals throughout the tissues. Its cause is unknown.

Several types of compounds undergo esterification with sulfate in the body. The liver utilizes sulfate for the "detoxication" of phenol and indoxyl, for example. Other compounds forming sulfate esters in the body are the estrogens, androgens, tyrosine, and the amino sugars. Organic sulfate esters which are excreted in the urine are called "ethereal sulfates." The reactant in all sulfate conjugations is "active sulfate," 3′-phosphoadenosine-5′-phosphosulfate (PAPS), synthesized as follows:

$$ATP + SO_4^{=} \longleftrightarrow \text{adenosine-phosphosulfate} + \text{pyrophosphate}$$

$$\text{Adenosine-phosphosulfate} + ATP \longrightarrow \text{phosphoadenosine-phosphosulfate} + ADP$$

Transfer of the sulfate group to various acceptors is catalyzed by specific sulfotransferases.

It may be of interest to outline the overall fate of sulfur-bearing compounds in the mammalian organism. Inorganic sulfate is ingested only in small amounts, and, although it can be utilized for esterification, is not ordinarily a significant source of this form of sulfur; it is also not appreciably reduced to lower states of oxidation. Small quantities of mercaptans derived from intestinal putrefaction may be absorbed into the blood and excreted in the urine. The major sources of urinary sulfur, however, are the cystine, cysteine, and methionine moieties of the dietary proteins. Normally, a certain (relatively small) proportion of these amino acids is metabolized via pathways leading to the excretion of taurine, thiosulfate, or thiocyanate. Traces of the amino acids themselves are also excreted. All compounds in the urine containing sulfur in a lower state of oxidation than sulfate are classified as "neutral sulfur." The major metabolic pathway of the sulfur-bearing amino acids results in complete oxidation to sulfate. A minor fraction of the total sulfate in the urine is ester or "ethereal" sulfate, the major fraction being free, inorganic sulfate. Quantitative aspects of sulfur partition in the urine are discussed elsewhere (p. 846).

Methionine

The essentiality of methionine for growth and nitrogen equilibrium was formerly believed to be due to its methyl group, since its demethylated derivative, homocysteine, could not replace it when administered to animals on certain restricted diets ("methyl-free" but otherwise mistakenly believed at the time to be complete) unless a source of methyl groups (e.g., choline) was provided also. Since it has been discovered that methyl groups can be synthesized in the organism, since homocysteine can replace methionine in a methyl-free diet provided with the proper vitamins, and since the keto acid of methionine can take its place in the diet, it appears that the structure in methionine which cannot be synthesized by the animal is the sulfur-carbon skeleton,

$$-S-CH_2-CH_2-\overset{|}{\underset{|}{C}}-COOH.$$

Despite its close relation to cysteine, methionine does not behave as a glucogenic amino acid. This is difficult to explain, since α-ketobutyrate (a major metabolite) is believed to form propionate, which is glucogenic.

Although methionine can be deaminated, there is no evidence that any significant part of its metabolism proceeds via the keto acid. In fact, there appear to be only two important metabolic routes open to methionine or its constituent chemical fragments: (1) transfer of sulfur to the carbon chain of serine to form cysteine and α-ketobutyrate; (2) utilization of the methyl group in transmethylations and the related reactions of the "formate"-"formaldehyde" group. The former pathway has been discussed in detail in connection with the metabolism of cysteine; the latter will be considered here.

Metabolism of One-Carbon Units: Methyl

A general scheme of methyl donors and acceptors is shown in Figure 21–16, which is not to be interpreted to mean that there is a general "pool" of methyl groups in the sense that there is a pool of ammonia or acetyl, since transmethylations have been found to be not only very specific for donor and acceptor, but also largely irreversible. The methyl donors listed do not correspond exactly to the compounds commonly regarded in the older literature as possessing "labile" methyl groups. These labile groups were com-

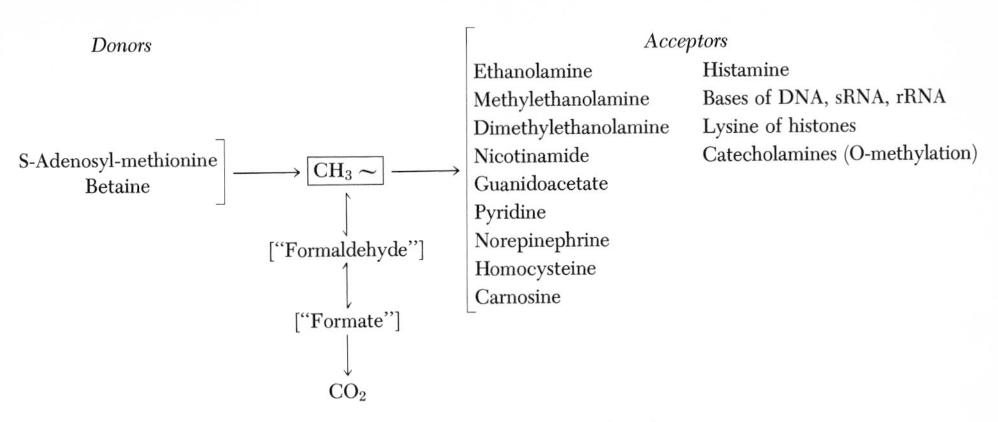

Figure 21-16. Donors and acceptors of methyl groups.

monly detected by testing a given compound for its ability to replace methionine for the growth of rats on a methyl-free, homocysteine-supplemented diet. (As shown by later experiments, the diets used chanced to be deficient in folate and vitamin B_{12}, precluding synthesis of methyl groups from "formate"-"formaldehyde" [p. 592].) The possession of labile methyl groups by this criterion did not prove that the compound in question was itself a methylating agent, e.g., the case of choline (discussed below), but did indicate that it could act as a source of methyls, even if only by way of intermediary reactions. The same type of information has been obtained in tracing the course of methyl groups in the body by labeling them with isotopic carbon or hydrogen. Although lipotropism was used in the past as an indication of the possession of labile methyl groups (p. 504), there is no direct correlation between the lipotropic activity of a compound and its transmethylating ability. Detailed information on certain direct methyl donors has become available from experiments in vitro with more or less purified systems.

In addition to betaine and S-adenosylmethionine, compounds which also act as in vitro methylating agents include S-methylmethionine, dimethylthetin, and dimethylpropiothetin (sulfonium compounds), and the ester, methyl phosphate. The first two are the only physiological methylating agents known to occur in the animal organism; dimethylpropiothetin is found in algae, S-methylmethionine occurs in higher plants, whereas dimethylthetin and methyl phosphate, so far as is known, are purely synthetic products of the laboratory. All of these compounds bear a marked resemblance to the alkylating agents of the organic chemist, containing methyl groups linked either to an "-onium" atom (quaternary nitrogen or tertiary sulfur) or esterified with an inorganic acid (methyl phosphate being analogous to dimethyl sulfate). It seems reasonable to assume that all biological methyl donors have structures similar to those indicated.

Transmethylations are highly exergonic. In most cases, a hydrogen ion is released in the reaction, contributing to the liberation of free energy at physiological pH. The free energy of transmethylation approximates that of hydrolysis of a high-energy bond.

The apparent ability of dietary choline to serve as a source of methyl groups obviously must be explained by its prior oxidation to betaine:

$$\underset{\text{Choline}}{(CH_3)_3\overset{+}{N}CH_2CH_2OH} \longrightarrow \underset{\text{Betaine aldehyde}}{(CH_3)_3\overset{+}{N}CH_2\overset{H}{C}{=}O} \longrightarrow \underset{\text{Betaine}}{(CH_3)_3\overset{+}{N}CH_2COO^-}$$

Indeed, it has been observed that the in vitro efficacy of choline as a methylating agent is contingent upon aerobiosis and the possession by the tissue in question of choline and betaine aldehyde dehydrogenases, whereas transmethylations from betaine are independent of these factors. A specific transmethylase catalyzes the transfer of methyl groups from betaine to homocysteine:

$$(CH_3)_3\overset{+}{N}{-}CH_2COO^- \text{ (Betaine)} + HSCH_2CH_2CH\overset{+}{N}H_3COO^- \text{ (Homocysteine)} \rightarrow (CH_3)_2N{-}CH_2COO^- \text{ (Dimethyl glycine)} + H^+ + CH_3{-}SCH_2CH_2CH\overset{+}{N}H_3COO^- \text{ (Methionine)}$$

The demethylated remainder of betaine is dimethylglycine, which is not a direct methyl donor. It can, however, re-form betaine in the cyclic series of reactions shown in Figure 21–17. The second methyl group of betaine (one of the two methyl groups of dimethylglycine) is oxidized to a "formaldehyde" fragment (p. 592), as is the third methyl group (the single methyl group of sarcosine, monomethylglycine). Complete removal of methyl groups leaves glycine, which is interconvertible with serine by addition or removal of a "formaldehyde" unit. By decarboxylation, serine produces ethanolamine, which is methylated in three successive steps to form choline, from which betaine is finally produced by oxidation. It should be pointed out that certain of these interconversions are of importance in connection with the phospholipids (p. 484) and the phenomenon of lipotropism (p. 504). As a matter of fact, there is evidence that the portion of the sequence from serine through choline occurs while the bases are integral parts of phospholipids. The interconversion of methyl groups and "formaldehyde" shown in Figure 21–17 will be discussed later.

It has been known for some time that methylations from methionine involve some sort of "activation," since ATP is required. The direct methyl donor, a reaction product of ATP and methionine, has proved to be S-adenosylmethionine. In the activation reaction, ATP donates its entire adenosine moiety to methionine and loses three moles of phosphate (one as orthophosphate, two as pyrophosphate):

$$\text{Ad-R-}Ⓟ\sim Ⓟ\sim Ⓟ + CH_3{-}S{-}CH_2CH_2CHNH_2COOH \rightarrow Ⓟ + Ⓟ\sim Ⓟ + \text{Ad}{-}\text{R}{-}\overset{+}{\underset{CH_3}{S}}{-}CH_2CH_2CHNH_2COOH$$

Transmethylations from activated methionine to various acceptors may be depicted as shown in Figure 21–18. Hydrolysis of S-adenosylhomocysteine would provide the homocysteine required for the synthesis of cysteine. Ethionine, an antimetabolite (p. 666) of methionine, can be activated and will transethylate to various acceptors.

The sources and ultimate disposal of methyl groups are topics which have stimulated much investigation. Preformed methyl groups are available to the organism from the methionine and choline (and betaine) of the diet. The methyl groups of such substances as creatine, N^1-methylnicotinamide, and epinephrine are not "labile," which is another way of stating that their initial methylations are irreversible. (The only methylation

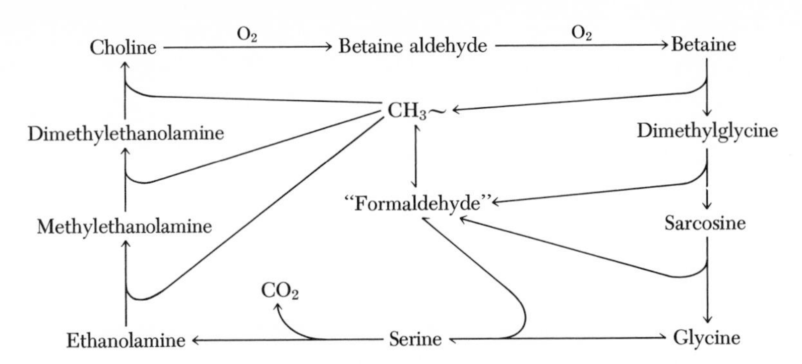

Figure 21-17. Interrelations of glycine and choline derivatives in transmethylation.

which could be considered reversible, in fact, is that of homocysteine to methionine, but the route involves ATP, as has been seen, and cannot be considered direct.) It is now known that the animal organism has at its disposal metabolic pathways for the synthesis of methyl groups from other 1-carbon units (discussed below), provided certain vitamins are present in the diet. These pathways are sufficiently effective (except, possibly, for a short period after birth) to supply the growing organism with all of the methyl groups it requires on diets devoid of methyl donors, but containing homocysteine, the "essential" portion of methionine.

The ultimate fate of methyl groups is oxidation to CO_2. Formaldehyde and formate, or compounds readily interconvertible with them, appear to be the intermediates in this oxidation. The metabolic route may proceed through dimethylglycine and sarcosine

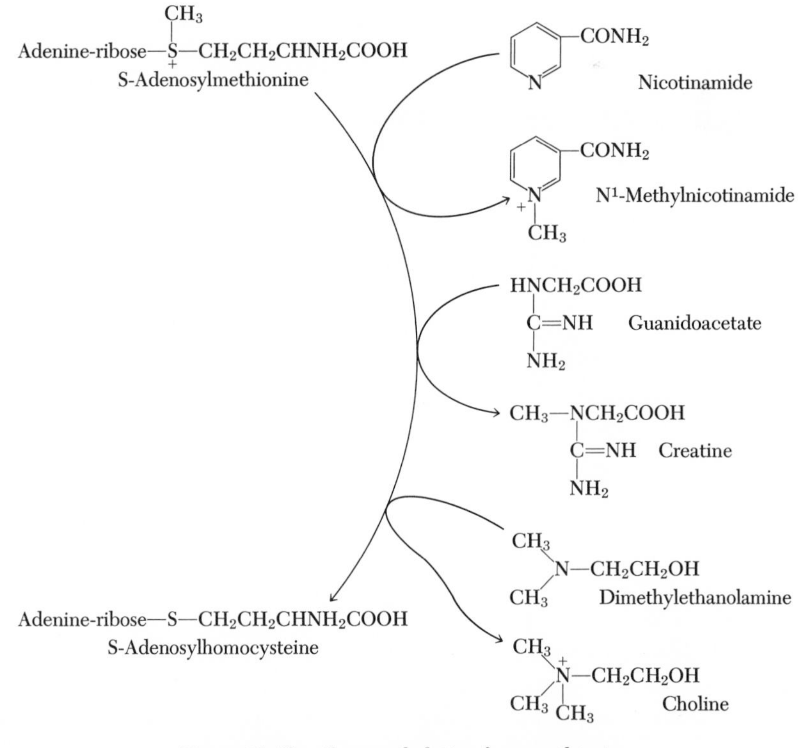

Figure 21-18. Transmethylation from methionine.

(Fig. 21–17), since enzyme systems are known which oxidize N-methyl amino acids to the free amino acids and formaldehyde. Formaldehyde is readily oxidized to formate, which is in turn rapidly converted to CO_2. Since formaldehyde and formate are closely related to the 1-carbon fragments mentioned in connection with the synthesis of methyl groups, it appears that the anabolic and catabolic pathways of methyl groups may be very similar, if not identical.

Metabolism of One-Carbon Units: Methyl, Hydroxymethyl, and Formyl

Sporadic reference has been made, in this and previous chapters, to certain 1-carbon units, frequently called "formate" or "formyl," and "formaldehyde" or "hydroxymethyl," in addition to the methyl group itself. An outline of the donors, acceptors, interconversion, and mode of transport of these fragments is presented in Figure 21–19. The coenzyme which transports the fragments, shown in the figure as FH_4, is tetrahydrofolate, which is

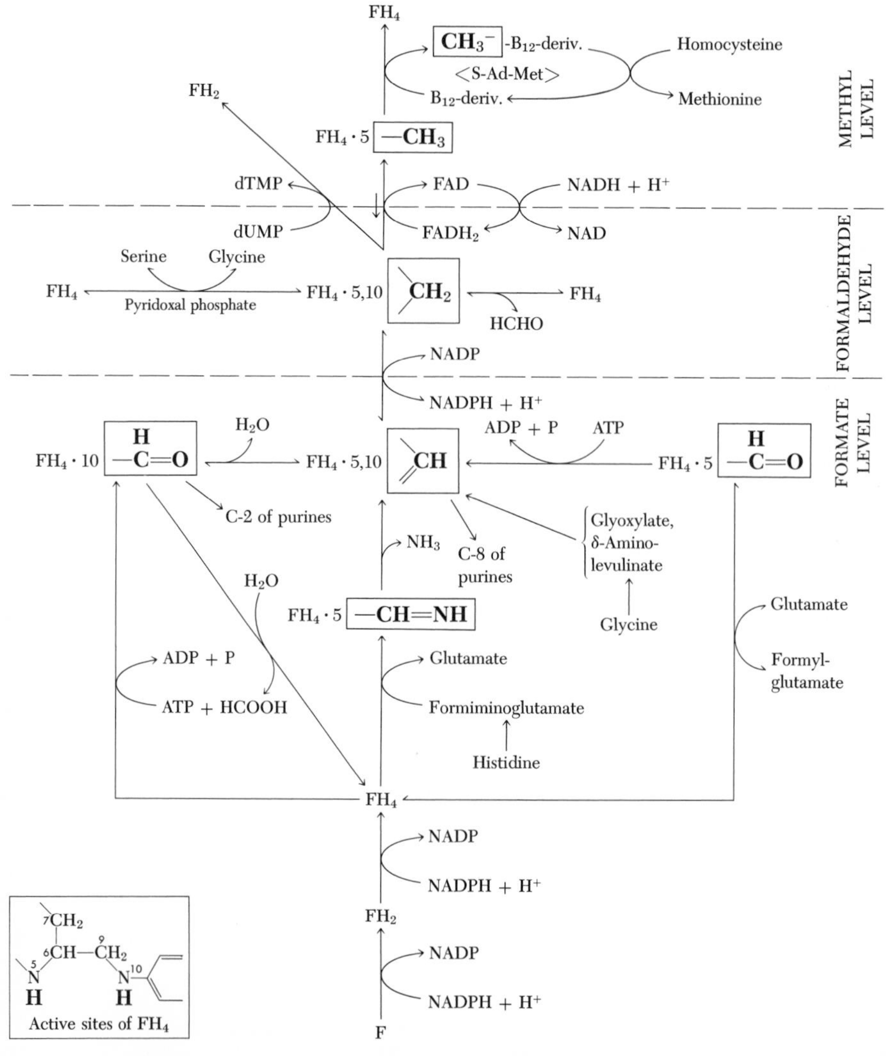

Figure 21–19. Metabolism of 1-carbon fragments. *F, FH_2, FH_4,* folate, dihydrofolate, tetrahydrofolate.

derived from the stepwise reduction of folate. Free formaldehyde (derived from sources such as oxidation of the methyl groups of sarcosine and dimethylglycine) and the β-carbon of serine are direct sources of the hydroxymethyl fragment, whereas the formyl group is derived from free formate (from sources such as formylkynurenine, a metabolite of tryptophan [p. 596]), the α-carbon of glycine, via glyoxylate (p. 577) or δ-aminolevulinate (p. 609). Formiminoglutamate, a metabolite of histidine (p. 583) is the source of the formimino fragment. Other, less important, sources of 1-carbon fragments are cyanide and the methyl carbons of methanol and acetone. That portion of the carbon-nitrogen skeleton of tetrahydrofolate which is involved in transporting these fragments is shown in the insert in Figure 21–19. The active sites are N^5, N^{10}, or both together.

It will be noted in Figure 21–19 that, including methyl, the 1-carbon fragment can exist at three levels of oxidation. Several different types of fragments exist on the formate level: a formimino group carried on position N-5 of tetrahydrofolate, formyl groups carried either on position N-5 or N-10, and an anhydroformyl (methenyl) group carried between positions N-5 and N-10. One-carbon fragments at the formaldehyde or hydroxymethyl level appear to react solely in the form of the $N^{5,10}$-methylene (anhydrohydroxymethyl) group on tetrahydrofolate. The methyl fragment is carried on N^5.

In the catabolic direction, hydroxymethyl and formyl groups are oxidized to CO_2. It is not certain whether this oxidation, which undoubtedly occurs at the formate level, is necessarily preceded by liberation of free formate from tetrahydrofolate.

As indicated in Figure 21–19, 1-carbon fragments are involved in the synthesis of several important products. It is probable that, in the human adult, the imidazole ring of histidine is synthesized by a mechanism similar (but in reverse) to that involved in its degradation, consequently requiring the incorporation of a formyl group. In the synthesis of purines, "formate" has been shown to produce carbons 2 and 8. It is a curious fact that two different types of formyl groups are involved in these reactions, as shown in the figure. The attachment of a "formaldehyde" group to glycine in the conversion of that amino acid to serine has been discussed previously. Fragments of the hydroxymethyl type also are precursors of the methyl group of thymine, in an unusual reaction in which the coenzyme, tetrahydrofolate, acts not only as transfer agent, but also as reductant (becoming dihydrofolate), simultaneously adding the hydroxymethyl group to deoxyuridylate and reducing it to a methyl group, thus forming (deoxy)thymidylate. Continuous synthesis of thymine requires continuous regeneration of tetrahydrofolate from dihydrofolate, a reaction inhibited by the "antifolate" drugs used in cancer chemotherapy (p. 673).

Synthesis of the methyl group of methionine, which is the parent of most methyl groups in the organism (other than that of DNA thymine), has been a difficult process to clarify. Since this pathway is currently under intensive investigation, the reactions shown in Figure 21–19 should be regarded as tentative. In a reaction, the equilibrium point of which is far toward the side of the products, 5,10-methylene-tetrahydrofolate is reduced to 5-methyl-tetrahydrofolate. Reduced FAD is the coenzyme directly involved, maintained in its reduced state by reduced NAD. The methyl group is ultimately accepted by homocysteine, forming methionine, probably by way of intermediary reactions. It is believed that a methylated form of a derivative of vitamin B_{12} is the intermediate carrier, thus explaining the well-known requirement of this vitamin (as well as of folate) in the de novo synthesis of methyl groups. Catalytic amounts of S-adenosylmethionine also participate in some unknown fashion. Conditions of vitamin B_{12} deficiency may lead to the accumulation of 5-methyl-tetrahydrofolate in the tissues, constituting a "folate trap," resulting in diminished efficiency of reactions requiring adequate supplies of tetrahydrofolate for 1-carbon fragment metabolism.

Although cyanide can scarcely be recommended for inclusion in the diet, this noxious substance may be metabolized in small amounts. The administration of small amounts of radioactive cyanide to experimental animals results in the appearance of cyanide in the urine and HCN in the expired air. The carbon of the cyanide makes its way into thiocyanate, respiratory CO_2, the methyl groups of choline and methionine, and the ureide carbon atom of allantoin, which is derived from C-2 and C-8 of the purines. Obviously, metabolic pathways are available for the conversion of cyanide to "formate" and labile methyl groups.

Lysine

In the case of lysine, there is no evidence for net glucogenicity or ketogenicity, although fragments of the ketogenic type may be produced during its catabolism (Fig. 21–7, p. 576). Lysine is an essential amino acid for growth and maintenance of nitrogen equilibrium, and is one of the few amino acids which does not participate in the ammonia pool, that is, it can lose its nitrogen to the pool, but cannot be reaminated from it. The relationship between free lysine and the hydroxylysine of skin collagen is analogous to that between free proline and hydroxyproline (p. 582). The ε-amino nitrogen atom of lysine is the site of attachment of the biotin prosthetic group of many carboxylases. Although of unknown physiological significance, the same site in the lysine residues of histones is capable of accepting methyl groups from S-adenosylmethionine.

Tryptophan (Fig. 21–20)

This essential amino acid is neither glucogenic nor ketogenic in the intact organism (Fig. 21–7, p. 576), although it appears to produce both types of fragments in the course of its catabolism. Since only small quantities of tryptophan are metabolized daily, it is possible that the rate of formation of glucogenic and ketogenic products is insufficient to influence the usual tests.

Serotonin pathway. Tryptophan is the precursor of "serotonin," a vasoconstrictor found in serum and a number of tissues, including the gastrointestinal tract and central nervous system. Serotonin may be involved in the regulation of gastric secretion and intestinal peristalsis. It is apparently stored in blood platelets, producing local vasoconstriction when liberated by platelet disintegration. The role of serotonin in the nervous system is currently under intensive investigation, since it has been shown that the "tranquilizing" action of Rauwolfia alkaloids (e.g., reserpine) is accompanied by release of serotonin (and norepinephrine) from bound forms in the brain (and other tissues), and that the action of certain hallucinogenic indolic drugs may be due to antagonism of the normal functions of serotonin (p. 672). Since oxidation is a major pathway of catabolism (in brain) of amines such as serotonin and norepinephrine, the concentration of these amines in the brain increases when inhibitors of monoamine oxidase are administered. Since this rise in amine concentration has an excitatory effect on the central nervous system, mental depression has been treated by administration of inhibitors of monoamine oxidase (so-called "psychic energizers") such as isopropyl isonicotinyl hydrazine (iproniazid). Owing to these and other findings, it has been hypothesized that certain mental aberrations have a biochemical basis.

The major end-product of the serotonin pathway is hydroxyindoleacetate, which is normally excreted in small amounts in the urine. This excretion is increased many-fold in

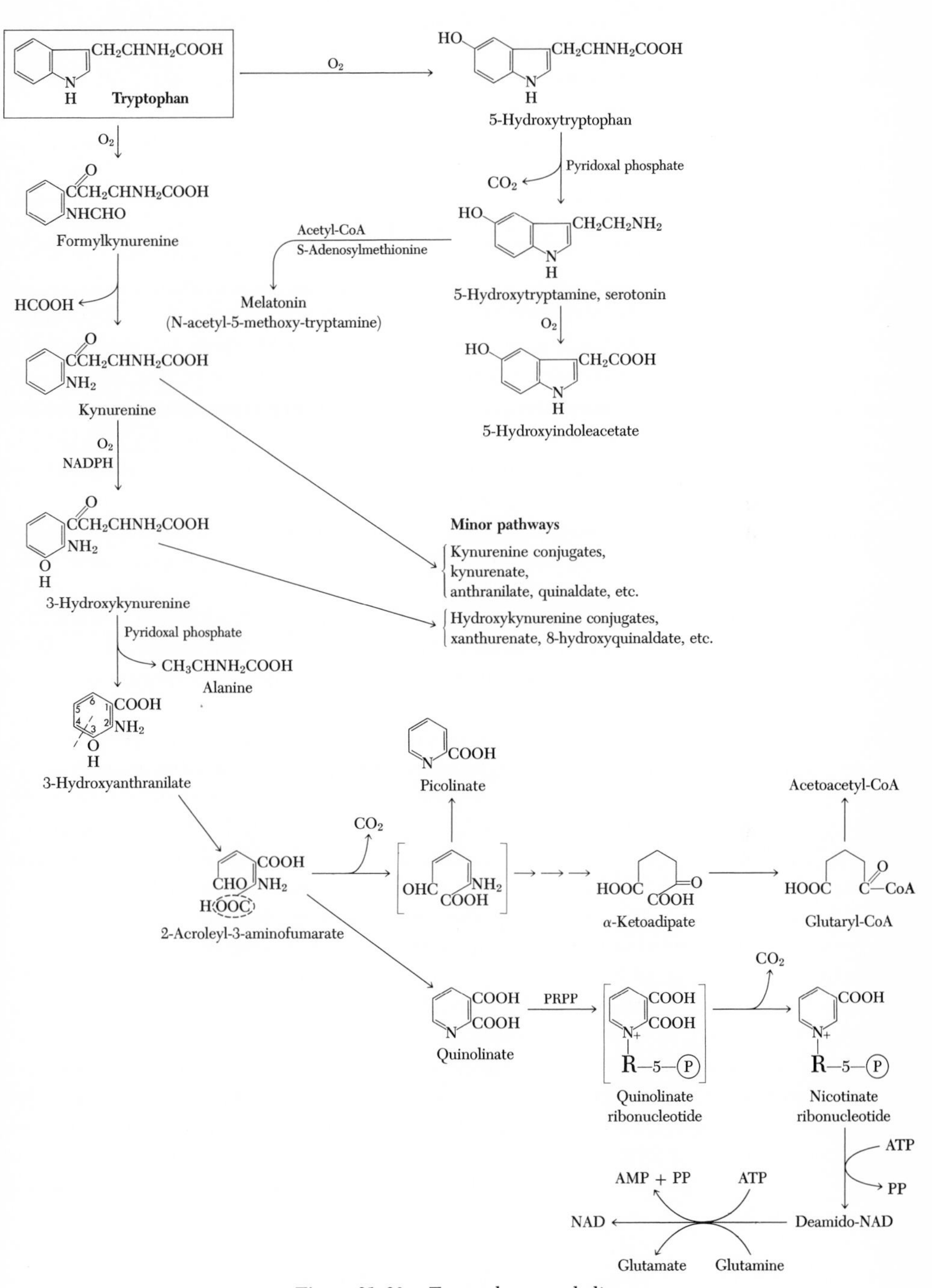

Figure 21-20. Tryptophan metabolism.

malignant carcinoid, in which case as much as 60 per cent of tryptophan metabolism may be directed to the serotonin pathway, rather than the usual 1 per cent.

Acetylation and methylation of serotonin lead to the formation of melatonin, a hormone of the pineal gland and peripheral nerve of man and other mammals. This hormone lightens the color of frog melanocytes and blocks the action of melanocyte-stimulating hormone and ACTH. Its function in mammals has not been established.

Nicotinamide pathway. The major metabolic pathway of tryptophan is unusual in its end-products, derivatives of the vitamin nicotinamide. Although provision of the vitamin does not appear to affect the dietary requirement for tryptophan, the amino acid reduces the vitamin requirement to a certain extent.

Tryptophan is initially acted upon by tryptophan pyrrolase (oxygenase) to yield formylkynurenine. The enzyme presents a number of unusual characteristics. In contrast to other similarly conjugated proteins, its heme prosthetic group is rather easily dissociated. The pyrrolase is adaptive, responding with an increase in activity within a few hours of the administration of substrate or glucocorticoids, and also as a result of the "alarm reaction" (p. 741). Induction by hormones is inhibited by actinomycin, demonstrating the participation of RNA synthesis (p. 554) in the de novo synthesis of the enzyme. On the other hand, induction by substrate is inhibited by puromycin, but not by actinomycin, localizing the site of this action at the ribosomal level (p. 556).

Formylkynurenine is hydrolyzed to kynurenine and formate. Kynurenine is excreted in the urine of animals following administration of test doses of tryptophan and, with other tryptophan metabolites, in pyridoxine deficiency. The oxidation of kynurenine to 3-hydroxykynurenine is severely depressed in riboflavin deficiency, although the enzyme system exhibits no requirement for flavin in vitro. Kynureninase catalyzes the cleavage of 3-hydroxykynurenine into alanine and 3-hydroxyanthranilate, pyridoxal phosphate being the cofactor.

Ring cleavage of 3-hydroxyanthranilate forms 2-acroleyl-3-aminofumarate, a branch-point in tryptophan catabolism. Decarboxylation produces an unstable intermediate which can (a) cyclize to form picolinate or (b) lose ammonia and undergo several further transformations, terminating in ketone bodies by a pathway identical with that of lysine (Fig. 21–7, p. 576).

Direct cyclization of acroleylaminofumarate forms quinolinate, which is converted to its ribonucleotide by reaction with phosphoribosyl-pyrophosphate. Decarboxylation then produces nicotinate ribonucleotide. Interaction with ATP adds an adenylate moiety, thus forming a precursor of NAD which requires only formation of the amide group to complete the synthesis of the coenzyme. The further metabolism of nicotinate and its derivatives is discussed in connection with the vitamins (p. 185).

Minor pathways. As indicated in Figure 21–20, several minor pathways branch off from the main series of reactions in the catabolism of tryptophan. Certain of the end-products indicated are excreted under normal circumstances, but there is great variation among species. The excretion of others is generally associated with vitamin deficiencies, and can be seen to correlate closely with the suggested locus of action of each vitamin. Thus, anthranilate and derivatives are excreted in riboflavin deficiency (blockage of oxidation of kynurenine), whereas pyridoxine deficiency leads to excretion of xanthurenate (defect in kynureninase action). Since the major pathway leads to synthesis of nicotinate, it is evident that these are examples of mechanisms whereby deficiency in one vitamin may lead to deficiency (or increased requirement) in another.

The small amounts of indoleacetate excreted daily in the urine may be formed from tryptophan either by deamination of the amino acid and oxidative decarboxylation of the resulting α-keto acid, or by decarboxylation of the amino acid to tryptamine and oxidation of the latter by monoamine oxidase.

Certain metabolites of tryptophan (indole, skatole), resulting from microbial action in the intestine, are excreted in the feces and urine, in the latter medium following "detoxication" in the liver after absorption from the intestine.

Hartnup disease (H disease, Hart's syndrome) is an inborn defect of amino acid absorption in both the intestine and kidney, affecting tryptophan and other neutral amino acids. The symptoms, involving the skin and frequently the nervous system, appear to reflect deficiencies of tryptophan, nicotinate, or both.

In phenylketonuria, an inborn error of phenylalanine metabolism (see following section), the excretion of indolelactate, indoleacetate, and indican is increased, whereas excretion of hydroxyindoleacetate is decreased, suggesting that the abnormality in phenylalanine metabolism is accompanied by serious derangements of tryptophan metabolism. It has been suggested that the mental deficiency occurring in this condition may be caused by a decrease in the formation of serotonin in the central nervous system.

Although no extended discussion of comparative biochemistry will be attempted, a few data of general interest may be mentioned at this point. 3-Hydroxykynurenine is the precursor of an eye pigment (ommochrome) of Drosophila, the fruit-fly; much work in biochemical genetics has been done in connection with this pigmentation. In certain bacteria, an enzyme system (tryptophanase) catalyzes the cleavage of tryptophan into indole, pyruvate, and ammonia. Pyridoxal phosphate is the coenzyme. Tryptophan can be synthesized in microorganisms from indole and serine, pyridoxal phosphate again being the coenzyme. These reactions of indole with 3-carbon units are probably analogous to the kynureninase reaction in which the same coenzyme is involved.

Aromatic Amino Acids (Fig. 21-21)

Reactions of phenylalanine. The metabolism of phenylalanine and tyrosine is even more complicated than that of tryptophan. Phenylalanine itself undergoes few reactions unrelated to tyrosine metabolism. It may be deaminated (probably by transamination) to phenylpyruvate, which may be reduced to phenyllactate. Although traces of phenylpyruvate may be decarboxylated to phenylacetate (conjugated to glutamine and excreted in the urine of men and apes), both phenyllactate and phenylpyruvate are largely reconverted to phenylalanine for further catabolism.

The relationship between phenylalanine and tyrosine is of considerable interest. Phenylalanine is an essential amino acid, whereas tyrosine is not. The conversion of phenylalanine to tyrosine is irreversible, so that tyrosine cannot wholly replace phenylalanine in the diet. However, since most of the functions of phenylalanine in the body (except that of incorporation into proteins *as phenylalanine*) are performed subsequent to its conversion to tyrosine, it is not surprising that tyrosine is capable of sparing approximately one-half the daily requirement of phenylalanine for growth, and three-quarters of the requirement for nitrogen equilibrium.

The conversion of phenylalanine to tyrosine occurs in the liver. Two enzymes, molecular O_2, Fe^{++}, NADPH, and a pteridine-like cofactor are required. The reaction occurs in two steps, the first of which, the oxidation of phenylalanine to tyrosine, is catalyzed by a hydroxylase, with a reduced form of the pteridine cofactor acting as hydrogen donor to the molecular oxygen. In the second step, the oxidized pteridine is reduced by NADPH, the reaction catalyzed by an enzyme of wider distribution, occurring in many tissues, and apparently having functions in addition to those involved in phenylalanine oxidation. The

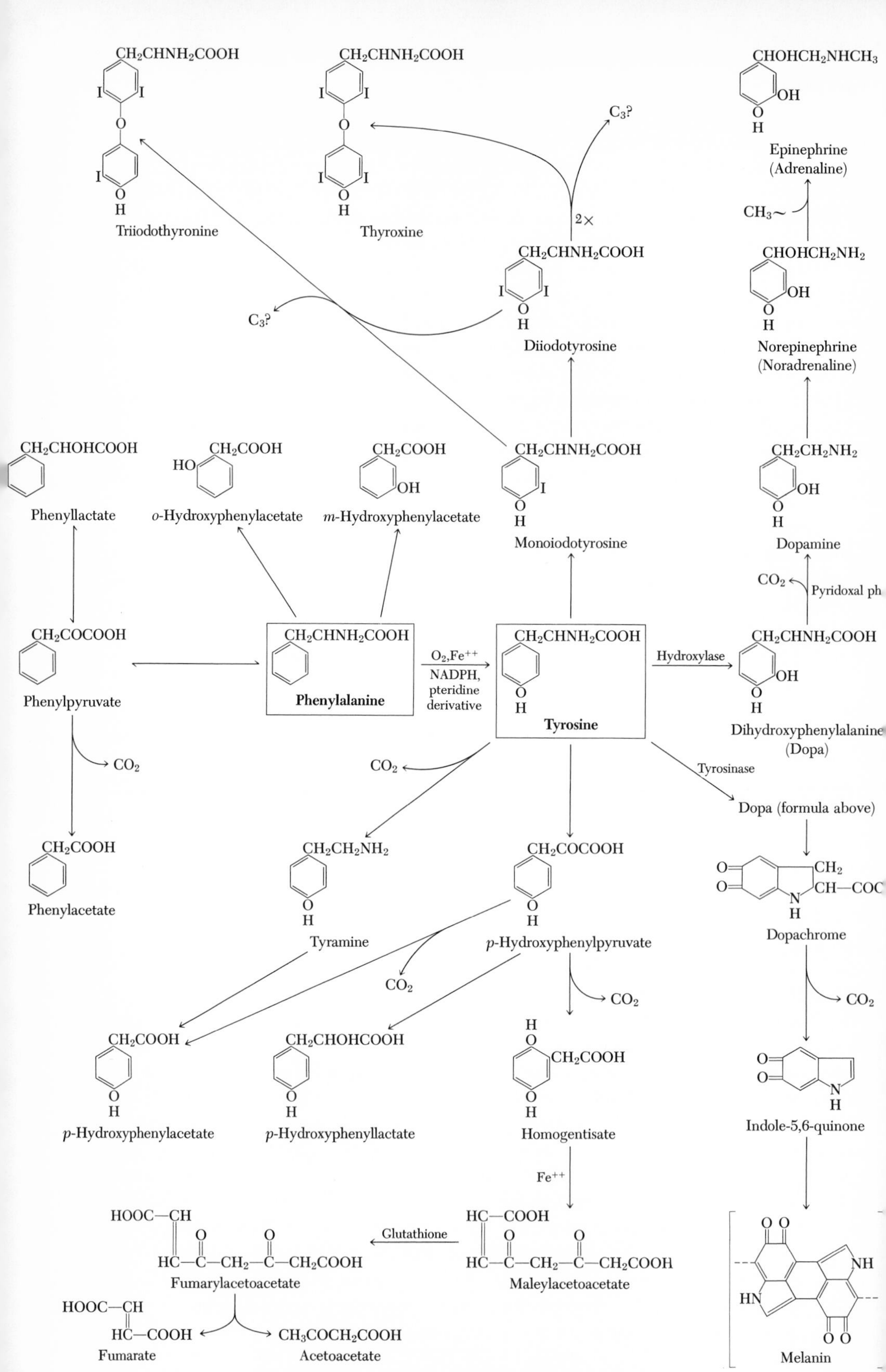

Figure 21-21. Metabolism of phenylalanine and tyrosine.

first enzyme, the specific hydroxylase protein, is absent in fetal liver and in an inborn error of metabolism known variously as phenylpyruvic oligophrenia, imbecillitas phenylpyruvica, or simply phenylketonuria. The metabolic defect is coupled, in some unknown fashion, with mental deficiency. It is characterized by the excretion in the urine of phenylalanine and phenylpyruvate, phenyllactate, phenylacetate (as its glutamine conjugate) and *o*-hydroxyphenylacetate. (Phenylpyruvate usually predominates.) *m*-Hydroxyphenylacetate, a normal excretory product, is either greatly diminished in quantity or absent. The diminished ability of the liver to hydroxylate phenylalanine results in the appearance of significant quantities of this amino acid in the blood. In the kidney, the excess phenylalanine is deaminated, deaminated and reduced, or deaminated and decarboxylated, to form the products which are excreted together with the phenylalanine. (Presumably the excessive circulating phenylalanine results also in increased ortho-hydroxylation, only an insignificant proportion of the amino acid traversing this pathway under normal conditions.) Although the hypothesis that the mental defect in phenylketonuria is caused by accumulation of a toxic metabolite of phenylalanine has received little support in the past, it must be accorded more weight in view of recent findings. Thus, phenylketonuric children on low-phenylalanine diets not only excrete smaller amounts of abnormal metabolites in the urine, but also exhibit improvement in their mental condition.

It has been reported that several phenylketonuric mothers have had offspring who are mentally retarded but not phenylketonuric. The suggestion is made that these children, who are evidently heterozygous for phenylketonuria, are suffering from brain damage produced in utero by the high concentration of circulating phenylalanine in the maternal organism.

Other secondary effects occurring in the phenylketonuric, due to the presence of excessive circulating phenylalanine, include inhibition of certain normal pathways of tyrosine metabolism, such as the formation of melanin (resulting in light pigmentation of the skin and hair of many phenylketonuric children), decreased production of epinephrine, and interference with the metabolism of tryptophan, mentioned previously. Such inhibition of the pathways of tyrosine metabolism probably accounts for the reports of increased excretion of compounds such as *p*-hydroxyphenylpyruvate, *p*-hydroxyphenyllactate, and *p*-hydroxyphenylacetate in phenylketonuria.

The remainder of the metabolic pathways of the aromatic amino acids may be considered solely as various aspects of the metabolism of tyrosine. The material subdivides naturally into the separate metabolic routes discussed in the following sections.

Pathway to acetoacetate and fumarate. The route from tyrosine to acetoacetate and fumarate is normally the most important from a quantitative point of view, accounting for most of the several grams of phenylalanine and tyrosine catabolized per day. It also accounts for the classification of these amino acids as both ketogenic and glucogenic.

Tyrosine is converted reversibly into *p*-hydroxyphenylpyruvate by transamination with α-ketoglutarate. The transaminase is inducible by glucocorticoid hormones, pyridoxine, and, under certain conditions, by substrate. Hormonal induction appears to require RNA synthesis, whereas substrate or coenzyme induction (as in the case of tryptophan pyrrolase) functions at the ribosomal site. To a minor extent, *p*-hydroxyphenylpyruvate may be reduced to *p*-hydroxyphenyllactate or decarboxylated to *p*-hydroxyphenylacetate, neither of which is believed to be metabolized further.

The major pathway of catabolism of *p*-hydroxyphenylpyruvate involves its transformation to 2,5-dihydroxyphenylacetate (homogentisate). This conversion is the site of a "metabolic error," tyrosinosis, which may be "inborn," although too few cases have been described and too little is known of its heritability to state this with certainty. The patient in the first case to be described excreted *p*-hydroxyphenylpyruvate on an ordinary diet; administration of increasing quantities of tyrosine brought about the excretion of tyrosine itself and *p*-hydroxyphenyllactate, in addition to the keto acid. (Dopa is reported to have been excreted following large doses of tyrosine.) Since homogentisate was readily oxidized in this subject, the metabolic lesion is obviously located earlier in the sequence of reactions than is the lesion in alcaptonuria (see below).

"Hydroxyphenyl" compounds are excreted by scorbutic guinea pigs and monkeys, human infants (especially if premature) and adults on scorbutogenic diets, patients with untreated pernicious anemia, and folate deficient rats. Treatment with ascorbate usually decreases the excretion of hydroxyphenyl compounds in those subjects obviously suffering from a lack of this vitamin. The effect of ascorbate is explained by the finding that it protects the enzyme, *p*-hydroxyphenylpyruvate hydroxylase, from inhibition by its own substrate. The role of folate or vitamin B_{12} in tyrosine metabolism is uncertain; however, it should be noted that a pteridine derivative possibly related to folate is involved in the conversion of phenylalanine to tyrosine. In any event, the next step in the catabolic sequence involves the oxidation and decarboxylation of *p*-hydroxyphenylpyruvate to homogentisate, an unusual reaction involving migration of the side chain on the aromatic ring.

The further degradation of homogentisate is blocked in the inborn error of metabolism, "alcaptonuria," due to lack of homogentisate oxygenase. Frequently this anomaly is discovered in infancy, since the homogentisate which is excreted is readily oxidized to black products in the air, especially if the urine undergoes ammoniacal fermentation on standing and becomes alkaline. Although several grams of homogentisate may be excreted per day, no harmful effects result directly from this condition. In later life, an accumulation of dark pigment in the cartilage (ochronosis) has been reported to accompany arthritic changes in the joints. Homogentisate normally is oxidized and its ring opened to form maleylacetoacetate, which is isomerized (*cis* → *trans*) under the influence of an enzyme requiring glutathione as cofactor to fumarylacetoacetate, which is in turn hydrolyzed to fumarate and acetoacetate. A minor pathway from homogentisate leads to the production of the next lower homolog, gentisate, which is found in the urine of alcaptonurics and scorbutic guinea pigs.

Under most test conditions, tyrosine and phenylalanine appear to be ketogenic (owing to acetoacetate); under certain circumstances, however, they are glucogenic (owing to fumarate). The underlying factors favoring one or the other of these results are unknown.

Minor pathways: decarboxylation, sulfatation. To a very minor extent, tyrosine may be decarboxylated to tyramine in the kidney. This reaction was considered formerly to be a step in the synthesis of epinephrine. It is now regarded as too slow to be of any importance. In a reaction involving "active sulfate" and derivatives of tyrosine in which the amino group is free but the carboxyl is blocked, the phenolic hydroxyl of tyrosine is conjugated to form tyrosine-O-sulfate. This unusual ester is a constituent of the peptide liberated in the fibrinogen → fibrin transformation and also constitutes about half of the bound tyrosine of human urine.

Pathway to epinephrine. In the initial step of this series, tyrosine is oxidized to 3,4-dihydroxyphenylalanine ("dopa"), an intermediate common to the synthesis of both epinephrine and melanin, but by a specific hydroxylase (contrast with tyrosinase in the next section) found in brain, adrenal medulla, and sympathetic nervous tissue, requiring a reduced pteridine cofactor.

An active decarboxylating enzyme for dopa is found in several tissues, but is particularly potent in the kidney. Pyridoxal phosphate is the coenzyme. Hydroxytyramine, or "dopamine," is the product of the reaction. The same decarboxylase is believed to act upon dopa, tyrosine, 5-hydroxytryptophan, and probably histidine. α-Methyl-dopa (p. 671) inhibits this decarboxylation, and has been shown to decrease the synthesis of serotonin, tryptamine, and tyramine and to lower the blood pressure in man. Dopamine, in addition to serving as precursor of the other catecholamines, probably also possesses specific functions. Thus, it is deficient in the motor centers of the forebrain in parkinsonism.

The next step is the oxidation of the proximal carbon atom in the side chain of dopamine to yield norepinephrine, a reaction catalyzed by dopamine hydroxylase, requiring molecular oxygen and ascorbate. Norepinephrine is probably the sympathetic hormone of peripheral nerves, whereas its methylated derivative, epinephrine, is the sympathetic hormone of the adrenal medulla. Epinephrine is synthesized from norepinephrine by transmethylation, S-adenosylmethionine being the source of the methyl group. The biological functions of epinephrine and norepinephrine are discussed elsewhere (p. 701).

Pheochromocytomas are tumors of the adrenal medulla or sympathetic ganglia which secrete excessive quantities of norepinephrine and epinephrine, the increased concentrations of these catecholamines in the body fluids accounting for the symptoms which are observed.

The catabolic pathway for catecholamines (dopamine, norepinephrine, and epinephrine) depends upon their location in the body. In the central nervous system, the pathway parallels that of serotonin, involving oxidation (monoamine oxidase) to the corresponding phenylacetate and mandelate derivatives, whereas catecholamines which have been released into the general circulation (the major route) are catabolized by a pathway involving, first, O-methylation on the 3-hydroxyl group, followed by oxidation of the methoxy derivatives to the corresponding acids. Methylated epinephrine, "metanephrine," is a major excretory product in the urine. Pyrogallol (1,2,3-trihydroxybenzene) and other catechols act as competitive inhibitors of the O-methylation of catecholamines.

Pathway to melanin. Melanin may be defined as a brown to black pigment, resulting from the polymerization of oxidation products of dopa. Its formation is apparently the result of the action of a single enzyme, tyrosinase, functioning in a specialized cell, the melanocyte (formerly, melanoblast), located in the skin and eyes and in melanomas. Melanin functions in mammals as a protection against ultraviolet rays. In albinism, an inborn error of metabolism, melanin pigmentation is absent, owing to an hereditary lack of tyrosinase in the melanocytes.

Although the melanogenic enzyme is commonly called "tyrosinase," the name implies an unwarranted specificity. It is one of a family of copper-containing *o*-diphenol oxidases, occurring to some extent in animal tissues, but more widely distributed in plants. These enzymes are not only relatively nonspecific toward their diphenolic substrates, but also are capable of oxidizing monophenols to diphenols.

It is not certain exactly how many of the steps in the synthesis of melanin are catalyzed by tyrosinase and how many are spontaneous. Most of the quinonoid intermediates are capable of reacting nonenzymatically with the polyphenolic intermediates, resulting in reduction of the former and oxidation of the latter. Consequently, the entire sequence of reactions appears to be capable of autocatalysis of a most complex type. Ignoring for the sake of simplicity the autocatalytic features of the reaction, tyrosinase may be regarded as oxidizing tyrosine to dopa, which is oxidized, cyclized, and then further oxidized to the red pigment, "dopachrome." Dopachrome is spontaneously decarboxylated to 5,6-dihydroxyindole, which is oxidized to its corresponding quinone. Polymerization of indole-5,6-quinone produces melanin, a tentative structure for which is shown in Figure 21–21. Owing to its quinone groups, melanin can exist in both oxidized (black) and reduced (brown) forms. As found in nature, melanin is combined with proteins (probably by interaction between the quinone groups of the melanin and sulfhydryl groups of the proteins), forming "melanoproteins."

The activity of melanocytes in the lower vertebrates is under the control of "intermedin," a hormone from the intermediate lobe of the pituitary. It has been suggested, but not proved, that a similar control obtains in man. Melatonin, a hormone also affecting the melanocytes, has been mentioned previously.

Pathway to thyroxine. Inasmuch as the synthesis of thyroxine is discussed in considerable detail elsewhere (p. 714), with particular attention being given to the reactions of iodine and to regulatory and inhibitory factors, this discussion will be confined to a brief outline of the changes undergone in the organic molecule.

Tyrosine is iodinated in the thyroid gland, probably by iodine (I_2), successively to monoiodo- and diiodotyrosine. Two molecules of diiodotyrosine may then be coupled, with the loss of one alanine side chain, to form a molecule of thyroxine (tetraiodothyronine). The nature of the 3-carbon fragment which is ejected is not known. Triiodothyronine (about five times more active than thyroxine in most assays) is formed in and secreted by the thyroid gland together with thyroxine. The intermediates of thyroid hormone synthesis may undergo the conversions mentioned while in protein-bound form.

Little is known of the catabolism of the thyroid hormones. Liver converts both thyroxine and triiodothyronine to the corresponding arylpyruvates (deamination), which are then excreted in the bile together with the unchanged hormones, each partly free, partly conjugated as the glucuronide. Extensive deiodination may occur in the liver and other tissues, such as the salivary glands. Kidney deiodinates thyroxine and triiodothyronine and also converts both compounds to the corresponding arylacetate derivatives. A sulfate conjugate of triiodothyronine is formed in the liver and excreted in the bile. A similar conjugate of triiodothyroacetate is found in bile, blood, and urine. Small amounts of thyroxine are excreted in the urine, both free and conjugated. Evidence has been presented for an enterohepatic circulation of thyroid hormones. Thyroxine itself constitutes only a minor fraction of the total thyroxine-related metabolites excreted in feces and urine, the feces being the major avenue of excretion.

Inborn errors of thyroid hormone metabolism have been described, involving defects probably localized in (a) conversion of inorganic iodine to the organically bound form, (b) dehalogenation of the iodotyrosines, (c) conversion of iodotyrosines to thyroglobulin-bound thyroxine and triiodothyronine, and (d) conversion of the last-named substances to the physiologically active circulating hormones bound to plasma proteins.

INTERRELATIONS OF THE METABOLISM OF PROTEINS AND OTHER FOODSTUFFS

The major interrelations between proteins, fats, and carbohydrates are outlined in Figure 21–22. The importance of proteins in the metabolism of all types of compounds is too obvious to require elaboration, inasmuch as enzymes and many hormones are proteins (or amino acid derivatives). Synthesis of specialized products, such as purines, pyrimidines, and porphyrins, is likewise an important function of proteins and amino acids, as has been discussed previously. The subject of interest in this section is the relationship between the metabolism of proteins and that of the two other major foodstuffs, as exemplified by direct interconversion and by caloric substitution.

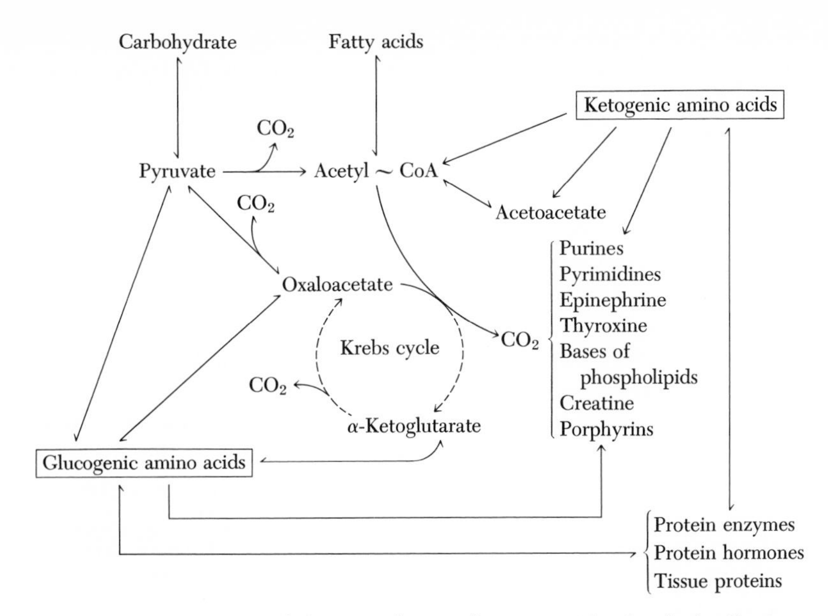

Figure 21-22. Metabolic interrelations of proteins with other foodstuffs.

The ketogenic amino acids and certain fragments derived from the metabolism of non-ketogenic amino acids form acetate or acetoacetate, thus contributing directly to the synthesis of fatty acids. The glucogenic amino acids can function similarly, but subsequent to initial conversions to pyruvate or ketoacids yielding pyruvate. Certain specialized lipid moieties are also derived from amino acids, viz., serine, ethanolamine, sphingosine, and choline. The pathway from the carbon skeletons of the ketogenic or glucogenic amino acids to the fatty acids is irreversible.

The majority of amino acids can form carbohydrate. In certain cases, viz., alanine, aspartate, and glutamate, the conversion to precursors of carbohydrate is direct; in others the pathway may be quite devious. The conversion is reversible for most of the non-essential, glucogenic amino acids. It must be emphasized in connection with glucogenicity that the α-keto acids produced from the amino acids (pyruvate, oxaloacetate, α-ketoglutarate) function not only as raw materials for the synthesis of glucose, but also as catalysts in the channeling of acetyl units from all classes of foodstuffs through the tricarboxylic acid cycle (α-ketoglutarate and pyruvate being easily converted to oxaloacetate, the actual catalytic compound of the cycle) for the provision of energy.

The energy content of the diet influences protein metabolism, as reflected in the nitrogen balance. Nitrogen excretion is increased when the caloric intake is lowered to sub-maintenance levels. Conversely, increasing the caloric intake causes a decrease in urinary N excretion. At any given adequate level of dietary protein, the nitrogen balance is determined, in part at least, by the caloric intake. This relationship can be demonstrated in another manner. When the caloric intake is adequate, increasing the dietary protein from sub-maintenance levels leads to improvement in N balance. However, if the energy intake is below about 25 per cent of that required, this response to an increased protein intake is not obtained. Under these restricted conditions, the caloric intake is apparently a limiting factor in the utilization of dietary proteins.

On diets grossly inadequate in caloric value, nitrogen equilibrium may still be maintained, especially in obese subjects and if adequate amounts of protein and a small amount of carbohydrate are provided. During the initial days of such a regimen (or of a fast), the N excretion is lower than on subsequent days, owing to utilization of glycogen stores. Later, body fat is utilized for energy, exerting the beneficial effect on N balance indicated above for dietary fat.

These effects of the energy content of the diet are apparently largely independent of the nature of the energy-providing materials, being essentially identical, except temporarily (see below), with equicaloric amounts of carbohydrate, fat, or alcohol. They are not influenced by the time of feeding of the latter in relation to that of the protein. The mechanism of production of these effects is not known.

Dietary carbohydrate exerts an influence on protein metabolism not shared by other substances. This is independent of its caloric effect, which is shared equally by fat and alcohol; it is referred to as the specific "protein-sparing" action of carbohydrate. It manifests itself in several ways:

1. Isocaloric substitution of fat for carbohydrate in the diet is followed by an increase in nitrogen excretion. This is of relatively brief duration, however, the original level of N balance being restored after several days. This effect is observed whether or not the energy and protein contents of the diet are adequate.

2. If the protein and carbohydrate components of an adequate diet are ingested separately, at wide time intervals, there is a transitory increase in N excretion. No such effect is exhibited by fat.

3. On an exclusively fat diet, the nitrogen output is the same as during starvation, whereas administration of carbohydrate reduces the nitrogen output.

The mechanism underlying this phenomenon is not known for certain. As discussed elsewhere, it involves, in part, certain complex interrelationships between dietary and hormonal influences on protein metabolism as such, and on translocation of nitrogen between tissues. It is probably also a reflection of the fact that carbohydrate, in addition to its function as a fuel, also provides the major source of oxaloacetate for the tricarboxylic acid cycle and the carbon skeletons of non-essential amino acids. In the absence of carbohydrate, protein is called upon specifically to assume these functions, since fat cannot. The increased degradation of protein and loss of nitrogen are necessarily greater than would occur if fat were omitted from the diet instead of carbohydrate.

BIBLIOGRAPHY

GENERAL

Annual Review of Biochemistry
Annual Review of Physiology
Baldwin, E.: Dynamic Aspects of Biochemistry, London, Cambridge University Press, 1963, Chapters 10–13.
Meister, A.: Biochemistry of the Amino Acids, Vols. 1 and 2, New York, Academic Press, Inc., 1965.
Munro, H. N., and Allison, J. B. (eds.): Mammalian Protein Metabolism, Vols. 1 and 2, New York, Academic Press, Inc., 1964.

DIGESTION, ABSORPTION

Wilson, T. H.: Intestinal Absorption, Philadelphia, W. B. Saunders Company, 1962, Chapters 5 and 10.

SPECIAL TOPICS IN PROTEIN METABOLISM

Chantrenne, H.: The Biosynthesis of Protein, New York, Pergamon Press, 1961.
Perutz, M. F.: Proteins and Nucleic Acids, Amsterdam, Elsevier Publishing Company, 1962.
Putnam, F. W. (ed.): The Plasma Proteins, Vols. 1 and 2, New York, Academic Press, Inc., 1960.
Wiseman, A.: Organization for Protein Biosynthesis, New York, American Elsevier Publishing Company, 1965.
Wuhrmann, F., and Wunderly, C.: The Human Blood Proteins, New York, Grune & Stratton, 1960.

SPECIAL TOPICS IN AMINO ACID METABOLISM

Cohen, P. P., and Brown, G. W., Jr.: Ammonia metabolism and urea biosynthesis, Chapter 4 in Florkin, M., and Mason, H. S. (eds.): Comparative Biochemistry, Vol. 2, New York, Academic Press, Inc., 1960.

Cohen, P. P., and Sallach, H. J.: Nitrogen metabolism of amino acids, Chapter 13 in Greenberg, D. M. (ed.): Metabolic Pathways, Vol. 2, New York, Academic Press, Inc., 1961.

Greenberg, D. M.: Carbon catabolism of amino acids, Chapter 14 in Greenberg, D. M. (ed.): Metabolic Pathways, Vol. 2, New York, Academic Press, Inc., 1961.

Greenberg, D. M.: Biosynthesis of amino acids, Chapter 15 in Greenberg, D. M. (ed.): Metabolic Pathways, Vol. 2, New York, Academic Press, Inc., 1961.

Greenberg, D. M.: Biological methylation, Advances Enzymol. *25:*395, 1963.

Guirard, B. M., and Snell, E. E.: Vitamin B_6 function in transamination and decarboxylation reactions, Chapter 5 in Florkin, M., and Stotz, E. H. (eds.): Comprehensive Biochemistry, Vol. 15, Amsterdam, Elsevier Publishing Company, 1964.

Henderson, L. M., Gholson, R. K., and Dalgliesh, C. E.: Metabolism of aromatic amino acids, Chapter 6 in Florkin, M., and Mason, H. S. (eds.): Comparative Biochemistry, Vol. 4, New York, Academic Press, Inc., 1962.

Hsia, D. Y.: Inborn Errors of Metabolism, Part 1, Chicago, Year Book Medical Publishers, 1966.

Kun, E.: Metabolism of sulfur-containing amino acids, Chapter 16 in Greenberg, D. M. (ed.): Metabolic Pathways, Vol. 2, New York, Academic Press, Inc., 1961.

Lyman, F. L. (ed.): Phenylketonuria, Springfield, Ill., Charles C Thomas, 1963.

Mudd, S. H., and Cantoni, G. L.: Biological transmethylation, methyl-group neogenesis and other "one-carbon" metabolic reactions dependent upon tetrahydrofolic acid, Chapter 1 in Florkin, M., and Stotz, E. H. (eds.): Comprehensive Biochemistry, Vol. 15, Amsterdam, Elsevier Publishing Company, 1964.

Roy, A. B.: The synthesis and hydrolysis of sulfate esters, Advances Enzymol. *22:*205, 1960.

Shapiro, S. K., and Schlenk, F. (eds.): Transmethylation and Methionine Biosynthesis, Chicago, University of Chicago Press, 1965.

Thomson, R. H.: Melanins, Chapter 13 in Florkin, M., and Mason, H. S. (eds.): Comparative Biochemistry, Vol. 3, New York, Academic Press, Inc., 1962.

HORMONAL INFLUENCES

Litwack, G., and Kritchevsky, D. (eds.): Actions of Hormones on Molecular Processes, New York, John Wiley & Sons, Inc., 1964.

Manchester, K. L., and Young, F. G.: Insulin and protein metabolism, Vitamins and Hormones *19:*95, 1961.

CHAPTER 22

METABOLISM OF PORPHYRINS AND RELATED SUBSTANCES

THE PORPHYRINS are cyclic tetrapyrroles, which, in combination with iron, form iron porphyrins or hemes. The union of a heme and a specific protein constitutes a hemoprotein. Bile pigments are open-chain tetrapyrroles resulting from the biological degradation of the hemoproteins. Skeleton structures of porphyrins, heme, and bile pigments are given in Figure 22–1.

The hemoproteins are of great importance in the economy of the animal organism. Oxygen from the atmosphere is transported in the bloodstream by a hemoprotein (hemoglobin), is stored temporarily, to a limited extent, attached to another hemoprotein in the tissues (myoglobin), and is finally utilized in that combination with hydrogen atoms and electrons which marks the last phase of the biological oxidation of most substrates, a reaction catalyzed by still other hemoproteins (cytochromes, cytochrome oxidase). Incidental roles in biological oxidations are played also by catalases and peroxidases, both of which are hemoproteins. The metabolism of such important compounds is naturally a matter of great practical as well as theoretical interest, in both its normal and abnormal aspects.

Owing to its quantitative predominance and relative ease of investigation, much more is known of the metabolism of hemoglobin than of the other hemoproteins, a fact which is reflected in the space devoted to consideration of each of the several substances in this category. A brief survey of the overall metabolism of porphyrins and their derivatives is followed by a discussion of their synthesis, including a consideration of certain abnormalities regarded as "inborn errors." The discussion of the degradation of the hemoproteins to bile pigments and of the minor pathways of catabolism of porphyrins is followed by a consideration of their normal and abnormal excretory metabolites. The chapter concludes with a brief treatment of the metabolic interrelations of porphyrins, carbohydrates, and proteins.

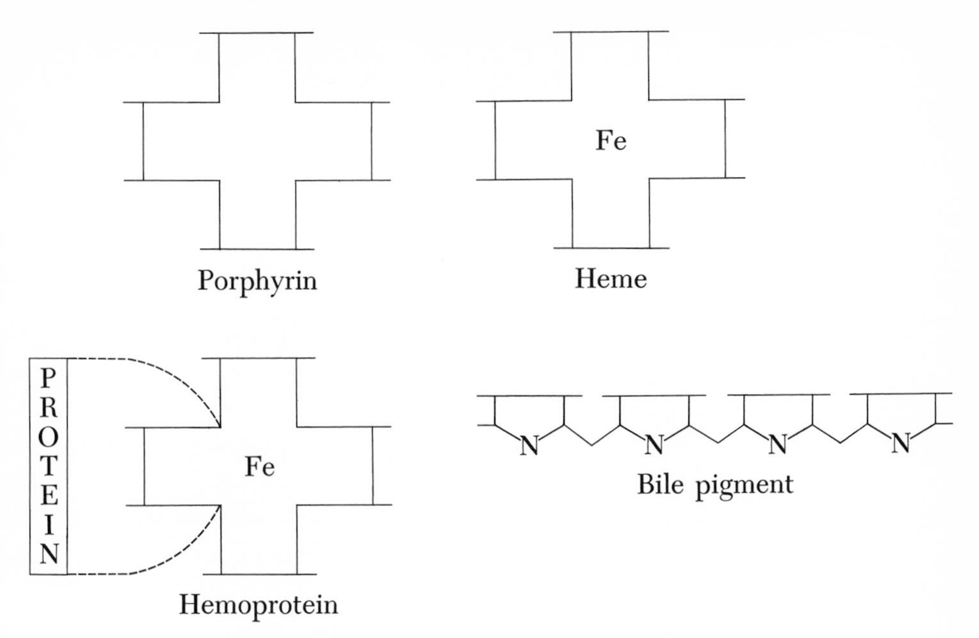

Figure 22-1. Skeleton structures of porphyrin derivatives.

OVERALL SURVEY OF PORPHYRIN METABOLISM

A scheme illustrating the overall metabolism of the porphyrins is presented in Figure 22-2. The complex porphyrin ring is synthesized from small units, i.e., glycine and succinate. Two isomeric types of porphyrins are produced. Type I porphyrins form a minor metabolic path and are excreted unutilized (after minor structural modifications). Although small amounts of Type III porphyrins are also excreted, the major metabolic path of these compounds involves eventual union with iron (forming hemes) and specific proteins to yield hemoproteins.

Small amounts of open-chain tetrapyrrolic compounds, the bile pigments, are formed during the synthesis of the hemoproteins, either from precursors of the porphyrins or from unutilized heme. Traces of bile pigments may arise also from the catabolism of myoglobin, catalases, peroxidases, and cytochromes. The major source of the bile pigments, however, is the hemoglobin of the erythrocytes, liberated upon destruction of the latter at the end of their "life" span of approximately 125 days. The small amount of bilifuscins excreted per day originates during the synthesis of the porphyrins and may be derived from dipyrrole precursors of the latter.

As indicated in the figure, hemoglobin is the dominant hemoprotein in the body, by sheer weight in a static sense, and by the magnitude of its metabolic turnover from the dynamic standpoint. It accounts not only for most of the porphyrin compounds synthesized daily (i.e., most of the bile pigments excreted, 300 mg.), but also for a sizeable turnover in protein (about 8 gm. of globin daily) and iron (27 mg./day, which exceeds the daily dietary requirement). Although the bile pigments and traces of porphyrins which are excreted represent sheer waste, this is not a loss of great magnitude. The iron and protein moieties of the hemoproteins are reutilized.

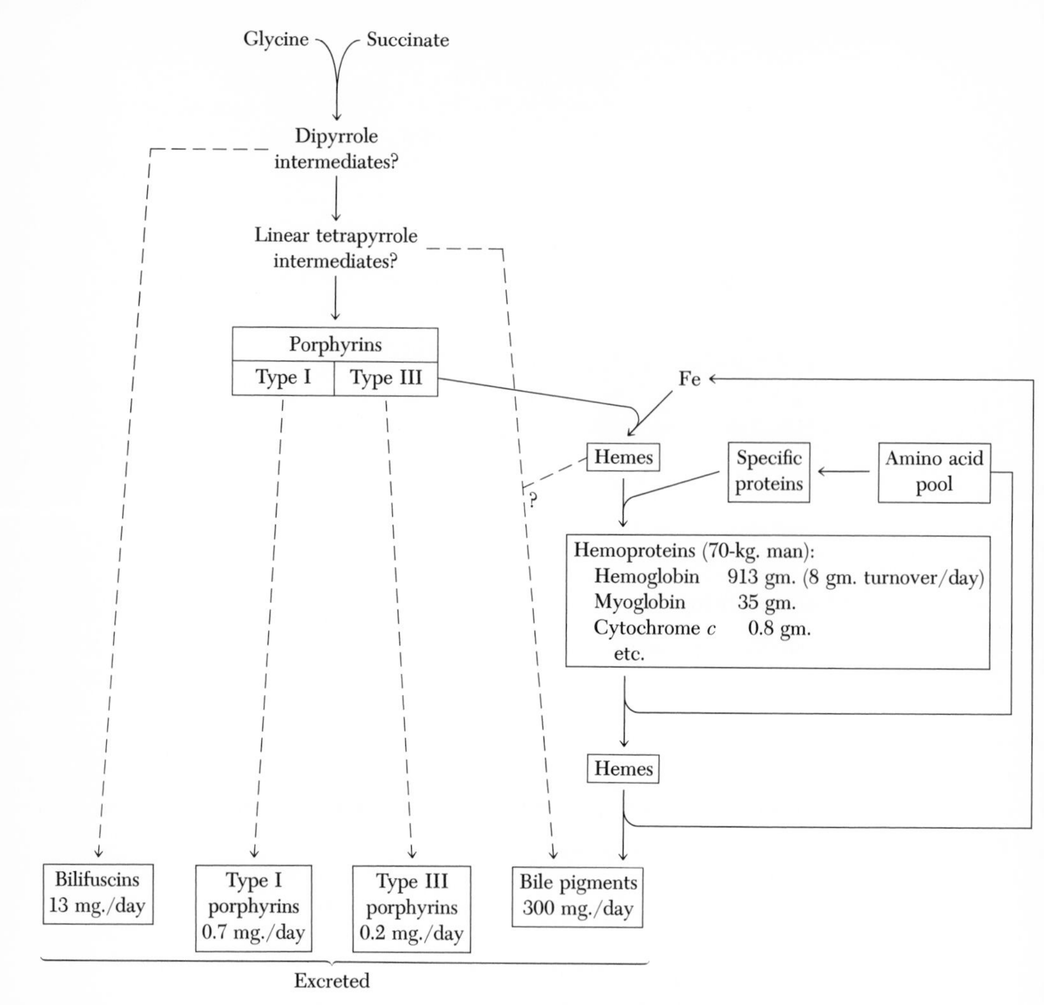

Figure 22-2. Overall metabolism of porphyrins.

SYNTHESIS

It is probable that most of the various types of hemoproteins of the body (e.g., catalases, peroxidases, cytochromes) are synthesized in situ, suggesting that all cells may have the ability to construct porphyrins. However, the synthesis of hemoglobin is a special case, being limited to the hemopoietic organs (mainly red bone marrow in adults). For convenience, general aspects of porphyrin synthesis will be discussed first, followed by consideration of specific hemoproteins.

General Synthesis of Porphyrins

(*a*) ***Formation of porphyrin ring.*** As indicated in Figure 22–3, the synthesis of porphyrins begins with the condensation (catalyzed by δ-aminolevulinate synthetase) of succinyl-CoA and glycine, the latter probably reacting as a complex with pyridoxal phosphate, a cofactor for the condensation. The initial product of the condensation,

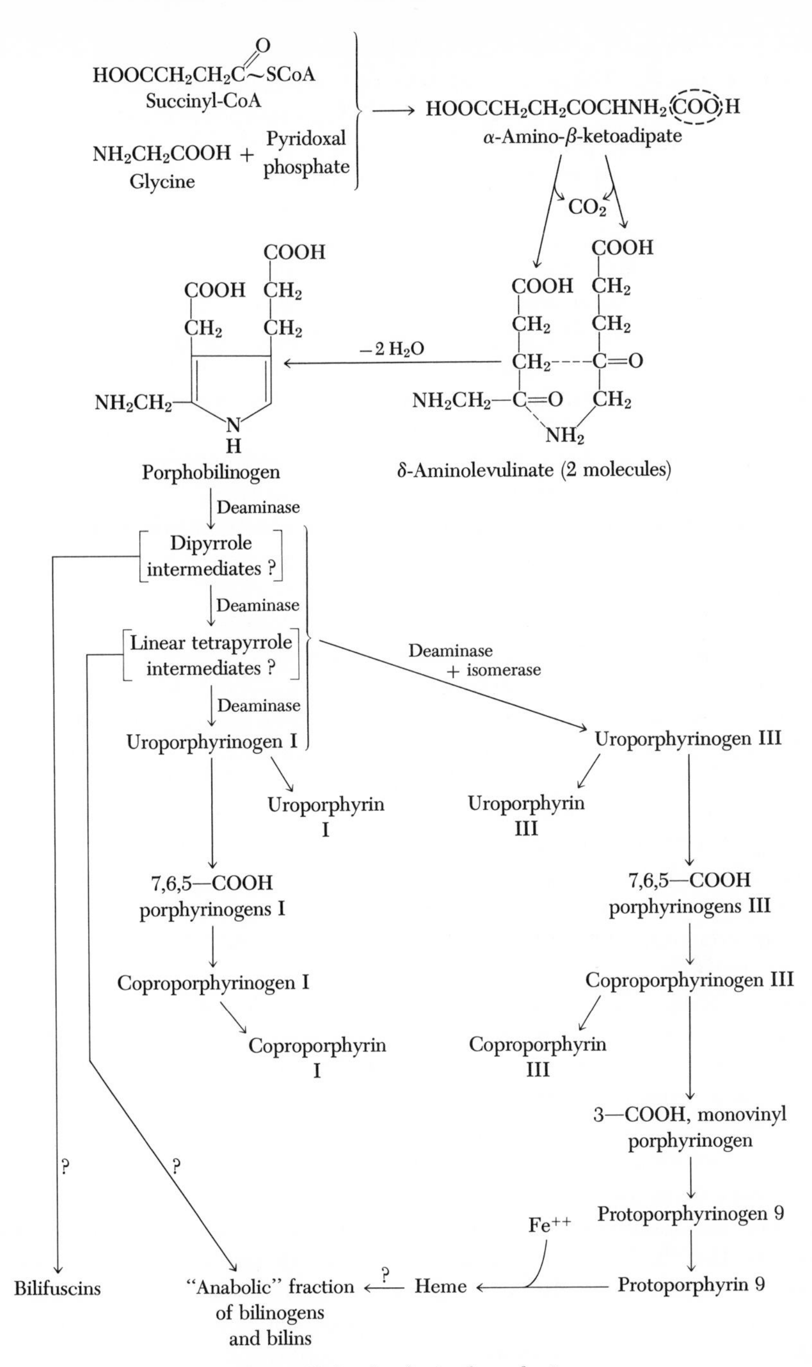

Figure 22-3. Synthesis of porphyrins.

α-amino-β-ketoadipate, is decarboxylated to δ-aminolevulinate. In the pathway of porphyrin synthesis, two molecules of δ-aminolevulinate condense (catalyzed by δ-aminolevulinate dehydratase, for which copper may be a cofactor) to form porphobilinogen, the parent monopyrrole of the porphyrins.

In an alternate path, δ-aminolevulinate may be deaminated to form α-ketoglutaraldehyde, which may form, by oxidation, α-ketoglutarate or may lose a "formate" fragment to form succinate directly. The α-ketoglutarate also can form succinate in the Krebs cycle. In any case, regeneration of succinate or succinyl-CoA completes the so-called "succinate-glycine cycle," a possible pathway in the catabolism of glycine.

The mechanism is not known whereby four molecules of porphobilinogen unite to form a cyclic tetrapyrrole, although it is established that the porphyrinogens, reduction products of the porphyrins, are formed in this condensation and participate in the subsequent reactions. As indicated in the figure, it is not known whether dipyrroles and linear tetrapyrroles are intermediates in this condensation, although this is probable. In any event, in the presence of a porphobilinogen deaminase (uroporphyrinogen I synthetase), four molecules of porphobilinogen are condensed, with the loss of four molecules of ammonia, to form uroporphyrinogen I (minor series) in which the acetic and propionic side chains alternate throughout. Concomitant operation of an isomerase (uroporphyrinogen III cosynthetase) results in the reversal of one porphobilinogen residue so that the cyclization results in the formation of uroporphyrinogen III (major series). In both cases, the first cyclic tetrapyrroles formed are of the uro type (tetra-acetic, tetra-propionic side chains). Oxidation of the uroporphyrinogens produces the uroporphyrins, minute amounts of which may be excreted normally.

(*b*) ***Formation of copro- and protoporphyrins.*** Decarboxylation (catalyzed by uroporphyrinogen decarboxylase) of the four acetic acid side chains of the uroporphyrinogens to methyl groups (probably stepwise) results in coproporphyrinogens (tetramethyl, tetrapropionic). As in the case of the uroporphyrinogens, the coproporphyrinogens give rise to the coproporphyrins on oxidation. Coproporphyrin I, formed in the minor pathway, is excreted without being utilized. Although traces of coproporphyrin III and its porphyrinogen are also excreted, most of the latter is converted to a protoporphyrin.

The steps between coproporphyrinogen III (tetramethyl, tetrapropionic) and protoporphyrin (tetramethyl, divinyl, dipropionic) are obscure at the present time. An oxidative decarboxylase system, which may contain flavin and may consist of more than one enzyme, converts coproporphyrinogen III to protoporphyrinogen. Although, on a structural basis, derivatives of mesoporphyrin (tetramethyl, diethyl, dipropionic) and hematoporphyrin (tetramethyl, di-hydroxyethyl, dipropionic) might be anticipated as intermediates, only a tripropionic, monovinyl compound has been detected thus far. Protoporphyrinogen is converted to protoporphyrin by an oxidase system. Protoporphyrin, although derived from porphyrins of Type III, is frequently designated Type 9 (or IX) for reasons discussed elsewhere (p. 122).

(*c*) ***Formation of hemes and hemoproteins.*** Insertion of an atom of iron into the central position of protoporphyrin 9 is catalyzed by ferrochelatase (heme synthetase), which for optimal function requires anaerobiosis and reducing agents such as glutathione. It is possible that both the iron and protoporphyrin participate in the reaction as protein-bound intermediates. (In vitro, cobalt can replace iron.) The heme which is produced then may be coupled to various proteins to produce the conjugated hemoproteins, such as hemoglobin, myoglobin, cytochrome *c*, catalases, and peroxidases. Certain hemoproteins (e.g., cytochrome oxidase) contain porphyrins other than protoporphyrin, but these prosthetic groups are probably derived from protoporphyrin and hence are synthesized via the same general pathway.

(*d*) ***Intracellular localization, regulatory influences, and effects of inhibitors.*** In liver cells, the synthesis of δ-aminolevulinate is intra-mitochondrial, the steps from formation of porphobilinogen through formation of coproporphyrinogen are extra-mitochondrial, and the remainder of the pathway through formation of heme is again intra-mitochondrial. It has been suggested, although no evidence is available, that the exit of δ-aminolevulinate from and the entry of coproporphyrinogen and iron into the mitochondrion are possible sites of metabolic regulation.

The effect of oxygen on heme synthesis is complex. In vivo, the overall synthesis of hemoglobin is known to be stimulated by low oxygen tension (e.g., living at high altitude), an effect mediated by erythropoietin (p. 751). In vitro, the conversion of porphobilinogen to uroporphyrinogen and the conversion of protoporphyrin to heme are both inhibited by oxygen, but on the other hand, oxygen is required for the oxidative decarboxylation of coproporphyrinogen and the oxidation of protoporphyrinogen.

The enzymes which catalyze the synthesis and utilization of δ-aminolevulinate are important sites of regulation. Heme, the end-product of the metabolic sequence, inhibits the activity of the synthetase. (In photosynthetic bacteria, heme in addition represses formation of the enzyme.) As discussed in a later section, a number of drugs which cause experimental porphyrinuria have been shown to induce de novo formation of the synthetase. To a lesser extent, such compounds also increase the activity of the dehydratase. Administration of δ-aminolevulinate to experimental animals also results in greater activity of the dehydratase, but in a curious, cyclical pattern, with successive peaks of activity.

Regulatory mechanisms which coordinate the synthesis of heme with that of globin will be discussed subsequently. At this point it may be noted that there is evidence that globin facilitates the formation of heme from protoporphyrin.

Lead, which is known to cause profound abnormalities in porphyrin metabolism, has been shown to inhibit δ-aminolevulinate synthetase, δ-aminolevulinate dehydratase, and heme synthetase in vitro.

Synthesis of Hemoglobin

In adult man, this synthesis is restricted normally to the immature red cells in bone marrow. Three components are required: (1) protoporphyrin 9, synthesized as described above; (2) globin, produced by the usual mechanisms of protein synthesis; (3) iron, the sources, absorption, transport, and storage of which are considered elsewhere (p. 640).

In addition to the actual constituents of hemoglobin, certain cofactors are required, viz., pantothenate, pyridoxine, folate, vitamin B_{12} and the "intrinsic factor" necessary for its absorption, and copper. Synthesis of hemoglobin and maturation of the erythrocyte proceed concomitantly, rendering a decision difficult as to whether a given cofactor is concerned in one process or the other. Pantothenate and pyridoxine are necessary for the synthesis of coenzyme A and pyridoxal phosphate, cofactors involved in the δ-aminolevulinate synthetase reaction. The requirement for folate and B_{12} may not be concerned directly with the formation of the porphyrins. For example, the rapid rate of cell growth and division occurring during erythropoiesis results in a correspondingly rapid rate of nucleic acid synthesis, requiring folate and B_{12} to insure adequate supplies of formate for purine synthesis. No satisfactory explanation of the role of copper can be offered, unless its participation in the δ-aminolevulinate dehydratase reaction is confirmed.

Erythropoietin, a low molecular weight glycoprotein originating in the kidney, stimulates production, maturation, and release of red cells from the blood-forming tissues.

As stated previously, synthesis of hemoglobin appears to proceed concurrently with the maturation of the erythrocyte. The primitive red cell contains free porphyrins rather than hemoglobin. As the cell matures, the content of porphyrin decreases and that of hemoglobin increases. These changes are correlated with alterations in staining properties of the cell. The circulating red cell contains traces of protoporphyrin, the amount being related to iron deficiency or other factors that inhibit the synthesis of hemoglobin, and coproporphyrin (mostly Type III), the quantity of which varies with the rate of erythropoiesis.

Regulatory mechanisms exist which coordinate the synthesis of heme with that of globin. In addition to the previously mentioned facilitation of heme synthesis by globin, heme has been shown to stimulate the synthesis of globin on the ribosomal level.

The average "life" of the erythrocyte and other features of the chemistry of this cell are discussed in connection with the formed elements of the blood (p. 803). It is of interest that the substances incorporated in the red cell (protoporphyrin, iron, and globin) are effectively isolated from the dynamic state and metabolic pools of the other constituents of the body for the "lifetime" of the cell. The iron and globin are returned to the community of metabolites upon disintegration of the cell; the porphyrin moiety is exceptional in this respect, as it is not reutilized.

In the adult human (70-kg. man), approximately 8 gm. of hemoglobin is synthesized (and degraded) per day, corresponding to about 300 mg. of porphyrin (porphyrin rings are about 4 per cent by weight of hemoglobin molecule). As discussed later, only traces of porphyrins are involved in other, minor metabolic pathways. Increased synthesis of hemoglobin (compensatory polycythemia) occurs as a result of chronic exposure to low partial pressures of oxygen.

The chemistry of the various normal adult and fetal hemoglobins and their abnormal variants has been discussed previously, along with consideration of the genetic and evolutionary implications (p. 124). There appear to be four structural genes in the normal human, specifying the synthesis of α, β, γ, and δ peptide chains, respectively. Normally, there is continuous production of α chains. In the fetus, γ chains are produced in place of β and δ, thus forming hemoglobin F ($\alpha_2^A\gamma_2^F$). A "switch" mechanism, beginning well before birth and completing its action at about 6 months of age, represses formation of γ chains and turns on production of β and δ chains, thus permitting formation of hemoglobins A ($\alpha_2^A\beta_2^A$) and A_2 ($\alpha_2^A\delta_2^{A_2}$). In thalassemia and hemolytic conditions, the forced differentiation of young cells results in formation of significant amounts of hemoglobin F in the adult. Deficient synthesis of α or, more usually, β chains is seen in the thalassemias, which may be due to defective controlling genes.

During its residence in the erythrocyte, a small fraction of hemoglobin is normally oxidized to the ferric form, methemoglobin. This process is accelerated by exposure to certain chemicals and drugs. In the normal individual, methemoglobin is reduced to the functional ferrous form by several enzyme systems, chiefly utilizing NADH produced by glycolysis, and to a lesser extent NADPH formed by the pentose shunt pathway. The former appears to act on methemoglobin through a flavoprotein intermediary, the latter through glutathione, or as yet poorly characterized hemoproteins. Genetic deficiency of glucose-6-phosphate dehydrogenase, since it affects the less important pathway, does not lead to methemoglobinemia, although hemolytic tendencies may be present due to lack of protection (via NADPH and glutathione) against peroxide-forming drugs. On the other hand, homozygous deficiency of the diaphorase-like flavoprotein involved in the major, NADH, pathway results in methemoglobinemia. There also exist hemoglobins of abnormal structure which preferentially remain in the ferric form (p. 132), giving rise to another type of inherited methemoglobinemia.

Synthesis of Other Hemoproteins

Little is known of the synthesis of the catalases or peroxidases. The rate of turnover of iron in the catalase of red cells is the same as that of the iron of hemoglobin, but this is only one-eighth of that of the iron in liver catalase.

There appear to be two pools of myoglobin in rat skeletal muscle, a minor fraction with a half-life less than that of hemoglobin and a major fraction with a half-life greater than that of hemoglobin.

Cytochrome *c* is synthesized by mitochondria of liver and heart. Cytochrome *c* turnover (incorporation of radioactive glycine) is much more rapid than that of hemoglobin in regenerating liver after partial hepatectomy. On the other hand, the turnover of cytochrome *c* is rather slow in skeletal muscle and heart. In liver and kidney cytochrome *c* turnover is about the same as that of tissue protein, whereas in skeletal muscle it is higher than that of tissue protein. It is of considerable interest that the concentration of cytochrome *c* in all tissues is directly related to the state of thyroid function. In conditions of protein deprivation, preference is given to the synthesis of cytochrome *c*, as is the case with hemoglobin.

Abnormalities in Synthesis of Poryphyrins and Heme

This topic is mentioned again (p. 619) in connection with the excretion of porphyrins, since it is chiefly by detection and characterization of abnormalities in the excretion of porphyrins that the underlying dysfunctions have been discovered and classified.

In general, accumulation and excretion of excessive quantities of Type I porphyrins result from a greatly accelerated rate of synthesis of heme, whereas interference with the synthesis of heme usually results in accumulation and excretion of a preponderance of Type III porphyrins. The former condition (i.e., Type I) occurs in hemolytic anemias, the latter (i.e., Type III) in lead poisoning.

Inborn errors of metabolism involving the porphyrins are designated porphyrias. Two general types are recognized:

1. *"Erythropoietic" porphyrias.* In these inborn errors, the bone marrow appears to be the site of the abnormality. The classical condition of this type, transmitted as a rare autosomal recessive characteristic, is manifested by the development, early in life, of photosensitivity, due to the accumulation of porphyrins in the skin. Large amounts of uro- and coproporphyrins of Type I appear in the urine and feces, along with increased quantities of "shunt" stercobilin (p. 618). The preponderance of Type I porphyrins suggests an abnormality in the isomerase reaction which produces Type III porphyrins from porphobilinogen or intermediates. However attractive, such a simple explanation ignores a number of observations. Although some degree of anemia occurs, the actual rate of formation of type III porphyrins is increased, the protoporphyrin content of the erythrocytes is elevated, and the excretion of type III porphyrins in urine and feces, although a small fraction of the total, is increased in absolute amount. The suggestion has been made that a mutation in a regulator gene could result in lack of repression of a key enzyme, such as δ-aminolevulinate synthetase, leading to general overproduction of porphyrins. If the isomerase were limiting as compared with the deaminase under these conditions, then the observations would be accounted for.

A type of erythropoietic protoporphyria has been described recently, characterized by dominant inheritance, photosensitivity, elevated protoporphyrin concentration in the erythrocytes, and moderate increase in fecal protoporphyrin and coproporphyrin III, and in urinary coproporphyrin III.

2. *"Hepatic" porphyrias.* In these conditions (which are due to autosomal dominant genes), the organ responsible for the dysfunction is the liver, in which there occurs abnor-

mal and excessive production of porphyrins (chiefly Type III), their precursors, and related compounds. The hepatic porphyrias may be subdivided into three groups: (1) that accompanied by gastrointestinal, neurological, and psychological symptoms, often designated "acute intermittent" or "paroxysmal" porphyria; (2) that characterized by photosensitivity, "porphyria cutanea tarda"; (3) a mixed or combined type, with both abdominal-neurological and cutaneous symptoms. All varieties of the hepatic porphyrias are characterized by the urinary excretion of uroporphyrin and coproporphyrin III and I, as zinc complexes, and largely in the form of the porphyrinogens. Porphyrins containing intermediate numbers of carboxyl groups also are found. The acute intermittent type differs from porphyria cutanea tarda by the presence of porphobilinogen and δ-aminolevulinate in the urine in the former case. The pattern of urinary metabolites in mixed porphyria resembles that of intermittent acute porphyria when abdominal and nervous symptoms are prominent; when photosensitivity is prominent, the pattern resembles that of porphyria cutanea tarda. The hepatic porphyria occurring in the white population of South Africa has been called "variegate," since cutaneous symptoms predominate in the male, acute symptoms in the female. Porphobilinogen is excreted, hence this type of porphyria bears resemblance to the "mixed" type. Many cases of hepatic porphyria are latent, the symptoms appearing after exposure to alcohol or barbiturates.

Whether all types of hepatic porphyria share a common biochemical lesion is questionable. The excretory pattern of the purely cutaneous variety suggests a possible block in the area of the uro- and coproporphyrinogen decarboxylases. In contrast, the excretion of precursors (δ-aminolevulinate and porphobilinogen) together with porphyrins in the acute intermittent type seems to reflect a condition of overproduction, possibly due to uncontrolled formation of δ-aminolevulinate synthetase, which enzyme in fact has been found to be increased in activity in the liver in these cases. A poorly functioning repressor system, easily inhibited by alcohol or barbiturates, would provide a possible explanation.

CATABOLISM OF HEMOPROTEINS AND PORPHYRINS

There is little information available on the mechanisms of degradation of hemoproteins other than hemoglobin. It has been suggested, on the basis of tenuous evidence, that myoglobin is catabolized to bile pigments; evidence of an indirect and circumstantial nature is also available with regard to catalase in this regard. Nothing is known of the pathway of catabolism of the cytochromes. The small quantities of methemoglobin which may be present normally in the erythrocyte are reduced to hemoglobin by enzyme systems in the cell; a small fraction may be degraded and excreted as porphyrin.

Catabolism of Hemoglobin

The degradation of hemoglobin (about 8 gm. daily) is initiated with the breakdown of the erythrocytes at the end of their "life" span, and results in the formation of bile pigments, as indicated in Figure 22–4. The chief normal sites of this degradation are the reticuloendothelial cells of the spleen, bone marrow, and liver, although it may occur in all tissues into which blood has extravasated, as witness the fine play of colors resulting from a "black eye."

For convenience, the conversions undergone by the bile pigments in the intestine are considered separately, after the discussion of the breakdown of hemoglobin to the stage of bilirubin.

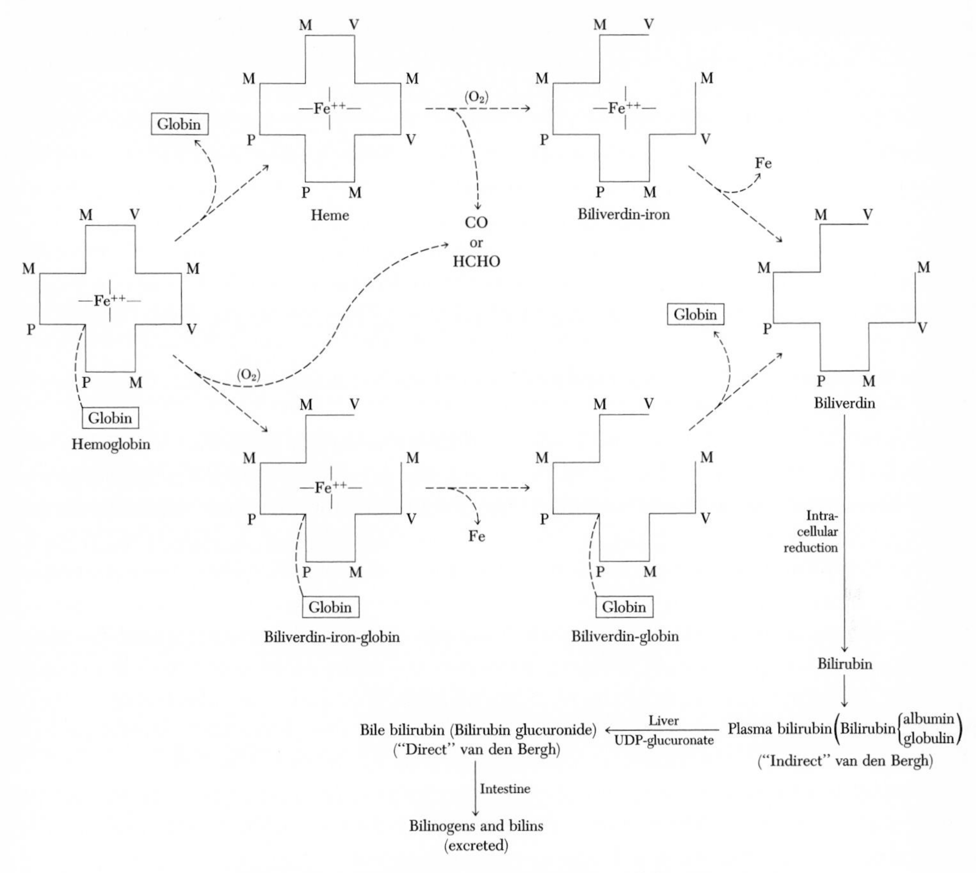

Figure 22–4. Degradation of hemoglobin to bile pigments.

(*a*) ***Conversion of hemoglobin to bile pigments.*** Many of the specific details in this pathway are uncertain, several of the debated points being indicated in Figure 22–4. The main point of controversy concerns the stage at which the tetrapyrrole groups are dissociated from the globin.

1. According to one hypothesis, a methyne group in the heme ring is oxidized, opening the ring and producing a compound of globin, biliverdin (green pigment), and iron. The metal is removed next, yielding biliverdin-globin. The globin moiety is then split off, releasing biliverdin, which undergoes reduction to bilirubin, which enters the bloodstream. Bilirubin is transported in the plasma to the liver attached chiefly to albumin, partly to a fraction of the plasma globulins.

2. Another possibility which has been suggested involves an initial cleavage into heme and globin, and breakdown of the heme to bilirubin by the reactions already indicated, but involving the free prosthetic group, unattached to globin.

It has long been known that exposure of hemoglobin to hydrogen peroxide and ascorbate in the test tube results in the formation of "choleglobin," a substance containing globin, iron, and biliverdin. The suggestion has been made that such non-enzymatic degradation may represent the physiological pathway of conversion of hemoglobin to bile pigments. Indeed, this type of reaction has been demonstrated in liver slices and homogenates, where oxidation of purines provides the hydrogen peroxide. However, the search for a more specific enzymatic pathway has turned up two mechanisms of a more "physiological" character: (1) either hemoglobin or free heme is oxidized by mitochondria of the blood-destroying organs (e.g., spleen) to biliverdin and carbon monoxide (from the α-methenyl group); (2) an oxygenase in the non-particulate fraction of the cytoplasm of liver or kidney, in the presence of O_2, NADPH, Fe^{++}, —SH groups, and an activator from the nucleus, oxidizes the complex of hemoglobin-haptoglobin (or the artificial hemochromogen of heme-pyridine) to a green intermediate, which yields biliverdin and formaldehyde under the influence of a hydrolase.

(*b*) ***Bilirubin in plasma and bile.*** It has been found that bilirubin migrates in normal plasma largely combined with albumin, a minor fraction being attached to an α_1-globulin. In this form (normally 0.1 to 1.0 mg./100 ml.), it is carried to the liver, where it is separated from its protein carrier by either the Kupffer or polygonal cells. The latter excrete the bilirubin into the bile canaliculi, from which it ultimately enters the duodenum in the bile (about 300 mg. daily).

The bilirubin normally present in plasma differs chemically from that which has been "processed" by the liver. In hemolytic disorders, the excessive breakdown of hemoglobin causes the accumulation of abnormally large amounts of the "normal" type of bilirubin in the plasma. On the other hand, in biliary obstruction, bilirubin is reabsorbed from the bile canaliculi into the plasma, where it migrates with the albumin. This "liver-processed" bilirubin behaves chemically in a manner quite different from the bilirubin of normal plasma. It has been shown to be a diglucuronide of bilirubin, accompanied by minor quantities of monoglucuronide. These compounds are much more polar than the original "plasma" bilirubin. The conjugation of bilirubin with glucuronate is effected by a microsomal transferase utilizing UDP-glucuronate. Absence of the glucuronyl transferase from the liver accounts for the jaundice often observed in the human newborn.

In addition to glucuronides, an appreciable fraction of the bilirubin of human bile exists in the form of a sulfate conjugate accompanied by a minor fraction of bilirubin conjugated with substances which are as yet unidentified.

The conjugated and unconjugated types of bilirubin may be differentiated by the van den Bergh reaction, the chemistry of which is discussed elsewhere (p. 138). Essentially, the test consists in treatment of the sample with a diazonium compound to produce an azo dye (blue-violet under usual conditions of the test). The test may be performed qualitatively or quantitatively, the latter procedure being more sensitive to small quantities of bilirubin.

When the diazo reagent in aqueous solution is added to normal serum or plasma (direct van den Bergh reaction), no coupling occurs within 30 to 45 seconds (no color; negative prompt direct reaction). Coupling will occur, however, gradually, after longer periods of time (delayed direct reaction). Addition of alcohol to the reaction mixture (indirect van den Bergh reaction) results in prompt coupling, probably by facilitating access of the diazonium salt to the methylene bridge of the relatively non-polar bilirubin. Alcohol is not necessary for immediate coupling of "liver-processed" bilirubin (conjugated), e.g., in bile, which consequently gives a prompt direct van den Bergh reaction. This reaction is also obtained with serum in certain abnormal conditions of the liver or bile passages, when the "processed" bilirubin of the bile has re-entered the bloodstream (e.g., in biliary obstruction). Both forms of bilirubin give the indirect van den Bergh reaction, which therefore can be employed in the quantitative determination of total bilirubin.

Serum (or plasma) contains 0.1 to 1.0 mg. of bilirubin per 100 ml. When the direct reaction (i.e., in aqueous solution) is applied quantitatively, coupling occurs within one minute to the extent of 0.00 to 0.24 mg. of bilirubin per 100 ml. (one-minute, direct-reacting bilirubin). This amount of rapidly reacting pigment apparently is not sufficient to produce a visible color in the qualitative van den Bergh procedure. Increase in this fraction of the serum bilirubin is abnormal, even though the total is within normal limits.

(*c*) ***Inborn errors of bilirubin metabolism.*** The "hyperbilirubinemias" of genetic origin are characterized by elevated levels of unconjugated bile pigment in the blood, unaccompanied by glucuronide forms. "Congenital non-hemolytic jaundice with kernicterus" is a recessive abnormality of this type, which is severe and often fatal early in life. It is caused by the lack of bilirubin-glucuronyl transferase. The same lack occurs in a dominant form, which is mild in its effects. A so-called "shunt" type (p. 618) may be due to overproduction of bilirubin in bone marrow. In addition to the pure hyperbilirubinemias, a genetically caused "bilemia" has been found. Since it is characterized by elevation in the blood levels of both bilirubin itself and its glucuronides, it has been postulated to involve a defective hepatic biliary secretory system.

(*d*) ***Further metabolism of the bile pigments.*** The reactions undergone by the bile pigments are outlined in Figure 22–5. Structural formulas and other chemical characteristics of these compounds are presented elsewhere (p. 136).

As indicated previously, hemoglobin is converted to biliverdin by an oxidative reaction, and biliverdin (34 H atoms) is reduced to bilirubin (36 H atoms), both reactions being catalyzed by enzyme systems in the tissues. Most of the remaining reactions of the bile pigments are the result of the action of intestinal bacteria; a few are due to spontaneous autoxidation.

There is evidence that free bilirubin can be absorbed from the intestine and thus may undergo an entero-hepatic circulation. Whether this occurs in the adult, after hydrolysis of the glucuronides, is uncertain. The pathway may be significant in the newborn, when some free bilirubin is excreted by the liver, and may be a contributing factor in neonatal jaundice.

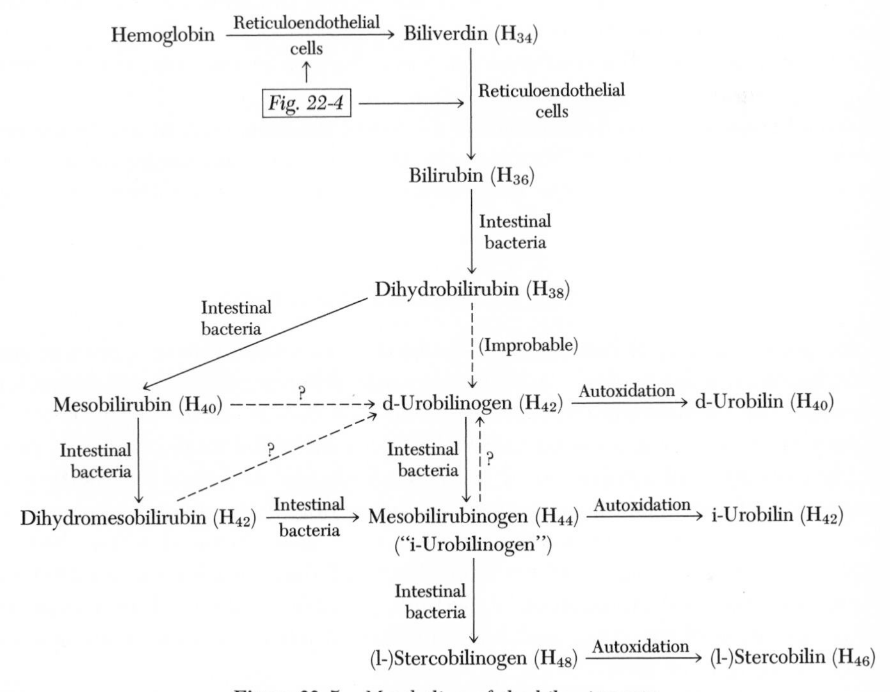

Figure 22–5. Metabolism of the bile pigments.

In the intestinal lumen, bacterial enzyme systems reduce bilirubin (presumably after hydrolysis of conjugating groups) to dihydrobilirubin, mesobilirubin, dihydromesobilirubin, and mesobilirubinogen ("i-urobilinogen"), a member of the "bilinogen" category.

Some of the mesobilirubinogen is reduced further to (l-)stercobilinogen, another component of the bilinogens. A third bilinogen, d-urobilinogen, occurs in the urine and feces of patients who have received broad spectrum antibiotics. Since its structure is not definitely established, the place of d-urobilinogen in the metabolic sequence is uncertain. However, its occurrence in circumstances in which bacterial reductions are at least partially inhibited, coupled with a diminution or cessation of formation of other bilinogens in these cases, suggests that d-urobilinogen may be a normal precursor of the other bilinogens. Bilinogens are excreted to a certain extent, unchanged, in both urine and feces. A variable fraction of the bilinogens undergoes spontaneous autoxidation to the class of "bilins," stercobilinogen forming (l-)stercobilin, mesobilirubinogen forming a compound known variously as "urobilin-IX-α," "K-urobilin," or "i-urobilin," whereas d-urobilinogen, when it occurs, forms d-urobilin. Although stercobilin generally has been considered the major component of the bilin group, more recent investigations indicate that i-urobilin is preponderant in the urine of some individuals, the variations probably being due to differences in bacterial activity and intestinal absorption.

A variable portion of the bilinogens and bilins is excreted in the feces (40 to 280 mg. daily, average, 200). The remainder is reabsorbed from the intestine, passing into the portal circulation. The major part of this fraction is removed from the blood by the liver; its exact fate is unknown, but it does not appear to be re-excreted normally in the bile in significant amounts. The small amount of bilinogens and bilins that escapes the liver and enters the systemic circulation is excreted in the urine. The fraction of the total daily output of bilinogens and bilins which appears in the urine depends to some extent on conditions for reabsorption in the intestine, being increased in constipation and decreased in diarrhea. In the presence of normal liver and bowel function, the amount excreted daily in the urine does not exceed 4 mg.

For clinical purposes, the combined bilinogen fraction of the urine (called "urobilinogen") is determined by means of the Ehrlich aldehyde reagent (p. 139). Total urinary bilins plus bilinogens may be determined by the use of the same reagent, following reduction of the former to the latter. Alternatively, the bilinogens may be oxidized to bilins, and total bilins determined by the fluorescence of their zinc derivatives, or by spectrophotometry.

"Extra-erythrocytic" Sources of Bile Pigments and Dipyrroles

If the porphyrin ring of hemoglobin is labeled by administration to a normal man of isotopic glycine in a single dose, several apparently different pathways of formation of bile pigments can be demonstrated, as seen in the excretion of labeled end-products. The major pathway, normally amounting to 80 to 85 per cent of the total, reaches its peak at about 140 days after administration of the labeled glycine, and clearly is derived from the breakdown of hemoglobin, synthesized when labeling of the glycine pool was at its highest, incorporated into erythrocytes at that time, and liberated when these cells began to disintegrate in large numbers after about 125 days. In addition, a rather small, slow, but long-continued excretion of labeled bile pigments is observed, now believed to be due to operation of the major pathway, but derived from retention of small amounts of isotope in the glycine pool.

The most striking finding from experiments of the type described is the appearance of a significant peak of labeled bile pigments in the first four days. This "early" or "shunt" fraction, which amounts to 10 to 20 per cent of the total normally, increases to as much as 70 per cent in pernicious anemia, erythropoietic porphyria, thalassemia, hemorrhagic conditions, and in the "over-production" variety of hyperbilirubinemia. Further investigation has subdivided this fraction into two, the first reaching its peak in 1 to 24 hours, and apparently being independent of heme synthesis. It is probably derived from precursors of the porphyrins, possibly linear tetrapyrrole intermediates. The second subfraction reaches a maximum in three to four days, is dependent on complete heme synthesis, and probably originates from heme or hemoglobin accidentally escaping during maturation of the erythrocytes.

"Anabolic" pathways also appear to be responsible for the formation of the dipyrrolic bilifuscins, which largely determine the color of the feces.

EXCRETION OF PRODUCTS OF PORPHYRIN METABOLISM

Although much of this material has been mentioned in connection with each of the several aspects of porphyrin metabolism, it may be helpful to collect and coordinate the information here, together with certain other data on the excretion of porphyrin metabolites.

Bile Pigments and Dipyrroles

The bilinogens and bilins, which constitute the major final catabolites of porphyrins in the body, are excreted in the total amount of about 300 mg. daily, most of which is in the feces. Bilirubin is not a normal constituent of the urine or feces. Mesobilifuscin, partly in the form of a dark brown pigment, partly as a colorless chromogen, occurs to the extent of 1 to 3 mg. per day in urine, 11 mg. per day in feces.

Porphyrins

(*a*) ***Normal excretory pattern.*** Traces of porphyrins are excreted normally, mainly in the feces. The average daily output of coproporphyrin I is about 0.7 mg., that of coproporphyrin III, 0.2 mg. Urinary coproporphyrin ranges from 60 to 280 μg. (average 160) daily, of which 60 to 80 per cent is Type I, 20 to 40 per cent Type III. Fecal coproporphyrin amounts to 300 to 1400 μg. daily, of which 70 to 90 per cent is Type I. Uroporphyrins are excreted normally only in traces, 15 to 30 μg. daily in urine, mostly Type I; fecal uroporphyrin is excreted in a range of 20 to 60 μg. daily. The small amount of protoporphyrin found in the feces is probably derived mainly from the hemoglobin of the meat in the diet. Traces are found also in the bile, but not normally in the urine.

It should be mentioned that much of the coproporphyrin in normal urine is excreted as a "porphyrinogen," or precursor, which is converted to coproporphyrin spontaneously on standing, or by chemical treatment with mild oxidants.

(*b*) ***Porphyrinurias.*** Under certain conditions, excessive amounts and "abnormal" types of porphyrins are excreted. Table 22-1 summarizes data on the general conditions characterized by excretion of large quantities of porphyrins in the urine (and feces).

The porphyrias have been discussed previously. It is of interest that the porphyrins excreted in the urine in "hepatic" porphyrias are present as Zn complexes, whereas those of "erythropoietic" porphyria are in the free state. Certain varieties of the former conditions are characterized also by the excretion of porphobilinogen and δ-aminolevuli-

TABLE 22-1. PORPHYRINURIAS

GENERAL TYPE	SPECIFIC CONDITIONS	CHIEF URINARY PORPHYRINS	OTHER CHARACTERISTICS
Hereditary	Erythropoietic porphyria	Uroporphyrin I Coproporphyrin I	Increased porphyrins in bone marrow
	Erythropoietic protoporphyria	Coproporphyrin III	Increased protoporphyrin in erythrocytes
	Hepatic porphyrias	Uroporphyrin and coproporphyrin III and I; 7-COOH III	Increased porphyrins in liver. Porphobilinogen and δ-aminolevulinate in urine in certain types.
Acquired	Toxic agents: Chemicals Heavy metals Acute alcoholism Cirrhosis in alcoholics	Coproporphyrin III	
	Certain liver diseases: Infectious mononucleosis Viral hepatitis Cirrhosis in non-alcoholics	Coproporphyrin I	
	Certain blood dyscrasias: Hemolytic anemias Iron-deficiency anemias Pernicious anemia Leukemia	Coproporphyrin I	
	Obstructive jaundice	Coproporphyrin I	
	Miscellaneous conditions: Poliomyelitis Aplastic anemias Hodgkin's disease	Coproporphyrin III	

nate. The excretion of porphyrins containing 7, 6, and 5 carboxyl groups in the hepatic porphyrias has been noted previously.

Coproporphyrin III is excreted in excessive quantities as the result of (1) exposure to certain toxic chemicals and heavy metals (e.g., lead), (2) acute alcoholism (temporary increase in output), (3) cirrhosis of the liver in chronic alcoholics (persistent porphyrinuria), and (4) in certain miscellaneous disorders.

Abnormally large quantities of coproporphyrin I are found in the urine in (1) obstructive jaundice (deviation from biliary excretion), (2) certain liver diseases (including cirrhosis in non-alcoholics), and (3) certain blood dyscrasias.

A type of porphyrinuria resembling acute intermittent porphyria may be induced in experimental animals by administration of allylisopropylacetylcarbamide ("Sedormid," a hypnotic) or, better, allylisopropylacetamide. Uroporphyrin and coproporphyrin, mostly Type III, appear in the urine along with porphobilinogen, and concentrations of these substances are greatly increased in the liver. Similar results are obtained by administration of barbiturates containing allyl groups or of 2,4,6-trimethyl-1,4-dihydro-3,5-dicarbethoxypyridine. Some of these compounds have been shown to induce formation of δ-aminolevulinate synthetase in the liver in vivo and in cell culture. (An isozyme of succinyl-CoA synthetase is induced even earlier.) Poisoning with hexachlorobenzene, which has occurred on a large scale in Turkey from consumption of seed wheat treated with this fungicide, results in a type of porphyrinuria resembling cutanea tarda. Experimental porphyrinuria resembling erythropoietic porphyria has been produced in rabbits by the combined administration of phenylhydrazine, lead, a photosensitizer, and ultraviolet light. Although the urinary uroporphyrin is mainly Type I and porphyrins are greatly increased in the bone marrow, this condition differs from the analogous human porphyria by the excretion of Type III coproporphyrin and porphobilinogen.

RELATION OF PORPHYRIN METABOLISM TO THAT OF OTHER METABOLITES

Figure 22–6 illustrates the major interrelations between the porphyrins (and their derivatives) and the carbohydrates and proteins. Carbohydrate provides the succinyl portion; protein, the glycine part of the porphyrin ring. Combination with iron produces the hemes (iron porphyrins), which are coupled with specific proteins to form the hemoproteins.

In the degradation of the hemoproteins, the iron and protein moieties are returned to their respective pools for reutilization. The non-metallic portion of the prosthetic group (derived from glycine and succinate, originally) is discarded completely by the organism, largely in the form of the bile pigments.

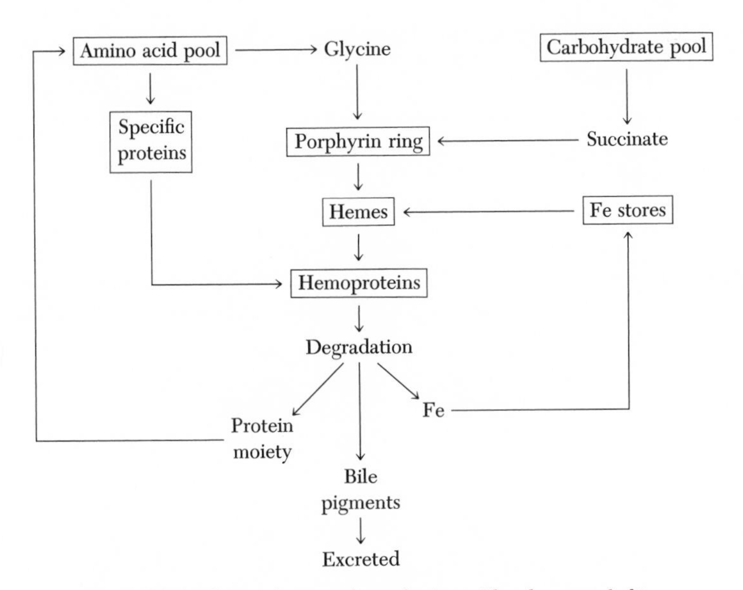

Figure 22–6. Interrelations of porphyrins with other metabolites.

BIBLIOGRAPHY

Annual Review of Biochemistry.
Annual Review of Physiology.
Bogorad, L.: The biogenesis of heme, chlorophylls, and bile pigments, Chapter 5 in Bernfeld, P. (ed.): Biogenesis of Natural Compounds, New York, The Macmillan Company, 1963.
Dean, G.: The Porphyrias, Philadelphia, J. B. Lippincott Company, 1963.
Goldberg, A., and Rimington, C.: Diseases of Porphyrin Metabolism, Springfield, Ill., Charles C Thomas, 1962.
Granick, S.: Metabolism of heme and chlorophyll, Chapter 20 in Greenberg, D. M. (ed.): Metabolic Pathways, Vol. 2, New York, Academic Press, Inc., 1961.
Gray, C. H.: The Bile Pigments, London, Methuen & Company, 1953.
Gray, C. H.: Bile Pigments in Health and Disease, Springfield, Ill., Charles C Thomas, 1961.
Ingram, V. M.: Hemoglobin and its Abnormalities, Springfield, Ill., Charles C Thomas, 1961.
Ingram, V. M.: The Hemoglobins in Genetics and Evolution, New York, Columbia University Press, 1963.
Lascelles, J.: Tetrapyrrole Biosynthesis and its Regulation, New York, W. A. Benjamin, Inc., 1964.
Lemberg, R., and Legge, J. W.: Hematin Compounds and Bile Pigments, New York, Interscience Publishers, Inc., 1949, Chapters 10–13.
Vanotti, A.: Porphyrins, London, Hilger & Watts, 1954.

CHAPTER 23

INORGANIC METABOLISM

SODIUM, POTASSIUM, AND CHLORIDE METABOLISM

Related Physiological Mechanisms

The metabolism of sodium, potassium, and chloride is intimately related to certain fundamental physiological mechanisms which are considered elsewhere in detail and will therefore be mentioned here only briefly:

(*a*) ***Water balance and osmotic pressure (p. 309).*** The maintenance of normal hydration and osmotic pressure depends primarily on the total cation content of the body fluids. Since sodium constitutes the largest fraction of the total cations of the extracellular fluids (142/155), it plays a dominant role in this connection.

(*b*) ***Acid-base balance (p. 312).*** At any given H_2CO_3 concentration, the H^+ ion concentration of extracellular fluids depends upon the bicarbonate concentration (p. 320). Since the latter is determined by the amount of total cations in excess of anions other than HCO_3^-, since Cl^- constitutes by far the largest fraction of the total anions of the extracellular fluids (103/155), and since the total concentration of anions depends essentially on that of Na^+, it follows that the maintenance of the normal pH of these fluids depends largely on the presence of normal concentrations of Na^+ and Cl^- (p. 313).

(*c*) ***Neuromuscular irritability.*** Neuromuscular irritability and excitability are influenced by the relative proportions of certain ions, which may be expressed as follows:

$$\text{Irritability} \propto \frac{Na^+ + K^+}{Ca^{++} + Mg^{++} + H^+}$$

Sodium is the chief cation and chloride the chief anion of extracellular fluids, whereas potassium is the chief cation of intracellular fluids (p. 301). Some movement of potassium occurs continually from cells to extracellular fluids (including plasma). It is accelerated under abnormal conditions of excessive loss of intracellular fluid, the mobilized potassium being usually excreted promptly in the urine. Some movement of sodium occurs continually in the opposite direction, i.e., from extra- to intracellular fluid, and is accelerated under conditions discussed elsewhere (p. 307). Any considerable increase or decrease of potassium in the extracellular fluids produces serious and at times fatal disturbances in muscle irritability, respiration, and myocardial function. No other cation can replace considerable amounts of potassium in the intracellular fluids without affecting the functional activity of the cell.

Absorption and Excretion

An average adequate diet contains about 3 or 4 gm. (75 to 100 mEq.) of potassium and 8 to 15 gm. (130 to 250 mEq.) of sodium chloride daily, the latter being contributed to by the addition of salt to the food. Normally, sodium, potassium, and chloride are practically completely absorbed from the gastrointestinal tract, less than 2 per cent of ingested sodium and less than 10 per cent of the potassium being eliminated in the feces. In subjects with diarrhea, large amounts are lost in the feces, owing in large measure to failure of reabsorption of constituents of digestive fluids, the electrolyte composition of which is indicated in Figure 13–2 and Table 23–1. Sodium and chloride are eliminated chiefly in the urine and, to a lesser extent, in the perspiration. Potassium is normally eliminated almost entirely in the urine.

Excretion in urine. The amounts excreted in the urine are indicated elsewhere (p. 847). Under normal conditions the daily urinary excretion of these electrolytes approximates the intake except under conditions of sudden increase of sodium chloride intake following a period of restriction. Sodium and chloride are removed from the circulating plasma by glomerular filtration, over 1000 gm. of sodium chloride entering the renal tubules daily in the glomerular filtrate. Under normal conditions 99 per cent or more undergoes reabsorption into the bloodstream by the tubular epithelium. About 80 to 85 per cent of this is reabsorbed in the proximal portion of the tubule, the remainder in the distal portion (p. 825). Adrenocortical hormones, particularly aldosterone, enhance reabsorption of sodium (and therefore, indirectly, of chloride). Mainly in the distal portion, too, about 1 or 2 per cent of the Na^+ reabsorption occurs in exchange for H^+ ions (also for K^+) (p. 317) as part of the mechanism of acidification of the urine. Under normal conditions the regulation of sodium and chloride reabsorption and conservation is so efficient that equilibrium can be maintained on a sodium chloride intake as low as 0.5 gm. daily, sodium virtually disappearing from the urine.

Potassium is removed from the plasma by glomerular filtration and, like sodium and chloride, normally undergoes extensive reabsorption in the tubules (p. 825). However, unlike sodium and chloride, it is also excreted into the tubular lumen by the cells of the distal portion of the renal tubules. This active process apparently competes with H^+ ions in the Na^+ exchange mechanism (p. 318). In the presence of normal kidney function,

TABLE 23-1. APPROXIMATE CONCENTRATIONS OF CERTAIN ELECTROLYTES IN BODY FLUIDS (mEq./LITER)

FLUIDS	Na	K	Cl	HCO_3
Gastric juice	20	8	145	0
Pancreatic juice	140	5	40	110
Jejunal juice	138	5	110	30
Bile	140	8	108	38
Perspiration	82	5	85	0
Blood serum	140	4.3	100	25
Interstitial fluid	145	3.3	110	28

potassium is removed from the blood plasma promptly and efficiently even in the face of a considerably increased supply, preventing undue increase in its concentration in the extracellular fluids.

Excretion by the skin. The sodium and chloride content of perspiration is usually lower than that of blood plasma (Table 32-1). Their concentrations in sweat are decreased by the salt-active adrenal cortical hormones (q.v.), which are secreted in increased amount during acclimatization to heat. This constitutes an adaptive mechanism for conservation of body sodium and chloride, the sweat glands producing a progressively more dilute fluid. In normal subjects, the loss of sodium and chloride in the perspiration is compensated by a corresponding diminution in their urinary excretion. However, considerable amounts may be lost from the body under conditions of prolonged strenuous exertion at extremely high temperatures and humidity. If, under such circumstances, large amounts of salt-poor water are taken to alleviate thirst, the concentration of sodium and chloride in the body fluids may fall to the point of producing symptoms (muscle cramps, intense headache, exhaustion, mental dullness). These may be relieved by administration of sodium chloride.

Excretion in digestive fluids. The approximate electrolyte compositions of certain digestive fluids are indicated in Figure 13–2 (p. 322) and in Table 23-1. Under normal conditions these fluids are virtually completely reabsorbed in the bowel but, in the presence of protracted vomiting or diarrhea, large amounts of water and electrolytes may be lost from the body. This is of importance in the treatment of the dehydration and dislocations of acid-base balance that occur under these circumstances.

Sodium, Chloride, and Potassium in Blood

The normal amounts of sodium, chloride, and potassium in 100 ml. of blood plasma (or serum) are as follows: sodium, 300 to 335 (average 320) mg. (132 to 144 mEq./liter); chloride, 340 to 370 mg. (96 to 105 mEq./liter), or 570 to 620 mg. expressed as sodium chloride; potassium, 14 to 19 (average 16) mg. (3.6 to 4.8 mEq./liter). In man, erythrocytes contain little or no sodium, smaller amounts of chloride than does the plasma, and large amounts of potassium (about 370 mg./100 gm.). The distribution of Cl^- between plasma and erythrocytes is similar and intimately related to that of HCO_3^-, in accordance with Donnan's law governing the distribution of diffusible monovalent ions (p. 290). The factors which influence this distribution and the changes that occur under physiological conditions are considered elsewhere (p. 291). Suffice it to recall here that shifts of Cl^- and HCO_3^- between the plasma and the erythrocytes play an important role in the maintenance of a constant pH in the blood.

The concentrations of sodium, chloride, and potassium in the plasma vary but slightly under physiological conditions. The plasma chloride may fall somewhat during periods of active gastric secretion of hydrochloric acid and may rise again in the post-digestive period (reabsorption from intestine). It is affected only slightly by marked variations in chloride intake; the same is true of the plasma sodium and potassium concentrations. The plasma potassium decreases somewhat during periods of increased carbohydrate utilization (oxidation and glycogen deposition), as following administration of glucose or insulin. This is due to its passage from extracellular fluids into the cells in increased amount under these circumstances (p. 308).

The influence of adrenal cortical hormones (especially aldosterone) in increasing plasma sodium and decreasing potassium is considered elsewhere in detail (p. 709). It is the result of their effect on renal tubular reabsorption of these ions and on their distribution between intra- and extracellular fluids.

Distribution and Intermediary Metabolism

Differences in the composition of intra- and extracellular fluids are illustrated in Figure 12–3 (p. 301). We are concerned here mainly with the striking differences in the concentrations of sodium, potassium, and chloride in these fluid compartments. It should be understood that the concentrations of electrolytes vary in the intracellular fluid of individual tissues, but the general pattern is rather uniform. Skeletal muscle is the tissue studied most thoroughly in this connection. The rather strict localization of relatively large amounts of potassium in the intracellular and of sodium and chloride in the extracellular fluid is attributable to a rather high degree of selective relative impermeability of most cell membranes to these ions. However, this impermeability is neither absolute nor fixed. In different functional states and under certain abnormal circumstances the composition of the intracellular fluid may be altered as a result of loss of potassium from and entrance of sodium into the cells. These changes are often accompanied by alterations in the concentrations of Cl^- and HCO_3^- in the extracellular fluid, which may seriously affect the state of acid-base balance (p. 319).

Some sort of equilibrium is maintained normally between the high cellular (150 mEq./liter) and low extracellular (5 mEq./liter) concentrations of potassium, and the reverse situation with regard to sodium, although the factors operating are not well understood. The adrenal cortical hormones and the kidneys are perhaps involved, as well as the oxidative energy of the cell (p. 307). Under normal conditions, sodium and potassium entering the body are distributed rapidly throughout the extracellular fluids, an equivalent amount being excreted within a short time, almost entirely in the urine. Very little sodium is transferred to the cells; studies with radioactive potassium indicate that its transfer through the cell membrane is slow as compared to that of water, the labeled potassium attaining equilibrium with the intracellular potassium only after 15 hours, whereas deuterium-labeled water attains equilibrium with the total body water in two hours. As indicated elsewhere (p. 308), the addition of sodium to the extracellular fluids is followed by a temporary shift of water to that compartment from the cells, osmotic equilibrium being thus preserved. The addition of potassium is followed promptly by increased renal excretion of potassium (diuresis), preventing its accumulation in excess in the extracellular fluids. Certain of the factors which influence renal excretion of potassium are discussed elsewhere, viz., adrenocortical hormones (pp. 709, 848), potassium concentration in the cells (p. 318), and the state of acid-base balance (p. 319).

Potassium moves into cells during periods of cell growth and repair, i.e., increased protein anabolism, occurring spontaneously or induced by such agents as growth hormone or androgen. Deposition of 1 gm. of cell protein requires retention of approximately 3 ml. of intracellular fluid containing 0.45 mEq. of potassium. Movement of potassium in the same direction occurs also during periods of increased glucose utilization under normal conditions, e.g., after administration of glucose or insulin (p. 308). Deposition of 1 gm. of glycogen (liver, muscle) involves retention of approximately 1 ml. of intracellular fluid and, therefore, 0.15 mEq. of potassium. Potassium enters cells also at an accelerated rate during periods of rehydration and, in the absence of complicating factors, in alkalosis.

Excessive loss of extracellular fluid (dehydration), e.g., as a result of vomiting, diarrhea, diuresis, or intestinal fistulas, is followed by transfer of intracellular fluid, and therefore potassium, to the extracellular compartment. This occurs also when glycogen is lost (diabetes mellitus) and in conditions of accelerated protein catabolism, e.g., starvation, trauma, disease, excessive amounts of adrenocortical (stress) and thyroid hormones. About 2.7 mEq. of potassium are released for every gram of nitrogen lost under such circumstances. Acidosis and anoxia are accompanied by similar transfer of potassium from intra- to extracellular fluids.

In the presence of normal renal function passage of excessive quantities of K^+ out of the cells is accompanied by movement of Na^+ and H^+ in the opposite direction. A considerable portion of the intracellular K^+ is thus replaced by Na^+ and a decrease in H^+ concentration in extracellular fluid is accompanied by an increased H^+ concentration within the cell. The excess potassium in the extracellular fluid is excreted in the urine, chiefly with chloride, with consequent decrease in the concentration of Cl^- in the extracellular fluid and a corresponding increase in HCO_3^-. This increases the tendency toward production of a metabolic type of alkalosis instigated by the initial passage of H^+ into cells in exchange for Na^+. Impaired renal function interferes with this exchange of sodium for potassium in the cell and with excretion of the excess potassium in the blood plasma, resulting at times in hyperpotassemia. Appreciation of the occurrence and significance of these electrolyte shifts in a variety of common clinical disorders has been of great practical value.

SULFUR METABOLISM

Sulfur is a nutritionally essential element, occurring in proteins in the form of the amino acids, methionine, cystine, and cysteine. It is present in enzymes and certain hormones (anterior pituitary, insulin) and also in such substances as glutathione, thiamine, taurocholic acid, and chondroitin sulfuric acid. The normal requirement is undoubtedly satisfied by an adequate protein intake.

Absorption

Sulfur is ingested in (1) inorganic (sodium, potassium, magnesium sulfates) but mainly in (2) organic forms. It is provided chiefly by the sulfur-containing amino acids, methionine and cystine (pp. 584, 588), and also by sulfolipids and glycoproteins (mucoitin and chondroitin sulfuric acids). Inorganic sulfate is absorbed as such from the intestine, as are the amino acids methionine and cystine, liberated by digestion of protein. A small amount of sulfide may be formed in the bowel by the action of bacteria (p. 274). This may be excreted in the feces; if absorbed it is rapidly oxidized to sulfate.

Intermediary Metabolism

Sulfur reaching the liver (exogenous or endogenous) undergoes the following changes:

(1) The bulk of the organic sulfur is oxidized in the liver to inorganic sulfate (SO_4). A portion of the latter, together with a portion of the inorganic sulfate absorbed as such, enters the systemic circulation and is excreted in the urine.

(2) A portion of the organic sulfur escapes oxidation. Some of this fraction is utilized for the formation of sulfur-containing substances, such as insulin, anterior pituitary hormones and other proteins, taurocholic acid (p. 267), glutathione (p. 577), melanin (?) (pp. 601, 780), etc. The small remainder is excreted in the urine as neutral sulfur.

(3) A portion of the inorganic sulfate is combined in the liver with various phenolic substances produced in the bowel largely by bacterial decomposition of amino acids (p. 271) or entering the body as such (e.g., benzene in certain occupations), forming "ethereal" sulfates (e.g., indican, p. 279), which are excreted in the urine. These sulfata-

tion reactions are mediated by an "activated sulfate"-containing compound that has been identified as 3′-phosphoadenosine-5′-phosphosulfate (p. 238). Sulfate conjugation (liver) is also an important phase of the intermediary metabolism of certain steroid hormones, e.g., androgen (p. 686) and estrogen (p. 691). In addition to the participation of inorganic SO_4 in these "detoxication" processes, the amino acid cysteine may form conjugation products (mercapturic acids) in the liver with certain toxic compounds, such as bromobenzene (p. 280).

(4) Sulfate, in the "active" form, is incorporated into certain acid mucopolysaccharides (p. 23). The most important of these are chondroitin sulfates (p. 24), keratosulfate (p. 776), and heparin (p. 802).

Transport and Excretion

Sulfur is present in the blood plasma as inorganic sulfur, 0.5 to 1.1 mg., ethereal sulfur, 0.1 to 1.0 mg., and neutral sulfur, 1.7 to 3.5 mg./100 ml. Whole blood contains 2.2 to 4.5 mg. neutral S/100 ml., the higher value being due in large measure apparently to the presence of thioneine and glutathione in the erythrocytes.

Sulfur is excreted almost entirely in the urine in the three forms in which it occurs in the blood plasma. The total sulfur output, since it is usually derived mainly from protein, varies with the protein intake and tissue protein catabolism, averaging about 1.0 gm. (0.7 to 1.5 gm.) daily under normal conditions. The urinary N:S ratio normally ranges from 13 to 16 in the fasting state or when meat comprises the bulk of the protein intake.

The normal urinary total sulfate (inorganic plus ethereal sulfate) on an average mixed diet ranges from 0.6 to 1.0 gm. daily, comprising 85 to 95 per cent of the total S output. The proportion as well as the absolute amount excreted varies directly with the protein intake. The total SO_4 excretion may be diminished in the presence of renal functional impairment (retained in the blood plasma) and is increased in conditions accompanied by excessive tissue protein catabolism (e.g., fever, increased metabolism).

Inorganic sulfate (sodium, potassium, calcium, magnesium, ammonium sulfates) normally comprises 85 to 95 per cent of the total urinary SO_4, the remainder being ethereal sulfate (0.06 to 0.12 gm. daily). This fraction consists of sodium and potassium salts of aromatic sulfuric acid compounds (phenyl sulfate, indican, etc.) and therefore varies with the quantity of phenolic substances produced in the intestine or otherwise entering the body (e.g., occupational or accidental exposure). Increase in urine indican (potassium indoxyl sulfate, p. 279), absolute or relative, may occur in conditions accompanied by intestinal stasis (increased bacterial action on protein). In subjects having abnormally high occupational exposure to benzene the proportion of the total urinary sulfate in the form of ethereal sulfate may rise to as high as 75 to 80 per cent, a phenomenon of diagnostic importance.

The neutral sulfur of the urine, normally about 5 per cent of the total sulfur, is in the form of such substances as methionine, cystine, urochrome, taurocholic acid, thiosulfate, and thiocyanate, each in very small amounts. This fraction increases in cystinuria (p. 586), melanuria (?), and obstructive jaundice (increased taurocholic acid).

IODINE METABOLISM

The metabolism of iodine is of particular significance in connection with the formation of thyroid hormone, which is considered in detail elsewhere (p. 714). Normal adults require about 25 μg. daily but the recommended optimal daily intake for adults is 100 to 200 μg., for children 50 μg., and for infants 20 to 40 μg. The requirement is probably increased during pregnancy. The iodine of most common foodstuffs is apparently readily available to the organism but is not superior to inorganic iodides. Because of the high iodine content of sea water, marine vegetation, sea foods, and vegetables and fruits grown on the seaboard are particularly rich in this element. Plants (and animal tissues) grown far inland, especially at high altitudes, may be deficient in iodine because of its low concentration in the water. In such regions, iodide is commonly added to the drinking water or to table salt in concentrations of 1:5000 to 1:200,000 to insure an adequate intake and to prevent the development of simple goiter (iodine-deficiency goiter).

Absorption and Excretion

Iodine and iodides can be absorbed from any portion of the alimentary tract, most readily perhaps from the small intestine, free iodine and iodates probably being first converted to iodide. Organic iodine compounds, e.g., diiodotyrosine and thyroxine, are in part absorbed as such and in part broken down in the stomach and intestines with the formation of iodides. Absorption can occur from other mucous membranes, the lungs, and the skin.

Iodine is excreted by the kidneys, liver, skin, lungs, and intestine, and also in milk and saliva. It is almost entirely in the form of inorganic iodide, and may be either endogenous (including liberation from degradation of thyroxine and diiodotyrosine) or exogenous (food, water). Thyroxine is not demonstrable in excreta except after administration.

The quantity excreted normally varies with the intake. About 40 to 80 per cent is usually excreted in the urine (20 to 70 μg. daily in adults; 20 to 35 μg. in children). The urinary fraction of the total elimination is largest when the intake is lowest. Urine iodine is increased by exercise and other factors that increase metabolism (increased rate of turnover of thyroid hormone), except in the event of profuse sweating, when relatively large amounts are lost by this route. Urine iodine increases during pregnancy.

Iodine in the feces (2 to 11 μg. daily; 3 to 27 per cent of intake) is almost entirely exogenous (iodine in unabsorbed food), the remainder being derived from the bile and intestinal secretions. Bile contains 4 to 14 μg./100 ml. in the fasting state and about 50 μg./100 ml. after eating. A portion of this is reabsorbed in the intestine (enterohepatic circulation). Biliary iodine is chiefly of alimentary origin (exogenous) but is also in part endogenous (degradation of thyroid hormone in liver).

Under ordinary atmospheric conditions, negligible amounts of iodine are excreted by the skin. With profuse perspiration (heat, humidity, exercise), up to 2 per cent of the total may be lost by this route. The amount in expired air varies enormously, but may be as much as 10 to 30 μg. daily. The quantity present in milk varies with the iodine intake and may be increased by administration of iodides. Saliva contains 0 to 350 μg./100 ml., also depending on the intake.

Blood Iodine (p. 716)

Practically all of the iodine in the blood is in the plasma, the concentration in the resting state being 4 to 10 μg./100 ml. plasma (or serum). If no iodine has been administered for several days, less than 30 per cent of the plasma iodine is in inorganic form (iodide), practically all (4 to 8 μg./100 ml.) being bound to protein and precipitated with the latter by protein-precipitating agents. It is largely in the form of thyroid hormone.

Measurement of the amount of this protein-bound iodine (PBI), reflecting the concentration of circulating thyroid hormone, is therefore of value in the clinical evaluation of the state of thyroid function. High values occur in hyperthyroidism (8 to 30 μg.) and low values in hypothyroidism (0 to 3 μg.).

In the fasting state the plasma inorganic iodide is quite constant even in the face of wide variations in thyroid activity (which affect only the plasma PBI) but increases strikingly after iodine is ingested, applied to the skin, or administered for purposes of cholecystography, bronchography, or urography.

Distribution and Intermediary Metabolism

The body normally contains about 20 to 30 mg. of iodine, which is distributed approximately as follows: muscles, 50 per cent; thyroid, 20 per cent; skin, 10 per cent; skeleton, 6 per cent. The concentration in the thyroid (10 to 40 mg./100 gm.) is higher than in other tissues (e.g., 0.03 mg./100 gm. muscle). The amount in all tissues diminishes when the intake is lowered, but the normal thyroid retains its capacity for trapping and storing iodine even under such circumstances. This aspect of thyroid function, its mechanism and control, are considered in detail elsewhere (p. 715). Suffice it here to recall that one of the important initial phases of the formation of thyroid hormone involves this remarkable capacity of thyroid cells for trapping and concentrating iodine.

The normal adult thyroid contains 2 to 28 mg. of iodine (0.1 to 0.55 per cent dry weight), varying with the iodine intake and state of thyroid function. By far the largest part is in organic combination, stored in the follicular colloid as "iodothyroglobulin," a composite protein molecule containing thyroxine, diiodotyrosine, and smaller amounts of triiodothyronine. On demand (p. 715), these substances are mobilized from this compound and passed into the systemic circulation. They undergo metabolic degradation apparently chiefly in the liver, their iodine component being excreted in the bile largely as inorganic iodide, but also in some organic combination (thyroxine metabolites). In the tissues, thyroxine may be at least in part converted to triiodothyronine, and perhaps to acetic acid analogs (p. 716).

The liver usually contains 0.5 to 2.3 mg. of iodine, exhibiting wide variations during periods of absorption and excretion. Iodine entering the portal vein from the intestine in part passes through the liver into the systemic circulation and is in part removed by the hepatic cells and excreted in the bile. Organic compounds containing iodine, exogenous or endogenous, are partly or completely degraded in the liver, the iodine being liberated as iodide.

MAGNESIUM METABOLISM

Magnesium is an essential constituent of the tissues and body fluids, but little is known regarding its metabolism or requirement. It is undoubtedly provided in adequate amounts by diets adequate in other respects because of its wide distribution in vegetable (chlorophyll) and animal tissues. It ranks next to potassium among the cations of intracellular fluids (p. 302).

Mg^{++} ions serve as activators of important enzymes involved in intermediary metabolism, including phosphorylase, phosphoglucomutase, and enolase; it inhibits ATP-ase. It exerts an effect on neuromuscular irritability similar to that of Ca^{++}, high levels inducing anesthesia and low levels tetany. However, the marked depression of the central and peripheral nervous system associated with hypermagnesemia is reversed promptly by intravenous administration of calcium.

Absorption and Excretion

The absorption of magnesium from the bowel resembles that of calcium in many respects. An excessively high intake of fat, phosphate, calcium, and alkalies appears to diminish its absorption from the upper intestine. A high magnesium intake apparently increases urinary excretion of calcium. The influence of the factors mentioned above probably depends on their influence on the solubility of magnesium salts. Little information is available regarding the effect of vitamin D on magnesium absorption. The fact that the magnesium content of the bones in rickets is not decreased and is usually actually increased argues against the importance of vitamin D in this connection.

Like calcium, magnesium is excreted in the feces and urine. Under normal conditions about 50 to 80 per cent is excreted in the feces (magnesium of food, bile, digestive secretions) and the remainder by the kidneys. Administration of acidifying substances (e.g., NH_4Cl) is followed by increased urinary elimination of magnesium (as of calcium, p. 638).

Blood Magnesium

Magnesium, unlike calcium, is present in both erythrocytes and plasma, its concentration in the former being 5.4 to 7.8 mg./100 gm. (average 6.6 mg.) and in the latter 1.7 to 2.3 mg./100 ml. (1.4 to 1.9 mEq./liter). About 70 to 85 per cent (average 80) of the serum magnesium is diffusible, the remainder being bound to plasma proteins. The magnesium content of cerebrospinal fluid is higher than that of blood plasma, averaging about 3.0 mg./100 ml. (2.5 mEq./liter).

Little is known regarding the factors involved in the regulation of the magnesium content of the blood. There is in certain respects a reciprocal relationship between magnesium and calcium in the serum; e.g., in oxalate poisoning, a decrease in serum calcium is accompanied by an increase in magnesium, whereas the hypermagnesemia induced by injection of magnesium salts is accompanied by a fall in serum calcium. Under other conditions the relationship is with the serum phosphate concentration rather than calcium; e.g., administration of vitamin D produces an increase in serum phosphate and a decrease in serum magnesium, whereas administration of parathyroid hormone produces a decrease in serum phosphate and an increase in serum magnesium.

Hypomagnesemia, experimental and clinical, has been described as occurring in association with defective intestinal absorption (steatorrhea), severe dehydration, chronic alcoholism, and excessive loss of magnesium in the urine (renal tubular reabsorptive defect). The chief manifestations are those of neuromuscular hyperirritability.

CALCIUM AND PHOSPHORUS METABOLISM

Although over 99 per cent of the body calcium and 80 to 85 per cent of the phosphorus is in the bones, important functions of these elements are exerted in directions other than preservation of skeletal structure. Calcium ions (1) decrease capillary and cell membrane permeability, (2) decrease neuromuscular excitability, and are necessary for (3) muscle contraction, (4) normal transmission of nerve impulses, and (5) blood coagulation. Calcium ions also activate certain enzymes, including lipase, succinate dehydrogenase, adenosine triphosphatase, and some proteases.

The vital functions of phosphorus in various phases of organic metabolism have been referred to repeatedly. It is necessary merely to recall here the fundamental role of high-energy phosphate bonds in the storage, liberation, and transfer of energy (e.g., ATP, phosphocreatine), the importance of hexose- and triose-phosphates in the intermediary metabolism of carbohydrate, and the metabolic significance of such phosphorus-containing substances as phospholipids, nucleic acids, and nucleotides (NAD, NADP, etc.). These subjects are discussed in detail elsewhere. We shall be concerned here mainly with the role of phosphate in inorganic metabolism.

Absorption

Calcium and phosphate are absorbed in the small intestine, more readily in the upper than in the lower portions. Absorption in the ileum is an active process and can occur against a considerable concentration gradient. In the course of digestion of nucleoproteins and phosphoproteins, phosphate may be split off and absorbed as such. If ester forms are present, they may undergo hydrolysis (enzymes of pancreatic and intestinal juice) prior to absorption. It has been suggested that because of this fact a considerable fraction of the dietary phosphate is absorbed later than the major portion of the calcium. This may permit better absorption of both elements, especially in regions of relatively low acidity.

Factors influencing degree of absorption. Several factors influence the degree of absorption of calcium:

(*a*) *Concentration in Intestine.* Other factors being equal, absorption of calcium is roughly proportional to its concentration in the intestine. The same appears to be true of phosphate.

(*b*) *Intestinal pH.* Calcium salts, particularly phosphates and carbonates, are quite soluble in acid solutions and are relatively insoluble in alkaline solutions. Consequently, factors which increase intestinal acidity favor absorption of calcium, and vice versa. Under conditions of normal gastric acidity, calcium salts of weak organic acids are converted to the soluble chloride and, if retained in the stomach for a sufficient period, even the less soluble basic phosphate may go into solution. The acidity in the duodenum is of considerable importance, determining whether more of the calcium is in the form of the more soluble acid phosphate or less soluble basic phosphate. Calcium chloride and acid phosphate are probably absorbed from the duodenum before the gastric juice acidity is neutralized. Subsequently, absorption of calcium may be favored by the presence of organic acids (e.g., lactic, citric, amino acids, fatty acids).

(*c*) *Other Substances in the Food Mixture.* An excess of magnesium apparently diminishes absorption of calcium, especially if the latter is not present in adequate amounts. Considerable interest has centered in the calcium : phosphorus ratio, the optimum ratio for absorption of both elements being about 1 : 1 (1 : 2 to 2 : 1). An excessively high ratio is accompanied by decreased absorption of phosphate (rachitogenic diet, p. 164). It is stated that a low ratio does not result in decreased calcium absorption. This effect is apparently related to the influence on solubility of the products (calcium phosphates) formed under these conditions. Such substances as iron, beryllium, lead, manganese, aluminum and strontium, which form insoluble phosphates, likewise interfere with absorption of phosphate, and can induce rickets (p. 164).

Phytic acid (inositol hexaphosphate), which occurs in cereal grains, forms insoluble salts (phytin) with calcium and magnesium (insoluble above pH 3 to 4), with consequent impairment of absorption of these elements. This phenomenon is regarded as the basis of the rachitogenic effect of such cereals as oatmeal. Poorly absorbed compounds are formed also with fatty acids (calcium soaps). Hydroxyacids such as lactic (favored by high lactose intake in young), citric, and tartaric shift the precipitation point of calcium phytate toward a higher pH (see also action of vitamin D, below and p. 163), and favor absorption, which is facilitated, too, by lysine and arginine and by a high protein intake (with normal digestion and absorption).

(*d*) *Vitamin D* (*p. 163*). Vitamin D is essential for normal intestinal absorption of calcium. It enhances the active transport of calcium across the ileum, apparently, in part at least, by promoting release of mitochondria-bound calcium. The presence of adequate amounts of vitamin D is required for enhancement of intestinal absorption of calcium by the parathyroid hormone. Absorption of phosphate is apparently increased somewhat.

Vitamin D apparently counteracts the effect of phytic acid in binding the calcium ions and thus diminishing calcium absorption. In adequate amounts and with a high calcium intake, it suppresses the rachitogenic and anticalcifying effect of phytic acid. This may be due, in part at least, to enhancement of activity of phytase in the mucosal cells, with consequent increased destruction of phytic acid.

Blood Calcium and Phosphate

The inorganic phosphate of blood plasma ranges from 3 to 4.5 mg./100 ml. (expressed as phosphorus) (1.7 to 2.5 mEq./liter) in adults and from 4.5 to 6.5 mg. (2.5 to 3.6 mEq./liter) in children. It is somewhat higher in summer than in winter (solar ultraviolet irradiation). It decreases during periods of increased carbohydrate utilization (administration of glucose or insulin), owing presumably to increased utilization for phosphorylation of carbohydrate metabolites (hexose- and triose-phosphates). A slight increase follows ingestion of large amounts of calcium and a considerable drop follows parenteral administration of magnesium.

There is no calcium in erythrocytes. The calcium content of plasma (usually determined in serum) is 8.5 to 11.5 mg./100 ml. (usually 9 to 11 mg., or 4.5 to 5.5 mEq./liter). During infancy and early childhood (to 12 years) the average values approach the upper limit of this range, falling with advancing years.

Calcium exists in the plasma in physiologically different fractions, designated (1) diffusible, mainly ionized, but in part bound as a non-ionized complex (e.g., citrate), and (2) non-diffusible or non-ionized. The diffusible fraction (50 to 60 per cent of total) is capable of passing through an artificial semipermeable membrane (cellophane, collodion) and through the living capillary wall; the non-diffusible fraction (40 to 50 per cent of total) cannot pass through, owing to its combination with plasma proteins. Although these fractions may vary independently under certain abnormal circumstances (e.g., hypoproteinemia, in which the non-diffusible calcium alone may be decreased), they seem to be in a state of rather unstable equilibrium. The parathyroid hormone exerts its influence primarily on the diffusible (ionized) fraction, which probably is the only physiologically active portion of the serum calcium.

Maintenance of the plasma Ca^{++} concentration within a narrow range is of vital concern to the well-being of the organism inasmuch as this ion has a profound influence on certain fundamental processes affecting cell function (e.g., membrane permeability, neuromuscular excitability). A few of the factors concerned in the preservation of the normal level of calcium in the plasma deserve special mention.

(*a*) ***Parathyroid hormone.*** Active absorption of calcium from the ileum is stimulated by the parathyroid hormone, adequate amounts of vitamin D being required for this action. In the fasting state (i.e., no absorption from intestine), the plasma calcium concentration is maintained primarily by the mobilization of calcium from the bones through the action of the parathyroid hormone. The metabolic actions and regulation of secretion of this hormone are considered in detail elsewhere (pp. 730, 733). It is one of the most important factors in the regulation of the concentration of calcium ions in the body fluids. Its effect in lowering the serum phosphate concentration is probably due to a direct action on the renal tubular epithelium, decreasing reabsorption of phosphate.

(*b*) ***Vitamin D.*** As indicated elsewhere (p. 163), the action of vitamin D in maintaining the normal plasma calcium concentration depends chiefly on its effect in enhancing absorption of calcium from the intestine. It also is involved in the mobilization of calcium from the bones. In the presence of vitamin D deficiency, the plasma phosphate usually falls sooner than the calcium concentration. This is in part the result of stimulation of parathyroid activity, which tends to maintain the plasma calcium concentration and, simultaneously, to lower the plasma phosphate (p. 731). In addition, intestinal absorption of phosphate diminishes as calcium accumulates within the lumen.

(*c*) ***Plasma proteins.*** Calcium exists in the plasma in higher concentration than would be possible in the absence of protein. As indicated above, about half of the plasma calcium (non-diffusible fraction) is bound to plasma proteins, principally albumin, decrease in which may be accompanied by a decrease in the serum calcium concentration (Fig. 23–1). The calcium-binding potentialities of the plasma proteins may not be "satu-

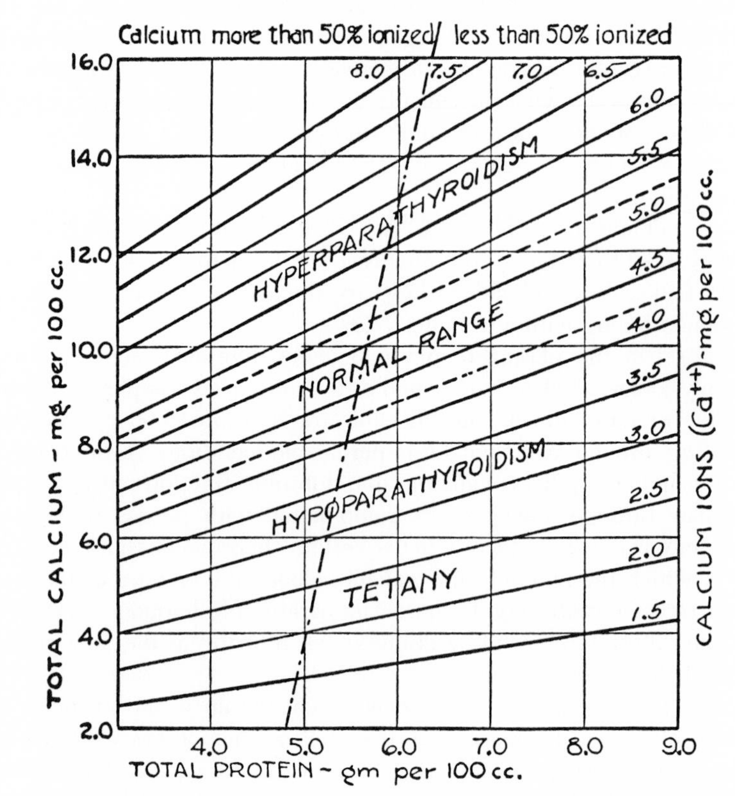

Figure 23–1. Chart for calculation of [Ca^{++}] from total protein and total calcium of serum or plasma. (From McLean, F. C., and Hastings, A. B.: Am. J. Med. Sc. *189*:601, 1935.)

rated" under normal conditions, so that frequently no significant fall in serum calcium occurs at slight or moderate levels of hypoproteinemia. Such variations, since they are confined to the non-diffusible calcium fraction, are not accompanied by manifestations of altered calcium metabolism or neuromuscular excitability (e.g., tetany), and hypocalcemia of this type (i.e., due to hypoproteinemia) does not cause stimulation of parathyroid function (p. 733).

(*d*) ***Plasma phosphate.*** There is a roughly reciprocal relationship between the concentrations of Ca^{++} and $HPO_4^{=}$ ions in solutions in vitro. In the body fluids this relationship is exhibited to a limited extent and usually only in one direction; i.e., rather marked increase in serum $HPO_4^{=}$ may cause a fall in serum Ca^{++} concentration, the mechanism being unknown. This occurs clinically in advanced renal insufficiency with high serum phosphate concentrations. Tetany may occur under these circumstances.

Deposition and Mobilization of Bone Minerals

Bone formation involves two distinct fundamental processes: (1) construction of an organic matrix and (2) deposition of bone salts in this matrix. In areas of developing bone, reticular cells of the invading marrow turn into osteoblasts, which appear to be responsible for laying down the intercellular organic matrix (osteoid). This has two main components: (a) the protein, collagen, arranged in bundles of long parallel fibers; (b) the so-called ground substance, consisting mainly of mucoprotein and mucopolysaccharide, resembling chondroitin sulfate, but not yet definitely characterized. The collagen fibers are embedded in this mucopolysaccharide ground substance, which may be regarded as a sort of cementing material. Moreover, the mucopolysaccharide component is necessary for the preservation of the normal structure and orientation of the collagen fibers.

Other constituents of preosseous cartilage of probable physiological significance include alkaline phosphatase, present in high concentration in osteoblasts, and components of the glycolytic cycle, particularly glycogen, phosphorylase, ATP, and lactic acid. The cell types are apparently interconvertible, osteoblasts turning into osteocytes, the mature bone cells. When bone undergoes degradation, the osteocytes and osteoblasts form osteoclasts, which are actively involved in the breakdown of bone; these can in turn be transformed to osteoblasts or reticular cells.

The formation of the osteoid matrix is influenced by certain vitamins and hormones. Ascorbic acid is essential for normal function of fibroblasts and osteoblasts, and, therefore, for the normal formation of collagen fibers and mucopolysaccharides of the ground substance (p. 777). Adequate amounts of vitamin A are also necessary for normal bone development (p. 150). Growth hormone (somatotropin) has a specific stimulating influence on the growth of bone (p. 745), and thyroid hormone hastens maturation of the skeleton, i.e., appearance and differentiation of epiphyseal ossification centers and their fusion to the diaphysis. There is evidence that the adrenal glucocorticoids interfere with synthesis of chondroitin sulfate and, consequently, with formation of the bone matrix. Over and above these presumably specific effects, these hormones influence the formation of osteoid tissue by virtue of their effects on protein metabolism in general. Protein anabolism, and therefore osteoid formation, is favored by somatotropin, androgen, and thyroid hormone in physiological amounts, whereas protein catabolism, and therefore inhibition of osteoid formation, is favored by adrenal glucocorticoids and excessive amounts of thyroid hormone. The important action of the parathyroid hormone in stimulating resorption of bone is considered elsewhere (p. 730). The influence of estrogens on the development and metabolism of bone varies widely in different species (p. 695). Their role in this connection in man is suggested by the common occurrence of a form of osteoporosis (defective matrix formation) following the menopause.

Mineralization of Bone

Two sets of factors are required for normal mineralization of bone: (1) a calcifiable matrix, constituting the local mechanism; (2) adequate concentrations of calcium and phosphate ions in the extracellular fluid, constituting the humoral mechanism. The humoral mechanism involves factors concerned with the regulation of the concentrations of calcium and phosphate ions in the blood plasma, concerning which there is considerable information. However, little is known of the essential nature of the local mechanism, i.e., what makes a properly prepared bone matrix calcifiable, whereas other tissues rich in collagen, ground substance, and phosphatase do not possess this property.

The basic structure of the bone salt is that of a hydroxyapatite ($[Ca_3(PO_4)_2]_3 \cdot Ca(OH)_2$). The fundamental problem concerns the manner in which the local factors initiate the precipitation of crystals of this compound out of the calcium and HPO_4 ions provided from the blood plasma.

Key roles in this connection have been attributed to various substances, but none of the hypotheses proposed has as yet been substantiated. The view that alkaline phosphatase serves to increase the concentration of phosphate ions by hydrolyzing some phosphoric acid ester is apparently untenable; current opinion favors its participation in the construction of the calcifiable protein matrix. The possibility has been suggested that glycolysis may be involved in bone mineralization. Preosseous cartilage contains glycogen, phosphorylase, ATP, and lactic acid, important components of the glycolytic cycle. Cartilage cells preparatory to mineralization accumulate large amounts of glycogen, which disappears abruptly just before or during the course of deposition of bone salts. Whether glycolysis provides a source of phosphoric ester substrate for phosphatase, or whether its main purpose is the provision of energy for some phase of the mechanism of bone formation is not clear. There are indications that the protein, collagen, serving as a template, and the ground substance mucopolysaccharide, with its polyelectrolyte characteristics in its highly polymerized state, are involved in this local mechanism.

The current concept is that the blood plasma is supersaturated (Ca and HPO_4 ions) with respect to hydroxyapatite; consequently, once crystal formation has been initiated, crystal growth continues spontaneously to completion as in crystallization in aqueous solutions.

The unit of bone mineral may be visualized as a crystal complex, comprising the crystal itself surrounded by a hydration shell within which are ions bound to the surfaces of the crystal and other ions in solution. Various ions can penetrate this crystal complex to different depths. Sr, Ra, Pb, Ca, F, HPO_4, and OH ions can reach the crystal lattice itself, exchanging with Ca, HPO_4, and OH ions already present; Pb, U, Mg, and Na may replace Ca adsorbed on the surface of the crystal, and HPO_4 in this situation may be replaced by CO_3 or citrate; other ions, including K and Cl, are present in solution in the hydration shell. The ground substance in which these mineral units are imbedded being a direct extension of the extracellular fluid, the crystal complex is in direct contact with this medium and its ionic constitution will be influenced by that of the blood plasma.

The rate of interchange of ions between the bone and the extracellular fluid decreases from the outermost layer of the hydration shell to the interior of the crystal lattice. Exchanges occur more readily in newly formed trabecular bone than in older compact bone. From a functional standpoint, it is convenient to regard the skeletal calcium as existing in two forms: (1) a stable component, the calcium of the crystal lattice, not readily exchangeable with the calcium of the extracellular fluids, and perhaps requiring degradation of bone substance for its mobilization; (2) a more labile component, calcium adsorbed on the surface of the crystal, and in more or less immediate equilibrium with that in the extracellular fluids. The functional significance of this labile deposit of calcium, as of other ions adsorbed on the surface of the crystals and in solution in the hydration shell, is indicated by the fact that the fundamental crystal lattice is of such dimensions that its surface area of contact with the extracellular fluid is very large, approximately 100 sq.m./gm. of bone. The readily availability of this reservoir of inorganic ions other than calcium is illustrated by the observation that, in experimental acute sodium depletion, 25 per cent of the sodium lost from the body comes from the skeleton.

In common with other tissues, bone undergoes continual metabolic turnover, its various components undergoing degradation, mobilization, and replacement. This applies to both organic and mineral constituents. This turnover is more active in newly formed, incompletely mineralized osteones, the older compact bone being metabolically quite stable. Normal degradation processes are apparently related to osteoclastic activity, presumably influenced by the parathyroid hormone and vitamin A (p. 150). The mechanisms involved in the dissolution of bone and the mobilization of calcium are not known, but citric acid may play an important role in this connection.

Interrelations of citrate and calcium metabolism. Skeletal citrate comprises a large portion of the total body citrate (about 70 per cent in the mouse). Its intimate relation to the metabolism of calcium may be indicated as follows:

(1) Citrate forms a soluble, poorly ionized complex with calcium, and therefore can effectively remove calcium ions from solution (basis of anticoagulant and tetanic effects).

(2) Local increases in citrate concentration resulting from cellular activity might conceivably be a factor in promoting dissolution of bone salt, even at comparatively high pH levels.

(3) In general, changes in plasma citrate are paralleled by changes in calcium, e.g., after nephrectomy, parathyroid hormone or vitamin D administration, and after injection of calcium chloride or neutral citrate.

Regulation of Serum Calcium Concentration

The concentration of calcium in the blood plasma and other extracellular fluids is maintained within quite narrow limits, even in the face of extensive loss of this element, so long as the regulatory mechanisms and the skeletal stores remain adequate. That some regulatory factor or factors other than the parathyroid hormone must be involved is indicated by the following observations: (1) in the absence of the parathyroid glands the serum calcium concentration is maintained rather constantly at about 3 to 3.5 mEq./liter; (2) sudden removal of calcium ions from the bloodstream is followed rather promptly by restoration of the serum calcium concentration to the original level in both intact and parathyroidectomized animals; (3) these rapid, almost immediate, and automatic adjustments in response to changes in extracellular fluid calcium concentration cannot be attributed to the relatively slowly acting parathyroid hormone.

A dual mechanism has been postulated: one, which acts rapidly and independently of the parathyroid hormone, is concerned with transfer or exchange of ions between the extracellular fluid and the more labile fractions of the skeletal calcium (p. 636), perhaps representing merely a physicochemical equilibrium between these two media. Another, which is mediated by the parathyroid hormone, regulates the rate of degradation and mobilization of the organic and stable mineral components of bone, liberating calcium and other ions from the hydroxyapatite crystal lattice and also the more labile deposits on the crystal surface and in the hydration shell. Increased production of citric acid may be an essential feature of this mechanism.

Parathyroid secretory activity is regulated by the concentration of calcium ions in the blood plasma, being stimulated by a decrease in the latter and depressed by an increase. Any tendency for the serum calcium concentration to fall is therefore counteracted automatically by mobilization of calcium (a) from the labile deposits in the bones, perhaps by a simple transfer of ions, and (b) from the hydroxyapatite crystal lattice through the medium of increased secretion of parathyroid hormone, other inorganic and organic constituents being mobilized simultaneously as a result of increased degradation of the bone. There is evidence that a rapidly acting, serum calcium-lowering factor, polypeptide in nature ("thyrocalcitonin"), is produced in the thyroid gland in response to rise in the serum calcium concentration. Its effect is produced presumably by inhibiting release of calcium from skeletal deposits. This agent, with the parathyroid hormone (hypercalcemic factor), would constitute a very efficient mechanism for regulation of the serum calcium concentration.

Excretion

Normal adults on an adequate calcium intake are in a state of calcium equilibrium. Calcium is excreted in the urine, bile, and digestive secretions. Much of that in the feces is food calcium which has escaped absorption. This represents a variable but considerable fraction of the intake, since even under optimal conditions dietary calcium (e.g., in milk) is not more than 50 per cent absorbed. The remainder of the fecal calcium is unabsorbed calcium of the digestive fluids. Conditions which interfere with absorption of calcium from the intestine will increase the amount excreted in the feces (p. 632).

The "renal threshold" for calcium excretion lies between 6.5 and 8.0 mg. per 100 ml. plasma, little being eliminated at lower serum calcium concentrations. Under normal conditions, and despite wide variations in calcium intake, the amount excreted in the urine remains rather constant at about 100 to 150 mg./day. Since approximately 9 gm. of calcium leave the blood plasma daily in the glomerular filtrate, about 99 per cent is normally reabsorbed in the tubules. Even in states of marked hypercalcemia, only a relatively small fraction of the increment in the glomerular filtrate escapes in the urine. Moreover, following intravenous injection of as much as 1 gm. of calcium within a few hours, the serum calcium concentration returns rapidly to normal, although only 30 to 50 per cent of the injected calcium appears in the urine within the next 24 hours. The kidneys therefore do not play an important role in the mechanism of regulation of the serum calcium concentration. This apparent relative indifference of the kidney to the level of calcium in the blood plasma (above the threshold concentration) is illustrated also by certain abnormal situations. An increase in urinary calcium occurs in thyrotoxicosis, acidosis, or skeletal immobilization, without demonstrable increase in the serum calcium concentration. In vitamin D deficiency, urinary excretion of calcium decreases even though the serum calcium concentration may be normal; administration of vitamin D is followed promptly by an increase in urine calcium, with little or no significant change in the serum calcium concentration. The mechanism of action of vitamin D in influencing renal excretion of calcium is not known.

One of the initial actions of the parathyroid hormone is to increase renal tubular reabsorption of calcium and, therefore, to decrease its urinary excretion. If the dosage of the hormone is such as to produce hypercalcemia, this initial effect is subsequently masked by the hypercalciuria incident to the increased glomerular filtration of calcium due to hypercalcemia.

Inorganic phosphate is excreted in the urine and feces, the relative proportions varying under different conditions, e.g., those which influence absorption from the intestine (p. 632). The source of urinary inorganic phosphate is chiefly that of the blood plasma, although it may be contributed to by hydrolysis of phosphoric acid esters by phosphatase activity in the kidneys. On a balanced diet, urine phosphate constitutes about 60 per cent of the total excretion. As the calcium intake is decreased, the proportion of phosphate eliminated in the urine increases (increased intestinal absorption), being about 75 per cent on a low calcium, moderately high phosphate intake. The "renal threshold" for phosphate excretion is about 2 mg./100 ml. of plasma, excretion falling to very low levels at lower concentrations. Reabsorption of phosphate from the glomerular filtrate by the renal tubular epithelium is apparently inhibited by the parathyroid hormone. Administration of this agent (or clinical hyperparathyroidism) causes increased urinary excretion of phosphate. Although vitamin D may have a similar effect under certain experimental conditions (e.g., parathyroidectomized animals), it seems to have an opposite effect (i.e., increases tubular reabsorption of phosphate) in the normal subject. Negative calcium balance may occur in subjects with hyperthyroidism or hyperfunction of the adrenal cortex. This may be due to the protein catabolic action of excessive amounts of thyroid hormone and the adrenal 11-oxysteroids, affecting primarily the osteoid matrix and secondarily, therefore, skeletal mineralization.

Decreased alkalinity of the body fluids (acidosis), due to any cause, may result in increased urinary excretion of calcium. The excess is presumably removed from the bones because of the increased solubility of the labile calcium deposits in a more acid medium.

Defective skeletal growth (in children) and undermineralization of the skeleton occur in the presence of disturbances of fat absorption (steatorrhea) from the intestine (sprue, celiac disease). There may be hypocalcemia and hypophosphatemia. These abnormalities are probably due in large measure to inadequate absorption of vitamin D under these conditions. The increased amounts of fatty acid in the intestine in these disorders, by binding Ca^{++} in the form of insoluble soaps, together with the incident diarrhea, may also contribute to the decreased absorption of calcium (increased excretion in feces).

Similar skeletal disorders also occur in the presence of hypophosphatemia resulting from defective reabsorption of phosphate by the renal tubular epithelium, with consequent increased urinary excretion (Fanconi syndrome).

Tetany (increased neuromuscular excitability) occurs whenever the concentration of Ca^{++} ions in the plasma and tissue fluids falls to sufficiently low levels, regardless of the cause of the hypocalcemia. It also occurs as a characteristic manifestation of alkalosis (p. 324), without hypocalcemia, owing perhaps to decreased ionization of the plasma calcium at decreased H^+ ion concentrations. Vitamin D deficiency is discussed elsewhere (p. 164).

Calcium and Phosphorus Requirement

The adult daily requirement for phosphorus is 1 to 1.5 gm., or about 1.5 times the calcium intake. Diets adequate in other respects provide an adequate amount of phosphorus because of its wide distribution in common foods (phosphoproteins and phospholipids, inorganic phosphate), especially milk and milk products, wheat, meats, and fish.

The minimal daily adult requirement for calcium is 0.45 gm., but the recommended allowance is 0.8 gm. (10 to 13 mg./kg. body weight), increasing to 1.5 gm. or more during pregnancy and lactation. Growing children require about 45 mg./kg. body weight. Even under optimal conditions, not more than 35 to 50 per cent of dietary calcium is absorbed. Milk (1.0 gm. per quart) and dairy products constitute the most important dietary source of this element, cereals, meats and most vegetables being low in calcium. Even those which contain relatively large amounts (viz., certain vegetable greens, and shellfish) are usually not eaten in sufficient quantities to be of practical value in this regard. The calcium requirement may be supplied satisfactorily in the form of inorganic or organic salts (e.g., phosphate, lactate, chloride, gluconate).

IRON METABOLISM

Although the amount of iron in the body is small (about 45 mg./kg. body weight), the fact that it is an essential constituent of hemoglobin and of cytochrome and other components of respiratory enzyme systems (cytochrome oxidase, catalase, peroxidase) makes it an element of great fundamental importance. Its chief functions lie in the transport of oxygen to the tissues (hemoglobin) and in cellular oxidation mechanisms (cytochrome system).

Absorption and Excretion

Iron differs from other electrolytes in that the quantity in the body is controlled by regulation not of its excretion, but rather of its absorption into the organism. The body stores of iron are conserved very efficiently, only minute amounts being excreted in the urine and feces, usually less than 1 mg. daily. Relatively large amounts are, of course, lost in the menstrual flow. That present in the body in various substances, e.g., hemoglobin, is almost completely reutilized following its liberation in the course of metabolic degradation of these substances. The bulk of the iron of the feces is unabsorbed food iron; a very small amount enters the intestine in the bile and escapes in the feces.

Several factors make absorption of iron difficult, regardless of the form in which it is ingested: (1) the relatively high pH in the jejunum favors the formation of insoluble iron compounds; (2) iron salts of bile acids are relatively insoluble; (3) the presence of relatively large amounts of phosphate favors the formation of insoluble iron phosphates; (4) absorption of iron is interfered with, therefore, in the absence of free HCl in the stomach (achlorhydria) and by administration of alkalies.

Absorption occurs chiefly in the upper duodenum, but to a lesser extent, in the stomach and throughout the small intestine. In general, ferrous iron is better absorbed than ferric, and the iron of inorganic salts is better absorbed than that of foodstuffs. The mechanism of regulation of absorption of iron has not been established with certainty. The "mucosal block" theory has been the one most widely accepted. This postulates that acceptance or rejection of iron by the gastrointestinal mucosa is regulated by the amount of ferritin in the mucosal epithelial cells. This is an Fe^{+++}-protein complex (23 per cent iron), containing aggregates of ferric hydroxide and a protein, apoferritin (m.w. 450,000). Apoferritin has vasodepressor and antidiuretic properties, the latter being mediated by the neurohypophysis. Ferritin occurs also in other parenchymal cells, e.g., the liver and spleen, and in the bone marrow and reticuloendothelial calls generally. It is believed to be the chief physiological storage form of iron.

According to this theory, only the Fe^{++} ion is transferred across cell membranes.

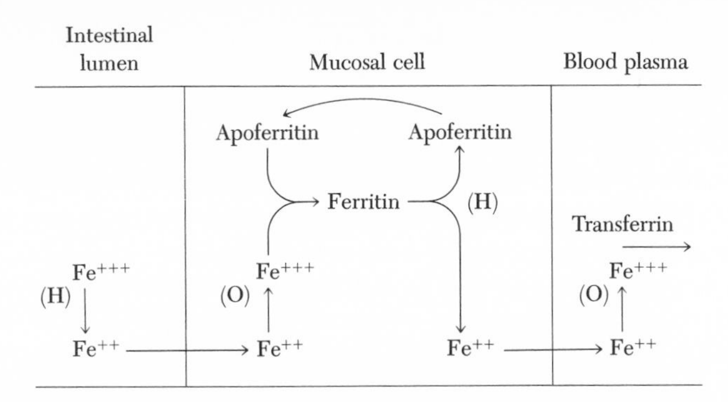

Figure 23-2. Mechanism of absorption, transport, and mobilization of iron. (After Charley, P. J., Stitt, C., Shore, E., and Saltman, P.: J. Lab. Clin. Med. *61*:397, 1963.)

Fe^{++}, on entering the mucosal epithelial cell, is oxidized to Fe^{+++}, which combines with the protein, apoferritin, synthesized in the cell, forming ferritin (Fig. 23-2). Apoferritin is present in very small amounts and is apparently unstable, breaking down quickly unless iron is present to convert it to ferritin, which is more stable. The equilibrium between these intracellular forms of iron is potentially reversible. Entrance of iron into the cell ceases when its capacity for storing ferritin is exhausted. According to this view, therefore, absorption of iron from the gastrointestinal tract is regulated by the amount of ferritin in the mucosal cells.

In recent years there has been increasing doubt of the validity of the "mucosal block" hypothesis. However, no satisfactory alternative mechanism has been proposed. It has been suggested that iron crosses cell walls not as Fe^{++} ion, but as a soluble chelate. It is postulated that both Fe^{++} and Fe^{+++} in the intestinal lumen combine with chelating substances in the diet or intestinal secretions and that these complexes enter the cell and interact with other intracellular chelating agents, the resulting complexes passing into the bloodstream.

Transport

Whatever the form may be in which iron enters the blood, it is transported in the plasma as Fe^{+++} firmly bound to a specific β_1-globulin. This compound, transferrin (siderophilin), is present in a concentration of about 0.25 gm./100 ml. plasma. Each molecule can combine with two atoms of iron. The iron content of plasma is 50 to 180 μg./100 ml.; this is the transport iron (ferric). Under normal conditions this represents only about one-third of the iron-binding capacity of the plasma transferrin.

The iron content of whole blood is normally 40 to 60 mg./100 ml., averaging 45 in women and 52 in men. Practically all of this is in organic form, as hemoglobin, which contains about 0.335 per cent iron (ferrous) (p. 123), all of which is in the red blood cells.

Utilization and Storage

In the tissues, as needed, the plasma iron is apparently released from transferrin and enters the cells, where it may be utilized or stored (as ferritin and hemosiderin). Although the plasma contains only a small amount of iron, the turnover rate is rapid, averaging about 0.56 mg./kg. body weight per day, or, in a 70-kg. man, about 40 mg./day. The liver, spleen, and intestinal mucosa are the chief storage sites, but other organs (e.g., pancreas, adrenals) and all reticuloendothelial cells contain ferritin. When iron enters the body in abnormally large amounts, the excess is deposited mainly as hemosiderin, a compound similar to ferritin, but containing more iron (up to 35 per cent).

Iron is utilized chiefly in synthesis of hemoglobin, myoglobin (muscle hemoglobin), and certain respiratory enzymes (cytochromes, peroxidase, catalase). The latter are probably formed in all cells, myoglobin in muscle cells, and hemoglobin in the developing red blood cells (normoblasts, reticulocytes) in the erythropoietic tissues, principally the bone marrow in man. The approximate distribution of iron in the body is as follows (Fig. 23–3): (1) circulating hemoglobin, 70 per cent; (2) myoglobin, 5 per cent; (3) storage iron, 20 per cent, mainly in the liver; (4) functional tissue iron (respiratory enzymes), 5 per cent. Thus, about 75 per cent of the body iron is in the form of hemoglobin, 20 per cent is in storage form, available for utilization, and 5 per cent is functional tissue iron, not readily available for other purposes. The iron of erythrocyte hemoglobin is readily available, but not that of myoglobin.

The quantity of iron liberated within the organism daily far exceeds the exogenous supply. About 0.8 per cent of the circulating erythrocytes undergo disintegration daily (life 225 days), liberating about 7 to 8 gm. of Hb (0.34 per cent iron). In the course of its degradation, this gives rise to about 20 to 25 mg. of iron, the bulk of which is immediately utilized in the resynthesis of hemoglobin (p. 611). Some, however, may enter the blood plasma for transport to other tissues. Synthesis of hemoglobin, and consequently utilization of iron for this purpose, requires among other things adequate amounts of folic acid and vitamin B_{12} (pp. 201–204).

Inasmuch as there is no efficient excretory mechanism for iron, when amounts exceeding the capacity for its utilization and normal storage are released in or introduced into the body, the excess is deposited in various tissues, mainly in the liver (siderosis). This may occur in conditions of excessive hemolysis, excessive parenteral iron therapy, or repeated blood transfusions. One form of siderosis in the South African Bantu is due to high intake of iron-rich foods and use of iron cooking pots. In idiopathic hemochromatosis, relatively enormous amounts of iron (hemosiderin) accumulate in the liver, pancreas, lymph nodes, and other tissues. Its deposition in the skin frequently produces a rather characteristic bronze-slate pigmentation, and its accumulation within cells of the liver and pancreas is followed by degeneration and replacement fibrosis, producing hepatic cirrhosis and diabetes mellitus.

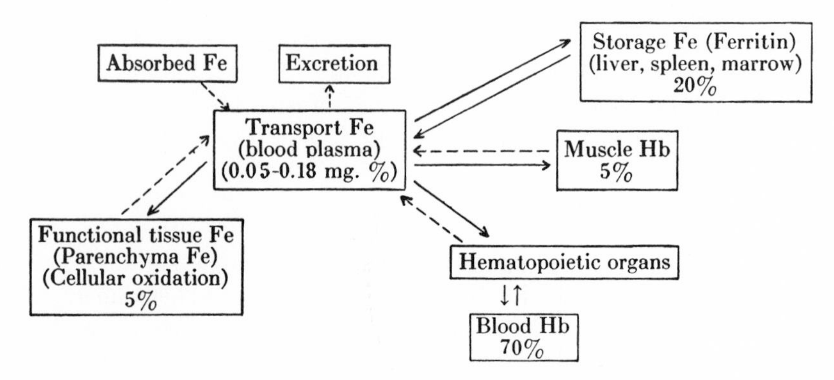

Figure 23–3. Approximate distribution of iron in the body.

Excretion

The efficiency of utilization of endogenous iron is such that only small quantities are lost under normal conditions, averaging about 0.5 to 1.5 mg./day in men and approximately double this amount in women (menstrual loss). Small amounts are lost in the sweat (<0.5 or 1.0 mg.), minute quantities in the hair, and the remainder largely in the feces (0.3 to 0.75 mg.). The latter (fecal) is contributed to by (1) true excretion, (2) desquamated mucosal cells, and (3) incompletely reabsorbed biliary iron.

Requirement

Since only minute amounts of iron are excreted, the exogenous requirement should be correspondingly low. However, it is recommended that adults take 5 to 15 mg. daily to meet ordinary and unanticipated requirements; perhaps 15 to 20 mg. is more satisfactory for women (menstruation, pregnancy, lactation). Young children (4 to 8 years) require about 0.6 mg./kg. body weight and infants (to 1 year) 1 to 2 mg./kg.

TRACE ELEMENTS

This term is applied to elements which occur in body tissues and fluids in minute amounts. Essential physiological functions have been established for certain of these, viz., copper, cobalt, zinc, iodine (p. 630), manganese, and molybdenum. Others may be accidental contaminants, although there is suggestive evidence of the possible biological importance of fluorine, barium, strontium, and arsenic. In view of the fact that their essential activities are exerted by mere traces of these elements, it would appear that their functions are catalytic in nature, i.e., that they act as direct activators of certain enzymes, or, indirectly, as essential components of vitamins or hormones.

Copper

Absorption, Excretion, Metabolism

Only small amounts of copper are absorbed, apparently only from the upper small intestine. Under normal conditions, 85 to 99 per cent of the quantity ingested is excreted in the feces, partly via the bile, 0 to 15 per cent escaping in the urine (0 to 0.05 mg./day). The concentration in milk, except in colostrum, is lower than in blood plasma. The amount retained in the body apparently depends mainly on the copper status of the tissues, being influenced relatively slightly by the intake.

In the blood, copper is distributed approximately equally betwen erythrocytes and plasma, except in late pregnancy, when the concentration rises in the plasma (increased ceruloplasmin). It is present in the erythrocytes in the form of erythrocuprein. About 96 per cent of the plasma copper is firmly bound to an α_2-globulin (8 copper atoms per molecule) as ceruloplasmin (20 to 35 mg./100 ml.), an oxidative enzyme, the main transport form; a variable but smaller amount is less firmly bound to albumin; a very small quantity is dialyzable. The normal concentration of copper in the plasma is 85 to 110 (average 100) μg./100 ml. in adults, and 45 to 100 (average 75) μg./100 ml. in the newborn. It increases during pregnancy, from the third month on, being approximately doubled at term, owing mainly to an increase in ceruloplasmin.

Copper is distributed widely throughout the tissues, in highest concentrations in the liver (hepatocuprein), kidneys, heart, bone marrow, brain, and hair. The amount in the tissues decreases with inadequate intake; the liver is apparently the main storage site, its copper content reflecting the state of copper nutrition under most circumstances.

Function, Deficiency Manifestations

Copper is an essential component of the respiratory pigments (hemocyanins) of certain marine "blue-blooded" species, i.e., gastropods and arthropods, and of phenol oxidases in plants, the only representative of this category of importance in mammals being tyrosinase (p. 354). It is present also in cytochrome oxidase.

All available evidence points to a role in hemopoiesis as the main function of copper, the exact nature of which is unknown. Copper deficiency results in a microcytic anemia, similar to that resulting from iron deficiency, which, however, cannot be corrected by administration of iron. There is impairment of erythropoiesis and decrease in erythrocyte survival time. Associated reductions in tissue catalase and cytochrome *c* and in cytochrome oxidase activity suggest that copper is involved in the metabolism of iron, acting perhaps as a catalyst for its incorporation into these substances, and also into hemoglobin.

In certain species, in addition to anemia, copper deficiency is accompanied by impaired growth, coarsening and depigmentation of hair, decreased reproductive capacity and milk production, and, e.g., in sheep, symmetrical demyelination in the cerebral hemispheres and motor tracts of the cord, producing a characteristic incoordination of gait.

In man, a condition of hepatolenticular degeneration (Wilson's disease) is characterized by abnormally large accumulations of copper in the brain and liver, increase in urine copper, decrease in plasma copper and ceruloplasmin, and positive copper balance. There is also increased urinary excretion of amino acids and dicarboxylic amino acid peptides, due to decreased renal tubular reabsorption, apparently secondary to local deposition of excessive amounts of copper. The fundamental defect is impaired capacity for synthesis of ceruloplasmin, a hereditary condition transmitted by a single autosomal recessive gene. A similar deficiency with respect to tyrosinase results in albinism.

Requirement

The average daily diet, adequate in other respects, contains about 1.5 to 4 mg. of copper. The minimum daily requirement for man is not known, but has been estimated to be 0.6 to 2 mg. It has been found that, in infants, administration of 1 to 2 mg./day is distinctly superior to administration of iron alone in maintaining normal hemoglobin levels.

Zinc

Zinc is poorly absorbed from the intestine, virtually all zinc in food being excreted in the feces, and only small amounts in the urine (0.2 to 1.0 mg./day). The amount excreted in the urine is not influenced significantly by the intake or by the concentration in the blood plasma, suggesting that the zinc contained in the urine is derived from metabolic processes in the kidney. Traces are present in bile, and somewhat more in pancreatic juice and milk.

Zinc is distributed widely in plant and animal tissues, and is essential to growth and health. In man, it occurs in the prostate, hair, bones, liver, kidneys, muscles, pancreas, gastrointestinal tract, spleen, and blood, in order of decreasing concentrations. Like lead, it tends to accumulate in bone. The zinc in the pancreas exhibits very active metabolic turnover, a large proportion being excreted in the pancreatic juice.

The average concentration in the blood is 900 μg./100 ml., about 75 per cent of which is in the erythrocytes (mainly in carbonic anhydrase), 3 per cent in the leukocytes, and 22 per cent in the plasma, bound mainly to albumin (loosely) and an α-globulin (firmly).

Zinc is present in certain purified enzyme preparations, viz., carbonic anhydrase, liver alcohol dehydrogenase, glutamate dehydrogenase, uricase, and kidney phosphatase. In erythrocytes, its concentration parallels carbonic anhydrase activity. Zinc is apparently also a component, probably not an essential one, of insulin, as ordinarily prepared. In the pancreas of diabetics, however, the zinc content is not significantly low, despite the decreased insulin content of this organ.

Deficiency manifestations have been reported in the rat, but none is recognized in man, whose requirement for this element is not known. Because of the wide distribution of zinc in nature, all ordinary diets undoubtedly provide adequate amounts.

COBALT

Cobalt is readily absorbed from the intestine (70 to 80 per cent), about 65 per cent of the amount ingested being excreted in the urine, the remainder in the feces. Only minute amounts are present in tissues, the largest in the liver (storage site). Its nutritional importance in man apparently arises mainly out of the fact that it is a component of vitamin B_{12} (4.5 per cent cobalt), which is discussed elsewhere (p. 199).

In ruminants, but not other species, cobalt deficiency results in anorexia, wasting, a profound macrocytic anemia, fatty liver, and hemosiderosis of the spleen. In certain species, a moderately excessive intake of cobalt results in polycythemia. This may be a pharmacological effect, due to the action of cobalt in inhibiting certain respiratory enzymes, e.g., cytochrome oxidase, succinate dehydrogenase.

As indicated above, the only established function of cobalt is in hemopoiesis, by virtue of its presence in the vitamin B_{12} molecule, which, an essential substance for animals, originates apparently only in microorganisms. Cobalt is firmly bound in the B_{12} molecule, and in this form undergoes no significant interchange with inorganic cobalt.

If cobalt is required in man only for vitamin B_{12} formation (by intestinal bacteria), its requirement is much lower than for any other trace mineral. As little as 1 to 2 μg. of B_{12} daily, containing 0.045 to 0.09 μg. cobalt, suffices to maintain normal bone marrow function in pernicious anemia. An average American diet supplies many times this amount. In contrast, the requirement for ruminants is relatively high (0.1 mg./day for sheep); these are the only species in which cobalt deficiency has been demonstrated.

MANGANESE

Manganese is poorly absorbed and retained. It is excreted largely in the feces, less than 0.1 mg./24 hours being eliminated in the urine on intakes of 8 to 9 mg. It occurs in the tissues in very small amounts, the highest concentrations being in the liver, muscles, and bones. Blood contains 12 to 18 μg./100 ml., about two-thirds of which is in the cells.

It is an activator of liver arginase and several other enzymes, e.g., mitochondrial respiratory enzyme systems and cholinesterase.

Manganese deficiency in certain species results in defects in bone. Rats exhibit defective ovulation, testicular degeneration, and nervous system manifestations (also chick). No deficiency manifestations are recognized in man. The usual American diets provide about 6 to 8 mg. manganese per day.

Molybdenum

Molybdenum is absorbed in the intestine and is excreted mainly in the urine and to a lesser extent in the feces, perhaps via the bile. There is little tissue retention of this element except in the bones, and, in smaller amounts, in the liver and kidneys.

Interest in molybdenum has centered mainly in the demonstration of its function as an essential component of certain metalloflavoproteins, viz., xanthine oxidase, aldehyde oxidase, nitrate reductase, and hydrogenase.

In certain species (sheep, cattle, rat), ingestion of excessive amounts of molybdenum results in a disease known as "teart," characterized by persistent scouring, and decreased copper retention, with anemia and skeletal and muscle lesions. In sheep, this effect of molybdenum on copper is exerted only in the presence of inorganic sulfate.

No manifestations of molybdenum deficiency are recognized in man, and the human requirement is not known.

Fluorine

Fluorine occurs in many tissues, notably the bones, teeth, thyroid, and skin, but there is no evidence that it is a nutritional essential for general health. Interest in this element arises chiefly out of its efficacy in preventing dental caries.

It is readily absorbed from the intestine, about 75 per cent being excreted in the urine, the remainder mainly in the sweat. Intake of abnormally large amounts (in drinking water) during childhood results in "dental fluorosis" ("mottled enamel"), characterized by a patchy, chalky, or brownish mottling of the enamel, frequently with pitting of the surface and fracture and chipping of the enamel, which is abnormally fragile. This is a reflection of imperfect formation of the enamel.

Of special practical importance is the observation that ingestion of amounts of fluoride (1.0 to 1.5 parts per million in drinking water) too small to produce mottling renders the teeth more resistant to caries. This has led to widespread fluoridation of water supplies, with encouraging results. Topical application is also apparently somewhat effective. It is believed that fluorine may undergo surface adsorption by the hydroxyapatite crystals of the enamel, forming a protective layer of acid-resistant fluorapatite. The F^- ion may also act by inhibiting the metabolism of oral bacterial enzymes, diminishing local production of acids (from carbohydrates) that are believed by many to be important in the production of dental caries. It is known to inhibit enzymes requiring calcium, magnesium, manganese, zinc, and copper, e.g., enolase, certain esterases, and bone alkaline phosphatase.

Selenium

Formerly, biological interest in selenium was restricted to its toxic properties. Its potentialities as a health hazard stem from the fact that it becomes incorporated in cystine and methionine, replacing sulfur, in plants grown in soil rich in selenium. Recently, attention has been directed toward its possible nutritional significance. A rather characteristic form of liver necrosis occurs in rats fed purified diets deficient in vitamin E, cystine, and a substance referred to as "Factor 3," the active component of which has been identified as selenium. Addition of certain inorganic and organic selenium compounds to these deficient diets affords complete protection, the mechanism of its action being unknown. Selenium in large doses also protects against the exudative diathesis in vitamin E-deficient chicks and muscle dystrophy in E-deficient lambs, but not against other manifestations of vitamin E deficiency in other species, e.g., reproductive failure in rats, muscle dystrophy in rabbits. It has been suggested that selenium is a component of an enzyme essential for an oxidation-reduction reaction involving cystine, and that vitamin E is also involved as an antioxidant.

BIBLIOGRAPHY

Albright, F., and Reifenstein, E. C., Jr.: Parathyroid Glands and Metabolic Bone Disease, Baltimore, Williams & Wilkins Company, 1948 (calcium and phosphorus).

Annual Review of Biochemistry.

Annual Review of Physiology.

Berliner, R. W.: Relationship between acidification of the urine and potassium metabolism, Am. J. Med. *11:*274, 1951.

Bland, J. H. (ed.): Clinical Metabolism of Body Water and Electrolytes, Philadelphia, W. B. Saunders Company, 1963.

Bourne, G. H. (ed.): The Biochemistry and Physiology of Bone, New York, Academic Press, Inc., 1956.

Bourne, G. H., and Kidder, G. W. (eds.): Biochemistry and Physiology of Nutrition, Vol. 2, New York, Academic Press, Inc., 1953.

Brown-Grant, K.: Extrathyroidal iodide concentrating mechanisms, Physiol. Rev. *41:*189, 1961.

Care, A. D.: Secretion of thyrocalcitonin, Nature *205:*1289, 1965.

Charley, P. J., Stitt, C., and Saltman, P.: Studies in the intestinal regulation of intestinal absorption of iron, J. Lab. Clin. Med. *61:*397, 1963.

Christensen, H. N.: Body Fluids and the Acid-Base Balance, Philadelphia, W. B. Saunders Company, 1964.

Comar, C. L., and Bronner, F.: Mineral Metabolism, New York, Academic Press, Inc., 1960 and 1961.

Copp, D. H.: Parathyroids, calcitonin, and control of plasma calcium, Recent Progress in Hormone Research *20:*59, 1964.

Cotzias, G. C.: Manganese in health and disease, Physiol. Rev. *38:*503, 1958.

Darrow, D. C.: Body fluid physiology: The role of potassium in clinical disturbance of body water and electrolytes, New England J. Med. *242:*978, 1014, 1950.

Darrow, D. C., and Hellerstein, S.: Interpretation of certain changes in body water and electrolytes, Physiol. Rev. *38:*114, 1958.

Elkinton, J. R., and Danowski, T. S.: The Body Fluids, Baltimore, Williams & Wilkins Company, 1955.

Fourman, P.: Calcium Metabolism and the Bone, Springfield, Ill., Charles C Thomas, 1960.

Gamble, J. L.: Chemical Anatomy, Physiology and Pathology of Extracellular Fluid, Cambridge, Harvard University Press, 1950.

Gamble, J. L.: Companionship of Water and Electrolytes in the Organization of Body Fluids (Lane Medical Lectures), Stanford, Calif., Stanford University Press, 1951.

Granick, S.: Structure and physiological functions of ferritin, Physiol. Rev. *31:*489, 1951.

Greep, R. O., and Talmage, R. V. (eds.): The Parathyroids, Springfield, Ill., Charles C Thomas, 1961.

Josephs, H. W.: Absorption of iron as a problem in human physiology, Blood *13:*1, 1958.

Josephson, B.: Chemistry and Therapy of Electrolyte Disorders, Springfield, Ill., Charles C Thomas, 1961.

MacIntyre, I.: Magnesium metabolism, The Scientific Basis of Medicine: Annual Reviews, 1963, p. 216.

Macy Foundation Conferences on Metabolic Interrelations, I, II, III, IV, New York, Josiah Macy, Jr., Foundation, 1949 to 1952 (calcium and phosphorus).

McLean, F. C., and Budy, A. M.: Chemistry and physiology of the parathyroid hormone, Vitamins and Hormones *19:*165, 1961.

Moore, C. V.: Iron metabolism and nutrition, The Harvey Lectures *55:*67, 1961.

Neuman, W. F., and Neuman, M. M.: Emerging concepts of the structure and metabolic functions of bone, Am. J. Med. *22:*123, 1957.

Nicolaysen, R.: Physiology of calcium metabolism, Physiol. Rev. *33:*424, 1953.

Pitts, R. F.: Physiology of the Kidney and Body Fluids, Chicago, Year Book Medical Publishers, 1963.

Rasmussen, H.: Parathyroid hormone, nature and mechanism of action, Am. J. Med. *30:*112, 1961.

Rasmussen, H., and Craig, L. C.: The parathyroid polypeptides, Recent Progress in Hormone Research *18:*269, 1962.

Rawson, R. W. (ed.): Modern concepts of thyroid physiology, Ann. New York Acad. Sci. *86:*311, 1960.
Roche, J., and Michel, R.: Nature and metabolism of thyroid hormones, Recent Progress in Hormone Research *12:*1, 1956.
Salter, W. T.: The Endocrine Function of Iodine, Cambridge, Harvard University Press, 1940.
Strauss, M. B.: Body Water in Man, Boston, Little, Brown & Company, 1957.
Tenenhouse, A., Arnaud, C., and Rasmussen, H.: The isolation and characterization of thyrocalcitonin, Proc. Nat. Acad. Sci. *53:*818, 1965.
Underwood, E. J.: Trace Elements in Human and Animal Nutrition, New York, Academic Press, Inc., 1956.
Underwood, E. J.: Mineral metabolism, Ann. Rev. Biochem. *28:*499, 1959.
Vallee, B. L.: Physiology and pathology of zinc, Physiol. Rev. *39:*443, 1959.
Welt, I. D.: Water balance in health and disease, in Duncan, G. G. (ed.): Diseases of Metabolism, ed. 5, Philadelphia, W. B. Saunders Company, 1964, p. 449.

CHAPTER 24

GENERAL BIOCHEMICAL ASPECTS OF DIET

In general terms, an adequate diet is one which permits normal growth, maintenance, and reproduction. More specifically, its minimum requirements for the adult are fulfilled (1) when the organism is in a state of equilibrium with regard to (a) calories, (b) nitrogen, and (c) inorganic elements; (2) when there is an adequate supply and utilization of vitamins and other factors (e.g., trace minerals, essential fatty acids) necessary for maintenance of special functions; (3) when reproduction is normal. In the immature organism, growth and development must proceed normally.

The functions served by the essential components of the diet and the quantities required for optimum nutrition are considered in detail elsewhere in discussing the role of each of these factors in biochemical processes and need not be repeated here. However, certain general aspects of the subject of diet merit independent consideration.

It is necessary to appreciate the difficulties involved in arriving at satisfactory standards of diet that can be applied to large groups of peoples of different dietary habits and economic status. The bulk of present information regarding fundamental aspects of nutrition has emerged from studies in experimental animals. Despite the existence of important species differences in many respects, fortunately it has been found possible to utilize much of this information directly in practical problems of nutrition in man. Nevertheless, there are still large areas of uncertainty in important fields. For example, even in experimental animals, there is no assurance that an adequate diet, as described above, is an optimum diet. There are, in fact, indications that such is not the case. Moreover, because of the integration of various phases of intermediary metabolism and the functional interdependence of several of the factors involved, construction of a satisfactory diet must include consideration of quantitative relationships between certain of these principles or their precursors in the foods. For example, the protein requirement is influenced by the level of carbohydrate in the diet and also by the caloric intake; the requirement for various B vitamins is influenced by the carbohydrate, caloric, or protein intake. These and other difficulties, some recognized and some unknown, make it necessary to provide for a rather wide margin of safety in order to insure satisfactory nutrition. The valuable recommen-

Table 24-1. Recommended Daily Dietary Allowances* Revised 1963*

	AGE[1] YEARS	WEIGHT KG. (LBS.)	HEIGHT CM. (IN.)	CALORIES	PROTEIN GM.	CALCIUM GM.	IRON MG.	VITAMIN A I.U.	THIAMINE MG.	RIBOFLAVIN MG.	NIACIN EQUIV.[2] MG.	ASCORBIC ACID MG.	VITAMIN D I.U.
Men	18–35	70 (154)	175 (69)	2900	70	0.8	10	5000	1.2	1.7	19	70	
	35–55	70 (154)	175 (69)	2600	70	0.8	10	5000	1.0	1.6	17	70	
	55–75	70 (154)	175 (69)	2200	70	0.8	10	5000	0.9	1.3	15	70	
Women	18–35	58 (128)	163 (64)	2100	58	0.8	15	5000	0.8	1.3	14	70	
	35–55	58 (128)	163 (64)	1900	58	0.8	15	5000	0.8	1.2	13	70	
	55–75	58 (128)	163 (64)	1600	58	0.8	10	5000	0.8	1.2	13	70	
	Pregnant (2nd and 3rd trimesters)			+ 200	+20	+0.5	+ 5	+1000	+0.2	+0.3	+ 3	+30	400
	Lactating			+1000	+40	+0.5	+ 5	+3000	+0.4	+0.6	+ 7	+30	400
Infants[3]	0–1	8 (18)		kg. × 115 ±15	kg. × 2.5 ±0.5	0.7	kg. × 1.0	1500	0.4	0.6	6	30	400
Children	1–3	13 (29)	87 (34)	1300	32	0.8	8	2000	0.5	0.8	9	40	400
	3–6	18 (40)	107 (42)	1600	40	0.8	10	2500	0.6	1.0	11	50	400
	6–9	24 (53)	124 (49)	2100	52	0.8	12	3500	0.8	1.3	14	60	400
Boys	9–12	33 (72)	140 (55)	2400	60	1.1	15	4500	1.0	1.4	16	70	400
	12–15	45 (98)	156 (61)	3000	75	1.4	15	5000	1.2	1.8	20	80	400
	15–18	61 (134)	172 (68)	3400	85	1.4	15	5000	1.4	2.0	22	80	400
Girls	9–12	33 (72)	140 (55)	2200	55	1.1	15	4500	0.9	1.3	15	80	400
	12–15	47 (103)	158 (62)	2500	62	1.3	15	5000	1.0	1.5	17	80	400
	15–18	53 (117)	163 (64)	2300	58	1.3	15	5000	0.9	1.3	15	70	400

* Food and Nutrition Board, National Academy of Science—National Research Council, revised 1963. Designed for the maintenance of good nutrition of healthy persons in the United States. Allowances are intended for persons normally active in a temperate climate. The allowance levels are intended to cover individual variations among most normal persons as they live in the United States under usual environmental stresses. The recommended allowances can be attained with a variety of common foods, providing other nutrients for which human requirements have been less well defined.

[1] Entries on lines for age range 18–35 years represent the 25-year age. All other entries represent allowances for the midpoint of the specified age periods, i.e., line for children 1–3 is for age 2 years (24 months); 3–6 is for age 4½ (54 months), etc.

[2] Niacin equivalents include dietary sources of the preformed vitamin and the precursor, tryptophan. 60 mg tryptophan represents 1 mg niacin.

[3] The calorie and protein allowances per kg for infants are considered to decrease progressively from birth. Allowances for calcium, thiamine, riboflavin, and niacin increase proportionately with calories to the maximum values shown.

dations of the Food and Nutrition Board of the National Research Council, indicated in Table 24–1, constitute an important contribution to this subject.

The food intake is influenced by geographical and economic factors as well as by personal idiosyncrasies. The diet of the Eskimo is limited by his environment largely to meat and fish. Large numbers of Orientals are forced to subsist mainly on rice, with variable supplements of other vegetables and fish. As a general principle, any type of rigid dietary restriction, voluntary or forced, carries with it the danger of deficiency in some essential factor. The greater the variety of foods, the more remote this danger becomes. Of less practical importance, perhaps, in normal subjects, is the manner of preparation of foods, i.e., seasoning, flavoring, cooking, except in that improper procedures may destroy or remove certain vitamins (q.v.) or impair the quality of the food proteins. These matters may assume importance, however, in maintaining adequate nutrition in disease since increased palatability of the food causes stimulation of appetite.

Dietary considerations of vitamins (p. 142ff.) and inorganic elements (p. 623) are discussed elsewhere. It seems desirable to review here certain pertinent points regarding the caloric, carbohydrate, fat, and protein intakes insofar as they bear on biochemical aspects of the diet. Data on the composition of foods are available in standard works on nutrition and dietetics.

Caloric Content of Diet

The daily caloric requirements under various physiological conditions are considered elsewhere (p. 333). These are, of course, contributed by the three classes of organic foodstuffs, carbohydrate, fat, and protein. From the standpoint of adequate nutrition, of these the protein requirement is the most rigid, the accepted recommendation being not less than 1 gm. per kilogram of body weight daily. This amount (e.g., 70 gm. = 280 cal.) would contribute about 10 per cent of the energy requirement of a moderately active 70-kg. man. It is somewhat higher in pregnant and lactating women and in children (p. 332). The relative proportions of carbohydrate and fat contributing the remainder could vary widely, but it is recommended that carbohydrate contribute at least 50 per cent and fat at least 20 per cent of the total calories. Increased energy demands incident to increased activity may be met by either of the two latter foodstuffs. However, ketone bodies may accumulate in excess if carbohydrate provides much less than half of the total calories on a high-fat diet (p. 469).

If the caloric intake is insufficient to meet current demands, the body tissues will supply the deficit. If the protein intake is adequate and caloric restriction of only moderate degree, this will be derived from depot fat after the small glycogen reserves have been depleted. However, with progressive reduction in caloric intake, a deleterious influence is exerted on protein metabolism, as reflected in nitrogen balance (p. 603), this effect becoming more evident after the fat reserves have been depleted. With severe, prolonged restriction, virtually all tissues lose weight, but not equally, fat, liver, and muscle suffering considerably, whereas brain, plasma proteins, and bones are maintained for relatively long periods.

The organism adapts itself to caloric restriction to a certain extent by an associated decrease in the rate of oxidations. The BMR may decrease by about 50 per cent after prolonged semi-starvation, owing in part to the above phenomenon, but mainly to the decreased mass of metabolizing tissue.

The requirement for certain vitamins is influenced by the caloric intake. This is particularly true of the B vitamins concerned in oxidative mechanisms (q.v., p. 353), the requirements for which diminish as the caloric content of the diet is reduced. In fact, frank vitamin deficiency manifestations are not often seen in total starvation, but may develop during subsequent feeding if the intake of vitamins is not increased in proportion to the caloric intake.

Dietary Carbohydrate

Inasmuch as all biologically significant carbohydrates can be synthesized in the body, their main function in the diet is to provide a readily utilizable source of energy for the maintenance of cell functions. Under usual conditions, carbohydrate should provide 50 per cent or more of the calories of the diet (p. 333), i.e., about 5 to 7 gm. per kg. of body weight in the average moderately active adult.

Undue restriction of dietary carbohydrate influences both fat and protein metabolism adversely, even if the caloric intake is adequate. Fat mobilization from the depots and utilization are exaggerated (p. 503), ketogenesis is increased (p. 469), and ketosis may develop. The effect on protein metabolism is apparently of a specific nature, not shared by other substances (e.g., fat, alcohol), and not related to its calorigenic action. This is referred to as the "protein-sparing action" of carbohydrate (pp. 447, 604). During a total fast, an adult may lose about 80 gm. of protein daily. This may be reduced to about 35 gm. by a daily intake of 100 gm. of glucose, which represents approximately its maximum protein-sparing effect under these circumstances. It has been estimated that a maximum effect in this connection is accomplished by 5 gm. of glucose per 100 Cal. produced.

Celluloses, indigestible plant polysaccharides, contribute bulk to the intestinal contents and, therefore, in normal amounts promote intestinal motility. When present in excess, they may be irritating to the intestinal mucous membrane, producing diarrhea or a spastic type of constipation. All other dietary carbohydrates are readily digested and absorbed. Ingestion of excessive amounts, especially in infants, may occasionally produce intestinal disturbances due to irritation induced by products of bacterial fermentation (p. 271). There is some evidence in experimental animals (rat) that continued ingestion of supertolerance amounts of galactose may result in the formation of cataract. A similar phenomenon has been suggested as possibly occurring in man, especially in children, in the presence of hepatic functional impairment, in which condition the conversion of galactose to glucose (or glycogen) may be impaired, with consequent elevation of the blood galactose concentration. It should be recalled in this connection, however, that the incidence of cataract is relatively high also in uncontrolled diabetes, a phenomenon presumably related in this case to maintenance of a persistently elevated blood glucose concentration.

Dietary Lipid

A wide variety of lipids is provided in a balanced diet. Inasmuch as, under normal circumstances, all components of biologically significant lipids, with the exception of certain "essential" fatty acids (p. 462), can be synthesized in the body from non-lipid precursors, the main function of dietary lipids, like that of carbohydrates, is to provide energy, largely through their constituent fatty acids (p. 450). The dietary lipids serve another, indirect function in serving as carriers of certain vitamins and provitamins (e.g., A, D, E, K, q.v.), which, because of their solubility in fats, occur in nature mainly in association with these substances. There is also some indication that they may exert a relatively minor protein-sparing effect, apart from their caloric contribution (p. 604).

Neutral fats, comprising the largest fraction of food lipids, are quantitatively the most important of these substances. Under usual conditions, fat provides 20 to 35 per cent of the calories of the diet (p. 333), i.e., 1 to 2 gm. per kg. of body weight in the average moderately active adult.

The nutritional significance of the polyunsaturated "essential" fatty acids is discussed elsewhere (p. 462). They are provided in ample amounts by a balanced diet that contains an adequate quantity of naturally occurring lipids (linoleic mainly in plants, arachidonic of animal origin). Not all vegetable fats are rich in linoleic acid (low content in coconut oil), nor are all animal fats deficient in this substance (high content in chicken fat). There is currently considerable interest in the influence of dietary fat on the plasma cholesterol concentration in relation to the pathogenesis of atherosclerosis. Although there is considerable species variation, it is generally agreed that in man elevated plasma cholesterol levels of certain types may be lowered by (a) restriction of fat intake or (b) substitution of polyunsaturated for saturated fatty acids (p. 494).

Inasmuch as most of the common food fats contain mainly the same few fatty acids, viz., oleic, palmitic, and stearic, although in different proportions, there is little significant difference in their digestibility or biological value, whether of plant or of animal origin. When ingested in amounts that are not excessive, all of those commonly used in cooking or as foods are well digested and absorbed, most of them to the extent of about 95 per cent, but somewhat less in the case of beef and mutton fat. Of more academic than practical importance is the fact that triglycerides with unusually high proportions of longer-chain saturated fatty acids, resulting in high melting points (above 38° C.), may remain solid at body temperature, and, therefore, are less readily absorbed.

An excessively high fat intake inhibits gastric secretion and motility, producing anorexia and gastric discomfort. Intestinal irritation and diarrhea may result from excessive amounts of fatty acids in the intestine. Although of little practical importance, it is of interest that cottonseed oil contains a pigment, gossypol, which has antioxidant and antitryptic activity, diminishes appetite, and interferes with protein digestion.

Dietary Protein

The large amount of information available on nutritive aspects of food proteins has been obtained mainly from studies in the albino rat and to a limited extent in the dog (especially plasma proteins and hemoglobin). The relatively few observations that have been made on human subjects support the view that, with occasional exceptions, the results of studies in these experimental animals may be generally applied to man.

Food proteins perform a vitally important function different from that served by dietary carbohydrates and fats, the main purpose of which is to provide an adequate amount of energy. The proteins of the diet are the ultimate source of amino groups, and of the carbon skeletons of the essential amino acids required for synthesis of body proteins, which comprise the bulk of the metabolic machinery (e.g., enzymes) and of other structural and functional components of the tissues and body fluids. Taken in excess, they may also be utilized for the production of energy; they may be converted to carbohydrate or to fat. Inasmuch as all body proteins are continually undergoing degradation (p. 542) and there is an obligatory loss of nitrogen in the urine, at least this amount of nitrogen must be supplied in the diet if protein anabolism is to keep pace with its catabolism, even in the adult, non-growing state. The diet must also provide certain "essential" amino acids that cannot be synthesized in the body.

Inasmuch as growth involves formation of tissue proteins at a rate exceeding that of their degradation (i.e., positive N balance), the dietary protein is much more critically concerned in growth and tissue repair than are carbohydrates and lipids. This influence may be demonstrated readily in the growing animal, whose weight curve reflects the adequacy (quantity and quality) of the protein intake. There is evidence also that the latter determines to a significant extent the ultimate adult size of the individual, over and above genetic influences. Adult heights and weights of peoples in various geographic areas apparently vary directly with the amount and quality of protein in their diets. For example, members of certain African tribes subsisting largely on vegetables are small in stature, whereas neighboring tribes of similar origin, subsisting mainly on meat and milk, are tall. Similar correlations have been obtained in studies of genetically comparable groups of individuals in this and other countries.

Emphasis was placed originally almost exclusively on the quantitative protein requirements. With the development of more satisfactory analytical methods for amino acids, and the accumulation of information on "essential" amino acids, it became apparent that the "quality" of dietary proteins is just as important as their quantity in contributing to adequate protein nutrition.

Nitrogen equilibrium can be maintained, i.e., protein requirements can be satisfied, just as satisfactorily by intravenous as by oral administration of adequate mixtures of amino acids. The same is true of plasma proteins. Moreover, apart from the influence of certain unknown factors present in natural animal proteins (e.g., "animal protein factor"), intravenous injection of such mixtures can completely replace oral protein feeding, at least for periods of several days. Properly fortified protein (e.g., casein) hydrolysates and various mixtures of pure amino acids are commercially available for this purpose, and have aided considerably in maintaining satisfactory nutrition in patients in whom adequate oral feeding is impossible or undesirable, e.g., after operations on the gastrointestinal tract.

Quality of food proteins (biological value). Food proteins vary considerably in the efficiency of their utilization for synthesis of body proteins (e.g., tissues, hemoglobin, plasma proteins). Any one of several procedures may be employed for evaluation of the "quality" of a protein: (1) measurement of its influence on the weight increase of weanling animals $\left(\text{"protein efficiency ratio"} = \dfrac{\text{weight increase (gm.)}}{\text{gm. protein consumed}}\right)$; (2) determination of its "biological value" in terms of the percentage of absorbed nitrogen retained by the organism; (3) measurement of its influence on the rate of regain of body weight or of liver protein by previously depleted animals; (4) measurement of its influence on the rate of restoration of plasma proteins or of hemoglobin in animals previously depleted of these specific proteins (e.g., by plasmapheresis). In the case of hemoglobin, a conjugated protein, consideration must be given to other factors, including iron (p. 641) and requirements for porphyrin synthesis (p. 607) and erythropoiesis (viz., vitamin B_{12}) (p. 202).

Evaluated on the basis of these criteria, animal proteins generally are of higher "quality" than those of vegetable origin. Whole egg and milk (especially lactalbumin) proteins rank highest in this respect, meats and glandular tissues somewhat lower. Gelatin, commonly used in desserts, although a protein of animal origin (not occurring naturally as such), is a wholly inadequate protein, lacking tryptophan and being low in tyrosine and cystine. It is prepared from collagen (cartilage, bone, tendon, skin) by boiling in water.

Certain factors are known to influence the biological value of proteins: (1) the amounts and relative proportions of their constituent amino acids; (2) the nutritional availability (rates of liberation and absorption) of their constituent amino acids under conditions of digestion in the gastrointestinal tract. Moreover, factor 2 may be influenced, adversely or beneficially, by various methods of processing (commercial) or preparation (cooking) of foodstuffs.

Amino acid composition. The most important single factor, but not the only one, that influences the nutritional "quality" of a protein is its amino acid composition. The significance of the "essential" amino acids in this connection is discussed elsewhere (p. 546). These must be provided in the diet if nitrogen equilibrium is to be maintained. Inasmuch as they must all be presented to the organism virtually simultaneously for purposes of protein synthesis (p. 547), a "complete" food protein must contain all of them. However, the biological value of a protein is apparently related to the proportionality relationships among its constituent essential amino acids. The following proportional values, relative to tryptophan as unity, have been found to be optimal for growth of the rat: lysine 5, leucine 4, valine 3.5, phenylalanine 3.5, methionine 3, isoleucine 2.5, threonine 2.5, histidine 2, arginine 1, tryptophan 1. There is evidence that these ratios hold, approximately, for man. The following daily intake values (in gm.) have been recommended tentatively: isoleucine 1.4, leucine 2.2, lysine 1.6, methionine 2.2, phenylalanine 2.2, threonine 1.0, tryptophan 0.5, valine 1.6. These are about double the minimal requirements and should provide an adequate excess, from which each cell may select the proper mixture for its specific protein synthesis requirements.

Despite the fact that the organism can manufacture the "non-essential" amino acids, when a mixture of the "essential" amino acids is the only source of dietary nitrogen, growth is not as satisfactory as when the same amount of nitrogen is supplied in the form of intact complete proteins or their hydrolysates, under otherwise comparable conditions (i.e., carbohydrate and fat contents). This is apparently due, in part at least, to the fact that the presence in the diet of a "non-essential" amino acid, e.g., cystine, may reduce the requirement for an "essential" amino acid, in this case methionine. It has been suggested that when the former are not provided, the necessity for their synthesis may constitute an excessive burden on the metabolic activities of the cell. This is particularly true under conditions of rapid growth (childhood, pregnancy, convalescence from wasting diseases).

Balance of dietary amino acids. Proper balance of dietary amino acids is particularly important when the protein intake is inadequate, i.e., deficient with respect to certain amino acids. For example, in the rat, addition of an excess of leucine to a previously adequate diet increases the requirement for isoleucine. Addition of methionine to a low protein diet deficient in this amino acid may cause threonine deficiency. Addition of lysine to a diet low in histidine increases the requirement for histidine and the urinary excretion of cystine. Several other examples of this phenomenon have been observed, the situation being analogous to the exaggeration of certain vitamin deficiencies by addition of amino acids to the deficient diets.

These types of imbalance may be indicated as follows:

(1) When the protein intake is inadequate, addition of the most limiting amino acid may precipitate deficiency in the next most limiting amino acid. Conversely, addition of the latter may induce deficiency in the former.

(2) When the diet contains only minimally adequate amounts of certain B vitamins, addition of an excess of certain amino acids may precipitate or exaggerate the vitamin deficiency.

(3) Under certain circumstances, addition of an excess of one amino acid to a previously adequate diet may reduce utilization of another amino acid to such an extent that deficiency occurs.

Provision of excessive amounts of single amino acids may alter the requirement for certain vitamins. For example, addition of glycine and leucine to a sucrose diet increases the requirement for niacin, and an excess of methionine increases the pyridoxine requirement.

Availability of amino acids of foods. Different proteins with similar amino acid compositions may not liberate a given amino acid at the same rate during the course of digestion, and the rates at which different amino acids are liberated may vary widely. An apparent determining factor in this connection is the nature of the amino acid linkage within the protein molecule. Digestibility of various proteins and the rates of release of amino acids may be affected by the manner of preparation of foods (e.g., heating), in some cases adversely, in others beneficially. On this basis, wide differences in the time of absorption of individual amino acids from the intestinal lumen may diminish the nutritional usefulness of a protein of satisfactory chemical constitution because of the importance of the time element in the utilization of amino acids for protein synthesis (p. 547).

Supplementary relationships; time factor. If a relatively low-quality protein food, such as white bread (low in lysine), is supplemented by a small amount of lysine, raising its content of this amino acid from 0.29 per cent to 0.67 per cent, its biological value is more than doubled. The utilization of an "incomplete" protein for protein synthesis is limited by the amino acid least available ("law of the minimum"). Similarly, mixtures of food proteins, each of which is "incomplete" in different respects, may provide a satisfactory amino acid balance for optimum protein nutrition.

Analysis of various types of staple protein foodstuffs reveals that their most significant deficiencies are in lysine, methionine, threonine, and tryptophan. For example, wheat, which is an important dietary protein, is deficient in lysine; this is true of cereal grains generally. Rice is, in addition, poor in threonine, and corn in tryptophan. Leguminous (peas, beans) and root vegetable proteins are generally deficient in methionine, the former also in tryptophan. The combination of wheat (low in lysine, but adequate in methionine) and potatoes or peas (adequate in lysine, but low in methionine) raises the biological value of each of these relatively low-quality proteins considerably. Similar enhancement of the utilization of relatively low-quality (vegetable) proteins is accomplished by the addition of high-quality (animal) proteins.

A protein molecule can be synthesized only if all of its constituent amino acids are available simultaneously in proper amounts. If an interval of longer than one hour is allowed to elapse between ingestion of an incomplete amino acid mixture and administration of the missing essential amino acids, these amino acid constituents are not utilized for protein synthesis. Under these circumstances, weight loss is much the same as on an equicaloric diet containing no amino acids. The same applies, of course, to mixtures of dietary proteins that supplement one another's deficiencies; they must be ingested simultaneously in order to be maximally utilized. There is evidence, too, that even high-quality dietary proteins are utilized more efficiently when distributed evenly throughout the three daily meals than if concentrated in one or two meals. The time of administration of carbohydrate in relation to protein is also of importance in this connection (p. 604).

Quantity of protein. If the intake of protein is reduced gradually, urinary nitrogen excretion diminishes correspondingly and the organism may remain in nitrogen equilibrium until a critical intake level (about 0.25 to 0.33 gm. per kg. of body weight) is reached, below which the nitrogen balance becomes negative. However, continuation of such low-protein intakes for prolonged periods may endanger health and is certainly undesirable. Animals maintained on such diets are more susceptible to subsequent protein depletion than are those receiving high-protein diets.

It has been found that protein nutrition is maintained satisfactorily in adults by a daily intake of 0.66 gm. per kg. of body weight. Larger amounts are required during pregnancy (growth of fetus, placenta, uterus, breasts), lactation (production of milk proteins), childhood (body growth), and convalescence from wasting diseases (tissue repair). In order to provide for variations in nutritional quality and for fluctuations in requirement incident to contingencies of everyday existence, the Food and Nutrition Board of the National Research Council has recommended the following daily allowances (Table 24-1, p. 650) per kg. of body weight: normal adults, 1 gm.; during the latter half of pregnancy, 1.45 gm.; during lactation, 1.8 gm.; infants, 3.5 gm.; early childhood, 2.2 to 3.3 gm.; late childhood through adolescence, 1.4 to 2 gm.

The daily requirement is, of course, influenced by the quality of the food protein. For example, whereas nitrogen equilibrium can be maintained on 0.6 gm. (per kg. of body weight) of milk protein daily, over 1 gm. (per kg. of body weight) of white flour protein is required for this purpose. The dietary protein recommendations indicated presuppose that the diet is adequate in other respects and that high-quality proteins (whole egg, milk, meats, liver) comprise at least half of the total protein intake in the case of normal adults, half to two-thirds during pregnancy and lactation, and two-thirds to three-quarters during childhood and adolescence.

Although there is evidence that an extremely high protein intake may produce kidney damage in the rat, there is no substantial evidence that this is true in man within feasible limits of dietary protein content.

Consequences of protein deficiency. If the protein intake does not meet the immediate requirements, protein anabolism cannot be maintained at the required rate. In the child, growth is retarded; in the adult, weight is lost; wound healing is delayed. Hemoglobin synthesis is impaired, with consequent anemia. If the deficiency is marked, excessive amounts of fat may accumulate in the liver (p. 504), a consequence of deficiency in methionine, and degenerative changes and fibrosis (cirrhosis) may occur. Prolonged deficiency may result in inadequate synthesis of plasma proteins. If this progresses to the point of significant decrease in the plasma albumin concentration, edema may develop (p. 306), and also increased susceptibility to shock. Resistance to infections may be diminished as a result of impaired capacity for forming γ-globulins (antibodies) (p. 562). In severe protein restriction, certain hormones, protein in nature, such as those of the anterior pituitary (p. 736), may not be synthesized in adequate amounts, and endocrine abnormalities may appear, e.g., amenorrhea (gonadotropin deficiency). Since enzymes are proteins and must be synthesized in the body, the enzyme content of certain tissues (e.g., liver) and secretions (e.g., pepsin in gastric juice) falls in advanced deficiency states. This may result in disturbances of function of the organs affected.

Beneficial and deleterious factors in foods. Apart from their protein content, certain animal foodstuffs (e.g., milk, liver) contain an unidentified factor (or factors) which enhances protein synthesis and growth. This has been termed "animal protein factor" (APF), and perhaps will eventually be found to belong in the category of vitamins (p. 198); vitamin B_{12}, before it was separated from this "factor," was included under this designation. This APF may contribute to the biologic superiority of animal over vegetable proteins.

Certain foodstuffs, in their natural state, may contain nutritionally deleterious components. For example, soybeans contain a principle with antitryptic activity which depresses appetite and interferes with protein digestion, an effect similar to that of gossypol in cottonseed oil (p. 653). This substance, presumably protein in nature, is inactivated by heat, which explains, in part at least, the fact that the nutritional value of soybean is increased considerably by proper cooking techniques.

Toxic materials may be present in certain foods, as consumed, as a result of either natural occurrence or processing. These include such factors as lead, arsenic, selenium, and copper, and a substance present in wheat flour bleached with agene (NCl_3), which causes serious nervous system manifestations (e.g., "canine hysteria"). Protection is afforded against many of these recognized hazards by appropriate legislation. A sensitizing factor in fava beans may induce a hemolytic disorder, favism. Spoiled sweet clover hay contains dicoumarin (p. 664), which, when ingested by cattle, produces a hemorrhagic condition characterized by prothrombin deficiency.

BIBLIOGRAPHY

Allison, J. B.: Biological evaluation of proteins, Physiol. Rev. *35:*664, 1955.
Annual Review of Physiology.
Elvehjem, C. A., and Harper, A.E.: Importance of amino acid balance in nutrition, J.A.M.A. *158:*655, 1955.
Food and Nutrition Board, National Academy of Sciences-National Research Council: Recommended Dietary Allowances, Revised 1963, Washington, D. C.
Geiger, E.: Extracaloric function of dietary components in relation to protein utilization, Federation Proc. *10:*670, 1951.
Heinz Handbook of Nutrition (B. T. Burton, Ed.), New York, McGraw-Hill Book Company, 1959.
Heinz International Symposium on Nutrition, Federation Proc. *18,* Suppl. 3, No. 2, Part II, 1959.
McHenry, E. W.: Basic Nutrition, Philadelphia, J. B. Lippincott Company, 1957.
McLester, J. S., and Darby, W. J.: Nutrition and Diet in Health and Disease, ed. 6, Philadelphia, W. B. Saunders Company, 1952.
Nutritional Reviews.
Pollack, H., and Halpern, S. L.: Therapeutic Nutrition, Pub. No. 234, National Academy of Sciences-National Research Council, 1952.
Proceedings, Fifth International Congress on Nutrition, Federation Proc. *20,* Suppl. 7, No. 1, Part III, 1961, General Biochemical Aspects of Diet, p. 621.
Sherman, H. C.: Chemistry of Food and Nutrition, ed. 8, New York, The Macmillan Company, 1952.
Symposia on Nutrition, Federation Proc. *18:*1075, 1125, 1959.

CHAPTER 25

METABOLIC ANTAGONISM

The term "metabolic antagonism" is applied to the phenomenon of interference with the metabolism or function of a given chemical compound by a structurally related compound, the basis of the interference being their structural similarity. The metabolic antagonist also may be designated an "antimetabolite" or a "substrate analog." The topic of metabolic antagonism would scarcely merit extended treatment if it were as completely abstruse as might be suggested by this rather vague definition. As a matter of fact, the phenomenon of metabolic antagonism not only finds constant use in current biochemical investigations of a fundamental nature, but also forms the basis of many major advances in pharmacology, chemotherapy, and cancer research.

The concept of metabolic antagonism is not entirely new. Interference with the metabolism of succinate by structurally related compounds, e.g., malonate, represents an example of this phenomenon which was recognized many years ago. However, the wide applicability of the concept was not realized until the now famous explanation of the mode of action of sulfonamides forcibly brought this subject to the attention of the scientific public.

After the efficacy of sulfonamides as antibacterial agents was demonstrated, it became of interest to inquire into the mechanism of their action. Certain natural extracts were found to be capable of "antagonizing" or abolishing the antibacterial action of the sulfonamides, and it was shown that the substance responsible for this effect is *p*-aminobenzoic acid. It was hypothesized, without much supporting evidence at the time, that *p*-aminobenzoic acid is an essential nutrilite of bacteria, that it is concerned in a specific enzyme reaction, and that its combination with that enzyme is interfered with by the sulfonamides, which, by virtue of the similarity of their structures, could competitively combine with the enzyme in place of the natural substrate.

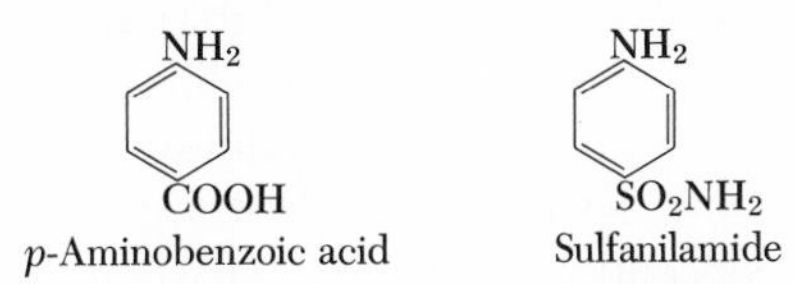

p-Aminobenzoic acid Sulfanilamide

This theoretical "shot in the dark" proved to be well directed. *p*-Aminobenzoic acid was soon found to be a nutrilite of bacteria; indeed, it is a dietary requirement or "vitamin" for many species. It was eventually discovered that bacteria require *p*-aminobenzoic acid for the synthesis of folic acid, and that the sulfonamides interfere specifically with the enzyme reaction in which *p*-aminobenzoic acid is incorporated into the pteroylglutamic molecule. The sulfonamides have no such effect on the animal host, since no comparable reaction occurs in animal tissues; preformed folic acid is required by the animal organism.

With this extraordinary elucidation of a chemotherapeutic phenomenon, arrived at by the application of the concept of metabolic antagonism, the theory has received increasing attention and application. It would be no exaggeration to state that a significant segment of current research in the basic medical sciences and in clinical medicine is influenced, if not directly guided, by it.

GENERAL THEORY OF ANTAGONISM

Various types of enzyme inhibition other than that by substrate analogs have been described (p. 222); they are not of concern in connection with the topic at hand.

The general hypothesis of inhibition by analogs states that, whereas the specificity of enzymes with respect to the catalysis of given chemical reactions may be high, thus requiring specific chemical groups in the substrates, the specificity of enzymes with respect to simple *combination* with various molecules is much lower. Consequently, the "combining sites" on the enzyme surface may unite with molecules other than the natural substrate, if the analogs are sufficiently similar structurally to the substrate to fit the site of combination. Since sites occupied by the analog obviously are inaccessible to substrate, and since the structure of the analog ordinarily precludes its participation in the same type of chemical reaction as the normal substrate, the velocity of an enzyme-catalyzed reaction is decreased when analogs are present in addition to substrate.

Competitive Inhibition

The simplest type of metabolic antagonism, or inhibition by substrate analogs, is termed "competitive" and is illustrated in Figure 25–1. Substrate is shown combining reversibly with the enzyme to form an activated complex, which splits to yield the products of the reaction and liberate the enzyme. An analog similarly combines reversibly with the enzyme at the same type of site, but forms an inactive complex.

The tenacity with which substrates or analogs combine with the enzyme may be described quantitatively by standard constants of equilibrium or dissociation. Ordinarily, but not invariably, the normal substrate is held more tightly than any analog. Since the equilibrium constants are fixed for any enzyme, substrate, and analog, the degree of inhibition of the reaction varies with the ratio of concentrations of inhibitor to substrate. Sufficiently high concentrations of substrate can force the analog molecules from the enzyme sites and relieve the inhibition. The ratio of concentration of inhibitor to that of substrate required to produce a given degree of inhibition (usually set at 50 per cent) is termed the "inhibition index." True competitive inhibition is characterized by the constancy of the inhibition index over a range of inhibitor and substrate concentrations. To put the matter more concretely, let us suppose that a given enzyme reaction is inhibited 50 per cent at a substrate concentration of 0.001 M when the antimetabolite is used at a concentration of 0.01 M. Raising the concentration of substrate alone will decrease the inhibition, raising the concentration of analog will increase it, whereas raising both in the

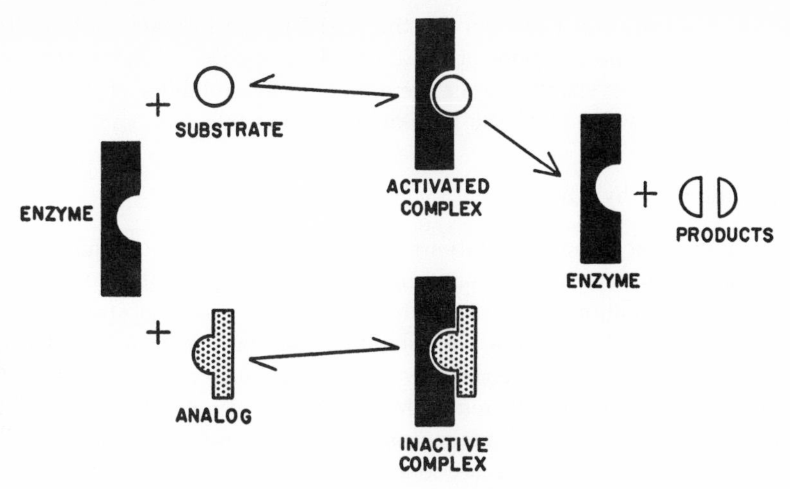

Figure 25-1. Competitive inhibition.

same ratio will preserve the same degree of inhibition. A substrate concentration of 0.005 M and an analog concentration of 0.05 M will result in the same 50 per cent inhibition as concentrations of 0.001 M and 0.01 M, respectively, the inhibition index being 10 in both cases. Such behavior is characteristic of competitive inhibition.

Analysis of the kinetics of reversible, competitive inhibition indicates that the presence of the inhibitor causes an apparent increase in the Michaelis constant (p. 221), as may be seen in a Lineweaver-Burk plot (Fig. 25–2). In the presence of a competitive inhibitor, the "apparent K_m" becomes greater by the factor $(1 + (I)/K_I)$, where (I) is the concentration of inhibitor and K_I is the dissociation constant of the enzyme-inhibitor complex. In molecular terms this means that the presence of the competitive inhibitor influences unfavorably the equilibrium between enzyme and substrate so that a greater

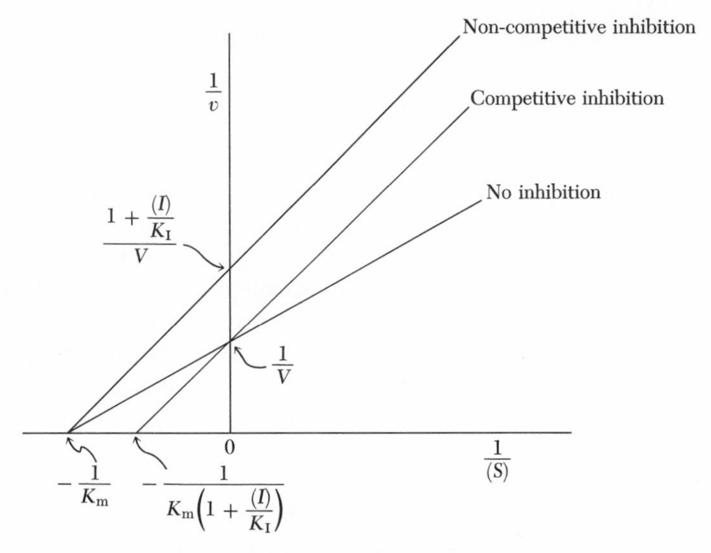

Figure 25-2. Lineweaver-Burk double reciprocal plot to differentiate types of inhibition. (I), Concentration of inhibitor; K_I, dissociation constant of enzyme-inhibitor complex; K_m, Michaelis constant; (S), substrate concentration; v, rate of enzyme reaction; V, maximum rate at high substrate concentration.

concentration of substrate is necessary for the reaction rate to reach half-maximum. On the other hand, high concentrations of substrate can drive the inhibitor from the active sites (since it combines reversibly), hence the presence of an inhibitor of this type does not change the numerical value of V, the maximum reaction rate.

Irreversible Inhibition by Analogs

Unfortunately, the clear-cut relations outlined above do not obtain in all cases. Instances are known in which compounds, undoubtedly closely related to the substrate in structure, produce inhibitions not completely reversible by excess substrate at high inhibitor concentrations. At the extreme, the inhibition may be irreversible under all conditions. These inhibitions are characterized by lack of constancy of the inhibition index and by progressive increase in the degree of inhibition with time. They are, nevertheless, regarded as examples of metabolic antagonism, since the inhibitors are structurally related to the substrate, since the inhibitions are sometimes reversed by excess substrate, and since systems which are apparently irreversible in one species are at times reversible in another.

Irreversible inhibition by substrate analogs may result from various causes. The inhibitor may, for example, form so firm a union with the enzyme as to make the combination practically irreversible. This phenomenon is particularly liable to occur when the analog bears reactive groups other than those involved in combination with the ordinary enzyme site, these accessory groups then combining (frequently irreversibly) with adjacent chemical groups on the enzyme surface.

There is a special case of irreversible antagonism which is not due to substrate analogs, but is still related quite closely to this topic. In the case of the sulfonamides, it was stated that the inhibition of bacterial metabolism could be relieved by *p*-aminobenzoic acid. This phenomenon is of the competitive type. But sulfonamide inhibitions also may be relieved by folic acid, in an irreversible manner, in the sense that, at a given concentration of folic acid, increasing the sulfonamide concentration will not re-establish the former level of inhibition. Folic acid, being the *product* of the reaction in which *p*-aminobenzoic acid is involved, can bypass the inhibitor when supplied preformed. As a general rule, the product of an inhibited reaction antagonizes the inhibitor irreversibly.

Non-competitive and Uncompetitive Inhibition

A type of inhibition called "non-competitive" is caused by inhibitors which combine with the enzyme at sites other than those utilized by the substrate. Since these inhibitors do not compete with the substrate, they have no effect on its equilibrium with the enzyme or on the Michaelis constant. However, they exert other influences which alter the reaction kinetics, such as inhibition of the rate of decomposition of the enzyme-substrate complex. Consequently, they depress the maximum reaction rate (Fig. 25–2), since high concentrations of substrate do not remove the inhibitor from its combining sites. In other words, inhibition of this type is not abolished by excess substrate. The maximum reaction rate (V) is decreased by the factor $(1 + (I)/K_I)$, where the symbols have been defined previously.

Another type of inhibition, called "uncompetitive," has been distinguished. In this case, which is not encountered commonly, the inhibitor combines with the enzyme-substrate complex, not with the free enzyme.

Enzymatic Formation of Antimetabolites: "Lethal Synthesis"

Although it is certain that many analogs are effective antagonists as such, evidence is accumulating that a number of supposed antimetabolites resemble their corresponding normal substrates closely enough to undergo certain of the metabolic reactions of the latter. This phenomenon is probably a reflection of a certain lack of specificity in the enzymes involved. Eventually, however, the "abnormal" molecules thus produced encounter an enzyme system of greater specificity, at which point inhibition occurs. One of the first established instances of this sort concerns fluoroacetic acid (p. 666). Others for which evidence is available include analogs of vitamins, amino acids, purines, and pyrimidines. The thought that an organism's own enzymes may assist in the synthesis of a "lethal" molecule is not only intriguing philosophically, but may also be a useful working hypothesis in further investigations of the phenomenon of metabolic antagonism.

APPLICATIONS OF METABOLIC ANTAGONISM

The field of metabolic antagonism has been worked so thoroughly in recent years that the accumulated information has become unwieldy. Rather than catalog the hundreds of known antagonists to vitamins, amino acids, etc., it may be more instructive to discuss certain of the fields of application, the approaches taken by investigators in these fields, and a few actual examples of antagonism.

Fundamental Biochemistry

(*a*) ***Naturally occurring antimetabolites.*** One of the consequences of the realization of the wide applicability of the concept of biological antagonism has been the recognition of certain cases of antagonism involving naturally occurring antimetabolites. Among the oldest of these examples is ion antagonism, although in the past it was not generally regarded as belonging in this category. Illustrations of ion antagonism may be drawn from many sources. For example, certain of the transphosphorylations of glycolysis require K^+, which is antagonized by Na^+. The antagonism between certain divalent cations has been mentioned in connection with the properties of actin and myosin.

Inspection of the formulas of the steroid hormones reveals many similarities, suggesting the possibility that certain of these compounds may act as mutual antagonists. Evidence in support of this thesis has been obtained in the case of androgens versus estrogens, and estrogens versus progesterone.

A number of natural antagonisms have been discovered in the nutrition of microorganisms, involving purines, pyrimidines, nucleic acids, and amino acids. Antagonisms among amino acids in animal nutrition have been mentioned previously. The interference of high concentrations of circulating phenylalanine or its metabolites with the metabolism of tyrosine and tryptophan in phenylketonuria may be another example.

Certain antibiotics function as metabolic antagonists (Fig. 25–3). In the case of chloramphenicol (Chloromycetin), there is some evidence of antagonism with phenylalanine, although the relationship is not purely competitive. Chloramphenicol, the structure of which resembles that of phenylalanine, is synthesized by certain fungi. Its inhibitory action toward Escherichia coli is reversed by phenylalanine, but only at low concentrations of the antibiotic. Chloramphenicol inhibits protein synthesis at the ribosome level in micro-

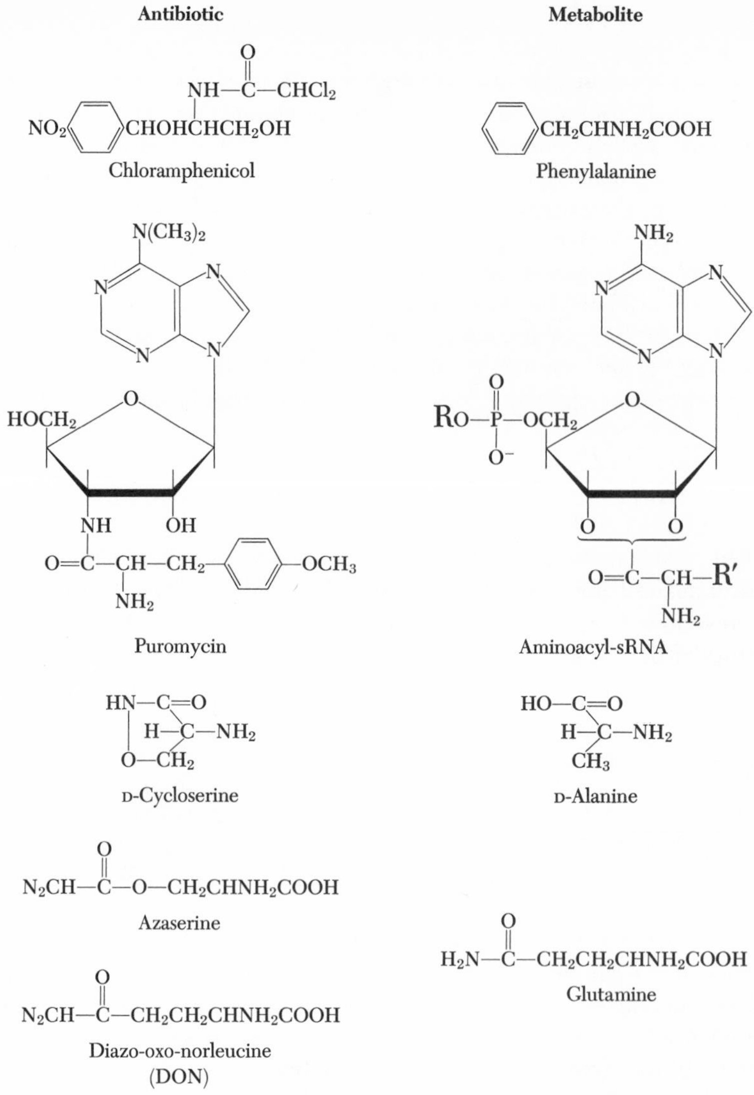

Antibiotic	Metabolite
$NO_2C_6H_4CHOHCH(NHCOCHCl_2)CH_2OH$ Chloramphenicol	$C_6H_5CH_2CHNH_2COOH$ Phenylalanine
$N(CH_3)_2$ (purine); $HOCH_2$ (ribose); NH, OH; $O{=}C{-}CH(NH_2){-}CH_2{-}C_6H_4{-}OCH_3$ Puromycin	NH_2 (purine); $Ro{-}P(O)(O^-){-}OCH_2$ (ribose); O, O; $O{=}C{-}CH(NH_2){-}R'$ Aminoacyl-sRNA
$HN{-}C{=}O$; $H{-}C{-}NH_2$; $O{-}CH_2$ D-Cycloserine	$HO{-}C{=}O$; $H{-}C{-}NH_2$; CH_3 D-Alanine
$N_2CH{-}C(=O){-}O{-}CH_2CHNH_2COOH$ Azaserine	
$N_2CH{-}C(=O){-}CH_2CH_2CHNH_2COOH$ Diazo-oxo-norleucine (DON)	$H_2N{-}C(=O){-}CH_2CH_2CHNH_2COOH$ Glutamine

Figure 25-3. Antibiotic analogs.

bial and a few animal systems, although it may not be functioning as an antimetabolite in these cases. The antibiotic puromycin, which resembles the "transfer end" of an aminoacyl-sRNA molecule, appears to labilize the attachment of nascent polypeptidyl-sRNA chains to mRNA. D-Cycloserine (oxamycin) interferes with the racemization of L- to D-alanine and the subsequent formation of D-alanyl-D-alanine, required for the synthesis of the cell wall mucopeptide in staphylococci. Two other antibiotics, azaserine and diazo-oxo-norleucine, antagonize glutamine in the synthesis of purines (amination of formylglycinamide ribotide). They have been tested in cancer chemotherapy. It must be emphasized that many antibiotics are not believed to function as metabolic antagonists.

Dicumarol (dicoumarin) is a particularly interesting example of a naturally occurring antimetabolite, because of its practical application in clinical medicine. Cattle suffer from a hemorrhagic condition after consuming spoiled sweet-clover hay. The causative agent is 3,3′-methylenebis-(4-hydroxycoumarin), commonly designated "Dicumarol."

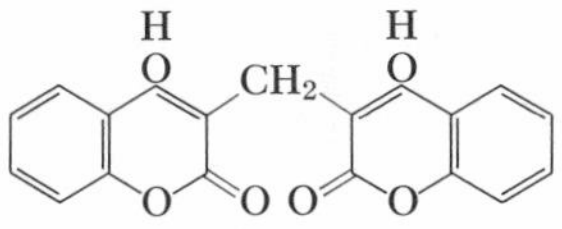

Dicumarol 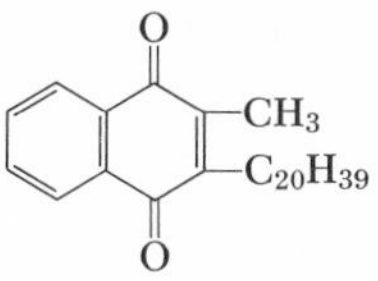 Vitamin K

The mechanism of production of the hemorrhagic condition involves the antagonism by Dicumarol of the vitamin K required for activation of prothrombin via formation of proconvertin. Large doses of the vitamin can counteract the effect of the antagonist, but the quantitative relation is not truly competitive. Dicumarol finds application in medicine in conditions in which excessive clotting or thrombosis must be prevented.

Fluoroacetic acid must be included among the naturally occurring antimetabolites. It is found in a South African plant which is toxic to cattle.

(*b*) ***Discovery of new metabolites.*** Elucidation of the pathways of intermediary metabolism is largely a matter of detection and identification of intermediates not ordinarily accumulated in the organism. Certain of the methods used in such investigations are discussed elsewhere (p. 336). The ability of a naturally occurring compound to counteract, in a competitive manner, the inhibitory action of a synthetic, structurally similar compound may be regarded as necessary but not conclusive evidence that the former compound is an intermediary metabolite in the system being tested. *p*-Aminobenzoic acid and the sulfonamides are a case in point.

Counteraction of the inhibitor, irreversibly, by a compound not structurally analogous suggests that the substance may be a product of the reaction being inhibited, e.g., folic acid in the case mentioned above. In addition to folic acid, bacterial inhibition by sulfonamides has been relieved (irreversibly) by methionine, purines, and pyrimidines. These phenomena are explicable on the basis that folic acid is involved in the metabolism of "formate" fragments, including interrelations with methyl groups and certain parts of the structures of purines and pyrimidines.

In addition to seeking compounds that may reverse the inhibition of a given antimetabolite, it is frequently profitable to search for the accumulation of intermediary metabolites in the inhibited system. An excellent example of this is the finding, in the medium of bacterial cells grown under conditions of slight inhibition by sulfonamides, of a precursor of the purines, aminoimidazole-carboxamide:

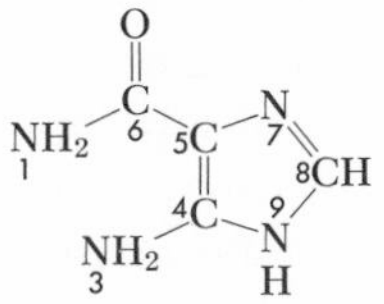

This molecule requires only a 1-carbon unit ("formate") to yield hypoxanthine. The intermediate accumulates because the formate cannot be introduced, the "transformylation" cannot occur because of the deficiency of "cotransformylase," and the coenzyme cannot be synthesized in adequate quantity owing to the sulfonamide blockage of the incorporation of *p*-aminobenzoic acid into the folic acid molecule. (It may be noted that the formylation which produces carbon 8 of the purine ring is not as severely inhibited; the intermediate would not be formed otherwise. The explanation seems to lie in the reversibility of the C-2 and the irreversibility of the C-8 formylation, so that deficiencies of tetrahydrofolic acid initially will affect the former process in greater degree.)

A related phenomenon is the excretion of formiminoglutamate, a metabolite of histidine, by rats treated with sulfonamides and by patients treated with folic acid antagonists. This provides evidence for the participation of folic acid in the transfer of formimino groups.

For experimental purposes, it is frequently desirable to inhibit the operation of the tricarboxylic acid cycle. As mentioned previously in various connections, the succinate → fumarate step is inhibited by malonic acid, an analog of succinic acid. An example of the specificity of structure involved in substrates and antimetabolites is illustrated by *trans*-aconitic acid, which interferes with the metabolism of *cis*-aconitic acid. The inhibitory action of fluoroacetic acid is most unusual. Fluoroacetate is apparently sufficiently similar in structure to acetate to undergo activation as well as condensation with oxaloacetate to form fluorocitrate. However, that is as far as the interloper can go, since the fluorocitrate acts as an antagonist of citrate in the aconitase reaction.

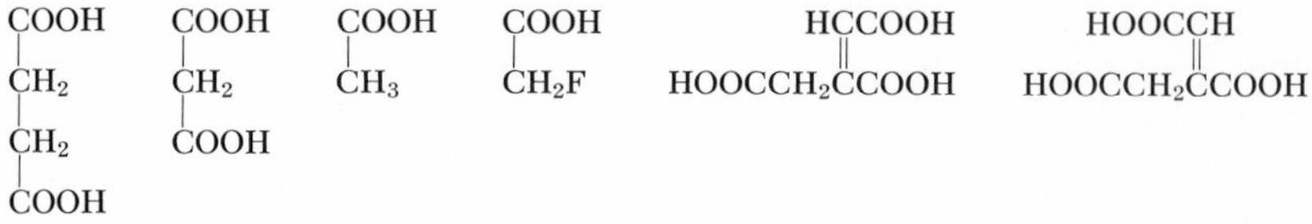

Succinate	Malonate	Acetate	Fluoroacetate	*cis*-Aconitate	*trans*-Aconitate
COOH	COOH	COOH	COOH	HCCOOH	HOOCCH
|	|	|	|	‖	‖
CH_2	CH_2	CH_3	CH_2F	$HOOCCH_2CCOOH$	$HOOCCH_2CCOOH$
|	|				
CH_2	COOH				
|					
COOH					

(*c*) ***Experimental dietary deficiencies.*** Much can be learned of the metabolic role of an essential dietary constituent by selective deprivation of that factor. The design of diets complete in all but one item, however, is frequently a difficult task, and often is made more difficult by the synthesis of certain essential factors by intestinal bacteria. The advent of anti-vitamins and anti-amino acids has consequently materially lightened the labors of investigators in nutritional biochemistry. Frequently, inclusion in the diet of an antimetabolite results in deficiency in the factor being antagonized, despite adequate quantities of that factor in the diet or derived from intestinal bacteria.

A selection of antagonists for vitamins and essential amino acids in animals is presented in Figure 25–4 on pages 668 and 669. Ethionine is toxic to rats, the effect being counteracted by methionine. The analog inhibits the incorporation of methionine into proteins; the analog itself is incorporated. It can form an S-adenosyl derivative and "transethylate," forming the triethyl analog of choline, itself a toxic antimetabolite (which, however, is lipotropic). In forming the S-adenosyl derivative, ethionine consumes an equivalent amount of ATP, hence this analog acts as an "ATP trap" and inhibits reactions (e.g., protein synthesis) which require a steady supply of the nucleotide. Thienylalanine retards the growth of rats, an effect that may be counteracted by phenylalanine.

Typical avitaminoses, cured by administration of the appropriate vitamin, are produced in test animals by pyrithiamine, β-acetylpyridine, deoxypyridoxine, and galactoflavin. A number of these and certain related B-antivitamins have been shown to form "unnatural" coenzymes (i.e., phosphates, pyrophosphates, mono- and dinucleotides) when incubated with the appropriate enzyme systems in vitro. The resultant unnatural coenzymes probably are the actual inhibitors in subsequent reactions requiring the corresponding normal coenzymes.

The apparent avitaminosis K produced by Dicumarol is reversed only by very large doses of the vitamin. Many of the analogs of folic acid produce effects which cannot be counteracted by folic acid. Although scurvy-like manifestations are produced in mice and rats (animals which ordinarily do not require ascorbic acid) by glucoascorbic acid, this condition is not cured by administration of ascorbic acid. In the guinea pig, a competition between ascorbic acid and its analog can be demonstrated, but the symptoms produced by the analog in this case are not typically scorbutic. Obviously, factors in addition to simple antagonism are operating in these cases.

(*d*) ***Active centers of enzymes.*** Research on the mechanism of action of enzymes has been aided by the use of metabolic antagonists. A normal substrate obviously contains the atomic groupings requisite for the performance of the enzymatically catalyzed reaction in question, whereas an inhibitory analog ordinarily does not. However, both types of compounds must bear whatever groups are necessary for combination with the enzyme surface. Consequently, study of the functional groups of typical substrates and analogs and of the results of stepwise variation in the character or position of these groups permits certain conclusions to be drawn concerning the possible character and topical distribution of the sites on the enzyme surface. Particularly valuable work in this direction has been performed in the case of acetylcholinesterase, an enzyme of considerable biochemical, physiological, and pharmacological interest (p. 212).

Neuropharmacological Applications

Actions of drugs involve the selective stimulation or inhibition of activity of one or, at most, a few organs, tissues, or receptors. Since many of these receptors are subject normally to chemical control by a specific organic compound (such as a neurohormone), the concept of antagonism by analog may be expected to be applicable in this field. As indicated below, several general types of phenomena appear to occur: (1) antagonists may be found which compete with the normal "control" compound for enzymes which destroy or otherwise inactivate the latter, thus intensifying the normal effect of the control ("mimetic" type); in addition, certain mimetic compounds resemble the control compound so closely that they themselves affect the receptor site; (2) other antagonists may compete with the control compound for the receptor site, thus decreasing the normal effect ("lytic" type); (3) antagonists may compete with precursors of the control compound and prevent the synthesis of the latter; (4) antagonists may prevent storage of the neurohormone in bound form by blocking the action of the storage mechanism or facilitating its reversal; (5) antagonists may inhibit the mechanism which effects release of the bound form from storage. These areas of application of antagonists may be pictured as follows:

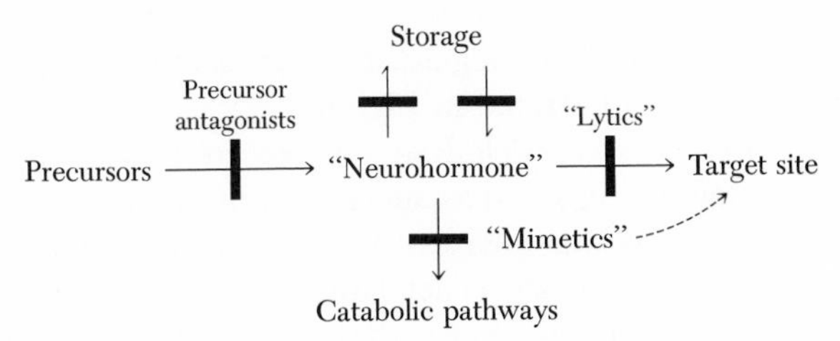

Although the concept of antagonism between chemical compounds has been employed widely in pharmacology for many years, the specific hypothesis that many pharmacological agents act as analogs of normal substrates has gained acceptance only slowly. Furthermore, it is undeniably true that the actual evidence in support of this hypothesis is deficient or lacking in many cases. For these reasons, the examples of purported

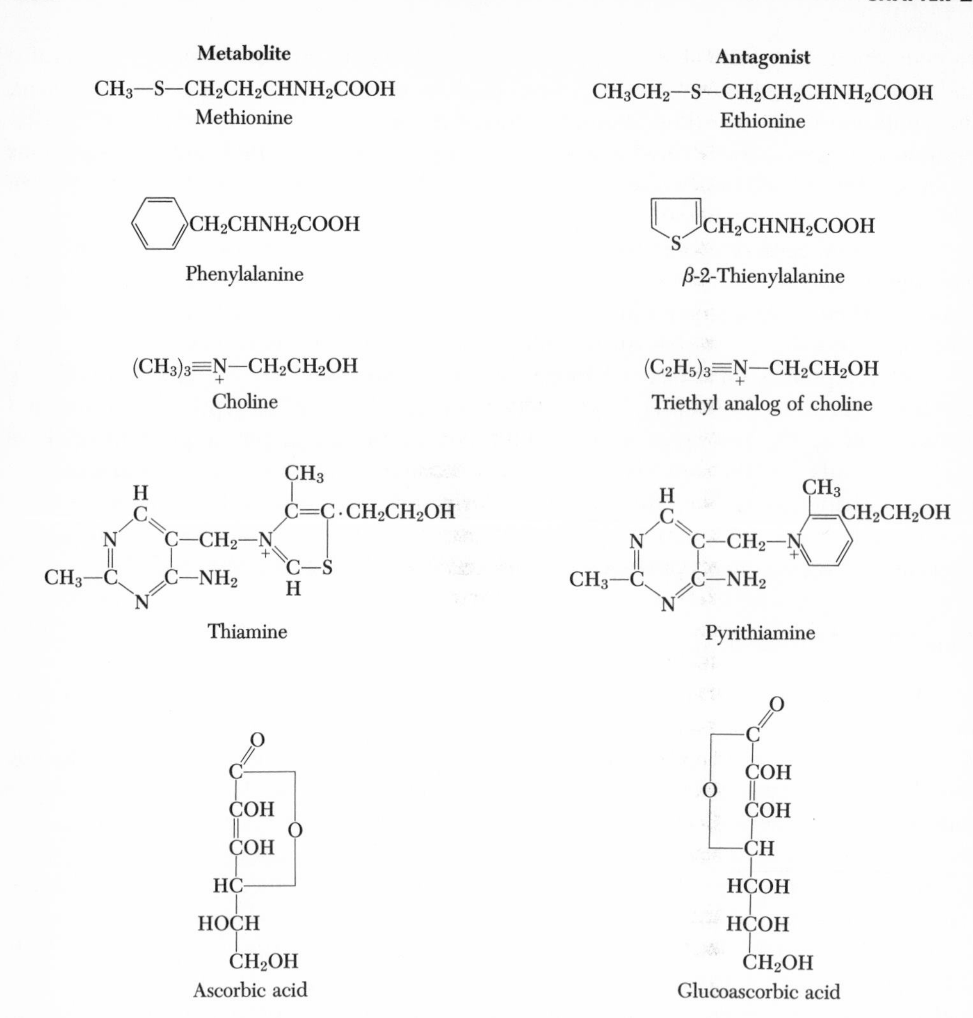

Figure 25-4. Antimetabolites used to produce nutritional deficiencies in animals. (See page 669 for continuation of this figure.)

antagonism mentioned here are to be regarded rather as suggested than as proved. Certain of these antagonisms are illustrated in Figure 25-5.

(*a*) ***Antagonisms involving acetylcholine.*** There are two opposing groups of compounds, both of which may be regarded as antagonists of acetylcholine. The parasympathomimetic drugs (such as neostigmine, a carbamate, and diisopropyl fluorophosphate [DFP], an organophosphate—Fig. 25-5) act largely by competition with acetylcholine for the enzyme, acetylcholinesterase. Since they block the enzyme responsible for the hydrolysis of acetylcholine, in effect they increase the concentration of the neurohormone at its receptor sites, hence the designation, "parasympathomimetic." Diisopropyl fluorophosphate is believed to react with the esteratic site of the enzyme, whereas neostigmine probably is attracted to both the anionic and esteratic sites.

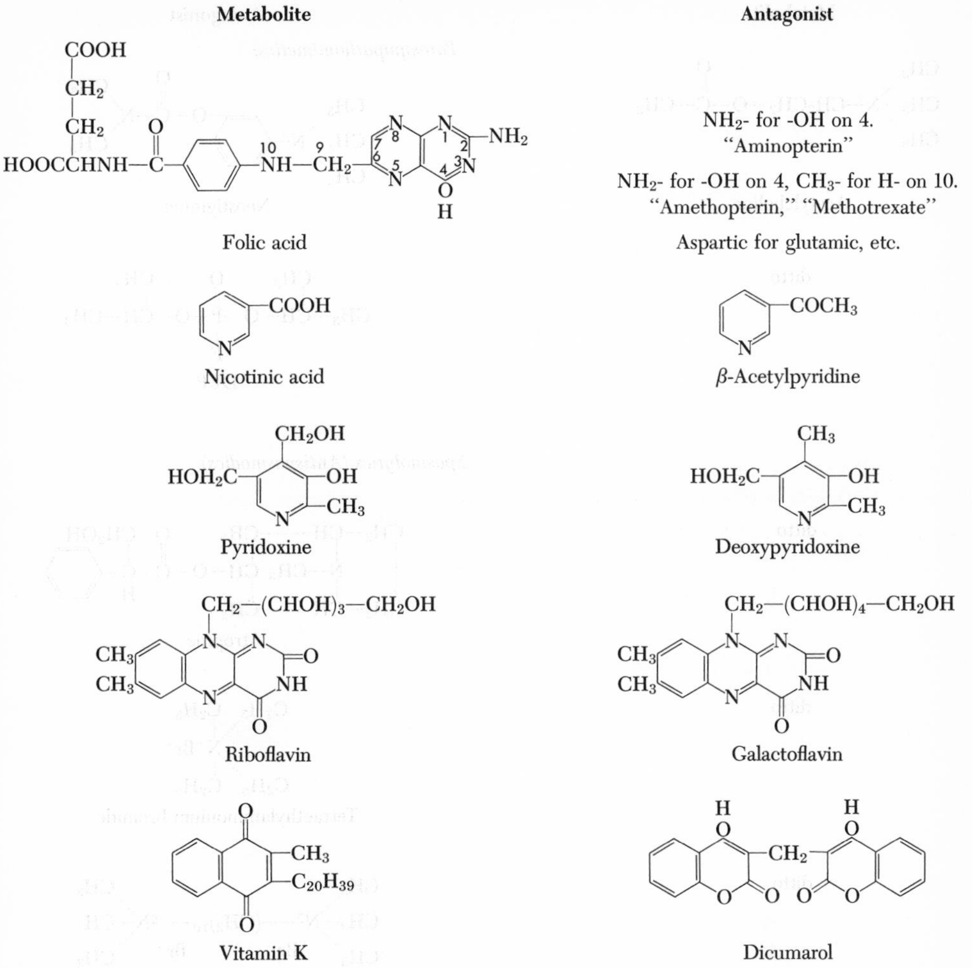

Metabolite	Antagonist
Folic acid	NH_2- for -OH on 4. "Aminopterin" NH_2- for -OH on 4, CH_3- for H- on 10. "Amethopterin," "Methotrexate" Aspartic for glutamic, etc.
Nicotinic acid	β-Acetylpyridine
Pyridoxine	Deoxypyridoxine
Riboflavin	Galactoflavin
Vitamin K	Dicumarol

Figure 25-4. *(continued).*

The second group of acetylcholine antagonists compete with it at the receptor sites, rather than at the surface of the esterase. Since they act as displacing agents, these compounds have the effect of lowering the concentration of acetylcholine in the vicinity of the receptors, and consequently are designated "spasmolytics", "parasympatholytics," or "antispasmodics." There appear to be three subdivisions of this group (Fig. 25-5): (1) the atropine type, which displaces acetylcholine from parasympathetic receptor sites (smooth muscle, glands); (2) the tetraethylammonium type, which blocks the action of the hormone in the ganglia; (3) the curare and decamethonium type, antagonizing the action of acetylcholine at the neuromuscular junction.

(*b*) ***Antagonisms involving catecholamines.*** The situation here is similar to that with acetylcholine. One class of antagonists to epinephrine and other catecholamines,

Metabolite	Antagonist
	Parasympathomimetics:
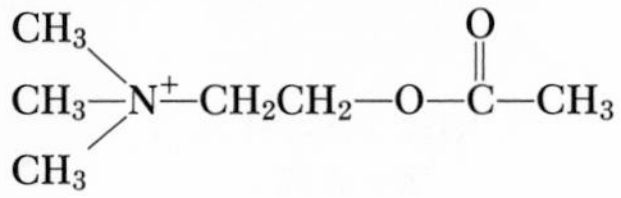 $(CH_3)_3N^{+}-CH_2CH_2-O-C(=O)-CH_3$ Acetylcholine	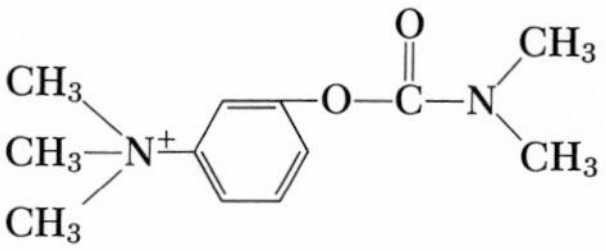 $(CH_3)_3N^{+}-C_6H_4-O-C(=O)-N(CH_3)_2$ Neostigmine
ditto	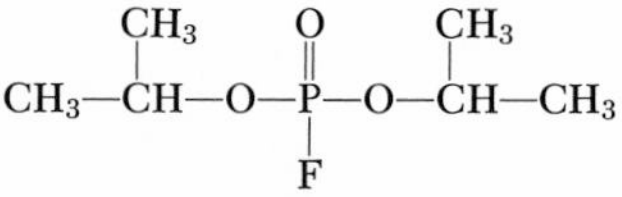 $CH_3-CH(CH_3)-O-P(=O)(F)-O-CH(CH_3)-CH_3$ DFP
	Spasmolytics (Antispasmodics):
ditto	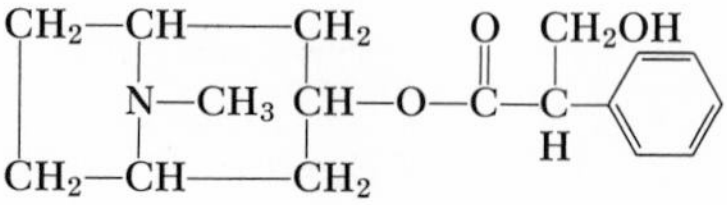 $CH_2-CH-CH_2$; $N-CH_3$; $CH-O-C(=O)-C(H)(CH_2OH)-C_6H_5$; $CH_2-CH-CH_2$ Atropine
ditto	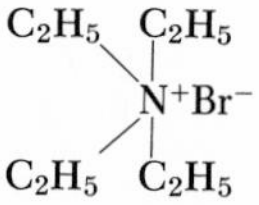 $(C_2H_5)_4N^{+}Br^{-}$ Tetraethylammonium bromide
ditto	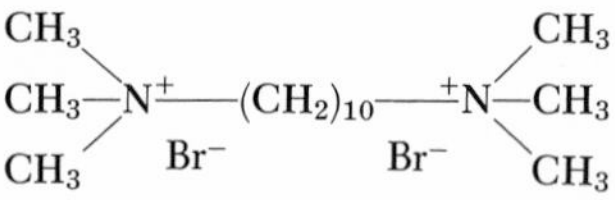 $(CH_3)_3N^{+}-(CH_2)_{10}-{}^{+}N(CH_3)_3$ Br^{-} Br^{-} "Decamethonium" bromide
	Sympathomimetics:
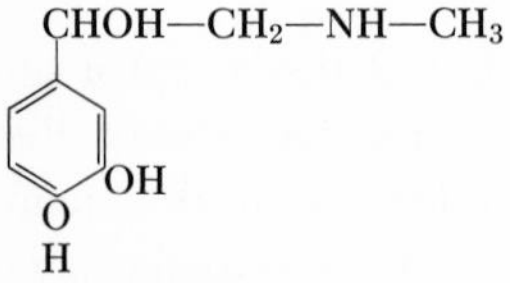 $CHOH-CH_2-NH-CH_3$ on benzene ring with OH, OH (O–H) Epinephrine (and other catecholamines)	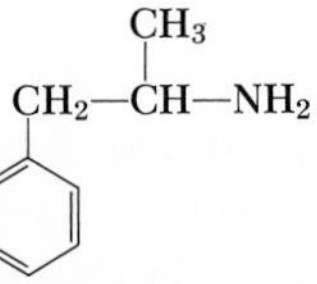 $C_6H_5-CH_2-CH(CH_3)-NH_2$ Amphetamine ("Benzedrine")
	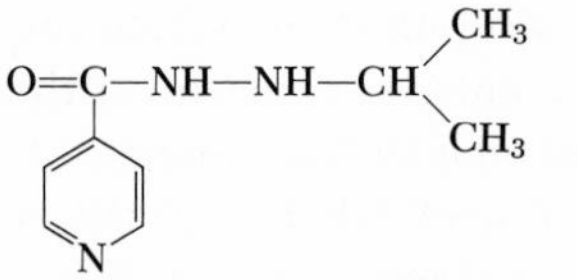 $O=C(C_5H_4N)-NH-NH-CH(CH_3)_2$ Iproniazid ("Marsilid")

Figure 25-5. Purported antagonisms of pharmacological agents. (See page 671 for continuation of this figure.)

Metabolite	Antagonist
	Sympatholytics (Adrenolytics):
Epinephrine (and other catecholamines)	"Dibenamine"
	Antihistaminics:
Histamine	"Pyribenzamine"
	Antiserotonins:
Serotonin	Psilocybin

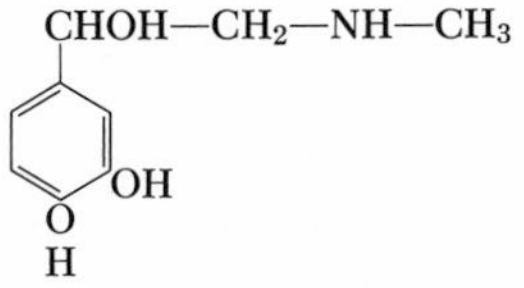

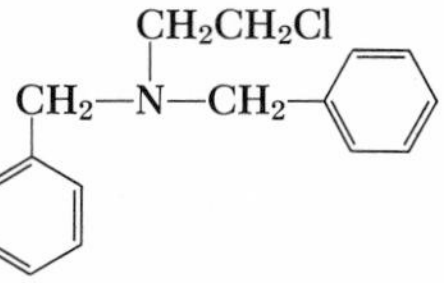

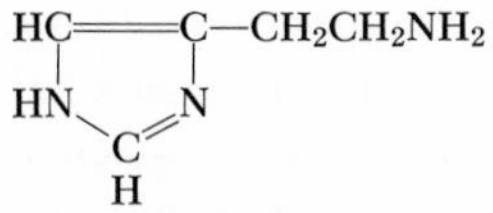

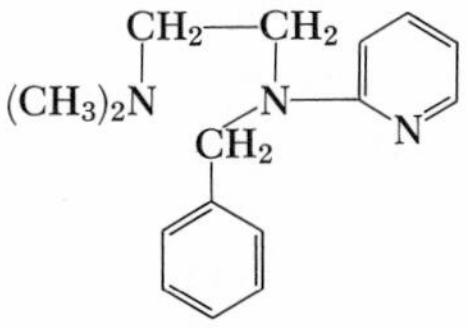

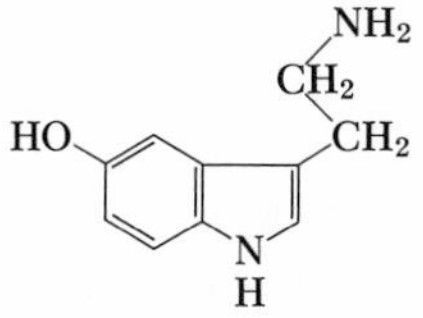

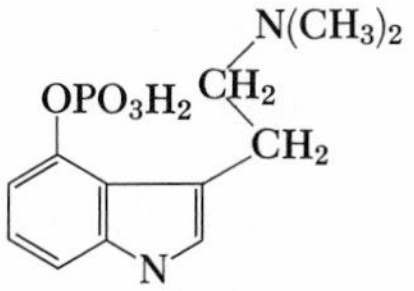

Figure 25-5. *(continued).*

the "sympathomimetics" apparently function either by directly affecting the receptor sites (probably the case with amphetamine [Fig. 25-5] and lysergic acid diethylamide [LSD]), or by blocking the action of monoamine oxidase, an enzyme which is of primary importance in the catabolism of catecholamines in the central nervous system (phenylcyclopropylamines, and hydrazides such as iproniazid [Fig. 25-5]). (Since the same enzyme is involved in the catabolism of serotonin in the central nervous sytem, the concentration of this "neurohormone" may be increased along with that of the catecholamines when the oxidase is inhibited). The detoxication of catecholamines circulating outside the nervous system is accomplished primarily by O-methylation. This catabolic pathway has been blocked in experimental animals by analogs such as catechol and pyrogallol and by guanidoacetic acid, which depletes the organism of methyl groups. Another type, the "sympatholytics" or "adrenolytics" (Dibenamine, Fig. 25-5) displace the catecholamines from their receptor sites. A similar action in the central nervous system is attributed to the tranquilizer, chlorpromazine. In one of the few known examples of precursor antagonism, α-methyldopa inhibits the decarboxylation of dopa to dopamine, itself a catecholamine and a precursor of norepinephrine and epinephrine. Agents are also known which impair the storage of catecholamines (reserpine, which also affects storage of serotonin), as well as others which block their release (Bretylium).

(*c*) ***Antagonisms involving histamine.*** The antihistaminics (Pyribenzamine, Fig. 25–5), currently used for the relief of allergies and related conditions, supposedly function by the displacement of histamine from receptor sites. Since the structures of certain antihistaminics bear little superficial resemblance to histamine, the applicability of the concept of antagonism by analog in this case is questioned by some.

(*d*) ***Antagonisms involving serotonin.*** The suggested role of serotonin in the central nervous system has been mentioned previously (p. 595). Certain hallucinogenic indoles, such as psilocybin, a compound found in some types of mushrooms in southern Mexico (Fig. 25–5), may function by antagonism of serotonin. The release of serotonin from its stores by reserpine has been mentioned previously.

Chemotherapy of Infection

The task of chemotherapy is the selective destruction or inhibition of the metabolism of the cells of invading microorganisms with minimal damage to the cells of the host. Since the major metabolic pathways of all living cells are much the same, from the bacterium to the bacteriologist, the design of effective and safe chemotherapeutic agents is quite difficult. The selectivity required in these cases favors an approach such as the search for selective antagonists, rather than the older application of noxious agents which are general tissue poisons.

In the most favorable instance, a metabolite or metabolic reaction may be found which is essential to the life or growth of the microorganism, but is absent from or of no consequence in the cells of the host. Such a case is the requirement for *p*-aminobenzoic acid by many bacteria. Obviously, discovery of such a differential requirement is only half the answer to the problem; the proper antimetabolite then must be synthesized.

In many cases no such qualitative difference in metabolism can be discovered. The investigator then must content himself with the exploitation of whatever quantitative differences may exist. The bacterium, being a rapidly growing and dividing cell, may not be able to withstand the induction of a temporary deficiency in the host, whose requirements for a given metabolite may be much more modest. This somewhat difficult approach may be aided by differences in cell permeability between microorganism and host toward the chosen antimetabolite.

The structural formulas of a number of chemotherapeutic agents and of the metabolites they are believed to antagonize are illustrated in Figure 25–6. A number of antibiotics acting as analogs have been discussed in an earlier section.

The example of the sulfonamides and *p*-aminobenzoic acid has been discussed at length already. Another probable antagonist of *p*-aminobenzoic acid is *p*-aminosalicylic acid, which has had some clinical application in the treatment of tuberculosis. Further investigation of sulfonamide-like compounds has led to the development of antibacterial sulfones used in tuberculosis and leprosy, while deliberate pursuit of certain side-effects of sulfonamide drugs has resulted in the discovery of useful diuretics (acetazolamide), uricosurics (probenecid), and oral hypoglycemics (sulfonylureas). The antithyroid properties of sulfonamides have not yet been utilized in therapy.

Phenylpantothenone has been tested experimentally as an antimalarial drug. It appears to inhibit the incorporation of pantothenic acid into CoA. Certain other antimalarials ("Daraprim") act as folic acid antagonists.

One of the few successful antiviral agents is the thymidine analog, iododeoxyuridine, which is effective against herpes virus infection of the cornea.

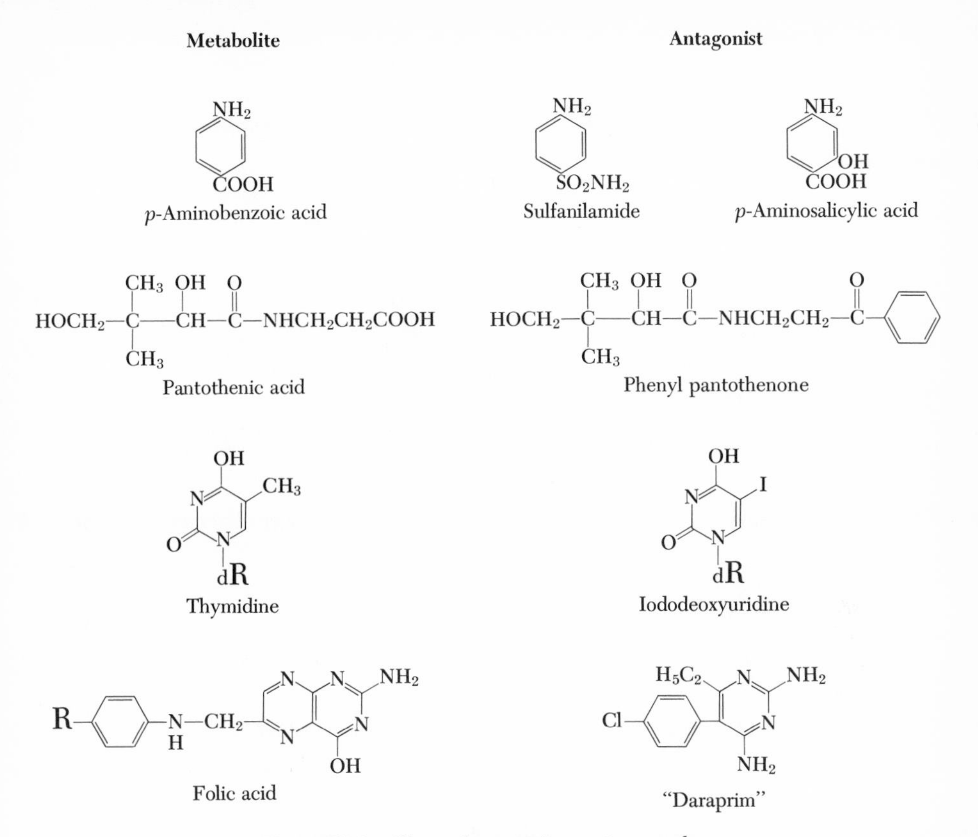

Figure 25-6. Chemotherapeutic agents as analogs.

Cancer Chemotherapy

Attempts at chemical control of neoplastic growth are based essentially on the same assumptions as those underlying the chemotherapy of infections. The problem is infinitely more difficult, however, since the cells to be inhibited or destroyed are "foreign" to the body largely in behavior, not in origin. Nevertheless, it is believed that the rapid rate of growth of neoplastic tissue may result in requirements for vitamins or other cofactors which differ, possibly qualitatively, but at least quantitatively, from those of normal cells. It is possible, also, that certain "primitive" metabolic pathways may be of more importance in tumors than in normal tissue, since the former resemble embryonic tissue in certain respects.

Examples of antimetabolites which have been or are being investigated in cancer chemotherapy are presented in Figure 25-7.

(a) ***Folic acid antagonists.*** Several factors have motivated the investigation of folic acid antagonists as tumor inhibitors. One is the rapid rate of multiplication of cancer cells, which would be expected to increase the requirements for raw materials used in the synthesis of nuclear components (nucleic acids, purines, pyrimidines), thus concomitantly increasing the need for folic acid. Another is the leukopenia which results from a deficiency in folic acid, suggesting application of antifolic compounds in the treatment of leukemias.

Folic acid is capable of chemical modification to yield active antagonists to the

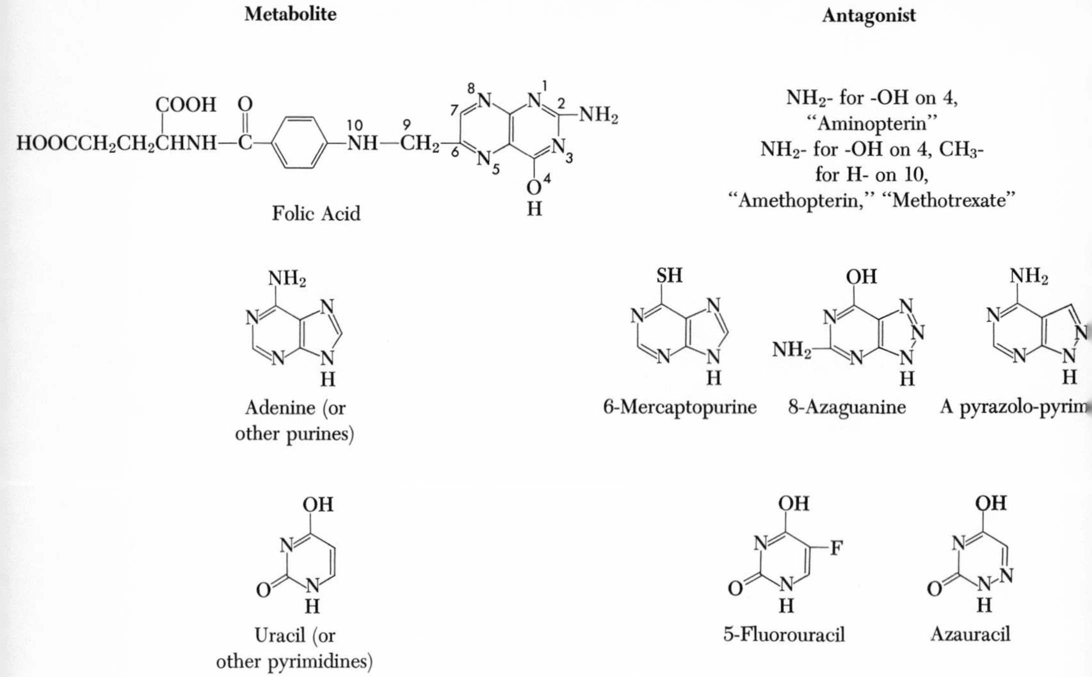

Metabolite	Antagonist
Folic Acid	NH_2- for -OH on 4, "Aminopterin"; NH_2- for -OH on 4, CH_3- for H- on 10, "Amethopterin," "Methotrexate"
Adenine (or other purines)	6-Mercaptopurine; 8-Azaguanine; A pyrazolo-pyrim
Uracil (or other pyrimidines)	5-Fluorouracil; Azauracil

Figure 25-7. Antimetabolites in cancer chemotherapy.

parent molecule. Replacement of the hydroxyl group at position 4 of the pteridine ring by an amino group (Aminopterin), or addition of a methyl group at position 10 of the *p*-aminobenzoyl moiety, together with the preceding change (Amethopterin, Methotrexate), is an example of changes which yield active antagonists.

The antifolics inhibit the reduction of folic and dihydrofolic acids to the tetrahydro derivative, which is the active coenzyme in transformylations and transhydroxymethylations. Although the insertion of formate units into the purine ring undoubtedly is inhibited in the presence of these analogs, probably the process most sensitive to inhibition is the transformation of uracil derivatives to thymine derivatives, since this involves not only transhydroxymethylation, but also reduction, with tetrahydrofolic acid being the reducing agent.

Positive results with these analogs have been reported in experimental animals and clinically in acute leukemia. The beneficial effects are only temporary, however, and are accompanied by toxic manifestations due to folic acid deficiency of the normal tissues.

(*b*) ***Purine antagonists.*** Such compounds as 6-mercaptopurine and 8-azaguanine have been somewhat effective in inhibiting growth of certain types of solid tumors and in leukemia. They, like the anti-folic compounds, have toxic side-effects. 6-Mercaptopurine forms the corresponding ribonucleotide, which in turn inhibits the conversion of inosinic to adenylic and guanylic acids. 6-Mercaptopurine nucleotide, in addition, participates in the negative feedback mechanism whereby purine nucleotides inhibit the synthesis of ribosylamine-5′-phosphate. In this connection, it has been found that tumor cells which are resistant to 6-mercaptopurine have a reduced capacity to convert it to the nucleotide. 8-Azaguanine is incorporated into RNA, replacing guanine. It is likely that this fraudulent RNA inhibits protein synthesis. Pyrazolo-pyrimidines also are effective purine antagonists.

(*c*) ***Pyrimidine antagonists.*** Azauracil (or better, the nucleoside, azauridine) is converted in the organism to azauridylic acid, an inhibitor of orotidylate decarboxylase. 5-Fluorouracil forms nucleotides which inhibit the incorporation of uracil nucleotides into RNA and are themselves incorporated, replacing uracil; of probable greater importance is the inhibition of the conversion of uracil to thymine derivatives by these compounds. Although fluorouracil does not prevent the incorporation of thymine into DNA, other halogenated uracils such as the bromo derivative may have this action, replacing thymine in DNA and producing inhibitory and mutagenic effects in the cell. The presence of halogenated pyrimidines in DNA sensitizes it to X-rays.

(*d*) ***Miscellaneous considerations.*** The mechanism of action of the antibiotics azaserine and diazo-oxo-norleucine has been discussed previously.

Mention should be made of the use of estrogens in the treatment of prostatic carcinoma, an excellent example of estrogen-androgen antagonism. The growth of the cancer and the concomitant elevation of serum acid phosphatase are both affected directly by the estrogen-androgen balance.

Diuretic Analogs

One of the interesting by-products of the research on sulfonamides was the discovery that certain of these compounds may be effective inhibitors of carbonic anhydrase. One of these, "Diamox" (Fig. 25–8), has found application as a diuretic agent. The inhibition of carbonic anhydrase decreases the hydrogen-sodium exchange across the renal tubule, thus decreasing the reabsorption of bicarbonate and sodium and causing a concomitant loss of water. However, inhibition of carbonic anhydrase may not be the underlying mechanism of the newer sulfonamide diuretics, since these compounds are less potent inhibitors of the enzyme and appear to have their main effects on the reabsorption of chloride and sodium.

A different type of diuretic analog is represented by the steroid-17-spirolactones (Fig. 25–8), which compete with aldosterone for the target site in the renal tubule at which it promotes the reabsorption of sodium.

Metabolite	**Antagonist**
Bicarbonate	Acetazolamide ("Diamox")
Aldosterone	"Aldactone"

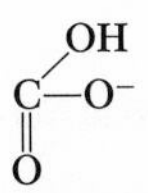

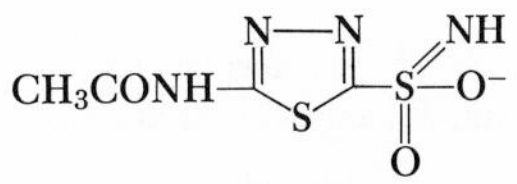

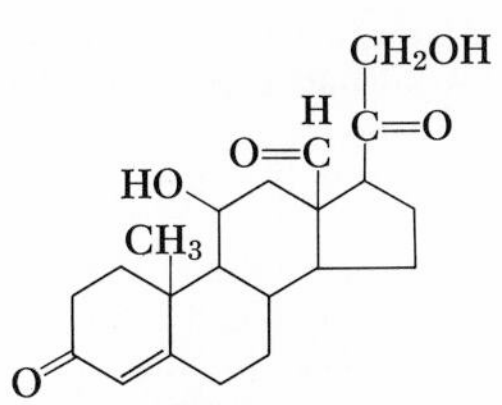

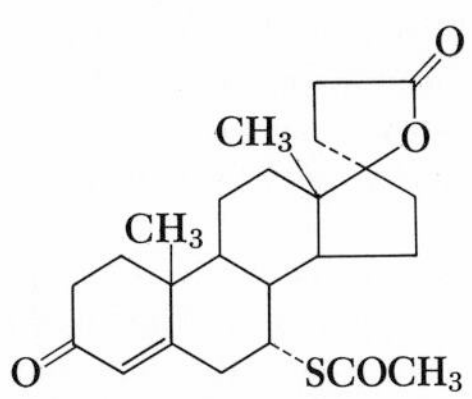

Figure 25-8. Diuretic analogs.

Organic Insecticides

Little information is available in this field, although much may be expected in the future. The paucity of data probably will not be remedied until more is known of the intermediary metabolism of insects. Examples of metabolic antagonism that have received attention in recent years are various organic phosphates and carbamates (similar to those in Fig. 25–5), which are antagonists of acetylcholine at the esterase site.

Herbicides

It has been suggested that certain "weed-killers," e.g., the chlorophenoxyacetic acids ("2,4-D") act either as antagonists of the natural plant hormones (i.e., auxins, such as indoleacetic acid) or, more probably, as direct substitutes which are lethal through overstimulation. 2,2′-Dichloropropionic acid is believed to inhibit the synthesis of pantothenate.

COMMENT

Many examples of metabolic antagonism have been omitted, since the aim has been the presentation of general principles rather than the accumulation of specific details. Nevertheless, it should be obvious that the concept of metabolic antagonism is widely applicable, It would be of importance if it merely aided the understanding of facts already available; however, it does much more. It places in the hands of the biochemist new tools for the systematic investigation of metabolic pathways, the discovery of intermediary metabolites, and the mechanism of enzyme action. It provides what has been called a "rational basis" for pharmacology and chemotherapy, substituting general theory for much of the empiricism formerly characteristic of those fields. It promises for the agriculturalist new weapons against insect pests and weeds, as well as agents for improving the performance of crops. In short, the phenomenon of metabolic antagonism potentially augments immeasurably the controls which can be exercised over the cells of our own bodies and those of our biological friends and foes.

BIBLIOGRAPHY

Handschumacher, R. E., and Welch, A. D.: Agents which influence nucleic acid metabolism, Chapter 39 in Chargaff, E., and Davidson, J. N. (eds.): The Nucleic Acids, Vol. 3, New York, Academic Press, Inc., 1960.

Hitchings, G. H., and Burchall, J. J.: Inhibition of folate biosynthesis and function as a basis for chemotherapy, Advances Enzymol. *27*:417, 1965.

Hochster, R. M., and Quastel, J. H. (eds.): Metabolic Inhibitors, Vols. 1 and 2, New York, Academic Press, Inc., 1963.

Martin, G. J.: Biological Antagonism, New York, Blakiston Division, McGraw-Hill Book Company, 1951.

Meister, A.: Biochemistry of the Amino Acids, Vol. 1, New York, Academic Press, Inc., 1965, Chapter 3, Amino Acid Antagonists.

Peters, R. A.: Biochemical Lesions and Lethal Synthesis, New York, The Macmillan Company, 1963, Chapters 6 and 7.

Škoda, J.: Mechanism of action and application of azapyrimidines, Progress Nucleic Acid Res. *2*:197, 1963.

Stekol, J. A.: Biochemical basis for ethionine effects on tissues, Advances Enzymol. *25*:369, 1963.

Webb, J. L.: Enzyme and Metabolic Inhibitors, Vols. 1 and 2, New York, Academic Press, Inc., 1963 and 1966.

Wooley, D. W.: A Study of Antimetabolites, New York, John Wiley & Sons, Inc., 1952.

Wooley, D. W.: The Biochemical Bases of Psychoses, or the Serotonin Hypothesis about Mental Diseases, New York, John Wiley & Sons, Inc., 1962.

CHAPTER 26

HORMONES

A HORMONE is commonly defined as a chemical substance which, formed in one part of the body, is carried in the bloodstream to other organs or tissues, which it influences in a specific manner. This definition is so broad that its usefulness is limited. For example, on this basis CO_2 has been referred to as a "hormone of respiration;" substances liberated by traumatized tissues as "wound hormones;" a number of factors secreted by digestive organs have been designated "gastrointestinal hormones;" acetylcholine, synthesized in nervous tissue, is frequently included in this category. It is generally agreed that the following structures should be included in the "endocrine system," i.e., tissues which produce "internal secretions" (hormones): the anterior and posterior pituitary, thyroid, parathyroid, adrenal cortex and medulla, pancreatic islands of Langerhans, ovary, testis, and placenta. Inclusion of other structures under this designation is a matter of individual preference. Of historical interest is the fact that the term "hormone" was first applied (Bayliss and Starling, 1902) to secretin, a substance produced in the duodenal mucosa, which has a stimulating effect on the secretion of pancreatic juice and bile (p. 752). It should be pointed out that although the term "hormone" implies an "exciting" influence, certain hormones are now known to exert a depressing effect on certain of their target tissues.

Information concerning the functions of hormones has been derived from (1) studies of the effects of removal or destructive disease of their tissues of origin, and (2) studies of the biological effects of excessive amounts of individual hormones resulting from either disease (hypersecretion) of various endocrine organs or experimental administration of tissue extracts or chemically pure products. The enormous advances in this field in recent years have been due largely to remarkable accomplishments in the chemical identification of several hormones, leading in important instances to their synthesis and, therefore, to their availability in amounts adequate for experimental purposes. These studies have indicated that certain hormones, in addition to biologically important actions on individual target organs (e.g., gonadotropic and sex hormones), are intimately concerned in a variety of integrated processes, metabolic and otherwise, which serve to maintain homeostasis, i.e., a "steady state," in the organism. We are concerned here mainly with the chemistry and metabolic effects of these substances.

Mode of Action of Hormones

It is often stated that hormones influence the activity or extent of certain processes in the body, but do not appear to initiate such processes. Hormones have therefore been likened to catalysts. The example of the thyroid hormone is often cited in this connection. The amount of this hormone in the circulation determines the level of oxidations, but the latter are merely lowered and not abolished by complete absence of thyroid hormone. In many instances the quantitative changes effected by a hormone cover so wide a range, raising the level of activity of a process from almost zero to $+4$, that what actually is a quantitative change appears to be qualitative at first sight. This is well illustrated by the changes in function and enzymatic activity of the uterine and vaginal mucosa induced by estrogens and progesterone.

The facts that hormones act in very low concentrations and that their actions amount to a rather specific type of control over certain metabolic events suggested that the targets of hormonal action may be the enzymes. It has been difficult to obtain definite evidence on this point. Attempts to demonstrate hormonal action in soluble enzyme systems have been largely unsuccessful. It has been found that natural estrogens, but not certain synthetic estrogens, activate a transhydrogenase of placental tissue. It has been shown that glucagon and epinephrine stimulate the enzymatic production of cyclic adenylic acid for the reactivation of phosphorylase in the liver. This same mechanism apparently also is involved in the activation of adrenal phosphorylase by ACTH.

It is believed by some that the action of hormones is "morphologic," i.e., that their immediate target is the cell membrane or the limiting membrane of an intracellular particle, e.g., the mitochondrion. On this basis it is assumed that the hormone facilitates contact of substrate and cofactor molecules with enzymes, thereby serving to increase the rate of specific enzyme reactions. For example, there is evidence that the action of insulin in stimulating utilization of glucose is due in part at least to an increase in the rate of penetration of glucose into the cell. The action of thyroxine as an "uncoupling agent" for aerobic phosphorylations appears to be due to an effect exerted on the mitochondrial membrane. It must be remembered, however, that demonstration of an effect of a hormone on an isolated system does not necessarily mean that this is involved in the production of its physiological effects in the intact organism or that other actions or mechanisms may not be involved. Injection of a hormone into an intact animal is frequently followed by a change in activity of one or more enzyme systems, as assayed in excised tissues of the animal. In such experiments the action of the hormone could be the result of increased synthesis or destruction of the enzyme, removal or addition of inhibitory substances or cofactors, or simply changes in tissue permeability, all of which are rather far removed from the enzymatic reaction proper. The same general ambiguities attend experiments performed with tissue slices.

There is increasing evidence that the metabolic effects of several hormones are preceded by and dependent upon production of increased amounts of mRNA in the target tissues. Because of the central role of mRNA in protein synthesis, it has been suggested that the regulatory actions of hormones are exerted through the medium of mRNA control of enzyme synthesis. Increased RNA production or enzyme induction or both have been demonstrated for certain important actions of a number of hormones: growth hormone, ACTH, FSH, LH, TSH, estrogen, androgen, adrenocortical hormones, thyroxine, insulin, and parathyroid hormone. On this basis, hormonal control of metabolic reactions and perhaps of certain transport processes is effected by altering the intracellular concentration of enzymes, coenzymes, or other activating or inhibiting factors.

Hormone and Target Tissues

Certain hormones exert their characteristic effects on a limited number of organs or tissues which have been termed the "target tissues" of the corresponding hormone. For example, the primary dramatic actions of adrenocorticotropin, thyrotropin, and gonadotropins are exerted on the adrenal cortex, thyroid, and gonads, respectively. On the other hand, such agents as insulin, thyroxine, and adrenal glucocorticoids influence basic metabolic reactions in cells of almost all tissues. Even such hormones as the estrogens and androgens, the dramatic effects of which are exerted upon specific sex organs and tissues, are known to influence certain metabolic reactions in a variety of tissues, e.g., liver, kidney, bone, and muscle. Stimulation of growth of certain specific tissues, induced by sex steroids and tropic hormones of the adenohypophysis, involves a large variety of metabolic processes, including synthesis of nucleic acids, proteins, lipids, and carbohydrates, as well as increased production of energy. Since similar and in some cases identical reactions occur continually in cells of other tissues also exposed to these circulating hormones, clearly some morphologic or functional characteristics of the target cells must underlie the difference in their responsiveness to these specific hormones. A number of factors may be involved: differences in penetrability of the hormone into the cell; differences in the rate of its metabolism to inactive or active compounds; structural differences in cellular enzymes that perform identical functions in different cells, as in the case of the phosphorylases of liver and muscle. In certain respects, responsiveness of a particular cell is related fundamentally to the mode of action of the hormone, concerning which little is known.

MECHANISMS OF REGULATION OF HORMONE SECRETION

Negative Feedback Mechanisms

In the interests of physiological efficiency, the concentrations in the circulation of substances as potent as hormones must be regulated rather precisely. This is accomplished by regulation of their production and secretion, metabolism, and excretion.

Although the nervous system is of primary importance in the case of a few hormones, humoral factors are generally involved in the fundamental control mechanism. Under normal conditions, production and discharge of thyroid, glucocorticoid and gonadal (estrogen, androgen) hormones are regulated by the concentrations in the blood of thyrotropic, adrenocorticotropic and gonadotropic hormones, respectively. As the concentration of circulating target organ hormone rises, secretion of the corresponding tropic hormone is depressed, either by direct action on the adenohypophysis or perhaps via depression of secretion of hypothalamic neurohumoral factors which reach the adenohypophysis in the hypophyseal portal circulation. This is a remarkably efficient autoregulatory mechanism operating on the negative feedback principle.

Secretory activity of other endocrine glands is regulated by the concentrations of certain blood constituents, in the metabolism of which the hormone is directly concerned. For example, secretion of insulin increases and decreases as the blood sugar concentration rises and falls; secretion of parathyroid hormone increases and decreases as the serum calcium concentration falls and rises. These are other examples of negative feedback types of mechanism. In this case, the effects of changes in the blood glucose and calcium concentrations are produced by direct action on the pancreatic islet cells and parathyroid glands. In effect, the blood glucose and calcium concentrations regulate themselves, each through the medium of changes in secretion of a single hormone.

Nervous System

Reference has been made previously to the role of the nervous system in determining or influencing hormonal effects on target tissues. It also influences production and release of certain hormones.

(1) Neurosecretory products, conventionally referred to as "neurohumoral" substances, are elaborated in certain hypothalamic nuclei; they pass along nerve fibers and are transferred to the blood of the portal system of the pituitary stalk; thus they reach the parenchyma of the adenohypophysis and stimulate secretion of anterior pituitary hormones. In view of the fact that the hypothalamic nuclei are connected with higher brain centers, the latter can influence liberation of these neurohumoral factors and thus indirectly that of pituitary hormones and, ultimately, secretion of gonadal, thyroid, and adrenocortical hormones.

(2) Certain hormones are actually elaborated in and secreted by nerve cells. Oxytocin and vasopressin are elaborated in certain hypothalamic nuclei, their production therefore being subject to influence by emotional factors and nerve impulses from other areas of the nervous system. Epinephrine and norepinephrine are manufactured and secreted not only by the adrenal medulla (itself a differentiated and specialized part of the nervous system), but also by ganglion cells and perhaps by brain cells. Sympathetic stimulation increases epinephrine secretion which, accordingly, occurs in response to a variety of emotional factors, particularly those of an unpleasant nature, such as pain, anger, apprehension, and fear. Increased production of epinephrine may, in turn, directly or indirectly increase secretory activity of the pancreatic islets, adenohypophysis, thyroid, and adrenal cortex.

In the case of most of the endocrine glands, these nervous influences are superimposed upon a fundamental regulatory mechanism of the negative feedback type.

TRANSPORT, METABOLISM, AND EXCRETION OF HORMONES

Major fractions of several hormones exist in the blood plasma in forms other than the free state in which they presumably initially entered the circulation. Certain hormones are transported largely in combination with plasma proteins, e.g., estrogens and androgens bound to albumin, corticosteroids bound to corticosteroid-binding globulin, and thyroxine bound to thyroxine-binding globulin. The protein-bound hormone is apparently in rather readily reversible equilibrium with the relatively small amounts present in the free form. This phenomenon of protein-binding, because of the relative non-diffusibility of the complex, serves to restrict passage of the hormone not only across the glomerular capillaries into the urine, but also across other capillaries, thereby limiting the amount of hormone coming into direct contact with cells of various tissues. It has been postulated that these hormone-protein complexes may stabilize the physiologically significant concentrations of unbound hormones in much the same manner that buffer salts stabilize the small concentration of hydrogen ion. In this sense, binding by plasma proteins is a regulatory mechanism, protecting the organism against sudden and undesirable fluctuations in concentrations of circulating hormones.

The liver plays an important role in endocrine homeostasis. Some hormones here undergo structural alteration to biologically less active or inactive compounds; these include androgens, estrogens, progesterone, corticosteroids, thyroid hormone, insulin, and epinephrine. Steroid hormones and their metabolites are also conjugated here (glucuronic acid and sulfate) to form compounds more readily soluble in water and therefore more readily excreted in the urine. Certain of the steroid hormones also are removed from the systemic circulation by the liver and are excreted in the bile.

Certain hormones may undergo metabolic inactivation in cells of target tissues, e.g., thyrotropin by the thyroid and gonadotropins by the gonads. It is possible, too, that certain hormones may be transformed in target cells to compounds of higher or different biological activity.

Chemical Nature of Hormones

Certain of the hormones are protein or polypeptide in nature (e.g., anterior pituitary, parathyroid, insulin), some are amino acid derivatives (e.g., thyroxine, epinephrine), and others are steroids (e.g., estrogens, androgens, progesterone, adrenal cortex). The multiplicity of possibilities of stereoisomerism and of metabolic reactions inherent in the multiple-ring structure of the steroid hormones has given rise to a rather complicated system of nomenclature, the more confusing since it is subjected to periodic revision. It seems desirable to present here an outline of the currently accepted system, which applies not only to this group of hormones but to all other steroids, e.g., bile acids, cholesterol, etc. (p. 42).

NOMENCLATURE OF STEROIDS

Introduction

The term "steroid" is applied to the members of a group of compounds which have in common the cyclopentanoperhydrophenanthrene nucleus. This skeleton structure consists of a cyclopentane ring, (D), fused to a completely hydrogenated phenanthrene (A-B-C):

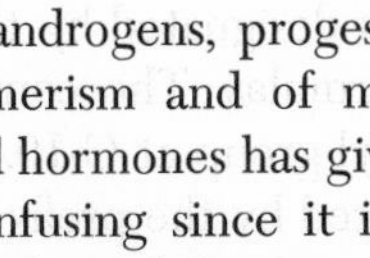

C D
A B

Substituents in the nucleus and on the commonly occurring side chains are located by a standard numbering system:

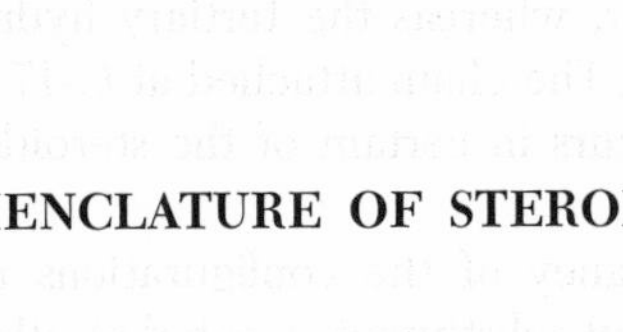

21 22 24 26
20 23 25
18 27
12 17
11 13 16
19 14 15
1 9
2 10 8
3 5 7
4 6

Examination of this formula and those of the substituted steroids reveals the existence of numerous asymmetric carbon atoms. Deoxycholic acid, a common bile acid, contains ten centers of asymmetry and can theoretically exist in 1024 stereoisomeric forms. Fortunately, only a few of the possible stereoisomers of the steroids actually exist in nature.

Nuclear Stereoisomerism

It is possible for each pair of adjacent rings in the nucleus to exist in two spatial configurations about the junction: *cis* and *trans*. In all naturally occurring steroids the configurations at the junctions of rings B-C and C-D are *trans*. At the junctions of rings A and B there is more natural variation. The estrogens, as will be seen below, do not have the possibility of isomerism at this locus because ring A is aromatic. All other steroids can be divided into two groups: the "normal," or *cis*-A/B, and the "allo-," or *trans*-A/B.

Stereoisomerism of Substituents

Most of the steroids which are of physiological interest carry methyl groups attached at positions 10 and 13, usually indicated merely by a short vertical line. By convention, the methyl group at C-10 is assigned a steric configuration with relation to this carbon atom such that it projects upward from the plane of the steroid nucleus, if the latter is written as above. This steric form is designated by the prefix "β-," and is indicated by a solid valence bond in structural formulas. The configurations of other substituents are assigned with reference to the methyl group at C-10. Groups projecting downward below the plane of the nucleus are designated by the prefix "α-," and are indicated in the structural formulas by valence bonds formed of broken lines.

Owing to the *trans* junctions involved in rings B, C, and D, the tertiary hydrogen atoms at C-9 and C-14 are α, whereas the tertiary hydrogen atom at C-8 and methyl group (No. 18) at C-13 are β. The chain attached at C-17 is β in all natural steroids. The 11-hydroxyl group which occurs in certain of the steroids of the adrenal cortex has the β configuration.

In contrast to the constancy of the configurations mentioned above, considerable variation is found in the case of substituents located at other positions on the ring system. The hydroxyl groups attached to the various bile acids have characteristic configurations (p. 479). The existence of "normal" and "allo-" series of compounds due to isomerism at junction A/B gives rise, respectively, to β and α tertiary hydrogen atoms at C-5/6 (*cis* and *trans* relations to the methyl group at C-10). Many steroids bear an alcoholic hydroxyl group at C-3, which also can exist in the two isomeric forms.

In the case of compounds bearing asymmetric centers in the side chain attached at C-17, by convention, α-oriented groups are written as projecting to the right and β-groups to the left, if the side chain is written vertically on the page.

Prefixes and Suffixes

In order to facilitate an understanding of the nomenclature rules presented below, the meanings of certain prefixes and suffixes are listed in Table 26-1. Certain of these are of common occurrence in organic chemistry; others are peculiar to the field of steroids.

Parent Hydrocarbons

All steroids may be considered derivatives of certain parent hydrocarbons. The estro-

TABLE 26-1. SUFFIXES AND PREFIXES FOR STEROIDS

SUFFIX OR PREFIX	MEANING
Suffix	
-ane	Saturated hydrocarbon
-ene	Unsaturated hydrocarbon
-ol	Hydroxyl group, as in an alcohol or phenol
-one	Ketone group
Prefix	
hydroxy- (oxy-)	Hydroxyl group
keto- (oxo-)	Ketone group
deoxy-	Loss of an oxygen atom
dehydro-	Loss of two hydrogen atoms
dihydro-	Gain of two hydrogen atoms
cis-	Refers to spatial arrangement of two groups on the same side of the molecule
trans-	Refers to spatial arrangement of two groups on opposite sides of the molecule
α-	Refers to group which is *trans* to the methyl at C-10
β-	Refers to group which is *cis* to the methyl at C-10
epi-	Isomeric in configuration to a reference compound; specifically α at location C-3.
iso-	Similar to epi-, but not restricted to C-3.
allo-	Differing from reference compound in having 5α instead of 5β configuration; rings A and B in *trans* instead of *cis* relation to each other
etio-	Refers to final degradation product of a more complex molecule which still retains the essential chemical character of the original molecule.
nor-	Refers to compound similar chemically to reference substance, but having one less carbon atom in side-chain
Δ^n-	Indicates position of unsaturated linkage.

gens, which are formed of monomethylated steroid nuclei, are derived from the parent compound, estrane:

Estrane   1,3,5:10-Estratriene

Since they are aromatic in ring A, the common estrogens are named systematically as derivatives of 1,3,5:10-estratriene.

All other steroids which are of physiological interest have in common a dimethylated nucleus, and, as indicated previously, may be grouped into two series, depending on the steric relations between rings A and B (seen as a *cis* or *trans* relation between the hydrogen atom at C-5 and the reference methyl group at C-10). Since four types of side chains are commonly attached at C-17 in these compounds, a total of eight parent hydrocarbons exists. These are listed in Table 26-2.

Compounds which, owing to structural modifications, have no asymmetry at C-5 are named from the parent compound (based on the side chain) which is italicized in the table. The term, "allo-," is used solely to indicate the replacement of a 5β by a 5α configuration. Reversals at any other asymmetric centers are indicated by a prefix, consisting of the location of the group and the appropriate term, α or β, followed by the name of the

Table 26-2. Parent Hydrocarbons of Steroid Hormones

5α, allo- or *trans* series	R—	5β, normal, or *cis* series
Androstane	—H	Testane (formerly etiocholane)
Allopregnane	$—C_2H_5$	*Pregnane*
Allocholane	$—CH(CH_3)—CH_2—CH_2—CH_3$	*Cholane*
Cholestane 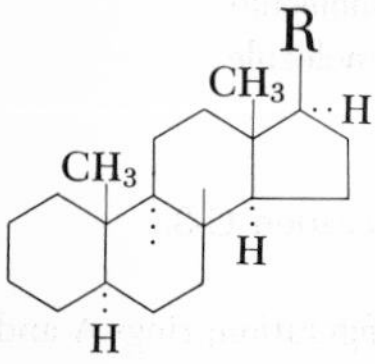	$—CH(CH_3)—CH_2—CH_2—CH_2—CH(CH_3)_2$	Coprostane 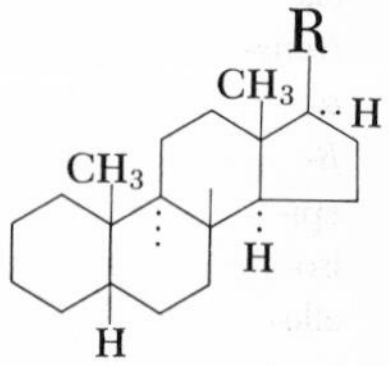

reference compound. Substituents are named in a similar fashion. Illustrations of the systematic method of naming steriods are presented in Table 26-1. Currently acceptable trivial designations are indicated.

ANDROGENS

Androgens are substances capable of producing certain characteristic masculinizing effects; i.e., they maintain the normal structure and function of the prostate and seminal vesicles and influence the development of secondary male sex characteristics, such as hair distribution and voice.

Chemistry

The naturally occurring androgens in man are testosterone, androsterone, 3β-androsterone (epiandrosterone), and dehydro-3β-androsterone (dehydro-epiandrosterone). For purposes of terminology, these may be regarded as derivatives of the saturated hydrocarbon, "androstane" (Fig. 26–1). All have methyl groups at C-10 and C-13 and contain 19 C atoms.

In compounds containing a ketone group at C-3 and a double bond at C-4-5, the grouping including C-3 to C-5 is termed an α,β-unsaturated ketone group. This is characteristic of the most active steroid hormones except estrogens (e.g., testosterone, progesterone, adrenal cortical hormones), and any change in this group reduces the specific activity of the hormone in question.

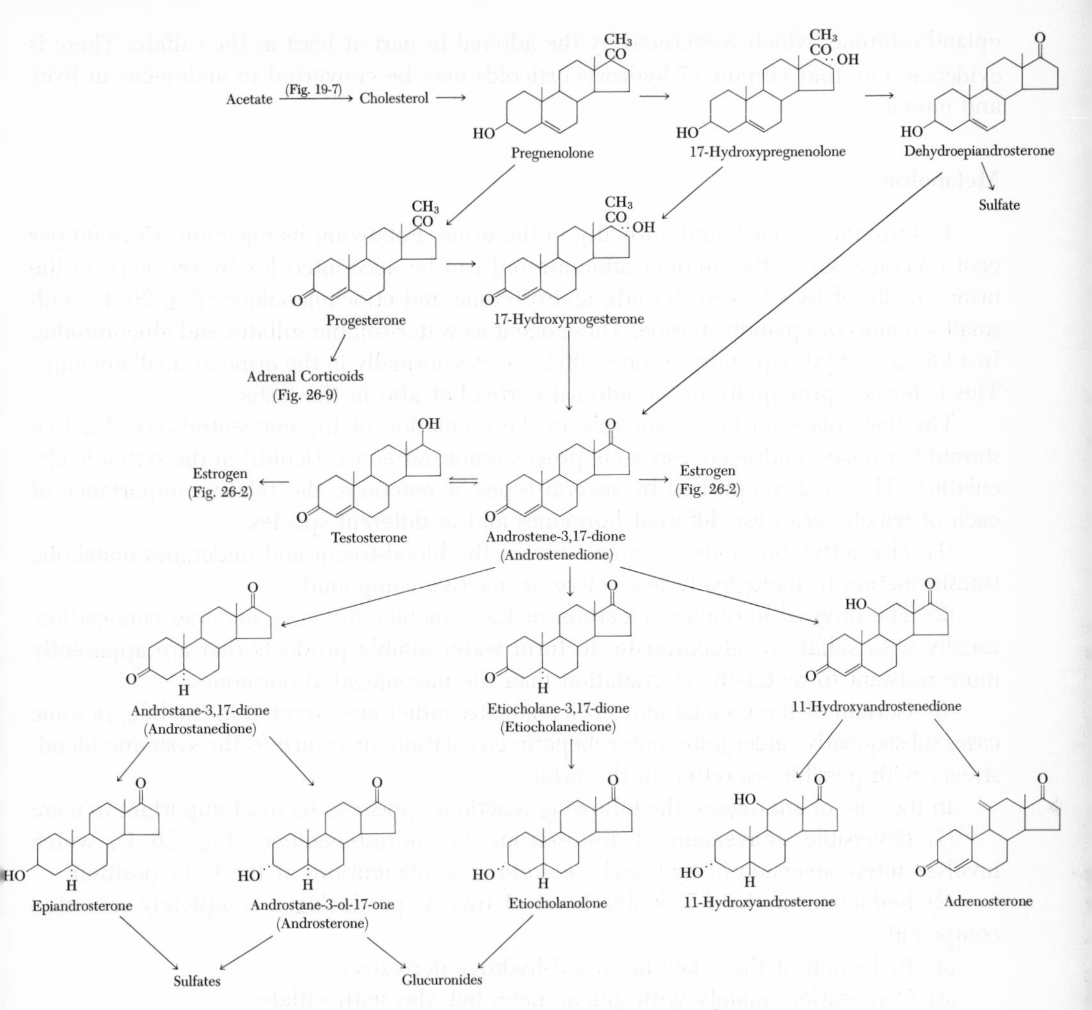

Figure 26–1. Biosynthesis and metabolism of androgens.

Biosynthesis

Androgens are produced in the testis (Leydig cells), adrenal cortex, and ovary. They may be formed from either acetate or cholesterol, pregnenolone being an important if not indeed an obligatory intermediate. Various demonstrated pathways of biosynthesis are presented in Figure 26–1. It is probable that most of these operate in all androgen-secreting tissues, but not equally. For example, in the testis, testosterone, the most active natural androgen, is the chief end-product of steroid hormone biogenesis, relatively little estrogen being formed and progesterone serving mainly as a metabolic intermediate. In the ovary, on the other hand, progesterone is itself an important end-product and testosterone serves mainly as a precursor of estrogen. In the adrenal cortex, under normal conditions, a large portion of the progesterone and 17α-hydroxyprogesterone formed is converted to adrenocorticoids, androgens being produced mainly perhaps via dehydroepiandrosterone, which is secreted by the adrenal in part at least as the sulfate. There is evidence, too, that certain 17-hydroxycorticoids may be converted to androgens in liver and muscle.

Metabolism

Testosterone is not found normally in the urine. Following its injection, 15 to 60 per cent (average 35) of the amount administered can be accounted for by recovery in the urine chiefly of two 17-ketosteroids, androsterone and etiocholanolone (Fig. 26–1), with small amounts of epiandrosterone. These occur as water-soluble sulfates and glucuronides. In addition, dehydroepiandrosterone sulfate occurs normally in the urine in small amounts. This is formed principally in the adrenal cortex but also in the testis.

The liver plays an important role in the regulation of the concentrations of active steroid hormones (androgen, estrogen, progesterone, adrenocorticoids) in the systemic circulation. This is accomplished by several types of reactions, the relative importance of each of which varies for different hormones and in different species.

(1) The active hormone is removed from the bloodstream and undergoes metabolic transformation to biologically less active or inactive compounds.

(2) The original hormone or certain of these metabolites may undergo conjugation, usually with sulfate or glucuronate, to form water-soluble products that are apparently more resistant to metabolic degradation than the unconjugated hormones.

(3) Certain of these metabolites or conjugates either are excreted in the bile, in some cases subsequently undergoing enterohepatic circulation, or return to the systemic bloodstream with possible excretion in the urine.

In the case of androgens, the following reactions appear to be most important in man:

(1) Reversible conversion of testosterone to androstenedione (Fig. 26–1), which involves interconversion of hydroxyl and ketonic configurations at the C-17 position.

(2) Reduction of the 4,5 double bond of ring A, producing a completely saturated compound.

(3) Reduction of the 3-ketone to a 3-hydroxy derivative.

(4) Conjugation, mainly with glucuronate, but also with sulfate.

At least in man, biliary excretion is apparently less important in the case of androgens than of estrogens. Tissues other than liver may be involved in the metabolism of androgens, especially kidney, which has been shown to be capable of forming 17-ketosteroids from testosterone and of destroying the α,β-unsaturated system in ring A. As is indicated in Figures 26–2 and 26–9, testosterone is a metabolic precursor of estrogens (ovary, placenta, adrenal cortex, testis).

Urinary Neutral 17-Ketosteroids

The term "17-ketosteroids" is applied to steroids which have a ketone group at position 17 (Fig. 26–1). This structural feature enables them to produce certain color reactions, such as the Zimmermann (*m*-dinitrobenzene) and Pincus (antimony trichloride) reactions, which are very useful in their quantitative determination. The urinary 17-ketosteroids may be further classified as either neutral or acidic. Estrone, containing a phenolic ring (Fig. 26–2, p. 690), is acidic; it can therefore be separated from the neutral 17-ketosteroids by washing with alkali. The neutral fraction contains metabolites of steroids produced mainly by the testis and adrenal cortex, and determination of urinary 17-ketosteroids (the designation "neutral" is usually omitted, but implied) is used chiefly in the

TABLE 26-3. NORMAL VALUES FOR TOTAL URINARY NEUTRAL 17-KETOSTEROIDS

	17-KETOSTEROIDS (mg./24 HOURS)
4–7 years	0.8–2.6
7–12 years	1.8–5.0
12–15 years	5.0–12.0
15+ years	
Males	8.0–20.0
Females	5.0–15.0
Pregnancy (4–7 mos.)	10.0–20.0

evaluation of the functional activity of these organs (p. 709). Since they are present in the urine as esters, they must first be freed by hydrolysis.

A number of 17-ketosteroids have been isolated from the urine. The most important of these in normal subjects are (Fig. 26–1): (1) androsterone; (2) testane-3α-ol-17-one (etiocholanolone); (3) dehydro-3β-androsterone (dehydroepiandrosterone); (4) small amounts of 3β-androsterone (epiandrosterone). In the first two of these the —OH groups at C-3 lie below the plane of the molecule, as indicated by the broken bond in Figure 26–1; these orientations are indicated by the designation "alpha" (α). In the last two, the —OH groups at C-3 lie above the plane of the molecule; they are, therefore, β-17-ketosteroids. The α-17-ketosteroids normally comprise 85 to 95 per cent of the total. Androsterone has about one-tenth and dehydro-3β-androsterone (dehydroepiandrosterone) about one-third the androgenic activity of testosterone; 3β-androsterone (epiandrosterone) is only weakly androgenic and testane-3α-ol-17-one (etiocholanolone) is inactive.

Children under 6 years of age usually excrete less than 1 mg. daily, the values increasing gradually to adult levels at 12 to 18 years of age. The daily excretion in normal adult women is 5 to 15 mg., presumably derived almost entirely from adrenal precursors. Somewhat higher values may be obtained in late pregnancy (placental origin?). In adult men, during the reproductive period, the usual average range is 7 to 20 mg., about two-thirds being derived from adrenal and one-third from testicular hormones.

Abnormally high values are obtained in conditions of increased adrenocortical (hyperplasia, tumor) and interstitial-cell (certain testicular tumors) function. Low values are obtained in male hypogonadism and in hypofunction of the adrenals and adenohypophysis (decreased gonadotropin and adrenocorticotropin).

Metabolic Actions

The characteristic biological effects of androgens, particularly in gonadal tissues, are accompanied by biochemical effects that reflect stimulation of functional activity of these tissues. Stimulation of growth of the immature or castrate seminal vesicles and prostate is accompanied by: (a) increased rate of incorporation of amino acids into protein; (b) increased rate of synthesis of fatty acids; (c) increased rate of synthesis of citrate; (d) increased rate of formation of messenger RNA associated with prostatic ribonucleoprotein particles (ribosomes), presumably related to stimulation of protein synthesis (p. 534); (e) increased production of fructose by the seminal vesicles; (f) increased level of prostatic acid phosphatase activity; (g) increased respiration of the seminal vesicles and the prostate (O_2 consumption; CO_2 production).

The dominant general metabolic effect of androgens is stimulation of protein anabolism. This is reflected in (1) a decrease in urinary nitrogen (urea) without an increase in blood NPN, and (2) increase in body weight, due chiefly to an increase in skeletal muscle. There is evidence that the associated increase in oxygen consumption by muscle tissue is due to increased activity of NADH-cytochrome *c* reductase. Creatine, which is virtually absent from the urine of normal men, increases after castration. This increase is abolished by testosterone, owing to increased storage of creatine in the muscles. After prolonged administration, the quantity of creatinine in the urine may increase, probably reflecting the increase in muscle mass. Administration of androgens is followed by decreased hepatic arginine synthetase activity. Inasmuch as this enzyme catalyzes conversion of citrulline to arginine, this would tend to diminish urea formation, an effect which would be in accord with the known action of androgens in decreasing urea excretion.

In the growing organism, a growth spurt is induced with increase in bone matrix and skeletal length. Mineralization of this added skeletal tissue is accompanied by decreased excretion of calcium and phosphate, i.e., a more positive balance with respect to these substances.

Androgens cause a rather selective increase in size and weight of the kidneys (renotropic action). This is accompanied by decrease in kidney alkaline phosphatase activity and by increase in activity of D-amino acid oxidase, arginase, and acid phosphatase in the kidney. The relation of these phenomena to the metabolic actions of testosterone is not clear.

The prompt increase in RNA in the prostate and seminal vesicles that follows administration of testosterone suggests that androgens produce their characteristic metabolic and biological effects through stimulation of synthesis or utilization of messenger RNA.

Androgen reduces (and estrogen increases) the excretion of citrate in the urine. This is due apparently to increased reabsorption of citrate by the renal tubular epithelium. The decreased urinary excretion of nitrogen (chiefly urea) that follows administration of androgens is accompanied by a lower urine volume and diminished escretion of Na, Cl, K, SO_4, and PO_4, with no increase in their concentrations in the blood plasma. The tissue retention of K, SO_4, and PO_4 is probably related to the increased storage of protein. The retention of Na, Cl, and water (increased renal tubular reabsorption) is apparently due to an action resembling that of the adrenocortical hormones (p. 709).

Biological Effects

The characteristic morphological effects of androgens are reflected in the changes induced in the male by castration, all of which are corrected by administration of adequate amounts of hormone. In the prepubertal castrate the prostate and seminal vesicles fail to develop; in adults, castration is followed by atrophy of these structures. The penis remains small in the former and regresses in the latter. In prepubertal castrates, beard growth is absent, the body and pubic hair are scant and the voice remains high-pitched. Closure of epiphyseal lines is retarded, resulting in disproportionately long arms and legs.

Abnormally large amounts of androgen in women produce two effects, (1) "virilization" and (2) suppression of ovarian function. The former includes: enlargement of the clitoris, growth of facial and body hair, development of a male forehead hairline, stimulation of secretion and proliferation of the skin sebaceous glands (often with acne), and deepening of the voice. The ovarian suppression takes place primarily because of the fact that androgens, in large doses, share with estrogens the capacity to inhibit production by the adenohypophysis of gonadotropins and, to a lesser extent, other tropic hormones ("shot-gun action"). This results in suppression of ovarian follicle maturation and ovulation (i.e., decreased estrogen and progesterone production) followed by atrophy of the uterus, vagina, and often the breasts.

ESTROGENS

Estrogens are substances capable of producing certain biological effects, the most characteristic of which are the changes which occur in mammals at estrus. They induce growth of the female genital organs, the appearance of female secondary sex characteristics, growth of the mammary duct system, and numerous other phenomena which vary somewhat in different species.

The naturally occurring estrogens are steroids, but estrogenic activity is exhibited also by certain derivatives of phenanthrene and dibenzanthracene. Certain of these compounds (e.g., diethylstilbestrol; dienestrol), synthesized commercially, have been of great therapeutic value.

Chemistry

The naturally occurring estrogens in the human are β-estradiol, estrone, and estriol, which, for purposes of terminology, may be regarded as derivatives of the saturated hydrocarbon, "estrane" (Fig. 26–2).

One of the essential features of these estrogens is the aromatic character of ring A (three double bonds), with absence of a methyl group at C-10. Because of this characteristic, the OH group at C-3 possesses the properties of a phenolic hydroxyl group (weakly acid). All contain 18 carbon atoms.

Estrone has three double bonds, a hydroxyl (at C-3) and a ketone (at C-17) group. Its systematic name is therefore "1,3,5 : 10-estratriene-3-ol-17-one." The designation 5 : 10 indicates the position of the ends of the double bond, since the use of 5 alone would be ambiguous. Applying the same system of nomenclature, β-estradiol is "1,3,5 : 10-estratriene-3,17(β)-diol." Estriol is "1,3,5 : 10-estratriene-3,16(α),17(β)-triol."

Natural estrogens are soluble in oil, ether, alcohol, acetone, and other lipid solvents. They are only very slightly soluble in water, but enter solution in alkaline aqueous media. They are also moderately soluble in solutions of certain bile acids and in serum.

Occurrence

Estradiol has been found in the placenta, in the urine during pregnancy, and in the testis of the stallion. Estrone is present in the urine of adult males, pregnant and non-pregnant women, pregnant mares, stallions, human placenta, the adrenal cortex, and stallion testes. Estriol is present in the urine of pregnant women and in human placenta. Other estrogens, viz., equilin, equilenin, and hippulin, are present in pregnant mare urine.

Site of Formation

In the ovary, estrogens are produced by the maturing follicles (thecal and probably granulosa cells) and by the corpus luteum. All three pituitary gonadotropic hormones (FSH, LH, LTH) are involved in stimulation of estrogen secretion by these structures (p. 741). Estrogen is formed also in the adrenal cortex, placenta, and testis.

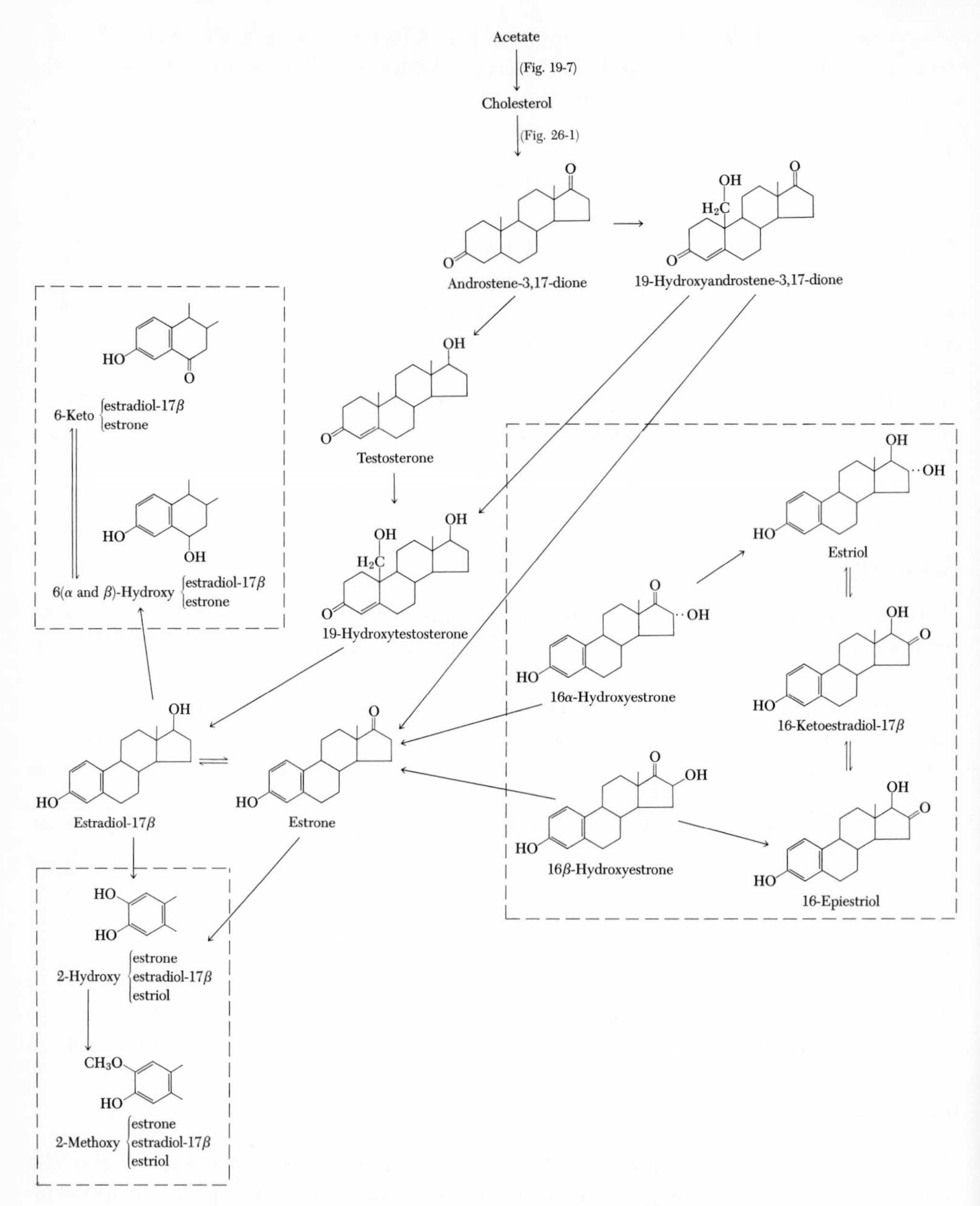

Figure 26-2. Biosynthesis and metabolism of estrogens.

Biosynthesis and Metabolism (Fig. 26-2)

Androgenic steroids are intermediates in the biosynthesis of estrogens. Transformation of these neutral C-19 steroids, e.g., 4-androstene-3,17-dione and testosterone, to estradiol and estrone involves (a) removal of the angular methyl group at C-10 and (b) aromatization of ring A. This is accomplished by three enzymes in the presence of oxygen and NADPH: (1) a 19-hydroxylase, producing 19-hydroxytestosterone and 19-hydroxyandrostenedione; (2) a 19-oxidase, producing 19-oxotestosterone and 19-oxoandrostenedione;

(3) an aldehyde lyase, which catalyzes removal of formaldehyde from the 19-oxo-compound, followed by spontaneous aromatization of ring A (Fig. 26–2).

Estrone and β-estradiol may be synthesized from acetate, via cholesterol, 4-androstene-3,17-dione, and testosterone. Estrone is irreversibly convertible to estriol.

The liver plays an important role in the metabolism of estrogens. Its functions in this connection may be summarized as follows: (1) it effectively removes estrogens from the systemic circulation by (a) biliary excretion and (b) metabolic degradation to less active and inactive compounds; (2) it conjugates estrogens and their metabolites with glucuronate and sulfate, converting them into water-soluble forms which return to the systemic circulation and are excreted in the urine. In certain species, estrogens excreted in the bile may subsequently undergo enterohepatic circulation, with gradual degradation in the liver to less active compounds.

Estradiol and estrone are interconvertible by the action of a specific 17β-hydroxysteroid dehydrogenase, the hydroxyl group being reversibly converted to the ketonic form, with NAD or NADP serving as hydrogen carriers. It has been suggested, on the basis of this type of reaction, that these and certain other steroid hormones may act as coenzymes in transhydrogenation reactions, accomplishing the transfer of hydrogen between the two pyridine nucleotides (p. 361).

Several types of reactions are involved in the intermediary metabolism of estrogens. Quantitatively, the most important of these involve: (1) substitutions at C-16, i.e., 16-hydroxyestrogens and 16-ketoestrogens; (2) substitutions at C-2, i.e., 2-hydroxyestrogens and 2-methoxyestrogens; (3) conjugation reactions, i.e., formation of estriol glucosiduronide (glucosidic linkage at C-16) and estrone sulfate (esterification at C-3). Substitutions also occur at C-6, 11, 17, and 18; the physiological significance of these reactions has not been established.

The hydroxylation reactions in the liver are catalyzed by the corresponding hydroxylases, and the methylation reaction by an O-methyl-transferase similar if not identical to that involved in the metabolism of catecholamines.

Secretion, Transport, Excretion

Estrogens are present in the blood plasma partly in free form and partly conjugated, about 50 to 75 per cent being closely bound to plasma proteins, mainly γ-globulin. They are excreted in the urine chiefly in conjugated forms, viz., estrone sulfate, estriol glucosiduronide. It is estimated that the urinary estrogens represent about 5 to 10 per cent of the activity of the estrogens secreted. The determination of urinary estrogens is therefore employed as an index of estrogen production (about 10 mg. estrone equivalent during a menstrual cycle); variations in metabolic "inactivation" may conceivably interfere with accurate interpretation of such data. Normal values under different physiological conditions are presented in Tables 26-4, 26-5, and 26-6 (p. 692).

The newborn infant is in a state of hyperestrogenism, the hormone being derived entirely from the maternal circulation and excreted during the first week or so of extrauterine life. During early childhood (male and female) the urine contains small amounts of estrogens, probably of adrenal origin. In adult men, estrogens continue to be formed, apparently at a relatively constant rate, in the adrenal cortex and from testosterone. Generally at about 8 to 10 years of age there is a significant increase in estrogen excretion by girls as compared to boys. Thereafter, it increases slowly progressively, with a sharp rise shortly before the menarche. During the reproductive years, in nonpregnant women, estrogen (also progesterone) production, as gauged by urinary excretion, follows a cyclic

Table 26-4. Normal Urine Estrogen Values (Fluorometric)

	µg./24 hours
Age 5–10	3.0–6.5
Age 31–37 (Men)	21.6–26.2
(Women)	10–50
Age 50–65 (Women)	0–23.4
Pregnancy (8–10 mos.)	365–1500

Table 26-5. Hormone Values in Normal Pregnancy

Weeks	Serum Estrogens (µg./100 ml.)*	Serum Gonadotropin (m.u./100 ml.)†	Urine Pregnanediol (mg./24 hours)
2	1.5–8		2–10
4	1.5–10	50–1000	5–15
8	3–12.5	500–33000	5–15
12	4–16.5	1000–33000	8–20
16	8–20	1000–33000	8–30
20	16.5–25	330–10000	16–32
24	16.5–33	200–500	20–60
28	10–40	200–500	35–80
32	25–60	200–500	40–80
36	33–75	200–500	50–100
40	33–150	200–500	50–120

* As µg. estrone equivalents.
† Mouse ovarian weight units.

Table 26-6. Normal Sex Hormone Values

Hormone	Women: Days of Menstrual Cycle 7	14	21	28	Menopause	Men
Gonadotropin						
Urine[1]	trace–12	8–40	trace–8	0–6	32–300	4–24
Serum[2]	0–trace	trace–3	0–trace	0	3–30	0
Estrogen						
Urine[3]	65–160	160–660	160–660	30–110	10–65	25–100
Serum[4]	trace–6	3–9	3–9	0–3	0–trace	
Pregnanediol						
Urine[5]	0	3–10	3–10	0–4	0	0

[1] Mouse uterine weight units per 24 hours.
[2] Mouse ovarian weight units per 100 ml.
[3] I.U. per 24 hours.
[4] Mouse units per 100 ml. (1 m.u. = 5 I.U.).
[5] Mg. pregnanediol glucuronidate per 24 hours.

pattern in accordance and conjunction with the rhythmic fluctuations in secretion of gonadotropins (Fig. 26–3). In the early follicular phase the titer is rather low; it rises progressively to an initial peak at about the time of ovulation, subsequently drops moderately for a few days, and increases again as the corpus luteum becomes well established. A second peak of estrogen production generally occurs at about the 21st to 24th day of the cycle, after which there is a rather abrupt drop during the immediate premenstrual phase. The estrogen curve is therefore biphasic, with two peaks, one at about the time of ovulation and the other at the height of corpus luteum activity. The first peak is usually, but not invariably, somewhat higher than the second.

After conception, the relatively high levels of estrogen and progesterone of the luteal phase persist, accounting for the amenorrhea of the first menstrual cycle. Estrogen produc-

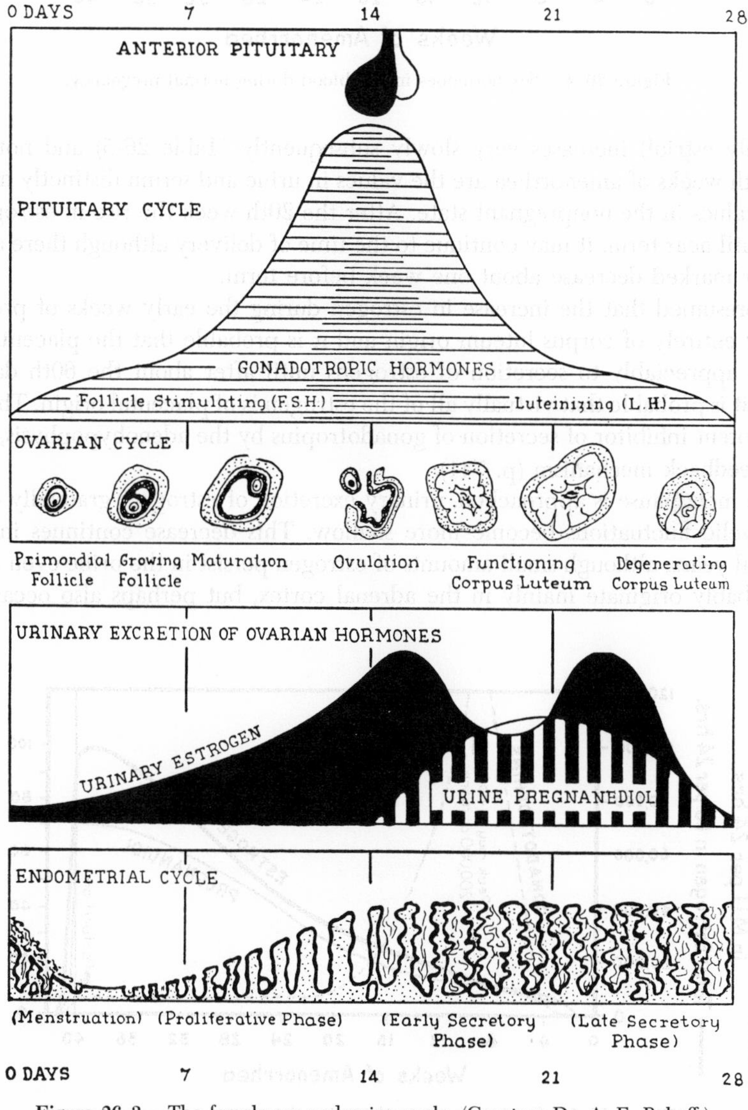

Figure 26–3. The female sex endocrine cycle. (Courtesy Dr. A. E. Rakoff.)

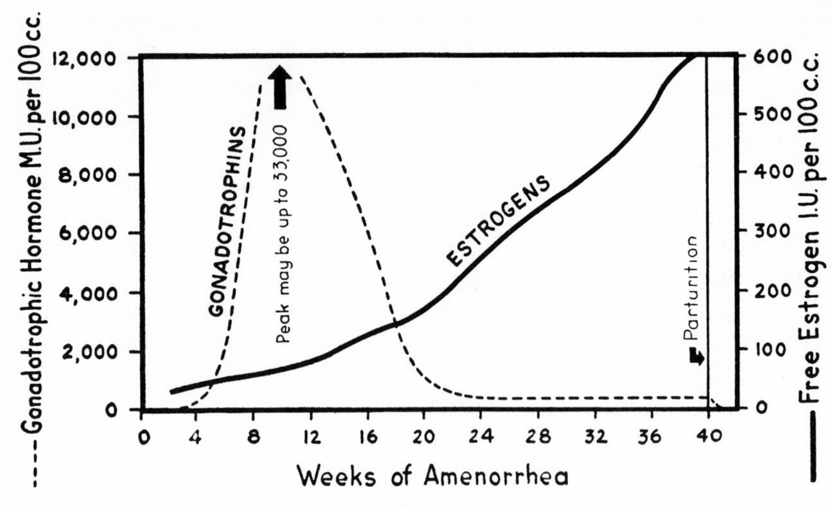

Figure 26-4. Sex hormones in the blood during normal pregnancy.

tion (mainly estriol) increases very slowly subsequently (Table 26-5) and not until the 12th to 16th weeks of amenorrhea are the values in urine and serum distinctly higher than the peak values in the nonpregnant state. After the 20th week the rise in estrogen is progressive until near term; it may continue to the time of delivery although there are reports of a rather marked decrease about one week before term.

It is presumed that the increase in estrogen during the early weeks of pregnancy is practically entirely of corpus luteum origin and it is probable that the placenta does not contribute appreciably to secretion of estrogens until after about the 60th day. By the 100th day it is probable that virtually all of the estrogen is of placental origin. This increase acts as a potent inhibitor of secretion of gonadotropins by the adenohypophysis, through a negative feedback mechanism (p. 741).

As the menopause is approached, urinary excretion of estrogens gradually diminishes and the cyclic fluctuations become more shallow. This decrease continues in the postmenopausal years, although small amounts of estrogen persist in the urine even in old age. These probably originate mainly in the adrenal cortex, but perhaps also occasionally in the ovary.

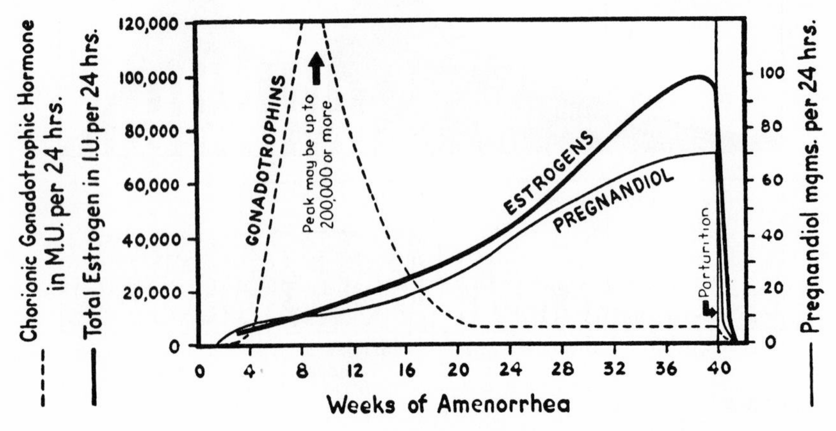

Figure 26-5. Sex hormones in the urine during normal pregnancy.

Actions

Estrogens cause growth of the epithelium and musculature of the fallopian tubes, stimulate their contraction and motility, and are responsible for cyclic changes in the tubal mucosa. They cause growth, increased tonus and rhythmic contractions of the uterine musculature, and development of the endometrial mucosa and blood vessels which plays an important role in normal menstruation. They increase the vascularity of the cervix and stimulate secretion by the cervical glands, increasing the amount of cervical mucus with a lowered viscosity, thus favoring migration, motility, and longevity of spermatozoa. Estrogens cause a characteristic proliferation of the vaginal epithelium which forms the basis for one of the methods of bioassay of estrogenic activity (Allen-Doisy). They are also responsible in large part for normal development of the external female genitalia, the duct system of the breasts and the nipples, and the secondary sex characteristics.

Administration of estrogens is followed by an increase in glycogen and alkaline phosphatase in the endometrium. Glycogen also increases in the vaginal epithelium, which is second only to the liver in glycogen content during the reproductive years (1.5 to 3 per cent). The vaginal glycogen is probably the source of the lactic acid which, by increasing the acidity of the vaginal secretion (pH 4.0 to 5.0), favors a homogenous flora of acid bacteria. Administration of estrogen results in acceleration of incorporation of amino acids into proteins of the uterus (increased protein synthesis), which is preceded by an increase in RNA polymerase activity and RNA synthesis. There is an increase in the rate of glycolysis, with accumulation of lactic acid; uterine lipogenesis from carbohydrate is increased. β-Estradiol, estrone, equilin, and equilenin, in vitro, produce an increase in oxygen consumption in endometrium, placenta, mammary gland, and adenohypophysis, owing to a quite specific effect upon an "estradiol-sensitive" isocitrate dehydrogenase (transhydrogenase). This action is not shared by estriol nor by several potent synthetic estrogens; its relation to estrogenic activity is therefore questionable.

The concept has been advanced that a fundamental action of certain estrogens, e.g., estradiol and estrone, is to activate a transhydrogenase which accomplishes the transfer of hydrogen between NAD and NADP. As in the case of other hormones, there is evidence that the characteristic metabolic and biological actions of estrogens on target tissues result from induction of synthesis of enzymes concerned with these reactions. This, in turn, is dependent upon increased availability or perhaps increased production of mRNA.

Estrogens exert an effect on metabolic processes independently of their actions on specific target tissues. They (particularly estradiol) cause slight retention of Na, Cl, and water, not nearly as pronounced, however, as that produced by adrenocortical hormones, testosterone, or progesterone. They apparently favor retention and skeletal deposition of calcium, producing hypercalcemia and hyperphosphatemia in birds (formation of egg shell), and hyperossification of long bones in mice. In birds, estrogens cause hyperlipemia; this does not occur in mammals, being related presumably to the influence of the ovarian hormones in the formation of the egg yolk. In certain mammalian species, however, estrogens may exert a lipotropic effect (p. 505), i.e., tending to prevent accumulation of lipids in the liver. There is evidence that their administration to subjects with hypercholesterolemia results in lowering of the plasma cholesterol concentration and a fall in the level of β-lipoproteins (p. 494).

PROGESTERONE

Progesterone is formed in the ovary, placenta, adrenal cortex, and testis. It is secreted by the corpus luteum of the ovary during the period of its functional activity. It appears suddenly on the day of ovulation or perhaps a day or two earlier, as indicated by the presence in the urine of its chief excretion product, pregnanediol. It is concerned, in the latter half of the menstrual cycle, mainly with preparing the endometrium for nidation of the fertilized ovum if conception has occurred (Fig. 26–3, p. 693). During early pregnancy, it is produced by the corpus luteum of pregnancy (stimulated by luteinizing and lactogenic hormones, q.v.), and perhaps by other ovarian luteinized cells, and later mainly by the syncytial cells of the placenta. During pregnancy, progesterone, in association with estrogen, appears to be concerned with maintenance of a state of quiescence of the uterine muscle.

Chemistry

Progesterone may be regarded as a derivative of "pregnane" (Fig. 26–6) and may be designated "4-pregnene-3,20-dione." It has methyl groups at C-10 and C-13 and contains 21 C atoms.

Progesterone is soluble in practically all organic solvents except petroleum ether and dilute alcohol, acetone, and pyridine. It is quite soluble in oil, moderately soluble in serum, and practically insoluble in water.

Biosynthesis and Metabolism (Fig. 26–6)

The role of progesterone as an intermediate in the biogenesis of adrenal corticoids and of androgens is referred to elsewhere (pp. 684, 706). Indirectly, i.e., via androstenedione and testosterone, it may serve as a precursor of estrogens (p. 690). Progesterone is formed from acetate or cholesterol, 5-pregnene-3-ol-20-one being its immediate metabolic precursor.

Progesterone is one of the main products of secretory activity of the corpus luteum and placenta. Progesterone metabolites have been found in the bile; the liver is involved in the removal of this hormone from the circulation, in its degradation to unidentified compounds, and in its reduction to pregnanediol, which is biologically inactive, via pregnane-3,20-dione and pregnane-3-ol-20-one. Progesterone is then conjugated with glucuronic acid (p. 278), passed into the systemic circulation, and excreted in the urine (Tables 26-5 and 26-6). It has been estimated that 10 to 30 per cent of the progesterone secreted during a normal menstrual cycle is converted to pregnanediol, the urinary excretion of which is a fairly satisfactory index of progesterone production and metabolism.

Excretion

Human urine contains only biologically inactive progesterone metabolites, chiefly the glucuronidate of pregnane-3(α),20(α)-diol, commonly referred to as pregnanediol. Other isomers present, especially during pregnancy, but in smaller amounts, are allopregnanediol-3(α),20(α), and allopregnanediol-3(β),20(α).

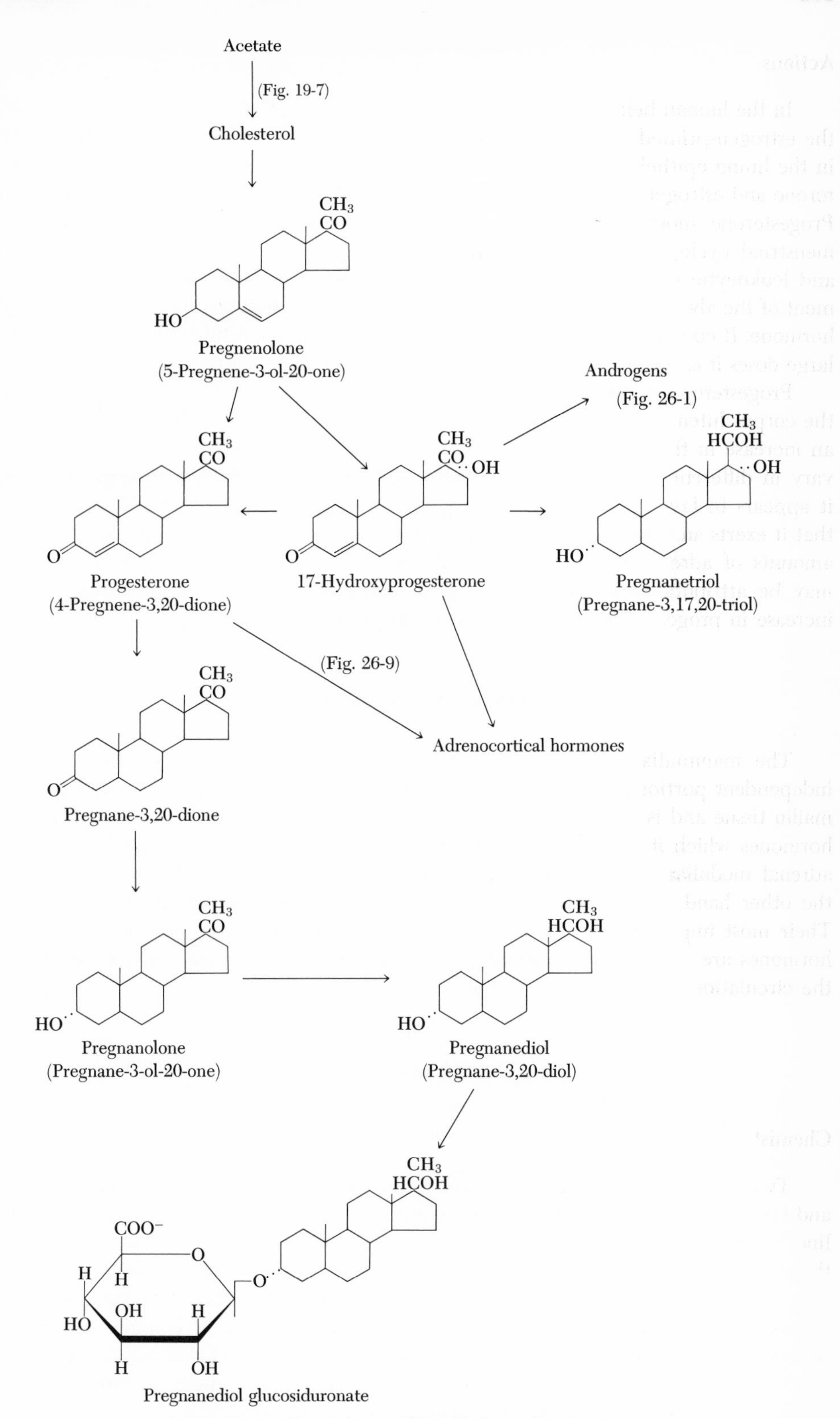

Figure 26-6. Biosynthesis and metabolism of progesterone.

Actions

In the human being, progesterone produces characteristic changes (progestational) in the estrogen-primed endometrium. It also causes an increase in glycogen, mucin, and fat in the lining epithelial cells. Alkaline phosphatase decreases. Sudden decrease in progesterone and estrogen leads to a series of changes culminating in bleeding or menstruation. Progesterone modifies the action of estrogen on the vaginal epithelium during the menstrual cycle, causing desquamation and basophilia of the superficial layer of cells and leukocytic infiltration. In conjunction with estrogen, progesterone causes development of the alveolar system of the breasts and sensitizes them for the action of lactogenic hormone. It counteracts the effect of estrogen on the fallopian tubes and uterine cervix. In large doses it exerts androgenic effects, perhaps by conversion to androgenic metabolites.

Progesterone is responsible for the rise in basal temperature which occurs during the corpus luteum phase of the normal menstrual cycle. This is believed to be related to an increase in the basal metabolic rate. Its effects on electrolyte and water metabolism vary in different species and under different hormonal conditions. In dogs and rodents it appears to favor retention of sodium, chloride, and water. In man, there is evidence that it exerts an opposite effect, which is particularly evident in the absence of adequate amounts of adrenocortical hormones. It has been suggested that premenstrual edema may be attributable in part to increased secretion of aldosterone, accompanying the increase in progesterone, rather than to a direct action of the latter.

ADRENAL HORMONES

The mammalian adrenal gland consists of two embryologically and functionally independent portions, the medulla and the cortex. The adrenal medulla consists of chromaffin tissue and is essentially a portion of the autonomic nervous system. Although the hormones which it secretes have pronounced pharmacological effects, extirpation of all adrenal medullary tissue is followed by no important changes. The adrenal cortex, on the other hand, an epithelial structure, secretes hormones which are essential for life. Their most important actions are metabolic in nature, whereas those of the medullary hormones are exerted predominantly on unstriated muscle, vasomotor mechanisms, and the circulation.

Adrenal Medullary Hormones

Chemistry

Two biologically active compounds have been isolated from the adrenal medulla and synthesized, viz., epinephrine (adrenaline; adrenine) and norepinephrine (noradrenaline; Arterenol) (Fig. 26–7). The naturally occurring forms are levorotatory, the synthetic are racemic, the former being almost twice as active as the latter. These substances are catecholamines, closely related to tyrosine and phenylalanine. Epinephrine differs from tyrosine in the following respects (Fig. 26–7): (1) it contains an additional phenolic OH in *meta* position to the side chain; (2) it has an OH attached to the β-carbon of the side chain; (3) it has no carboxyl group; (4) it has a methyl group attached to the N atom; this is lacking in norepinephrine.

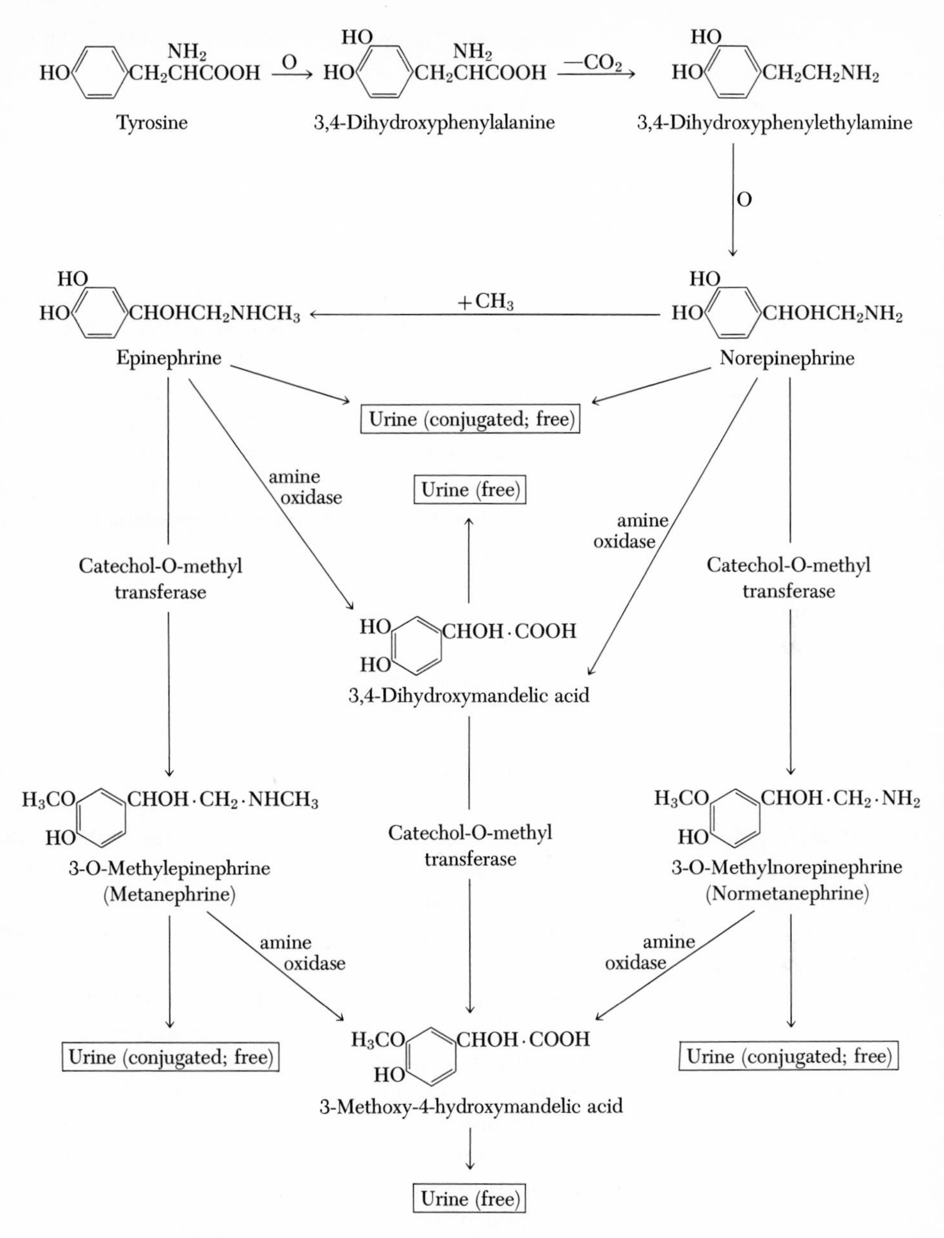

Figure 26-7. Biosynthesis and metabolism of adrenal medullary hormones.

Extracts of the adrenal glands of cattle and man have been found to contain epinephrine and norepinephrine in the approximate proportions of 4:1. Relatively larger amounts of the latter have been found in adrenal medullary tumors.

The term "chromaffin tissue" has been applied to tissues in which the "chromaffin reaction" can be developed, i.e., oxidation of epinephrine and certain related compounds by bichromate or iodate, with the production of a colored compound. In man, in addition to the adrenal medulla, substances giving this "chromaffin" reaction are present in cells of the paraganglia and various parts of the sympathetic nervous system. The material in these situations, originally designated "sympathin," is norepinephrine. This is apparently formed in postganglionic sympathetic fibers upon stimulation and is regarded as the chemical transmitter of adrenergic nerves.

Regulation of Secretion

Epinephrine and norepinephrine are secreted by the adrenal medulla in response to splanchnic stimulation. They are stored in the chromaffin granules, their discharge (i.e., secretion) being effected by a variety of factors, including fear, anger, pain, and other undesirable emotional states, hypoglycemia, hypotension, muscular activity, and anesthetic and hypnotic drugs. Certain of these influences exert a preferential action, epinephrine being released predominantly in response to hypoglycemia and norepinephrine in response to hypotension; various types of hypothalamic stimulation produce different proportions of the two hormones. It has been suggested that adrenal medullary stimulation may be involved in the initiation of the "alarm reaction" (p. 741), the discharged epinephrine stimulating secretion of ACTH by the adenohypophysis, perhaps indirectly through mediation by a hypothalamic mechanism.

Biosynthesis and Metabolism

Tyrosine or phenylalanine is the primary precursor; conversion to norepinephrine and epinephrine has been demonstrated by radioactive tracer techniques in intact animals, isolated adrenals, and sympathetic ganglia and nerves.

The generally accepted pathway of biosynthesis of these substances is indicated in Figure 26–7. Tyrosine is oxidized (tyrosine hydroxylase) to 3,4-dihydroxyphenylalanine (dopa). This undergoes decarboxylation (dopa decarboxylase) to 3,4-dihydroxyphenylethylamine (hydroxytyramine; dopamine), which is in turn oxidized to norepinephrine. The latter is methylated (S-adenosylmethionine) to epinephrine.

The three catecholamines (dopamine, norepinephrine, epinephrine) may possess hormonal activity. All are present in the adrenal medulla, the synthetic process proceeding to epinephrine as the major end-product under normal conditions. In nervous tissue, biosynthesis stops at the norepinephrine level, but dopamine may also possibly be an effector substance. It has been suggested that dopamine may act as a local hormone in the lungs, intestine, and liver, in which it is the end-product of catecholamine biosynthesis.

Epinephrine and norepinephrine are present in the blood plasma in both free and conjugated (sulfate, glucuronide) forms; epinephrine is almost completely bound to plasma proteins, chiefly albumin, and norepinephrine to a lesser extent.

The relatively brief duration of action of epinephrine and norepinephrine reflects their active metabolism. They disappear rapidly following injection; less than 5 per cent of the amount administered is excreted as such in the urine during the subsequent 24 hours. The bulk of the remainder appears in the urine in the form of inactive metabolites, the most abundant of which are 3-methoxy-4-hydroxymandelic acid, 3,4-dihydroxymandelic acid, 3-O-methylepinephrine (metanephrine), and 3-O-methylnorepinephrine (normetanephrine) (Fig. 26–7). The most important reactions involved in these transformations are oxidative deamination (amine oxidase) and methylation (catechol-O-methyl transferase). There are also sulfate and glucuronide conjugates of epinephrine and norepinephrine as well as of certain of the metabolites.

Small amounts of these hormones are excreted normally in the urine, 3 to 35 μg. (average 16) of epinephrine and 25 to 135 μg. (average 55) of norepinephrine daily.

The major metabolite, 3-methoxy-4-hydroxymandelic acid (vanilmandelic acid) may be excreted normally in the urine in amounts up to 3 mg. daily.

Excessive amounts of epinephrine and norepinephrine are produced by certain tumors of chromaffin tissue (pheochromocytomas), with consequent increased urinary excretion of catecholamines and mandelic acids, quantitative determination of which is of diagnostic value.

Normal values for these hormones in the blood vary with the method employed for their determination; according to one procedure (ethylenediamine) the normal concentration of norepinephrine is 0.5 to 6.5 μg./liter and that of epinephrine 0 to 0.6 μg./liter; with another procedure (trihydroxyindole), normal values for norepinephrine range from 0.09 to 0.5 μg./liter and for epinephrine from 0.05 to 0.2 μg./liter.

Metabolic Actions

Injection of epinephrine is followed promptly by an increase in blood sugar and lactic acid concentrations, due to acceleration of glycogenolysis in the liver (glucose) and glycolysis in muscles (lactic acid), associated with stimulation of phosphorylase activity (activation of phosphorylase kinase by increased formation of cyclic adenylic acid, p. 400). The hyperglycemic effect of norepinephrine is about one-twentieth that of epinephrine. This mobilization of glycogen is one of the major metabolic effects of epinephrine.

Glucose uptake by muscle cells is apparently depressed somewhat; this has been attributed to depression of hexokinase activity by the increased concentration of glucose-6-phosphate incident to accelerated breakdown of glycogen. However, uptake of glucose in adipose tissue is stimulated by epinephrine and norepinephrine. Here, the most important action of these hormones is stimulation of hydrolysis of triglycerides and release of increased amounts of free fatty acid into the bloodstream, thyroid and adrenocortical hormones being required for production of the latter effect. The increased concentration of free fatty acids in the blood plasma results in increased uptake by the liver, with consequent increased ketogenesis. This stimulation of mobilization of lipids from adipose tissue is inhibited by prostaglandins (p. 36), which exert a similar effect upon the activity of glucagon in this connection.

Epinephrine and norepinephrine increase oxygen consumption in the intact animal. This is probably due mainly to accelerated turnover of triglycerides and acceleration of fatty acid oxidation. Simultaneous increase in blood ketone acids and lactic acid produces a decrease in blood bicarbonate. Oxygen consumption (basal metabolism) increases, according to some representing a specific calorigenic effect and, according to others, merely reflecting general sympathetic stimulation and increased muscle tonus.

Hormones of the Adrenal Cortex

Chemistry

The hormones secreted by the adrenal cortex are steroids. They can be classified as of four main types on the basis of biological activity and structure: (1) estrogens (18 carbon atoms) (p. 689); (2) androgens (19 carbon atoms) (p. 684); (3) progesterone (21 carbon atoms) (p. 696); (4) "corticoids," the characteristic adrenocortical hormones

(21 carbon atoms) (Fig. 26–8). The first three are considered in detail elsewhere, and therefore only the fourth will be discussed here.

The characteristic (i.e., excluding estrogen, progesterone, androgen) adrenocortical hormones (corticoids) that have been isolated are derivatives of "pregnane" (21 C atoms) (Fig. 26–6, p. 697). Inasmuch as "corticosterone" was the first "common" name applied to an adrenal cortical hormone, it has become customary to name the others according to their relation to corticosterone. The latter is designated systematically as 4-pregnene-11(β),21-diol-3,20-dione. Several compounds of importance in this category have been isolated from the adrenal (Fig. 26–8). Three structural features are essential for all known biological actions of the natural adrenocortical hormones: (1) a double bond at C-4-5, (2) a ketonic group (C=O) at C-3 (i.e., an α,β-unsaturated ketone group), and (3) a ketonic group at C-20.

Certain additional structural features have a profound effect upon the biological activity of these compounds:

(1) A hydroxyl (OH) group at C-21 enhances sodium retention and is necessary for activity in carbohydrate metabolism.

(2) The presence of O either as —OH or as =O, i.e., hydroxyl or ketonic groups, at C-11 is necessary for carbohydrate activity and decreases sodium retention.

(3) A hydroxyl (OH) group at C-17 increases carbohydrate activity.

Corticosterone

11-Dehydrocorticosterone

11-Dehydro-17-hydroxycorticosterone

17-Hydroxycorticosterone

11-Deoxycorticosterone

11-Deoxy-17-hydroxycorticosterone

(hemiacetal) ⟵ (aldehyde)

Aldosterone

Adrenosterone (androgenic)

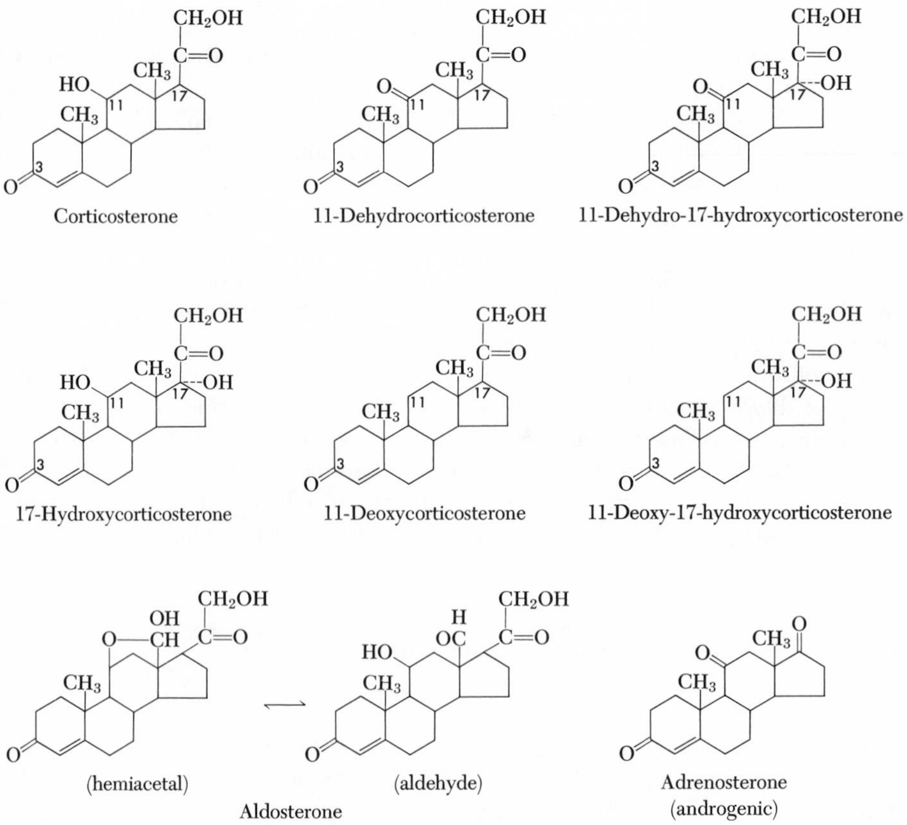

Figure 26–8. Hormones of the adrenal cortex.

On the basis of these relationships between structure and biological activity, the adrenal cortical hormones may be classified in three categories:

(1) Those possessing O at the C-11 position (either hydroxyl or ketonic), with activity in carbohydrate and protein metabolism and relatively minor effect on electrolyte and water metabolism. These have been referred to as the "11-oxygenated corticosteroids" or "11-oxysteroids," and include corticosterone (compound B), 11-dehydrocorticosterone (compound A), 11-dehydro-17-hydroxycorticosterone (compound E; cortisone), and 17-hydroxycorticosterone (compound F; hydrocortisone; cortisol).

(2) Those without O at the 11-C position, with virtually no activity in carbohydrate or protein metabolism and major effect on electrolyte and water metabolism. The most important representatives of this group are 11-deoxycorticosterone and 17-hydroxy-11-deoxycorticosterone (compound S; 11-deoxycortisol).

(3) Aldosterone, which, in solution, exists in two tautomeric forms, with hemi-acetal and aldehyde structures, respectively. This differs from the other corticoids in that the usual methyl group at C-18 is replaced by an aldehyde group. The fact that this is spatially adjacent to a hydroxyl group at C-11 permits the compound to occur also as the C-11-hemi-acetal (Fig. 26–8). The two forms are in equilibrium, the hemi-acetal predominating.

Aldosterone exerts effects in both mineral (Na, K, Cl) and organic metabolism. It is the most active known "mineralocorticoid" and, in appropriate dosage, it produces effects in carbohydrate, lipid, and protein metabolism resembling those of the other 11-oxygenated corticoids (e.g., 17-hydroxycorticosterone). It is the main hormonal factor in the regulation of Na and K metabolism, its biological activity in this connection being 20 to several hundred times that of deoxycorticosterone, depending upon the method of assay. For example, its potency in maintaining life and electrolyte balance in adrenalectomized dogs has been found to be 10 to 30 times that of deoxycorticosterone and 500 times that of 17-hydroxycorticosterone (cortisol; compound F).

Of the more than 40 steroids that have been isolated from the adrenal cortex, all but a few are biologically inactive and probably represent precursors, metabolites, or artifacts. Studies of adrenal-vein blood indicate that cortisol, corticosterone, and aldosterone are the major corticosteroid secretory products in mammals. In man, cortisol is the major glucocorticoid (corticosterone in rodents) and aldosterone the major mineralocorticoid.

Sex hormones isolated from adrenal cortex. Estrone, progesterone, adrenosterone (4-androstene-3,11,17-trione), and 4-androstene-3,17-dione have been isolated from adrenal tissue. The two latter possess androgenic activity, but there is some question as to whether they may not be artifacts arising during the extraction and purification procedures. However, an androgenic compound which gives a reaction for 17-ketosteroids has been isolated from adrenal-vein blood.

Methods of Assay

These may be divided into two categories, (a) biological and (b) chemical.

(*a*) ***Bioassay procedures.*** These are based on certain biological actions of the adrenocortical hormones in adrenalectomized animals: (1) maintenance of life and/or growth; (2) improvement of work performance; (3) effect on urine Na/K ratio; (4) prolongation of life during exposure to cold, or (5) to trauma; (6) promotion of glycogen deposition in the liver; (7) promotion of thymus involution; (8) cytocidal action on rabbit lymphocytes in vitro; (9) changes in electroshock seizure threshold; (10) decrease in circulating eosinophils; (11) anti-inflammatory action. Several of these have been used successfully for quantitative purposes, particularly the liver glycogen deposition, cold, and trauma tests, which, however, measure only those adrenal steroids oxygenated at C-11 (11-oxysteroids), and appear to be specific for these substances. However, these procedures are time-consuming and expensive, and have been largely supplanted, for routine purposes, by less specific chemical methods.

(*b*) ***Chemical procedures.*** All of the known biologically active adrenal steroids contain an α-ketol side chain at C-17 (ring D) and an α,β-unsaturated 3-ketone grouping (ring A) (Fig. 26–8, p. 702). These structural features constitute the basis for chemical assay procedures (colorimetric).

(1) *Formaldehydogenic Method.* The α-ketol or glycol side-chains of steroids react with periodic acid (glycol cleavage) with generation of formaldehyde, which may be determined quantitatively.

(2) *Phosphomolybdic Acid Reduction.* Steroids containing a primary or secondary (but not tertiary) α-ketol grouping, or an α,β-unsaturated 3-ketone grouping, can reduce phosphomolybdic acid (e.g., corticosterone, deoxycorticosterone, progesterone, etc.).

(3) *Copper Reduction.* Copper is reduced by steroids containing an α-ketol grouping. An α,β-unsaturated 3-ketone grouping does not reduce copper; consequently, compounds such as progesterone do not interfere with this procedure.

(4) *Color Reaction with Phenylhydrazine and Sulfuric Acid.* This reaction (Porter-Silber) is given by 17,21-dihydroxy-20-ketosteroids, i.e., 11-dehydro-17-hydroxycorticosterone (compound E), 17-hydroxycorticosterone (cortisol; compound F), and 11-deoxy-17-hydroxycorticosterone (11-deoxycortisol; compound S), and their reduced tetrahydro derivatives, which are biologically inactive. This procedure has largely superseded the others in studies of adrenal hormone excretion in man, inasmuch as the human adrenal cortex produces cortisol predominantly.

These chemical reactions are not specific for cortical hormones, being given by other normal constituents of body fluids. However, a rather satisfactory degree of specificity is attained, particularly in urine, which is relatively free from lipid material, by the extraction and chromatographic procedures employed preliminary to application of the chemical assay reactions. Chemical methods yield consistently higher values (in urine) than do biological methods. The closest correlation is obtained with the phenylhydrazine-sulfuric acid procedure, which is now employed most widely. By the application of chromatographic techniques, it has become possible to separate, identify, and measure adrenocortical steroids in amounts of a few micrograms.

Biosynthesis

Administration of adrenocorticotropic hormone (ACTH) is promptly followed by increased secretory activity of the adrenal cortex and increased excretion of certain adrenal hormones and their metabolites in the urine (p. 708). Simultaneously, there is a decrease in the cholesterol and, in most species, also in the ascorbic acid content of the adrenal cortex (p. 740). This suggests that cholesterol is a biological precursor of at least certain of the adrenal cortical steroids. Although ascorbic acid is not an obligatory participant in this process, its decrease in the adrenal cortex following injection of ACTH is the accepted basis for assay of ACTH. The action of this hormone in stimulating formation of adrenocortical hormones involves increased formation of cyclic

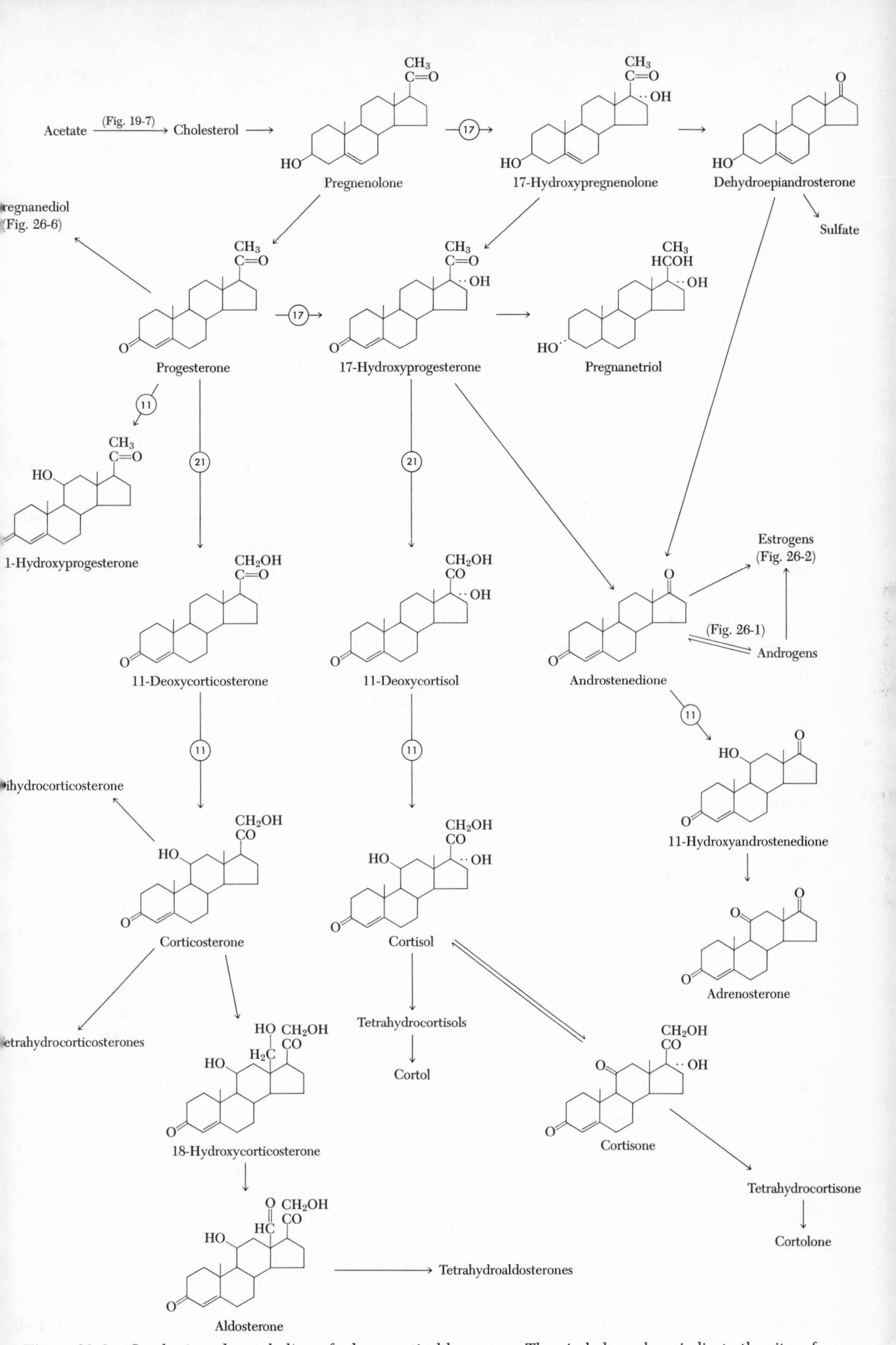

Figure 26-9. Synthesis and metabolism of adrenocortical hormones. The circled numbers indicate the sites of specific hydroxylation reactions.

adenylic acid which, by increasing phosphorylase activity in the adrenal, provides increased amounts of NADPH required for certain hydroxylation reactions. 17-Hydroxycorticosterone (cortisol), corticosterone, and aldosterone are the most important end-products of corticosteroid biosynthesis in mammalian species, cortisol predominating in man and corticosterone in rodents.

The pathway of biosynthesis from acetate and cholesterol (Fig. 26–9) is via pregnenolone, ring A of which undergoes oxidation to form progesterone, with the α,β-unsaturated ketonic structure essential for the characteristic biological activities of the corticoids. Two metabolic pathways are taken by progesterone in its subsequent transformations.

(1) The major pathway in man involves: (a) 17-hydroxylation (i.e., at C-17) to 17-hydroxyprogesterone; (b) 21-hydroxylation of the latter to 11-deoxycortisol; (c) 11-hydroxylation of the latter to cortisol.

(2) A minor pathway in man involves, successively: (a) 21-hydroxylation of progesterone to deoxycorticosterone; (b) 11-hydroxylation to corticosterone; (c) conversion of the C-18 methyl to an aldehyde, forming aldosterone.

The enzymes, 17-hydroxylase, 21-hydroxylase, and 11-hydroxylase, occupy key positions in the biosynthesis of the adrenocortical hormones. Deficiencies in the latter two, particularly, form the basis for the metabolic abnormalities and clinical manifestations of certain aberrations of adrenocortical function (adrenogenital syndrome).

(3) In another pathway, pregnenolone undergoes 17-hydroxylation to 17-hydroxypregnenolone; the latter enters into the formation of (a) cortisol by oxidation to 17-hydroxyprogesterone and (b) androgens and estrogens by oxidation to dehydroisoandrosterone (Fig. 26–9). The latter is formed in and secreted by the adrenal cortex in the form of the sulfate ester.

(4) Synthesis of androgens and estrogens in the adrenal cortex occurs via formation of androstenedione by oxidation of both 17-hydroxyprogesterone and dehydroisoandrosterone (Fig. 26–9).

Regulation of Secretion

Cortisol (glucocorticoid) is produced in the zona fasciculata and zona reticularis, and aldosterone (mineralocorticoid) in the zona glomerulosa. Corticosterone is produced in all three zones. It would appear that the 18-hydroxylase is present only in the glomerulosa and the 17-hydroxylase only in the other two zones. Although there is some species difference with respect to this zonal segregation of secretory activities, the zona fasciculata in most cases (including man) is stimulated strikingly by ACTH, and the glomerulosa to a relatively minor extent, if at all. Different mechanisms must exist, therefore, for the regulation of secretion of glucocorticoids and mineralocorticoids.

Administration of ACTH is followed by marked increase in the concentration of glucocorticoids in the adrenal-vein blood and peripheral blood and increased excretion of these hormones and their metabolites in the urine. All of these values decrease sharply after hypophysectomy. The regulation of ACTH secretion under basal conditions and in response to stress is discussed elsewhere (p. 740). The level of circulating adrenal hormones appears to be the major controlling factor under basal conditions, increased concentrations depressing and decreased concentrations stimulating secretion of ACTH (negative feedback mechanism). Adrenalectomy results in elevated levels of ACTH in the bloodstream. The regulatory effect of adrenocortical hormones on discharge of ACTH into the bloodstream is probably exerted both at the level of the hypothalamus, influencing secretion of corticotropin releasing factor (CRF), and at the level of the adenohypophysis, influencing directly its secretory activity with respect to ACTH. There is some evidence, also, that cortisol may exert an effect at the level of the adrenal cortex. Fluctuations in the production of these adrenal hormones may therefore be induced by a variety of emotional and other nervous stimuli.

The fact that life and electrolyte balance can be maintained without replacement therapy in animals after hypophysectomy but not after hypophysectomy-adrenalectomy indicates that the adrenal secretes some "electrolyte-active" material independent of pituitary (ACTH) stimulation. In most species studied, secretion of aldosterone is not affected as much as that of glucocorticoids by hypophysectomy or by administration of ACTH. However, the similarity of changes in aldosterone and corticosterone under these circumstances supports the view that corticosterone is the immediate precursor of aldosterone in a major biosynthetic pathway. On this basis, ACTH is involved indirectly in the production of aldosterone through its profound influence upon adrenal steroidogenesis.

Secretion of aldosterone is increased when the intake of sodium is restricted or that of potassium excessive; it is decreased by excessive sodium or restricted potassium intake. Decrease in the serum sodium concentration is a stimulus to increased output of aldosterone. However, aldosterone secretion is responsive not only to changes in ionic concentrations but also to changes in extracellular fluid volume, a decrease in which is a physiological stimulus to aldosterone secretion. It has been suggested that these changes may be detected by volume or stretch receptors in the atria, great veins, or head, similar to the mechanism operating in the case of the antidiuretic hormone (p. 747).

Although there is much that is not known concerning this mechanism, the net effects of its operation seem clear. Aldosterone increases reabsorption of sodium by the renal tubular epithelium, causing sodium retention. This results in increase in the volume or sodium concentration of the extracellular fluid. These in some way in turn inhibit secretion of aldosterone. This mechanism is apparently more sensitive to Na^+ concentration than to changes in volume. Volume receptors therefore probably play a minor role in controlling aldosterone secretion except under conditions of extreme depletion of body water. Secretion of aldosterone is stimulated also by the renin-angiotensin system (p. 837). The active factor is angiotensin II; this action is not dependent upon the rise in blood pressure produced by this powerful pressor agent.

Transport, Metabolism, Excretion

The average concentrations of corticoids in the blood plasma in man are as follows: 17-hydroxycorticosterone (compound F; cortisol) 12 μg./100 ml. (5 to 25 μg.); corticosterone (compound B) 1.0 (0.04 to 2.0) μg./100 ml.; aldosterone 0.05 (0.03 to 0.08) μg./100 ml. The concentrations of F and B in adrenal-vein blood have been found to be about 300 μg. and 80 μg./100 ml., respectively. Under conditions of normal plasma cortisol concentration, only about 10 per cent is in the free state, 90 per cent being bound to protein—30 per cent to albumin and 60 per cent to a specific α_2-globulin, transcortin. At concentrations exceeding the binding capacity of transcortin (about 20 μg./100 ml.) the proportions bound to albumin and in the free state increase.

In normal subjects the plasma cortisol concentration exhibits a diurnal rhythm with maximum values at 8 A.M., falling subsequently to about 50 per cent or less between 4 P.M. and midnight. This fluctuation apparently results from nervous system influences that produce cyclic variations in secretion of ACTH.

In addition to facilitating transport of these steroids in an aqueous medium, this protein binding may serve to limit the activity of these hormones at the cellular level by restricting their diffusion across the capillary walls. It may in this manner also protect them from excessively rapid metabolic inactivation. The increment in plasma cortisol that occurs normally during the third trimester of pregnancy and following administration of estrogen is almost entirely bound to protein, and is therefore not associated with manifestations of hyperadrenocorticism.

The adrenocortical hormones undergo rapid changes in the organism, with loss of biological activity. In the liver the α,β-unsaturated 3-ketone group in ring A undergoes reduction. The side chain may be removed by oxidation, forming 17-ketosteroids, or the C-20 ketone may be reduced to glycol configuration. The terminal steroid derivatives are excreted as conjugates (glucosiduronides, sulfates). About 75 per cent is excreted in the urine, the remainder in the feces, the latter representing mainly metabolites excreted in the bile that had escaped reabsorption in the intestine and bacterial action. The most abundant urinary metabolites are the tetrahydro derivatives, e.g., urocortisol and urocortisone and their derivatives, cortol and cortolone. Corticosterone and aldosterone are also excreted presumably as tetrahydro derivatives.

17-Hydroxycorticosterone (cortisol: compound F). This gives rise to essentially the same metabolites as does 11-dehydro-17-hydroxycorticosterone (cortisone; compound E).

(1) They are in part excreted in the urine unchanged (except largely conjugated, as glucuronides).

(2) They undergo reduction at carbons 3, 4, 5, and in part also at C-20, giving rise mainly to dihydro and tetrahydro derivatives, losing the α,β-unsaturated 3-ketone grouping in ring A, and are therefore biologically inactive (e.g., urocortisol; urocortisone). These are excreted in the urine, mainly as glucuronides. Reduction of the ketonic structure at C-20 gives rise to cortol and cortolone.

(3) By virtue of the 17-hydroxy group, the side chain can be oxidatively removed, with the formation of 17-ketosteroids of the C-19 type, e.g., 11-hydroxy- and 11-keto-androsterones and etiocholanolones, which are excreted in the urine, mainly as sulfates and glucuronides and account for about 10 per cent of the cortisol secreted. These androsterones are responsible for the androgenic effects of cortisol and cortisone when given in large amounts.

Corticosterone (compound B). This undergoes reduction, giving rise to dihydro and tetrahydro derivatives that are biologically inactive due to loss of the α,β-unsaturated 3-ketone grouping in ring A. Corticosterone cannot give rise to 17-ketosteroids, owing to absence of the 17-hydroxy group.

Aldosterone. This, too, undergoes reduction, apparently to a tetrahydro derivative, which is excreted in the urine. A small amount of aldosterone is present in the urine, mainly conjugated with glucuronic acid.

Corticoids and their metabolites occur in the urine, therefore, mainly in the following forms:

(1) Biologically active corticoids in their original forms (e.g., cortisol, corticosterone, aldosterone), except largely conjugated (glucuronides).

(2) Biologically inactive reduction products, free and conjugated.

(3) 17-Ketosteroids, mainly conjugated (sulfates; glucosiduronides), some biologically active (androgenic), others not.

(4) Pregnanediol glucuronide, biologically inactive. Pregnanetriol may be excreted in the urine in significant quantities in certain forms of adrenocortical functional disturbance resulting from congenital defects in essential hydroxylation mechanisms (adrenogenital syndrome).

Evaluation of adrenocortical functional activity may be approached by measuring urinary excretion of these substances in the resting state or after administration of ACTH. Certain of the procedures employed may be outlined as follows:

Neutral 17-Ketosteroids. These substances, determined colorimetrically (Zimmermann reaction), give a measure of metabolites of adrenal and testicular hormones (p. 686) excreted as 17-ketones. In normal adult subjects, the adrenal is responsible for about two-thirds of the total urinary neutral 17-ketosteroids in men (total, 7 to 20 mg. daily) and for the total quantity in women (5 to 15 mg. daily). They can result from the catabolism of adrenal hormones of the C-21 type (corticoids) and from secretion of adrenal hormones of the C-19 type (androgens) (p. 701).

Biologically Active Corticosteroids. The urine contains steroids which exert biological effects characteristic of adrenal cortical hormones (p. 703), as indicated above. The most important in man are cortisol (F) and aldosterone, excreted mainly in conjugated form from which they can be liberated by hydrolysis (acid or β-glucuronidase).

Aldosterone may be assayed by chromatography or by procedures involving measurement of Na retention following administration of a test dose of NaCl to adrenalectomized rats. The normal 24-hour excretion is approximately 2 to 15 μg. of aldosterone.

The carbohydrate-active (i.e., 11-oxygenated) corticoids may be measured by the liver-glycogen deposition procedures (p. 703). Normal 24-hour values are about 0.05 to 0.4 mg. in men and 0.1 to 0.3 mg. in women (mg. equivalents of 11-dehydrocorticosterone). This and other bioassay procedures have been generally supplanted by chromatographic and chemical methods (p. 704).

17,21-Dihydroxy-20-ketosteroids. These substances, which include the biologically active compounds E, F, and S, and certain of their inactive reduced metabolites, may be measured by means of the Porter-Silber procedure (p. 704). This is widely employed clinically because of the fact that compound F is the adrenal corticoid secreted in largest amount in man. Normal resting values, after hydrolysis with β-glucuronidase, range from 3 to 9 mg. in 24 hours (mg. equivalents of compound F) in normal adults. Approximately 10 per cent of this is in the free state.

Neutral Formaldehydogenic Steroids. Substances in this category include, in addition to cortisone (E), cortisol (F), and certain of their inactive metabolites, also corticosterone, 11-deoxycorticosterone, and aldosterone, as well as certain of their inactive metabolites and other steroids with α-ketol or glycol side chains. This procedure, which is much less specific than the Porter-Silber method, has been superseded by the latter for purposes of clinical evaluation of adrenocortical function. Normal 24-hour values range from 7 to 18 mg. equivalents of deoxycorticosterone.

Metabolic Effects

Absence of adrenal cortical hormones (adrenalectomy; Addison's disease) or administration of excessive amounts of these hormones are accompanied by characteristic metabolic changes, which may be grouped broadly under two headings: (1) electrolyte and water metabolism; (2) carbohydrate, protein, and fat metabolism. The latter category is influenced principally by cortisol and corticosterone (11-oxysteroids; "glucocorticoids"), whereas the former is influenced predominantly, but by no means exclusively, by aldosterone ("mineralocorticoid").

Electrolytes and water. The adrenocortical hormones exert a regulatory influence on the distribution of sodium and potassium between extracellular and intracellular fluids and upon their excretion by the kidney. Accordingly, they are involved in regulation also of the volume and composition of the body fluid compartments. The adrenocortical hormones exhibit both qualitative and quantitative differences with respect to these actions.

Aldosterone promotes passage of K^+ ions from intracellular to extracellular fluids in exchange for Na^+ and H^+ ions, which pass in the opposite direction. Aldosterone acts on renal tubular epithelial cells to promote reabsorption of Na^+. This is accompanied by reabsorption of increased amounts of Cl^+ and water and, in the distal tubule, by increased excretion (exchange mechanism, p. 826) of K^+ and H^+ ions and ammonia, increased amounts of HCO_3^- ion being returned to the blood plasma. Similar effects on sweat, salivary, and intestinal mucosal glands are reflected in decreased amounts of Na and Cl and increased amounts of K in their secretions. The overall effects are increased retention of Na and water, increased loss of K, increase in extracellular fluid volume, with a tendency toward increased concentration in this fluid of Na^+ and HCO_3^- ions and decreased concentrations of K^+ and Cl^-, i.e., a condition of hypochloremic alkalosis (p. 320).

Similar electrolyte abnormalities may occur in individuals with generalized adrenocortical hyperfunction (Cushing's syndrome), accompanied by abnormalities of carbohydrate, protein, and lipid metabolism, or in subjects with hyperaldosteronism, without such associated manifestations. In Cushing's syndrome, the condition of osteoporosis resulting from inadequate production of osteoid tissue (antianabolic action of glucocorticoids, p. 712), is reflected in increased urinary excretion of calcium.

The Na-retaining potency of aldosterone is 20 to several hundred times that of deoxycorticosterone, and that of the latter two to four times that of the glucocorticoids. There are also qualitative differences in the actions in this connection of these hormones. In the absence of the adrenals, neither water nor Na is excreted adequately when unusually large quantities are given. This difficulty is aggravated by aldosterone, which further increases retention of Na, but is corrected by glucocorticoids. Moreover, the elevation of plasma Na resulting from excessive doses of aldosterone or deoxycorticosterone in intact animals may be counteracted by simultaneous administration of glucocorticoids or ACTH, perhaps through the medium of increased glomerular filtration.

In addition to the renal effect, the glucocorticoids influence K metabolism by their protein anti-anabolic action in extrahepatic tissues, releasing intracellular K to the extracellular fluids. Their action in increasing glycogen storage (especially liver) is accompanied by increase in K in the cells involved in this process.

The effects of corticoids on water excretion vary considerably depending upon (1) the amount and nature of the steroid and (2) the conditions under which it is acting, e.g., the extent of the simultaneous water (hydration) or Na load. In animals hydrated with isotonic NaCl solution, aldosterone usually, but not invariably, has little or no effect on water excretion, although Na retention occurs. On the other hand, under these conditions deoxycorticosterone decreases water excretion in proportion to Na retention, whereas the effects of corticosterone, cortisone, and cortisol differ among themselves and from the effects of the other steroids.

Although adrenocortical insufficiency is characterized by excessive Na and water excretion (and dehydration), it is also associated with inability to excrete a large water load at a normal rate. Normal excretion is restored by glucocorticoids, but not by aldosterone or deoxycorticosterone.

Adrenalectomized animals and patients with Addison's disease, if untreated, exhibit the following phenomena: (1) increased urine volume, with (2) disproportionately increased excretion of Na and Cl, leading to (3) decreased concentration of Na and Cl in blood plasma, (4) decrease in body water (dehydration) and (5) decrease in plasma volume. Ultimately there is a fall in blood pressure, with circulatory collapse and impaired renal glomerular filtration, which are aggravated by, but not necessarily entirely dependent upon the changes in electrolyte and water balance. Simultaneously with the changes in Na, the urinary excretion of K decreases and the concentration of K in the plasma increases.

In the absence of adrenal hormones, the renal tubular epithelial cells are unable to reabsorb Na (also Cl and water) adequately from the glomerular filtrate in spite of a low plasma Na concentration. They also are unable to excrete K adequately despite the increased plasma K concentration. At the same time there is a disturbance in the equilibrium between the extracellular (plasma and interstitial fluids) and intracellular fluid compartments (extrarenal effect), characterized by an increase in intracellular (muscle) K and a decrease in extracellular Na and Cl. Inadequate Na^+:H^+ exchange in the kidney results in decrease in the plasma HCO_3^- concentration (metabolic acidosis). An increase in blood urea nitrogen reflects the diminished glomerular filtration, apparently a primary effect of decrease in glucocorticoids, aggravated by the superimposed state of dehydration and circulatory collapse.

Carbohydrate metabolism. The 11-oxygenated (glucogenic) adrenocortical hormones play an important role in carbohydrate metabolism. Their chief effects, which vary somewhat in different species, are to increase the blood glucose concentration, to diminish glucose tolerance, and to increase liver glycogen. These effects result from the actions of these hormones in: (1) increasing the output of glucose by the liver; (2) diminishing peripheral uptake and utilization of glucose, i.e., for oxidation, lipogenesis, extrahepatic synthesis of protein; (3) increasing gluconeogenesis.

Glucocorticoids depress synthesis of acid sulfated mucopolysaccharides in extrahepatic tissues. In the case of bone, this defective formation of chondroitin sulfate, in addition to that of protein, underlies the development of osteoporosis in subjects with adrenal hyperfunction (Cushing's syndrome).

The livers of animals treated with cortisol show selectively increased activity of glucose-6-phosphatase and fructose-1,6-diphosphatase. Inasmuch as these enzymes occupy key positions in reversal of the enzymatic reactions of glycolysis in the liver, such changes could contribute to the hyperglycemic action of the glucocorticoids. The increased gluconeogenesis may be related to their action in stimulating activity of certain transaminases (p. 573). Hepatic glycogen synthetase activity is also increased.

Cortisol possesses the highest activity in carbohydrate metabolism; 11-dehydro-17-hydroxycorticosterone (cortisone; compound E) is about two-thirds as active and corticosterone or 11-dehydrocorticosterone (compound A) about one-third as active. Aldosterone, too, causes glycogen deposition in fasting adrenalectomized animals, its activity being about one-third that of cortisone and two-thirds that of corticosterone.

The fasted, untreated, adrenalectomized animal (or patient with Addison's disease) exhibits the following changes in carbohydrate metabolism: (1) striking decrease in liver glycogen; (2) less marked decrease in muscle glycogen; (3) hypoglycemia; (4) decreased intestinal absorption of glucose (corrected by administration of NaCl). These changes do not occur if a sufficient quantity of carbohydrate is given, and are prevented or corrected by administration of 11-oxygenated adrenal hormones.

(5) Adrenalectomized animals exhibit increased sensitivity to insulin.

(6) Adrenalectomy results in amelioration of diabetes produced by pancreatectomy or alloxan. Administration of 11-oxygenated adrenal hormones or cortical extracts aggravates the diabetes.

Protein metabolism. Administration of relatively large amounts of glucocorticoids to fasting intact animals is followed by an increase in total urinary nitrogen and free amino acids and a negative nitrogen balance. This is accompanied by an increase in total body carbohydrate, and G:N ratios indicate that about 50 to 70 per cent of the extra protein catabolized was converted to glucose. The negative nitrogen balance results from a decreased rate of incorporation of amino acids into protein in extrahepatic tissues in the face of continuing protein degradation at a normal rate (antianabolic effect). There is also a decrease in the rate of synthesis of acid sulfated mucopolysaccharides in the tissues, but not of those in the blood plasma.

In the liver, on the other hand, glucocorticoids cause increased incorporation of amino acids into protein. This apparently results from increased availability of free amino acids reaching the liver from extrahepatic tissues and it is accompanied by striking increase in certain hepatic enzymes involved in the metabolism of carbohydrate and amino acids. These include glucose-6-phosphatase, fructose-1,6-diphosphatase, glycogen synthetase, alanine α-ketoglutarate transaminase, tyrosine α-ketoglutarate transaminase, and tryptophan pyrrolase. This increase, at least in the case of tyrosine transaminase, is preceded by increased synthesis of RNA. This suggests that the hormonal induction of these enzymes, with the consequent effects on protein metabolism, and perhaps on gluconeogenesis, is exerted primarily on production of messenger RNA.

Lipid metabolism. The major effects of glucocorticoids on lipid metabolism appear to be secondary to their effects on carbohydrate metabolism. They are therefore conditioned by other factors, including the adequacy of carbohydrate intake and of insulin secretion. Under conditions of inadequate insulin secretion, particularly if carbohydrates are simultaneously restricted, glucocorticoids cause an increase in release of unesterified fatty acids from adipose tissue (increased lipolysis). This effect is presumably a consequence of the action of these hormones in depressing utilization of glucose in this as in other tissues. It has been suggested that the resulting decreased supply of α-glycerophosphate may retard re-esterification of fatty acids in adipose tissue, thus favoring their passage into the bloodstream, particularly since these cells do not possess a mechanism for direct phosphorylation of free glycerol.

In the absence of an adequate supply of insulin and carbohydrate, the increased amounts of free fatty acid reaching the liver exceed its oxidative capacity and enter other metabolic pathways, i.e., ketogenesis, and synthesis of cholesterol, phosphatides, and triglycerides. This is reflected in the production of ketonemia and ketonuria, hypercholesterolemia, hyperlipemia, and increase in liver fat. Because of their action in stimulating gluconeogenesis, glucocorticoids are actually antiketogenic in the presence of adequate secretion of insulin.

Anti-inflammatory Action

Cortisol is a potent inhibitor of the inflammatory reaction induced by physical, chemical, or bacterial agents. Cortisone is less than 2 per cent as active in this respect, corticosterone is virtually inactive, and aldosterone and deoxycorticosterone apparently antagonize this action of cortisol. This anti-inflammatory action includes inhibition of the vascular margination of leukocytes, of the migration of leukocytes from the capillaries, and of the formation of fibrin and accumulation of edema fluid. There is also suppression of the increase in capillary permeability in the inflamed area. Although these effects may in certain respects be detrimental in the case of bacterial infections, they may be desirable in other types of inflammation. Among these are rheumatoid arthritis and rheumatic fever, in which the inflammation of affected joints often responds dramatically to administration of active corticosteroids. Several synthetic derivatives are available which are highly active in this respect and which exhibit less biological activity in other directions that are therapeutically undesirable.

Effect on Immune Reactions

Certain of the glucocorticoids, including cortisol and cortisone, exert a pronounced anti-allergic action. They can not only inhibit the production of antibodies following the introduction of an antigen, but also produce prompt alleviation of serious manifestations of hypersensitivity, e.g., anaphylactic shock. The mechanism of their action in this connection is not known.

They are effective in breaking down genetic barriers to heterotransplantation of tissues. For example, certain tumors will grow in heterologous hosts pretreated with these hormones.

Miscellaneous Effects

Administration of glucocorticoids is followed promptly by a decrease in the number of circulating lymphocytes and eosinophils. The lymphopenia is due to active destruction of lymphocytes in lymphatic tissues (intestinal mucosa, lymph nodes, thymus); the mechanism of production of the eosinopenia is not known. Conversely, adrenocortical insufficiency, as in Addison's disease, may be accompanied by increase in circulating eosinophils and lymphocytes and in hypertrophy of lymphoid tissue.

One of the undesirable consequences of prolonged therapy with adrenocortical hormones is the development of ulcerations of the gastrointestinal tract. Their pathogenesis is not clear, but it may be related to the observation that these hormones induce increased gastric (HCl and pepsin) and pancreatic (trypsinogen) secretion.

THYROID HORMONE

Chemistry

The thyroid gland contains an iodized glycoprotein, "thyroglobulin," characteristically present in the colloid of the thyroid follicles, which is apparently the "storage form" of the thyroid hormone. It has a molecular weight of about 680,000. Hydrolysis yields several iodine-containing derivatives of tyrosine, viz., mono- and diiodotyrosine, di- and triiodothyronine (two forms), and thyroxine (tetraiodothyronine) (Fig. 26–10). 3,5,3′-Triiodothyronine has four to 10 times the biological activity of thyroxine. The naturally occurring forms are levorotatory; synthetic thyroxine shows no optical rotation, being a mixture of D- and L- forms (racemic), the former exhibiting relatively low activity in vivo.

A number of substances have been shown to exhibit thyroid hormone activity (relief of human myxedema); these contain iodine substituted in the inner aromatic ring (3–5) of a compound termed "thyronine" (4-4′-hydroxyphenoxy-phenylalanine). Several analogs of thyroid hormone have been prepared which exert anti-thyroxine activity (e.g., 2′,6′-diiodothyronine). These probably act as competitive antagonists of the hormone (p. 660), differing fundamentally in this respect, therefore, from the so-called "anti-thyroid agents."

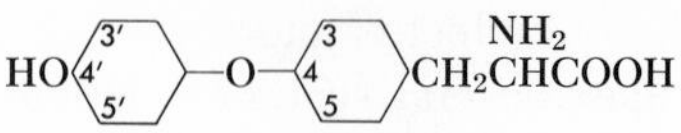

"Thyronine"
(4-[4′-hydroxyphenoxy]phenylalanine)

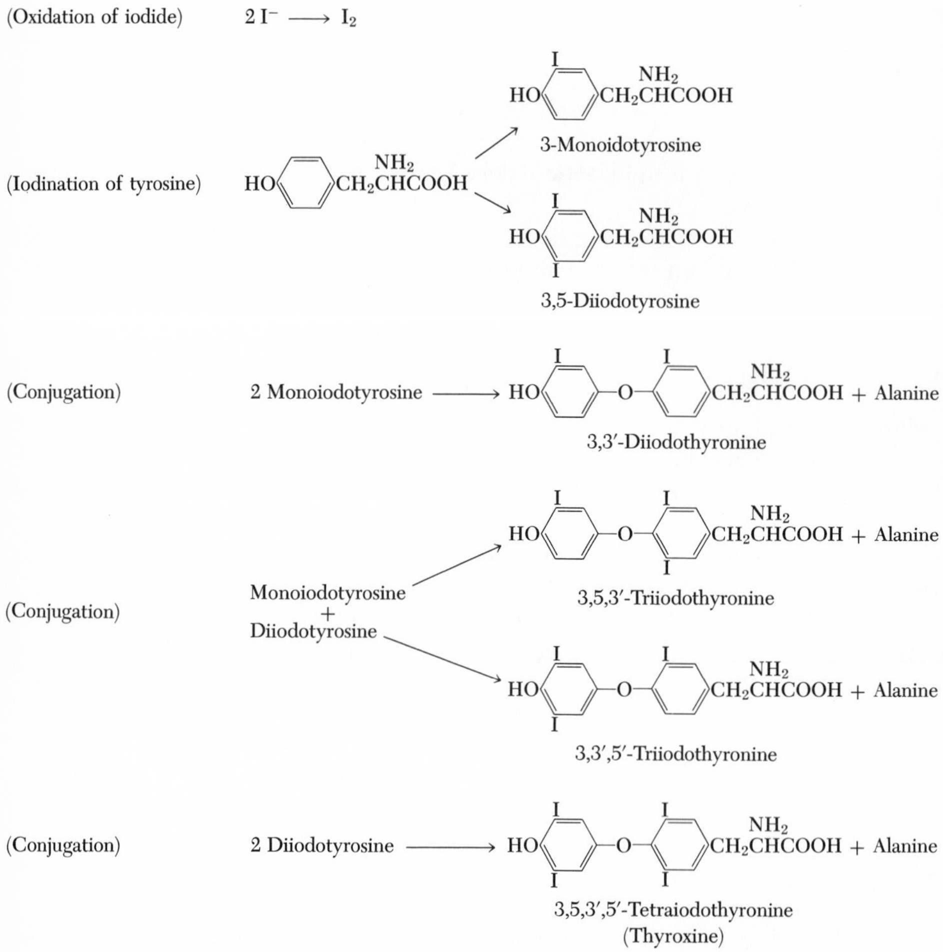

(Oxidation of iodide) $2\,I^- \longrightarrow I_2$

(Iodination of tyrosine) Tyrosine $\longrightarrow$ 3-Monoidotyrosine; $\longrightarrow$ 3,5-Diiodotyrosine

(Conjugation) 2 Monoiodotyrosine $\longrightarrow$ 3,3′-Diiodothyronine + Alanine

(Conjugation) Monoiodotyrosine + Diiodotyrosine $\longrightarrow$ 3,5,3′-Triiodothyronine + Alanine; $\longrightarrow$ 3,3′,5′-Triiodothyronine + Alanine

(Conjugation) 2 Diiodotyrosine $\longrightarrow$ 3,5,3′,5′-Tetraiodothyronine (Thyroxine) + Alanine

Figure 26-10. Biosynthesis of thyroid hormones.

There is evidence that the thyroid gland produces "thyrocalcitonin," a polypeptide which lowers the serum calcium concentration, this effect being produced by inhibiting release of calcium from skeletal deposits. Secretion of this substance is presumably stimulated by an increasing concentration of calcium in the blood plasma.

Biosynthesis and Secretion

The function of the thyroid in the formation and secretion of thyroid hormone may be divided into six phases: (1) Entry of inorganic iodide from the circulation; (2) concentration of inorganic iodide in the gland; (3) synthesis of thyroglobulin in follicular cells; (4) storage of thyroglobulin in colloid; (5) liberation of thyroxine and triiodothyronine from thyroglobulin; (6) passage of these compounds into the circulation.

Accumulation of iodine in thyroid. Inorganic iodide, present in the blood plasma in low concentration (<2 μg. per cent, except after administration), is actively removed by the acinar cells of the thyroid and passes into the follicle, which is able to "trap" iodine in enormously higher concentration (several hundred times) than that in the circulation. Under physiological conditions, inorganic iodide comprises only about 1 per cent of the total iodine of the thyroid gland and, in 15 minutes after administration of tracer doses of I^{131} to rats, over 90 per cent of the radioactivity in the gland is organically bound. This suggests that the selective accumulation of this element by the thyroid is related to its ability to incorporate iodine in organic compounds. However, after administration of large doses of iodide or certain anti-thyroid agents (p. 720), which inhibit synthesis of thyroid hormone, inorganic iodide may accumulate in the gland in high concentration, indicating the presence of a mechanism independent of that involved in the organic conversion reactions.

Accumulation of iodine in the thyroid is accelerated and increased by administration of thyrotropic hormone (TSH) and is markedly reduced by thiocyanate and perchlorate (p. 721).

The thyroid contains inorganic iodide, monoiodotyrosine, diiodotyrosine, thyroxine, triiodothyronine, and other as yet unidentified iodinated compounds. Almost all (about 97 per cent) of the iodine in the gland is firmly bound to protein (thyroglobulin), the organic compounds mentioned above being liberated by hydrolysis. Free thyroxine (possibly loosely linked to protein), although present in small amounts (0.5 per cent of the total I), nevertheless exists in over 100 times the concentration of protein-bound iodine in the plasma.

Synthesis of thyroid hormone (Fig. 26–10). Although all details have not been definitely established, present evidence supports the following sequence of events.

Oxidation of Iodide. Normally, iodide entering the thyroid promptly undergoes oxidation to an active form, possibly iodinium ion (I^+) or hypoiodite (HIO) or both. This is accomplished through the action of an iodide peroxidase on H_2O_2. The transition from iodide, through an oxidized form, to incorporation in the benzene ring of tyrosine, as indicated below, may occur almost as a single step.

Iodination of Tyrosine and Coupling. It is believed that the process of iodination involves tyrosine that is attached in peptide linkage to a large globulin molecule. The "activated" iodine is introduced first at the 3-position, forming monoiodotyrosine, and then at the 5-position, forming diiodotyrosine. Two molecules of diiodotyrosine, still in peptide linkage with globulin, then undergo oxidative coupling, with the elimination of one alanine side chain, to form thyroxine (tetraiodothyronine). One molecule each of diiodotyrosine and monoiodotyrosine may couple to form triiodothyronine, and two molecules of monoiodotyrosine to form diiodothyronine (Fig. 26–10). Triiodothyronine may possibly be formed also by partial deiodination of thyroxine. These iodothyronines in peptide linkage with the globulin comprise the thyroglobulin molecule, which is stored in the colloid material within the lumen of the thyroid follicles.

The iodination and coupling reactions are accelerated by TSH and are inhibited by certain anti-thyroid agents (e.g., thiocarbamides; aminobenzenes) (p. 722).

Under physiological conditions there is little diurnal variation in the iodine content of the thyroid, the uptake of I and release of I-containing hormone occurring simultaneously, continuously, and at approximately constant rates.

Secretion of thyroid hormones. In accordance with demand, under stimulation by TSH, the thyroglobulin in the gland undergoes hydrolysis by a proteolytic enzyme or enzymes, with release of its iodinated compounds. It is probable that this is the manner in which the hormones are secreted, passing from the colloid, through the acinar cells, into the lymphatics or bloodstream. This process is accelerated by TSH. It has been estimated that the equivalent of about 80 to 95 μg. of thyroxine is secreted daily under physiological conditions.

Secretion of TSH by the anterior pituitary is regulated by the level of circulating thyroid hormone. Decrease in the latter stimulates and an increase depresses secretion of TSH, apparently mainly by a direct action on the pituitary, but also in part via the hypothalamus (p. 738). Formation and release of thyroid hormone are therefore automatically adjusted to the demand, as reflected in the rate of its removal from the bloodstream.

Circulating thyroid hormone. The plasma normally contains iodine in the form of inorganic iodide (small amounts, <2 μg. per cent, except after administration), thyroxine (6 to 12 μg. per 100 ml.), and a relatively small amount of triiodothyronine (p. 713). When present in normal amounts, thyroxine is loosely bound to a specific α-globulin, thyroxine-binding globulin (a glycoprotein), with an electrophoretic mobility intermediate between the α_1- and α_2-globulins. A small amount is bound to pre-albumin, a serum protein of somewhat greater electrophoretic mobility than albumin. Triiodothyronine is present largely in the free state. When abnormally large amounts of hormone are present (over 2 to 3 times normal), the excess is bound to albumin. The constituent iodine is referred to and determined as protein-bound iodine (PBI), ranging normally from 4 to 8 μg. per 100 ml. plasma.

Metabolism of Thyroid Hormones

Thyroxine, injected intravenously, leaves the circulating plasma rapidly, only about 50 per cent remaining in the bloodstream after 3 minutes, the bulk of the remainder being recoverable from the liver. This organ plays an important role in the regulation of the concentration and biological activity of thyroid hormone in the blood. The most important demonstrated actions of the liver in this connection are as follows:

(1) Deiodination, with excretion of the iodine as inorganic iodide in the bile and urine. This results in abolition of biological activity.

(2) Conjugation of the iodothyronines with glucuronic acid, the resulting glucuronides being excreted in the bile. These undergo hydrolysis in the intestinal lumen, the free hormone being reabsorbed into the portal circulation. This enterohepatic circulation may be an important part of the mechanism of regulation of circulating thyroid hormone. Triiodothyronine may undergo sulfate conjugation.

(3) Removal of the amino group from the alanine substituent, with the formation of the pyruvic and acetic acid analogs of certain of the iodothyronines.

(4) Excretion in the bile of small amounts of hormones in the free state, with subsequent reabsorption (enterohepatic circulation).

(5) Disruption of the thyronine molecule with formation of such compounds as tyrosine, 3,4-dihydroxyphenylalanine, and *p*-hydroxyphenylpyruvic acid.

Complete deiodination occurs in extrahepatic tissues, as in the liver, with excretion as inorganic iodide in the urine. However, the postulated conversion of tetraiodothyronine (thyroxine) to triiodothyronine has not been established. The greater biological activity and more rapid action of the latter have suggested that it (or one of its derivatives) may be the active form of the hormone at the target tissue level. Triiodothyronine may also be metabolized to triiodothyroacetic acid, presumably by initial transamination, i.e., conversion to triiodothyropyruvic acid, and oxidative decarboxylation of the latter; these reactions are similar to those undergone by alanine (p. 576). The acetic acid analog is less active biologically but acts more rapidly than triiodothyronine.

Small amounts of the iodothyronines are excreted by intestinal mucosal cells (with subsequent reabsorption) and in the urine. The quantities excreted in the feces and urine increase after parenteral administration of large doses of hormone. The relatively slow metabolic degradation and disposal of thyroid hormone is indicated by its estimated biological half-life of 7 to 12 days, and by the fact that the calorigenic effect (increase in BMR) of a therapeutic dose of thyroxine persists for 30 to 50 days in hypothyroid subjects.

Metabolic Effects

The action of thyroid hormone is characteristically evidenced in the relief of the manifestations of human myxedema. A great variety of effects is involved in the production of this phenomenon. Some of the important body functions influenced by thyroid activity are:

- Metabolic rate (oxygen consumption)
- Growth and tissue differentiation
- Metabolism of carbohydrate, lipids, protein, electrolytes, and water
- Vitamin requirements
- Temperature sensitivity
- Gastrointestinal activity
- Central nervous system activity
- Reproduction
- Hematopoiesis
- Cardiovascular function
- Muscle activity
- Resistance to infection
- Sensitivity to acetonitrile

Consideration will be given here only to the metabolic effects of the thyroid hormone which are of immediate biochemical interest. The biological activity of triiodothyronine is about five to 10 times that of thyroxine, the relative activities differing for different functions and by different assay methods, and also in different species. It is to be understood that where reference is made, here or elsewhere, to actions of thyroxine, the same statements apply (qualitatively) also to triiodothyronine, and only to the L-forms of the hormones.

Calorigenic effect. Thyroid hormone increases the rate of energy exchange and oxygen consumption of all normal tissues except the thyroid gland itself. This is reflected in an increase in the basal metabolic rate (BMR), which is the sum of the effects, of different magnitude, on various tissues.

This calorigenic effect is of smaller magnitude in young than in old subjects and is greater at low (e.g., in hypothyroidism) than at normal or high levels of metabolism. In subjects with myxedema, 1 mg. of thyroxine produces about 2.8 per cent increase in BMR. In the absence of thyroid hormone, the BMR (i.e., resting level of oxygen consumption) decreases by about 30 to 45 per cent (p. 332). Possible mechanisms of production of this effect are discussed elsewhere (p. 384).

Protein metabolism. In physiological doses, thyroid hormones favor protein anabolism, leading to increased retention of nitrogen (positive nitrogen balance). This explains the growth arrest of young thyroidectomized animals and hypothyroid children, and the resumption of growth following administration of thyroid hormones. Thyroxine promotes incorporation of amino acids into protein; this is depressed following thyroidectomy and may be restored to normal by appropriate replacement therapy. Large, unphysiological doses stimulate protein catabolism, leading to a negative nitrogen balance.

Thyroidectomy (in man) is followed by accumulation of extracellular fluid rich in a hyaluronic acid–containing mucoprotein, apparently similar in composition to fetal mucin. This forms the basis of clinical myxedema.

Administration of thyroid hormone is followed by increased urinary excretion of creatine. This may be due in part to increased catabolism of muscle protein, or decreased conversion of phosphocreatine to creatinine, and in part to a decreased capacity for synthesizing phosphocreatine (p. 428) by the muscle cell.

Carbohydrate metabolism. Although direct evidence is lacking, thyroid hormone is believed to increase the rate of intestinal absorption of monosaccharides. This is regarded as one of the factors responsible for the frequently excessive rise in blood sugar concentration following ingestion of glucose by patients with thyrotoxicosis (decreased oral glucose tolerance); this may not occur following intravenous injection of glucose. Decreased glucose tolerance may be contributed to also by acceleration of degradation of insulin. Diabetes mellitus is aggravated by coexisting thyrotoxicosis or by administration of thyroid hormone. Hyperglycemia may be contributed to also by the increase in hepatic glucose-6-phosphatase activity which has been observed in animals treated with thyroxine.

In the case of most of the observed effects of thyroid hormones on carbohydrate metabolism, it is difficult to distinguish direct actions from those exerted indirectly through influences on the actions of epinephrine and insulin. Thyroid hormone causes a decrease of glycogen in the liver and, to a lesser extent, in the myocardium and skeletal muscle. This stimulation of glycogenolysis may be due to increased sensitivity of the organism to epinephrine in the presence of excessive amounts of thyroid hormone.

Thyroxine enhances gluconeogenesis, but in a manner different from adrenocortical hormone. For example, thyroidectomy, in contrast to adrenalectomy, does not alleviate pancreatic diabetes in the cat or dog, and administration of thyroid hormone, in contrast to adrenocortical hormone, does not increase glycosuria in the Houssay dog (hypophysectomized-depancreatized). However, diabetes can be produced in the partially depancreatized dog and rat by administration of thyroid hormone (metathyroid diabetes, p. 445).

In the otherwise normal animal, the hyperglycemic effects of increased hepatic glycogenolysis and gluconeogenesis are usually effectively offset by simultaneously increased utilization of glucose in the tissues generally.

Thyroid hormones stimulate glycolysis as well as oxidative metabolism of glucose via the Krebs cycle and phosphogluconate pathway. Administration of thyroxine results in increase of glucose-6-phosphate dehydrogenase activity in the liver.

Lipid metabolism. The stimulation of oxidative processes which follows administration of thyroid hormones may include fatty acids. However, the metabolism of these substances is influenced also indirectly. Thyroid hormones promote release of unesterified fatty acids from adipose tissue, with consequent increase in their concentration in the blood. This effect is believed to be due to increased sensitivity of the tissue to the fat-mobilizing actions of epinephrine in the presence of increased amounts of thyroid hormone. Under such circumstances there may be increased ketogenesis and ketosis, particularly in the absence of adequate amounts of carbohydrate and insulin. Thyroid hormones also enhance the fat-synthesizing effect of insulin, i.e., depression of release of fatty acids from adipose tissue.

Despite the fact that hepatic synthesis of cholesterol and phospholipid is depressed following thyroidectomy and is increased in thyrotoxicosis, the concentration of cholesterol (and to a lesser degree phospholipid) in the plasma is frequently increased in hypothyroidism and decreased in hyperthyroidism. This is explicable in part on the basis that although thyroid hormones increase the rate of biosynthesis of cholesterol, they increase the rate of its degradation, transformation (e.g., to bile acids) and excretion (biliary) to an even greater extent, accounting for the lowered blood concentration. The concentration of plasma lipoproteins of the S_f 10 to 20 class is frequently increased in hypothyroidism and decreased in thyrotoxicosis, or following administration of thyroid hormone to normal subjects.

Electrolyte and water metabolism. In hypothyroidism, there is an increase in interstitial water and a decrease in plasma volume. Adequate thyroid therapy results in prompt diuresis with increased excretion of Na, Cl, K, and N, indicating loss of fluid from both the extracellular and the intracellular compartment. In thyrotoxicosis, the calorigenic and catabolic effects of excessive amounts of thyroid hormone are reflected in increased urinary excretion of K (also N and PO_4), and increased water loss, mainly by vaporization from the skin and lungs (insensible loss); the plasma volume may be increased.

In young, growing subjects, small doses of thyroxine enhance calcium retention. This may be secondary to increased formation of bone matrix (osteoid), resulting from stimulation of protein anabolism. Excessive amounts of thyroid hormone lead to increased mobilization of calcium from the skeleton, with increased calcium excretion in the urine and feces. This may be part of the general catabolic effect of the hormone and not a specific influence on calcium metabolism. There is no significant alteration in serum calcium.

Vitamins. Administration of large amounts of thyroid hormone increases the requirement for certain members of the vitamin B complex (thiamine, pyridoxine, pantothenic acid) and for vitamin C. These relationships and the mechanisms involved are obscure, but are presumably related to the stimulation of oxidative and catabolic processes.

Growth and development. Absence of the thyroid during the growth period is accompanied by retardation of growth, which is corrected by administration of thyroid hormone. There is evidence that this growth-enhancing and perhaps the protein-anabolic effect of physiological amounts of thyroid hormone may be mediated by the growth hormone of the anterior pituitary.

Thyroid hormone also induces tissue differentiation and maturation. In man, early absence of this hormone not only arrests longitudinal growth, with consequent dwarfing, but also delays the appearance of epiphyseal centers of ossification. This defect is corrected by administration of thyroid hormone.

The effect of this agent in hastening metamorphosis of amphibians has been employed for bioassay purposes. In the absence of thyroid hormone, i.e., in the thyroidectomized tadpole, metamorphosis does not occur, e.g., the limbs do not extend and the gill and tail do not regress, although the tadpole continues to grow. Metamorphosis can be induced at any stage by administration of minute amounts of thyroid hormone. Very small tadpoles can be metamorphosed into minute frogs.

This effect in inducing tissue differentiation and development is not related directly to the calorigenic action of thyroxine, since dinitrophenol, which increases metabolism, lacks this morphogenetic effect, whereas acetylthyroxine, which exerts this effect, has no calorigenic action. Moreover, certain stages of amphibian metamorphosis, although stimulated by thyroid hormone, are not accompanied by increase in metabolic rate.

Mechanism of Action

The mechanism of action of the thyroid hormone is not known. Principally because of the wide variety of their effects, many believe that the hormones exert a single primary action, perhaps on energy metabolism, to which other actions are secondary, depending upon specific local target-organ mechanisms and responsiveness. However, they may have a function in tissue differentiation and development independent of effects on energy transformations and oxygen consumption. There is evidence which suggests that the thyroid hormones may produce their metabolic effects by inducing or regulating the induction (via mRNA) of certain key enzymes, including several in the electron transport chain of mitochondria, $NADPH_2$ cytochrome *c* reductase, and microsomal steroid reductases. The concept has been advanced that the thyroid hormones regulate all metabolic functions by controlling the level of cytochrome *c* in the tissues; this is increased in hyperthyroidism and decreased in hypothyroidism.

Interest has been centered upon observations that, in vitro, thyroid hormone can (a) induce mitochondrial swelling, reversible by ATP, and (b) uncouple phosphorylation from oxidation reactions in the oxidation of beta-hydroxybutyrate with isolated tissue preparations. If the latter occurs in vivo, a portion of the energy produced during cellular oxidation processes might be lost in heat instead of being utilized for synthesis of high-energy phosphate compounds. This could account for the calorigenic action of thyroid hormone. However, these effects have been produced only with unphysiologically high concentrations of thyroxine and are produced also by other substances, some calorigenic, others not, which exert none of the other biological actions of thyroid hormone. Moreover, the mitochondrial swelling produced by thyroxine, which has been related to the uncoupling phenomenon, is counteracted by dinitrophenol, which itself uncouples oxidative phosphorylation, and other in vitro uncoupling agents do not produce a calorigenic effect. Although the physiological significance of these observations is still speculative, an action of thyroid hormone on the mitochondrial membrane, if such be the case, would have a profound effect on the oxidative metabolism of the cell and the production and transfer of energy.

Agents Interfering with Synthesis of Thyroid Hormone

A number of chemical agents can interfere with the formation of thyroid hormone by affecting different phases of the mechanism involved in its synthesis. These may be classified conveniently as follows: (1) thyroid hormone; (2) iodine; (3) thiocyanate; (4) antithyroid agents.

Thyroid Hormone

Administration of thyroid hormone results in regressive changes in the thyroid gland and diminished formation of hormone. This may be due in part to suppression of thyrotropin (TSH) secretion by the pituitary; however, thyroid hormone apparently also inhibits the action of TSH upon the thyroid gland.

Iodine

Deficiency in iodine intake leads to deficient synthesis of thyroid hormone and compensatory hyperplasia of the thyroid gland (iodine-deficiency goiter). Conversely, administration of iodine to subjects with hyperthyroidism is followed by regressive changes in the gland and diminished output of hormone. High levels of circulating iodide also have a less pronounced and temporary inhibitory effect on thyroid hormone synthesis by the normal thyroid. The mechanism is not clear.

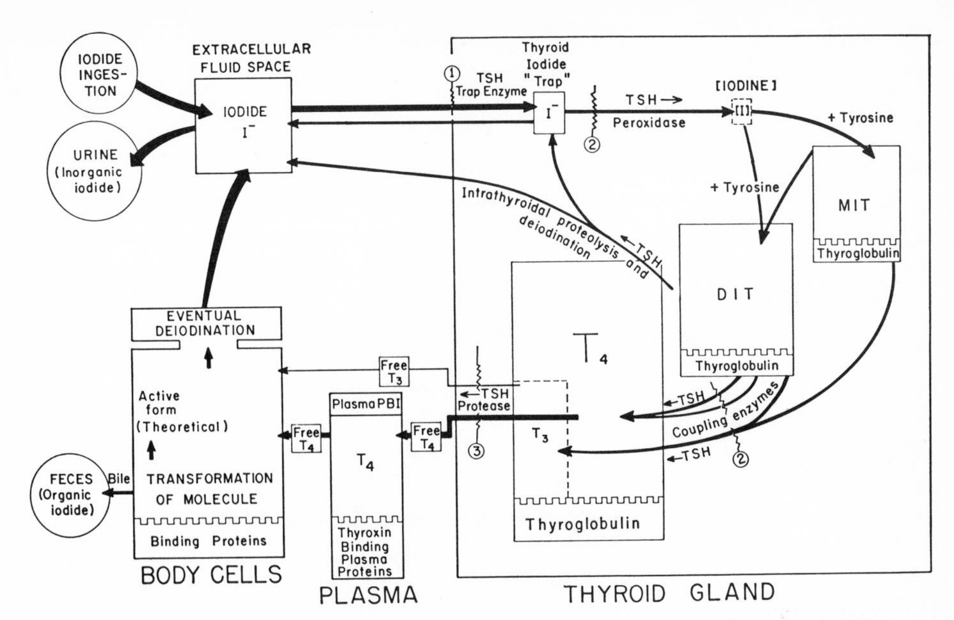

Figure 26-11. Pathways of iodine metabolism. (The relative size of the arrows and squares attempts to approximate relative magnitudes.) In the upper left the inorganic iodide is absorbed from the gastrointestinal tract and completely transferred to the plasma and extracellular iodide pool. The iodide is carried to the thyroid gland (the large square), where the thyroid iodide trap then concentrates it. A smaller arrow indicates that some iodide returns to the plasma, but the majority is oxidized by the peroxidase system. The oxidized iodide (iodine) immediately iodinates tyrosine in globulin molecules in the acinar colloid, forming mono-idotyrosine (MIT)-globulin.

A second iodination forms diidotyrosine (DIT)-globulin. Specific coupling enzymes combine MIT and DIT to form triidothyronine (T_3) and two DIT's to form thyroxin (T_4), still within the thyroglobulin matrix. Proteolytic enzymes may split some of these iodoproteins, and peptidases may free the iodotyrosines. Free iodotyrosines are promptly deiodinated, and most of the released iodide re-enters the hormonogenesis chain without escaping from the thyroid. However, some does escape, especially after stimulation by TSH.

Before thyroid hormone can be secreted from the gland, a protease is needed to free T_3 and T_4 from the thyroglobulin. The secreted hormone, over 90 per cent T_4, is bound to one of the plasma thyroxin-binding carrier proteins, forming the PBI. Some free (unbound) T_3 is also present. When the hormone is carried to the peripheral body cells, intermediate compounds are formed either with or without hormonal calorigenic activity. Some conjugates are excreted through the liver, but the majority are deiodinated and the released inorganic iodide returns to the plasma iodide pool where it is again cleared by the kidney and thyroid. The steps accelerated by TSH are indicated. The site of action of three types of inhibitors is shown:

1 The monovalent anions (i.e., perchlorate).
2 The thiocarbamides (i.e., methimazole).
3 Therapeutic iodide may act at this site.

(From Williams, R. H. and Balle, J. L. in Williams: Textbook of Endocrinology, ed. 3, W. B. Saunders Co., 1962.)

Thiocyanate

Administration of thiocyanate results in enlargement of the thyroid (goiter), if the blood iodide concentration is low, and decreased synthesis of thyroid hormone. This effect is due to inhibition of the uptake, concentration, and accumulation of iodine by the thyroid, the gland being obliged to form hormone from the iodine which enters by passive diffusion. If the level of circulating iodine is elevated sufficiently by administration of iodine, enough may enter the gland to permit adequate function, inasmuch as thiocyanate does not influence the synthesizing mechanism per se (i.e., oxidation, iodination of tyrosine, and coupling). The mechanism of its action is unknown.

Thiocarbamide derivatives

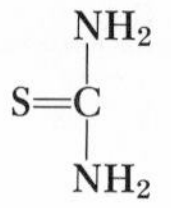

NH_2—C(=S)—NH_2
Thiourea

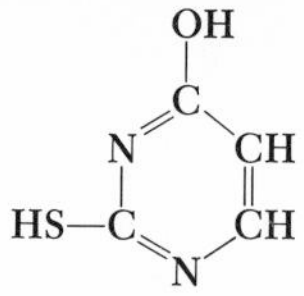

Thiouracil

Aniline derivative

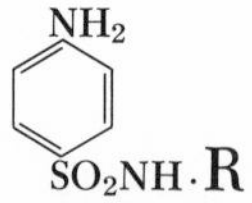

NH_2—C_6H_4—$SO_2NH \cdot R$
Sulfonamides

Thiocyanate KSCN

Figure 26-12. Examples of important classes of anti-thyroid agents.

Anti-thyroid Agents (Fig. 26-12)

This designation is applied to a large number of substances which inhibit synthesis of thyroid hormone, apparently by interfering in some way with the oxidation of inorganic iodide, necessary for iodination of tyrosine.

Most of these compounds fall into two categories: (1) those containing a thiocarbamide grouping (e.g., thiourea, thiouracil, and related compounds); (2) those containing an aminobenzene grouping (aniline derivatives, e.g., sulfonamides). However, other types of compounds are also active in this respect, e.g., 5-vinyl-2-thiooxazolidone (from rapeseed) and 1-methyl-2-mercaptoimidazole.

Administration of these anti-thyroid compounds leads to hyperplasia of the thyroid (goitrogenic action) as a result of excessive stimulation by TSH, secretion of which by the pituitary is no longer adequately restrained by circulating thyroid hormone.

The mechanism of action of these agents is uncertain. The thiourea-like compounds react rapidly with iodine, reducing free iodine to iodide at neutral pH, a phenomenon which could effectively interfere with iodination of tyrosyl groups. However, other substances which react similarly with iodine, such as glutathione, cystine, and thioglycolic acid, do not inhibit thyroid function. Moreover, the aminobenzene derivatives, which apparently inhibit thyroid hormone formation at this same stage, react only very slowly with iodine. Other possible mechanisms include (1) inhibition of the oxidizing enzyme system, (2) competition for hydrogen peroxide, or (3) competition as a substrate.

PANCREATIC HORMONES

The endocrine functions of the pancreas are performed by the islands of Langerhans. These contain three main types of cells, designated α, β, and γ, respectively. Insulin, which lowers the blood sugar, is produced in the beta cells and glucagon, a glycogenolytic-hyperglycemic factor, in the alpha cells.

Insulin

Chemistry

Insulin is a protein (m.w. 5700), composed of two polypeptide chains, containing 21 and 30 amino acid molecules respectively, joined at two points by disulfide bridges (i.e., cystine). It therefore contains a ring which resembles the disulfide ring structure of oxytocin, suggesting that this configuration may have biological significance. At different pH levels, two or more insulin molecules are associated (dimers, trimers, etc.) in rather firm combinations; e.g., at pH 6 to 7 a species predominates having a molecular weight of about 36,000 (Fig. 26–13). Crystalline insulin contains zinc, in amounts of 0.15 to 0.6 per cent depending upon the pH of crystallization.

Insulin is irreversibly inactivated by proteolytic enzymes or acid hydrolysis. It is therefore inactive when taken orally. Reduction of the disulfide linkages results in loss of activity, as does treatment with alkali, which liberates ammonia and hydrogen sulfide. The physiological activity of insulin appears to be a property of the entire molecule. Insulin from different species exhibits the same maximum activity.

Assay

The physiological activity of insulin is expressed in international units (I.U.), a unit being the activity contained in (1) 0.125 mg. of the international standard preparation or (2) $\frac{1}{22}$ mg. of a standard preparation of crystalline zinc-insulin.

Two procedures are generally employed for determining the activity of insulin preparations:

(1) Comparison of the incidence of convulsions in groups of mice injected intraperitoneally with unknown and standards.

(2) Comparison of the hypoglycemic effect of unknown preparations and standards after subcutaneous injection in groups of rabbits (2 kg.) previously starved for 18 to 24 hours.

Other methods are employed for the assay of the small amounts of insulin present in blood plasma.

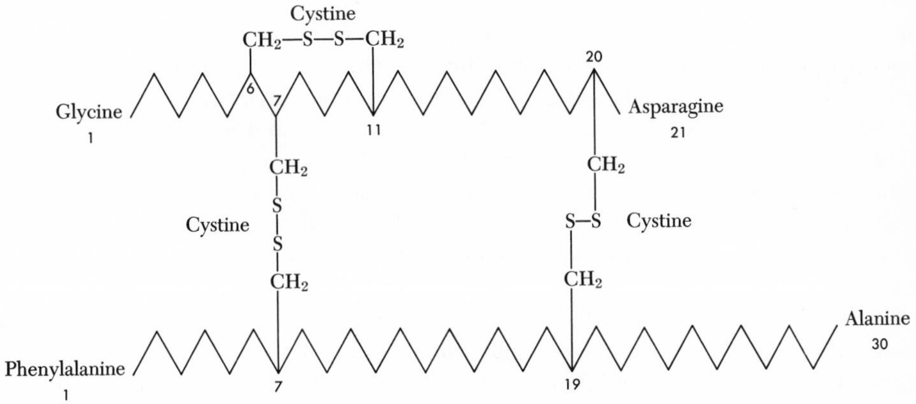

Figure 26-13. Structure of insulin.

(*a*) ***In vivo assay.*** Procedures in this category measure the blood glucose lowering effect of plasma injected into rats or mice whose sensitivity to insulin has been increased by hypophysectomy, adrenalectomy, adrenal demedullation, or administration of alloxan. The results are highly variable and nonspecific, and these methods have been replaced by more satisfactory techniques.

(*b*) ***In vitro bioassay.*** Measurements are made of the glucose uptake of diaphragm (rat or mouse) or of epididymal fat pad (rat) incubated with plasma. Although these procedures are more sensitive than the in vivo methods, the results vary considerably with variations in technique.

(*c*) ***Immunologic assay.*** The procedure employed most commonly currently, and the most sensitive, depends upon the fact that unlabeled insulin competes with beef insulin-I^{131} for binding by insulin antibodies in the serum of guinea pigs immunized with beef insulin. The free radioactivity of the separated fractions is measured. The amount of unlabeled insulin in the plasma is related linearly to the decrease in the bound insulin: free insulin ratio.

Regulation of Secretion

Secretion of insulin is regulated by the blood sugar level. Increase in the blood glucose concentration causes an increase in the insulin content of the pancreas and increased secretion into the blood. Decrease in blood sugar causes the reverse. This feed back control mechanism is of fundamental importance in the regulation of the blood sugar concentration (p. 435). There is no unequivocal evidence that secretion of insulin is influenced directly by any other physiological mechanism; however, any of the great variety of factors that can affect the blood sugar concentration can thereby indirectly influence insulin secretion. Of therapeutic importance in certain cases of diabetes is the fact that the blood sugar concentration may be lowered by a number of sulfonylurea derivatives. Their hypoglycemic effect is apparently due mainly to stimulation of release of insulin from the pancreas, but it may be due in part, under certain circumstances, to a direct effect upon the liver, diminishing its output of glucose.

Transport and Metabolism of Insulin

By immunoassay, the plasma insulin concentration of normal fasting subjects has been found to range from 0 to 60 (mean 30) μU/ml. A small fraction of the plasma insulin is apparently in the free state, migrating as an α_1-globulin; most of the insulin-like activity of normal plasma is associated with the β-and γ-globulins, suggesting that insulin secreted into the bloodstream circulates largely bound by protein carriers in the plasma.

Normal subjects excrete less than 1 I.U. of insulin daily in urine; only a slight increase follows administration of insulin. Nevertheless, it disappears rapidly from the circulating blood, having a half-life of about 35 minutes. It undergoes enzymatic degradation, principally in the liver, but to a lesser extent in skeletal muscle, kidney, and perhaps other tissues, by "insulinase" (glutathione-insulin dehydrogenase), which catalyzes reductive cleavage of the interchain disulfide bonds of insulin in the presence of glutathione, which serves as the hydrogen donor. It is also degraded in liver by proteolytic enzymes and by nonenzymatic reduction (by reduced glutathione and cysteine). Preservation of a proper balance between secretion and destruction may constitute one of the central mechanisms regulating the quantity of circulating insulin. Insulinase activity is inhibited by glucagon and by indoleacetic acid, a tryptophan derivative.

Insulin Antagonists

The metabolic effects of insulin are counteracted by a number of factors that exert influences on carbohydrate metabolism antagonistic to those exerted by insulin. These include: (a) epinephrine, which increases hepatic and muscle glycogenolysis and decreases glucose utilization; (b) somatotropin (growth hormone), which increases hepatic glucogenesis and otherwise decreases utilization of glucose (increased insulin resistance); (c) glucocorticoids, which increase gluconeogenesis and hepatic glucogenesis and otherwise decrease utilization of glucose (increased resistance to insulin); (d) glucagon, which increases hepatic glycogenolysis. Epinephrine also acts to accelerate the degradation of insulin in the liver.

In addition to these counter-insulin actions due to antagonistic metabolic effects, there is a type of more direct insulin antagonism which is exerted by factors associated with certain of the plasma protein fractions. One of these is a dialyzable, thermostable substance associated with but separable from plasma albumin (synalbumin factor). It is present in small amounts in normal subjects and increases in uncontrolled diabetes, particularly of the juvenile type and in the presence of ketoacidosis, and following administration of somatotropin or glucocorticoids. It disappears following hypophysectomy or adrenalectomy and reappears upon administration of somatotropin and glucocorticoids, both being necessary for the formation and action of this factor. No such direct insulin antagonism is exerted by these hormones in vitro. Another such factor occurs in the β_1-lipoprotein fraction of the plasma of diabetic rats; it exhibits the same dependence upon the presence of adequate amounts of somatotropin and glucocorticoids.

Insulin antibodies comprise another type of direct insulin antagonist. They appear in the blood plasma of virtually all subjects who have received insulin for several weeks. Occasionally they may be present in such high concentrations (high insulin-binding capacity) as to produce marked resistance to insulin, interfering materially with therapeutic control of the diabetes.

Metabolic Actions of Insulin

The overall effects of insulin on the organism are illustrated by certain observable metabolic consequences of (1) pancreatectomy (diabetes mellitus) and (2) administration of insulin to normal or depancreatized animals.

(1) *Pancreatectomy* (p. 443) is followed by:
- (a) Decreased glucose tolerance.
- (b) Hyperglycemia and glycosuria.
- (c) Depletion of glycogen in liver and muscle.
- (d) Decreased rate of oxidation of glucose (decreased R.Q.).
- (e) Increased gluconeogenesis.
- (f) Negative nitrogen balance.
- (g) Increased mobilization of depot fat; increased liver fat and ketogenesis.
- (h) Increase in triglycerides, free fatty acids, phospholipids, and cholesterol in the plasma.

(2) *Insulin administration* is followed by:
- (a) Decrease in blood sugar.
- (b) Increased oxidation of glucose (increased R.Q.).
- (c) Increased muscle glycogen.

(d) Decreased gluconeogenesis.
(e) Decreased ketogenesis.
(f) Increased lipogenesis.
(g) Increased protein synthesis.

Increase in muscle glycogen is usually readily demonstrable following administration of insulin. However, increased hepatic glycogenesis may be masked by the effects of the existing hypoglycemia, which itself accelerates hepatic glycogenolysis (p. 433), e.g., via increased secretion of epinephrine.

The glycogen of the brain and myocardium differs from that of the liver and skeletal muscle with reference to insulin action. This hormone has little or no effect upon glycogen in nervous tissue, which is also influenced slightly, if at all, by the level of blood sugar. Although, under certain experimental conditions, administration of insulin may result in an increase in myocardial glycogen, the latter may be maintained in depancreatized animals. It would appear to be dependent more on the level of blood sugar than upon the presence of insulin. However, high values for cardiac muscle glycogen have been obtained in phlorizinized animals with low blood sugar concentrations. There is evidence that growth hormone plays an important role in the deposition of myocardial glycogen.

Effects on acid-base, electrolyte, and water balance are secondary to those on carbohydrate, fat, and protein metabolism and are discussed elsewhere (p. 444).

Carbohydrate metabolism. On the basis of these overall effects, insulin may be considered to promote the utilization of glucose in every direction, including its oxidation, glycogenesis, and lipogenesis; it also promotes protein synthesis. The sites of action of insulin in producing these effects have not been established with certainty, much of the evidence being of an indirect nature. Liver slices from insulin-deficient animals exhibit the following changes in carbohydrate metabolism, all of which are corrected by supplying insulin:

(a) Decreased uptake and phosphorylation of glucose, resulting in its decreased utilization in every known direction.

(b) Increased glucose-6-phosphatase activity, resulting in increased output of glucose from the liver, contributing to hyperglycemia.

(c) Decreased glucose-6-phosphate dehydrogenase activity, resulting in depression of oxidation by the phosphogluconate oxidative pathway.

(d) Decreased activity of UDPG glycogen transferase, the final step in biosynthesis of glycogen, resulting in decreased glycogenesis.

(e) Oxidation of fructose by livers of diabetic animals, contrary to that of glucose, is normal, thus localizing the metabolic block (and the action of insulin) in the conversion of glucose to fructose-6-phosphate, which includes the hexokinase and phosphohexose isomerase reactions.

(f) Decreased activity of glycerol phosphate dehydrogenase.

Passage of glucose from the extracellular fluid into the cell is, of course, a prerequisite for its metabolic utilization. In extrahepatic tissues, and perhaps also in liver, this involves a transport process, referred to as membrane transport of glucose. In skeletal and cardiac muscle, and perhaps in other extrahepatic tissues, one of the principal actions of insulin is to accelerate this process, i.e., entrance of glucose into the cell. On the other hand, it has no such effect on the liver cell, which is freely permeable to glucose and other monosaccharides. Of importance in this connection is the ready reversibility of glycolysis in the liver, and not in other tissues, arising out of the presence in the liver of glucose-6-phosphatase (reversing the hexokinase reaction) and fructose-1-6-diphosphatase (reversing the phosphofructokinase reaction). The direction of flow of glucose, whether into or out of the liver cell, depends therefore to a large degree upon the relative activities of the opposing enzymes in these two reactions. Liver hexokinase activity is therefore important in determining the direction of flow of glucose. Insulin exerts a regulatory influence upon the activity of glucokinase in liver, but not in skeletal muscle. It would appear, therefore, that the first point at which insulin acts to increase glucose utilization is on phosphorylation by hexokinase in the liver and upon membrane transport of glucose in extrahepatic tissues. Transport of galactose is also enhanced, but phosphorylation of galactose and fructose are unaffected.

The hormonal imbalance in insulin deficiency (adrenocortical preponderance) results in increased glucose production from amino acids (excessive gluconeogenesis) with associated increased protein catabolism (p. 712). This increased production of glucose, together with its decreased utilization, contributes to the hyperglycemia associated with insulin deficiency.

The hypoglycemia induced by insulin could conceivably result from one or both of two processes: (a) decreased rate of entrance of glucose into the bloodstream from the liver; (b) acceleration of removal of glucose from the blood and the interstitial fluid, that is, increased rate of entry into and utilization in the cells. According to one view, the initial effect of insulin is to reduce the output of glucose by the liver. Another maintains that the initial effect is to increase the utilization of glucose. There is general agreement, however, that both of these phenomena occur as later manifestations of insulin action.

Lipid metabolism. The importance of insulin in lipid metabolism is perhaps best illustrated by the consequences of insulin deficiency (uncontrolled diabetes mellitus). This is characterized by progressive loss of adipose tissue fat, increase in liver fat, excessive ketogenesis, and increase in blood fat, free fatty acids, phospholipids, and cholesterol. These phenomena are reversed by administration of insulin, which produces the following effects on lipid metabolism:

(*1*) *Increased Free Fatty Acid Synthesis.* Insulin causes increased synthesis of long-chain fatty acids from glucose or acetate in both adipose tissue and liver. This is apparently related to its effects on the metabolism of glucose, which is both a source of fatty acid carbon and, in the phosphogluconate oxidative pathway, of NADPH required for elongation of the fatty acid chain from acetyl-CoA. However, insulin also acts to induce synthesis of acetyl-CoA carboxylase, a rate-limiting step in the synthesis of fatty acid from carbon fragments, and also of a microsomal oxygenase necessary for monoene synthesis from saturated fatty acids. This is believed to be accomplished through increased synthesis of messenger RNA.

(*2*) *Increased Synthesis of Triglyceride.* In both adipose tissue and liver, insulin increases esterification of fatty acids, either synthesized in situ or liberated by hydrolysis of triglycerides of chylomicra or lipoproteins. Glycerol cannot be used for this purpose in adipose tissue because of the absence of glycerol kinase. Synthesis of triglyceride here requires α-glycerol phosphate, which must be derived from the metabolism of glucose and which is provided in increased amounts through the action of insulin. Although this mechanism operates also in liver, this tissue can use glycerol for esterification of fatty acids because of the presence of glycerol kinase.

(*3*) *Decreased Release of Free Fatty Acid.* In adipose tissue, fatty acids are continually being produced by synthesis and by hydrolysis of triglyceride. The amount produced in excess of the capacity of these cells to form triglyceride by esterification with α-glycerol phosphate enters the blood stream and is transported mainly bound to plasma albumin (p. 495). Insulin, by increasing the capacity of adipose tissue for resynthesis of triglyceride, decreases the rate of release of free fatty acid from adipose tissue and causes a decrease in the concentration of fatty acids in the blood plasma.

(4) *Decreased Ketogenesis.* This effect of insulin is best illustrated by its action in correcting the hyperketonemia associated with diabetes mellitus. In this condition, increased ketogenesis results mainly from mobilization of excessive quantities of unesterified fatty acids from adipose tissue which, in the liver, produce amounts of acetyl-CoA in excess of the capacity of that tissue to dispose of it by oxidation or by synthesis of fatty acids or cholesterol. Administration of insulin causes reversal of these processes in both adipose tissue and liver.

Protein metabolism. Although consistent effects of insulin on protein metabolism in normal intact animals are not readily demonstrable, there is abundant evidence that it promotes protein synthesis. Depancreatized or alloxanized animals are in a state of negative nitrogen balance. An adequate supply of insulin is required for the protein anabolic activity of somatotropin. This promotion of protein synthesis may result in part from the provision of increased amounts of available energy derived from the increased rate of oxidation of glucose. However, independently of its effect on glucose utilization, it accelerates the entry of amino acids into cells and augments their incorporation into proteins.

There is evidence that insulin increases synthesis of messenger RNA and perhaps ribosomal RNA, either of which could account for the protein anabolic action of this hormone. Reference has been made previously to the possibility that at least certain of its actions on lipid and perhaps also carbohydrate metabolism may be due to increased production of key enzymes through the medium of increased formation of mRNA. On this basis, many of the important effects of insulin on carbohydrate and lipid metabolism may be linked to its effects on protein synthesis.

Stimulation of glucose utilization, by administration of either glucose or insulin, is accompanied by a decrease in the concentration of potassium and inorganic phosphate in the blood. These electrolyte changes are apparently associated with two phenomena: (1) acceleration of entrance of glucose (or other hexoses) into the tissue cells, and (2) deposition of K and PO_4 with glycogen in liver and muscles. The closely parallel changes in blood glucose, K, and PO_4 that follow administration of insulin are apparently dependent upon common cellular metabolic mechanisms, probably involving phosphorylation processes.

GLUCAGON

A factor is present in extracts of the pancreas, as well as in most commercial insulin preparations, which causes an increase in blood sugar when injected intravenously. This hyperglycemic factor is called glucagon. It is apparently formed in the alpha cells of the islets, and may be regarded as a hormone. The hyperglycemic effect of certain extracts of other tissues, including the gastric mucosa (dog), attributed to glucagon, may be due to other substances. Glucagon has been isolated in relatively pure form and has been characterized as a small protein (m.w. 3485) containing 29 amino acid residues arranged in a straight chain.

When glucagon is injected intravenously, the blood sugar begins to rise immediately, reaches a maximum in about 30 minutes, and falls to the original level in about an hour. Liver slices incubated with this factor show a decrease in glycogen and an increase in glucose-l-phosphate, due to increased phosphorylase activity.

Liver phosphorylase undergoes continual enzymatic inactivation and resynthesis (activation); glucagon (and also epinephrine) accelerates its resynthesis (reactivation). The glycogenolytic action of glucagon is restricted to the liver, whereas epinephrine exerts a similar effect in both liver and muscle, with consequent increase in glucose and lactic acid in the bloodstream. Active phosphorylase (liver) contains phosphate, and its inactivation involves removal of phosphate (forming "dephosphophosphorylase") by an inactivating enzyme (phosphorylase phosphatase). Reactivation consists in addition of phosphate to the molecule by a phosphokinase system, i.e., "dephosphophosphorylase kinase" (p. 400). This reaction is greatly accelerated by glucagon (also by epinephrine), which acts on a particulate component of the liver cell in the presence of ATP and Mg^{++} to produce a cyclic adenine ribonucleotide (adenosine-3′,5′-phosphoric acid), which is the activating cofactor.

Glucagon exerts influences also on lipid and protein metabolism. It depresses synthesis of long-chain fatty acids and increases mobilization of adipose tissue fat, with consequent hyperlipemia and increased ketogenesis. It stimulates protein catabolism, as reflected in increased urinary excretion of urea and creatinine, and decreased muscle mass.

The brief duration of the hyperglycemia induced by glucagon is due to its rapid proteolytic degradation in the liver, a process which is inhibited by insulin in vitro. Whether or not it plays any role in the regulation of carbohydrate metabolism and of blood sugar concentration is not known.

PARATHYROID HORMONE

The parathyroid glands are intimately concerned with regulation of the concentrations of calcium and phosphate ions in the blood plasma. This is accomplished by secretion, by the chief (principal) cells, of a hormone, the net effect of which is to increase the concentration of calcium and decrease that of phosphate. There is evidence that a factor, "thyrocalcitonin," which causes lowering of the concentration, is produced by the thyroid.

Nature of the Parathyroid Hormone

The parathyroid hormone has been obtained in pure form, and has been characterized as a straight-chain polypeptide with a molecular weight of approximately 8500 and a biological potency of 2500 units/mg. Smaller polypeptide preparations exhibit similar but lower activity. This substance exhibits both the calcium-mobilizing and the phosphaturic activities of cruder preparations. It has now been established that these two effects are produced by a single agent acting upon different target tissues, and not by two different hormones, as had been suggested. It is generally believed that the parathyroid hormone controls the level of plasma calcium by a negative feedback mechanism whereby hypocalcemia stimulates release of the hormone from the gland while hypercalcemia inhibits it. The mechanism is supplemented by the action of thyrocalcitonin, a rapidly acting hypocalcemic factor secreted by the thyroid in response to an increase in the serum calcium concentration.

Assay

The U.S.P. unit is defined as 0.01 of the amount of extract required to raise the serum calcium of not less than 20 normal dogs (8 to 16 kg.) an average of 1 mg. per cent within 16 to 18 hours after subcutaneous injection.

Metabolic Action

The actions of the parathyroid hormone are reflected in the consequences of (1) its administration and (2) removal of the parathyroid glands.

The most conspicuous metabolic consequences of administration of parathyroid hormone are: (1) increase in serum calcium concentration; (2) decrease in serum inorganic phosphate concentration; (3) increased urinary phosphate; (4) increased urinary calcium following an initial decrease; (5) increase in citrate content of blood plasma, kidney, and bones.

Removal of the parathyroid glands is followed by changes in each of these factors in the opposite direction. As the concentration of calcium in the extracellular fluids falls, manifestations of neuromuscular hyperexcitability develop, eventuating in death with the clinical picture of tetany. Fibrillary muscle twitchings pass successively into generalized tremors, increased muscle tonus, painful clonic and, finally, tonic spasms and violent generalized convulsions, with laryngeal spasm and asphyxia. The autonomic nerves and smooth muscles are also affected, with involvement of the heart and the gastrointestinal and urinary tracts.

Calcium. The increase of serum calcium concentration induced by parathyroid hormone results from: (1) increased absorption of calcium from the intestine (in the presence of adequate amounts of vitamin D); (2) increased rate of mobilization of calcium (and other components) from the skeleton; (3) increased renal tubular reabsorption of calcium. The initial effect of the latter is to reduce the urinary calcium excretion. However, as the plasma calcium concentration rises, even the enhanced tubular reabsorption process cannot prevent the escape in the urine of increased amounts of calcium out of the enormously increased quantity entering the tubules in the glomerular filtrate.

Inasmuch as parathyroid hormone produces hypercalcemia and hypercalciuria in the absence of an exogenous supply of calcium, clearly the excess must be derived from the only tissue in which significant amounts of calcium are stored, i.e., the bones. Under physiological conditions this hormone is believed to be involved in the normal process of osteoclastic resorption of bone, which includes degradation of the organic components of the matrix as well as dissolution of the bone salt and mobilization of mineral components.

Effect on skeleton. Repeated injection of parathyroid hormone produces the characteristic skeletal picture of diffuse osteitis fibrosa cystica. The severity of the lesions varies with age, species, dosage, and duration of the state of hyperparathyroidism. In mild cases there may be no gross changes, the histologic changes consisting in osteoclastic lacunar resorption of the more compact bone, with little or no fibrous replacement, destruction and phagocytosis of megakaryocytes, and degeneration of erythroid marrow cells. In severe cases there is rapid resorption of trabecular and cortical bone, with numerous osteoclasts, degeneration of the marrow cells, with necrosis and hemorrhage, and replacement fibrosis of the marrow. The blood vascular spaces may become greatly dilated, giving the appearance of cysts, osteoid may proliferate, and fractures and deformities develop. The process is most rapid in the vicinity of most recent bone formation, but there is no unanimity of opinion regarding its exact nature. The mineral elements are mobilized most readily from the trabecular portions of the bones. Healing is accompanied by reversal of the process, with disappearance of osteoclasts, diminution in connective tissue, reappearance of osteoblasts, and resumption of bone formation.

The serum calcium concentration begins to rise about four hours after intravenous injection of a large dose of parathyroid hormone, reaching a maximum in about 12 hours and returning to the preinjection level in about 24 hours. Injections of 100 to 300 units repeated at intervals of four to eight hours lead to sustained hypercalcemia at dangerously high levels. In dogs treated in this manner the serum calcium concentration rises to a maximum of 20 to 25 mg./100ml. in 18 to 24 hours, remaining at this level for some hours, after which it may fall somewhat despite continuous administration of the hormone. At about 36 hours, manifestations of renal functional insufficiency supervene, with nitrogen retention and increasing levels of serum phosphate. The animal exhibits anorexia, diarrhea, vomiting, lassitude, muscular hypotonia, and eventually coma terminating in death. The blood shows increased viscosity and the blood volume is decreased, with associated signs and symptoms characteristic of progressive dehydration and circulatory failure. Parathyroid hormone induces a greater increase in serum calcium in young than in adult animals, and skeletal changes can also be produced more readily. This difference in age response is probably related to the more rapid rate of mineral metabolism during the period of active skeletal growth. Pregnancy seems to enhance the skeletal effects of the hormone.

When parathyroid administration is continued in a dosage inadequate to produce acute hyperparathyroidism, the response diminishes after a time until eventually no change in serum calcium and phosphate occurs and the skeletal lesions may heal. This refractoriness to the hormone is attributed to the development of an antihormone. However, there are reports of continued effectiveness of parathyroid therapy in hypoparathyroidism, particularly if the phosphate intake is restricted. It has been reported also that this condition of refractoriness does not develop when highly purified preparations of the hormone are used.

Inorganic phosphate. Intravenous injection of parathyroid hormone is followed promptly, usually within one hour, by decreased urinary excretion of phosphate and, somewhat later, by decrease of the concentration of inorganic phosphate in the blood plasma. Available evidence supports the view that these effects are produced by a primary action of the hormone on the kidney to reduce renal tubular reabsorption of phosphate. In certain species there may be stimulation of renal tubular secretion of phosphate, but this has not been demonstrated to occur in man.

It has been suggested that this practically immediate effect upon renal excretion of phosphate, as contrasted with the comparatively slow action in stimulating osteoclastic resorption of bone, may be explained on the basis of the striking difference in the volume of blood perfusing these tissues. The blood flow through the kidneys is approximately 25 per cent of the resting cardiac output, whereas that through the total mass of skeletal tissue is approximately 5 per cent. Accordingly, the renal tubular epithelial cells would be exposed to much larger quantities of the hormone than would the bone cells during the first few hours following its injection.

Citrate. The relationship between the metabolism of citrate and that of calcium is indicated elsewhere (p. 637). Administration of parathyroid hormone is followed by a rise in the citrate content of bone, blood plasma, kidney, and urine. Citrate forms a soluble, non-ionized complex with calcium, and it has been suggested that this chelating action plays an important role in the mechanism of mobilization of calcium from the bones. Inasmuch as calcium is probably actively reabsorbed in the renal tubules only in ionic form, such non-ionized complexes entering the glomerular filtrate from the blood plasma will be largely excreted in the urine. Citrate enters the plasma mainly from the skeleton and leaves it mainly in the kidneys. The fact that these two important target organs of parathyroid hormone are also involved fundamentally in the production of its hypercalcemic and hypercalciuric effects suggests the possibility of an intimate relationship between calcium and citrate. However, a role of citrate in the mobilization, transport, and excretion of calcium has not been definitely established, nor has its role in the mechanism of action of the parathyroid hormone.

Other effects of parathyroid hormone. Administration of parathyroid hormone is followed by evidence of depolymerization of skeletal mucopolysaccharides, presumably a reflection of stimulation of dissolution of the osteoid matrix. There have been reports of an associated increase of mucoprotein in the blood plasma and increased excretion of mucopolysaccharide components in the urine.

In chronic hyperparathyroidism, clinical or experimental, there is frequently increase in the alkaline phosphatase activity of the blood plasma and, less frequently, increase of acid phosphatase activity. The latter is regarded as a reflection of increased osteolytic activity, whereas the former is believed to reflect (a) increased osteoblastic activity secondary to the weakening of the bone and (b) the proliferation of fibroblasts that constitutes a characteristic feature of the skeletal lesion. Both osteoblasts and fibroblasts are unusually rich in alkaline phosphatase.

Effect on parathyroid glands. The hypercalcemia incident to administration of parathyroid hormone results in decrease in size and functional activity of the parathyroid glands. The cells are reduced in size, and exhibit degenerative changes and alterations in the Golgi apparatus and mitochondria. Mitosis is apparently inhibited.

Hypocalcemia has been observed in guinea pigs several days after discontinuing prolonged parathyroid hormone administration. This may be due either to rapid redeposition of calcium in the previously depleted bones or to temporary hypofunction of the parathyroid glands induced by hypercalcemia.

Effect on other tissues. When parathyroid hormone is injected repeatedly, e.g., every four hours, a state of acute hyperparathyroidism is induced. This is accompanied by degeneration and necrosis in the myocardium, kidneys, stomach, thyroid, liver, and skeletal muscle. Degenerative changes occur most frequently in the renal tubular epithelium and myocardium. There may be hemorrhagic manifestations, varying from petechiae in the stomach and small intestine to large extravasations of blood into the stomach and duodenum. The lungs may be dry and cyanotic, or may exhibit congestion and edema, which may be generalized throughout the viscera.

Calcific deposits are found in the myocardium, kidneys (particularly tubular epithelium), stomach, arteries, duodenum, thyroid, bronchi, and pulmonary alveoli. This is frequently referred to as metastatic calcification, but there is evidence that the calcium is deposited in areas of regressive change and not in previously normal tissue. However, factors operative in true metastatic calcification, i.e., relative alkalinity in affected cells, seem to have some influence upon the localization of the calcific deposits, as in the acid-producing cells of the gastric mucosa and the renal tubular epithelium. The hormone may exert a direct toxic effect on the tissues, entirely independently of the induced hypercalcemia. The absence of degenerative and calcific phenomena in living fetuses of mothers (dogs) exhibiting all of these changes suggests that the parathyroid hormone does not pass the placental barrier in significant amounts.

Parathyroid hormone has been reported to exert an influence on magnesium metabolism. Primary hyperparathyroidism has been found to be associated with excessive urinary excretion of magnesium and negative magnesium balance. In such cases parathyroidectomy has been followed by a positive magnesium balance and lowering of the serum magnesium concentration. The significance of such observations has not been established.

Mechanism of Action

Although the principal results of the actions of the parathyroid hormone on bone, renal tubule, and intestine appear to have been established, the mechanisms underlying the production of these effects are not clearly understood. As is true of other hormones, there is evidence that these mechanisms may involve enhancement of biosynthesis of mRNA, with consequent stimulation of production either of some structural protein component of cellular or subcellular membranes (facilitating transport of calcium and phosphate) or of enzymes concerned with transport mechanisms or osteoclasis. This concept is supported by the observation that both the hypercalcemia and the skeletal changes induced by parathyroid hormone are inhibited by administration of actinomycin D, an antibiotic which blocks biosynthesis of mRNA. However, the effects of the hormone on renal excretion of calcium and phosphate apparently are not affected by this agent.

Control of Parathyroid Secretory Activity

Influence of serum calcium concentration. There is abundant evidence that decrease in the concentration of calcium ions in the plasma stimulates the parathyroid gland cells to increased activity. Conversely, increase in the concentration of calcium ions in the plasma depresses parathyroid secretory activity. Enlargement of the glands, with cellular hypertrophy and hyperplasia, has been produced in various species by administration of diets low in calcium as well as by hypocalcemia induced by various other means. Evidence of stimulation has been reported in the parathyroid glands of animals injected with oxalate and in isolated parathyroid glands perfused with decalcified blood. This phenomenon plays an important role in the maintenance of a relatively normal serum calcium concentration in clinical disorders characterized by a tendency toward hypocalcemia. This compensatory state of "secondary hyperparathyroidism" occurs in such conditions as renal functional insufficiency, vitamin D deficiency (rickets, osteomalacia), chronic steatorrhea, the Fanconi syndrome, etc., and perhaps also in normal pregnancy and lactation.

The parathyroid hormone increases the level of circulating calcium by (a) increasing the rate of its mobilization from the skeleton, (b) increasing its absorption from the intestine, and (c) increasing its reabsorption by the renal tubular epithelium. Consequently, regulation of its secretion by the level of calcium in the blood plasma constitutes a very efficient autoregulatory mechanism; i.e., in effect, the serum calcium concentration regulates itself through the medium of parathyroid stimulation or depression.

There is no satisfactory evidence that parathyroid secretory activity is influenced directly by factors other than the concentration of calcium ions in the plasma. Such influence has been attributed to the level of inorganic phosphate, the adenohypophysis, and gonadal and adrenocortical hormones. However, the present consensus is that any stimulation of parathyroid secretory activity by these agencies is produced through the medium of lowering of the plasma calcium ion concentration. The common denominator in many of the observed actions of various hormones is apparently an increase in plasma inorganic phosphate, which directly depresses release of calcium from the bone.

Parathyroid hormone : vitamin D interrelationships. The effects of administration of parathyroid hormone and of vitamin D have certain points of similarity. Both induce increased absorption of calcium from the intestine and increased resorption of bone, with consequent hypercalcemia and hypercalciuria, and increase of citrate in the skeleton, kidney, blood, and urine. However, the view that vitamin D exerts its effect through the parathyroid mechanism is not tenable. It can effectively increase the serum calcium concentration in the absence of the parathyroid glands. Moreover, under certain circumstances, the effect of the vitamin on urinary excretion of phosphate differs from that of the parathyroid hormone. The significance of these differences is difficult to evaluate because they vary with dosage of the vitamin (i.e., whether physiological or pharmacological), and with the functional status of the organism, (e.g., whether parathyroidectomized or in a state of vitamin D deficiency). For example, vitamin D increases the serum phosphate concentration in rickets only in the presence of the parathyroid glands. It has the opposite effect in their absence, resembling therefore, the action of the parathyroid hormone in this respect. Then, too, when large, therapeutically effective doses of vitamin D are administered to subjects with hypoparathyroidism, there is relatively little phosphaturic response as compared to that which occurs following administration of parathyroid hormone.

Evidence of relationship between the parathyroids and vitamin D is manifested in two different areas:

(1) The parathyroid glands are usually, but not invariably enlarged in experimental and clinical states of vitamin D deficiency (rickets, osteomalacia). It is assumed that this hypertrophy and hyperplasia is accompanied by hyperactivity, i.e., a state of "secondary hyperparathyroidism." This is a compensatory mechanism, evoked by a falling serum calcium concentration, whereby the latter may be effectively maintained within normal limits for considerable periods, at the expense, however, of the skeleton.

(2) There is increasing evidence that the parathyroid hormone cannot produce its characteristic effects in the total absence of D vitamins. This is regarded as reflecting a so-called permissive action of the vitamin, a certain level of which is required to permit production of the characteristic effect of the hormone, i.e., on bone resorption, intestinal absorption of calcium, and renal tubular reabsorption of phosphate.

Endocrine interrelationships. There is no satisfactory evidence of any direct effect of the parathyroid glands on any of the other endocrine glands, or vice versa. Whatever influences are exerted are mediated by changes in the metabolism of calcium or phosphate.

Adenohypophysis. Enlargement of the parathyroid glands, occasionally with hypercalcemia, has been reported following administration of anterior pituitary extracts in experimental animals. Diminution in size and degenerative lesions, however without hypocalcemia, have also been reported to occur following hypophysectomy. Parathyroid hyperplasia and adenomas, with hypercalcemia, have been observed in patients with eosinophilic pituitary tumors with acromegaly. Although the nature of this relationship is not established, the prevailing view is that stimulation of the parathyroids by an excess of growth hormone is attributable to the effect of the latter in raising the level of plasma inorganic phosphate, with consequent lowering of the plasma calcium ion concentration. Any influence exerted by other hormones of the adenohypophysis, e.g., ACTH, TSH, or gonadotropins, is presumably mediated by the hormones of the target glands of these hormones.

Adrenocortical hormones. There is no evidence that the parathyroid glands are involved in the production of any of the demonstrated effects of adrenal glucocorticoids on calcium metabolism or skeletal mineralization. The osteoporosis that occurs in clinical and experimental states of adrenocortical hyperfunction is attributable to the protein catabolic and antianabolic actions of the glucocorticoids and to their effect in interfering with synthesis of mucopolysaccharides, all of which contribute to defective formation of the osteoid matrix.

In man and most experimental animals (but not in the rat) hypercalcemia occurs quite consistently in adrenal functional insufficiency. Although the mechanism is not clear, there is evidence that this hypercalcemia does not involve an increase in concentration of calcium ions but is related to (a) the increased plasma protein concentration associated with hemoconcentration, (b) an increase in the affinity of plasma proteins for calcium, and (c) an increase in filtrable non-ionized calcium complexes, especially calcium citrate.

Cortisol is effective in lowering the elevated plasma calcium concentrations in such clinical disorders as hypervitaminosis D, sarcoidosis, idiopathic infantile hypercalcemia, and, occasionally, metastatic malignant disease. The hypercalcemia of hyperparathyroidism is relatively resistant to such treatment, but this may be merely a matter of dosage rather than of more fundamental differences. Administration of glucocorticoids is followed also by decrease in the concentration of citrate in the plasma. This may be related to the action of these hormones in depressing utilization of glucose. This difference in responsiveness of the hypercalcemia of hyperparathyroidism and that due to other causes is frequently helpful in differential diagnosis.

Gonadal hormones. The effects of gonadal hormones on mineral metabolism vary widely in different species. The profound effect of estrogens on calcium and phosphate metabolism in birds and on ossification of the skeleton in the rat are not observed in other mammals. However, the protein anabolic action of androgens extends also to the bone matrix, as does a similar but considerably less marked action of estrogens. Both hormones are necessary for optimal osteoblastic activity and this action, in conjunction with the general enhancement of protein synthesis, promotes bone formation and mineralization. So-called "postmenopausal osteoporosis" is a reflection of inadequate bone formation resulting from gonadal hormone insufficiency.

The hypercalcemia that develops at times following administration of gonadal hormones to patients with metastatic malignant disease is believed to be due to increased osteolysis incident to stimulation of growth of the neoplastic cells and not to a direct hypercalcemic action of the hormones.

In addition to these effects, androgen characteristically accelerates growth of long bones and hastens closure of the epiphyses, an action responsible for the growth spurt of adolescence.

Thyroid hormones. There are several indications of important actions of thyroid hormone on calcium metabolism and the bones. (1) Hypothyroidism in infancy causes retardation of skeletal development, including a characteristic epiphyseal dysgenesis. This is a reflection of the requirement for physiological amounts of thyroid hormone for normal maturation and protein synthesis. (2) Perhaps mainly as a result of the protein catabolic effect of excessive amounts of thyroid hormone, hyperthyroidism is accompanied by evidences of acceleration of bone degradation, including increased mobilization of calcium, and hypercalciuria. Hypercalcemia may occur occasionally, but the serum calcium concentration usually remains within normal limits. (3) In patients with both hypoparathyroidism and hypothyroidism, elevation of the serum calcium concentration is facilitated by administration of thyroid hormone.

Evidence has been presented that the thyroid gland secretes a factor that lowers the serum calcium concentration ("thyrocalcitonin"). Together with the parathyroid hormone, this would constitute a hormonal feedback mechanism that provides much more precise control of the level of plasma calcium than could be accomplished by the hypercalcemic factor alone. Thyrocalcitonin is reported to be rapidly active, producing a maximal response within 20 minutes, the plasma calcium concentration returning to normal within one hour. There is evidence that this is probably a polypeptide, which produces its effect by inhibiting release of calcium from the bones.

HYPOPHYSEAL (PITUITARY) HORMONES

Three anatomical divisions of the hypophysis yield extracts which, on injection, exert well-defined effects in various animal species. These divisions are (1) the neurohypophysis (posterior lobe), (2) the pars intermedia, and (3) the adenohypophysis (anterior lobe). In man and other mammals, the latter is by far the most important, inasmuch as it controls the functional activity and structural integrity of other important endocrine glands, e.g., the thyroid, adrenal cortex, and gonads, through its so-called "tropic" hormones. In addition, it produces the growth hormone (somatotropin), which exerts direct actions in certain fundamental phases of intermediary metabolism.

Anterior Lobe (Adenohypophyseal) Hormones

Following hypophysectomy, the thyroid gland, adrenal cortex, and gonads undergo atrophy, and the animal loses weight. In addition, in young animals, longitudinal growth is arrested, closure of epiphyseal lines is delayed, and the gonads fail to mature, the animals remaining infantile. Certain metabolic defects are apparent. Oxidative processes are depressed; liver and muscle glycogen are depleted; fat oxidation is decreased; ketosis does not appear readily following procedures which usually induce increased ketogenesis; fat turnover is decreased, as reflected in its decreased mobilization from the fat depots. These animals are exceedingly sensitive to insulin.

All of these morphological and metabolic abnormalities can be prevented or corrected by administration of adenohypophyseal extracts. Several principles have been separated and purified, which exert rather characteristic effects and which are assumed to be different hormones. All are protein or polypeptide in nature. They may be placed in two categories. (1) The so-called "tropic" (trophic) hormones are responsible for the structural integrity and functional activity of certain specific "target" endocrine glands. Their most characteristic effects are due to stimulation of their respective target glands, although they may exert important actions on other tissues. They include the following: (a) thyrotropic, (b) adrenocorticotropic, and (c) three gonadotropic hormones, follicle-stimulating, luteinizing, and lactogenic. (2) At least one factor, growth hormone (Somatotropin) exerts a direct metabolic effect on protein, carbohydrate, and fat metabolism, not mediated by other endocrine glands. It is believed, but not established conclusively, that the growth and lactogenic hormones are produced in the eosinophils and the other factors in the basophils of the adenohypophysis. All are proteins or polypeptides.

Such fundamentally important regulatory functions must themselves be under rather precise control. Little is known concerning the mechanism of regulation of growth hormone secretion. There are apparently two mechanisms which regulate elaboration and release of the tropic hormones. Apparently the most precise, basic, and immediate regulation is accomplished by a type of negative feedback mechanism (servo-mechanism), whereby the rate of secretion of each of the tropic hormones is decreased or increased by increase or decrease, respectively, in the concentration in the bloodstream of the hormone(s) of the corresponding specific target gland. This provides for virtually automatic regulation of secretion of the latter in accordance with the needs of the organism. Excessive amounts of one of the secondary hormones, acting over relatively long periods of time, may suppress not only the specific tropic hormone but others as well ("shot-gun" action). For example, administration of large amounts of estrogen to young animals results not only in atrophy of the gonads, but also in thyroid atrophy and dwarfing.

Another type of control of adenohypophyseal secretion of tropic hormones is exercised by the central nervous system, mediated mainly through the hypothalamus. The available evidence suggests that neurohumoral substances (neurohormones), secreted in the region of the median eminence, pass through the hypophyseal portal system to the anterior lobe of the pituitary, where they stimulate secretion of specific hormones. By virtue of the extensive connections of the hypothalamus with other parts of the nervous system, this mechanism provides for hormonal responses to a great variety of nervous and emotional stimuli. These are particularly important in the case of gonadal and adrenocortical hormones (gonadotropic and adrenocorticotropic). In addition, certain of the target organ hormones may exert a direct influence on these hypothalamic centers, depressing secretion of the neurohumoral factors.

Thyrotropic (Thyroid-Stimulating) Hormone

Chemistry

Thyrotropic hormone (TSH) has not been isolated in pure form, but rather highly purified preparations are available. It is apparently a glycoprotein, containing glucosamine and galactosamine, with a molecular weight of about 30,000 and an unusually high cystine content.

Assay

Several methods have been employed: (1) determination of the number of colloid droplets in the cells of guinea pig thyroid following injection of preparations containing TSH; (2) measurement of increase in thyroid acinar cell height, and increase in extension of the hindlimb of the stasis (starved, non-metamorphosing) tadpole following injection of preparations containing TSH; (3) increased uptake or release of I^{131} by the thyroid.

Actions

TSH is an important factor in the regulation of thyroid function. Removal of TSH (hypophysectomy) is followed by: (a) involution of the thyroid, progessing to atrophy; (b) decrease in thyroid uptake of iodine ("trapping" function, p. 715); (c) depression of transformation of diiodotyrosine to thyroxine ("coupling"); (d) inhibition of release of thyroid hormone from the thyroid; (e) consequent fall in the level of circulating thyroxine (protein-bound iodine, p. 716).

Injection of TSH is followed by morphological and metabolic evidences of increased thyroid function. The following phenomena have been observed: increase in thyroid acinar cell height; resorption of follicular colloid; increase of Golgi apparatus, proteolytic activity, oxidase granules, and O_2 consumption of thyroid cells; increase of thyroid RNA and protein; increase in the iodine content of the gland as well as in the "protein-bound" iodine of the plasma; increase in uptake of radioactive iodine by the thyroid. There is evidence that TSH is necessary for coupling of diiodotyrosine to form thyroxine (p. 715). However, under ordinary circumstances, its primary physiological action is probably to stimulate release of thyroid hormone from the intrafollicular thyroglobulin. This is apparently accomplished by activation of a proteolytic enzyme which hydrolyzes thyroglobulin, the released thyroxine being transported across the follicular cells into the bloodstream. Administration of TSH therefore produces effects on the organism (except on the thyroid) identical with those produced by thyroxine. There is evidence that it also may exert a direct effect upon extraocular retrobulbar structures (fat, muscle, connective tissues), with consequent protrusion of the eyeball (exophthalmos). This may be due to an independent factor separable from TSH.

Secretion and Metabolism

Production and release of TSH are regulated by (a) the level of circulating thyroid hormone and (b) a hypothalamic neurohumoral factor, and are influenced by (c) other hormones, and (d) certain nutritional and environmental factors.

The rate of secretion of TSH varies in inverse relation to the concentration of thyroid hormone in the bloodstream. This negative feedback or servo-mechanism provides for delicate and practically automatic maintenance of a normal level of circulating thyroid hormone in the presence of a normally responsive hypophysis and thyroid. Primary depression of thyroid activity (e.g., thyroidectomy, anti-thyroid agents, p. 722) is accompanied by increased secretion of TSH and increase in size and number of pituitary basophils, many showing vacuolation ("thyroidectomy cells"). Conversely, TSH secretion is depressed in thyrotoxicosis.

Evidence for hypothalamic control of TSH secretion is still incomplete. It appears likely that neurohumoral factors produced in the hypothalamus may exert a modifying influence upon its production and release. Apart from psychogenic and other nervous stimuli that may operate by this mechanism, it has been suggested that thyroid hormone may depress TSH secretion indirectly by an action at the hypothalamic level as well as directly at the hypophyseal level.

Thyroid function may be depressed by administration or excessive secretion of epinephrine, ACTH, or adrenocortical hormones, or by exposure to a variety of nonspecific "alarming" stimuli (e.g., formalin injection). It is probable that this depression of thyroid activity is mediated by the adenohypophysis, TSH secretion being decreased. In certain species estrogens appear to exert a similar effect. There have been reports of increased thyroid secretion following ovariectomy and decrease in thyroid function following administration of estrogen, these changes being attributed to corresponding changes in TSH secretion.

Variations in secretion of TSH, with consequent variations in thyroid activity, play an important part in adaptations of the organism to certain changes in environment and nutrition. Exposure to low environmental temperatures results in increased TSH secretion, with stimulation of thyroid activity; conversely, secretion of TSH and thyroid hormone is decreased in a hot environment. Thyroidectomized animals do not tolerate prolonged exposure to cold. TSH secretion and thyroid activity are decreased in chronic starvation.

Exogenous TSH leaves the bloodstream quite rapidly, more than 97 per cent being removed within one hour. It is apparently metabolized (inactivated) in the thyroid and other tissues as well. A small amount is excreted in the urine.

Adrenocorticotropic Hormone

Chemistry

Adrenocorticotropic hormone (ACTH; corticotropin) is a straight-chain polypeptide containing 39 amino acid residues. Two forms have been isolated: α-corticotropin and β-corticotropin. Studies of these preparations from different species indicates that the biological activity of ACTH probably resides in the sequence of the first 24 amino acids. The hormones isolated from sheep, beef, and hog pituitaries exhibit differences in the arrangement of amino acids in positions 25 to 33, which have no effect upon their biological activity.

The ACTH polypeptide chain also contains a sequence of seven amino acids present also in the melanocyte-stimulating hormones (MSH). This is the basis for the melanophore-expanding activity exhibited by all active ACTH preparations (p. 749).

Assay

Several methods of assay of ACTH activity have been proposed:

(*a*) ***Repair test.*** This consists in determination of the reappearance of lipid material in the regressed adrenal cortices of hypophysectomized rats following injection of preparations containing ACTH.

(*b*) ***Maintenance test.*** This consists in determination of the quantity of ACTH-containing material required to maintain the adrenal weights of rats injected immediately after hypophysectomy.

(*c*) ***Measurement of decrease in adrenal ascorbic acid.*** Measurement of the decrease in adrenal ascorbic acid of hypophysectomized rats one hour after intravenous injection of the ACTH-containing material is a highly specific and sensitive method.

Actions

The principal actions of corticotropin are exerted on the adrenal cortex. However, certain effects produced by purified preparations in adrenalectomized animals suggest that influences exerted on extra-adrenal tissues may be of physiological significance.

Actions on adrenals. ACTH is the most important physiological regulator of the production and secretion of all hormones of the adrenal cortex except aldosterone. The adrenals of hypophysectomized animals are reduced in size and lipid content, and the concentration of 17-hydroxysteroids in the blood and their excretion in the urine fall to very low levels, as does urinary excretion of 17-ketosteroids; output of aldosterone decreases by only 50 or 60 per cent, in contrast to about 90 per cent decrease in glucocorticoids. The most striking metabolic consequences are fasting hypoglycemia and increased insulin sensitivity, with relatively minor changes in electrolyte and water balance. All of these morphologic, hormonal, and metabolic abnormalities can be reversed by administration of ACTH.

Injection of excessive amounts of ACTH in either normal or hypophysectomized animals can produce hypertrophy of the adrenal cortex with decrease (temporary) in adrenal lipid and ascorbic acid (pp. 158, 704), striking increase in secretion and urinary excretion (five- to ten-fold) of glucocorticoids and, to a lesser extent, in urinary excretion of 17-ketosteroids; secretion of aldosterone may increase two- or three-fold. The metabolic consequences include most of those observed after administration of cortical hormones, including hyperglycemia, negative nitrogen balance, hyperlipemia and hypercholesterolemia, ketonemia, eosinopenia, lymphopenia, and evidence of excessive retention of Na, Cl, and water (p. 709 ff.).

ACTH stimulates formation of cyclic AMP in the adrenal, activating phosphorylase (p. 400) and thereby providing an increased supply of glucose-6-phosphate and, consequently, NADPH via the hexose monophosphate shunt pathway. This may be one of the fundamental mechanisms of action of ACTH on the adrenal, since NADPH is a requirement for several reduction and hydroxylation reactions in adrenal steroidogenesis. However, there is evidence that ACTH-stimulated steroidogenesis may be dependent primarily on increased synthesis of protein (i.e., enzymes) secondary to increased production of RNA.

Extra-adrenal actions. Administration of ACTH is followed by increased mobilization of unsaturated fatty acids from adipose tissue into the blood plasma. This "adipokinetic action," which is shared also by somatotropin, requires the presence of adrenocortical hormones but is not mediated by the adrenal cortex. Other extra-adrenal effects on lipid metabolism include increased ketogenesis and decrease in the respiratory quotient.

Direct effects on carbohydrate metabolism include lowering of the blood glucose concentration and increase in glucose tolerance. Deposition of glycogen in adipose tissue is increased, regarded as due to stimulation of insulin secretion. The rate of urea formation from exogenous amino acids is reduced, an action similar to that of growth hormone and due presumably to enhancement of transport of amino acids into cells of extrahepatic tissues. ACTH retards metabolic degradation and conjugation of corticosteroids in the liver, prolonging the biological half-life of these hormones in the plasma. It may therefore augment adrenocortical activity in this manner as well as by stimulating corticosteroid secretion.

ACTH possesses melanocyte-stimulating activity, about 1 per cent of that of the melanocyte-stimulating hormone (p. 749), due to the fact that these polypeptides share a common sequence of amino acids responsible for this activity. This phenomenon is characterized by dispersion of melanin granules in the melanophores of frog skin. The relation of this action of ACTH to the increased pigmentation of Addison's disease is not clear, since purified ACTH preparations have not been demonstrated to produce increased pigmentation in man.

Secretion, Metabolism

The rate of discharge of ACTH from the adenohypophysis is controlled mainly by a neurohypophyseal factor produced by neurons in the region of the infundibular nuclei and median eminence. This factor, designated corticotropin releasing factor (CRF), is believed to be a polypeptide related to but not identical with other active peptides of the neurohypophysis, such as oxytocin and vasopressin, which produce similar effects when given in large amounts. That this factor is not necessary, however, for basal secretion of ACTH or for its regulation by circulating adrenocortical hormones, is indicated by the fact that these continue after removal of the hypothalamus (dog).

Increase in the concentration of glucocorticoids in the blood causes depression of ACTH secretion and, if sufficiently high, can result in adrenal atrophy comparable to that which follows hypophysectomy. Conversely, decrease in the level of blood glucocorticoids leads to increased secretion of ACTH. There are differences in the relative effectiveness of different adrenal hormones in this regard, 17-hydroxycorticosterone (cortisol), the major physiological glucocorticoid in man, being most active, and aldosterone having little or no effect on ACTH secretion. This effect is probably exerted both at the level of the hypothalamus, influencing secretion of CRF, and at the level of the adenohypophysis, influencing directly its secretory activity with respect to ACTH. There is some evidence, also, that cortisol may exert an effect at the level of the adrenal cortex.

This automatic regulation of ACTH secretion in accordance with physiological demands, as reflected in the level of circulating adrenocortical hormones, constitutes an important phase of the mechanism of regulation of adrenal cortical activity (negative feedback mechanism). A similar mechanism exists for thyrotropin (p. 738) and gonadotropins (p. 741). However, in conditions of stress (e.g., pain, emotion, injury, infection, etc.) ("alarm reaction"), there is increased secretion of ACTH and, secondarily, of adrenocortical hormones. An additional mechanism must operate to produce this stimulation.

Stimulation of certain areas of the median eminence results in increased secretion of ACTH, and, conversely, lesions in this area prevent the increased ACTH secretion that otherwise occurs in response to "alarming" stimuli. Morphine and reserpine also exert potent inhibitory effects. These effects are attributed to influences of nerve impulses and drugs upon the state of sustained inhibition of these hypothalamic centers exerted by the reticular formation or the limbic system.

Exogenous ACTH disappears from the circulating blood very rapidly. It has been reported that only about 2 per cent of the injected dose remains in the blood stream after six minutes.

Gonadotropic Hormones

The anterior pituitary secretes three hormones which exert important effects on the gonads and are therefore termed "gonadotropic hormones." These are: (1) follicle-stimulating hormone (FSH); (2) luteinizing hormone (LH) (interstitial cell-stimulating hormone; ICSH); (3) prolactin (lactogenic hormone; luteotropic hormone; LTH). In the female, they are responsible for the growth, maturation, and expulsion of the ova and with the production of the internal secretions of the ovary. In the male, they stimulate spermatogenesis and production of androgen. Gonadotropins from different species differ in chemical structure.

Hypophysectomy is followed by atrophy of the gonads, with abolition of their hormone production and, consequently, atrophy of the target organs of these hormones, viz., uterus, vaginal mucosa, prostate, and seminal vesicles. All of these structures and functions are restored by administration of the gonadotropic hormones.

Release of gonadotropic hormones from the pituitary is stimulated by neurohumoral factors originating in the hypothalamus and reaching the pituitary via the hypophyseal portal system and/or the systemic circulation. This hypothalamic control of gonadotropin release is itself influenced by stimuli reaching the hypothalamus via nerve pathways, e.g., from the retina, genital tract, breast. Secretion and release of FSH in the female are regulated also by the level of estrogen in the circulating blood, an increased concentration causing depression and a decreased concentration producing stimulation (negative feedback control). Androgens are much less effective in this connection.

Hormonal influences on secretion of LH are not as well defined. This is depressed in the female by large doses of progesterone and in the male by testosterone. The actions of these steroid hormones are apparently exerted at the levels of both the hypothalamus and the adenohypophysis. Although there is no doubt of the importance of the hypothalamus in controlling secretion and release of prolactin, there is little evidence of the influence of gonadal steroid hormones in this connection. Release of prolactin from the adenohypophysis is apparently inhibited when secretion of FSH and LH is increased. There is evidence that oxytocin, secretion of which is increased by nerve impulses reaching the hypothalamus, e.g., by suckling, may stimulate release of prolactin.

Normal gonadotropin levels in blood and urine are given in Figure 26–3 (p. 693) and Tables 26-5 and 26-6 (p. 692). The gonadotropic activity of blood plasma is associated with the α_2- and β-globulin fractions.

As the menarche is approached, production of gonadotropins (largely FSH), as reflected in urinary excretion, increases progressively. A high level may persist for many months before the onset of the first menstrual period; this reflects the time at which the ovary is capable of responding to this marked outpouring of gonadotropins and regular cyclic function is assumed. Appreciable amounts of LH are probably not released by the hypophysis until the ovarian follicles are capable of secreting substantial amounts of estrogen, inasmuch as a certain concentration of the latter in the blood appears to be the normal physiological stimulus for release of LH from the hypophysis.

In the non-pregnant sexually mature woman, gonadotropic hormones are produced in a characteristic cyclic fashion. FSH is the chief gonadotropin produced during the follicular phase of the cycle; it is present in only very small amounts during the first week or 10 days of the average menstrual cycle but subsequently increases rapidly during the preovulatory phase, during which time a rather high peak of FSH may be present for two or three days. More than one such peak can sometimes be demonstrated. A minimal amount of LH is perhaps also secreted during the early phase of the cycle, acting synergistically with FSH in stimulating production of estrogens by the growing follicle. As the mid-cycle is approached, there is a sudden increase in LH which, together with the increased output of FSH, acts upon the rapidly maturing follicle to induce ovulation. After the latter has occurred, FSH apparently diminishes rapidly, although LH continues to be produced in moderate amounts until the premenstrual phase is reached. During this time LH appears to be concerned with the luteinization of granulosa and thecal cells in producing a corpus luteum. Functional activity of the corpus luteum however appears to be dependent largely upon the presence of both LH and LTH (prolactin), which stimulate the luteal cells to produce both progesterone and estrogen. The precise status of LTH in the human being is not clear.

During pregnancy, production of gonadotropins by the adenohypophysis is depressed as a result of the increasing level of estrogens and progesterone. The huge amount of gonadotropin, which is one of the characteristics of pregnancy, is produced by the chorionic epithelium (chorionic gonadotropin). This is entirely of the luteinizing variety and is distinguishable biologically from LH in only a few respects.

For several years prior to the onset of the menopause the aging ovary becomes progressively less capable of responding to gonadotropic stimulation. Consequently, increased concentrations of FH are required to produce follicular development and estrogen production. When ovulation ceases, gonadotropin production not only is increased but now consists almost entirely of FSH. When menstruation ceases, the blood level of FSH increases and usually shows no definite cyclic pattern. This increase usually persists for many years, into the sixth and seventh decades; eventually the hypophysis apparently becomes exhausted and gonadotropin production ceases.

Follicle-Stimulating Hormone

Chemistry. Follicle-stimulating hormone (FSH) is apparently a water-soluble glycoprotein (m.w. about 30,000), containing 3 to 11 per cent carbohydrate. FSH preparations from sheep and hog pituitaries exhibit essentially identical biological activity but apparently significant structural differences. Both are hexose- and hexosamine-containing glycoproteins with different molecular weights, isoelectric points, and carbohydrate contents.

Assay. Inasmuch as the activity of FSH is influenced by LH, quantitative data regarding the former can be obtained only in hypophysectomized animals. The following procedures may be employed: (1) production of increase of ovarian weight or follicular development in hypophysectomized female rats; (2) production of increase in weight of testes without stimulation of secondary sex organs in hypophysectomized male rats.

Actions. In the female, FSH stimulates the growth and maturation of ovarian follicles and prepares them for ovulation. In pure form, this hormone does not cause secretion of estrogen by the ovary, but does so in the presence of even minute amounts of luteinizing hormone (ICSH; LH) (below). In the male, FSH stimulates spermatogenesis.

Luteinizing Hormone

Chemistry. Luteinizing hormone, LH (ICSH), has been isolated in pure form. It is apparently a homogeneous, water-soluble, carbohydrate-containing (mannose; hexosamine) protein. LH prepared from different species exhibits differences in immunological specificity, chemical composition, isoelectric point, and molecular weight (human 26,000; sheep 40,000; swine 100,000).

Assay. LH activity may be assayed in several ways, the following being commonly employed: (1) increase of ovarian weight and corpora lutea production in normal immature rats primed by FSH; (2) repair of ovarian interstitial cells in hypophysectomized rats; (3) increase in weight of seminal vesicles in normal immature male rats; (4) increase in weight of the ventral lobe of the prostate in hypophysectomized male rats.

Actions. In the female, LH acts synergistically with FSH to cause ovulation of mature follicles and secretion of estrogen by the thecal and granulosa cells. It is also concerned with corpus luteum formation and, in conjunction with luteotrophic (lactogenic) hormone (LTH), it is concerned with the production of estrogen and progesterone by the corpus luteum.

In the male, LH stimulates the development and functional activity of Leydig (interstitial) cells, and, consequently, the production of testicular androgen (p. 684). Its administration, therefore, produces effects in the organism (except on the testis) similar to those which follow administration of testosterone (p. 687).

Prolactin

Chemistry. Prolactin (lactogenic hormone; luteotropic hormone; LTH) has been isolated in pure form. It is a protein with a molecular weight of about 24,000.

Assay. The method usually employed depends upon the increase in weight of the crop sac of the pigeon after injection of prolactin. An international unit (I.U.) has been defined as "the specific activity contained in 0.1 mg. of the standard preparation (international standard)."

Actions. Prolactin (LTH) is responsible for lactation in the postpartum woman, the breast having been prepared by estrogen and progesterone. It is also necessary for stimulation of functional activity (estrogen and progesterone production) for the corpus luteum in certain species (human?). In certain species prolactin has a protein-anabolic effect, resembling somatotropin in this respect. Its function in the male is unknown.

Chorionic Gonadotropin

The placenta produces a gonadotropic hormone which differs from the pituitary gonadotropins but resembles LH in its biological actions. It is a glycoprotein with a molecular weight of about 30,000 and a carbohydrate content of about 28 per cent (man). It reaches a maximum concentration in blood and urine usually in 50 to 70 days after the last previous normal menstrual period, this phenomenon constituting the basis for certain of the most valuable pregnancy tests (Tables 26-5, 26-6, p. 692).

The rising titer of chorionic gonadotropin in the blood during pregnancy causes persistence and continued function of the corpus luteum until the placental syncytiotrophoblast is capable of producing sufficient estrogen and progesterone to support the pregnancy.

Growth Hormone (*Somatotropin*)

Chemistry

Growth (somatotropic) hormone has been prepared in crystalline form from the hypophyses of several species, including man. All of these exhibit immunological, structural, and physicochemical differences. The molecular weights vary from 25,400 (monkey) to 47,800 (sheep); the isoelectric points range from 4.9 (man) (m.w. 29,000) to 6.85 (beef); those of man and monkey consist of a single polypeptide chain, whereas the beef and sheep hormones contain two chains. These differences are reflected in species differences in biological activity. Beef growth hormone is ineffective in man and monkey, but is biologically active in rats and fish. Human and monkey somatotropins are effective in all species tested. The nature of the biological activity, when present, is essentially the same in all species.

Certain of these preparations may be partially hydrolyzed by chymotrypsin without loss of biological activity. This suggests that, as in the case of other hypophyseal hormones, activity resides in an identical core of amino acid sequences.

Assay

The method that has been employed most widely consists in measurement of the increase in width of the proximal epiphyseal cartilage of the tibia of the hypophysectomized female rat following injection of the growth hormone. Other methods involve measurement of the increase in body weight of normal, plateaued, or, better, hypophysectomized female rats following injection of the hormonal preparation. The availability of purified somatotropin has made possible the application of highly sensitive immunological assay methods. With such procedures, fractions of a microgram may be detected.

Actions

Animals hypophysectomized before fully grown are dwarfed; administration of pituitary extracts results in gigantism or, if given after full growth is attained, in acromegaly. These effects on both skeletal and visceral growth are attributable to the growth hormone, but involve also participation of other factors, e.g., thyroxine and insulin, for their maximal expression. This is to be expected, inasmuch as the complicated phenomenon of growth must be dependent upon a number of interrelated metabolic processes and the state of nutrition of the organism. In man, too, inadequate growth hormone production in early life (period of growth) results in dwarfism, and overproduction (prior to epiphyseal closure) in gigantism. Hypersecreting tumors (acidophilic) in adults result in acromegaly, characterized by overgrowth of certain portions of the skeleton and of other tissues.

Unfractionated extracts of the anterior pituitary produce effects on various metabolic processes, in part indirectly (e.g., TSH, ACTH), but also by a direct action not mediated by other glands. It is probable that most (but not all) of these direct metabolic actions may be due to somatotropin.

Protein metabolism; skeletal growth. Growth hormone is a protein-anabolic principle. It induces a positive nitrogen balance, accompanied by increase in tissue nitrogen, and decrease in urea nitrogen, amino nitrogen and total NPN of the blood plasma and urine. Catabolism of amino acids is apparently retarded and their entry into cells and incorporation into body proteins accelerated. This anabolic action of growth hormone is facilitated by the presence of normal amounts of insulin, adrenocortical hormones, and thyroxine and simultaneous stimulation of fat and carbohydrate metabolism.

Somatotropin stimulates erythropoiesis and growth of the liver, intestines, and kidneys, with augmentation of renal function (renal clearance and tubular excretion). The effect on bones is primarily stimulation of chondrogenesis, with secondary increase in osteogenesis. This action involves increased synthesis of chondroitin sulfate; there is also increased synthesis of acid mucopolysaccharides in the skin.

The mechanism of action of somatotropin in stimulating protein synthesis probably involves production of increased amounts of mRNA.

Carbohydrate metabolism. Hypophysectomy leads to the following changes in carbohydrate metabolism: (1) tendency to hypoglycemia on fasting; (2) decrease in liver and muscle glycogen on fasting; (3) increased sensitivity to insulin; (4) increased utilization of carbohydrate; (5) amelioration of diabetes in depancreatized or alloxanized animals. Certain of these manifestations are due in part to adrenocortical hypofunction (p. 711) resulting from loss of ACTH. However, they are completely reversed only by administration of growth hormone (or crude pituitary extracts) in addition to adrenocortical hormones (or ACTH).

Conversely, administration of growth hormone produces the following changes in carbohydrate metabolism, the effects varying in different species: (1) hyperglycemia (dog, cat) and aggravation of diabetes in depancreatized hypophysectomized animals ("diabetogenic" effect); (2) inhibition of insulin action ("anti-insulin" effect), with decreased utilization of carbohydrate and lowering of the respiratory quotient; (3) increase in muscle glycogen in hypophysectomized animals ("glycostatic" effect). The permanent diabetes produced in certain species by growth hormone is due to destruction of the islands of Langerhans. This effect is probably due to the primarily induced hyperglycemia, which in turn causes hyperactivity and hyperplasia of the islet beta cells and, subsequently, functional exhaustion and atrophy (p. 445).

The mechanism of action of growth hormone in producing these effects has not been established definitely. It has been suggested that whereas insulin acts to accelerate entry of glucose into cells, somatotropin (and adrenocortical steroids) inhibits its subsequent phosphorylation. This concept is still controversial.

Administration of growth hormone causes an increased output of glucose by the liver. Inasmuch as the rate of turnover of glucose in the intact organism is simultaneously increased, any postulated peripheral inhibition of glucose utilization must be overcome by this provision of increased amounts of glucose or by the operation of other components of the homeostatic mechanism. There is suggestive evidence that growth hormone may depress glucose-6-phosphate dehydrogenase activity, with consequent decreased oxidation of glucose via the hexose monophosphate oxidative pathway.

Lipid metabolism. Administration of growth hormone stimulates mobilization of fat from the fat depots, with consequent decrease in carcass fat, increase in plasma fat and unesterified fatty acids and liver lipids and increased fatty acid oxidation and ketogenesis. This fat-mobilizing and catabolic effect is facilitated by simultaneous depression of carbohydrate utilization. Conversely, hypophysectomy results in retardation of mobilization of depot fat, and amelioration of ketosis in diabetic animals.

The effects of somatotropin on lipid metabolism resemble those of ACTH and adrenocortical steroids, i.e., decrease of adipose tissue fat, increased mobilization of unesterified fatty acids with rise in their concentration in the blood plasma, increased ketogenesis, and decrease in the respiratory quotient.

Posterior Lobe (Neurohypophyseal) Hormones

Injection of an extract of the posterior lobe (neurohypophysis) produces three well-recognized effects: (1) increase in blood pressure (pressor effect); (2) contraction of the mammalian uterus (oxytocic effect) and milk ejection; (3) decreased urine volume in mammals, with increased concentration of urinary solids (antidiuretic effect). A fourth effect, induced in lower vertebrates, i.e., melanophore expansion or melanophore dispersion, is due to a principle formed in the pars intermedia, but present as a contaminant in unfractionated extracts of the posterior lobe. In animals that have no pars intermedia (e.g., whale, chicken), this principle occurs in extracts of the anterior lobe only.

Vasopressin and Oxytocin

The pressor and antidiuretic effects are produced by the same substance (pressor principle; vasopressin), and the oxytocic effect is produced by a second principle, oxytocin, separable from the former.

The structures of these two hormones have been established, and they have been synthesized, an accomplishment of historical importance, representing the first successful laboratory syntheses of polypeptide hormones. Both are octapeptides, containing eight different amino acids, three of which are present in the form of amides (Fig. 26–14). Each contains glycine (amide), proline, aspartic acid (amide), glutamic acid (amide), tyrosine, and cystine, the latter represented by two cysteinyl residues linked by a disulfide bridge, the structure therefore being that of a cyclic disulfide. In addition, oxytocin contains leucine and isoleucine, whereas vasopressin contains phenylalanine and either lysine (hog) or arginine (beef). Replacement of the leucine of oxytocin with either arginine or lysine, and the isoleucine with phenylalanine, produces a vasopressin. These hormones are not present in non-mammalian vertebrates (e.g., the frog), being replaced by vasotocin, which

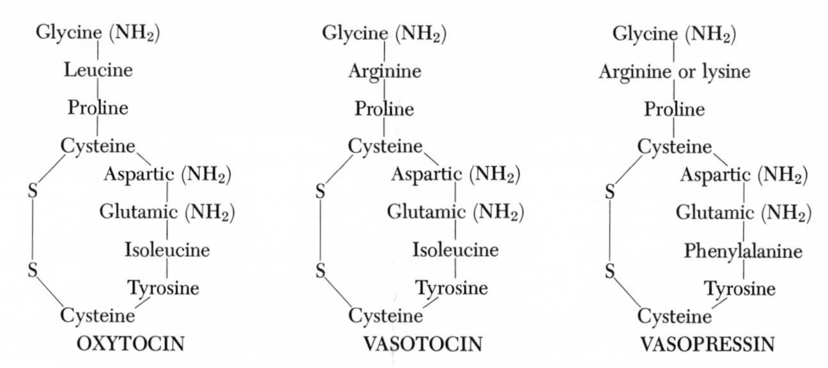

Figure 26-14. Structures of oxytocin, vasotocin, and vasopressin.

has relatively weak vasopressor and oxytocic activity. This substance is of interest from the standpoint of biochemical evolution; it possesses the 5-membered ring structure of oxytocin and the tripeptide chain of vasopressin and has been suggested as the evolutionary precursor of these hormones.

The functional significance of certain amino acid sequences in these polypeptide chains is indicated by the overlapping of biological activities of these hormones. Vasopressin possesses 6 per cent of the oxytocic and 20 per cent of the milk-ejecting potency of oxytocin; the latter possesses about 1 per cent of the pressor and about 0.5 per cent of the antidiuretic potency of vasopressin.

Secretion

These hormones are formed in neuronal cells of the supraoptic and paraventricular nuclei, migrate along their axons, and are stored in nerve cell endings in the neurohypophysis, from which they are discharged into the bloodstream upon appropriate stimulation. Information concerning factors that influence the release of hormones from the neurohypophysis ("secretion") relates mainly to vasopressin (antidiuretic hormone; ADH). There is evidence that secretion of vasopressin may be influenced independently of that of oxytocin. Discharge of ADH from the hypophysis, with consequent decrease in urine volume and increase in urine specific gravity (p. 825), is influenced by at least four types of stimuli:

1. Neurogenic. The neurohypophysis is responsive to a great variety of nonspecific stimuli by virtue of its direct nervous connections with the hypothalamic nuclei and, through the latter, with higher brain centers. Discharge of ADH is effected by traumatic and emotional stimuli, including pain and fear. Epinephrine may possibly be involved in this reaction; small doses have been found to increase discharge of ADH (large doses inhibit). Emotional factors may also depress release of ADH, with consequent diuresis.

2. Osmotic. Perhaps the most important of the regulatory mechanisms involves osmoreceptors, located in the diencephalon, responsive to changes in osmotic pressure of the blood. Increase in osmotic pressure, e.g., in dehydration, stimulates these receptors, with resulting release of ADH from the hypophysis and retention of increased amounts of water in the body; decrease in osmotic pressure of the blood, e.g., in excessive hydration, produces the opposite effect.

3. Volume Changes. Release of ADH may be stimulated by factors which decrease the volume of extracellular fluid independently of changes in osmotic pressure (e.g., hemorrhage, venous occlusion, change from recumbent to sitting position). Conversely, it may be decreased (with consequent diuresis) by factors which increase extracellular fluid volume (e.g., infusion of isotonic solutions, change from sitting to recumbent position). This mechanism is believed to involve volume receptors ("stretch receptors") located in the left atrium and probably elsewhere, which communicate with the antidiuretic system by way of vagal impulses.

4. Drugs. Release of ADH is stimulated by a number of drugs, including morphine, anesthetic agents (ether), nicotine, ferritin, etc. These effects are apparently mediated by acetylcholine and are therefore cholinergic in nature.

Assay

Pressor activity is assayed by comparing the rise in blood pressure, following intravenous injection in anesthesized dogs, spinal cats, or anesthetized rats, with that produced by known amounts of a standard preparation.

Oxytocic activity is assayed by comparing the degree of contraction of the isolated, virgin guinea pig uterus, in vitro, with that produced by known amounts of a standard preparation. Another method is based upon the blood pressure lowering effect of the oxytocic principle in the anesthetized chicken.

Antidiuretic activity is assayed by comparing the reduction in urine volume following intravenous injection in hydrated unanesthetized rats or hydrated rabbits with that produced by a standard preparation.

Functions

Despite the pronounced pressor effect of vasopressin, there is no satisfactory evidence that this factor plays a role in the physiological regulation of vascular tone or of blood pressure. Similarly, there is merely suggestive and contradictory evidence that the oxytocic principle may be implicated in the regulation of uterine contraction during parturi-

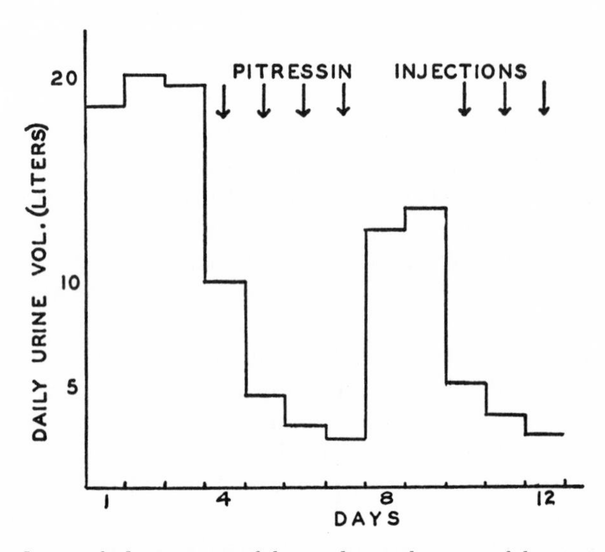

Figure 26-15. The influence of administration of the antidiuretic hormone of the pituitary on the daily urine output of a patient with diabetes insipidus.

tion. It also causes ejection of milk from the lactating breast. Oxytocin secretion is increased by suckling; it has been suggested that it stimulates release of prolactin. Another action of oxytocin, possibly of physiological significance, is to stimulate contraction of the gallbladder, intestine, urinary bladder, and ureters. On the other hand, there is unequivocal evidence that the antidiuretic hormone (vasopressin) is important in the regulation of water balance in mammals. This antidiuretic effect is dependent on a specific action of ADH on the epithelial cells of the distal portion of the uriniferous tubule, enhancing reabsorption of water independently of solids, and resulting in concentration of the urine (pp. 310, 825). In its absence the urine cannot be concentrated, and large volumes (up to 20 liters or more daily) of low specific gravity are excreted (diabetes insipidus). This condition can be produced by destruction of the hypothalamic nuclei (supraoptic and paraventricular) or by interruption of their connections with the neurohypophysis, e.g., by section of the infundibular stalk.

Melanocyte-Stimulating Hormones

Almost all cold-blooded vertebrates (e.g., amphibians, reptiles, fishes) are able to adapt their skin coloring to their surroundings to a greater or lesser extent, a protective or deceptive device of obvious benefit to the animal. This property is due to the presence, in the skin, of certain cells, with branching processes, termed "chromatophores," which contain mobile pigment granules. In the majority of such cells the pigment is black, and the cells are called "melanophores" (melanocytes); xanthophores contain yellow and erythrophores red pigment granules.

These pigment granules may be concentrated in a single mass near the center of the cell, in which case the skin becomes pale. They may, on the other hand, be dispersed throughout the cell and its processes, in which case the color of the skin is intensified. Scattering of these granules from their central position is effected by the action of the melanocyte-stimulating hormones (MSH). In most species these are elaborated by the pars intermedia of the pituitary; in animals in which this structure is absent (e.g., whale, chicken), they are apparently produced in the anterior lobe. Variable amounts are secreted, with consequent variations in skin color, in response to reflexes originating in the retina and initiated by the color of the immediate visible environment of the animal. Hypophysectomy (e.g., in the toad) results in paling of the skin; injection of MSH restores the normal color. This forms the basis for the bioassay procedure.

Two melanocyte-stimulating factors (α-MSH and β-MSH) have been isolated and characterized as straight-chain polypeptides containing 13 to 18 amino acid residues, respectively. Both possess an identical internal sequence of seven amino acids, which occurs also in ACTH. It is on this basis that ACTH possesses melanophore-expanding activity, approximately 1 per cent of that of α-MSH. The function of these hormones in man is unknown. It has been suggested that they may be involved in normal and abnormal cutaneous pigmentation, but there is no satisfactory evidence that this is the case.

MELATONIN

The action of MSH is blocked and the color of the frog skin lightened (aggregation of pigment granules) by melatonin (N-acetyl-5-methoxytryptamine), which has been isolated from the pineal gland of several species, including man. This substance is formed by O-methylation of acetylserotonin, the methyl donor being S-adenosylmethionine and the enzyme, hydroxyindole-O-methyl-transferase, present in high concentration apparently only in the pineal gland. This enzyme is also responsible for the production of methyoxytryptophol from hydroxytryptophol, another serotonin product present in the pineal. Although small amounts of melatonin, or a similar substance, have been demonstrated in brain and peripheral nerve tissue, it seems probable that the melatonin is initially secreted by the pineal and is then taken up by other tissues.

Melatonin causes marked skin lightening in certain animals, such as the frog and certain fish, by its action on the pigment cells, an effect which is the opposite of that produced by the pituitary melanocyte-stimulating hormones.

There is increasing evidence that melatonin and methoxytryptophol influence gonadal function. Both of these substances depress ovarian weight and the incidence of vaginal estrus in rats. When rats are placed in continuous light, the capacity of the pineal to synthesize melatonin is decreased, and the activity of the melatonin-synthesizing enzyme varies according to a diurnal cycle, dependent upon the state of environmental lighting. These observations suggest that the pineal may serve as a primal "biologic clock," which helps to regulate certain endocrine rhythms.

RELAXIN

During pregnancy and parturition, in certain mammalian species, including man, a phenomenon occurs, known as "pelvic relaxation." This consists in separation of the symphysis pubis (or sacroiliac union), with consequent increase in size of the pelvic cavity and decrease in its rigidity, facilitating parturition. Relaxin is a hormone concerned with this relaxation phenomenon, operating in conjunction with other factors.

Relaxin is produced, during pregnancy, in tissues of the reproductive system, e.g., ovaries, placenta, uterus, the relative amounts formed in these tissues varying in different species. Its production is stimulated by progesterone and by related adrenocortical steroids, e.g., deoxycorticosterone and pregnenolone. It is apparently a polypeptide.

The action of this hormone on the connective tissue of the symphysis pubis requires preceding sensitization of this structure by estrogen. The specific effect of relaxin consists in increased vascularity of the connective tissue of the symphysis, followed by imbibition of water, dissolution and splitting of collagen fibers, and disorganization of the fibrous structure. There is apparently depolymerization of the mucoproteins of the ground substance (p. 776).

Other reported effects of this hormone include:

(1) Synergism with estrogen and progesterone in mammary development (rat).
(2) Antidiuretic action (rabbit).
(3) Inhibition of rhythmic uterine contractions (rat, guinea pig).

PLACENTAL HORMONES

The extent of secretory activity of the placenta has not been established with certainty. In primates, the placenta produces chorionic gonadotropin (p. 742) and there is good evidence that it also produces steroids with estrogenic (p. 689), progesteronic (p. 696), and adrenocorticoid (p. 709) activity, and relaxin, a protein hormone. These endocrine functions of the placenta play an important role in the maintenance of normal pregnancy. It has been reported that the placenta also produces a substance or substances with prolactin-like and growth hormone-like activity.

NEUROHORMONES

The theory of humoral (i.e., chemical) transmission of nerve impulses embodies the view that stimulation of nerves releases substances which act on the effector cells. The case is perhaps strongest for autonomic nerves, but has been invoked also for the central nervous system and somatic nerves. These neurohumoral factors include acetylcholine, norepinephrine and epinephrine, concerned with the transmission of excitatory impulses, e.g., in vagal and sympathetic fibers. Interest has been focused upon the possible role of γ-aminobutyric acid and serotonin in the transmission of inhibitory impulses in the brain. The validity of designating these agents as hormones is questionable because, under physiological conditions, the minute amounts formed or released at effector cells probably act only at the point of release, and are not carried to other effector cells; this criticism, of course, is not applicable to epinephrine and norepinephrine as secreted by the adrenal medulla. These neurohumoral substances are therefore considered in the discussion of metabolism in nervous tissues (p. 785).

The scope of the concept of "neurohormones" has been greatly enlarged as a result of the demonstration of the importance of the hypothalamus in regulating secretory activity of the adenohypophysis and in the formation of hormones formerly believed to originate in the neurohypophysis. These factors are considered in discussions of the secretion of ACTH (p. 740), gonadotropins (p. 741), and vasopressin (anti-diuretic factor) (p. 747).

ERYTHROPOIETIN

There is now general acceptance of the concept of a circulating erythropoietic-stimulating factor (or factors) which acts upon the bone marrow to increase the rate of maturation, production, and release of erythrocytes. Originally designated hemopoietin, the terms "erythropoietin" and "erythropoietic-stimulating factor (ESF)" have been applied to the substance(s) in the plasma and urine which exhibit this activity. ESF has been found to increase: (1) the rate of incorporation of iron into erythrocytes, (2) the rate of reticulocyte formation, and (3) the number of red blood cells (red cell mass).

Its presence in normal adults has not been demonstrated unequivocally, but there is evidence that it may be present in the blood of pregnant, fetal, and newborn animals. It is present in the urine of patients with severe anemia and in the plasma of animals treated with erythropoietic metals, such as cobalt, or rendered anoxic by (a) bleeding, (b) administration of hemolytic agents such as phenylhydrazine, and (c) exposure to reduced barometric pressures. This mechanism for controlling production of red cells in accordance with the needs of the tissues for oxygen is superimposed upon the well-recognized nutritional and hormonal factors that influence hemoglobin synthesis and red cell production.

Erythropoietin (ESF) is a glycoprotein of low molecular weight. It is formed in the kidney, and perhaps also in other tissues. It disappears rapidly from the bloodstream, the liver and hematopoietic tissues apparently being implicated in its utilization or inactivation. Excretion in the urine may contribute to its removal.

GASTROINTESTINAL HORMONES

Secretory activities of certain digestive glands are regulated by hormones produced in localized areas of the intestinal and perhaps also the gastric mucosa, in response to the local action of foodstuffs and non-specific agents. The actions of these humoral factors supplement those of the autonomic nervous system. Inasmuch as their only known effects are exerted on digestive functions, they will be considered here only briefly.

Of the many such substances for which hormonal status has been claimed, only two have been conclusively established as such by demonstration of release under physiological conditions, viz., secretin and cholecystokinin. The evidence is very strong but not conclusive for three others, viz., pancreozymin, enterogastrone, and gastrin.

Secretin

The term "hormone" was first applied to this substance by Bayliss and Starling (1904). It is produced by the upper intestinal mucosal glands, in highest concentration in the duodenum and jejunum, in response to the local action of a number of agents, the most important physiological factors being acidity, water, polypeptides, certain amino acids, and fatty acids. Other active agents include NaCl solution, alcohol, soaps, and buffer solutions. Produced in this manner, secretin enters the bloodstream as a true internal secretion and exerts a characteristic effect on the flow of pancreatic juice and bile.

Secretin has been isolated in crystalline form, suitable for parenteral administration. Its chemical structure is not known, but it is believed to be a polypeptide of low molecular weight (5000). It is freely soluble in water, dialyzable, thermolabile, unstable in alkaline solution, and resistant to pepsin, trypsin, and chymotrypsin.

Administered parenterally, and by rectum, but not orally, it increases the flow of bile from the liver (cholagogue effect) and the flow of pancreatic juice. The acinar cells of the pancreas are stimulated directly (increased O_2 consumption) to produce a secretion of increased volume and bicarbonate content but relatively low enzyme concentration (as compared with vagus stimulation).

The effect of a single injection of secretin lasts about 30 minutes, the hormone disappearing rapidly from the circulation. It is inactivated by an enzyme, "secretinase," present in the blood and also probably in the gastrointestinal tract. Small amounts of secretin are excreted in the urine.

Cholecystokinin

This substance is produced in the same areas as secretin (upper intestine), in response to similar stimuli, especially fat, fatty acids, dilute acids, and peptones. Its chemical structure is not known (dialyzable). It produces contraction and evacuation of the gallbladder when injected, especially intravenously, and also when administered rectally (but not orally). It is inactivated by an enzyme present in the blood.

Pancreozymin

This agent, which stimulates secretion of enzymes by the pancreatic acinar cells (amylase, lipase, trypsin, chymotrypsin), is produced in the same situations as secretin (upper intestine) and in response to the same stimuli. It is soluble in water, slowly dialyzable, thermolabile, sensitive to alkali, and resistant to pepsin, but is apparently attacked by trypsin. It is inactivated by an enzyme present in the blood and tissues.

Enterogastrone

This term may include two or perhaps three separate principles, presumably elaborated in the duodenal mucosa in response to the presence of fat in the duodenum. The active agent (or agents) is soluble in water, dialyzable, thermostable (in acid solution), is sensitive to alkali, and is attacked by pepsin. When injected intravenously or subcutaneously, three types of effect are produced: (1) inhibition of gastric motility (hunger contractions and peristalsis), which is dependent on an intact vagus innervation; (2) inhibition of gastric acidity (parietal cell secretion); (3) protection against development of gastrojejunal ulcer in "Mann-Williamson" dogs.

Gastrin

This agent is presumably elaborated by the pyloric mucosa in response to mechanical distention and the local action of secretagogues in the food. It may also be released by cholinergic impulses (vagus stimulation; acetylcholine). Secreted into the bloodstream, it stimulates secretion of HCl in the fundus of the stomach (parietal cell secretion), and is believed to be important in the gastric phase of gastric secretion.

Other Postulated Factors

Other effects of various extracts of the mucosa of the upper intestine have been described, the physiological significance of which has not been established. The term "enterocrinin" has been applied to a purported principle, elaborated in the intestinal mucosa in response to the presence of foodstuffs, which stimulates secretion by the jejunum and ileum. The term "duocrinin" has been applied to another factor (?), produced in the same manner, which stimulates secretion by the duodenum (Brunner's glands). Other intestinal factors have been reported to stimulate motor activity of the intestine and splenic contraction. Still others have been reported to lower the blood sugar (insulin synergist). The identity of the principles responsible for these effects as hormones has not been established.

BIBLIOGRAPHY

GENERAL

Annual Review of Biochemistry.
Annual Review of Physiology.
Antoniades, H. N. (ed.): Hormones in Human Plasma; Nature and Transport, Boston, Little, Brown & Company, 1960.
Eisenstein, A. B. (ed.): The Biochemical Aspects of Hormone Action, Boston, Little, Brown & Company, 1964.
Gray, C. H., and Bacharach, A. L. (eds.): Hormones in Blood, New York, Academic Press, Inc., 1961.
Karlson, P.: New concepts on the mode of action of hormones, Perspectives in Biol. and Med. *6*:203, 1963.
Litwack, G., and Kritchevsky, D.: Actions of Hormones on Molecular Processes, New York, John Wiley & Sons, Inc., 1964.
Paschkis, K. E., Rakoff, A. E., Cantarow, A., and Rapp, J.: Clinical Endocrinology, ed. 3, New York, Hoeber Medical Division, Harper & Row, Inc., 1966.
Pincus, G., and Thimann, K. V. (eds.): The Hormones, New York, Academic Press, Inc., 1948, 1955.

Recent Progress in Hormone Research (annual volumes), New York, Academic Press, Inc.
Scharrer, E., and Scharrer, B.: Neuroendocrinology, New York, Columbia University Press, 1963.
Vitamins and Hormones (annual volumes), New York, Academic Press, Inc.

GONADS

General references.
Breuer, H.: The metabolism of the natural estrogens, Vitamins and Hormones *20:*285, 1962.
Dorfman, R. I., Forchielli, E., and Gut, M.: Androgen biosynthesis and related studies, Recent Progress in Hormone Research *19:*251, 1963.
Dorfman, R. I., and Shipley, R. A.: The Androgens: Biochemistry, Physiology, and Clinical Significance, New York, John Wiley & Sons, Inc., 1956.
Eik-Nes, K. B.: Effects of gonadotrophins on secretion of steroids by the testis and ovary, Physiol. Rev. *44:*609, 1964.
Heard, R. D., et al.: Biogenesis of the sterols and steroid hormones, Recent Progress in Hormone Research *12:*45, 1956.
Mason, H. L.: The 17-ketosteroids: Their origin, determination and significance, Physiol. Rev. *30:*321, 1950.
Merrill, R. C.: Estriol: A review, Physiol. Rev. *38:*463, 1958.
Talalay, P.: Enzymatic mechanisms in estrogen metabolism, Physiol. Rev. *37:*362, 1957.

ADRENAL

General references.
Ashmore, J., Cahill, G. F., Jr., and Hastings, A. B.: Effect of hormones on alternate pathways of glucose utilization in isolated tissues, Recent Progress in Hormone Research *16:*547, 1960.
Axelrod, J.: Metabolism of epinephrine and other sympathomimetic amines, Physiol. Rev. *39:*751, 1959.
Ball, E. G., and Jungas, R. L.: Some effects of hormones on the metabolism of adipose tissue, Recent Progress in Hormone Research *20:*183, 1964.
deBodo, R. C., Steele, R., Altszuler, N., Dunn, A., and Bishop, J. S.: On the hormonal regulation of carbohydrate metabolism, Recent Progress in Hormone Research *19:*445, 1963.
Dorfman, R. I.: Steroid hormone metabolism, in Pincus, G., and Thimann, K. V. (eds.): The Hormones, Vol. 3, New York, Academic Press, Inc., 1955, p. 589.
Eder, H. A.: The effect of hormones on human serum lipoproteins, Recent Progress in Hormone Research *14:*405, 1958.
Farrell, G.: Regulation of aldosterone secretion, Physiol. Rev. *38:*709, 1958.
Gaddum, J. H., and Holzbauer, M.: Adrenaline and noradrenaline, Vitamins and Hormones *15:*151, 1957.
Gaunt, R., Renzi, A. A., and Chart, J. J.: Aldosterone: A review, J. Clin. Endocrinol. & Metab. *15:*621, 1955.
Haines, W. J.: Studies on the biosynthesis of adrenal cortex hormones, Recent Progress in Hormone Research *7:*255, 1962.
Harrison, T. S.: Adrenal medullary and thyroid relationships, Physiol. Rev. *44:*161, 1964.
Hechter, O., and Pincus, G.: Genesis of the adrenocortical secretion, Physiol. Rev. *34:*459, 1954.
Jeanrenaud, B.: Dynamic aspects of adipose tissue metabolism, Metabolism *10:*535, 1961.
Liddle, G. W., Istand, D., and Meader, C. K.: Normal and abnormal regulation of corticotropin secretion in man, Recent Progress in Hormone Research *18:*125, 1962.
Malmejac, J.: Activity of the adrenal medulla and its regulation, Physiol. Rev. *44:*186, 1964.
Mason, H. L.: The 17-ketosteroids: Their origin, determination and significance, Physiol. Rev. *30:*321, 1950.
Mirsky, I. A.: The etiology of diabetes mellitus in man, Recent Progress in Hormone Research *7:*437, 1952.
Noble, R. I.: Physiology of the adrenal cortex, in Pincus, G., and Thimann, K. V. (eds.): The Hormones, Vol. 3, New York, Academic Press, Inc., 1955.
Olson, R. E.: Nutrition-endocrine interrelationships in the control of fat transport in man, Physiol. Rev. *40:*677, 1960.
Rosen, F., and Nichol, C. A.: Corticosteroids and enzyme activity, Vitamins and Hormones *21:*136, 1963.
Sayers, G.: The adrenal cortex and homeostasis, Physiol. Rev. *30:*241, 1950.
Scow, R. O., and Chernick, S. S.: Hormonal control of protein and fat metabolism in the pancreatectomized rat, Recent Progress in Hormone Research *16:*497, 1960.
Tomkins, G., and Isselbacher, K. J.: Enzymatic mechanisms of hormone metabolism, Recent Progress in Hormone Research *12:*125, 1956.
von Euler, U. S.: Noradrenaline: Chemistry, Physiology, Pharmacology and Clinical Aspects, Springfield, Ill., Charles C Thomas, 1956.
Weber, G., Singhal, R. L., and Srivastava, S. K.: Action of glucocorticoid as inducer and insulin as suppressor of biosynthesis of hepatic gluconeogenic enzymes, Advances in Enzyme Regulation *3:*43, 1965.
Weber, G., Singhal, R. L., Stamm, N. B., Fisher, E. A., and Mentendiek, M. A.: Regulation of enzymes involved in gluconeogenesis, Advances in Enzyme Regulation *2:*1, 1964.
Wertheimer, E., and Shafrir, E.: Influence of hormones on adipose tissue as a center of fat metabolism, Recent Progress in Hormone Research *16:*467, 1960.
Winegrad, A. I.: Endocrine effects on adipose tissue metabolism, Vitamins and Hormones *20:*142, 1962.

Wolstenholme, G. E. W., and Cameron, M. P. (eds.): The Human Adrenal Cortex, Boston, Little, Brown & Company, 1955.
Yates, F. E., and Urquhart, J.: Control of plasma concentrations of adrenocortical hormones, Physiol. Rev. *42:*359, 1962.

THYROID

General references.
Barker, S. B.: Thyroid, Ann. Rev. Physiol. *17:*417, 1954.
Bush, I. E.: Chemical and biological factors in the activity of adrenocortical steroids, Pharmacol. Rev. *14:*317, 1962.
Care, A. D.: Secretion of thyrocalcitonin, Nature *205:*1289, 1965.
Charriper, H. A., and Gordon, A. S.: The biology of antithyroid agents, Vitamins and Hormones *5:*274, 1947.
Gross, J., and Pitt-Rivers, R.: Triiodothyronine in relation to thyroid physiology, Recent Progress in Hormone Research *10:*109, 1954.
Harrison, T. S.: Adrenal medullary and thyroid relationships, Physiol. Rev. *44:*161, 1964.
Hoch, F. L.: Biochemical actions of thyroid hormones, Physiol. Rev. *42:*605, 1962.
Pitt-Rivers, R.: Mode of action of antithyroid compounds, Physiol. Rev. *30:*194, 1950.
Rawson, R. W. (ed.): Modern concepts of thyroid physiology, Ann. New York Acad. Sci. *86:*311, 1960.
Rawson, R. W., Rall, J. E., and Sonenberg, M.: The chemistry and physiology of the thyroid, in Pincus, G., and Thimann, K. V.: The Hormones, Vol. 3, New York, Academic Press, Inc., 1955, p. 433.
Roche, J., and Michel, R.: Nature and metabolism of thyroid hormones, Recent Progress in Hormone Research *12:*1, 1956.
Tapley, D. F., and Hatfield, W. B.: The peripheral action of thyroxine, Vitamins and Hormones *20:*251, 1962.
Tenenhouse, A., Arnaud, C., and Rasmussen, H.: The isolation and characterization of thyrocalcitonin, Proc. Nat. Acad. Sci. *53:*818, 1965.
Werner, S. C. (ed.): The Thyroid, ed. 2, New York, Harper & Row, Inc., 1962.
Wolff, J.: Transport of iodide and other anions in the thyroid gland, Physiol. Rev. *44:*45, 1964.
Wolstenholme, G. E. W., and Millar, E. C. P. (eds.): Regulation and Mode of Action of Thyroid Hormones, Boston, Little, Brown & Company, 1957.

PANCREAS

General references.
Ashmore, J., Cahill, G. F., Jr., and Hastings, A. B.: Effect of hormones on alternate pathways of glucose utilization in isolated tissues, Recent Progress in Hormone Research *16:*547, 1960.
Ball, E. G., and Jungas, R. L.: Some effects of hormones on the metabolism of adipose tissue, Recent Progress in Hormone Research *20:*183, 1964.
Behrens, O. K., and Bromer, W. W.: Glucagon, Vitamins and Hormones *16:*263, 194 1958.
deBodo, R. C.: Insulin hypersensitivity and physiological insulin antagonists, Physiol. Rev. *38:*389, 1958.
deBodo, R. C., Steele, R., Altszuler, N., Dunn, A., and Bishop, J. S.: On the hormonal regulation of carbohydrate metabolism, Recent Progress in Hormone Research *19:*445, 1963.
Eder, H. A.: The effect of hormones on serum lipoproteins, Recent Progress in Hormone Research *14:*405, 1958.
Foa, P. P., Galansino, G., and Pozza, G.: Glucagon, a second pancreatic hormone, Recent Progress in Hormone Research *13:*473, 1957.
Fritz, I. B.: Factors influencing the rate of long-chain fatty acid oxidation and synthesis in mammalian systems, Physiol. Rev. *41:*52, 1961.
Goldner, M. G. (ed.): Chlorpropamide and diabetes mellitus, Ann. New York Acad. Sci. *74:*407, 1959.
Jeanrenaud, B.: Dynamic aspects of adipose tissue metabolism, Metabolism *10:*535, 1961.
Krahl, M. E. (ed.): The Action of Insulin on Cells, New York, Academic Press, Inc., 1961.
Levine, R. (ed.): Symposium on diabetes, Am. J. Med. *31:*837, 1961.
Levine, R., and Goldstein, M. S.: On the mechanism of action of insulin, Recent Progress in Hormone Research *11:*343, 1955.
Lukens, F. D. W.: Insulin and glucagon, Ann. Rev. Physiol. *21:*445, 1959.
Manchester, K. L., and Young, F. G.: Insulin and protein metabolism, Vitamins and Hormones *19:*95, 1961.
Mirsky, I. A.: Insulinase, insulin-inhibitors, and diabetes mellitus, Recent Progress in Hormone Research *13:*429, 1957.
Olson, R. E.: Nutrition-endocrine interrelationships in the control of fat transport in man, Physiol. Rev. *40:*677, 1960.
Scow, R. O., and Chernick, S. S.: Hormonal control of protein and fat metabolism in the pancreatectomized rat, Recent Progress in Hormone Research *16:*497, 1960.
Vallance-Owen, J., and Wright, P. H.: Assay of insulin in blood, Physiol. Rev. *40:*219, 1960.
Weber, G., Singhal, R. L., and Srivastava, S. K.: Action of glucocorticoid as inducer and insulin as suppressor of biosynthesis of hepatic gluconeogenic enzymes, Advances in Enzyme Regulation *3:*43, 1965.
Winegrad, A. I.: Endocrine effects on adipose tissue metabolism, Vitamins and Hormones *20:*142, 1962.

PARATHYROID GLANDS

General references.
Albright, F., and Reifenstein, E. C., Jr.: Parathyroid Glands and Metabolic Bone Disease, Baltimore, Williams & Wilkins Company, 1948.
Copp, D. H.: Parathyroids, calcitonin, and control of plasma calcium, Recent Progress in Hormone Research *20:*59, 1964.
Fourman, P.: Calcium Metabolism and the Bone, Springfield, Ill., Charles C Thomas, 1960.
Greep, R. O., and Talmage, R. V. (eds.): The Parathyroids, Springfield, Ill., Charles C Thomas, 1961.
McLean, F. C.: The parathyroid hormone and bone, Clinical Orthopaedics *9:*46, 1957.
McLean, F. C., and Budy, A. M.: Chemistry and physiology of the parathyroid hormone, Vitamins and Hormones *19:*165, 1961.
Rasmussen, H.: Parathyroid hormone, nature and mechanism of action, Am. J. Med. *30:*112, 1961.
Rasmussen, H., and Craig, L. C.: The parathyroid polypeptides, Recent Progress in Hormone Research *18:*269, 1962.

HYPOPHYSIS

General references.
Ashmore, J., Cahill, G. F., Jr., and Hastings, A. B.: Effect of hormones on alternate pathways of glucose utilization in isolated tissues, Recent Progress in Hormone Research *16:*547, 1960.
Ball, E. G., and Jungas, R. L.: Some effects of hormones on the metabolism of adipose tissue, Recent Progress in Hormone Research *20:*183, 1964.
Cowie, A. T., and Folley, S. J.: Physiology of the gonadotropins and the lactogenic hormone, in Pincus, G., and Thimann, K. V. (eds.): The Hormones, Vol. 3, New York, Academic Press, Inc., 1955, p. 309.
deBodo, R. C., and Altszuler, N.: The metabolic effects of growth hormone and their physiological significance, Vitamins and Hormones *15:*206, 1957.
deBodo, R. C., Steele, R., Altszuler, N., Dunn, A., and Bishop, J. S.: On the hormonal regulation of carbohydrate metabolism, Recent Progress in Hormone Research *19:*445, 1963.
Eder, H. A.: The effect of hormones on human serum lipoproteins, Recent Progress in Hormone Research *14:*405, 1958.
Eik-Nes, K. B.: Effects of gonadotrophins on secretion of steroids by the testis and ovary, Physiol. Rev. *44:*609, 1964.
Engel, F. L.: Extra-adrenal actions of adrenocorticotropin, Vitamins and Hormones *19:*189, 1961.
Everett, J. W.: Central control of reproductive functions of the adenohypophysis, Physiol. Rev. *44:*373, 1964.
Fields, W. S., Guillemin, R., and Carton, C. A. (eds.): Hypothalamic-Hypophyseal Interrelationships, Springfield, Ill., Charles C Thomas, 1956.
Frieden, E. H., and Hisaw, F. L.: The biochemistry of relaxin, Recent Progress in Hormone Research *8:*333, 1953.
Friesen, H., and Astwood, E. B.: Hormones of the anterior pituitary body, New England J. Med. *272:*1216, 1272, 1328, 1965.
Hechter, O.: Concerning possible mechanisms of hormone action, Vitamins and Hormones *13:*293, 1955.
Heller, H. (ed.): The Neurohypophysis, London, Butterworths Scientific Publications, 1957.
Hofmann, K.: Chemistry and function of polypeptide hormones, Ann. Rev. Biochem. *31:*213, 1962.
Jeanrenaud, B.: Dynamic aspects of adipose tissue metabolism, Metabolism *10:*535, 1961.
Lerner, A. B., and Lee, T. H.: The melanocyte-stimulating hormones, Vitamins and Hormones *20:*337, 1962.
Li, C. H.: The chemistry of gonadotropic hormones, Vitamins and Hormones *7:*224, 1949.
Li, C. H.: Synthesis and biological properties of ACTH peptides, Recent Progress in Hormone Research *18:*1, 1962.
McKenzie, J. M.: Assay of thyrotropin in man, Physiol. Rev. *40:*398, 1960.
Munson, P. L., and Briggs, F. N.: The mechanism of stimulation of ACTH secretion, Recent Progress in Hormone Research *11:*83, 1955.
Olson, R. E.: Nutrition-endocrine interrelationships in the control of fat transport in man, Physiol. Rev. *40:*677, 1960.
Sawyer, W. H.: Neurohypophyseal hormones, Pharmacol. Rev. *13:*225, 1961.
Scow, R. O., and Chernick, S. S.: Hormonal control of protein and fat metabolism in the pancreatectomized rat, Recent Progress in Hormone Research *16:*497, 1960.
Smith, R. W., Jr., Gaebler, O. H., and Long, C. N. H. (eds.): The Hypophyseal Growth Hormone, Nature and Actions, New York, Blakiston Division, McGraw-Hill Book Company, 1955.
Sonenberg, M.: Chemistry and physiology of the thyroid-stimulating hormone, Vitamins and Gormones Hormones *16:*206, 1958.
Thorn, N. A.: Mammalian antidiuretic hormone, Physiol. Rev. *38:*169, 1958.
van Dyke, H. B., Adamsons, K., and Engel, S. L.: Aspects of the biochemistry and physiology of the neurohypophyseal hormones, Recent Progress in Hormone Research *11:*1, 1955.
Velardo, J. T. (ed.): Endocrinology of Reproduction, New York, Oxford University Press, 1958.

Wertheimer, E., and Shafrir, E.: Influence of hormones on adipose tissue as a center of fat metabolism, Recent Progress in Hormone Research, *16:*467, 1960.
Winegrad, A. I.: Endocrine effects on adipose tissue metabolism, Vitamins and Hormones *20:*142, 1962.
Yates, F. E., and Urquhart, J.: Control of plasma levels of adrenocortical hormones, Physiol. Rev. *42:*359, 1962.

GASTROINTESTINAL HORMONES

General references.
Grossman, M. I.: Gastrointestinal hormones, Physiol. Rev. *30:*33, 1950.

NEUROHORMONES

General References.
Elliott, K. A. C., and Jasper, H. H.: Gamma-aminobutyric acid, Physiol. Rev. *39:*383, 1959.
Gerard, R. W.: The actylcholine system in neural function, Recent Progress in Hormone Research *5:*37, 1950.
Nachmansohn, D.: Chemical mechanisms of nerve activity, in Barron, E. S. G. (ed.): Modern Trends in Physiology and Biochemistry, New York, Academic Press, Inc., 1952, p. 230.
Sawyer, W. H.: Neurohypophyseal hormones, Pharmacol. Rev. *13:*225, 1961.
Symposium on neuropharmacology, Federation Proc. *17:*1004, 1958.
Tainter, M. L., and Luduena, F. P.: Sympathetic hormonal transmission, Recent Progress in Hormone Research *5:*3, 1950.
van Dyke, H. B., Adamsons, K., and Engel, S. L.: Aspects of the biochemistry and physiology of the neurohypophyseal hormones, Recent Progress in Hormone Research *11:*1, 1955.
Whitelock, O. v St. (ed.): Amine oxidase inhibitors, Ann. New York Acad. Sci. *80:*551, 1959.

ERYTHROPOIETIN

Gordon, A. S., and Root, W. S. (eds.): Hematopoietic mechanisms, Ann. New York Acad. Sci. *77:*407, 1959.
Stohlman, F., Jr.: Erythropoiesis, New England J. Med. *267:*342, 392, 1962.

CHAPTER 27

METABOLIC REGULATORY MECHANISMS

MANY references have been made previously to various mechanisms for the control of metabolism, including such regulatory influences as genes, nervous system, endocrine glands, induction-repression, and end-product inhibition. These references have been brief and highly specific. It seems appropriate at this point to consider regulatory mechanisms in their more general aspects, as examples of machinery developed by the organism for biochemical homeostasis.

Viewed very broadly, the regulation of metabolism may be considered to occur on three levels of biological organization, at least with regard to man and other multicellular organisms. The most general level is that of the species, an intermediate level is that of the individual whole organism, while the most circumscribed level is that of the cell. Metabolic regulatory mechanisms at these levels will be considered in sequence in the following discussions.

REGULATION AT THE LEVEL OF THE SPECIES

One does not ordinarily think of regulation of metabolism as occurring at the level of the species. However, the metabolic machinery available to the organism derives ultimately from the genotypes which have survived during the evolution of the species. These surviving genotypes, in turn, are the result of mutation and selection.

It is probable that most mutations occurring at the present time would be deleterious. This is because, in the course of evolution, the species has already adjusted its genetic heritage optimally to the environment. In the distant past, those mutations which led to superiority in the production of progeny (in relation to the environment) were retained, whereas those which led to inferior fitness in this regard were discarded by the decreased probability of reproduction of their bearers.

In the course of evolution, man has both gained and lost genetic material. From the structural similarities among myoglobin and the various normal hemoglobins (p. 126), it has been concluded that an original, primeval hemoprotein (or, more strictly, the genetic apparatus determining its structure) has evolved through structural changes (i.e., alterations in the structure of DNA) to the modern molecule of myoglobin and the peptide chains of the hemoglobins. In addition, since each hemoglobin molecule consists of two types of chains (one having evolved from the other, or both from a common ancestor), it has been concluded that duplication and separation of genes has occurred, an example of augmentation of the genetic complement of the species. In contrast to most mammals, man and his fellow primates have lost the genes for the metabolism of uric acid and for the synthesis of ascorbic acid. As a general rule (to which there are exceptions, as has been seen), the more highly differentiated and specialized forms of life have evolved with the loss of genetic material, and hence of metabolic pathways.

It should be noted that, although deleterious genetic information may be expected to be eliminated from the species, some apparently useless but harmless genes may continue to be transmitted and even to form potentially functional but in reality functionless products, corresponding to the "vestigial" organic structures found in the anatomy of man. Two possible examples are hepatic glucose dehydrogenase, which may be a vestige of a primitive non-phosphorylative pathway of glucose metabolism, and an hepatic acetylase which is of such little use in man that it is deficient in half the North American population. Despite the energy wasted by the organism in manufacturing such products, the extent of the waste apparently is not great enough to be a factor in natural selection, hence one cannot generalize that disuse leads to disappearance.

REGULATION AT THE LEVEL OF THE ORGANISM: INTERCELLULAR MECHANISMS

In contrast to the preceding area of regulation, wherein alterations in metabolic patterns may require hundreds of millions of years, regulatory systems operating at the organismic level accomplish their tasks in relatively brief periods of time, although these may vary from fractions of a second to days or weeks.

Although there are examples of control (or, at least, of influence) of one cell upon another by transfer of substrates, the majority of intercellular regulatory mechanisms are neural, endocrine, or neuroendocrine in nature. Whether any are purely neural is conjectural, and perhaps a matter of definition, since detailed investigation of cases of neural influence upon metabolic processes has usually brought to light a chemical mediator which is the actual effector (i.e., a "neurohormone").

Prime examples of neuroendocrine regulation are the emergency stress reactions influencing the metabolism of carbohydrate (p. 434) and lipid (p. 499) via the pituitary-adrenal axis (p. 741). Brief descriptions of purely endocrine control have been given in connection with the metabolism of carbohydrate (p. 436), lipid (p. 506), and protein (p. 563); more detailed information is presented in the chapter on hormones (Chapter 26, p. 677).

Within the area of hormone metabolism itself, there may be found a number of examples of a widely used regulatory mechanism, "negative feedback," in which a biological process generates a counteracting process which contains the first process within prescribed limits. Thus, the adenohypophysis produces several tropic hormones which stimulate target tissues to secrete their respective hormones; these, in turn, suppress the production or release of specific tropic hormones by the hypophysis (p. 679). Regulation of the glucose level in the blood is an example of negative feedback involving metabolite and hormone as the active participants (p. 433).

Homeostatic regulation of acid-base balance (p. 316) and water balance (p. 309) makes use of the same general type of mechanism.

Although the nature of the active agents is not known, the differentiation of tissues during embryonic development is controlled (or at least modified) by intercellular influences from adjacent tissues.

INTRACELLULAR MECHANISMS

The intercellular mechanisms are concerned with regulation of cell by cell in a multicellular organism, for the purpose of coordinating the activities of many potentially independent units into a biologically successful entity, the whole organism. They represent a relatively late development in evolution, and are superimposed upon (and, in some cases, function by means of) intracellular regulatory systems developed during the evolution of the unicellular organism.

Genetic Potential of the Individual Cell: Structural Genes

The metabolic pattern of each cell is determined ultimately by its genetic constitution, which specifies what it can and cannot do. On the other hand, it is apparent that a given cell does not do all that it can from a genetic standpoint, since virtually every cell in a multicellular organism is genetically identical, yet each exhibits a specific metabolic pattern appropriate to the tissue of which it forms a part. Moreover, the metabolic pattern changes, despite genetic constancy, in response to intracellular and even extracellular stimuli. It is obvious from these observations that, whereas the genetic potential of the cell is fixed (genotype), the expression of this potential (phenotype) is subject to extragenetic influences.

As discussed previously in connection with the genetic code (p. 556), the structures of the proteins (including enzymes) of the cell are determined by sequences of nucleotides in the nuclear DNA, a trinucleotide unit being the codeword (codon) for each amino acid residue in the protein. When it was found, largely on the basis of experiments with microorganisms, that mutation of individual genes caused specific losses of individual enzymes, the "one gene-one enzyme" or "one gene-one protein" hypothesis was advanced. Although correct in approach, this hypothesis has had to be refined, as each of its terms has been found imprecise.

In the first place, many enzymes and other proteins have been found to consist of two or more different polypeptide chains, each type of chain being under independent genetic control (true also of the sub-units comprising isoenzymes, p. 216). Secondly, the characteristics of the "gene" vary with the different types of experiments used to study it. Operational definitions of the hereditary unit have been proposed, viz., the smallest unit of mutation ("muton"), recombination ("recon"), and function ("cistron"). This last unit (with which we shall be concerned primarily) refers to the minimal segment of DNA which must be present in intact state ("wild type") on one of the two homologous chromosomes ("cis") of a diploid cell in order to specify the structure of a given polypeptide chain. Actually, the cistron corresponds very closely to the biochemist's working definition of the gene, and there is a growing tendency in current biochemical genetics to use the term "gene" with the properties of the cistron in mind. Accordingly, the fundamental hypothesis of biochemical genetics may be restated as, "one gene (cistron)-one polypeptide."

One final qualification must be mentioned. Genes of the type just discussed, which specify the amino acid sequence of polypeptides, appear to be under the control of other genes which have regulatory, not structural, functions. Consequently, genes of the former type have been termed "structural."

Expression of the Genetic Potential: Control Genes

Although there would seem to be no a priori reason why the functional expression of structural genes could not be influenced directly by extra-genetic factors, studies on the genetics of certain plants and, more recently, bacteria have provided evidence that control genes act as intermediaries. Whether this is true also in the animal cell is not known at this time, although there are suggestions of similarity. In the subsequent discussions, the general characteristics of the bacterial system (model of Jacob and Monod) will provide the basic concepts, which will be adapted, on paper, to the diploid cell, as illustrated in Figure 27–1.

It will be noted that each structural gene (cistron) is preceded by an operator gene which has the ability to "switch on" the function of the former. In bacteria, several structural genes specifying the synthesis of chemically or metabolically related polypeptides (i.e., the constituent units of a multi-chained protein, or the enzymes in a metabolic sequence) often are contiguous and controlled by the same operator. (The resulting mRNA may carry structural information for several peptides. It is said to be polycistronic or polygenic.) A similar situation may obtain in the animal cell. The functional biological unit of operator + structural gene(s) is called an "operon." An operator gene functions only within its own chromosome.

Operator genes are controlled, in turn, by regulator genes, which need not be on an adjacent segment of the chromosome, and indeed, need not be on the same chromosome. Regulator genes function indirectly, by producing a "repressor" substance. It is not known at this time whether the repressor is a protein, nucleic acid, or nucleoprotein. In any case, it exerts a repressive influence on the operator genes, so that gene regulation is of an essentially negative nature, resembling an electrical switching system of the "normally off" type.

An important characteristic of the repressor is that it can leave the chromosome. Whether it actually enters the cytoplasm of nucleated cells is uncertain; the essential fact

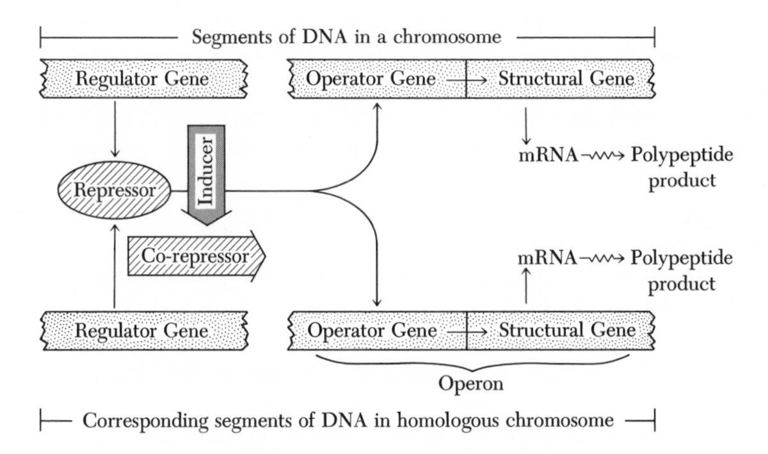

Figure 27–1. Possible arrangement of structural and control genes in a diploid cell.

is that it can exist outside the chromosome. Consequently, a repressor produced by one chromosome can influence another. In addition, its extra-chromosomal existence renders it amenable to influences existing in or coming from the cytoplasm. According to some, native repressors are inactive. They are made functional as repressors by interaction with "co-repressors" from the cytoplasm, a process counteracted by cytoplasmic "inducers" (i.e., "de-repressors").

The preceding hypotheses were constructed in order to explain the genetics of "adaptive" enzymes. In both bacteria and animals, the presence of a substrate often elicits increased synthesis of an enzyme attacking that substrate. In this case the substrate, or compounds structurally similar to it, may act as inducers by reaction with the repressor so as to lessen its inhibitory influence on the operator genes. Conversely, it is often observed that the presence of ample quantities of the end-product of a metabolic sequence results in decreased synthesis of an enzyme functioning early in the sequence. Here, the end-product, acting as co-repressor, reacts with the repressor to convert it to its fully inhibitory form. It should be noted that, in addition to substrates, end-products, and compounds related to these structurally, certain hormones are believed to induce and repress the formation of enzymes in a similar manner. Finally, a word of caution is in order: the preceding mechanisms, even if firmly established in animal cells in the future, need not be exclusive. Some "inducers" in animal systems have been shown to function at the ribosomal, not the chromosomal, level (p. 770).

Not all enzymes (or all other proteins, for that matter) have been demonstrated to be adaptive. Such non-inducible or non-repressible types are said to be "constitutive." Whether this means that the structural genes of the latter type have no functional linkage with operators and regulators, or that the differentiation of the cell results in permanently "fixing" the control systems in a certain pattern for each characteristic type of cell, is debatable and perhaps academic at this point.

Gene Mutations and their Biochemical Sequelae

Structural gene mutations. A diploid organism homozygous for a given structural gene bears one such gene on each homologous chromosome (excluding from consideration the sex chromosomes), i.e., a "double dose" of the characteristic. In the absence of repressive phenomena, a double dose of mRNA will be formed and an equivalent quantity of the final enzyme or other protein will be synthesized.

A heterozygous mutant in such a gene (Fig. 27–2) will form one dose of normal product, and from zero to one dose of abnormal (mutant) product, the amount of the latter depending upon the type of mutation. Mutation caused by insertion or deletion of nucleotides in the DNA may result in formation of so abnormal an mRNA that the specified polypeptide chain cannot be made at the ribosomal site. The same may be true also of substitution of nucleotides, if the replacement causes analogous replacement of an amino acid in a position along the polypeptide chain which is critical for the structural stability of the finished protein. Less critical substitution may permit a certain amount of synthesis (even up to one full dose), although the product will be abnormal in primary structure.

The biological activity of structurally abnormal products is quite variable, and is not necessarily related to the quantity produced. For example, a mutant enzyme bearing an abnormal amino acid residue in or near its active site may be completely inactive, yet may be produced in full dose.

From the preceding considerations, an organism heterozygous in a structural gene might be expected to form from 50 to 100 per cent of the normal *quantity* of total product

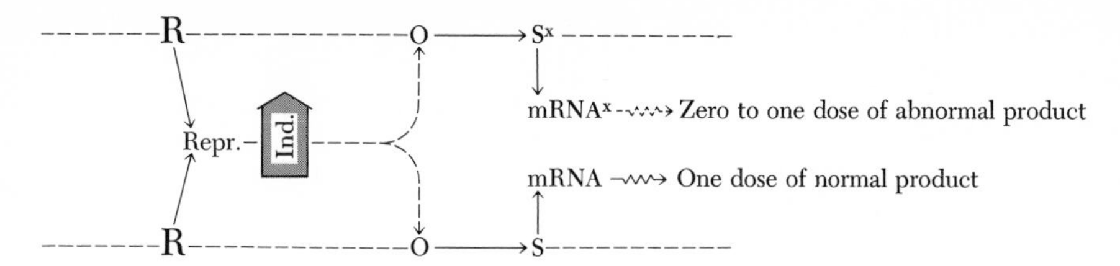

Figure 27-2. Heterozygous state of mutant in structural gene, system activated by induction. *Ind.*, Inducer; *mRNA*, normal messenger RNA; *mRNA*^{x}, "mutant" messenger RNA; *O*, operator gene; *R*, regulator gene; *Repr.*, repressor; *S*, normal structural gene; S^x, mutant structural gene.

(normal plus abnormal) possessing from 50 to 100 per cent of the normal total *activity*. The synthesis of the product should exhibit normal responses to induction and repression.

Extending these considerations to an organism homozygous in a mutant structural gene, one might anticipate synthesis of 0 to 100 per cent of the normal quantity of product (all abnormal in structure) possessing 0 to 100 per cent of the normal activity. Insofar as any synthesis occurs, it should be normally inducible and repressible. If the product is sufficiently abnormal to be inactive biologically, its detection may be difficult. Resort is usually had to immunochemical techniques, which permit detection of substances reacting with antisera to the normal product ("cross-reacting material," CRM).

The preceding several calculations of quantity of product were based on the assumption that the structural gene in question is autosomal; calculations of gene dosage are more complex in the case of genes located on the sex chromosomes. A gene located on the X chromosome, although it would appear to be present in double dose in human females (XX) as against males (XY), in fact forms about the same normal amount of product in both sexes. The hypothesis of gene dosage compensation states that one of the two X chromosomes in the female is inactivated in a random fashion among the cell population. As a consequence, females heterozygous for a mutant structural gene on the X chromosome may exhibit a wide range of quantity (or activity) of product, but averaging 50 per cent of normal. This has been observed in deficiency of erythrocyte glucose-6-phosphate dehydrogenase.

Originally, all inborn errors of metabolism in man were regarded as due to mutation of structural genes. With the discovery of control genes, the situation has become more complicated. Complete absence of product from one or both chromosomes, as will be noted in the next section, can result from mutation of a control gene as well as a structural gene. The most compelling evidence of a structural gene mutation is afforded by those instances in which at least some synthesis of the mutant product occurs; only in the case of a structural gene mutation will this product have an abnormal structure. If the product has very specific biological functions or certain characteristic physical properties, these may well be altered in the mutant.

The best-known examples of mutation of structural genes are the abnormal hemoglobins, which have been discussed in detail elsewhere (p. 124). It is interesting that, in heterozygotes for an abnormal hemoglobin, the abnormal protein frequently is synthesized more slowly than the normal, so that it makes up less than 50 per cent of the total. It is also of interest that the mutant hemoglobins, most of which differ structurally from the normal in only a single amino acid residue in a pair of identical peptide chains, exhibit a range of biological and physicochemical properties varying from normal to grossly abnormal.

In contrast to the hemoglobins, it is difficult to obtain sufficient quantities of a sus-

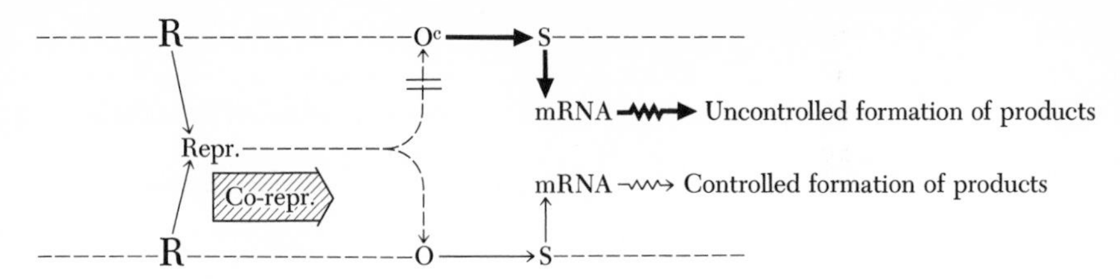

Figure 27-3. Heterozygous state of constitutive operator mutation in repressible system. *Co-repr.*, Co-repressor; O^c, mutant operator gene; other symbols as in Figure 27-2.

pected mutant enzyme to perform analyses of amino acid sequence or "fingerprinting" (p. 126). Hence, the identification of probable structural mutations currently rests largely on the detection of altered physicochemical properties or specific enzyme activity. One example is an atypical serum pseudocholinesterase, which hydrolyzes the muscle-relaxing drug, succinylcholine, so much more slowly than the normal enzyme that affected individuals may die of respiratory arrest if so treated. Other examples are two variants of erythrocyte glucose-6-phosphate dehydrogenase with properties different from the normal.

Control gene mutations: (a) operators. In all cases of mutation of control genes, the product, insofar as it is formed at all, should possess normal structure and normal specific biological activity. Variations from the normal situation should be exclusively quantitative.

Two types of operator mutation have been described in bacteria. In the constitutive operator mutation (O^c), the operator becomes insensitive to the repressor substance. If such a mutation occurs in the diploid animal cell (Fig. 27-3), the organism heterozygous for such a mutation should produce the normal quantity of product (one dose) from the normal chromosome, and this should be subject to the normal effects of induction and repression. The homologous chromosome should produce one dose of product independently of these regulatory influences. Homozygotes would be expected to exhibit maximum formation of product, uninfluenced by induction or repression. Since, even in the heterozygote, abnormally large quantities of product would be formed, O^c mutations probably would appear to be inherited as dominants. The hepatic porphyrias may be examples of this defect (p. 613).

In the operator negative mutation (O^o), the operator, and hence the entire operon, becomes non-functional, so that no transcription of mRNA occurs. Applying this condition to the diploid cell (Fig. 27-4), the heterozygote should be able to form 50 per cent of the normal total amount of product, and this quantity should be normally inducible or repressible. The homozygote should form no product whatsoever. In the case of enzymes, at least, even 50 per cent of the normal quantity usually more than satisfies biological needs, hence O^o mutations will appear to be inherited as recessives.

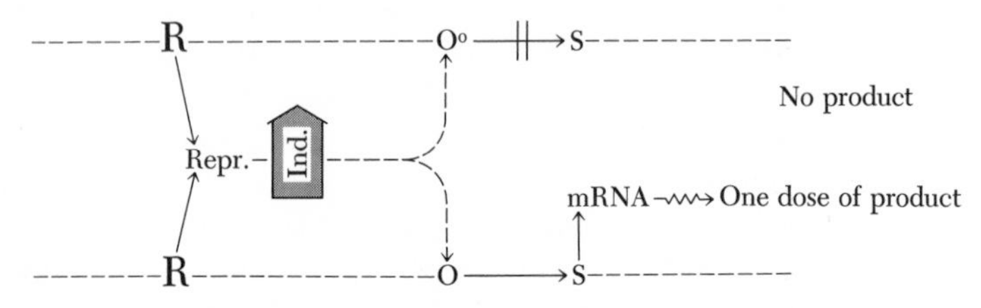

Figure 27-4. Heterozygous state of operator-negative mutation in inducible system. O^o, Mutant operator gene; other symbols as in Figure 27-2.

It has been suggested that the "high fetal" hemoglobin condition represents an operator mutation (presumably of the O^o type). The usual "switch" from production of γ to β and δ chains (p. 612) fails to occur on one (heterozygote) or both (homozygote) chromosomes, so that the hemoglobins present in the adult are either half adult and half fetal (in the heterozygote) or entirely fetal (in the homozygote). As support for the contention that the genes for β and δ chains are closely linked (and indeed, probably belong to the same operon), it may be noted that the "high fetal" homozygote produces no hemoglobin A_2.

Whether the thalassemias (p. 612) represent operator gene mutations is controversial. Some believe that their characteristics are more consistent with mutation of a structural gene, the mutation being so drastic that little or no product is formed. For example, many cases of the β-chain type of thalassemia exhibit no deficiency of hemoglobin A_2, which, in fact, may be increased in concentration together with hemoglobin F. The formation of A_2 reflects synthesis of δ chains in the absence of β, which would be difficult to explain on an operator basis (if these two genes are on the same operon, as seems likely).

Recessive genetic loss of an enzyme, such as occurs in many human inborn errors of metabolism, may be due to O^o mutation, although, as noted previously, the same 50 per cent loss of activity in the heterozygote and 100 per cent loss in the homozygote can occur in certain types of structural gene mutation. Definitive differentiation of the latter from the former requires isolation of the abnormal product in the latter case and proof of its structural abnormality. If no abnormal product is formed, the situation remains ambiguous. Two genetic variants of erythrocyte glucose-6-phosphate dehydrogenase appear to have normal properties, but are produced in subnormal amounts; they may represent operator mutations. In acatalasemia, the mutant gene forms no cross-reacting material, an example of the ambiguous case.

Control gene mutations: (b) regulators. In bacteria, mutation of a regulator gene to a non-functional form ("constitutive regulator mutation," R^-) leads to loss of inductive and repressor functions. Inducible systems become fully active in the absence of inducers, and repressible systems become constitutive. In a diploid cell (Fig. 27–5), since the repressor substance can affect operators on both homologous chromosomes, a heterozygous mutant of this type will form normally induced and repressed product, i.e., the defect will be a recessive type, exhibiting liberation of synthesis from control of inducers and corepressors only in the homozygous state. It has been suggested that erythropoietic porphyria (p. 613) represents a defect of this type.

Another regulator mutation in bacteria gives rise to a repressor substance which is completely insensitive to inducers ("super-repressed regulator mutation," R^s). Since both homologous operators in the diploid are repressed, even in the heterozygote (Fig. 27–6), this defect manifests itself as a dominant loss of function. The relatively few known

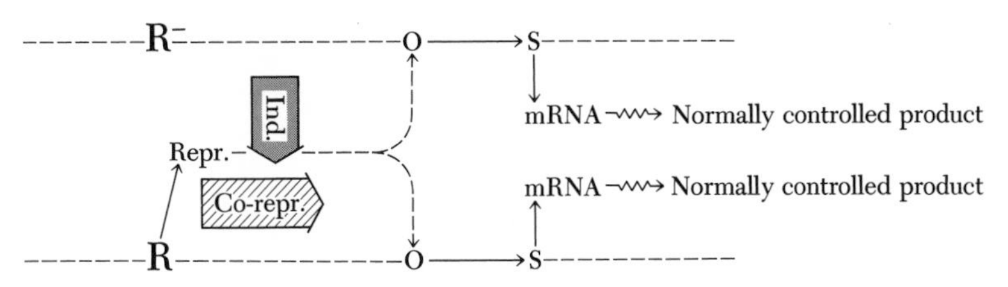

Figure 27-5. Heterozygous state of constitutive regulator mutation. R^-, Mutant regulator gene; other symbols as in Figure 27–2.

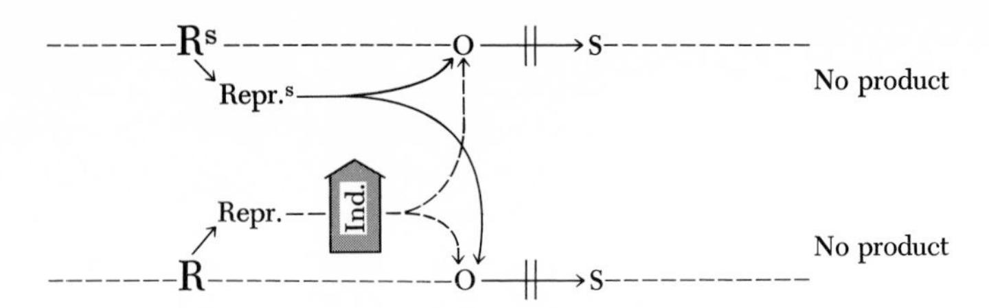

Figure 27-6. Heterozygous state of super-repressed regulator mutation. R^s, Mutant regulator gene; *Repr.*^{s}, mutant repressor; other symbols as in Figure 27-2.

autosomal dominant inborn errors of metabolism may represent super-repressed mutations, viz., hereditary spherocytosis, a mild variety of familial non-hemolytic jaundice, and renal glycosuria.

Hereditary loss of two enzymes simultaneously may be due to mutation of operators or regulators. In oroticaciduria (p. 521), both orotidylate pyrophosphorylase and decarboxylase are deficient. An operator defect seems to be excluded, since the heterozygote has considerably less than 50 per cent of the normal activity. The metabolic error has been attributed to a regulator defect, somewhat similar to the super-repressive type, but with only a somewhat enhanced affinity of repressor for operators. The result in this case appears as an autosomal recessive, since, evidently, more than enough enzyme is produced in the heterozygote to carry on normal metabolism. Certain reported multiple deficiencies in the glycogenoses (p. 401) have not been sufficiently substantiated or characterized to permit even hypothetical classification.

Inborn errors of metabolism in man. Table 27-1 lists the major types of hereditary metabolic errors. No attempt is made to classify these anomalies as mutants of structural or control genes, since this would be premature in most cases. Specific characteristics of many of these disorders have been presented in the various discussions of intermediary metabolism. This section will be confined to a survey of the occurrence and general properties of these abnormalities.

Inborn errors of metabolism were originally believed to involve the enzymes catalyzing the reactions of intermediary metabolism, although cystinuria, a member of the original group of defects compiled by Garrod in 1909, eventually turned out to be a renal tubular malfunction. In any case, the similarity in the genetics and other characteristics of cellular transport mechanisms to those of enzymes certainly supports the inclusion of inherited anomalies of the former with those of the latter. In like manner, the more recently discovered "molecular diseases" (e.g., abnormal hemoglobins) are now usually considered together with these other abnormalities. Broadly speaking, of course, all structural gene mutations are "molecular diseases," even if they involve the structure of enzymes rather than proteins of the blood.

The incidence of inborn errors of metabolism varies over a wide range. Certain "classic" inborn errors, such as alcaptonuria, pentosuria, and phenylketonuria, are quite rare, occurring in frequencies of only 1 to 4 per 100,000 population in the United States and Britain. The atypical pseudocholinesterase occurs with a frequency of 35 per 100,000 in Canada. Frequencies of an inborn error may vary in different populations; albinism has an incidence of 13 per 100,000 in Northern Ireland, but 470 per 100,000 among the San Blas Indians of Panama.

In contrast to the preceding, certain inborn errors have a high incidence. Predisposition toward diabetes mellitus has an incidence of 5 per cent. The liver acetylase which

TABLE 27-1. INBORN ERRORS OF METABOLISM

Circulating Proteins
- Abnormal hemoglobins
- Thalassemia
- Methemoglobin reductase deficiency
- Spherocytosis (erythrocyte glycolysis deficiency)
- Glucose-6-phosphate dehydrogenase deficiency
- Bisalbuminemia
- Analbuminemia
- Agammaglobulinemia
- Ceruloplasmin deficiency
- Clotting factor deficiencies
- Hypophosphatasia
- Pseudocholinesterase deficiency

Carbohydrate Metabolism
- Diabetes mellitus
- Pentosuria
- Fructosuria
- Fructose intolerance
- Glycogen storage defects
- Galactosemia
- Intestinal disaccharidase deficiencies
- Gargoylism (mucopolysaccharidosis)

Lipid and Steroid Metabolism
- Hyperlipemia, essential
- Hypercholesterolemia, essential
- Lipidoses
- Adrenogenital syndrome(s)

Amino Acid Metabolism
- Maple syrup urine disease
- Phenylketonuria
- Tyrosinosis
- Alcaptonuria
- Albinism
- Cretinism, familial
- Hyperoxaluria
- Citrullinuria
- Hyperammonemia
- Cystinosis
- Glycinemia
- Hydroxyprolinemia
- Prolinemia
- Homocystinuria
- Argininosuccinicaciduria
- Cystathioninuria
- Histidinemia

Purine and Pyrimidine Metabolism
- Gout
- Xanthinuria
- Oroticaciduria
- β-Aminoisobutyricaciduria

Porphyrin and Bile Pigment Metabolism
- Porphyrias
- Bilirubin UDP-glucuronyl transferase deficiency (familial non-hemolytic jaundice)

Renal Tubular Defects
- Diabetes insipidus, nephrogenic
- Renal glycosuria
- Resistant rickets
- Cystinuria
- Fanconi syndrome
- Hartnup disease
- Glycinuria

inactivates the tuberculostatic drug, isoniazid, is defective in half the population of North America. As compared with other mammals, all primates suffer from genetic lack of uricase and (together with the guinea pig) L-gulonolactone dehydrogenase, an enzyme necessary for synthesis of ascorbic acid.

Various consequences may follow from an inborn error of metabolism. In some cases, there may be no ill effects at all (e.g., pentosuria). There may be lack of formation of an important product (melanin in albinism, thyroid hormones in certain forms of cretinism). Alternately, the product may be formed, but be so abnormal in structure that it performs its biological function poorly, if at all (certain abnormal hemoglobins). In certain cases, blockage of a metabolic pathway causes accumulation of a toxic metabolite (galactose-1-phosphate in galactosemia).

Curiously, possession of an inborn error sometimes has survival value. Heterozygosity in the sickle cell hemoglobin gene apparently confers resistance against the malarial parasite, thus maintaining this gene in the population along the Mediterranean and African "malarial belt," although homozygosity proves fatal relatively early in life.

Although it is impossible to alter the genotype of affected individuals or to supply missing enzymes other than the digestive type, certain forms of therapy are possible. Dietary restriction of phenylalanine (phenylketonuria) and galactose (galactosemia) is effective, although there are complications in the former case due to the essentiality of phenylalanine. A missing essential product sometimes can be supplied, e.g., thyroid preparations in familial cretinism. When an environmental factor is largely responsible for the deleterious effects of the inborn error, treatment involves removal or avoidance of this factor, e.g., sunlight in the cutaneous porphyrias, various antimalarial drugs and fava beans in deficiency of erythrocyte glucose-6-phosphate dehydrogenase, succinylcholine in deficiency of plasma pseudocholinesterase. Harmful accumulations of metabolic products sometimes can be removed from the body (uric acid deposits in gout, by uricosuric drugs).

Genetic counselling of the parents of a child with an inborn error of metabolism frequently requires the study of siblings, parents, and relatives of the parents, with the object of ascertaining the mode of inheritance. This study may require the detection of heterozygotes, sometimes a difficult task. As noted previously, most enzymes are synthesized in such excess that loss of half the normal amount has no apparent effect on metabolism. In a few favorable cases, actual assay of the enzyme activity is possible in the peripheral blood or red cells. In other cases, "loading" tests (similar to the glucose tolerance test) serve to detect the heterozygote, who, although his subnormal enzyme activity suffices for normal metabolism, cannot cope with a large influx of precursor of the partly blocked step.

Regulatory Mechanisms not Involving the Genetic Apparatus

Mechanisms of the types already discussed, even including those of the bacterial cell, represent a rather advanced degree of metabolic sophistication. It is conceivable, and indeed probable, that these regulatory mechanisms were preceded by simpler, more primitive types in the course of evolution. Many of the latter are still of great significance in biochemical homeostasis, functioning in parallel with the more complex mechanisms. It may be stated as a generalization (to which there are a few exceptions), that the regulatory mechanisms involving the genetic apparatus are concerned primarily with the quantity of enzyme (or other protein) in the cell, whereas the more "primitive" regulatory mechanisms influence chiefly the specific activity of such protein as already exists. The former mechanisms are generally slow-acting, requiring several hours to several days for perceptible effects (in the animal organism), whereas the latter mechanisms operate rapidly.

Compartmentalization. A structural or topographic type of control is possible, because of the existence of the limiting membranes of cells and intracellular organelles. A reaction may be regulated in rate and even in its occurrence or non-occurrence by the ability of substrates or cofactors to reach the intracellular locale of the enzyme.

The gross presence of enzyme in one compartment or another in the cell specifies the metabolic pathways that can occur there, e.g., glycolysis in the particle-free cytoplasm, the Krebs cycle in the mitochondria. If a substance required for a pathway in one compartment can be sequestered in another, a control mechanism is established. This may be the explanation of the Pasteur effect (p. 416).

Cell membranes and the mechanisms of active transport located therein are the targets of action of a number of hormones (e.g., insulin, p. 726, and somatotropin, p. 745), an example of an intercellular regulatory mechanism functioning through regulation of the intracellular concentration of substrate, which in turn controls the rate of reactions utilizing the substrate. Glucose and amino acids appear to be particularly amenable to this type of regulation.

Regulation of metabolism by variation in the permeability of membranes of intracellular organelles is not well understood. Its probable significance is suggested, however, by the many factors which can influence the mitochondrial membrane (p. 386).

Plethora of enzyme. Many enzymes are synthesized in great excess over metabolic requirements. It has been calculated, for example, that the adult human liver contains sufficient homogentisate oxygenase to metabolize over 1600 gm. of substrate per day, although the normal daily turnover of homogentisate is only a few grams. In such situations, the rate of a reaction is not limited by the amount of available enzyme; increases and decreases in the amount of substrate are automatically compensated for by corresponding alterations in its turnover.

Mass action in reversible reactions. Readily reversible reactions might be expected to be subject to control by concentration of product, increase of which may retard or even reverse the reaction. Despite its simplicity, few examples of this type of regulation have been found. One is the Lohmann reaction (p. 379), by means of which surplus quantities of ATP transfer "high-energy" phosphate bonds to creatine for storage as phosphocreatine, the reverse occurring when the concentration of ATP falls to low levels. A more complex example is the self-regulation of oxidative chain phosphorylation (p. 385). Due to "tight," obligatory, coupling of mitochondrial electron transport to generation of ATP, the rate of oxidation of substrates is retarded by elevated values of the ratio ATP/(ADP) (PO_4), which in turn is determined by the balance between the rate of oxidation of substrates and the rate of utilization of ATP in the performance of work.

Competition for shared reactants. Participation of a metabolite or cofactor in two or more metabolic pathways renders each pathway susceptible to control by the other(s), a so-called "bottleneck effect." For example, the NADH formed in the oxidative step of glycolysis in muscle can be reoxidized by two competing paths, either via the lactate dehydrogenase reaction (working "in reverse") or via the oxidative chain. The extent to which the latter pathway competes successfully with the former depends upon the degree of aerobiosis. Consequently, the amount of lactate formed in a given muscle cell is controlled by its supply of oxygen (p. 429).

More complex examples arise from the fact that many components of the Krebs cycle form parts of other metabolic pathways. α-Ketoglutarate, for instance, is a participant also in the glutamate dehydrogenase reaction, whereby it forms glutamate in the presence of reducing equivalents and ammonia. (This reaction may be followed by conversion of glutamate and ammonia to glutamine.) Such binding of ammonia can form a mechanism for its detoxication. However, by so functioning, the concentration of ketoglutarate and the rate of operation of the Krebs cycle may be depressed. It has been suggested that hepatic coma may be explained on the basis of such a sequence of events occurring in brain (p. 570).

End-product inhibition. In addition to the co-repressor action of the end-product of a metabolic pathway upon the *synthesis* of an early enzyme in the sequence, a more direct inhibitory effect on the *activity* of the enzyme is frequently observed. If the end-product combines with the active site of the enzyme, the inhibition is of the competitive type. Although this does occur, more frequently the end-product combines with other, "allosteric," sites on the enzyme, in some cases altering the conformation of the protein, in others affecting the association-dissociation equilibrium of a multi-chain protein system.

One of the earliest recognized examples of end-product inhibition in the animal organism is the regulation of cholesterol synthesis in the liver by the level of dietary cholesterol (p. 477). The target site is the conversion of β-hydroxy-β-methylglutarate to mevalonate in the microsomal fraction, the specific inhibitor being a low-density cholesterol-lipoprotein complex formed from exogenous (but probably not endogenous) cholesterol.

An extreme example of such regulation by remote control is provided by the inhibition of phosphofructokinase in the glycolytic pathway, by citrate in the Krebs cycle (p. 402).

Apparent "induction" at the cytoplasmic level. In addition to derepression of the genetic apparatus, it is conceivable that increases in enzyme (protein) concentration could result from: (1) inhibition of degradative pathways with no change in the rate of synthesis, or (2) facilitation of the process of polypeptide chain formation or release at the ribosome.

The first possibility has been observed in the case of hepatic arginase, the final enzyme in urea formation through the ornithine cycle. Influx of increased amounts of amino acids (as dietary protein) into the organism is followed by an apparent increase in arginase activity, due to decreased degradation, not to increased synthesis. It has been suggested that the presence of substrates (and cofactors, in some instances), by their combination with enzymes, serves to stabilize the latter and protect them from degradative reactions.

The second type of cytoplasmic "induction" may serve to explain the elevation in concentration of hepatic tryptophan pyrrolase and tyrosine-ketoglutarate transaminase following administration of substrates or cofactors (pp. 596, 599). As indicated elsewhere, glucocorticoids induce synthesis of these two enzymes by a process that can be inhibited by actinomycin, suggesting the participation of DNA-directed synthesis of mRNA at the nuclear level. In contrast, synthesis induced by substrates or cofactors is inhibited by puromycin, not by actinomycin, thus localizing the site of action at the ribosome. Acceleration of protein synthesis at this locus could be accomplished by a number of mechanisms, such as (a) a type of mass-action, in which substances that can combine with the nascent protein facilitate its removal from the ribosome, thus making room for initiation of new polypeptide chains, or (b) facilitation, by substances normally attracted to the functional form of the enzyme, of the three-dimensional folding of the polypeptide chain to its proper conformation even while attached to the ribosome, thus accelerating the overall process, as in (a).

Miscellaneous activating influences. The conversion of zymogens (proenzymes, pre-enzymes) to active enzymes (p. 216) may be considered a form of regulation, since this mechanism allows such enzymes to exert their effects only in the appropriate environment at the appropriate time.

Cyclic adenylic acid (3′,5′-AMP) activates the kinases which phosphorylate glycogen phosphorylase (p. 400) and synthetase (p. 398), acting as a mediator for certain hormones in this respect. The activation is probably of the allosteric type.

SUMMARY (FIG. 27-7)

One may conclude that the individual cell of a multicellular organism represents a rather complex focus of regulatory mechanisms. As heir to many millions of years of evolution, the cell contains the genetic information for performance of the multitude of biochemical reactions common to the species of organism in which it occurs, with certain variations characteristic of the lineage of the particular organism. In the course of differentiation, the cell is subjected to outside influences (largely unknown) which limit the

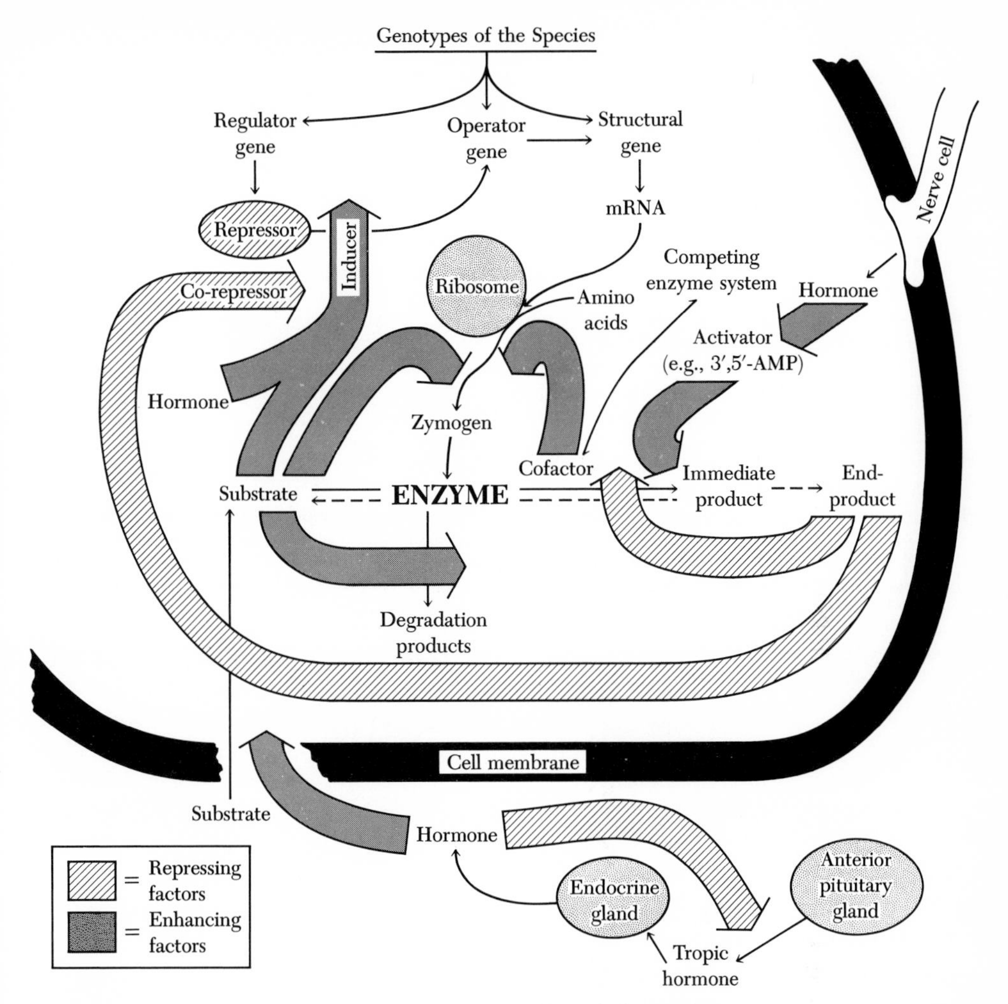

Figure 27-7. Various types of metabolic regulation.

expression of its total genetic potential to those characteristics which are required of a specific group of cells performing specific functions in a specific tissue.

Once matured, the cell is exposed to additional regulatory influences. Some are intercellular, at least in their mechanics, although their eventual effector mechanisms may operate by way of intracellular devices. Examples are intercellular exchanges of substrates (and possibly cofactors), and the well-known integrative functions of the nervous system and endocrine glands.

Intracellular regulatory mechanisms may be subdivided, for didactic purposes, into those which involve interaction with the genetic apparatus and those which do not. Among the former are those mechanisms of induction and repression which control the informational output of structural genes. Among the latter are the "topographic" controls (due to structural elements), as well as a series of relatively simple mechanisms such as provision of excess enzyme, mass action, competition for reactants, and end-product inhibition. Somewhat more complex mechanisms of the latter group are the examples of "cytoplasmic induction."

It is evident that biochemistry has come a long way since the days when the cell was regarded as a "bag of enzymes."

BIBLIOGRAPHY

Ames, B. N., and Martin, R. G.: Biochemical aspects of genetics: The operon, Ann. Rev. Biochem. *33:*235, 1964.

Bryson, V., and Vogel, H. J. (eds.): Evolving Genes and Proteins, New York, Academic Press, Inc., 1965.

Davis, B. D.: The teleonomic significance of biosynthetic control mechanisms, Cold Spring Harbor Symposia on Quantitative Biology *26:*1, 1962.

Garrod, A. E., Inborn Errors of Metabolism, reprinted with supplement by Harris, H., London, Oxford University Press, 1963.

Ingram, V. M.: The Hemoglobins in Genetics and Evolution, New York, Columbia University Press, 1963.

Jacob, F., and Monod, J.: On the regulation of gene activity, Cold Spring Harbor Symposia on Quantitative Biology *26:*193, 1962.

Krebs, H. A.: Control of cellular metabolism, Chapter 12 in Allen, J. M. (ed.): The Molecular Control of Cellular Activity, New York, McGraw-Hill Book Company, 1962.

Monod, J., and Jacob, F.: Teleonomic mechanisms in cellular metabolism, growth, and differentiation, Cold Spring Harbor Symposia on Quantitative Biology *26:*389, 1962.

Pardee, A. B.: The control of enzyme activity, in Boyer, P. D., Lardy, H., and Myrbäck, K. (eds.): The Enzymes, Vol. 1, New York, Academic Press, Inc., 1959, p. 681.

Pollock, M. R.: Induced formation of enzymes, in Boyer, P. D., Lardy, H., and Myrbäck, K., (eds.): The Enzymes, Vol. 1, New York, Academic Press, Inc., 1959, p. 619.

Popják, G., and Grant, J. K., (eds.): The Control of Lipid Metabolism, London, Academic Press, 1963.

Stanbury, J. B., Wyngaarden, J. B., and Fredrickson, D. S. (eds.): The Metabolic Basis of Inherited Disease, New York, The Blakiston Division—McGraw-Hill Book Company, 1966.

Weber, G. (ed.): Advances in Enzyme Regulation, 3 vols., Oxford, Pergamon Press Ltd., 1963 to 1965.

Wilson, A. C., and Pardee, A. B.: Comparative aspects of metabolic control, in Florkin, M., and Mason, H. S. (eds.): Comparative Biochemistry, Vol. 6, New York, Academic Press, Inc., 1964, p. 73.

Wolstenholme, G. E. W., and O'Connor, C. (eds.): Ciba Foundation Symposium on the Regulation of Cell Metabolism, Boston, Little, Brown and Company, 1959.

CHAPTER 28

CHEMICAL COMPOSITION OF TISSUES

WATER comprises somewhat less than 70 per cent of the body mass of the average well-nourished adult, the remainder of the body being solids. Entirely apart from the fact that these proportions can vary considerably with variations in the amount of stored fat, which occur without significant changes in water content, such figures have little biochemical significance, except perhaps to suggest the physiological importance of water. However, the amount of a substance present does not necessarily reflect its biological importance, and, therefore, isolated quantitative data on the elemental or even molecular composition of the body as a whole are of little biochemical import. On the other hand, knowledge of the substances present in a specific tissue may contribute to a better understanding of certain of its functions.

Whereas the important constituents of various organs and tissues have been known for some time, only recently has it been possible to secure detailed and precise information concerning their intracellular localization. By the use of differential centrifugation of tissue homogenates, various particulate components of cells (nuclei, mitochondria, lysosomes, microsomes) may be separated from each other and from the soluble constituents of the cytoplasm. Analysis of these isolated fractions has revealed that certain substances are restricted to certain cell components, and studies of this nature have yielded valuable information on many fundamental aspects of biochemistry and physiology. Additional information in this direction has been obtained by studies on intact cells, employing special staining techniques (e.g., for enzymes, nucleic acids, steroids, lipids, etc.) and ultraviolet absorption measurements (for nucleic acids).

INTRACELLULAR DISTRIBUTION OF CHEMICAL COMPONENTS (CYTOCHEMISTRY)

Liver has been employed more extensively than other tissues in studies of isolated cell fractions because it is composed of essentially a single type of cell, which is large, readily disrupted, and provides good yields of nuclei, mitochondria, and microsomes. The quantitative data indicated here, therefore, apply specifically to liver cells (mainly rat), but there is every reason to believe that the general pattern exhibited by these cells applies also to others.

Mitochondria

These are the largest particulate components of the cytoplasm, and represent up to 15 to 20 per cent of the dry weight of the liver cell. About 35 per cent of the total protein of the liver is in this fraction. Mitochondria are rich in lipids (25 per cent), two-thirds of which are phospholipids. In proportion to their mass, they contain a relatively small quantity of nucleic acid, i.e., <15 per cent of the total cell RNA and a small amount of DNA.

Mitochondria vary in shape (spherical, filamentous, sausage-shaped) and size (0.5 to 3μ long, 0.1 to 0.6 μ wide). Electron microscopic studies show them to be surrounded by a double membrane, the outer component of which is smooth and the inner infolded, frequently appearing in sections as shelf-like extensions of varying width (internal ridges or cristae). The number, size, shape, and internal structure vary in different tissues.

A large number of enzymes and coenzymes are localized in the mitochondria, which are the chief if not the sole sites of oxidative phosphorylation reactions. A number, but perhaps not all, of the Krebs cycle enzymes are localized exclusively in these structures, which contain also the electron transport mechanisms concerned with the delivery to oxygen of the electrons evolved in the oxidation reactions of the citric acid cycle. Inasmuch as the energy released by these processes is incorporated here in high-energy phosphate bonds, mainly as ATP, the mitochondrion may be regarded, therefore, as a sort of "powerhouse," producing energy for use here and elsewhere in the cell, required for synthetic and other purposes.

The mitochondria also contain dehydrogenases and other enzymes concerned with catabolism of fatty acids and of certain amino and keto acids, the metabolism of which is intimately linked to the reactions of the tricarboxylic acid cycle.

Formation of amino acids in these structures is suggested by the high levels of transaminases (also glutamate dehydrogenase). They contain enzymes concerned with certain aspects of the biosynthesis of long-chain fatty acids, phosphatides, porphyrin, heme, hippuric acid, and urea. They are apparently the exclusive sites of occurrence of transhydrogenases and contain also large amounts of adenylate kinase, glutaminase, and enzymes concerned with phosphorylation of nucleoside diphosphates and carboxylations.

Microsomes

These are the smallest particulate components of the cytoplasm separable by differential centrifugation of a tissue homogenate and represent fragments of an intricate system of membranes in the cytoplasm, called the "endoplasmic reticulum." It is a heterogeneous group of particles which collectively contain 20 to 25 per cent of the total nitrogen of the cell and are rich in nucleic acid, which is exclusively RNA (50 per cent of total cell RNA). Lipid, mainly phospholipid, comprises about 40 per cent of their dry weight. Microsomes vary considerably with respect to their RNA content. One fraction, rich in RNA (50 per cent), is termed "ribosomes." They consist mainly of particles of two sizes, one with a sedimentation constant of 50S, the other 30S (S = Svedberg units). The two particles combine to give one particle with a sedimentation constant of 70S. The ribosomes are the site of the final stages of protein synthesis, i.e., the union of "activated" amino acids in peptide linkage. The RNA of the ribosomes is referred to as rRNA. In addition to the enzymes concerned with these stages of protein synthesis, the following enzymes occur in these particles: steroid reductases (metabolism of cholesterol and steroid hormones), phosphatases, hydroxylases, hydrolases, glucuronyl transferase, and ATPase.

Lysosomes

These are cytoplasmic particles intermediate in size between mitochondria and microsomes, apparently surrounded by a lipoprotein membrane. This designation was applied to them because of their richness in hydrolytic enzymes. They have a mean diameter of about 0.4 μ, possess no oxidative enzymes, but are characterized by the presence of high levels of acid hydrolases, including acid phosphatase, cathepsins, acid deoxyribonuclease, acid ribonuclease, β-glucuronidase, aryl sulphatases, β-galactosidase, phosphoprotein phosphatase, and others.

Soluble Cytoplasmic Material

The supernatant fluid from centrifugation of mitochondria, microsomes, lysosomes, and nuclei contains the soluble constituents of the cytoplasm, lipid droplets, and possibly other very small particles. It is a complex mixture of proteins (35 to 40 per cent of total cell nitrogen), RNA, and other organic and inorganic compounds of low molecular weight.

This fraction contains the enzymes involved in the initial stages of protein synthesis, i.e., activation of amino acids and the formation of aminoacyl-sRNA (aminoacyl-sRNA synthetases) for transfer to the ribosomes, where the amino acids are joined in peptide linkage. An important phase of fatty acid biosynthesis (non-mitochondrial system) occurs in the soluble cytoplasmic fraction, i.e., formation of fatty acids of chain lengths up to palmitic acid. It contains also the following enzymes: those concerned with glycolysis, the hexose monophosphate oxidative pathway, glycogenesis and glycogenolysis; those concerned with catabolism of purines and pyrimidines; transaminases and peptidases.

Nuclei

The nucleus contains about 15 per cent of the protein of the cell and about 30 per cent of the RNA (20 per cent in the nucleolus, 10 per cent in the chromosomes). Most of the DNA of the cell is present in the nucleus (almost exclusively in chromosomes). The biological significance of these nucleic acids is discussed elsewhere (Chapter 19). Although other types of proteins are present, those associated with the DNA (deoxyribonucleoproteins) are basic proteins, either histones or, in sperm cells, protamines.

NAD synthesis (NAD synthetase) is apparently localized in the nucleus (liver cells). The same is true also of enzymes concerned with synthesis of DNA and other aspects of nucleic acid metabolism, e.g., DNA polymerase, DNA nucleotidyl transferase, nucleoside phosphorylase, adenosine deaminase, guanase.

ATP is readily synthesized in the nucleus. In some cases this may be accomplished as a result of glycolysis, the nuclei of many cells having been shown to possess glycolytic activity; an additional possibility is suggested by the presence of adenylate kinase, which mediates conversion of two molecules of ADP to AMP plus ATP. Esterase is apparently present in all nuclei, and other enzymes are present in some tissues and not in others (e.g., arginase, catalase).

CONNECTIVE TISSUE

Connective tissue is distributed widely throughout the body in tendons, sheaths, aponeuroses, subcutaneous tissue, supporting tissues in all organs, and, in modified form, as cartilage and bone. It is characterized by three types of components: (1) fibroblasts and their derivatives (chondroblasts, osteoblasts, etc.), concerned with the formation of collagen and mucopolysaccharides; and mast cells, which contain histamine, serotonin, and heparin; (2) fibrous proteins, mainly collagen and elastin; (3) an amorphous ground substance, the distinguishing components of which are acid mucopolysaccharides.

There are three main types of connective tissue fibers: (1) collagenous fibers (tendons, aponeuroses, ligaments, cartilage and bone, etc.); (2) elastic fibers (matrix of lungs, blood-vessel walls, loose areolar tissues, ligaments, etc.); (3) reticular fibers (matrix of bone marrow, lymphoid structures and many viscera, e.g., liver, kidney, etc.). These fibers and connective tissue cells are imbedded in intercellular material (ground substance), the quantity and consistency of which vary in different regions.

Proteins

The most important of these are (1) the scleroproteins (albuminoids), collagen, elastin, and reticulin, and (2) a mucoprotein (mucoid). There are also small amounts of albumin and globulin.

Collagen. This scleroprotein is insoluble in the usual protein solvents but, unlike keratin, it is digestible, although slightly, by pepsin and trypsin. It is further characterized by the fact that, on boiling in water or acid solution, it is transformed to gelatin, which is more soluble and readily digested by proteolytic enzymes. This transformation probably represents a denaturation process. Collagen has an unusually high content of glycine (25 per cent), and of proline and hydroxyproline (30 per cent). Collagen and elastin are the only natural animal proteins that contain significant amounts of hydroxyproline and hydroxylysine. Collagen and gelatin are lacking in tryptophan and cystine, and contain only small amounts of methionine and tyrosine.

Collagen comprises about 85 per cent of the solids of collagenous fibers (white connective tissue) and about 20 per cent of the solids of elastic fibers (yellow elastic tissue). It is also present in cartilage and in the organic matrix of bone ("ossein").

Soluble precursors of collagen, or a soluble form of collagen, are formed within fibroblasts and other connective tissue cells and pass into the intercellular ground substance. The mechanism of transformation here to fibrous collagen is not clear.

Elastin. This scleroprotein differs from collagen chiefly in not being converted to gelatin in boiling water, and in being more readily digested by pepsin and trypsin. It is particularly abundant in elastic fibers, in which it comprises about 75 per cent of the solids, as compared to about 4 per cent of the solids of collagenous fibers. The characteristic differences in staining reactions of these two types of fibers are due probably to these differences in protein, collagen and elastin having quite different amino acid constitutions.

Reticulin. This scleroprotein, present in reticular fibers, is closely related to collagen in composition.

Mucoprotein. All connective and supporting tissues contain mucoproteins (mucoids; glycoproteins) (p. 54) which are essentially the same as those in cartilage and bone, although different designations are commonly applied to them, i.e., tendomucoid, chondromucoid, osseomucoid. They contain as prosthetic groups mucopolysaccharides (chondroitin sulfates) containing multiple units of acetyl galactosamine sulfate and glucuronic or iduronic acid in glycosidal linkage. These mucoproteins are quite soluble in water and relatively resistant to denaturation, presumably because of their carbohydrate component. They comprise about 3 per cent of the solids of both collagenous and elastic fibers.

Mucopolysaccharide (p. 22)

Acid mucopolysaccharides occur in certain tissues and fluids in the free state or in combination with small amounts of protein. They are large anionic polymers (alternating units of acetylated hexosamines and hexuronic acids or hexoses). The most important include: (1) chondroitin sulfates A, B, and C; (2) keratosulfate, which differs from the above in containing glucosamine instead of galactosamine and galactose instead of a uronic acid; (3) hyaluronic acid (present in synovial fluid, umbilical cord, vitreous humor, skin, and connective tissue), which differs from chondroitin sulfates A and C in not containing sulfuric acid groups; (4) heparin, which contains five sulfuric acid groups in each tetrasaccharide unit, instead of two. Heparin is apparently produced in mast cells, is an anticoagulant (p. 802), and is present particularly in the liver and lungs; it acts as a cofactor for or activator of the enzyme, lipoprotein lipase, which is important in regulating the pattern of distribution of plasma lipids (p. 492). The chondroitin sulfates and hyaluronic acid are extremely hydrophilic and form viscous solutions; much of the water in connective tissues appears to be bound in this way. The mucopolysaccharides contribute viscosity and bulk to the tissues because of this property of highly polymerized hexoses.

The permeability of a tissue is determined by the amount and consistency of the ground substance, which consists largely of mucoproteins and mucopolysaccharides. The resistance of epithelium to penetration by fluids and particulate matter (including bacteria) is high, whereas that of subcutaneous tissue, which contains relatively few cells and fibers in proportion to ground substance, is low. Certain agents which act chemically on mucopolysaccharides alter the physical nature of the ground substance and, therefore, its viscosity and permeability. Among these are certain mucolytic enzymes found in animal tissues (p. 244); they catalyze the breakdown of the large polysaccharide molecules (depolymerization and hydrolysis). In the tissues, this phenomenon results in decreased viscosity and increased permeability, and these enzymes are sometimes designated "spreading-factors." Hyaluronidase (p. 244) falls into this category.

The integrity of the ground substance is influenced by certain vitamins and hormones,

TABLE 28-1. AVERAGE COMPOSITION OF WHITE AND YELLOW CONNECTIVE TISSUES

	WHITE (%)	YELLOW (%)
Water	63	58
Solids	37	42
Proteins	35	40
Collagen	30	7.5
Elastin	2.5	32
Mucoid	1.5	0.5
Coagulable	0.2	0.6
Lipids	1.0	1.1
Extractives	0.9	0.8
Inorganic	0.5	0.5

particularly ascorbic acid (p. 156) and gonadal hormones. Ascorbic acid is apparently required for normal formation of the mucoproteins and mucopolysaccharides, certain of the manifestations of vitamin C deficiency (scurvy) being due to defective development of the intercellular ground substance. Metabolic turnover of hyaluronic acid (synthesis after breakdown by hyaluronidase) in the sex skin of monkeys and apes varies in different phases of the menstrual cycle and can be altered by administration of estrogens and progesterone. Deficiency in thyroid hormone (in man) results in accumulation of excessive amounts of mucopolysaccharide in the skin and subcutaneous tissues (myxedema). In effective dosage, and in certain species, the 11-oxygenated adrenal corticoids (glucocorticoids) decrease or modify the ground substance and temporarily diminish growth of connective tissue. Synthesis of mucopolysaccharides is impaired (diminished incorporation of radioactive sulfate).

CARTILAGE

Cartilage is a modified connective tissue which chemically resembles the organic matrix of bone. It consists of cartilage cells imbedded in a dense matrix of collagenous fibers. It is about 70 to 75 per cent water. Organic substances, mainly proteins, comprise about 95 per cent of the solids. The important protein constituents are: (1) collagen; (2) chondroalbuminoid, which resembles elastin; (3) chondromucoid, which resembles the mucoproteins of connective tissue (tendons) and bone. Ossifying cartilage contains glycogen, which apparently plays a role in the mineralization of bone (p. 636). Inorganic constituents (3 to 6 per cent of solids) include Ca, Mg, Na, K, P, and Cl.

BONE

Osseous tissue is a modified connective tissue consisting of an organic matrix, resembling cartilage, in which inorganic elements (bone salt) are precipitated (mineralization) (p. 636) and a characteristic architecture is developed. It contains 20 to 25 per cent water; of the solids, about 60 per cent is inorganic and 40 per cent organic.

The nature of "bone salt" and the mechanism of mineralization are considered elsewhere (p. 636). The organic material is largely protein; there is a small amount of glycogen. The proteins include: (1) "ossein" (collagen), (2) "osseoalbuminoid," which resembles elastin; and (3) osseomucoid, a mucoprotein probably containing chondroitin sulfuric acid as a prosthetic group. Certain enzymes have been identified, including proteinases, peptidases, phosphorylase, and an alkaline phosphatase which is formed by osteoblasts and is apparently involved in the mechanism of mineralization of bone.

Vitamins A (p. 150), D (p. 163), and C (p. 156) are important for normal development of bone; the latter (ascorbic acid) is involved in the production of intercellular materials of all connective and supporting tissues, i.e., collagen and mucopolysaccharides.

TEETH

In a general way the chemical composition of teeth resembles that of bone, both structures consisting of a protein-rich organic matrix, in which is incorporated a complex mineral salt. There are three morphologically and chemically distinct mineralized regions in the tooth, viz., dentin, cementum, and enamel. Dentin, the largest component, forms the bulk of the internal structure into which the pulp cavity extends, containing nerves and blood vessels. It is covered by enamel on the exposed surface and by cementum on the subgingival surface.

Enamel, the hardest tissue in the body, is about 5 per cent water, about 98 per cent of the solid matter being inorganic and the bulk of the remainder protein, with a little lipid. The protein is a scleroprotein, resembling but apparently not identical with the keratin of skin. The mineral phase resembles that of bone (p. 636). It contains more calcium and phosphorus, but less magnesium and carbonate than that of dentin, as well as trace amounts of several other elements, perhaps the most important of which is fluorine.

Dentin is harder than bone; inorganic matter, apparently similar to "bone salt," comprises about 77 per cent of the solids, the organic matrix being mainly protein (22 per cent of the solids), with a small amount of lipid. The protein is largely collagen. Cementum has a consistency approximating that of bone, the mineral phase comprising about 70 per cent of the solids, the remainder being chiefly protein (collagen).

As is true of bone, vitamins A, C, and D (q.v.) influence the structure and mineralization of the teeth, and their effects are exerted particularly during the period of dental development, i.e., during fetal and early extrauterine life. However, studies with mineral isotopes indicate that at least the inorganic constituents of fully developed teeth undergo continual replacement, although they are infinitely less responsive than the bones to metabolic influences (Ca and P intake, parathyroid hormone, vitamin D, etc.). The rate of exchange of P^{32} in enamel is less than 1 per cent and in dentin less than 5 per cent of that in bone. Moreover, the largest fraction of this relatively small turnover may not represent the actual mineral lattice (hydroxyapatite), but rather deposits on the surface of the essential "bone-salt" (p. 636). Phosphate is apparently transferred from the saliva through the enamel to the dentin as well as from the blood plasma through the dentin to the enamel.

Fluorine, which occurs normally in bones and teeth in very small amounts, exerts an important influence on the structure of enamel and on its resistance to caries. This is referred to in greater detail elsewhere (p. 646).

SKIN AND APPENDAGES

The functions of the skin are, to a certain extent, reflections of its chemical constitution. Certain of its characteristics of toughness, elasticity, and flexibility are due to the high concentration of a characteristic fibrous protein, "keratin" (p. 81).

Proteins

The most important and characteristic protein in the epidermis is the scleroprotein, keratin. The deepest of the four epidermal layers, the stratum germinativum, the most active metabolically, has the highest water and glutathione content. Cells are being continually formed in this layer and pass toward the surface successively through the other layers, viz., the strata granulosum, lucidum, and corneum, their water content and metabolic activity decreasing until, in the superficial stratum corneum, the cells are dead and are lost by desquamation. The character of the proteins in these layers also differs. All are classed as scleroproteins. That in the stratum germinativum, termed "keratohyaline," occurs as irregularly scattered granules, which become more abundant in the stratum granulosum. This protein is regarded as the precursor of "eleidin," a scleroprotein present in the stratum lucidum, which undergoes further change to the characteristic "keratin" of the stratum corneum.

Keratin is not soluble in the usual protein solvents and is not digested by pepsin or trypsin. It has an unusually high cystine content, which imparts the characteristic odor to burning skin, hair and feathers, and probably contributes to the toughness of keratin by forming disulfide bridges between adjacent polypeptide chains. There are apparently two types of keratin, differing in amino acid composition and solubility, viz., "eukeratin" and "pseudokeratin," the former containing much more cystine and predominating in the hair and nails, the latter predominating in the epidermis. Skin also contains other scleroproteins, i.e., collagen, and smaller amounts of elastin and reticulin.

Lipids

The small amount of extractable lipids of the skin includes neutral fat, phospholipids, cholesterol, and cholesterol esters. Steroids comprise about 20 per cent of the lipid material, one important substance in this class being 7-dehydrocholesterol (provitamin D_3), which is apparently formed from cholesterol in the intestinal mucosa and, in the skin, is transformed to vitamin D_3 by the action of ultraviolet light (p. 159).

Miscellaneous

Skin contains a small amount of glycogen and most of the inorganic elements present in other tissues. Certain toxic heavy metals, e.g., arsenic, accumulate in the skin, hair, and nails when abnormally large amounts have entered the body.

Pigment

The term "melanin" is applied to the main pigment of the skin, hair, and choroid of the eye. It is not a chemical entity, but includes a variety of yellow, red, brown, or black pigments produced by polymerization of oxidation products of tyrosine and dihydroxyphenyl compounds (dopa, epinephrine, catechol, etc.) (p. 601) to relatively insoluble substances of high molecular weight. In some cases they occur in rather firm combination with tissue proteins (melanoproteins).

Melanin is formed in a specialized cell, the melanocyte (melanophore; chromatophore), present in the deeper layers of the epidermis (also in hair and choroid). It is produced in the form of rods (dark) or spheres (light). The depth of color depends on the degree of oxidation, the quantity of melanin and its dispersion and form of aggregation (i.e., rods or spheres). Partial or complete absence of this pigment (albinism) occurs as a recessive trait, in which melanocytes (which contain the enzyme tyrosinase) are absent from the skin, hair, and choroid.

The formation of melanin from tyrosine, catalyzed by the copper-containing enzyme, tyrosinase, is indicated elsewhere (p. 601). Normally, this enzyme is present in the skin (melanophores) in a partially inhibited state. This physiological inhibition may be due to (1) reducing substances, such as ascorbic acid or glutathione, or (2) copper-binding substances, such as organic compounds containing sulfhydryl groups (cysteine, glutathione). The increase in pigmentation which follows exposure to the sun (ultraviolet light) is apparently due to acceleration of the tyrosine-tyrosinase and "dopa"-tyrosinase reactions, the —SH groups which inhibit the enzyme being inactivated (oxidized) by the ionizing radiation. A similar mechanism (destruction of SH groups) may be involved in the pigmentation which occurs at the site of inflammatory skin lesions.

Androgens and estrogens cause pigmentation in certain specific areas, e.g., nipples, areolae, scrotum, apparently by direct action on melanocytes in these regions, the mechanism being unknown. In most cold-blooded vertebrates, the melanocyte-stimulating hormone (MSH) of the hypophysis (p. 749) causes darkening of the skin by expanding the cutaneous melanocytes. Inasmuch as these cells in mammals do not undergo such changes, the function of this hormone in mammalian species is not clear. However, there are reports of increased pigmentation following the administration of MSH in man, and it has been suggested that the cutaneous pigmentation that occurs characteristically in subjects with Addison's disease (adrenocortical insufficiency) may be due to the melanocyte-stimulating activity of ACTH (p. 740), which is increased in this condition. However, pigmentation has not been produced by purified preparations of ACTH in man.

Increased pigmentation may occur at the site of skin lesions in niacin deficiency (pellagra) and ascorbic acid deficiency (scurvy). This may result from inflammation with local destruction of SH groups and consequent increase in tryosinase activity. Depigmentation of hair and skin has been reported in children with multiple vitamin deficiencies, normal pigmentation being restored by administration of liver extract and a liberal diet. Similar depigmentation occurs in certain species maintained on diets deficient in pantothenic acid, *p*-aminobenzoic acid, biotin, tyrosine, and copper.

NERVOUS TISSUE

The chemical composition of nervous tissue differs in different portions of the nervous system and in different regions of the same organ. In general, the white matter has a higher solid content than the gray matter (30 per cent versus 15 per cent), owing chiefly to a larger amount of lipid material. The water content tends to decrease with age. Disregarding regional differences, the approximate average chemical composition of the adult brain is indicated in Table 28-2.

Lipids

One of the characteristic features of the chemical composition of nervous tissue is its high content of lipids, particularly phosphatides, in which it is richer than any other

TABLE 28-2. AVERAGE CHEMICAL COMPOSITION OF ADULT BRAIN

	WHITE MATTER (%)	GRAY MATTER (%)
Water	70	85
Solids	30	15
Total lipid	20	2.5
Cholesterol	5	1.2
Phosphatide	5.5	0.5
Glycolipid	9.5	0.8
Protein	8.5	7.5
Extractives	1.0	3.0

organ. The other lipids include galactolipids (p. 40), sulfolipids (p. 41), and cholesterol (p. 42). The fatty acid components are largely of the C-16 to C-24 series (even number) (p. 35), chiefly stearic and oleic, but also linoleic and arachidonic. Many are relatively highly unsaturated, especially in the spinal cord. Much if not all of the lipids may be present as lipoproteins.

In the brain (beef), the phosphatides are partitioned approximately as follows: cephalin, 55 per cent; lecithin, 25 per cent; sphingomyelin, 20 per cent. The designation, "cephalin," includes phosphatides with different nitrogenous components; e.g., about 75 per cent of their amino nitrogen is represented by ethanolamine and about 25 per cent by serine; about 50 per cent of their non-amino nitrogen is represented by choline, the remainder being unidentified. Inositol-containing phosphatides comprise about 25 per cent of the cephalin fraction of ox brain. Sphingomyelin is a prominent constituent of myelin sheaths; it is present in nerves in higher concentration than in the brain or cord. The white matter of the central nervous system is richer than the gray matter in total lipid (65 per cent versus 35 per cent of the dry weight), phosphatide (40 per cent versus 25 per cent), and cholesterol, but contains less sphingomyelin and a smaller proportion of unsaturated fatty acids. Medullated fibers contain more galactolipid than phospholipid; the reverse is the case in non-medullated fibers.

The lipid (and protein) content of the brain and cord varies with age and the state of development. During the first several weeks of life the water content decreases and the solids increase, due chiefly to an increase in lipid and protein. The increase in phosphatide is associated with myelination of axons (insulating lipid material). After 50 years of age, phosphatides decrease (especially unsaturated) and cholesterol increases.

Proteins

Relatively little detailed information is available regarding the proteins of nervous tissue. Perhaps the most characteristic is a scleroprotein, "neurokeratin," which is a component of neuroglia fibrils (supporting tissue). It contains less arginine than the keratin of the epidermis. Nerve cells contain nucleoproteins of both deoxyribose and ribose types. These have the same general intracellular distribution as in other tissues, i.e., DNA-proteins chiefly in the nucleus, RNA-proteins in the nucleolus and cytoplasm, and a relatively small amount in the nucleus. DNA predominates in young cells, diminishing (in concentration) as the cell develops and as RNA (and proteins) increases. In adult cells the RNA : DNA ratio is about 2 : 1. Globulins and collagen ("neurogelatin") are also present. White matter contains somewhat more protein than gray matter (8.5 per cent versus 7.5 per cent) but protein comprises about 50 per cent of the dry weight of the latter and about 30 per cent of that of the former.

The increase in solids in brain tissue during the first several weeks of life, as indicated above, is due in part to an increase in protein. This is a reflection of the increase in enzymes and other proteins during this period of increasing metabolic activity and functional and morphological development.

Carbohydrates

Glucose is present in somewhat lower concentration than in the blood plasma, and is by far the most important, virtually the only significant, energy-producing foodstuff of nervous tissue. The brain contains small amounts of glycogen (about 90 mg./100 gm.) and the cord somewhat more (0.2 to 0.3 gm./100 gm.). The functions of these carbohydrates are considered below. Galactose is present, in cerebrosides, presumably serving a structural (non-metabolic) function as a component of insulating and other lipids.

Enzymes

Nervous tissue contains all enzymes required for glycolysis and aerobic metabolism of glucose. Fructokinase has not been demonstrated. Important enzymes not involved in the utilization of glucose include cholinesterase (p. 239) and carbonic anhydrase (p. 250). Brain also contains glutaminase (p. 248) and transaminases (p. 234). The most active of the latter is glutamate-oxaloacetate transaminase, the glutamate-pyruvate and aspartate-pyruvate transaminations proceeding much less actively.

Miscellaneous

The so-called "extractives" of nervous tissue are similar to those of muscle and other tissues, with quantitative differences. Acetylcholine (p. 785) is of particular importance. It is apparently formed by stimulated nerve cells and is released at neuronal surfaces, playing a fundamental role in the transmission of nerve impulses. Norepinephrine (sympathin) is formed in sympathetic nerve fibers on stimulation, having a biological action resembling that of epinephrine.

Metabolism in Brain

Many constituents of the blood plasma which readily penetrate capillary walls and cell membranes in other situations do not do so in the brain. This is attributed to the existence of physiological barriers between the blood and the brain (and cerebrospinal fluid). The "blood-brain barrier" exhibits delayed permeability to practically all otherwise readily diffusible components of the plasma, including glucose, urea, Na, and K; is highly impermeable to large molecules, such as plasma proteins and bacterial toxins; and is apparently virtually impermeable to all amino acids except glutamine, in the concentrations in which they usually exist in the plasma. The permeability of this barrier tends to be increased in certain diseases of the central nervous system, e.g., meningitis, psychoses, cerebral arteriosclerosis, and brain tumors, a phenomenon which is utilized in certain diagnostic procedures.

Because of the existence of the blood-brain barrier, it has been difficult to evaluate the physiological significance of metabolic data obtained by in vitro studies. However, information concerning certain important aspects of brain metabolism appears to be established on a secure basis.

Carbohydrate metabolism. Although brain tissue contains all enzymes and metabolic intermediates of anaerobic and aerobic carbohydrate metabolism, glucose is the only carbohydrate that can enter from the blood plasma in significant amounts. Moreover, in vivo, under normal conditions, the amount of oxygen consumed is equivalent to that of glucose removed from the blood, as indicated by studies of arteriovenous differences of these two substances. Such observations suggest, too, that glucose is the chief physiological source of energy available for nerve cell function under ordinary circumstances. However, in hypoglycemia, the brain removes relatively more oxygen than glucose from the blood, indicating that some other substrate is being metabolized. Glutamine and glutamic acid may also function in this connection, as indicated below.

This large dependence on glucose for energy is the basis for the development of striking neurological manifestations (convulsions, coma) rather promptly after the blood glucose concentration falls to a low level. The cerebral glycogen falls during hypoglycemia, indicating that it may be drawn upon in this emergency, although it is not affected by other factors which profoundly influence liver glycogen, e.g., starvation, epinephrine, phlorizin.

The brain exhibits another peculiarity in carbohydrate metabolism in that glucose oxidation is not diminished after pancreatectomy. Moreover, it does not respond to administration of pituitary extracts by decreased glucose utilization, as do other tissues (p. 745). This may be due to failure of the pituitary growth hormone to pass the blood-brain barrier.

Anaerobic metabolism of glucose cannot supply the energy requirements of normal cerebral function; this is reflected in the comparatively large oxygen consumption of the brain, i.e., about 10 per cent of the basal body requirement (BMR), and at times as much as 25 per cent of the total consumption. Consequently, this organ is very sensitive to anoxia (convulsions; coma).

Amino acid metabolism. Glutamic acid and its amide, glutamine, apparently play important roles in brain metabolism. This is reflected in the fact that, together, they comprise almost half of the total NPN of mammalian brain. Moreover, the concentration of glutamic acid is usually higher in this organ than in other tissues, and that of glutamine approximates that in the liver. Their combined concentration is about two to three times that of glucose.

Glutamic acid is metabolized by brain slices in vitro, entering the tricarboxylic acid cycle via conversion to α-ketoglutaric acid (p. 568). It also undergoes decarboxylation to γ-aminobutyric acid (p. 582). However, it does not enter the brain from the blood plasma in significant amounts, even though its concentration in the latter be raised considerably above normal levels (blood-brain barrier). On the other hand, glutamine passes readily from the plasma to the brain and cerebrospinal fluid, and probably is an important metabolic precursor of the intracellular glutamic acid. The converse also occurs, i.e., formation of glutamine from glutamic acid. It is believed by some that this reaction may play an important role in the pathogenesis of hepatic coma. According to this concept, increased amounts of ammonia, originating in the intestinal lumen and escaping removal from the portal circulation by the damaged liver, reach the brain and react with glutamic acid to form glutamine. Decreased amounts of glutamic acid are therefore available for formation of α-ketoglutaric acid, an important component of the tricarboxylic acid cycle. The consequent impairment of oxidative metabolism may lower energy production to the point of producing unconsciousness, according to this hypothesis.

There is, however, no precise knowledge of the roles of these substances in brain metabolism. The following suggestions have also been advanced.

Glutamic acid may be used as a substrate instead of or in addition to glucose. It (and also glutamine) depresses anaerobic glycolysis in brain slices and raises aerobic glycolysis to the anaerobic level. The glutamic acid-glutamine system may act as one of the metabolic buffers regulating the rate of energy-producing processes in the nervous system.

Glutamine may serve as a source of glutamic acid and ammonia. It may also be involved in the synthesis of proteins and peptides.

Glutamic acid accelerates the in vitro synthesis of acetylcholine in brain tissue. K^+ ions have a similar effect (also on glycolysis), and it has been suggested that the influence of glutamic acid in these connections may be exerted via some influence on ionic composition, perhaps helping to maintain an effective level of K^+ ions.

Norepinephrine and serotonin are additional amino acid derivatives of importance in nervous tissue. The former is a metabolite of tyrosine (p. 600), the latter of tryptophan (p. 594). Their possible roles in the transmission of nerve impulses are discussed below.

Lipid metabolism. Fatty acids apparently are not utilized by nervous tissue as a significant source of energy, and acetoacetic acid possibly only to a limited extent. However, phosphatides, cholesterol, and fatty acids undergo continual degradation and resynthesis in the nervous system.

Nucleic acid and protein metabolism. RNA and protein also undergo continual catabolism and anabolism in nervous tissue, the rate varying in different functional states. At least in certain nerves, e.g., the vestibular, mild stimulation is followed by an increase in the amount of RNA and of protein. Repeated or prolonged nerve stimulation, or intense muscular activity, is accompanied by a decrease in the concentrations of these substances in the relevant nerve cells, with a subsequent increase during the recovery period. The changes in protein may be related to those in RNA (p. 534). Loss of function due to a variety of causes (e.g., trauma, virus infection, ischemia, drugs) is accompanied by decrease in the RNA content of the affected nerves. It has been suggested that the RNA content may reflect the functional state of neurons.

Neurohumoral Regulatory Factors

Interest is focused on this subject largely because of indications that factors regulating the transmission of impulses in autonomic and somatic nerves may be involved also in the regulation of cerebral processes influencing emotion and behavior. The factors believed to be of importance in this connection are (1) acetylcholine, (2) norepinephrine, (3) serotonin, and (4) γ-aminobutyric acid (GABA).

Acetylcholine. Stimulation of the vagus results in production of acetylcholine or in its liberation from combination with an unknown precursor. Stimulation of sympathetic fibers results in formation of norepinephrine, and also acetylcholine in certain instances. These nerve fibers are accordingly designated "cholinergic" and "adrenergic," respectively. Adrenergic fibers include most of the postganglionic sympathetic fibers. Cholinergic fibers include (1) preganglionic fibers, sympathetic and parasympathetic, (2) postganglionic parasympathetic fibers, (3) certain postganglionic sympathetic fibers, e.g., those to sweat glands, and (4) somatic motor fibers. Administration of acetylcholine produces effects that simulate those of parasympathetic stimulation (parasympathomimetic action); the response to administration of norepinephrine resembles that to sympathetic stimulation (sympathomimetic action).

There is considerable controversy over the physiological role played by these substances, particularly acetylcholine, in neuroeffector mechanisms, discussion of which is beyond the scope of a textbook of biochemistry. Classification of these agents as hormones is also questioned by some, chiefly on the basis that, under physiological conditions, the minute amounts formed or released at effector cells probably act only at the point of release, and are not carried to other effector cells. However, whereas the hormonal status of acetylcholine might be questioned on these grounds, that of epinephrine and norepinephrine is well established on the basis of their secretion by the adrenal medulla.

The chemical nature, biosynthesis, and metabolism of acetylcholine (p. 787) and norepinephrine (p. 698) are considered elsewhere. It is relevant to stress here the fact that rapid destruction of acetylcholine is an essential feature of certain theories of the activation of neuroeffector mechanisms. Acetylcholine is hydrolyzed to acetic acid and choline by a specific cholinesterase, present in nervous tissue and muscle, with a specific localization at synaptic junctions, i.e., at the sites of occurrence of bioelectrical phenomena (changes in action potential and membrane resistance and depolarization). Acetylcholine, synthesized as a result of nerve stimulation from choline by the enzyme choline acetylase in the presence of acetyl-CoA, and presumably involved in the transmission of the nerve impulse, must be inactivated rapidly in order to permit the initiation and transmission of another impulse. This specific cholinesterase acts only on acetylcholine, in contradistinction to pseudocholinesterase, which has a wider natural distribution, and catalyzes the hydrolysis of many other choline esters.

Norepinephrine. Demonstration of the presence of norepinephrine in certain areas of the brain has led to the view that it may play a role in the stimulation of psychomotor activity analogous to that which it occupies in stimulation of peripheral sympathetic effector organs. Its probable physiological importance for cerebral function is suggested, too, by the fact that it occurs in the brain in association with enzymes involved in its synthesis and in association with serotonin, the overall effects of which are in many respects antagonistic to those of norepinephrine. It is present in cerebral tissue in a bound, inactive form, from which it may be liberated by certain drugs, e.g., reserpine.

There is general agreement that norepinephrine is formed in and is the chemical transmitter of excitatory impulses in adrenergic nerves. It is stored within the axones of postganglionic fibers in bound form. The concept has been advanced that it serves a similar function in a subcortical cerebral system, probably the reticular formation, which coordinates autonomic, extrapyramidal motor, and psychic functions. The effects of certain drugs on behavior, emotional reactions, and psychomotor phenomena have been attributed to their actions in either (a) mimicking or blocking norepinephrine, (b) inhibiting its release or destruction (monoamine oxidase inhibitors), or (c) depleting its stored form (reserpine). Data obtained with such agents have provided much of the evidence to support the proposed concept of the central regulatory action of norepinephrine, and also of serotonin. Many of the observations are still controversial.

Serotonin (p. 594). This substance, 5-hydroxytryptamine, which is widely distributed in nature, has been found in relatively high concentration in mast cells, blood platelets, spleen, lungs, and brain. In these tissues it is present mainly in an inactive bound form, particularly in the mitochondria. Although interest previously was directed toward its potent action as a smooth muscle constrictor (arterioles, intestine, bronchioles), it is currently focused upon the possible participation of this substance in the mechanism of regulation of certain subcortical cerebral functions. Evidence that serotonin produces cerebral effects generally opposed to those of norepinephrine has suggested that it may act as a transmitter of inhibitory impulses, perhaps in the reticular formation as well as peripherally. As in the case of norepinephrine, much of this evidence is contradictory and indirect in nature, based on the effects of agents which mobilize serotonin from its bound form (reserpine) and of inhibitors of monoamine oxidase (Iproniazide). The suggestion has been made, too, that certain types of mental illness, such as schizophrenia, may be dependent fundamentally upon some abnormality of metabolism of serotonin. Although there are several conflicting features, the therapeutic effects of certain tranquilizing agents (reserpine) and psychic energizers (monoamine oxidase inhibitors) have been attributed to their effects on the metabolism of serotonin or norepinephrine.

γ-Aminobutyric acid (p. 582). High concentrations of this amino acid occur exclusively in the central nervous system. It is formed there by decarboxylation of glutamic acid by glutamate decarboxylase, with pyridoxal phosphate as an essential cofactor; it can be transaminated to form succinic semialdehyde, the latter in turn undergoing oxidation to succinate. This reaction sequence therefore constitutes a shunt mechanism around a portion of the tricarboxylic acid cycle.

Diminution in the concentration of γ-aminobutyric acid (GABA) is associated with increased excitability, and addition of exogenous GABA, under certain circumstances, with depression of certain aspects of cerebral activity. It has been suggested, therefore, that this amino acid may be an important transmitter substance of inhibitory neurons. In view of its high concentration in the brain, which would be unusual for a transmitter substance, it has been suggested, alternatively, that GABA may regulate the activity of the tricarboxylic acid cycle through the medium of the shunt mechanism indicated above. It is important in this connection that oxidation of α-ketoglutaric acid is regarded by some as an important rate-limiting step of the Krebs cycle in brain; a mechanism for short-circuiting this step may therefore be important for energy production. In vitro, respiration of brain tissue preparations is supported by GABA is readily as by glucose or glutamic acid.

Chemistry of Neural Transmission

Certain fundamental features of the mechanism of transmission of nerve impulses are still not understood, as is the case with muscle contraction (p. 428). However, there seems to be little doubt that this phenomenon involves: (1) exchanges of Na^+ and K^+ ions between the axon and the extracellular fluid; (2) changes in acetylcholine in the axon (except in postganglionic sympathetic fibers).

Changes in sodium and potassium. The passage of a nerve impulse along an axon is associated with a flow of small electric currents, which, in living cells, are carried by ions. As in other cells, the concentration of K^+ ions is much higher, and that of Na^+ much lower within nerve cells and axons than in the surrounding intercellular fluid. These large concentration gradients are the potential primary source of the action potentials and their resulting currents which propagate and are part of the nerve impulse.

When a nerve is stimulated, there is a sudden change in the permeability of the axon membrane, with a sudden influx of Na^+ from the intercellular fluid and an equivalent outflow of K^+. These shifts are reversed during the recovery phase. These ionic changes during nerve activity apparently constitute the mechanism whereby the action current is generated. The sudden changes in axon membrane permeability which underlie those in ionic distribution are apparently related to changes in acetylcholine, which is synthesized from choline and acetate by choline acetylase, in the presence of ATP, K^+, and Mg^{++}, and is rapidly hydrolyzed by acetylcholinesterase.

Changes in acetylcholine. The importance of this substance in this connection is reflected in the following observations. (1) It is present in all conducting systems (except postganglionic sympathetic fibers) in animals, and is localized, together with acetylcholinesterase, on the axon surface. (2) The voltage generated in the electric organ of the eel is directly proportional to the concentration of acetylcholinesterase, and inhibition of the latter is accompanied by a corresponding decrease in the nerve impulse.

The following explanation has been proposed of the role of acetylcholine in the transmission of the nerve impulse. Although it contains certain points on which there is not complete agreement, it will serve to indicate the general nature of acetylcholine participation in this phenomenon.

In the resting cell, acetylcholine is presumably present mainly in an inactive form, bound probably to protein. Upon nerve stimulation, it is released, the free acetylcholine combining with a receptor substance, probably another protein. This combination results in alteration in configuration of the receptor molecule, and this in turn to increased permeability of the axon membrane, in which these reactions occur, to Na^+ and K^+. As indicated above, this is responsible for generation of the action current.

The acetylcholine-receptor complex is in equilibrium with free acetylcholine and receptor. Hydrolysis of acetylcholine by acetylcholinesterase results in reversal of the above reaction, permitting the receptor to revert to its resting condition and axon permeability to return to the resting state, reestablishing the barrier to rapid movements of Na^+ and K^+. In the next stage of recovery, the inactive bound form of acetylcholine is resynthesized and the original ionic concentration gradients are restored.

The initial changes in Na^+ and K^+ during activity are in the direction of the concentration gradients, i.e., from high to low concentrations. They therefore require very little energy, particularly since they occupy an extremely short time (a few microseconds). During recovery, on the other hand, restoration of the resting ionic distribution, which occurs more slowly (a millisecond), requires movement of Na^+ and K^+ against their concentration gradients, and has a correspondingly large energy requirement. This is derived from reactions which provide energy to all cells (p. 372), i.e., from metabolism of carbohydrate, and also from hydrolysis of phosphocreatine.

As indicated elsewhere (p. 785), neurohumoral substances other than acetylcholine, e.g., norepinephrine, serotonin, and possibly γ-aminobutyric acid, influence transmission of nerve impulses and may be involved fundamentally in the mechanism of regulation of neuronal function, both central and peripheral. However, their exact role is still uncertain.

MUSCLE

Apart from its important structural and mechanical functions, muscle tissue plays a significant role in the total metabolism of the organism by virtue of the fact that it comprises about 40 per cent of the body mass. At rest, about 50 per cent, and during strenuous exercise about 75 per cent or more, of the total metabolism (as gauged by oxygen consumption) is due to muscle activity.

The three types of muscle, skeletal (striated), smooth, and cardiac, exhibit many points of similarity in chemical composition, but also certain rather characteristic points of difference, which may be of physiological significance. However, differences exist also in the same type of muscle in different parts of the body and in comparable muscles in different species. The significance of many aspects of these variations in chemical composition is not clearly understood, and in several particulars available quantitative data for human muscle are either lacking or unsatisfactory.

Muscle Proteins

Proteins comprise about 20 per cent of muscle tissue (weight) and about 80 per cent of its solid content. They may be classified, according to their location, as intracellular (fibrils and sarcoplasm) and extracellular (stroma). The latter are connective tissue proteins (p. 776), e.g., collagen, elastin. Interest is centered particularly in the intracellular proteins, which are intimately concerned with the functional activity of muscle. The most important of these are: (1) in the fibrils, (a) actin and (b) myosin; (2) in the sarcoplasm, (a) "myogen," (b) "globulin X," and (c) myoglobin. Actin and myosin are involved in the contractile process; "myogen" is a heterogeneous fraction which probably consists largely of enzymes; the functional significance of "globulin X" is not known; myoglobin probably acts as an oxygen carrier similar to hemoglobin.

Contractile Element: Actin and Myosin (p. 427)

These two proteins, present in the muscle fibril, combine to form actomyosin, the contractile unit, which has globulin characteristics. Together, they comprise 40 to 60 per cent of the total muscle protein. Actin exists in two forms: (1) G-actin, a globular protein of relatively low viscosity, which undergoes linear polymerization to (2) F-actin, a fibrous (linear) protein of high viscosity. The latter has a strong affinity for myosin, with which it combines in a weight ratio of approximately 1 (actin) : 3 (myosin) to form F-actomyosin. Contraction results from the action of ATP on F-actomyosin in the presence of proper concentrations of inorganic ions. The nature of these proteins and of the contractile process is considered in detail elsewhere (p. 428). A small amount of an ATPase is apparently intimately associated with myosin.

Sarcoplasmal Proteins

Few of the proteins of the sarcoplasm have been as completely characterized, chemically or functionally, as have those of the myofibrils. So far as is known, none of them participates directly in the structural changes of the process of contraction. However, certain of them are known to represent biologically active and important components, e.g., enzymes, which are fundamentally concerned with the vital activity of and energy production by the muscle cells.

Myogen. This term is applied to a heterogeneous fraction which comprises about 20 per cent of the muscle proteins, present in the sarcoplasm, and apparently unable to enter the fibril. At least two separate components have been isolated, designated "myoalbumin" and "myogen fibrin," respectively. It is believed that this protein fraction consists largely if not entirely of enzymes, among which the following have been identified: triosephosphate isomerase, aldolase, triosephosphate dehydrogenase, phosphorylase.

Other enzymes present in the sarcoplasm include: those involved in glycolysis (in addition to the above-mentioned) and aerobic carbohydrate metabolism; those of the cytochrome system; flavoproteins; pyridinoproteins; an ATPase which differs from that associated with myosin; myokinase, et al.

Globulin. This fraction, comprising 10 to 20 per cent of the total muscle protein, has globulin characteristics. Its functional significance is not known.

Myoglobin (muscle hemoglobin). Myoglobin, like hemoglobin, is a ferrous protoporphyrin globin complex (p. 124). It is present in the sarcoplasm in relatively low concentration (about 0.1 to 0.2 per cent in skeletal muscle), which, however, varies in different muscles (highest in myocardium) and in different species, being related apparently to the level of activity. In contrast to hemoglobin, which has a molecular weight of 66,800, and four iron atoms (i.e., four heme groups) per molecule, myoglobin has a molecular weight of 16,700 and one iron atom (i.e., one heme group) per molecule.

Myoglobin differs slightly from hemoglobin in its absorption spectrum and rather strikingly in its oxygen dissociation curve, its affinity for oxygen at relatively low P_{O_2} levels being considerably greater than that of hemoglobin. For example, at 40 mm. Hg P_{O_2}, myoglobin is 60 per cent saturated and hemoglobin 38 per cent. It may therefore provide a temporary reserve supply of oxygen under conditions of unduly prolonged restriction of circulation through a contracted muscle, or of excessive removal of oxygen from hemoglobin. It is interesting in this connection that its affinity for oxygen is intermediate between that of hemoglobin and of cytochrome oxidase. Its affinity for carbon monoxide is lower than that of hemoglobin.

Carbohydrate

The glycogen content of muscle varies considerably in different muscles, and under different conditions of activity and nutrition. Ranging from 0.4 to 1.8 per cent (usually 0.5 to 1.0 per cent) in the resting state (skeletal muscle), it may approach zero during prolonged, strenuous muscular exertion. It is usually included among the "muscle extractives" (p. 791), although only a minor fraction is extractable with hot water or cold trichloracetic acid, the greater part (65 per cent) being bound in some manner to proteins, particularly myosin ("desmoglycogen"). Muscle glycogen is derived from the blood glucose. In its aerobic (to CO_2 and H_2O) and anaerobic (to lactic acid) degradation, it serves as a source of high-energy phosphate bonds for resynthesis of adequate amounts of ATP (and phosphocreatine), depleted during the process of contraction (p. 429).

Lactic acid, the end-product of anaerobic metabolism of glycogen (and of glucose), is present in resting muscle in low concentration (0.02 per cent). At rest, or during moderate exercise, it is probable that the supply of oxygen to the muscles is adequate to provide for aerobic metabolism of carbohydrate; i.e., the bulk of the pyruvic acid formed enters the tricarboxylic acid cycle and relatively little lactic acid is produced. However, during sudden strenuous exercise, particularly in untrained subjects, the rate of breakdown of glycogen exceeds the capacity of the muscles to oxidize pyruvic acid, owing to temporary inability of the circulation to meet the increased metabolic requirement for oxygen. Under such conditions, increased amounts of lactic acid are produced (reaching concentrations of 0.25 per cent or higher in muscle) and pass into the bloodstream, with consequent rise in the blood lactic acid concentration.

In common with other tissues, muscle contains glucose in approximately the same concentration as in the blood plasma, per unit of water content (i.e., about 50 mg./100 gm. muscle). There are also small amounts of intermediates in carbohydrate metabolism, e.g., various hexose- and triosephosphates, pyruvate, and Krebs cycle intermediates.

Lipids

The lipids of muscle include neutral fat, phospholipids (phosphatides), glycolipids, cholesterol, and cholesterol esters. The quantity varies widely in different muscles and in comparable muscles in different species; e.g., the total lipid of striated muscle of the chicken (white muscle) averages about 7 per cent (of dry weight) and of the hog about 22 per cent. These differences are due mainly, but not entirely, to differences in amount of neutral fat. This is located largely in fat cells in the interstitial tissue, and resembles the other body depot (storage) fats in its chemical constitution.

Although the non-fat or "essential" lipids vary in different muscles and species (e.g., average 5 per cent [dry weight] in chicken, 9 per cent in frog), the comparative constancy of their quantitative distribution permits certain generalizations which may have functional significance. Phospholipids comprise the bulk of this fraction, as in other tissues. In most species, they constitute from 3 to 7 per cent (dry weight) of muscle tissue, whereas the glycolipid content is usually below 2 per cent and cholesterol below 0.7 per cent. In most muscles, the phospholipids consist almost entirely of lecithins and cephalins, the former usually predominating somewhat; sphingomyelin is present in small amounts. Human myocardium, for example, gives the following average values (per cent of dry weight): total phospholipid 7, lecithin 4.5, cephalin 2.2, sphingomyelin 0.3 Heart muscle usually contains more than skeletal and smooth muscle. In general, the phospholipid content varies with the level of habitual activity of the muscle; e.g., it is higher in muscles of active animals than in corresponding muscles of sedentary animals, even of the same species. Muscle phospholipids contain a higher percentage of unsaturated fatty acids than those of other tissues, averaging 65 to 75 per cent of the total fatty acids (e.g., liver about 60 per cent).

With few exceptions, cholesterol is largely in the free state. The quantity is apparently related to the degree of automatic activity of the muscle; e.g., in man, smooth muscle (0.8 per cent dry weight) invariably contains more than skeletal muscle (0.3 per cent), with heart muscle (0.5 per cent) occupying an intermediate position. Skeletal muscle generally contains more glycolipid than cholesterol, whereas this relationship is usually reversed in smooth muscle. Because of the fact that the cholesterol content of smooth muscle is invariably higher than that of skeletal muscle, whereas their phospholipid contents are approximately the same, the phospholipid: cholesterol ratio is lower in smooth (5:1) than in skeletal (10 to 16:1) muscle. The significance of these relationships is not known.

Muscle Extractives

The term "muscle extractives" is applied to the large and heterogeneous group of organic (nitrogenous and non-nitrogenous) and inorganic substances that go into solution when muscle is extracted with boiling water. The proteins are coagulated and lipids may be largely separated from the aqueous solution. Commercial beef extract or bouillon is a concentrate of beef muscle extractives. It will suffice here merely to enumerate the most important of these substances, their chemistry and functional significance having been discussed in detail elsewhere.

Nitrogenous. These include: adenosine tri- and diphosphates (ATP, ADP), adenylic acid (AMP), and inosinic acid (p. 517); phosphocreatine (p. 429); creatine (p. 578) and creatinine (p. 579); acetylcholine (p. 473); histamine (p. 583); two nicotinamide-adenine nucleotides (NAD, NADP; coenzymes I and II); amino acids; two dipeptides with high buffering capacities, but otherwise of unknown function, carnosine (β-alanylhistidine), and anserine (methylcarnosine) (p. 583); thiamine (p. 175).

Non-nitrogenous. These include: glucose, glycogen, and intermediates in their anaerobic and aerobic degradation (p. 395ff.); ascorbic acid (p. 153); inositol (p. 204); acetoacetic acid.

Inorganic. These include: K, Na, Mg, Ca, and Fe, in descending order of concentration; Mn, Co, Cu, Ni, and Zn, in trace amounts; HPO_4, Cl, SO_4. The concentrations of these ions are discussed elsewhere (p. 302) in connection with the electrolyte composition of intracellular fluid. The higher concentration of Na than of Mg in muscle extract is due to the inclusion of extracellular as well as intracellular components. In addition to the important functions of these ions in regulating osmotic and "acid-base" equilibrium, a proper balance between the cations is required for the maintenance of normal muscle irritability and contractility (p. 428), and enzyme functions (p. 216).

BIBLIOGRAPHY

Annual Review of Biochemistry.
Bloor, W. R.: Biochemistry of the Fatty Acids, New York, Reinhold Publishing Corporation, 1943.
Bourne, G. H. (ed.): The Biochemistry and Physiology of Bone, New York, Academic Press, Inc., 1956.
Brachet, J.: Biochemical Cytology, New York, Academic Press, Inc., 1957.

Brookhaven Symposium on the Chemistry and Physiology of the Nucleus, New York, Academic Press, Inc., 1952.
Buchthal, F., Svensmark, O., and Rosenfalck, P.: Mechanical and chemical events in muscle contraction, Physiol. Rev. *37*:503, 1957.
Chambers, R., et al.: Symposium on structure in relation to cellular function, Ann. New York Acad. Sci. *50*:815–1012, 1950.
Elliott, K. A. C., and Jasper, H. H.: Gamma-aminobutyric acid, Physiol. Rev. *39*:383, 1959.
Elliott, K. A. C., Page, I. H., and Quastel, J. H.: Neurochemistry, Springfield, Ill., Charles C Thomas, 1955.
Fourman, P.: Calcium Metabolism and the Bone, Springfield, Ill., Charles C Thomas, 1960.
Hebb, C. O.: Biochemical evidence for neural function of acetylcholine, Physiol. Rev. *37*:196, 1957.
Himwich, H. E.: Brain Metabolism and Cerebral Disorders, Baltimore, Williams & Wilkins Company, 1951.
Huxley, H. E.: Muscle cells, in Brachet, J., and Mirsky, A. E. (eds.): The Cell, Vol. 4, New York, Academic Press, Inc., 1960, p. 365.
Hydén, H.: The Neuron, in Brachet, J., and Mirsky, A. E. (eds.): The Cell, Vol. 4, New York, Academic Press, Inc., 1960, p. 215.
Korey, S. R., and Nurnberger, J. E. (eds.): Neurochemistry, New York, Paul B. Hoeber, Inc., 1956.
Macy Foundation Conferences on Metabolic Interrelations, I, III, and IV, New York, Josiah Macy, Jr. Foundation, 1949, 1951, 1952.
McIlwain, H.: Biochemistry and the Central Nervous System, Boston, Little, Brown & Company, 1955.
Mommaerts, W. F. H. M.: Muscular Contraction, New York, Interscience Publishers, Inc., 1950.
Nachmansohn, D., and Wilson, I. B.: Trends in the biochemistry of nerve activity, in Green, D. E. (ed.): Currents in Biochemical Research, New York, Interscience Publishers, Inc., 1956.
Page, I. H.: Serotonin (5-hydroxytryptamine); the last four years, Physiol. Rev. *38*:277, 1958.
Rothman, S.: Physiology and Biochemistry of the Skin, Chicago, University of Chicago Press, 1954.
Wolstenholme, G. E. W., and O'Connor, M. (eds.): Chemistry and Biology of Mucopolysaccharides, Boston, Little, Brown & Company, 1958.

CHAPTER 29

MILK

The importance of the chemical composition of milk arises out of the fact that it is the sole foodstuff of young mammals and should therefore provide for adequate nutrition during this critical period. As secreted, it is a nearly ideal food for human infants, being nutritionally seriously inadequate only in iron and vitamin D (perhaps also copper) (see Vitamins, p. 795).

Its composition varies considerably in different species, in different breeds of the same species, in different periods of lactation, and under different conditions of diet and hormonal secretion. In the breast, developed during pregnancy through the action of estrogen and progesterone, lactation is induced shortly before the onset of labor by the action of prolactin (p. 744), secreted by the anterior pituitary.

The fluid secreted during the few days before and for one to two weeks following parturition is called "colostrum." It differs from later milk in having a somewhat yellow color, more protein and mineral elements, and less fat and carbohydrate. The higher protein content is due mainly to the presence of globulins which are apparently identical with the γ-globulins of the blood plasma (main antibody fraction). In contrast to later milk, the protein of colostrum coagulates on boiling. The protein content falls and the fat and carbohydrate increase steadily to reach the true milk levels at three to five weeks post partum.

Proteins

Milk contains three important proteins (casein, lactalbumin, and lactoglobulin), the amounts and relative proportions of which differ in different species. The quantity of protein (and of mineral elements) varies directly, although not strictly quantitatively, with the rate of growth of the newborn, i.e., inversely as the time required to double its birth weight. The protein content of human (average 1.5 per cent) and cow's (average 4.0 per cent) milk is indicated in Table 29-1, this being one of the most important practical points of difference in the milk of these species. Casein comprises about 85 per cent of the protein of cow's milk and about 65 per cent of that of human milk. The amount of lactalbumin in cow's milk is two to 10 times that of lactoglobulin.

Probably none of these proteins is a homogeneous substance. A β-lactoglobulin has been isolated and its amino acid composition determined. All are quite complete proteins, nutritionally, with an unusually high content of essential amino acids.

Casein, the principal milk protein, is a phosphoprotein (0.7 per cent P), with an isoelectric point of pH 4.6. At the usual pH of fresh milk, 6.6 to 6.9 (owing to acid phosphates), it is probably present as a salt (calcium caseinate) and precipitates on acidification, as in souring (lactic acid fermentation, p. 271). The buffering capacity of milk is due largely to the presence of protein, phosphates, bicarbonate, and citrate. Casein is precipitated by mineral acids and by saturating neutral solutions with NaCl or $MgSO_4$. It does not coagulate on boiling, which, however, results in the formation of a film, consisting of a combination of casein and calcium salts. This film does not develop in acidified milk (e.g., sour milk).

Under the influence of milk-clotting (curdling) enzymes, e.g., rennin (p. 261), pepsin (p. 260), and chymotrypsin (p. 262), casein is hydrolyzed to soluble paracasein, which, in the presence of Ca^{++}, is converted to insoluble casein (calcium paracaseinate), or "milk curd." The residual clear fluid is called "whey." The casein of cow's milk is more readily precipitated by acid and coagulated by rennin than that of human milk. The curd formed in human milk is more flocculent and more readily digested.

Lipids

The lipids in milk are largely triglycerides (fats), with smaller amounts of cholesterol (0.01 per cent) and phospholipids (0.1 per cent). The average concentration in human and cow's milk is approximately the same, although there are wide variations (Table 29-1). The fat content of cow's milk (butter fat) varies considerably in different breeds and under different dietary conditions. The fats are present in a rather coarse emulsion; this is largely responsible for the white color of milk, which is contributed to also by the presence of casein in colloidal solution.

The fats of human milk differ from those of cow's milk in their fatty acid components. Oleic acid predominates in both (30 to 35 per cent of total), and fatty acids of the C_{12} to C_{18} series comprise 80 to 90 per cent of the total. However, about 10 per cent of human milk fatty acids are highly unsaturated (e.g., linoleic, linolenic), as compared to about 0.5 per cent in cow's milk. Moreover, human milk fats contain no short-chain fatty acids (i.e., below decanoic, C_{10} series), whereas these comprise 5 to 10 per cent of the fatty acids of cow's milk (e.g., caprylic, caproic, butyric acids). In this respect, butter fat (cow) differs strikingly from other body fats.

TABLE 29-1. COMPOSITION OF MILK

		SOLID	PROTEIN	CARB.	FAT	ASH	Ca	P	Mg	Na	K	Cl
		(gm./100 ml.)					(mg./100 ml.)					
Human	Max.		2.5	8.0	8.0	0.3						
	Min.		1.0	4.5	1.0	0.2						
	Av.	12.5	1.5	7.0	4.0	0.25	40	30	5	15	60	40
Cow	Max.		6.0	6.0	6.5	1.2						
	Min.		2.0	2.0	1.5	0.3						
	Av.	13.0	4.0	5.0	4.0	0.7	120	90	20	50	140	110

Available evidence (in cattle) supports the belief that milk fat is synthesized in the lactating breast, chiefly from glucose, which is supplied from the blood. It is contributed to by the blood fats or other lipids probably to only a limited extent, if at all. The fatty acids, particularly the short-chain acids (cow), are synthesized from 2-carbon precursors ("active acetate"), as in other tissues, derived mainly from glucose. The glycerol component of the milk fats, too, probably originates largely from glucose (via dihydroxyacetone phosphate, p. 419). It may, however, together with some of the fatty acids, be derived from glycerides of the blood plasma, but to a limited extent. Insulin stimulates the synthesis of fatty acids (and of fats) by the lactating breast. The fact that the R.Q. exceeds 1.0 under these circumstances suggests conversion of carbohydrate to fat (p. 330).

Carbohydrate

Lactose (milk sugar) is the characteristic carbohydrate of milk. Human milk (average 7 per cent) contains more than cow's milk (average 5 per cent) (Table 29-1). Its galactose component is formed by the alveolar cells of the lactating breast from blood glucose, these two sugars being then converted to lactose (p. 432).

On standing, milk undergoes souring, as a result of the production of lactic acid from lactose by fermentation, owing to the action of bacteria (e.g., Streptococcus lactis). As indicated elsewhere (p. 794), the incident increase in acidity causes precipitation of casein.

Inorganic Constituents

The inorganic content of cow's milk (average 0.7 per cent) is about three times that of human milk (average 0.25 per cent (Table 29-1). Both contain inadequate amounts of iron and copper for normal nutrition, the iron deficiency being particularly important in contributing to the development of anemia in infants. The high calcium content is of the greatest importance nutritionally, inasmuch as, for practical purposes, milk is the only food which can provide this element in amounts adequate for normal nutrition, even in adult life.

Vitamins

Under satisfactory dietary conditions, milk contains adequate amounts of vitamin A, and also carotenes (provitamins A). It is, however, rather low in B vitamins, except riboflavin and pantothenic acid, and is a poor source of vitamin D. The vitamin C content, which is relatively low in cow's milk, is further reduced by pasteurization. The average vitamin composition of human and cow's milk is indicated in Table 29-2. In most instances these values may be influenced considerably by the vitamin intake.

TABLE 29-2. VITAMINS IN MILK (PER 100 ML.)

	A (μg.)	D (I.U.)	C (mg.)	THIAMINE (μg.)	RIBOFLAVIN (μg.)	NIACIN (μg.)	PYRIDOXINE (μg.)	PANTOTHENIC ACID (μg.)
Human	50	5.0	4.5	15	45	180	10	200
Cow	35	2.5	2.0	45	200	80	50	350

Miscellaneous

Cow's milk contains variable quantities of vegetable pigments (dietary), including riboflavin (formerly designated lactoflavin), carotenes, and a small amount of xanthophylls. Vegetable pigments may also be found at times in human milk, the riboflavin content of which is usually much lower than that of cow's milk.

Certain enzymes are present, including proteases, lipase, amylase, catalase, peroxidase, phosphatase, and xanthine oxidase. The fact that the phosphatase is destroyed by pasteurization may be employed as a means of differentiating raw from pasteurized milk.

Certain foreign substances in the blood plasma may enter the milk. These include volatile oils of certain foods (e.g., onion, garlic), drugs (e.g., sulfonamides, salicylates, morphine, alcohol), and inorganic elements (e.g., As, Bi, Fe, I, Hg, Pb).

CHAPTER 30

BLOOD AND OTHER BODY FLUIDS

BLOOD

In so highly organized an aggregation of cells as the animal body, provision must be made for maintaining a certain degree of constancy of the immediate environment of these cells, i.e., the interstitial fluid which surrounds them, in the face of continual exposure to the entrance of variable amounts of exogenous (foodstuffs) and endogenous (metabolites) materials. This phenomenon of regulation, termed "homeostasis," is accomplished through the medium of the circulating blood, which carries nutritive materials (including oxygen) to the cells and waste products (including carbon dioxide) to excretory organs, and distributes other products of cell metabolism throughout the body for utilization in or action upon cells other than those in which they originate. This must be accomplished with a minimum degree of variation in the pH of the extracellular fluids, under widely varying conditions of metabolic activity. From a biochemical standpoint, these transport functions of blood are of paramount importance.

The plasma proteins play an important role in regulating the distribution of water between the intravascular and extravascular compartments of the extracellular fluid, fluid exchanges across capillary walls, and filtration through the renal glomeruli. The transport functions of plasma proteins are becoming increasingly apparent. A β_1-metal combining protein (siderophilin, transferrin) is the medium of transport of iron in the plasma, another (ceruloplasmin), of copper. Lipids, including an important fraction of the steroid hormones, are carried largely as lipoproteins, and certain fatty acids are bound by albumin.

The ability of the body to maintain a rather constant temperature is due largely to the high specific heat of water. Heat produced in the course of metabolic reactions in the cells is distributed throughout the body fluids via the bloodstream, the temperature in various tissues thereby tending to be equalized. Circulation of the blood at the body surface (skin, pulmonary alveoli) permits loss of excess heat by radiation and evaporation, an essential feature of the mechanism of temperature regulation.

The blood contains factors which form the basis of certain of the body's defenses against invading injurious agents. These include certain of the formed elements (granulocytes, monocytes) and antibodies (mainly γ-globulins) against microorganisms, toxins, and foreign proteins.

The phenomenon of blood coagulation may be regarded as a protective mechanism against undue loss of blood following disruption of the continuity of blood vessel walls, resulting from trauma to which they are frequently subjected.

General Characteristics

As it exists within the vascular system, blood consists of formed elements (erythrocytes, leukocytes, platelets) and a fluid portion, plasma, which contains a large number of organic and inorganic substances in solution. Apart from oxygen, which is carried virtually exclusively by hemoglobin (erythrocytes), and CO_2, which is carried in both plasma and erythrocytes, the important transport functions of the blood are served by the plasma. With the exception of considerations of respiration (O_2 and CO_2), biochemical interest is focused, therefore, on the composition of this medium, which reflects the adequacy of the homeostatic mechanisms of the body in health, and, frequently, disturbances in specific directions in disease.

The in vivo fluid state of the blood can be maintained in vitro only by interfering with the mechanism of coagulation, which otherwise begins to operate as soon as the blood comes in contact with most foreign surfaces (e.g., glass, metal). This may be accomplished by defibrination, i.e., by stirring freshly shed blood with a glass rod, to which the fibrin adheres as it forms. More commonly, an anticoagulant is added. Those employed most frequently for purposes of securing whole blood or plasma for examination act by removing Ca^{++} ions from solution, by formation of either insoluble calcium salts (oxalate, fluoride) or an undissociable calcium complex (citrate). Addition of heparin prevents coagulation of blood; it inhibits conversion of prothrombin to thrombin (antiprothrombin action), and also inactivates thrombin (antithrombin action). The formed elements can

Table 30-1. Miscellaneous Values for Venous Blood (Fasting)

	BLOOD	PLASMA	CELLS
Volume			
ml./kg.	63–80 (72)*	35–45 (40)	
liters/sq.M.	2.5–3.2 (2.9)	1.3–1.8 (1.5)	
pH	7.3–7.5 (7.4)	7.3–7.5 (7.4)	
Osmolar concentration (mOsM./liter)		320	
Specific gravity	1.052–1.061 (1.056)	1.022–1.031 (1.026)	1.095–1.107 (1.098)
Colloid osmotic pressure (mm. Hg)		20–35 (24)	
Hematocrit (% cells)	40–54 (47) 37–47 (42)		
Water content (%)	81–86 (83)	93–95 (94)	(65)

* Figures in parentheses are mean values.

readily be separated from the plasma by centrifugation. For analysis of blood gases (O_2, CO_2), the blood must be collected anaerobically (e.g., over mercury). The term "hematocrit value" is applied to the volume (in per cent) of packed red blood cells in a blood sample (usually 10 ml.) centrifuged under standardized conditions (Table 30-1).

Coagulation is essentially a plasma phenomenon, in which the platelets participate, however. The formed elements (erythrocytes, leukocytes, platelets) are trapped in the meshwork of the jelly-like fibrin clot, which, under normal conditions, shrinks on standing (retraction), squeezing out a straw-colored fluid termed "serum," which may be obtained by subsequent centrifugation. Serum differs from plasma chemically chiefly in that it contains no fibrinogen, which has been transformed to fibrin in the process of coagulation. With this exception, for all practical purposes, serum and plasma may be used interchangeably for chemical studies. Plasma obtained with such anticoagulants as sodium or potassium oxalate, fluoride, and citrate is obviously unsuitable for determinations of sodium, potassium, or calcium. Serum is usually employed routinely for such studies and, indeed, for many others, e.g., other electrolytes, pH, proteins, lipids, hormones, vitamins.

The total circulating blood and plasma volumes are indicated in Table 30-1. The values for women are about 7 per cent lower than for men. The methods employed for these determinations are outlined elsewhere (p. 296).

Blood Groups, Specific Substances

Human blood can be classified into four main groups and several subgroups on the basis of the presence (or absence) of specific substances in the erythrocytes, termed "agglutinogens." These are nitrogenous, neutral, heteropolysaccharides, containing amino acids or peptides as well as carbohydrate groups. They are mucopolysaccharides, containing N-acetyl-D-glucosamine, N-acetyl-D-galactosamine, L-fucose, and D-galactose, among other components. There are two major agglutinogens, designated A and B, and several minor ones, including M, N, P, and Rh. The blood group (or type) is determined by the nature of the specific agglutinogens (or their absence) in the red blood cells, a characteristic that is transmitted in mendelian fashion as a genetic dominant. These substances resemble the type specific polysaccharides present in certain bacteria (e.g., pneumococci). The A and B agglutinogens react specifically with α and β isoagglutinins, respectively. The isoagglutinins, globulin in nature, are present in the blood plasma. Erythrocytes containing A agglutinogen are agglutinated ("clumped") by plasma containing α isoagglutinin. Consequently, if a given agglutinogen occurs in the cells the corresponding isoagglutinin is never present in the plasma. These characteristics are of obvious importance in determining the compatibility of blood for transfusion and also in medicolegal situations involving questions of paternity. The group specific substances are present in practically all body cells and in certain body fluids (e.g., saliva, gastric juice).

Chemistry of Blood Coagulation

The process of blood coagulation is a vital mechanism of defense against loss of blood in the event of disruption of the continuity of blood vessels incident to trauma to which all organisms are subjected from time to time. Defense against abnormal blood loss involves: (1) constriction and retraction of blood vessels; (2) agglutination of platelets; (3) coagulation (clotting) of plasma. We are concerned here only with the latter, which is accomplished by a series of coordinated chemical events.

The only visible feature of the clotting process is the transformation of fibrinogen, a circulating soluble plasma protein, to fibrin, the solid clot.

According to the classical view, this is the terminal event in two main reaction sequences: (1) conversion of prothrombin to thrombin through the action of thromboplastin and Ca^{++}; (2) transformation of fibrinogen to fibrin under the influence of thrombin. This scheme does not reflect adequately present understanding of the blood coagulation mechanism, since several steps and several factors are involved in each of the two main reaction sequences of the classical theory.

Conversion of Prothrombin to Thrombin

Eleven plasma factors concerned with blood coagulation are listed in Table 30-2. All except fibrinogen are involved in the conversion of prothrombin to thrombin.

Prothrombin. This is a glycoprotein (m.w. about 65,000), containing hexose and glucosamine, present in the α_2-globulin fraction of the blood plasma. Vitamin K plays an essential part in the synthesis of prothrombin in liver cells (p. 172), but there is evidence also for an important role of this vitamin in the formation of proconvertin. Animals deficient in vitamin K exhibit decreased plasma levels of both prothrombin and proconvertin, the consequent delay in the process of blood coagulation being responsible for the hemorrhagic tendency in these animals.

Prothrombin may be regarded as a proenzyme, which is converted to the enzyme, thrombin, through the action, under various circumstances, of various combinations of Factors II to XII (Table 30-2).

Thromboplastin. This designation was originally applied to what was regarded as a component of tissue extracts, presumably a lipoprotein, the lipid component being mainly a mixture of phosphatides, which was believed to be a direct activator of prothrombin in the presence of calcium ions.

It is known now that optimal conversion of prothrombin to thrombin requires, in addition to "thromboplastin" and Ca^{++}, Factor V (proaccelerin) and Factor VII (proconvertin), which probably serve to activate the tissue extract component ("thromboplastin"). The reaction is accelerated also by Factor X (Stuart-Prower Factor). Clearly, the material originally called thromboplastin can no longer be regarded as the direct activator of prothrombin. The term prothrombinase has been suggested for the agent immediately concerned with conversion of prothrombin to thrombin, the ultimate product of interaction of the tissue extractive ("thromboplastin"), Factor V, Ca^{++}, and Factors VII and X.

TABLE 30-2. BLOOD COAGULATION FACTORS.

FACTOR	OTHER DESIGNATION
I	Fibrinogen
II	Prothrombin
III	Thromboplastin
IV	Calcium
V	Proaccelerin; plasma Ac-globulin; labile factor
VII	Proconvertin; stable factor; serum prothrombin conversion accelerator
VIII	Antihemophilic factor (AHF); antihemophilic factor A; antihemophilic globulin
IX	Plasma thromboplastin component (PTC); Christmas factor; antihemophilic factor B
X	Stuart-Prower factor
XI	Plasma thromboplastin antecedent (PTA); antihemophilic factor C
XII	Hageman factor; glass factor

Adapted from Gaston, L. W.: New England J. Med. *270*:236, 1964.

Formation of Thrombin

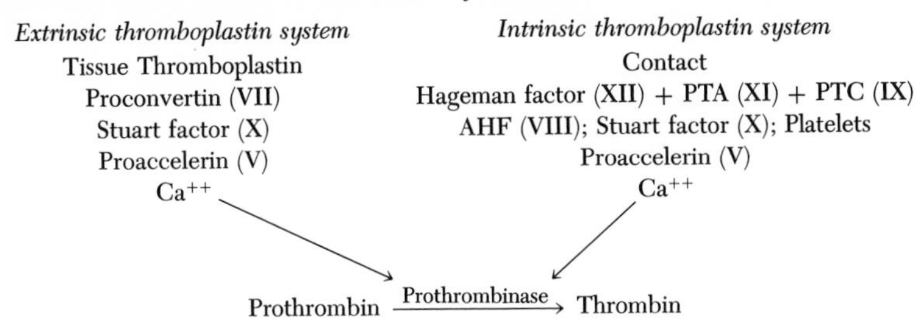

Conversion of Fibrinogen to Fibrin

Step 1. (Proteolysis)		Fibrinogen $\xrightarrow{\text{Thrombin}}$ Fibrin monomer (f) + Fibrinopeptides A and B
Step 2. (Polymerization)		Fibrin monomers (nf) $\longrightarrow$ Fibrin polymer (f_n)
Step 3. (Clotting)	(a)	Fibrin polymers (mf_n) $\longrightarrow$ Fibrin$_s$ (soft clot)
	(b)	Fibrin$_s$ $\longrightarrow$ Fibrin$_i$ (hard clot)

Figure 30-1. Mechanism of blood coagulation. (Adapted from Gaston, L. W.: New England J. Med. *270:*236, 1964.)

This is, of course, an artificial system, inasmuch as under normal conditions blood clots in the absence of tissue extracts. The current view is that under such circumstances a "blood thromboplastin" is formed by the interaction of certain factors derived from platelets, and Factors V (proaccelerin), VIII (antihemophilic factor), IX (plasma thromboplastin component), X (Stuart-Prower Factor), and, under certain conditions, Factors XI (plasma thromboplastin antecedent) or XII (glass factor). In the presence of calcium ions, the interaction of these agents results in the production of "prothrombinase," which catalyzes the conversion of prothrombin to thrombin.

Conversion of Fibrinogen to Fibrin

In the presence of thrombin, fibrinogen (soluble) produces fibrin (insoluble), with the formation of a firm clot. This reaction occurs in three main stages: (1) proteolysis; (2) polymerization; (3) clotting.

Proteolysis. Thrombin is a proteolytic enzyme which acts upon arginyl-glycine linkages in fibrinogen, producing two molecules of each of two types of peptides, fibrinopeptide A and fibrinopeptide B. The residual portion of the original fibrinogen molecule is termed "fibrin monomer." Thrombin does not act beyond this point.

Polymerization. The fibrin monomers promptly undergo polymerization by first an end-to-end and later a side-to-side alignment. If this reaction is conducted with purified reagents, in the absence of Ca^{++} and other serum factors, a so-called fine or soft clot is

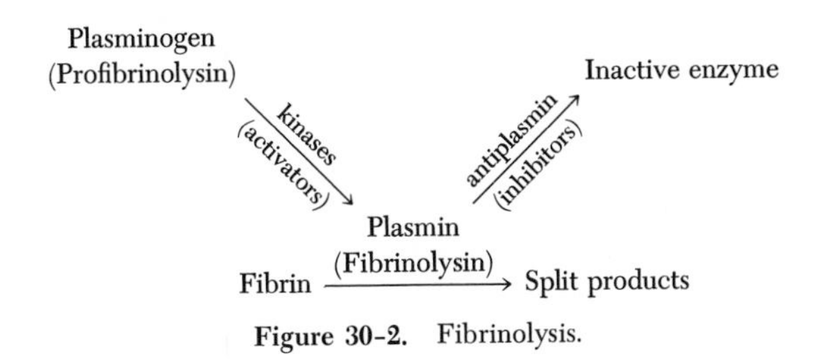

Figure 30-2. Fibrinolysis.

formed, which can be solubilized by adjustments of the pH or by certain concentrations of urea and sodium bromide. In the presence of Ca^{++} and a serum factor termed "fibrin stabilizing factor" or "fibrinase," the clot becomes coarse and hard, no longer capable of being solubilized by the manipulations indicated above. This change is believed to represent formation of new disulfide cross linkages.

Inhibitors of Coagulation

Artificial. Coagulation of blood can be prevented by removing calcium ions, which are necessary for conversion of prothrombin to thrombin. This can be accomplished by addition of oxalate, citrate, or fluoride, which form un-ionized calcium salts, and by other agents that bind calcium, such as ion-exchange resins, and ethylenediaminetetraacetate (EDTA), a chelating agent.

Natural. Under normal conditions, the fluidity of the circulating blood is insured by the unbroken continuity of the vascular endothelium, lacking therefore one of the factors necessary for development of thromboplastic activity, i.e., platelet disintegration, or contact with extravascular tissues or foreign surfaces. However, except under very unusual circumstances, disruption of the continuity of the vascular endothelium rarely results in more than local clotting, the fluidity of the circulating blood being preserved. This resistance to massive coagulation is due in part at least to the presence of anticoagulant systems in the blood. The most important known factors are heparin and antithrombin; there is suggestive evidence also of the presence of an antithromboplastin.

Heparin is an acid mucopolysaccharide (p. 24) containing glucuronic acid, glucosamine, and sulfate. It was originally isolated from liver but occurs in many tissues, particularly lung, arising apparently in mast cells, which are distributed widely along the walls of blood vessels. Heparin is rapidly destroyed in the body by the enzyme, heparinase, therefore exerting a rather transient anticoagulant effect (few hours) upon single administration. Although it has seldom been found in normal blood, it is believed to be present in minute amounts.

Heparin delays coagulation of blood both in vivo and in vitro, apparently acting at two points in the clotting mechanism: (1) in the presence of a cofactor associated with the serum albumin fraction, it inhibits conversion of prothrombin to thrombin; i.e., it acts as an antiprothrombin; (2) in the presence of this cofactor, it delays the conversion of fibrinogen to fibrin under the influence of thrombin; i.e., it acts as an antithrombin. There is evidence that the essential cofactor for heparin is an antithrombin. The action of heparin as an activator of plasma lipoprotein lipase (clearing effect, p. 492) is apparently not related to its anticoagulant effects.

Several apparently different antithrombins have been isolated from the blood under different conditions. All are proteins, migrating electrophoretically close to α- and β-globulins. Antithrombin II may be the heparin cofactor; it is an α-globulin. The plasma antithrombin serves to neutralize the vast excess of thrombin produced during the process of coagulation, thereby preventing extension of the clot beyond desirable limits.

Fibrinolysis

Under ordinary conditions, extravascular blood clots and, at times, intravascular thrombi disappear quite rapidly. This is due, in part at least, to a fibrinolytic system present in the blood plasma, in addition to tissue factors and leukocytes.

This system consists of a proenzyme, plasminogen (profibrinolysin), a globulin which, in the presence of an activator, is converted to plasmin (fibrinolysin), a proteolytic enzyme which actively hydrolyzes fibrin as well as a number of other proteins. Activators of plasminogen have been demonstrated in the blood plasma during periods of exercise, ischemia, and emotional stress, and following administration of epinephrine. Plasminogen may be activated also by factors present in tissues (fibrinolysinases), urine (urokinase), bacteria (streptokinase, staphylokinase), and by treatment with chloroform and other organic solvents. The blood plasma normally contains also inhibitors of plasminogen activation and of plasmin activity (antiplasmins).

Chemical Composition of Formed Elements

In contrast to the plasma, which serves as the main transport medium for nutrient materials, metabolites, vitamins, hormones, etc., the formed elements, apart from the respiratory functions of hemoglobin, have rather specific functions that are not intimately concerned in general metabolic processes. With the important exception of hemoglobin, therefore, general biochemical interest has been focused mainly upon the chemical constituents of the plasma rather than of the erythrocytes, leukocytes, and thrombocytes (platelets). Certain features of the chemical composition of the formed elements, however, have some bearing on their specialized functions, and will be reviewed briefly.

Erythrocytes

The erythrocytes are not living cells in the strict sense. They contain no nucleic acids or mitochondria, cannot reproduce, and have very little aerobic metabolism and no protein, fat, or carbohydrate synthetic activity. These substances and functions are lost upon conversion of normoblasts and reticulocytes to mature red blood cells. The erythrocytes' most important component, hemoglobin, in contrast to the proteins of other cells, undergoes no degradation or resynthesis during the "life" of the cell (about 120 days). The erythrocytes' chief function, by virtue of their hemoglobin content, is to make possible the transport of required amounts of oxygen from the lungs to the tissues, and of carbon dioxide in the reverse direction. The main functions of the other components must therefore be directed toward the support of the respiratory functions of hemoglobin, the chemistry and metabolism of which are considered elsewhere (pp. 124, 611, 614).

Erythrocytes have a solid content of about 35 per cent, almost all of which is Hb (32 per cent). Most of the remaining 3 per cent is represented by proteins and lipids, which form the stromal meshwork in which the Hb is held, and which also concentrate on the cell surface as a limiting membrane (cell wall). This membrane is perfectly permeable to water and apparently to certain small organic molecules, e.g., urea and creatinine (but not glucose), which consequently exist in similar concentrations in the water of the plasma and erythrocytes. The membrane is freely permeable to certain monovalent anions (HCO_3^-, Cl^-, SCN^-, OH^-). The predominant cation is potassium, and there is relatively little Na and Mg and virtually no Ca. H^+ ions cross the membrane readily, Zn^{++} (influencing carbonic anhydrase activity) somewhat less freely, and K^+ still less so. The phosphate content (50 to 100 mg. P/100 gm.) is much higher than that of plasma, but only about 1 mg. P/100 gm. is inorganic phosphate, the remainder being organic. About one-half of the latter is triosephosphate, about one-fourth each hexosephosphate and ATP, with traces of NAD and NADP. Phosphate apparently enters the cell by an active process, much more rapidly than it diffuses out, probably being utilized in phosphorylation reactions in the process of glycolysis, which apparently is a main source of energy for these cells.

The lipid content of the erythrocytes (450 to 700 mg./100 gm.) is lower than that of plasma, owing chiefly to the virtual absence of neutral fat, but the glycolipid and phospholipid contents are higher. Moreover, the proportion of cephalins is greater than that of lecithins, the reverse of the situation in plasma. The cholesterol concentration (125 to 150 mg./100 gm.) is lower than in plasma, all being in the free state in adults, whereas about 70 per cent of the plasma cholesterol is in the ester form.

Other organic constituents include: the blood group substances; glutathione and thioneine, which are not present in the plasma; amino acids (6 to 10 mg. amino acid N/100 gm.); intermediate- and end-products of glycolysis (e.g., hexose- and triosephosphates, lactic acid); and several enzymes. The latter include enzymes of the glycolytic and phosphogluconate oxidative pathways, catalase, peptidase, phosphatases, a more specific cholinesterase than that in plasma, carbonic anhydrase, which plays an important role in the mechanism of CO_2 transport (p. 287), methemoglobin reductase, and thiosulfate : cyanide sulfurtransferase, which catalyzes the transformation of cyanide to thiocyanate.

Energy is required for preservation of the integrity of erythrocyte morphology (e.g., biconcavity), composition, and function, including transport of many substances across the erythrocyte membrane, e.g., glucose, phosphate, sodium, and potassium. Because of the absence of a tricarboxylic acid cycle system, these energy requirments are met by glycolysis and the phosphogluconate oxidative pathway. In addition, the NADPH produced by the latter and NADH by the former play an important role in maintaining hemoglobin in a functional state (Fe^{++}), which requires continual reduction, by methemoglobin reductase, of the Fe^{+++} of methemoglobin which is produced slowly but continually by oxidation of hemoglobin. The importance of this reaction is reflected in the fact that in subjects with genetically determined deficiency of methemoglobin reductase (p. 612), up to 40 per cent of the total hemoglobin may be in the form of methemoglobin.

Aging of the red blood cells is accompanied by decreased formation of ATP and progressive loss of lipids, lipoproteins, and enzyme proteins. The spherical shape of the erythrocytes in hereditary spherocytosis (congenital hemolytic jaundice), which permits them to be more readily trapped and destroyed in the spleen, is associated with decreased capacity for ATP formation; the precise enzyme defect is not known. Increased susceptibility to hemolysis by certain antimalarial drugs, e.g., primaquine, is associated with a genetically determined deficiency in glucose-6-phosphate dehydrogenase (or in its activation) in the erythrocytes. The consequent deficient production of NADPH, which is a requirement for glutathione reductase, results in a low content of reduced glutathione. Glucose-6-phosphate dehydrogenase deficiency is present also in persons exhibiting increased sensitivity to the fava bean (favism) and to hemolysis by a number of other drugs, e.g., sulfonamides, acetophenetidin, acetanilid, and naphthalene. The nature of the relationship between the enzyme defect and the susceptibility to hemolysis is not known.

Leukocytes

The chemical composition of these cells resembles that of other tissue cells. The predominating proteins are compound proteins, chiefly nucleoproteins. Lymphocytes contain relatively large amounts of γ-globulin, probably serving as a storage site for this protein (antibodies [p. 562]), which is liberated upon lysis of the cell. The γ-globulins are probably formed mainly in plasma cells, which are probably also the site of production of Bence Jones protein in multiple myeloma. Heparin is produced in the basophilic mast cells. These cells also have a relatively high content of histamine, produced by decarboxylation of histidine (p. 583). Granulocytes and monocytes have a high content of phosphatases and of glycolytic and proteolytic enzymes, the latter perhaps being related to the phagocytic action of these cells on bacteria and cellular debris. The alkaline phosphatase of neutrophils is believed to be an evidence of maturity of these cells; it is characteristically absent or markedly decreased in chronic granulocytic leukemia. The cytoplasmic granules of granulocytes exhibit strong peroxidase activity, a fact which is utilized in the histochemical identification of this series of cells.

The adrenal glucocorticoids exert a striking influence on the production or destruction of eosinophils and lymphocytes, either depressing the former or accelerating the latter process. Administration of these hormones causes a prompt decrease in the number of these cells in the circulation and their continued administration results in virtually complete disappearance of lymphocytes from the tissues.

Thrombocytes (Platelets)

These small particles of megakaryocytes contain proteins and relatively large amounts of phospholipids, much of which is cephalin. Upon lysis, they liberate factors which participate in the mechanism of blood coagulation (p. 799), and also serotonin (p. 595) and histamine (p. 583).

Chemical Composition of Blood Plasma

The blood plasma is the medium of transport of nutrient materials from the alimentary tract to the tissues, of metabolites from one tissue to another, of hormones from their organs of origin to target tissues, and of waste products from the sites of their production to excretory organs. Being in equilibrium with the interstitial fluid across the semipermeable capillary walls (p. 306), the chemical composition of the blood plasma may be regarded as representative of that of extracellular fluids generally, recognizing the existence of certain regional variations in the latter. As would be anticipated, studies of its chemical components have yielded valuable information on various aspects of normal and abnormal metabolism. Plasma (or whole blood) is used extensively clinically for such studies because of its accessibility and because the concentration of a given constituent reflects, although at times imperfectly, the state of metabolism of that substance, e.g., normal or abnormal formation, normal or abnormal utilization or excretion.

Development of techniques that permit rapid quantitative determination of a number of substances in small volumes of blood has contributed enormously to diagnosis, prognosis, and treatment in virtually every clinical field. The availability of such procedures has also contributed in large measure to our present knowledge of the functional activities of various organs, e.g., the liver and kidneys, and the manner in which these functions may be altered in disease. A satisfactory understanding of the significance of deviations from the normal concentrations of plasma components is essential for modern clinical practice. Such abnormalities can be interpreted properly only on the basis of an understanding of the factors and mechanisms concerned in the preservation of normal levels of concentration of at least those plasma constituents that are of clinical significance.

These matters have been dealt with in detail in connection with discussions of the metabolism of proteins, nucleic acids, porphyrins, lipids, carbohydrates, inorganic elements, hormones, and vitamins, and of the regulation of "acid-base" balance and respiration. It seems desirable here to indicate again, for purposes of emphasis, the normal range of values for the substances that are of major clinical interest, with brief comments on the directions in which abnormalities may occur in certain important disease states. A comprehensive discussion of the significance of such abnormalities is beyond the scope of this book, and is available in works on clinical biochemistry. However, as indicated above, they can usually be readily interpreted as consequences of aberrations of normal control mechanisms. Fundamentally, abnormal increase or decrease in any constituent of the plasma must be due to an imbalance between the rate of its entrance into (production, liberation) and removal from (utilization, excretion) the bloodstream. If the factors concerned in these processes are understood, the general significance of the abnormality will be apparent. The quantitative data presented in the tables, unless otherwise specified, represent normal values, at rest, in the postabsorptive state, i.e., after an overnight fast, under which conditions variations are at a minimum.

Proteins (Table 30-3)

The nature, properties, functions, and metabolism of the plasma proteins are discussed in detail elsewhere (p. 558). It is necessary here only to review certain points of fundamental importance from the standpoint of abnormalities that may occur in disease.

The normal concentrations of the major protein fractions in serum are indicated in Table 30-3. It will be noted that although it is possible to obtain by a salting-out procedure (modified Milne method) values for albumin and globulins that approach those obtained by electrophoresis, this is not accomplished by other methods commonly employed (Howe). With many such procedures, about 1 gm. of globulin is included in the "albumin" fraction. With the Milne procedure, pseudoglobulin corresponds rather closely to the α-globulins, and euglobulin to the β- and γ-globulins. Serum contains no fibrinogen; this is removed from the plasma during the process of coagulation, and is incorporated in the clot (fibrin).

Albumin is affected more readily than globulins by nutritional factors, e.g., restricted protein intake. Because of its smaller molecular size, it is lost from the circulating plasma more readily than the other proteins by passage through capillary walls of increased permeability, as in inflammation (into inflammatory effusions into tissue spaces), glomerulonephritis, and nephrosis (albuminuria). Because of their different functions, metabolism, and sites of origin, plasma albumin and globulins are subject to different influences, and their concentrations may therefore vary independently of one another. Although it is possible for all fractions to be increased simultaneously, e.g., in sudden hemoconcentration, or to be decreased, e.g., in sudden hemodilution or severe malnutrition, in the majority of disease states in which the plasma proteins are altered the albumin is decreased and the globulins increased.

Albumin. The plasma albumin concentration falls somewhat in the later stages of

Table 30-3. Serum Protein Concentrations

PROTEIN	SALTING OUT		ELECTROPHORESIS	
	HOWE (gm. %)	MILNE (modified) (gm. %)	(gm. %)	(% of total)
Total	6–8 (7)*	6–8 (7)	6–8 (7)	100
Albumin	4.7–5.7 (5.2)	3.6–4.5 (4.0)	3.8–5.0 (4.4)	52–68 (60)
Globulin	1.3–2.5 (2.0)	2.1–4.2 (3.2)	2.0–4.0 (3.0)	32–48 (40)
Pseudo-		0.8–1.9 (1.3)	α 0.5–1.3 (0.9)	9–17 (12)
Eu-		1.3–2.5 (1.9)	β 0.6–1.2 (0.9)	8–16 (12)
			γ 0.8–1.6 (1.2)	10–22 (16)

* Figures in parentheses are mean values.

normal pregnancy, owing in part to hemodilution, and in part to decreased synthesis. The major causes for abnormal decrease in albumin (hypoalbuminemia) may be outlined as follows:

(1) Excessive loss (in urine, ascitic fluid, inflammatory exudates, etc.).

(2) Inadequate protein supply (dietary protein restriction, vomiting, diarrhea, etc.).

(3) Impaired synthesis (liver dysfunction, chronic infection, severe anemia, cachexia, etc.).

(4) Sudden plasma dilution (following sudden recovery from dehydration, as with intravenous salt solution in diabetic coma, infantile diarrhea, etc.).

If the plasma albumin concentration falls to a sufficiently low level, edema may occur. This is the most prominent clinical manifestation of hypoalbuminemia, and is due to the decrease in plasma colloid osmotic pressure, which favors retention of water in the tissue spaces (p. 306). The increase in globulins that often occurs simultaneously, e.g., in glomerulonephritis, hepatitis, chronic infections, is incapable of compensating adequately for the decrease in albumin because, their molecular size being greater, the globulins are much less effective in raising the osmotic pressure (pp. 560, 562).

Study of the plasma albumin concentration is of clinical importance in relation to the investigation not only of the cause of edema, but also of the state of liver function and of protein nutrition.

Globulins. The heterogeneity of the globulin fraction of the plasma proteins (p. 560) permits considerable variation in its individual components without significant alteration, at times, in the total, e.g., as determined by salting-out procedures. Further fractionation into pseudo- and euglobulin fractions may yield additional information, particularly since the latter includes the β- and γ-globulins, which are most frequently affected in disease. Reference is made elsewhere to the association of the β-globulins with plasma lipids (lipoproteins) (p. 489), and to the fact that most of the circulating antibodies are γ-globulins (p. 562). It would be anticipated, therefore, that an increase might occur in the β-globulins in conditions in which the plasma lipids are elevated, and in the γ-globulins in infections or other conditions in which the formation of antibodies is stimulated. The α-globulins also are increased frequently in febrile disorders.

Hyperglobulinemia occurs commonly in association with hepatitis and hepatic cirrhosis, glomerulonephritis, and many acute and chronic infectious diseases (increase in euglobulin and, at times, in pseudoglobulin). In multiple myeloma there is often a striking increase in the euglobulin fraction, due usually to appearance of an abnormal component, usually with somewhat slower or faster electrophoretic mobility than normal γ-globulins. In many of these conditions the plasma albumin is decreased, and the total protein concentration is either normal or subnormal. Occasionally (e.g., in multiple myeloma, certain cases of hepatic cirrhosis, certain chronic infections), however, the increase in globulin may be so large that the total protein concentration is elevated considerably.

At birth the serum γ-globulin, in approximately normal adult concentration, is derived solely from the maternal circulation. It decreases steadily to about 0.1 gm. per 100 ml. at 3 to 4 months, prior to which time there is little or no γ-globulin production by the infant, due to immaturity of the plasma cell system. The concentration rises subsequently to approximately adult levels at 8 to 12 months. This period of physiological hypogammaglobulinemia ($2\frac{1}{2}$ to $4\frac{1}{2}$ months of age) is associated with increased susceptibility to bacterial infections. Abnormal forms of hypogammaglobulinemia occur as a result of congenital defects in plasma cell production, acquired loss of ability to synthesize γ-globulin in later life, or extensive disease of the reticuloendothelial system (e.g., multiple myeloma, leukemia, total body irradiation).

The serum mucoproteins, which normally comprise about 25 per cent of the total α_1-globulin fraction, may vary in disease and be of diagnostic significance, e.g., in a decrease in certain types of liver disease and endocrine disorders, and an increase in certain neoplasms and infectious and inflammatory diseases.

The term "cryoglobulins," i.e., "cold-globulins," is applied to plasma proteins which precipitate from blood serum spontaneously usually only in the cold (7 to 11° C.), and which usually, but not invariably, redissolve at room temperatures. They resemble γ-globulins, and, although they have been found in normal blood, they occur in increased amounts most frequently in multiple myeloma and a few other diseases.

The term "pyroglobulins" has been applied to plasma proteins that gel on exposure to moderate elevation of temperature (e.g., 55° C.); they may not redissolve on returning to room temperature. They have been observed in multiple myeloma.

For clinical purposes, the technical difficulties inherent in accurate quantitative fractionation of the plasma globulins are commonly circumvented by employing certain simple qualitative reactions which are sensitive to significant increases in either β-globulins (thymol turbidity and flocculation tests) or γ-globulin (cephalin-cholesterol flocculation; zinc turbidity). These procedures have been found particularly useful in the study of patients with liver damage and biliary tract disease.

Fibrinogen. Formation of fibrinogen is apparently stimulated, and the plasma fibrinogen concentration increased, in many acute infections (normal: 0.2 to 0.4 [average 0.3] gm./100 ml.). This, together with the increase in globulins, is the cause of the increased rate of sedimentation of erythrocytes which occurs in such conditions (sedimentation test). Although it is formed exclusively in the liver, significant decrease in plasma fibrinogen seldom occurs in liver disease, except under conditions of virtually complete abolition of hepatic function (e.g., hepatectomy in experimental animals). A condition of afibrinogenemia may occur, rarely, as a congenital defect and, more commonly, as a serious complication of pregnancy. In the latter case, it is due to defibrination of the maternal blood as a result of entrance into the maternal circulation of amniotic fluid rich in thromboplastin or as a result of some placental abnormality.

Carbohydrates and Related Substances (Table 30-4)

Glucose is the most important carbohydrate in the blood plasma from both physiological and clinical standpoints. The several factors involved in regulation of its concen-

TABLE 30-4. CARBOHYDRATES AND CARBOHYDRATE METABOLITES IN BLOOD PLASMA (FASTING)

SUBSTANCE	CONCENTRATION (mg./100 ml.)
Glucose	70–110 (90)*
Fructose	5–9 (7)
Lactose (lactation)	0–2
Polysaccharides	90–140 (110)
Glucosamine	50–90 (70)
Lactic acid (resting)	5–20 (10)
Pyruvic acid	0.4–2 (1.2)
Citric acid	1.5–3.2 (2.3)

* Figures in parentheses are mean values.

tration in the blood are discussed elsewhere (p. 433). There is a small amount of pentose (2 to 3 mg./100 ml.), apparently mainly in the form of nucleosides and nucleotides.

The designations "polysaccharides" and "glucosamine" are undoubtedly overlapping, and include, in part, substances composed of galactose, mannose, and glucosamine, some of which are also in the form of mucoprotein. Their significance is not known.

Various intermediates of the tricarboxylic acid cycle occur in low and approximately equal concentration, e.g., citric, α-ketoglutaric, succinic, and malic acids. They, as well as pyruvic acid, increase in diabetes mellitus. Pyruvic and lactic acids (p. 430) increase during strenuous exercise and in the presence of congestive heart failure (stagnant hypoxia) and thiamine deficiency (p. 178). The lactic acid, originating mainly from muscle glycogen during the contraction process, is en route to the liver for reconversion to glycogen (or glucose); it may increase when liver function is impaired.

Certain interrelations between calcium and citrate metabolism are referred to elsewhere (p. 637). Parallel changes may occur in the concentrations of citrate and calcium in the blood plasma under certain conditions, e.g., after nephrectomy, administration of parathyroid hormone or vitamin D, and injection of calcium chloride or neutral citrate.

Lipids (Table 30-5)

The lipid content of the plasma varies widely in normal subjects, even in the postabsorptive state. The origin and significance of the various plasma lipids are discussed elsewhere (pp. 489, 493, 495, 496) as is the role of the plasma proteins, mainly α- and β-globulins, in their transport (lipoproteins, p. 489). Although the concentrations of the three major fractions, i.e., triglycerides (neutral fat), phosphatides (phospholipids), and cholesterol, frequently vary in the same direction, although not to the same degree, this is not always the case.

TABLE 30-5. LIPIDS, KETONE BODIES, AND BILE ACIDS IN PLASMA (FASTING)

SUBSTANCE	CONCENTRATION (mg./100 ml.)
Total lipid	385–675 (530)*
Neutral fat	0–260 (140)
Unesterified fatty acids	8–31 (26)
Phospholipids	110–250 (165)
Lecithin	80–200 (110)
Cephalin	0–30 (10)
Sphingomyelin	10–50 (30)
Cholesterol	140–260 (200)
Ester	90–200 (145)
Free	40–70 (55)
Total fatty acids	110–485 (300)
Neutral fat × 0.95	
Phospholipid × 0.65	
Cholesterol ester × 0.43	
Ketone bodies (as acetone)	0.2–0.9
Bile acids (as cholic)	0.2–3.0

* Figures in parentheses are mean values.

An increase occurs shortly after a high-fat meal (alimentary or postprandial hyperlipemia), returning to the fasting level in 3 to 6 hours. This is due largely to an increase in neutral fat, particles of which (chylomicrons), ranging in size from 35 mμ to 1 μ, may be seen with the microscope under darkfield illumination; if the concentration is sufficiently high the plasma may be opalescent. Dextran sulfate or heparin causes disappearance of this opalescence (p. 492), the effect of the latter being reversed by protamine. There is also some increase in phospholipid and cholesterol after meals rich in fat. The role of heparin in this "clearing" phenomenon is due apparently to its action either as a cofactor for or as an integral part of the molecule of the enzyme, "lipoprotein lipase" (p. 492).

The plasma lipids rise during normal pregnancy, particularly after the 12th week. They increase early in starvation (or carbohydrate restriction), owing to stimulation of mobilization from the fat depots, and fall later in the course of severe malnutrition (dietary inadequacy or wasting disease). The concentration of cholesterol tends to rise in individuals of advanced age. The important question of the possible relation of this increase to the incidence or development of atherosclerosis is being investigated intensively (see lipoproteins, p. 489).

The hyperlipemia and hypercholesterolemia that occur in diabetes mellitus are reflections of important metabolic aberrations resulting from deficiency in insulin (pp. 494, 727). Since the liver is the main, if not the only, source of plasma cholesterol, particularly the ester fraction, hypocholesterolemia, with a decrease in the ratio of the ester to the free fraction, occurs in the presence of severe liver cell damage (hepatocellular jaundice). Endocrine influences (e.g., thyroid, adrenocortical, insulin) on plasma lipids are considered in the discussions of the individual hormones (q.v.).

Ketone Bodies (Table 30-5)

The concentration of ketone bodies (acetoacetic acid, β-hydroxybutyric acid, acetone), normally very low, increases during dietary restriction or inadequate utilization of carbohydrate (excessive ketogenesis, pp. 448, 469).

Bile Acids (Table 30-5)

These substances, formed in the liver and excreted in the bile, undergo enterohepatic circulation (p. 267), only small amounts entering the systemic circulation under normal conditions. High concentrations (which are rarely encountered) are actively hemolytic, because of their powerful action in lowering surface tension. The quantity in the plasma increases in the presence of obstruction of the common bile duct, if the liver cells continue to function adequately (obstructive jaundice). This diversion of bile acids into the bloodstream is accompanied by and apparently related to an increase in plasma cholesterol (carried from the liver), a phenomenon of clinical importance at times in differentiating obstructive jaundice (hypercholesterolemia) from hepatocellular jaundice (hypocholesterolemia).

Non-protein Nitrogenous Substances (Table 30-6)

This is a heterogeneous group of nitrogen-containing substances not precipitated by protein-precipitating agents (e.g., tungstic acid). They are all metabolic intermediates or end-products. Of the total NPN, about 50 per cent is represented by urea, and about 25 per cent by free amino acids. The remaining 25 per cent includes a large number of substances of varied origin and metabolic significance, such as creatine, creatinine, uric acid, bilirubin, choline, epinephrine, thyroxine, adenosine-containing compounds (e.g., nucleotides, ATP), etc. Glutathione (p. 577) and thioneine are present in the erythrocytes, but not in appreciable amounts in the plasma.

***Urea nitrogen* (*Table 30-6*).** Urea is the chief nitrogenous end-product of protein metabolism, representing the amino groups ingested (or produced in the body) in excess of the requirements (or capacity) for synthesis of body proteins or other nitrogenous substances (p. 570). It is formed in the liver, from amino acids, is passed into the bloodstream, and is excreted in the urine (p. 827). It diffuses readily through capillary walls and cell membranes, and is present in intracellular and extracellular fluids in virtually identical concentration (per unit of water), and also occurs in cerebrospinal fluid, saliva, perspiration, and gastrointestinal secretions.

The blood urea nitrogen may rise temporarily to the upper limits of normal (Table 30-6) following a meal rich in protein. Low normal values are observed during periods of dietary protein restriction and also during pregnancy (increased nitrogen requirement for growth of fetus, placenta, uterus, breasts). The concentration falls also following administration of growth hormone and androgens (stimulation of protein anabolism).

Urea is the chief solid component of the urine under usual dietary conditions (p. 841); consequently, impairment of excretory function of the kidneys is reflected most consistently in a tendency toward urea retention in the body fluids. This is manifested first by decrease in urea "clearance" (p. 836) and later by abnormal increase in the blood urea nitrogen concentration. Low values may be obtained in the presence of very severe liver damage (diminished production).

***Free amino acids* (*Table 30-6*).** The "dynamic equilibrium" that exists between the various body proteins (e.g., tissues, plasma, hemoglobin) (p. 541) implies the existence of an amino acid "pool," which is contributed to continually by degradation of these proteins and which is drawn upon continually for their resynthesis. Accordingly, the concentration of free amino acids in the plasma, representing the extracellular fluids, is the resultant of these catabolic and anabolic processes.

The amino acid content of the plasma rises sharply after a protein meal, returning to the resting level in a few hours. It falls during stimulation of protein anabolism, e.g., by growth hormone or androgen, and also after insulin administration. A marked increase

Table 30-6. Certain Non-protein Nitrogenous Components of Venous Blood (Fasting)

Substance	Whole Blood (mg./100 ml.)	Plasma (mg./100 ml.)
Total NPN	16–40 (30)*	16–40 (30)
Urea N	8–23 (15)	10–23 (16)
Free amino acid N	5–8 (7)	3.5–6 (5)
Creatinine	1–2 (1.5)	0.8–1.0 (0.9)
Creatine	2.5–5 (4)	0.2–0.7 (0.4)
Uric acid	2–4 (3)	2.5–6 (4)
Ammonia	0.03–0.1	
Bilirubin		0.1–1.0 (0.4)
Glutathione	(40)	0

* Figures in parentheses are mean values.

may occur in the presence of severe liver damage (decreased deamination), with a corresponding decrease in urea.

In certain types of hepatic disease, the concentration of ammonia in the blood, normally negligible, may increase. Presumably, ammonia, originating in the intestine as a result of bacterial action and present in the portal circulation, is inadequately removed by the liver. According to some, this increase in blood ammonia may contribute to the development of the serious complication of hepatic coma.

***Uric acid* (*Table 30-6*).** Uric acid is the chief end-product of purine catabolism in man (p. 518). The site of its formation is probably liver (muscles; marrow?). It is excreted in the urine. Its concentration in the plasma is normally affected but slightly by changes in the intake of purine-rich foods. It increases slightly during pregnancy.

Being excreted by the kidneys, it tends to be retained in excess in the body fluids in renal insufficiency, as does urea. It may increase in the plasma also when excessively large numbers of cells are undergoing metabolic degradation (e.g., chronic myeloid leukemia). However, clinical interest is centered particularly in the increase that occurs in gout, owing apparently to increased production of uric acid, the underlying mechanism of which is not understood. Defective excretion (decreased uric acid clearance) occurs also in toxemia of pregnancy (eclampsia). The plasma uric acid may fall in the presence of severe acute liver damage (decreased production).

***Creatine and creatinine* (*Table 30-6*).** The metabolic origin and the significance of creatine and creatinine are discussed elsewhere (p. 578). The latter is a metabolic end-product of the former, is formed (in muscle) in relatively small amounts, passes into the bloodstream, and is excreted in the urine (p. 842). Its concentration in the blood increases in renal functional insufficiency, usually later than the increase in blood urea.

TABLE 30-7. IMPORTANT INORGANIC CONSTITUENTS (AND BICARBONATE) IN BLOOD PLASMA (FASTING)

SUBSTANCE	CONCENTRATION* (mg./100 ml.)	(mEq./liter)
Total "base"		142–158 (150)
Sodium	300–350 (325)†	132–152 (142)
Potassium	14–21 (17)	3.6–5.3 (4.4)
Calcium	8.5–11.5 (10)	4.2–5.7 (5)
Magnesium	1.7–2.8 (2.2)	1.4–2.4 (1.7)
Bicarbonate	55–72 (62) (vol. %)	24–31 (27)
Chloride	340–380 (360)	97–108 (103)
Phosphate (as P)	3–4.5 (3.5)	(HPO_4) 2.2–4.2 (3.2)
Sulfate (as S)	1–2 (1.5)	(SO_4) 0.7–1.5 (1.0)
Iron	0.05–0.18 (0.1)	
Iodine (protein-bound)	0.004–0.008 (0.006)	
Copper	0.08–0.16 (0.12)	
Lead	0.008–0.06 (0.03)	

* To convert mEq./liter to mg./100 ml., multiply mEq./liter by:

Na = 2.3 Cl = 3.5
K = 3.9 HCO_3 = 2.3 (vol. %)
Ca = 2.0 HPO_4 = 1.8
Mg = 1.2 SO_4 = 1.6

† Figures in parentheses are mean values.

Inorganic Elements (Table 30-7)

The significance of these plasma constituents is considered in the discussions of water (p. 293) and acid-base balance (p. 312) and of the metabolism of inorganic elements (pp. 623–647).

Enzymes (Table 30-8)

The blood plasma contains a number of enzymes, several of which have considerable clinical diagnostic significance. Apart from those concerned in coagulation, they probably perform no important metabolic function in the plasma and represent, in most cases, an overflow from their sites of origin. With certain important exceptions (decreased cholinesterase in liver disease; decreased alkaline phosphatase in hypophosphatasia; other genetically determined enzyme deficiencies), clinical significance is attached usually to increased activity of these enzymes. This may result from: (1) increased production (e.g., increased alkaline phosphatase due to osteoblastic proliferation); (2) interference with excretion (e.g., increased serum amylase activity in pancreatic duct obstruction); (3) sudden liberation of intracellular enzymes by massive tissue destruction (e.g., increased transaminase activity in myocardial infarction); (4) liberation into the bloodstream from malignant cells (e.g., increased acid phosphatase activity in metastatic prostatic cancer).

***Amylase* (*Table 30-8*).** The relatively small amount in normal plasma originates apparently in the pancreas and salivary glands. A marked increase occurs during the first 24 to 48 hours of certain forms of acute pancreatitis, owing to liberation of preformed amylase from the degenerating acinar cells directly into the bloodstream. This is of considerable diagnostic significance. An increase may occur in patients with obstruction of the pancreatic duct, particularly after administration of secretin or parasympathicomimetic agents (viz., β-methylcholine). The serum amylase may increase also in inflammation of the parotid gland (parotitis; mumps).

***Lipase* (*Table 30-8*).** This enzyme apparently originates mainly in the pancreas. It increases in the pancreatic disorders mentioned in connection with serum amylase and has the same diagnostic significance as the latter.

***Alkaline Phosphatase* (*Table 30-8*).** The alkaline phosphatase (optimum pH about 9) of normal plasma originates largely in the bones, being formed chiefly by osteoblasts (p. 635) and present also in osteoclasts. An increase in the plasma in skeletal disorders is

TABLE 30-8. CERTAIN CLINICALLY IMPORTANT ENZYMES IN BLOOD PLASMA

Pancreatic	*Transaminase*
Amylase	Glutamate-oxalacetate (Aspartate:oxoglutarate)
Lipase	Glutamate-pyruvate (alanine:oxoglutarate)
Glycolysis	*Phosphatase*
Phosphohexose isomerase	Alkaline
Aldolase	Acid
Lactate dehydrogenase	*Cholinesterase*
Krebs Cycle	
Malate dehydrogenase	
Isocitrate dehydrogenase	

regarded as a reflection of increased osteoblastic activity and is of great clinical value in differentiating between osteomalacia (high phosphatase activity) and osteoporosis (normal activity), as well as in the diagnosis of other skeletal diseases characterized by osteoblastic proliferation (e.g., Paget's disease of bone).

The serum alkaline phosphatase is increased also in biliary obstruction (obstructive jaundice) and, usually to a lesser degree, in certain cases of hepatic disease (hepatocellular jaundice). According to some, this represents retention in the blood of enzyme originating in the intestine, which is normally excreted in the bile. According to others, the enzyme that accumulates in the blood in these disorders originates in the liver (parenchyma or bile duct cells) and, biliary excretion being impaired, is absorbed into the lymphatic system and bloodstream.

Decreased serum alkaline phosphatase activity occurs in hypophosphatasia, a familial and probably genetically determined condition, characterized by defective skeletal mineralization. Alkaline phosphatase activity is low also in the bones and other tissues.

Acid phosphatase **(*Table 30-8*).** Normal plasma contains small amounts of acid phosphatase (optimum pH 4.9), which apparently originates mainly in the liver and spleen. Acid phosphatase activity is present in several organs, but in the adult prostate it is at least 100 times that in other tissues. This enzyme is formed by mature prostatic epithelial cells and is passed into the prostatic secretion. Immature prostatic cells (i.e., in preadolescent boy or castrate) do not form this enzyme, but do so under stimulation by androgens. The chief clinical significance of serum acid phosphatase lies in its relation to the diagnosis of prostatic carcinoma, especially metastatic, in which condition the enzyme gains access to the bloodstream and the activity in the serum increases. This may be distinguished from non-prostatic acid phosphatases in the serum (e.g., in extensive mammary cancer) on the basis of its (prostatic) inhibition by L-tartrate.

Transaminases **(*p. 234*).** Transaminase activity (glutamate-oxaloacetate [aspartate: ketoglutarate]; glutamate-pyruvate [alanine: ketoglutarate]) is demonstrable in normal serum. Markedly increased activity is present in patients with hepatocellular damage (e.g., hepatitis) and, to a lesser extent and more transiently, in those with myocardial infarction (glutamate-oxaloacetate). The excessive amounts of transaminase enter the blood as a result of tissue destruction, liver and heart muscle being particularly rich in these enzymes.

Glycolytic and Krebs cycle enzymes **(*p. 402*).** Increased activity of lactate dehydrogenase, isocitrate dehydrogenase, malate dehydrogenase, phosphohexose isomerase, and aldolase in the serum may occur in such conditions as acute hepatitis, myocardial infarction, extensive skeletal muscle damage, and extensive malignancy. This is due to liberation of preformed enzymes from the damaged tissue.

Cholinesterase **(*p. 240*).** The plasma pseudocholinesterase originates mainly in the liver. It may decrease as a result of impaired liver function.

Erythrocyte glucose-6-phosphate dehydrogenase **(*p. 417*).** Genetically determined inadequacy of this enzyme (in the red blood cells) apparently is a basis for increased susceptibility to hemolysis by a variety of agents (p. 804).

Vitamins (Table 30-9)

With a few exceptions, determination of the concentration of various vitamins in the blood has proved of little aid in the evaluation of nutritional adequacy in these substances. This matter is considered in the discussion of individual vitamins (pp. 142–206).

TABLE 30-9. VITAMINS IN BLOOD PLASMA (FASTING) UNDER AVERAGE ADEQUATE DIETARY CONDITIONS

VITAMINS	CONCENTRATION (μg./100 ml.)
Vitamin A	10–60 (24)*
Carotenoids	40–400 (150)
Vitamin D	1.5–4.5 (3.0)
Vitamin E	900–1900 (1200)
Ascorbic acid	400–1700 (900)
Thiamine	5–14 (9)
Niacin	20–150 (75)
Riboflavin	2–4 (3)
Pantothenic acid	6–35 (15)
Pyridoxine (monkey)	1–18 (8)
Biotin	(1)
Folic acid	1.5–5 (2)
Cobalamin (whole blood)	0.05–0.15 (0.1)

* Figures in parentheses are mean values.

OTHER BODY FLUIDS

Interstitial fluid, i.e., fluid in the tissue spaces, is in dialysis equilibrium with the blood plasma across the semipermeable capillary walls. In general, allowing for regional differences, the chemical composition of this fluid differs from that of plasma mainly in the concentrations of: (1) proteins, which are relatively non-diffusible through most capillaries but which vary considerably in fluids in different tissues; (2) other substances, either inherently non-diffusible or rendered so by adsorption by or combination with plasma proteins, e.g., lipids, certain dyes, bilirubin, calcium; (3) diffusible electrolytes, the distribution of which on the two sides of the capillary wall is influenced by the difference in protein content of the two fluids (Donnan phenomenon, p. 304). The composition of interstitial fluid is discussed in detail elsewhere (p. 300).

The small amounts of fluid normally present in the peritoneal, pleural, and pericardial spaces likewise have the characteristics of protein-poor dialysates of blood plasma, and may be regarded as a portion of the interstitial fluid. Synovial fluid, too, is apparently of similar origin, but contains, in addition, protein material derived from the periarticular connective tissue. Cerebrospinal fluid, however, exhibits features that indicate that it is not a simple dialysate or ultrafiltrate of plasma. Chemical studies of these and other body fluids are at times of diagnostic value. Certain of their most important characteristics will be reviewed briefly.

Lymph

Lymph is the fluid within the lymph vessels; this term is sometimes erroneously applied also to the interstitial fluid. The latter, i.e., the fluid in the extracellular space surrounding tissue cells, is derived from two sources, (1) the cells and (2) the blood plasma. Nutrient and other materials pass into the cells from these tissue spaces, which are drained by two channels, (1) the blood capillaries and (2) the lymphatic capillaries. The latter lead into larger lymphatic vessels, the course of which is interrupted by lymph nodes, and which empty ultimately into the subclavian veins. Lymphocytes, originating in these nodes and in intestinal lymphatic tissue, enter the bloodstream by this route.

Substances that can pass through blood capillary walls readily also enter the lymph without difficulty. Consequently, readily diffusible substances are present in blood plasma, interstitial fluid, and lymph in essentially identical concentrations (per unit water volume), e.g., glucose, urea, creatinine, amino acids. As would be expected in view of the fact that it is in direct equilibrium with the interstitial fluid rather than the blood plasma, lymph resembles the former rather than the latter in its content of protein and certain electrolytes, i.e., generally higher chloride, lower sodium and protein (p. 301), and lower calcium (p. 633) than plasma. Inasmuch as these discrepancies in concentrations of electrolytes are due to differences in protein content, they vary with the latter in lymph (and interstitial fluid) in different regions of the body. Lymph coming from the liver has a high protein content, about 5 per cent, representing an important pathway of delivery of plasma proteins from the liver cells to the bloodstream. Lymph coming from subcutaneous tissues, on the other hand, usually contains less than 1 per cent protein under normal conditions. That in the thoracic duct may contain 2 to 4 per cent. Lymph coagulates slowly when removed from the body, owing to the presence of small amounts of fibrinogen and other clotting factors.

The lymphatic capillaries are more permeable than the blood capillaries. Consequently, colloidal particles, e.g., India ink and certain dyes, injected subcutaneously, enter the lymph much more readily than the blood. The same is true of fat. During absorption of fat from the intestine, its concentration in the thoracic duct lymph may reach 5 to 15 per cent; the milky appearance of such fluid (chyle) is due to the large amount of suspended fat droplets. A similar situation exists, although not to the same degree, in lymph coming from regions of fat storage (depot fat, e.g., subcutaneous, mesenteric, perirenal, pericardial, omental) during periods of excessive mobilization of fat, e.g., carbohydrate restriction, starvation.

Synovial Fluid

This is a clear, straw-colored, viscous fluid, serving to lubricate articular surfaces. It has a specific gravity of 1.008 to 1.015 and a solid content of 1.2 to 4.4 per cent (postmortem specimens). It has the electrolyte and diffusible non-electrolyte (e.g., urea, urate, glucose) composition of extracellular fluids, supporting the view that it is fundamentally a dialysate of blood plasma, to which protein is added from the connective tissue surrounding the joint. The protein content ranges from 0.1 to 2.2 per cent, about half of which is albumin and globulin, and half mucoprotein, containing hyaluronic acid (acetyl-glucosamine-glucuronide) as a prosthetic group. It also contains certain enzymes, including hyaluronidase ("spreading factor"), dehydrogenases, protease, lipase, amylase, and systems capable of metabolizing glucose and fructose.

Cerebrospinal Fluid

Cerebrospinal fluid is formed in the choroid plexuses, enters the lateral ventricles, and passes through the third and fourth ventricles into the subarachnoid space, from which it is reabsorbed into the blood chiefly by the subarachnoid villi. It is a clear, colorless fluid, the total volume (adult) being about 100 to 150 ml., and the specific gravity (spinal fluid) 1.005 to 1.009. When collected with precautions to prevent escape of CO_2, the pH is essentially that of blood plasma, i.e., 7.35 to 7.4, and the HCO_3 40 to 60 volumes per cent (average 22.5 mEq./liter). Although in its chemical composition it corresponds in many respects to a dialysate of the blood plasma (i.e., interstitial fluid, p. 300), the few instances in which it does not (e.g., Mg, PO_4) indicate that it is, in part at least, a product of secretory activity of the choroid plexus.

Organic constituents. Cerebrospinal fluid contains but little protein (15 to 45 mg./100 ml. in that obtained from the spinal canal, with lower concentrations in the fluid from the cisterna and from the ventricles). Approximately 80 per cent of the protein is albumin, the remainder globulin, derived from the blood plasma.

The glucose concentration in the postabsorptive state, 45 to 80 mg./100 ml., varies with the plasma sugar concentration, but not quantitatively. There are small amounts of lactic acid present (10 to 25 mg./100 ml.), minute amounts of cholesterol (0.05 to 0.25 mg./100 ml.), and non-protein nitrogenous substances in approximately the same concentration as in blood plasma (e.g., urea nitrogen, 7 to 15 mg./100 ml.).

The fluid also contains certain hormones (e.g., anterior pituitary), enzymes (amylase, lipase, oxidases), and vitamins (e.g., ascorbic acid in same concentration as in blood plasma). Lactic dehydrogenase may be increased in certain cases of neoplastic disease of the central nervous system.

Inorganic constituents. The inorganic composition (mg./100 ml.; mEq./liter) is as follows: sodium, 300 to 350 mg. (130 to 150 mEq.); potassium, 11 to 16 mg. (average 4 mEq.); calcium, 4 to 6 mg. (average 2.5 mEq.); magnesium, 3 mg.; phosphorus, 1 to 1.5 mg.; chloride, 700 to 750 mg. (as NaCl) (average 125 mEq.).

The relatively higher concentration of chloride than in plasma accords with predictions based on the Donnan equilibrium, and the amount of calcium corresponds to that of the normal diffusible fraction of the serum calcium. However, changes in the latter are not always reflected quantitatively in the spinal fluid calcium. Moreover, the concentration of magnesium is usually higher and of inorganic phosphate lower than in the blood plasma. These facts indicate that this fluid is not a simple dialysate of the plasma.

Semen

Seminal fluid, as normally ejaculated, is a mixture of spermatozoa and secretions of the prostate, seminal vesicles, vas deferens, epididymis, and bulbourethral and urethral glands. It is quite viscid, and clots promptly (fibrinogen), but the clot undergoes liquefaction rapidly (minutes) owing to the presence of fibrinolysin (from prostate). Its quantitative composition varies widely, depending on the relative volume contribution from these sources at the time of collection. However, certain characteristics are of interest, although their significance may not be apparent.

The pH of semen approximates that of blood plasma, but semen contains much less protein, cholesterol, and chloride, and much more calcium, phosphate, and urea than does the latter fluid. The spermatozoa consist largely of nucleoproteins. The prostate contributes the polyamino compounds, spermine and spermidine; the latter is apparently responsible for the rather characteristic odor of seminal fluid.

Acid phosphatase (p. 814) is present in very high concentration (500 to 5000 units/ml.); it is derived from the prostate. The concentration varies with the functional activity of the prostatic epithelial cells, which is under androgenic control. The functional significance of this enzyme is not clear. Hyaluronidase is another enzyme present in abundance in semen that has aroused considerable interest. Because of its action in depolymerizing hyaluronic acid, it has been suggested that it may play an important role in facilitating penetration of the perifollicular gelatinous material in the ovum by the sperm, thus aiding fertilization. This hypothesis has not been supported by recent observations.

In contrast to other body fluids, the main carbohydrate in seminal fluid is not glucose but fructose, which originates in the seminal vesicles, and is present in high concentration (200 to 600 mg./100 ml.). Citrate and lactate are also present in much larger amounts than in blood plasma or other body fluids.

Amniotic Fluid

The fluid in the amniotic sac probably originates as a dialysate of the maternal and fetal blood plasma, its original composition being essentially the same as that of protein-poor interstitial fluids. As the fetus develops, this fluid apparently becomes progressively more diluted with the hypotonic fetal urine. One of its characteristic differences from the maternal blood plasma during this period is its relatively high uric acid content (2 to 9 mg./100 ml.).

BIBLIOGRAPHY

Albritton, E. C. (ed.): Standard Values in Blood, Philadelphia, W. B. Saunders Company, 1952.
Alexander, B.: Coagulation, hemorrhage and thrombosis, New England J. Med. *252:*432, 484, 526, 1955.
Annual Review of Biochemistry.
Annual Review of Physiology.
Biggs, R., and Macfarlane, R. G.: Human Blood Coagulation and Its Disorders, ed. 3, Philadelphia, F. A. Davis Company, 1962.
Cantarow, A., and Trumper, M.: Clinical Biochemistry, ed. 6, Philadelphia, W. B. Saunders Company, 1962.
Davidsohn, I., and Wells, B. B. (eds.): Clinical Diagnosis by Laboratory Methods, ed. 13, Philadelphia, W. B. Saunders Co., 1962, p. 558.
Elkinton, J. R., and Danowski, T. S.: The Body Fluids, Baltimore, Williams & Wilkins Company, 1955.
Gaston, L. W.: The blood-clotting factors, New England J. Med. *270:*236, 290, 1964.
Haurowitz, F.: Chemistry and Biology of Proteins, New York, Academic Press, Inc., 1950.
Lemberg, R., and Legge, J. W.: Hematin Compounds and Bile Pigments, New York, Interscience Publishers, Inc., 1949.
Merritt, H. H., and Fremont-Smith, F.: The Cerebrospinal Fluid, Philadelphia, W. B. Saunders Company, 1937.
Peters, J. P., and Van Slyke, D. D.: Quantitative Clinical Chemistry, ed. 2, Vol. 1, Interpretations, Baltimore, Williams & Wilkins Company, 1931, 1946.
Putnam, F. W. (ed.): The Plasma Proteins, Vol. 2, New York, Academic Press, Inc., 1960.
Sheraga, H. A.: Protein Structure, New York, Academic Press, Inc., 1961.
Sunderman, F. W., and Boerner, F.: Normal Values in Clinical Medicine, Philadelphia, W. B. Saunders Company, 1949.
Tullis, J. L. (ed.): Blood Cells and Plasma Proteins, New York, Academic Press, Inc., 1953.
White, L. P. (ed.): Enzymes in blood, Ann. New York Acad. Sci. *75:*1, 1958.
Wróblewski, F.: The clinical significance of transaminase activities of serum, Am. J. Med. *27:*911, 1959.

CHAPTER 31

URINE FORMATION—RENAL FUNCTION

As STATED by Homer Smith, the composition of the blood plasma is determined by what the kidneys keep rather than by what the mouth ingests. The kidneys are the chief ultimate regulators of the internal environment of the body, and the urine is a by-product of their regulatory activities.

In accomplishing their purpose, i.e., maintenance of a reasonable constancy of composition of the extracellular and, to a certain extent, the intracellular fluids, the kidneys are involved in:

(1) Elimination of water formed in or introduced into the body in excess of the amount required.

(2) Elimination of non-volatile end-products of metabolism.

(3) Elimination of inorganic elements in accordance with the needs of the organism.

(4) Elimination of certain foreign substances that gain access to the body.

TABLE 31-1. URINE-PLASMA CONCENTRATION RATIOS

	CONCENTRATION IN		
CONSTITUENT	URINE (mg. %)	PLASMA (mg. %)	CONCENTRATION RATIO
Urea	1800	30	60
Creatinine	75	1.5	50
Uric acid	60	3	20
Phosphate	160	4	40
Sulfate	150	3	50
Potassium	160	20	8
Chloride	500	350	1.4
Sodium	350	335	1
Calcium	15	10	1.5

Modified from Fishberg: Hypertension and Nephritis, ed. 5, Philadelphia, Lea & Febiger, 1954.

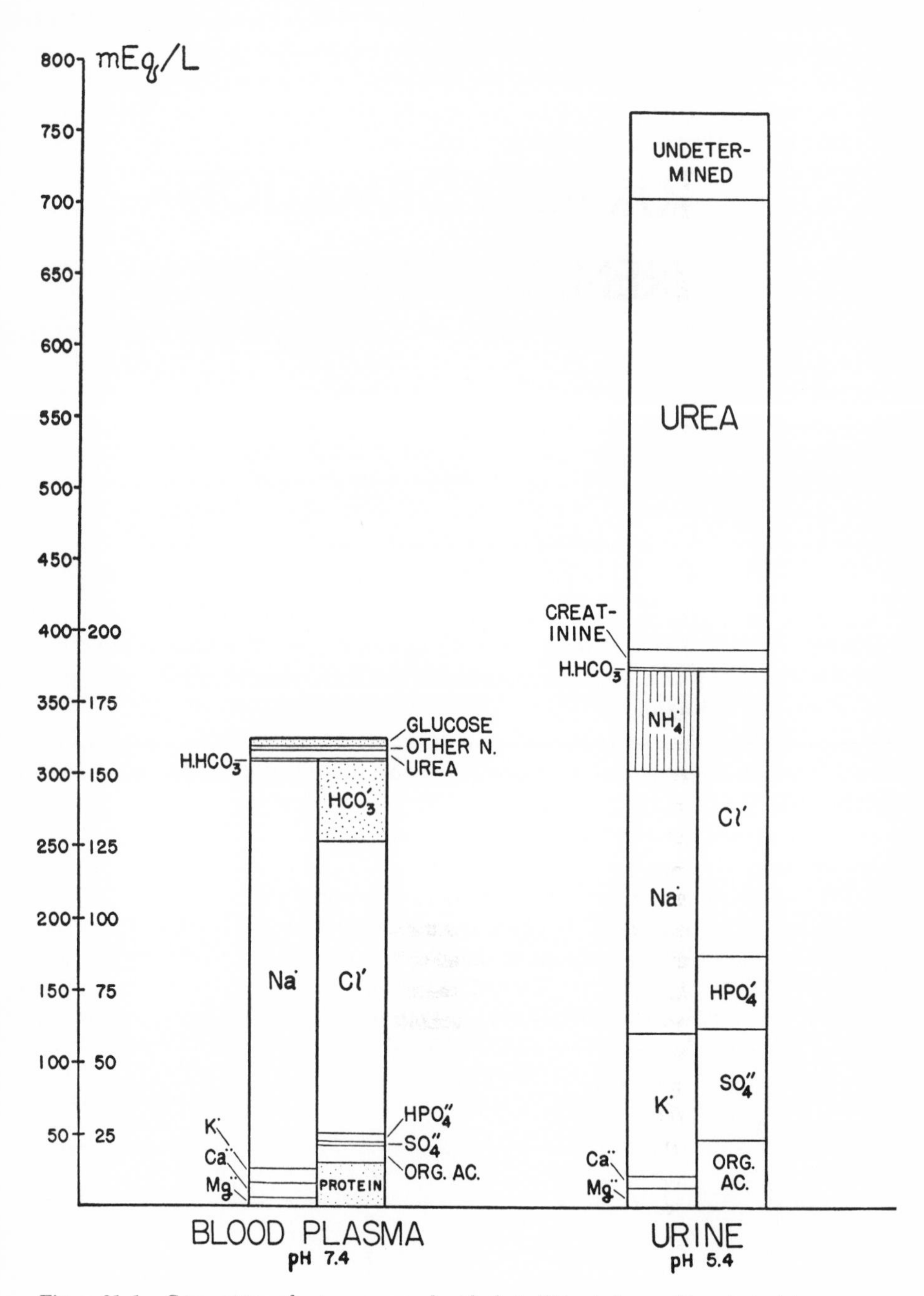

Figure 31-1. Composition of urine compared with that of blood plasma. Non-electrolytes are expressed as millimoles on the milliequivalent scale. (From Gamble: Chemical Anatomy, Physiology, and Pathology of Extracellular Fluid, Cambridge, Harvard University Press, 1950.)

(5) Retention in the body of substances necessary for the maintenance of normal functions, e.g., plasma proteins, glucose, amino acids, hormones, vitamins, etc.

(6) Formation and excretion of certain substances, e.g., ammonia and hydrogen ions.

As a result of these activities the kidneys play an important part in:

(1) The regulation of water balance (p. 293), electrolyte balance (p. 624), and osmotic pressure of the body fluids (p. 299).

(2) The regulation of acid-base balance (p. 316).

(3) The removal of metabolic waste products and certain toxic substances.

Considered in a broad sense, the chief excretory function of the kidney is to eliminate solid substances in solution in water. Many of these substances exist in the urine in much higher concentration than in the blood, the ratio of the average concentration in the urine to its concentration in the blood during the same period (concentration ratio) varying greatly for each of the urinary constituents. Thus, in the normal performance of its excretory functions the kidney must concentrate the eliminated substances, the necessary degree of concentration at any moment depending upon the relative quantities of solids and water present at that moment in the blood passing through the glomerular capillaries. One of the most important characteristics of the healthy kidney is its ability to eliminate the required quantity of solids regardless, within wide limits, of the amount of water available for their solution. In other words, the normal kidney exhibits a remarkable flexibility in its concentrating ability. Consequently, the concentration of solid constituents of normal urine, as evidenced by the specific gravity, varies considerably during the day in accordance with the ingestion of fluids and solid food and with the metabolic activity of the tissues. If large amounts of fluids are ingested the urine is of large volume and low specific gravity; if little water is ingested, or large amounts are lost through other channels such as the skin and gastrointestinal tract, the urine is of small volume and high specific gravity. Investigation of the concentrating ability of the kidney constitutes a most valuable measure for the determination of renal functional integrity.

Morphological Features of Functional Importance

The nephron (uriniferous tubule) is the functional unit, each kidney containing about 1,200,000 of these structures. The nephron consists of two functionally distinct units, (1) the glomerulus, primarily a vascular channel, and (2) the tubule, lined by epithelial cells of different types in different regions.

After entering the kidney, the renal artery divides, successively, into interlobar, arcuate, and interlobular branches, the latter eventuating in the afferent arterioles of the glomeruli. The afferent arteriole breaks up into a set of capillary loops, each of which is enveloped in and intimately bound to the external (basement) layer of Bowman's capsule, the invaginated glomerular end of the tubule, lined by flattened epithelial cells that are apparently functionless. The attached walls of the glomerular capillaries and of Bowman's capsule together form a semipermeable membrane, about 1 μ thick, across which substances pass from the blood plasma into the lumen of the tubule by a process of simple filtration.

The glomerular capillaries reunite to form the efferent arteriole of the glomerulus, the diameter of which is approximately one-half that of the afferent arteriole. This difference in caliber serves to maintain an effective "head" of filtration pressure in the capillaries under varying conditions of arteriolar tonus. The efferent arterioles pass to the several portions of the tubule, breaking up into an elaborate network of capillaries which lie in close approximation to the outer tubular lining, i.e., basement membrane of the tubular epithelial cells. They subsequently unite to form a venous plexus which leads, successively, into the interlobular, arcuate, and interlobar veins, and, finally, the renal vein.

These vascular features have an important bearing on certain important functional considerations, normal and abnormal. By far the bulk of the blood supplying the tubules passes first through the glomeruli, as indicated above. Consequently, interference with blood flow through glomeruli, e.g., in glomerulonephritis, is followed by degenerative changes (ischemia, hypoxia) in the tubular epithelial cells supplied by the corresponding efferent arterioles. This accounts for the almost invariable secondary occurrence of tubular lesions as a complication of primary glomerular damage, unless of brief duration. Moreover, the blood plasma reaching the tubules has an increased colloid osmotic pressure owing to the fact that, in passing through the glomerulus, it has lost about 18 to 20 per cent of its water and diffusible components, but virtually no protein. The resulting increased viscosity of the blood (hemoconcentration) helps to maintain the relatively high pressure in the glomerular capillaries, and the increased plasma colloid osmotic pressure aids in the extensive reabsorption processes that occur in the tubule.

In passing through the glomeruli, the blood loses an essentially protein-free plasma filtrate. In the course of its subsequent passage through the tubules, this filtrate is modified extensively by reabsorptive, excretory, and other activities of the tubular epithelial cells, the final product being urine. Largely as a result of the development of the clearance concept, various phases of renal function can be studied by rather precise quantitative methods. These are of value, not only in furthering understanding of the pathological physiology of certain disease states, but also in differential diagnosis, prognosis, and treatment of diseases of the kidneys or other conditions affecting renal function.

GLOMERULAR FILTRATION

Studies of glomerular fluid and plasma filtrate (protein-free) have shown that the pH, vapor pressure, conductivity, and concentrations of urea, glucose, chloride, inorganic phosphorus, uric acid, creatinine, bicarbonate, etc., in these fluids are practically identical. These observations indicate that the glomerulus acts merely as an ultrafilter and that glomerular urine is formed by a process of filtration alone, i.e., a purely mechanical process. The effective filtration pressure is the resultant of the blood pressure in the glomerular capillaries and the opposing forces of the colloid osmotic pressure of the blood plasma and the tension within Bowman's capsule (capsular pressure). The mean glomerular pressure may be regarded as about 70 per cent of the mean systemic arterial pressure (90 mm. Hg), thus averaging about 65 mm. Hg. This is subject to regulation by variation in the relative degree of constriction of the afferent and efferent arterioles of the glomerulus. Under stimulation, the latter may be constricted more than the former, with consequent increase in the pressure within the glomerular capillaries. If it is assumed that the colloid osmotic pressure is 25 mm. Hg in the blood entering the glomerulus, and that the capsular pressure is about 15 mm. Hg, it is obvious that the effective filtration pressure is approximately 65 minus (25 + 15) or 25 mm. Hg. As fluid (and diffusible solids, but little or no protein) leaves the plasma within the capillaries as a result of this force, the local plasma protein concentration increases and may reach a point where the effective filtration pressure is so reduced as to impair glomerular filtration. Further constriction of the efferent arteriole may then still increase the glomerular blood pressure, allowing filtration to continue. In addition to the influence of these pressure factors, the volume of glomerular filtrate is influenced significantly by (1) the surface area of the filter (glomerular capillary surface, normally 1.56 sq. meters) and (2) the minute volume flow of blood plasma over this surface (normally about 700 ml. plasma or 1200 ml. blood per 1.73 sq. meters body surface). Under normal conditions, the volume of glomerular filtrate averages about 125 ml. per minute per 1.73 sq. meters.

It is apparent that glomerular filtration may be diminished with a tendency toward retention of waste products in the blood, in the absence of primary morphological changes in the kidneys, by (1) extrarenal factors which diminish the renal blood flow and (2) factors which lower the effective filtration pressure by (a) decreasing the glomerular blood pressure, (b) increasing the plasma oncotic pressure, or (c) increasing the capsular pressure. Among the most important of these are clinical conditions characterized by marked lowering of the systemic blood pressure, dehydration or hemoconcentration, and cardiac failure. In such conditions, as in any condition of renal functional impairment, the tendency toward nitrogen retention may be aggravated by a simultaneous increase in protein catabolism or absorption of excessive amounts of protein end-products into the organism, e.g., in massive gastrointestinal hemorrhage.

In shock, both glomerular filtration and renal blood flow are decreased, approximately in proportion to the degree of shock. This decrease, which is greater than can be explained solely on the basis of the fall in blood pressure, results from active renal arteriolar constriction. Renal vasoconstriction plays a homeostatic role in shock, tending to maintain circulatory efficiency, for normally about 25 per cent of the resting cardiac output perfuses the kidneys. This, however, is effected at the expense of renal function, for oliguria and diminution in concentrating power result from the decreased renal circulation.

Decreased filtration due to increase in capsular pressure occurs commonly as a result of intrarenal or extrarenal obstructive lesions (e.g., urinary calculi, prostatic enlargement). Significant elevation of plasma colloid osmotic pressure is rarely encountered, since increase in the plasma protein concentration, when it occurs, is virtually invariably in the globulin fraction, which exerts relatively little influence on osmotic pressure.

TUBULAR FUNCTION

Reabsorption

The rate of formation of glomerular filtrate under normal conditions is approximately 125 ml. per minute, whereas the rate at which urine passes into the bladder under the same conditions is approximately 1 to 2 ml. per minute. Obviously, therefore, in its passage through the uriniferous tubules about 99 per cent of the water of the glomerular filtrate must have been reabsorbed. Furthermore, since the glomerular filtrate contains glucose in practically the same concentration as the blood plasma, whereas the bladder urine contains none, or very little, this substance, too, must have undergone practically complete reabsorption in the tubules. Quantitative studies of the excretion of other solids, such as chloride, phosphate, urea, uric acid, sodium, potassium, etc., in glomerular and bladder urine indicate a variable degree of reabsorption during their passage through the uriniferous tubules. Observations made in experimental animals have thrown considerable light upon the site of reabsorption of several of these solids in the renal tubules.

It was found (in amphibians) that reabsorption of glucose occurs entirely in the proximal segment, reabsorption of chloride and sodium throughout the tubule, and acidification of the urine in the distal segment. The proximal tubule appeared to be capable of actively reabsorbing phosphate.

Insofar as excretory functions are concerned, therefore, the function of the renal glomeruli may be regarded as that of ultrafiltration (essentially protein-free filtrate of the blood plasma) and that of the tubular epithelium, in part at least, as "selective" reabsorption (water, glucose, chloride, etc.). Inasmuch as the average rate of glomerular filtration is 120 to 130 ml. per minute (about 70 ml. per sq. meter of body surface) (p. 831), it follows that more than 170 liters are filtered through the glomeruli from the plasma daily, the tubules subsequently reabsorbing about 168.5 liters of water, 1000 gm. NaCl, 360 gm. $NaHCO_3$, 170 gm. glucose and smaller amounts of phosphate, sulfate, amino acids, urea, urate, etc., in order to excrete about 60 gm. of NaCl, urea and other waste products in about 1500 ml. of urine.

Several of the factors involved in the regulation of tubular reabsorption of various components of the glomerular filtrate are not entirely understood. However, information is available concerning certain constituents which aids materially in understanding abnormalities in disease. The extent to which any component of the glomerular filtrate is reabsorbed may be ascertained by determining its "clearance" simultaneously with the clearance of inulin or mannitol (p. 831), since the latter affords an index of the amount of material filtered through the glomeruli per unit of time.

Glucose. In normal men, under test conditions, the tubules can reabsorb 375 ± 80 mg. of glucose per minute (women, 305 ± 55 mg.). At a glomerular filtration rate of 125 ml./min., and a plasma glucose concentration of 280 mg./100 ml., 350 mg. of glucose would be entering the tubules each minute. The same quantity would be entering if the volume of glomerular filtrate were reduced to 75 ml./min. and the plasma glucose concentration were raised to 465 mg./100 ml. Under these circumstances, if tubular reabsorption were not impaired simultaneously, glucose would not necessarily escape in the urine despite the considerable elevation of blood sugar concentration (p. 000). The reabsorptive burden imposed upon the tubular cells is determined by the total quantity of substance presented to them per unit of time, i.e., concentration × volume, and not by its concentration alone. Reabsorption of glucose is largely an active process; it may involve phosphorylation in the tubular epithelial cells. This is blocked by phlorizin (p. 446), with consequent glycosuria. Similar types of renal glycosuria occur clinically (p. 446).

Water. Over 99 per cent of the large volume of water (about 180,000 ml. daily) that leaves the blood plasma in the glomeruli is normally returned to the blood in the tubules. Water is reabsorbed in different segments by different mechanisms, certain details of which have not yet been established but which may be represented as follows:

(*1*) *Proximal Convolution.* This segment is apparently freely permeable to Na, Cl, and water. Na and Cl are reabsorbed by an active transport mechanism, with passive isosmotic reabsorption of water. Under normal conditions about 85 to 90 per cent of the filtered solutes and water (125 ml./minute/1.73 sq. meters body surface) are reabsorbed in this region. The volume of fluid leaving the proximal convolution is therefore normally about 16 ml./minute, the actual amount in any case being conditioned primarily by the volume of glomerular filtrate and the rate of reabsorption of solutes. This phase of passive water reabsorption, representing over 85 per cent of the total, has been designated "obligatory" reabsorption. Although the fluid at this point in the tubule is approximately isotonic with the original glomerular filtrate (i.e., same total osmolar concentration of solutes), it differs considerably from the latter in respect to the concentrations of individual components, many of which have been reabsorbed in varying degrees.

(2) *Loop of Henle.* This segment is believed to be relatively impermeable to water. Active reabsorption of Na here results in dilution of the tubular contents. The fluid leaving the loop of Henle is therefore hypotonic with respect to the original glomerular filtrate; the interstitial fluid in this region (renal medulla) is correspondingly hypertonic.

(3) *Distal Convolution.* Active reabsorption of the Na (and other solutes) continues in this segment, which, however, is relatively impermeable to water in the absence of the antidiuretic hormone. Under such circumstances (diabetes insipidus), the tubular fluid would here become progressively more dilute. In the presence of ADH, water is absorbed isosmotically with Na and also by flowing along the osmotic gradient into the relatively hypertonic cortical interstitial fluid. Accordingly, depending upon the amount of ADH present, the fluid leaving the distal convolution may vary from hypotonicity to isotonicity with the original glomerular filtrate.

(4) *Collecting Ducts.* This segment is impermeable to Na and, in the absence of ADH, also to water. In the presence of adequate amounts of ADH, water flows along the osmotic gradient into the surrounding hypertonic medullary interstitial fluid. Under normal conditions, the consequent concentration of the tubular fluid in this segment (urine) may reach a maximum of 2100 milliosmoles per liter. The term "facultative reabsorption" has been applied to the phase of water reabsorption controlled by the antidiuretic hormone and occurring independently of the amount of solute being reabsorbed simultaneously. The mechanism of regulation of secretion of ADH is discussed elsewhere (p. 747). In its absence (diabetes insipidus), the specific gravity of the urine is very low (1.001 to 1.003) and the volume may be extremely large (as much as 20 liters daily).

Sodium; Chloride. Under average normal conditions, more than 99 per cent of the Na that leaves the plasma in the glomerular filtrate is reabsorbed in the tubules, 85 to 90 per cent in the proximal segment, the remainder in the loop of Henle and the distal segment. Several details of the mechanisms involved are not clearly understood and there are differences of opinion on certain important points. Reabsorption of Na by the tubular epithelial cells is generally regarded as an active process, stimulated by "salt-active" hormones of the adrenal cortex, the most potent of which is aldosterone; this plays an important role, therefore, in the regulation of Na balance (p. 309). The mechanism of regulation of aldosterone secretion in accordance with requirements for retention or excretion of Na is considered elsewhere (p. 707).

As Na^+ ions pass from the tubular fluid into the tubular epithelial cells, preservation of electrical neutrality on both sides of the cell membrane requires either (a) passage of an anion in the same direction or (b) passage of a cation in the opposite direction. Both of these occur, the former throughout the area of Na^+ reabsorption, the latter apparently in specialized segments. About 90 per cent of the Na^+ ions reabsorbed from the tubular fluid are accompanied by anions. In some instances this may be a passive process; in others an active transport mechanism is involved.

Inasmuch as the quantity of Na excreted is the resultant of the amount filtered through the glomeruli and that reabsorbed in the tubules, it is subject to influence by a number of variable factors, renal and extrarenal, which affect these functions. These include: (1) the glomerular filtration rate; (2) the concentration of Na in the plasma; (3) the Na intake; (4) the renal plasma flow; (5) the concentrations of other unabsorbed solutes in the tubular fluid; (6) endocrine influences, particularly adrenocortical and antidiuretic hormones; (7) the relative concentrations of associated anions, particularly Cl^- and HCO_3^-; (8) the rate of flow through the tubules; (9) the state of acid-base balance. Several of these factors are obviously interrelated and, under normal conditions, operate as components of a homeostatic mechanism which effectively regulates Na excretion in accordance with existing requirements.

Other things being equal, the rate of excretion of Na varies in the same direction as the quantity entering the tubules. It is therefore influenced by the plasma Na concentration and by the glomerular filtration rate, the latter being itself influenced by the renal plasma flow, the glomerular capillary surface area, the intratubular (capsular) pressure, and the colloid osmotic pressure of the blood plasma. In addition, the rate of excretion may vary, independently of variations in the rate of filtration, as a result of operation of factors acting at the tubular epithelial level to enhance or depress Na reabsorption. These include, among others, the state of acid-base balance, adrenocortical hormones, particularly aldosterone, and the relative concentrations of other solutes in the tubular fluid.

Enhancement of tubular reabsorption of Na by aldosterone (p. 710) and by stimulation of the hydrogen exchange mechanism, as occurs in acidosis (p. 317), are considered elsewhere. The influence of Cl^- and HCO_3^- ions is discussed below. Reabsorption of Na is depressed (excretion increased) in the presence of increased concentrations, in the tubular fluid, of relatively or absolutely unabsorbable solutes. In the case of anions in this category, such as sulfate, increased amounts of Na are retained in the tubular fluid to preserve a state of electrical neutrality. In the case of non-electrolytes, such as mannitol, citrate, and urea, the consequent retention of water in the proximal segment, by diluting the Na in the tubular fluid to a concentration below that of the plasma, may establish a progressively increasing concentration gradient which reduces the rate of Na reabsorption. The consensus is that regulation of Na excretion in man is accomplished mainly by influences exerted primarily on tubular reabsorption, although variations in glomerular filtration, when they occur, undoubtedly produce a significant effect.

Excretion of Cl usually parallels that of Na, and it is generally believed that tubular reabsorption of Cl occurs passively in association with reabsorption of Na (cation-anion pairing). However, some believe that Cl is reabsorbed actively; this is suggested by observations that under certain circumstances, e.g., in mercurial diuresis, urinary excretion of Cl may be increased out of proportion to that of Na. In man, Cl is reabsorbed at the rate of approximately 105 mEq./liter of filtrate under ordinary circumstances.

Acidification of urine; ammonia excretion. The mechanism of acidification of urine is discussed in detail elsewhere (p. 317). This is accomplished by the passage of H^+ ions from the tubular epithelial cell (derived from H_2CO_3) into the lumen of the tubule in exchange for Na^+ ions, which pass from the tubular fluid into the epithelial cells, then into the bloodstream paired with the HCO_3^- ions "released" by the excretion of H^+ ions (Fig. 13–1, p. 318).

The pH of the fluid leaving the proximal segment is identical with that of the glomerular filtrate (and the blood plasma), indicating that the process of acidification occurs in the distal segment. However, some believe that the Na^+:H^+ exchange mechanism operates also in the proximal tubule, the H^+ ions here participating in the mechanism of reabsorption of HCO_3 from the glomerular filtrate (also in the distal tubule). A portion of the H^+ ions entering the tubular fluid is therefore disposed of by the formation of H_2CO_3, which is converted to H_2O and CO_2, the latter diffusing across the epithelial cell into the bloodstream. An additional fraction of the H^+ ions is removed by the formation of NH_4^+ ions from NH_3 secreted into the tubular fluid in the distal segment. The NH_3 is formed in the tubular epithelial cells by deamination of glutamine and, to a lesser extent, α-amino acids (Fig. 13–1, p. 318).

The remaining H^+ ions are largely buffered by the $HPO_4^=$ ions in the tubular fluid (p. 317). The maximal attainable acidity of the urine is approximately pH 4.5.

Bicarbonate. Under conditions of normal urinary acidity the urine contains no HCO_3^- ions. The major portion (85 to 90 per cent) of the HCO_3^- of the glomerular filtrate (27 mEq./liter) is removed in the proximal segment. This may be accomplished by one or both of two mechanisms: (1) the HCO_3^- ion may be reabsorbed paired with a cation (for example, Na^+), in the same manner as Cl^-; (2) if, as some believe, the process of $Na^+:H^+$ exchange occurs in this segment, the H^+ entering the tubular fluid may, with the HCO_3^-, form H_2CO_3 and, in turn, H_2O and CO_2, the latter diffusing across the lining epithelium to the peritubular blood.

The concentration of HCO_3^- ions in the tubular fluid entering the distal segment is approximately the same as in the glomerular filtrate under normal conditions. In this region, removal of HCO_3^- is accomplished as a result of the entrance of H^+ ions, as indicated above, in the process of acidification of the urine; i.e., by formation of H_2O and CO_2, the latter diffusing back into the bloodstream.

In man, quantities of HCO_3^- in excess of 28 mEq./liter of glomerular filtrate usually escape reabsorption, the urine becoming correspondingly alkaline.

Potassium. The mechanism of excretion of K differs from that of Na in that it is actively secreted into, as well as reabsorbed from, the tubular fluid. It is probable that under physiological conditions the K^+ entering the tubule in the glomerular filtrate undergoes complete reabsorption, paired with an anion (for example, Cl^-), before reaching the distal segment. Excessive amounts entering in the glomerular filtrate, e.g., in dehydration, may escape reabsorption. The cells of the distal tubules actively remove K^+ from the peritubular blood and pass it into the tubular fluid in exchange for Na^+, which passes in the opposite direction. This is analogous to the process of $Na^+:H^+$ exchange, which occurs in this segment. In a general sense, reabsorption of Na^+ in this region may be visualized as occurring in exchange for an equal number of K^+ and H^+ ions; when the availability of one of the latter diminishes, the other competes more favorably in the exchange process.

Accordingly, the amount of K excreted by this mechanism depends upon the quantity of Na reabsorbed, stimulation of the latter (e.g., by aldosterone) resulting in increased urinary excretion of K (and decrease in urinary Na). It is probable that alterations in K excretion induced by adrenocortical hormones occur as a result of their effects upon Na reabsorption and not, as believed formerly, as a result of a direct action of the hormones on the mechanism of K excretion.

Although the kidneys conserve the K of the glomerular filtrate more efficiently than the Na (more complete reabsorption), because of active secretion of K into the tubular fluid the urine almost invariably contains some K, even when none is taken in (25 to 50 mEq./liter urine). Na and Cl, on the other hand, virtually disappear from the urine when withdrawn from the diet of subjects with normal renal function.

Urea. About 40 per cent of the urea which leaves the blood in the glomerular filtrate is reabsorbed in the tubules under average normal conditions. This is a passive process, i.e., diffusion, the extent of urea reabsorption depending, therefore, on the amount of water being reabsorbed and on the concentration gradient between the intratubular fluid (i.e., modified glomerular filtrate), and the fluid in the tubular cells and kidney interstitial spaces.

It is to be expected, therefore, that the amount of urea reabsorbed (and excreted) would vary, within certain limits, with changes in urine volume. At low urine volumes, i.e., more water reabsorption, more urea is reabsorbed and less is excreted; at high urine volumes, i.e., less water reabsorption, more urea is excreted. Maximum urea reabsorption (about 70 per cent) occurs at urine volumes of 0.35 ml. or less per minute. At a urine volume of 1 ml. per minute, about 60 per cent is reabsorbed, and at 2 ml. or more per minute 40 per cent is reabsorbed (p. 836). If marked diuresis is induced by intravenous injection of an osmotically active substance, e.g., glucose or sucrose, the extent of urea reabsorption may fall considerably below 40 per cent, and values for urea clearance will approach those for inulin clearance.

Miscellaneous. Practically all of the normal components of the glomerular filtrate are reabsorbed in the tubules to extents varying from practically 100 per cent (e.g., glucose) or over 99 per cent (e.g., Na, water) to negligible amounts (e.g., creatinine). Many if not most of these are reabsorbed by active "tubular transport mechanisms," i.e., enzyme systems which effect their passage from the tubular lumen into the cells, and from the latter into the adjacent interstitial fluid. Reference will be made to a few of these which are of some clinical interest.

Phosphate is absorbed in the proximal segment. This process is influenced by the parathyroid hormone, which increases phosphate excretion (p. 731), apparently by decreasing its reabsorption. It has been suggested that this mechanism may be influenced also by vitamin D.

It is generally believed that 90 to 95 per cent of the filtered uric acid is reabsorbed in the tubules. This is an active process, interest in which has been stimulated by the demonstration of a uricosuric effect of agents which block uric acid reabsorption, e.g., Benemid, carinamide. Such agents, particularly Benemid, are useful in the treatment of acute gout, lowering the plasma uric acid concentration as a result of their uricosuric action. There is evidence, however, that the urate of the glomerular filtrate is practically completely reabsorbed by the tubules, that excreted in the urine being actively secreted into the tubular fluid.

Under normal conditions, only small amounts of amino acids are excreted in the urine, the major fraction of what enters the glomerular filtrate being reabsorbed by active tubular transport mechanisms. Clinical conditions of excessive aminoaciduria occur in the presence of defects in these enzyme systems.

Tubular Excretion and Synthesis

The term "excretion" is applied to the active transport of substances by the tubule cells from the blood plasma to the lumen of the tubule. Synthesis refers to formation, in the tubule cells, of substances which are then passed into the lumen. Under physiological conditions, probably very few normal components of the plasma undergo significant active excretion by the renal tubular cells. Potassium is an important exception, and a portion of the urinary creatinine may be excreted by this route. However, a number of foreign substances that may be introduced into the body for therapeutic or diagnostic purposes are removed from the blood plasma extensively, and in certain instances even predominantly, by the tubular epithelium. Among these are penicillin, *p*-aminosalicylic acid, phenolsulfonphthalein (PSP), *p*-aminohippuric acid, and Diodrast. Recognition of this fact in the case of penicillin led to the use of transport-blocking agents for the purpose of maintaining effective plasma penicillin levels for longer periods by decreasing its excretion in the urine. The use of the other substances named in the study of renal function is referred to elsewhere (below).

There is evidence that in certain animals, compounds present in the urine are synthesized in the kidneys from precursors removed from the blood plasma, e.g., hippuric acid from glycine and benzoic acid. In man, such processes occur in the kidney to a very limited extent, if at all. However, the distal tubule cells do form two substances, hydrogen ions and ammonia, which, excreted into the lumen, play an extremely important part in the regulation of acid-base balance. This subject is discussed elsewhere in detail (p. 316).

Competition for Transport Mechanisms

There is evidence that several substances that are excreted by renal tubular cells are handled by a single mechanism, at least in one phase of their transport across the cell. The same is true of reabsorption of certain substances by these cells. The same mechanism, or one of its components, may be involved in reabsorption of certain compounds and excretion of others. Such substances may, under certain conditions, compete for these mechanisms, so that excretion or reabsorption of one or more is depressed by the presence of large amounts of another which utilizes the same mechanism.

Diodrast, *p*-aminohippurate, phenolsulfonphthalein, penicillin, and *p*-aminosalicylic acid, which are all actively excreted by tubule cells, exert mutually depressing effects on their urinary excretion when administered in sufficiently high dosage. Similar competition, in this instance for reabsorption, is exhibited between creatine, glycine, and other amino acids, between glucose and xylose, and between ascorbic acid and sodium chloride.

Reabsorption of ascorbic acid is depressed also by *p*-aminohippurate, which is excreted by the tubules. Carinamide and Benemid, although they are not actively excreted by the tubule, depress tubular excretion of Diodrast, phenolsulfonphthalein, *p*-aminohippurate, penicillin, and *p*-aminosalicylic acid. They also decrease reabsorption of uric acid. Observations such as these have led to improvements in therapy (infections; gout).

Abnormal Tubular Function

The functions of the renal tubular epithelium, particularly in reabsorption and urine acidification, may be disturbed as a result of: (1) endocrine abnormalities; (2) genetically determined enzyme defects in transport mechanisms; (3) acquired disease and morphological damage.

Adrenocortical hypofunction causes decreased reabsorption of Na and decreased excretion of K (converse in hyperfunction). In hypoparathyroidism there is increased reabsorption of phosphate (converse in hyperparathyroidism). Inadequate secretion of antidiuretic hormone, or interruption of the hypothalamic-neurohypophyseal connections, results in decreased reabsorption of water (diabetes insipidus).

Inherent defects in cell transport mechanisms, in some cases genetically determined ("inborn errors of metabolism"), in others of unknown etiology, may cause decreased absorption of one or more components of the tubular fluid. Clinical conditions in this category include: renal glycosuria; renal aminoaciduria (cystinuria); Fanconi syndrome; idiopathic hypercalciuria; vitamin D-resistant rickets (defective reabsorption of phosphate).

Disorders of tubular function due to acquired disease include: aminoaciduria (heavy metal poisoning; vitamin C deficiency; vitamin D deficiency); renal tubular acidosis (defective urine acidification); "salt losing nephritis" (defective reabsorption of Na and Cl); nephrogenic diabetes insipidus ("water losing nephritis").

CLEARANCE TESTS

In the performance of its excretory functions, the kidney may be said to "clear" the blood of certain waste and foreign products. Urea clearance is defined as the volume of blood which one minute's excretion of urine suffices to clear of urea. Inasmuch as all of the blood flowing through the kidneys is only partially cleared of urea (and other substances), a more exact definition would be "the number of milliliters of blood which contain the amount of urea removed per minute by renal excretion." The clearance also represents the minimum volume of blood required to furnish the amount of substance excreted in the urine in one minute. This concept of renal clearance has contributed largely to our present understanding of renal function in health and disease.

If U indicates the concentration (mg. per 100 ml.) of substance (e.g., urea) in urine, and V the volume (in ml.) of urine formed per minute, $U \times V$ equals the quantity of substance ($\times$ 100) excreted per minute. If B indicates the concentration (mg. per 100 ml.) of substance in the blood, UV/B indicates the virtual volume of blood "cleared" of substance per minute, i.e., the "clearance." It is essential that plasma be used instead of whole blood for clearance determinations if the substance investigated is not distributed uniformly between plasma and corpuscles (e.g., inulin, Diodrast, phenol red).

Theoretically, a substance may be excreted by (1) glomerular filtration alone, (2) filtration plus tubular excretion, or (3) filtration plus tubular reabsorption. If a substance is completely filtered at the glomerulus and is subsequently completely reabsorbed by the tubules, its clearance will be zero (e.g., glucose). As the degree of tubular reabsorption diminishes, the substance appears in the urine and its clearance increases (e.g., urea), until, if there is no reabsorption (e.g., inulin), the clearance will be equivalent to the rate of glomerular filtration. If a substance, in addition to being filtered through the glomeruli, is also excreted by the tubular epithelium (e.g., phenol red, Diodrast), its clearance will exceed the rate of glomerular filtration by an amount equal to the extent of tubular excretion. Inasmuch as the kidneys cannot excrete more of a substance per unit of time than is brought to them in the blood, the upper limit of renal clearance is determined by the renal blood flow. For example, if a substance undergoes glomerular filtration and tubular excretion, and if all that is contained in the blood passing through the kidneys is removed and is concurrently transferred to the urine, its clearance will be complete (e.g., Diodrast clearance); i.e., it will be equivalent to the volume of plasma flowing through the kidneys per minute. These facts constitute the basis for quantitative determination of various aspects of renal function.

Rate of Glomerular Filtration

Inulin is a polysaccharide which is not metabolized in the body and, following its intravenous injection, is excreted quantitatively by the kidneys within a short time. It is excreted entirely by glomerular filtration and undergoes no reabsorption in the tubules. Inasmuch as inulin, being freely filtrable at the glomerulus, exists in the blood plasma and glomerular filtrate in identical concentration, and since the quantity of inulin excreted per minute in the bladder urine is equal to the amount entering the glomerular filtrate per minute, it follows that the inulin clearance (UV/P) represents the volume of glomerular filtrate formed per minute. Employing this procedure, it has been found that the average rate of glomerular filtration is 125 ml. per minute (about 70 ml. per sq. meter of body surface). Similar figures are obtained with other carbohydrates, viz., mannitol, sorbitol, and dulcitol. Lower values (by 25 to 45 per cent) may be obtained in elderly (70 to 85 years of age), apparently normal subjects.

Determination of the rate of glomerular filtration (inulin clearance) has several important physiological applications: (1) The glomerular filtration rate minus the rate of urine flow (bladder) equals the quantity of water reabsorbed in the tubules per minute. (2) The inulin clearance minus the clearance of another substance (X) divided by the inulin clearance equals the proportion of substance X reabsorbed in the tubules. For example: inulin clearance (125) minus urea clearance (75), divided by inulin clearance (125), equals 0.4, indicating that 40 per cent of the urea of the glomerular filtrate is reabsorbed during its passage through the tubules. (3) When a substance has a clearance higher than that of inulin, it is excreted partly or entirely by the tubules. Such data have been found to be useful in studying the mode of action of diuretic agents and abnormalities in excretion of various subtances.

A decrease in inulin clearance may result from (1) decrease in renal blood flow, (2) partial obliteration of or decrease in the number of functioning glomeruli (glomerulonephritis, glomerulosclerosis, destructive or suppurative lesions of the renal parenchyma), or (3) decrease in the effective glomerular filtration pressure. The last (p. 822) is the resultant of (a) the glomerular blood pressure, (b) the plasma colloid osmotic pressure, and (c) the capsular pressure. Diminution in the first or increase in the last two forces result in a decrease in effective filtration pressure.

Determination of glomerular filtration (inulin or mannitol clearance) is of obvious value in investigating the pathological physiology of urine formation. Inasmuch as all of the normal constituents of the urine probably leave the bloodstream exclusively via the glomerular filtrate, with the exception of potassium (p. 827) and a relatively small fraction of the creatinine, reduction in glomerular filtration is usually the most important

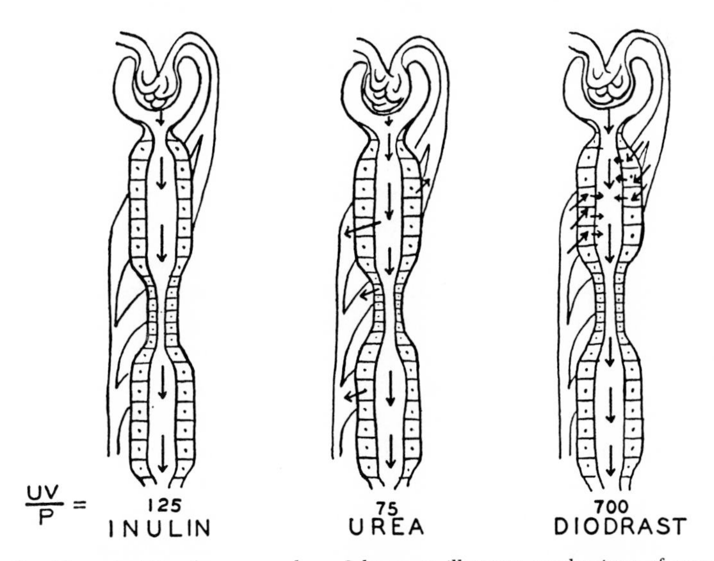

Figure 31-2. Characteristic clearance values. Scheme to illustrate mechanisms of excretion: Inulin is excreted by glomerular filtration alone, with no tubular reabsorption. Urea is excreted by glomerular filtration and is partially reabsorbed by the tubule. Diodrast (also *p*-aminohippurate) is excreted by both glomerular filtration and tubular excretion.

primary cause of abnormal retention of urinary waste products in the body fluids. The usefulness of inulin and mannitol clearance tests as routine clinical diagnostic procedures is limited by the necessity of injecting the test substances intravenously and by certain other technical difficulties.

Inasmuch as endogenous creatinine is not reabsorbed in the tubules, determination of endogenous creatinine clearance is often substituted clinically for these procedures. However, this is open to the criticism that the small amount of creatinine that enters the urine under normal conditions by tubular secretion may increase to a considerable and variable degree in conditions of impaired glomerular filtration.

In normal subjects, and often in disease states, under average conditions of urine flow, values for urea clearance usually parallel those for inulin clearance, and the latter may be calculated from the former according to the formula: Urea Clearance/0.6 = Inulin Clearance. This proportionality arises out of the fact that all of the urinary urea is removed from the blood by glomerular filtration and, at urine volumes of 2 ml. or more per minute, about 60 per cent is excreted in the urine (40 per cent reabsorbed) (p. 836). This substitution of urea clearance for inulin clearance is not valid at low urine volumes. Nevertheless, except under unusual circumstances, determination of urea clearance is quite satisfactory in the clinical study of renal function and for purposes of diagnosis and prognosis.

In interpreting deviations from normal values for glomerular, filtration rate (Table 31-2, p. 834), certain points should be kept in mind. Determinations should be made under carefully controlled and standardized conditions, including performance in the morning after an overnight fast (diurnal variation), adequate antecedent diet (dietary influences), avoidance of emotional disturbance (hormonal influences), and bed rest (exercise influence). Moreover, there may be some question of the validity of measurements of glomerular filtration in certain kidney diseases, particularly in the presence of severe acute tubular damage, e.g., mercury or carbon tetrachloride poisoning, severe pyelonephritis. In such conditions, a portion of the filtered inulin or mannitol may diffuse from the lumen across the damaged, non-functioning tubular cells, with the consequent production of spuriously low filtration values. However, this occurs rarely, even in advanced stages of the types of renal disease commonly encountered.

Renal Blood Flow

If a substance is completely removed from the blood plasma during its passage through the kidney, the "clearance" of that substance (i.e., volume of plasma "cleared" per minute; UV/P) (p. 830) would equal the renal blood plasma flow. Knowledge of the hematocrit value would permit calculation of the renal blood flow. This has been found to be true of Diodrast and *p*-aminohippurate, over 90 per cent of the plasma content of these substances being removed during a single passage through the kidneys ("extraction ratio") at relatively low plasma levels. Consequently, at least in normal subjects under standardized conditions, values for Diodrast or *p*-aminohippurate are approximately equivalent to the "effective" renal plasma flow, i.e., the flow through active renal excretory tissue. These have been found to be about 700 ± 135 ml. for men, and 600 ± 100 ml. for women, per 1.73 square meters of body surface. Corresponding values for renal blood flow are about 1275 ± 245 ml. and 1090 ± 180 ml., respectively. Lower values are obtained in elderly individuals.

Renal blood flow exhibits a diurnal variation, decreases during exercise, and is influenced by emotional states. These determinations must therefore be made under strictly standardized conditions. *p*-Aminohippurate (PAH) has largely placed Diodrast for estimation of renal blood flow because it possesses the following advantages over the latter substance: (1) it does not penetrate the erythrocytes; (2) it is less extensively bound to plasma proteins; (3) its quantitative determination is a simpler procedure. Values for PAH clearance in experimental animals correspond closely to those obtained by direct measurement of renal blood flow, amounting to about 30 per cent of the cardiac output and about 25 per cent of the total blood volume. Stated in other terms, all of the blood passes through the kidneys every four minutes, a fact which reflects the vital importance of these organs in maintaining a constant extracellular fluid composition.

Abnormal decrease in "effective" renal blood flow (PAH clearance) may result from:

(1) Decrease in cardiac output or arterial blood pressure, e.g., congestive heart failure, coronary artery occlusion, shock syndrome.

(2) Organic disease of the renal vascular system, e.g., renal arteriosclerosis, arteriolosclerosis (nephrosclerosis), intercapillary glomerulosclerosis, glomerulonephritis, periarteritis nodosa.

(3) Increased local resistance to the flow of blood, resulting from vasoconstriction of the afferent and/or efferent glomerular arterioles, e.g., early essential hypertension, systemic arterial hypotension.

(4) Decrease in the mass of functioning kidney tissue, e.g., renal hypoplasia, polycystic disease, pyelonephritis, tuberculosis, malignancy.

An absolute increase in renal blood flow may occur after administration of pyrogenic agents, e.g., typhoid vaccine, due to renal arteriolar dilatation. It may be increased temporarily by a high-meat diet. Following unilateral nephrectomy, the blood flow through the remaining kidney may increase more than 70 per cent in a short time.

The significance of diminished renal blood flow in contributing to reduction in glomerular filtration is referred to elsewhere (p. 823). The fact must be borne in mind that measurement of renal blood flow by the clearance procedure is valid only when renal extraction of PAH or Diodrast is almost complete, i.e., when over 90 per cent is removed during a single passage through the kidneys. Inasmuch as over 80 per cent of the normal excretion of these substances is accomplished by direct tubular cell action and less than 20 per cent by glomerular filtration, severe impairment of tubular excretory function may result in reduction in PAH or Diodrast clearance in the absence of corresponding diminution in renal blood flow. This will be reflected in decrease in the PAH extraction ratio, which can be determined by simultaneous measurements of PAH in the systemic arterial blood and in the renal-vein blood obtained by catheterization. By this means, low extraction ratios have been observed in subjects with severe kidney damage due to glomerulonephritis or nephrosclerosis. In such cases, the renal blood flow may be calculated by substituting the arterial-venous plasma difference in PAH (or Diodrast) concentration for "P" in the clearance formula, i.e., $U_{PAH} \cdot V/P(\text{art-ven})_{PAH}$. However, PAH extraction is usually normal in early stages of these conditions, and also in congestive heart failure.

Maximum Tubular Excretory Capacity

The process of renal tubular excretion is limited by the mass of functioning tubular tissue available for the transfer of a substance from the blood to the urine. Consequently the measurement of the maximal rate of excretion of a substance excreted by this mechanism reflects the "tubular excretory mass" of the kidneys. This value, designated Tm, is calculated from simultaneous determinations of inulin and Diodrast or *p*-aminohippurate

TABLE 31-2. NORMAL VALUES FOR VARIOUS PHASES OF RENAL FUNCTION DERIVED FROM CLEARANCE DATA AND CHARACTERISTIC VALUES IN CERTAIN TYPES OF KIDNEY DISEASE

(Expressed per 1.73 Square Meters Body Surface Area)

FACTORS	MEN	WOMEN	GLOMERULONEPHRITIS			CHRONIC PYELO-NEPHRITIS	BENIGN NEPHRO-SCLEROSIS
			ACUTE	CHRONIC			
				NEPHROTIC	TERMINAL		
Glomerular filtration rate (GFR) Inulin clearance / Mannitol clearance (ml./min.)	130 ± 20	115 ± 15	15–100 (50)	40–80 (55)	0–40 (10)	50–90 (75)	50–150 (100)
Renal plasma flow (RPF) PAH clearance / Diodrast clearance (ml./min.)	700 ± 135	600 ± 100	60–800 (400)	400–700 (500)	20–500 (100)	300–700 (425)	450–700 (500)
Renal blood flow (ml./min.)	1275 ± 245	1090 ± 180					
Filtration fraction (%)	18–20	18–20	10–25 (15)	10–20 (15)	10–30 (25)	15–20 (17)	10–30 (22)
Maximum tubular excretion (Tm) PAH Tm (mg./min.)	75 ± 13	70 ± 10	10–80 (50)	30–40 (35)	10–60 (30)	10–50 (35)	50–100 (75)
Diodrast Tm (mg. I/min.)	55 ± 15	50 ± 15					
Maximum tubular reabsorption (Tm) Glucose Tm (mg./min.)	375 ± 80	300 ± 55					
Plasma flow per unit excretory mass RPF/Dirodrast Tm (ml./mg.)	9 ± 1.5	8 ± 1.5					
RPF/PAH Tm (ml./mg.)	9 ± 1.5	8 ± 1.5	6–18 (8)	10–20 (12)	6–18 (10)		7–10 (8)
Plasma flow per unit reabsorption mass RPF/Glucose Tm (ml./mg.)	2 ± 0.4	2 ± 0.5					
Filtration per unit functioning nephrons Inulin clearance/PAH Tm (ml./mg.)	1.7 ± 0.4	1.5 ± 0.3	0.8–2.2 (1.2)	0.9–1.8 (1.2)	1.0–4.5 (1.5)		1.0–2.2 (1.5)

Figures in parentheses are mean values.

clearances at high plasma Diodrast or PAH levels. It is expressed as milligrams of Diodrast iodine or PAH eliminated per minute by tubular excretion, i.e., total excretion minus the amount excreted by glomerular filtration. Normal values for Diodrast and PAH Tm are indicated in Table 31-2 (p. 834).

It has been suggested that the Tm may be calculated indirectly as follows:

$$\text{Tm} = \frac{\text{Sp. Gr.} - 3.4}{4.8}\sqrt{\text{UC}}$$

where Sp. Gr. represents the second and third decimal place figures of the maximum urinary non-protein specific gravity obtained by the concentration test (p. 839) (e.g., 28 if the specific gravity is 1.028) and UC is the urea clearance in terms of per cent of average normal.

The value of this determination lies in the fact that, at effective plasma PAH or Diodrast concentrations and with adequate but not necessarily normal renal blood flow, the Tm is independent of glomerular activity and reflects the amount of functioning renal tubular tissue. For example, if one kidney were removed, Tm would be diminished by 50 per cent; if a portion of the excretory tissue were destroyed (either tubular destruction or obliteration of circulation), Tm would be reduced in proportion to the extent of destruction. If the glomeruli were entirely obliterated without impairing the circulation to the tubules, Tm would be unaltered.

The ratio of renal plasma flow to maximum tubular excretory capacity, i.e., of PAH or Diodrast clearance of PAH or Diodrast Tm, is an expression of the plasma flow per unit of functioning excretory renal tissue. Normal values are indicated in Table 31-2 (p. 834). Increased values may be obtained in the presence of fever (active hyperemia), and decreased values (relative ischemia) in the presence of intrarenal vasoconstriction, e.g., in shock, essential hypertension, peripheral circulatory failure, and in severe anemia.

Percentage Tubular Reabsorption

If another substance as freely filtrable through the glomeruli as inulin has a clearance value lower than the latter, it has undergone reabsorption in the tubules. The extent of this reabsorption may be calculated as follows:

$$\text{Reabsorption} = \frac{\text{Inulin Clearance (e.g., 125) minus Clearance of X}}{\text{Inulin Clearance (125)}}$$

By means of this calculation it is evident that about 40 to 50 per cent of the urea present in the glomerular filtrate is normally reabsorbed in the tubules under average conditions of urine flow (p. 827):

$$\frac{125 - 75}{125} = 0.4 \text{ or } 40\%$$

Filtration Fraction

The ratio of plasma inulin clearance (i.e., volume of glomerular filtrate) to plasma PAH or Diodrast clearance (i.e., renal plasma flow) represents the fraction of plasma filtered through the glomeruli. Under normal conditions this is about 0.18 (i.e., $^{125}/_{700}$), indicating that approximately 18 per cent of the water of the plasma flowing through the kidneys is filtered through the glomeruli into the lumen of Bowman's capsule.

Experimental studies have shown that increase or decrease in the filtration fraction is usually due to increase or decrease, respectively, in the tone of the efferent as compared to that of the afferent glomerular arteriole, with consequent increase or decrease, respectively, in intraglomerular blood pressure. Renal hyperemia produced by a pyrogen is probably due to predominantly efferent arteriolar dilation, since the renal blood flow increases and the filtration fraction decreases. The tone of the efferent arteriole is increased by administration of epinephrine and in orthostatic and psychogenic vasoconstriction, with consequent decrease in renal blood flow and increase in the filtration fraction. In early essential hypertension, as well as in hypertension induced by administration of renin or angiotonin (experimental), the renal blood flow (Diodrast clearance) is usually decreased, glomerular filtration (inulin clearance) is often normal, and the filtration fraction is frequently increased; this combination of circumstances can be produced practically only by predominantly efferent arteriolar constriction. Because of the increased filtration fraction, glomerular filtration and urea clearance may be maintained within normal limits until late in the course of essential hypertension (p. 834); under such circumstances, the normal urea clearance is not an expression of absolute integrity of renal function, but is usually an indication of renal vasoconstriction. An increase of filtration fraction from 0.2 to 0.3 is adequate to maintain urea clearance at 100 per cent of normal at a time when renal blood flow has fallen from a normal level of 1000 ml. per minute to an ischemic level of 600 ml. per minute.

Maximum Tubular Reabsorption Capacity

This may be studied in a manner similar to that employed for determination of excretory Tm, except that in this case a substance must be employed that is reabsorbed extensively rather than excreted by the tubular epithelial cells. Glucose is used for this purpose. When the plasma glucose concentration is maintained at a sufficiently high level, the amount of glucose entering the tubule will exceed the reabsorptive capacity and some will escape in the urine. Simultaneous determination of inulin clearance and mean blood glucose concentration permits calculation of the amount of glucose entering the tubule per minute, since all of it enters in the glomerular filtrate. Subtraction of the quantity escaping in the urine per minute gives the amount that has been reabsorbed.

Normal values for glucose Tm are indicated in Table 31-2 (p. 834). The significance of abnormalities in this factor is much the same as in the case of the excretory Tm (PAH or Diodrast), applying in this instance to tubular reabsorptive mass. The plasma flow per unit of functioning tubular reabsorptive mass may be calculated by determining the ratio of renal flow (PAH or Diodrast clearance) to the glucose Tm.

Glomerular function in terms of active nephrons may be expressed by the ratio of glomerular filtration rate (inulin clearance) to maximum tubular excretory capacity (PAH Tm). Normal values are indicated in Table 31-2. Increased values reflect hyperfiltration and decreased values hypofiltration in residual nephrons.

Other Clearance Procedures

Determination of urea clearance has been employed extensively clinically as a measure of renal functional efficiency. At urine volumes of 2 ml. or more per minute, normal urea clearance is 75 ± 10 ml. per minute (per 1.73 sq. meters body surface), indicating tubular reabsorption of about 40 per cent of the urea of the glomerular filtrate. With decreasing urine volumes below 2 ml. per minute (augmentation limit), the proportion of the filtered urea undergoing reabsorption increases progressively (p. 827). Under these circumstances, the volume of blood cleared of urea per minute is not directly proportional to the urine volume, and the usual clearance formula (UV/P) is not applicable. It has been proposed (Van Slyke) that with urine volumes below 2 ml. per minute an approximately accurate value for urea clearance may be obtained by applying the formula, $U\sqrt{V}/P$, designated "Standard Clearance." This is normally 55 ± 10 ml. per minute.

At physiological levels of plasma creatinine (i.e., endogenous), values for creatinine clearance correspond rather closely to those for unulin clearance in normal subjects. However, when the concentration in the plasma is raised by intravenous injection of creatinine, or in renal disease (glomerular damage), the clearance values exceed those for inulin, indicating partial tubular excretion of this substance under these conditions. Consequently, the creatinine clearance is not an invariably reliable index of the glomerular filtration rate.

Phenosulfonphthalein has an average clearance value of 400 ml., indicating that it is eliminated mainly (about 70 per cent) by tubular excretion. This fact serves to explain occasional discrepancies between values for PSP excretion and urea clearance in disease states (p. 834), urea being excreted entirely by glomerular filtration, a portion being reabsorbed subsequently.

Renal clearances of other substances are determined occasionally in studying the pathological physiology of certain conditions, e.g., uric acid in gout and eclampsia, sodium in congestive heart failure. However, they have little place in the clinical evaluation of renal functional efficiency.

RENIN

Hypertension can be produced experimentally by reducing the renal blood flow (ischemia), e.g., by placing a clamp on the renal arteries. This is due to the release into the bloodstream of a proteolytic enzyme "renin," produced in the renal tubular epithelial cells, which hydrolyzes angiotensinogen (hypertensinogen), a serum α_2-globulin produced in the liver, with the liberation of angiotensin I (hypertensin I), a polypeptide. This substance, which has no pressor activity, is acted upon by a peptidase in normal blood plasma with liberation of angiotensin II (hypertensin II), a powerful pressor substance. Under normal conditions this is rapidly destroyed by peptidases present in all tissues; certain forms of hypertension have been attributed to persistence of increased amounts of this material in the circulating blood. In addition to its pressor effect, angiotensin II is believed to be an important factor in the regulation of secretion of aldosterone by the adrenal cortex, stimulating release of this hormone with consequent increased retention of sodium and water (p. 707).

ERYTHROPOIETIN

This erythropoietic factor is produced in the kidney and is demonstrable in the blood plasma and urine of anemic or hypoxic subjects. Although its exact chemical nature has not been established, it is apparently a glycoprotein.

Erythropoietin stimulates erythropoiesis. Although it may act at later stages of the maturation process, its main action is to accelerate differentiation of stem cells into erythroid precursors, i.e., pronormoblasts and normoblasts. Inability to consistently demonstrate the presence of this factor in normal blood plasma is perhaps due to inadequacies of available assay methods.

URINE COMPOSITION

The urine is the most important medium of elimination of non-volatile substances from the body. Under normal conditions these include non-utilizable metabolites (e.g., urea, creatinine, uric acid), and materials ingested or produced in the organism in excess of metabolic requirements (e.g., water, electrolytes, etc.). The quantitative composition of the urine reflects the function of the kidneys in preserving important aspects of homeostasis and of the normal equilibrium between the organism and its environment. It will therefore vary widely in normal subjects at different ages and under different conditions of diet and activity. Detailed consideration of quantitative aspects of urine composition is not very profitable in a text of this nature. Attention will be directed chiefly toward its significant characteristics and toward the general principles and physiological factors governing the excretion of the most important normal constituents of the urine.

Color

The color of normal urine varies from light straw to reddish yellow, depending on the degree of concentration. This color is due largely to two pigments: (1) urochrome, a S-containing substance of unknown nature, an oxidation product (exposure to air) of the colorless urochromogen; (2) urobilin, an oxidation product (exposure to air) of the colorless urobilinogen, a product of the degradation of hemoglobin (p. 618). The color intensifies on standing.

Normal, freshly voided urine, acid in reaction, is clear and translucent. Alkaline urine may be turbid and turbidity develops on standing (ammoniacal fermentation), due to precipitation of phosphates which are relatively insoluble at alkaline reactions. Turbidity may also be due to uric acid, urates, calcium oxalate (excessive amounts in highly acid urine), to precipitation of mucin or nucleoprotein (usually on standing), or to abnormally large numbers of cells (epithelial, leukocytes, erythrocytes).

Certain drugs and foodstuffs may impart rather characteristic colors: e.g., santonin (orange-yellow), senna, rhubarb, cascara (brown-red), methylene blue (green), phenol (brown-black, on standing).

Odor

Normal, freshly voided urine has a slightly aromatic, rather characteristic odor, the origin of which is not known exactly. The odor is apparently contributed to by small amounts of certain volatile organic acids. On standing, urine develops an ammoniacal odor due to hydrolysis (bacterial) of urea to ammonia. Urine voided after eating asparagus has a rather typical odor, which has been attributed to the presence of methyl mercaptan. Certain drugs, which are not commonly administered, impart rather specific odors (e.g., turpentine, cubeb, copaiba, tolu).

Volume

The quantity of urine excreted daily by normal subjects varies widely and is determined chiefly by the fluid intake. Under ordinary dietary conditions it ranges from 1000 to 2000 ml. It is influenced somewhat by the protein and NaCl intake, the excreted urea and salt acting as diuretic agents. Excessive perspiration and strenuous exercise decrease the urine volume by pre-renal deviation of water (skin, lungs) (p. 294) and, under abnormal conditions, the same is accomplished by vomiting, diarrhea, and edema. The amount excreted during the day (8 A.M. to 8 P.M.) is two to four times that excreted during the night (8 P.M. to 8 A.M.). The minimum volume required for excretion of a given quantity of solids is determined by the concentrating capacity of the kidneys (below). Under conditions of average adequate food intake, it is about 300 ml./sq. meter body surface (i.e., about 500 ml. for a 70-kg. man).

Specific Gravity

The specific gravity of the urine is directly proportional to the concentration of solute and, therefore, with any given total solid excretion, varies inversely with the volume under usual normal conditions. The grams of solute per liter may be calculated roughly by multiplying the last two figures of the specific gravity (to the third decimal) by Long's coefficient, 2.6. This is only an approximation, particularly since all substances do not exert the same effect on specific gravity. For example, the specific gravity of a liter of urine is raised 0.001 by 3.6 gm. of urea, 1.47 gm. of NaCl, and 3.8 gm. of NaH_2PO_4 (also 2.7 gm. of glucose and 3.9 gm. of albumin).

Under ordinary dietary conditions, the specific gravity of the mixed 24-hour urine usually varies between 1.014 and 1.026. However, it may be as low as 1.001 on a very high water intake or as high as 1.040 if fluid is restricted or excreted in excess by other routes (skin, bowel, etc.). Expressed in other terms, under normal conditions the kidneys can form urine varying in solid content from 50 to 1400 milliosmoles/liter from a circulating plasma of approximately 300 milliosmoles/liter.

Normal kidneys eliminate the required amount of solids regardless, within wide limits, of the amount of water available for their solution. When their function is impaired, the kidneys lose this ability to dilute and concentrate the urine, and, with increasing damage, the osmolar concentration and specific gravity of the urine approach values for protein-free blood plasma (glomerular filtrate). The maximum attainable specific gravity falls and the minimum rises, the urine specific gravity being relatively fixed within narrowing limits below and above 1.007. The importance of the urinary specific gravity arises out of these facts, determination of the concentrating ability of the kidneys constituting an important test of renal function.

Acidity

Urinary acidity may be expressed in two ways: (1) its H^+ ion concentration (true acidity); (2) its titratable acidity. These two factors (and also urinary ammonia) are responsive to the same influences, but are not necessarily related quantitatively. The pH may be regarded as an "intensity" factor and the titratable acidity as a "capacity" factor. Secretion of ammonia into the tubular urine decreases its H^+ concentration, playing an important role in the renal regulation of acid-base balance (p. 316).

pH of normal urine. The extreme limits of urinary pH in health are 4.8 and 8.0, usually, under ordinary conditions, ranging between 5.0 and 7.0, averaging 6.0 in the mixed 24-hour sample. The mechanism of acidification of the glomerular filtrate (pH 7.4) is discussed elsewhere (p. 317).

Titratable acidity. The titratable acidity of the urine is expressed as milliliters of

N/10 alkali required to neutralize the 24-hour output of urine. This usually varies normally from 200 to 500, averaging about 350. If phenolphthalein is used as the indicator, values below 250 usually indicate an actual alkalinity, since an end-point is attained at about pH 8.3. Because of the intimate relationship between urinary acidity and urinary ammonia (p. 319), the latter (usually 300 to 500 ml. of N/10 alkali) should be included with the former in studies of acid-base balance (i.e., titratable acidity plus ammonia).

The urinary acidity and pH are reflections chiefly of the ratio, NaH_2PO_4:Na_2HPO_4, which is 1:4 at pH 7.4 (blood plasma; glomerular filtrate), about 50:1 at pH 4.8, and 9:1 at pH 6.0. This transformation of the dibasic to the monobasic salt effects considerable conservation of Na, which is returned to the plasma (p. 317). Acid urine contains virtually no bicarbonate (HCO_3^-). In alkaline urine, however, this ion is present and the pH may be determined largely by the ratio, H_2CO_3:$NaHCO_3$. The urinary acidity is normally also contributed to, but to a minor extent, by organic acids (lactic, uric, hippuric, β-hydroxybutyric).

The acidity of the urine is normally influenced chiefly by the nature of the diet (i.e., alkaline or acid ash). Ingestion of large amounts of protein (meats, bread, cereals), which yields acids in the course of metabolism (sulfuric, phosphoric), increases urinary acidity and ammonia. Most vegetables and fruits (orange, lemon, grape, apple, peach, pear) contain organic acids (e.g., citrate, oxalate) which form bicarbonate in the body and hence decrease urinary acidity. Certain fruits (plums, cranberries) contain benzoic acid and quinic acid, which are metabolized to and excreted as hippuric acid, increasing the urinary acidity and ammonia. These are increased also by starvation or dietary carbohydrate restriction, owing to increased catabolism of body protein and fat, with increased urinary excretion of sulfate, phosphate, and ketone acid (β-hydroxybutyric and acetoacetic).

Shortly after eating (within an hour) there is a decrease in urinary acidity and ammonia and H^+ concentration. This "postprandial alkaline tide" has been attributed generally to the increased secretion of HCl by the stomach, temporarily increasing the plasma bicarbonate. It is said not to occur in subjects with achlorhydria. This explanation is not accepted by some. On standing, normal urine becomes alkaline and ammoniacal owing to the action of bacteria on urea (ammoniacal fermentation).

Non-protein Nitrogenous Constituents

The term "non-protein nitrogen" (NPN) is applied to nitrogen present in compounds not precipitable by the usual protein-precipitating agents. These substances, occurring in the blood (p. 810) and other body fluids and in the urine, consist chiefly of intermediary or end-products of protein metabolism. They include urea, ammonia, amino acids, creatinine, creatine, uric acid, and a number of other compounds present in small amounts, not readily determined quantitatively, and referred to as "undetermined nitrogen" (peptides, hippuric acid, etc.).

The several components of this heterogeneous mixture have different origins and significance and are influenced by different factors; the amount of each excreted in the urine varies under different conditions of diet and metabolism. The most important features of the biogenesis and metabolic significance of these substances are considered in the section on intermediary metabolism of proteins (p. 544ff.) and nucleic acids (p. 513). Attention will be directed here mainly to their excretion in the urine of normal subjects.

Total non-protein nitrogen. Normal adults on an adequate protein diet are in a state of nitrogen equilibrium, the quantity excreted daily being equivalent to that ingested. This is not the case during periods of tissue growth (childhood, pregnancy, convalescence) (positive nitrogen balance, p. 545). Inasmuch as the amount of nitrogen excreted in the feces is relatively constant (p. 274) and that lost by other extrarenal channels is usually small and constant, the quantity in the urine may be regarded as reflecting the amount of protein ingested and the state of protein catabolism. It may vary from as little as 3 gm. daily on a low protein intake (20 gm.) to as much as 24 gm. or more on a very high protein diet (160 gm.); it ranges between 11 and 15 gm. on usual protein intakes (70 to 80 gm.).

Urea. Urea is the chief end-product of the catabolism of amino acids (p. 570) and is the substance in which is incorporated, for purposes of excretion, the bulk of the nitrogen provided to the organism in excess of its needs. Under usual dietary conditions it comprises about half of the total urine solids, and is therefore the most abundant urinary constituent (except water). Because of these facts, and because it is a metabolic end-product, virtually not utilizable, the quantity of urea excreted in the urine is the most significant index of the extent of protein catabolism and, consequently, is influenced more directly by the protein intake than are the other nitrogenous compounds.

The mechanism of excretion of urea is discussed elsewhere (p. 827). On a high protein diet, urea nitrogen (16 to 25 gm.) comprises 80 to 90 per cent of the urinary NPN. On very low protein intakes it may fall to 60 per cent or less of the total NPN, since variations in dietary protein are reflected almost exclusively in urinary urea and ammonia (p. 570ff.), the amounts of the other nitrogenous constituents remaining relatively constant (Table 31-3).

Ammonia. Unlike the other non-protein nitrogenous constituents of the urine, preformed ammonia is not removed by the kidneys from the bloodstream, in which ammonia is present in only minute amounts. It is formed in the renal tubular epithelium, chiefly (60 per cent) from glutamine (glutaminase), the remainder from other amino acids. It is passed largely into the tubular urine where, acting as a base, it combines with H^+ ions, forming NH_4, thus serving to lower the H^+ concentration and permitting further passage of H^+ ions into the lumen in exchange for Na^+ (p. 319). This mechanism is an important factor in the renal regulation of acid-base balance.

Under usual dietary conditions, normal adults excrete about 0.3 to 1.2 gm. (average 0.7 gm.) of ammonium N daily (20 to 70 mEq.), comprising 2.5 to 4.5 per cent of the total NPN. Inasmuch as the urea and ammonia of the urine are both derived ultimately

TABLE 31-3. URINARY NITROGEN PARTITION IN SAME INDIVIDUAL ON HIGH AND LOW PROTEIN DIETS

	HIGH PROTEIN		LOW PROTEIN	
	(gm./24 hours)	(% of total N)	(gm./24 hours)	(% of total N)
Urine volume	1170 ml.		385 ml.	
Total N	16.80		3.60	
Urea N	14.70	87.5	2.20	61.7
Ammonia N	0.49	3.0	0.42	11.3
Uric acid N	0.18	1.1	0.09	2.5
Creatinine N	0.58	3.6	0.60	17.2
Undetermined	0.85	4.8	0.29	7.3

After Folin: J.A.M.A. *69:*1209, 1917.

from amino acids, an increase in ammonia is accompanied by a corresponding decrease in urea, at any given level of NPN excretion. The quantity of ammonia in the urine of normal subjects is determined chiefly by the requirement for acidification of the urine. The chief immediate stimulus to its formation in the tubular epithelial cell is apparently a decrease in the pH of the plasma and, consequently, in that of the urine in the tubules (p. 319).

The output of ammonia increases with increasing levels of dietary protein, owing probably to the acid-producing properties of protein (oxidation of S and P) (p. 313). It is increased also by ingestion of acids or acid-forming substances (NH_4Cl, NH_4NO_3) and in association with acidosis (except renal), and is decreased by ingestion of alkalies or base-forming foods and in alkalotic subjects. As much as 10 gm. of ammonia may be excreted daily by individuals with severe diabetic acidosis. Administration of ammonium salts of mineral acids (viz., NH_4Cl, NH_4NO_3) is equivalent to administration of corresponding amounts of the free acids, since the ammonium is converted to urea in the body ($2NH_4Cl + CO_2 \longrightarrow \text{Urea} + 2HCl + H_2O$). These ammonium salts therefore increase urinary acidity and can induce acidosis. If urine is allowed to stand without a preservative, its ammonia content increases markedly as a result of hydrolysis of urea by bacteria ("ammoniacal fermentation").

Creatine and creatinine. The metabolic origin and significance of these substances are considered elsewhere (p. 578).

Creatine is not excreted in significant amounts in the urine of normal adult males. This is apparently due to the fact that it is completely reabsorbed from the glomerular filtrate in the renal tubules at normal plasma creatine levels ($<$0.6 mg./100 ml.). It is present in the urine (increased plasma level) of prepuberal children (4.2 mg./kg.) and certain normal women, periodically or constantly, and occasionally during pregnancy and the early puerperium.

Under normal conditions, creatine formed in or otherwise provided (food) to the organism over and above the requirements or capacity for storage in the muscles (as phosphocreatine, p. 429) is either transformed to creatinine or excreted as such. The creatine tolerance test is a measure of the capacity for utilization of creatine. Normal adult men excrete in the urine (in 24 hours) not more than 20 per cent and women not more than 30 per cent of a test dose (1.32 or 2.64 gm.) of creatine hydrate. Urinary creatine is increased in association with conditions accompanied by muscle wasting, muscle dystrophies, and thyrotoxicosis.

Creatinine (creatine anhydride) is formed from creatine in quite constant amounts daily (men, 1.0 to 1.8 gm.; women, 0.7 to 1.5 gm.), corresponding to about 2 per cent of the body creatine (p. 578), practically all of which is eliminated in the urine. The excretion of creatinine is therefore constant from day to day under quite varied conditions, being relatively uninfluenced by diet or urine volume, and being determined chiefly by the muscle mass (creatine content of body). Because of this fact, the daily excretion of creatinine is determined commonly in balance studies as a check on the accuracy of 24-hour urine collections. Endogenous creatinine is excreted in man by glomerular filtration and active tubular excretion, the value for creatinine clearance (about 145) exceeding that for inulin (p. 831).

The term "creatinine coefficient" is applied to the number of milligrams of creatinine (plus creatine, if any) nitrogen excreted daily per kilogram of body weight. Normal values are 20 to 26 for men and 14 to 22 for women. The corresponding values in terms of nitrogen are 7.5 to 10 for men and 5 to 8 for women. The creatinine coefficient may be regarded as an index of the amount of muscle tissue, and is therefore more directly proportional to the ideal than to the actual weight.

Amino acids. Amino acids are excreted in the urine in both free and combined form. The latter are present in peptide linkage, as in compounds such as hippuric acid (glycine). The free amino nitrogen ranges normally from 0.1 to 0.15 gm. daily, comprising 0.5 to 1.0 per cent of the total nitrogen. The total amino nitrogen output is 0.5 to 1.0 gm. daily (2 to 6 per cent of the total nitrogen). Increased amounts of several amino acids, principally threonine and histidine, are excreted in the urine during pregnancy. Larger amounts are found in the urine also during the first few months of life, due presumably to incomplete maturation of renal tubular reabsorption mechanisms. In normal adults, amino acids are conserved efficiently, the amount excreted varying but slightly with wide fluctuations in protein intake and even when amino acids are administered parenterally.

Pathological aminoaciduria may occur as a result of (a) increase in the concentration of one or more amino acids in the blood plasma (overflow aminoaciduria) or (b) defective renal tubular reabsorption of one or more amino acids (renal aminoaciduria). Both may occur as a result of either genetically determined defects or acquired disease. Overflow aminoaciduria may occur in severe liver damage (impaired deamination and urea formation) and in inherited defects in certain amino acid-metabolizing enzymes, e.g., phenylalanine hydroxylase (phenylketonuria), histidase (histidinemia), branched-chain keto-acid decarboxylase (maple syrup urine disease), proline oxidase (hyperprolinemia), cystathionine synthetase (homocystinuria). Renal aminoaciduria may occur as a result of renal tubular damage due to various causes and genetically determined defects in the renal tubular transport mechanism for one or more amino acids, e.g., cystinuria, glycinuria. Severe liver damage results in an increase in urinary amino acids and a corresponding decrease in urea (impaired deamination and urea formation). Increased excretion of amino acids occurs also in certain conditions in which their tubular reabsorption is impaired (e.g., cystinuria, pp. 586, 828).

Uric acid. Uric acid is the chief end-product of the metabolism of purines. Its metabolic origin is considered elsewhere (p. 518). Normal values for urate clearance range from 11 to 15 ml. per minute, indicating that 85 to 90 per cent of the urate filtered through the glomeruli is reabsorbed in the tubules. However, there is suggestive evidence that the urinary urate is largely if not entirely a product of active tubular excretion, that of the glomerular filtrate normally being completely or almost completely reabsorbed (p. 828).

In urine of average pH (6.0 or higher) uric acid is present largely as the soluble sodium and potassium urates, whereas in highly acid urine the relatively insoluble free acid may predominate and may precipitate from solution.

The amount of uric acid in the urine of normal subjects depends on the quantity of nucleoprotein ingested (exogenous) and that formed from tissue nucleic acids and nucleotides (endogenous). On purine-free diets, the urinary uric acid is of solely endogenous origin and is rather constant for the individual, usually 0.1 to 0.5 gm. daily. This may be increased somewhat by strenuous exercise and by a high protein of high caloric intake (stimulating endogenous metabolism).

On a high purine diet (meat, liver, kidney, sweetbreads, leguminous vegetables, etc.) the uric acid output may be as much as 2 gm. daily. In adults on the usual mixed diet the average daily excretion is about 0.7 gm., comprising 1 to 2 per cent of the total nitrogen. The urine of newborn infants contains relatively large amounts of uric acid

(0.2 gm./100 ml.), comprising about 7 to 8 per cent of the total nitrogen. Crystals of free uric acid and ammonium urate may be present and urate "infarcts" of the kidneys are not uncommon. A sharp drop to normal adult levels occurs after seven to 10 days. A considerable increase follows administration of cinchophen and salicylates. Caffeine and other methylpurines (in tea, coffee, cocoa) cause little or no increase, being either transformed largely to urea or undergoing more complete destruction in the body.

Urinary excretion of uric acid, reflecting nucleoprotein catabolism, is increased by 11-oxygenated adrenocortical hormones and by ACTH. It has been suggested that determination of the extent of rise in the urinary uric acid: creatinine ratio after administration of ACTH may be useful as a test of the reserve functional capacity of the adrenal cortex (p. 519), but this has not proved to be reliable. An increase occurs also after administration of certain reabsorption-blocking agents (p. 829).

Allantoin

Allantoin is formed from uric acid in the liver by the action of the enzyme uricase (p. 518). In man and anthropoid apes, the livers of which exhibit little or no uricase activity, allantoin is excreted in very small amounts (5 to 25 mg. daily). In other mammals it is the chief end-product of purine metabolism, accounting for 90 per cent or more of the excretion of purine metabolites. It was formerly believed that the metabolism of purines in the Dalmatian dog resembled that in man and apes (differing from that of other mammals) in having uric acid as its chief metabolic end-product. Present evidence indicates that the urinary excretion of relatively large amounts of uric acid is due to its incomplete reabsorption by the renal tubular epithelium and not to a difference from other breeds of dogs in capacity for forming allantoin from uric acid.

Oxalic Acid

Small amounts of oxalate (10 to 25 mg.) are excreted daily in the urine of normal subjects. Its origin is not well understood. Under normal conditions, the main source of urinary oxalate is probably dietary, it or certain metabolic precursors being present in many common foodstuffs (tomatoes, rhubarb, cabbage, spinach, asparagus, apples, grapes, etc.). Oxalate is also one of the end-products of the metabolism of ascorbic acid. Calcium oxalate, which precipitates from neutral or alkaline urine in the presence of abnormally high oxalate excretion, is an important constituent of urinary calculi.

Primary hyperoxaluria is a genetic disorder of glycine catabolism in which excessive amounts of oxalic acid are produced by oxidation of glyoxylic acid (p. 579). The precise nature of the defect is not known.

Glucuronic Acid (p. 21)

Glucuronic acid occurs in normal urine conjugated with a wide variety of compounds in two types of linkage, (1) ester and (2) glycosidic. The carboxyl groups of such compounds as phenylacetic acid and benzoic acid form ester linkages, whereas the hydroxyl groups of such substances as aliphatic or aromatic alcohols (chloral, camphor, phenol, menthol, indole, skatole, morphine, pregnanediol, estriol, etc.) form glycosidic linkages. This conjugation takes place in the liver, which is probably also the site of formation of glucuronic acid (p. 278).

The normal daily excretion of glucuronic acid is about 0.3 to 1.0 gm. This may be increased by administration of the substances indicated above, as well as acetylsalicylic acid, sulfonamides (except sulfanilamide), turpentine, antipyrine, and phenolphthalein. When present in relatively high concentration, the ester types reduce the usual copper reagents (e.g., Benedict's), probably owing to concomitant hydrolysis, and may therefore interfere with the interpretation of urinary tests for glucose. The glycoside types do not reduce these reagents unless previously hydrolyzed.

Hippuric Acid (Benzoylglycine) (p. 279)

Hippuric acid is formed by the conjugation, in peptide linkage, of benzoic acid and glycine. In man, this occurs largely if not solely in the liver; in certain species (e.g., dog), it occurs also in the kidney.

Benzoic acid (or benzoate) is present, as such, in many vegetables and fruits (e.g., cranberries, plums) and addition of sodium benzoate, as a preservative, to certain prepared foodstuffs is legally permissible. Quinic acid, another constituent of vegetables and fruits, is converted to benzoic acid in the body; the latter may arise also from intestinal bacterial action on aromatic compounds, viz., tyrosine and phenylalanine.

Glycine is normally invariably present in amounts adequate to convert all of the benzoic acid formed to hippuric acid. The latter, formed in the liver cells, enters the systemic circulation and is excreted in the urine in amounts ranging from 0.1 to 1.0 gm. (usually 0.5 to 0.7 gm.) daily, depending largely on the dietary intake.

Citric Acid

Citrate is excreted in the urine in amounts of 0.2 to 1.2 gm. daily. It is increased by administration of estrogen and decreased by androgen. Urinary citrate varies during the menstrual cycle, increasing during the first half (increasing elaboration of estrogen), persisting at a high level during the luteal phase (synergistic action of estrogen and progesterone), and falling in the premenstrual phase (drop in estrogen). The significance of these changes is not clear. Administration of alkalies or alkaline ash diets increases, and acidification decreases, urinary citrate.

Citric acid is formed in large amounts in the course of oxidative metabolism of carbohydrate. Whether or not this is the main source of urine citrate is not known. Citrate is present in the bones, apparently as a superficial deposit on the crystal lattice of apatite, which is the chief mineral complex in bone (p. 636). Citrate forms soluble and undissociable complexes with calcium, and these two ions exhibit certain interrelationships in their urinary excretion. Administration of parathyroid hormone or of very large doses of vitamin D, producing hypercalcemia, increases urine calcium and citrate (mobilization from skeleton?). Injection of citrate increases urinary excretion of calcium, perhaps by increasing its solution from bone.

Other Organic Acids

Lactic acid, the end-product of glycolysis in muscle, passes into the bloodstream, undergoing ultimate reconversion to glycogen or glucose in the liver (p. 392). About 50 to 200 mg. are excreted daily in the urine under ordinary conditions of activity. Much more may appear during periods of prolonged, strenuous muscular exercise or anoxia.

Minute amounts (up to 50 mg. daily) of fatty acids may be excreted in the urine.

These are mainly short-chain acids (formic, acetic, butyric), which arise chiefly during intermediary metabolism and as a result of intestinal bacterial action (p. 271).

Certain aromatic hydroxyacids may appear in the urine of normal subjects in small amounts. The most important are *p*-hydroxyphenylacetic and *p*-hydroxyphenylpropionic acids, which are formed in the intermediary metabolism and intestinal putrefaction of tyrosine. Other aromatic hydroxyacids (*p*-hydroxyphenylpyruvic, *p*-hydroxyphenyllactic, dihydroxyphenylacetic acids) may be excreted in abnormal states (tyrosinosis, vitamin C-deficiency in infants, certain cases of mental deficiency, alcaptonuria) (pp. 597–600).

Ketone Bodies

The substances designated "ketone bodies" include acetone, acetoacetic acid, and β-hydroxybutyric acid. These are formed in the liver in the course of metabolism of fatty acids (p. 467) and are conveyed in the bloodstream to the tissues for further oxidation. Under normal conditions, on the usual mixed diet, less than 125 mg. is excreted daily in the urine. Larger amounts may be eliminated on high-fat diets, during severe carbohydrate restriction and during pregnancy. Marked increases are encountered in a variety of abnormal states associated with excessive ketogenesis (p. 469), e.g., diabetes mellitus (p. 728).

Sulfur-Containing Compounds

Sulfur appears in the urine as (1) so-called neutral sulfur and (2) sulfate, the latter in (a) inorganic and (b) organic (ester; ethereal sulfate) combination. The bulk of the urinary sulfur is derived from the metabolism of the amino acids, methionine, cystine and cysteine, the amount excreted by normal subjects therefore varying with the protein intake.

The total sulfur excretion usually ranges from 0.7 to 1.5 gm. daily, averaging about 1.0 gm. The urinary N:S ratio is about 15:1. Neutral sulfur comprises about 5 to 15 per cent of the total (0.04 to 0.15 gm.), and sulfate-S 85 to 95 per cent. About 5 to 15 per cent of the latter is organic (ethereal) sulfate (0.06 to 0.12 gm.), the remainder inorganic (0.6 to 1.0 gm.).

Neutral sulfur includes such substances as cystine, methionine, methylmercaptan, taurine and its derivatives (taurocholic acid), thiocyanate, thiosulfate, and urochrome.

Ethereal (organic) sulfate consists largely of phenolic sulfates, formed in the liver from aromatic compounds arising from intestinal bacterial action on tyrosine and tryptophan (indole, skatole, cresol, phenol) (p. 271) or from benzene or other phenolic compounds entering the organism (as under conditions of industrial or accidental exposure). Certain hormones, including estrone and androsterone, are excreted largely as sulfates and fall into this category (pp. 691, 686). Indole, which arises almost entirely from intestinal putrefaction, is converted to indoxyl in the liver, is conjugated with sulfate, and appears in the urine as potassium (and sodium) indoxyl sulfate (indican). This is a rough index of the extent of intestinal putrefaction ($<$20 mg. daily normally).

Further details are considered in the section on sulfur metabolism (p. 628).

Phosphate

The metabolism of phosphorus is considered in detail elsewhere (p. 631). Phosphorus is excreted (urine and feces) largely as inorganic phosphate, and to a small extent in organic form (<4 per cent of total). Inasmuch as the phosphate is derived chiefly from the metabolism (oxidation) of phosphorus-containing organic foodstuffs (and tissue components), such as phosphoproteins, nucleoproteins, nucleotides, and phospholipids, the quantity excreted depends in large measure on the nature of the diet. It is therefore extremely variable.

The proportion of the total phosphorus excretion eliminated in the urine depends under normal conditions on dietary and intra-intestinal factors. On the usual mixed diet the daily urinary phosphorus excretion is 0.7 to 1.5 gm., averaging about 1.1 gm., almost entirely in the form of inorganic phosphate, comprising about 60 per cent of the total excretion (feces 40 per cent). If intestinal absorption of phosphate is diminished, as by high intake of calcium or magnesium (also aluminum, beryllium, iron), which tend to form relatively insoluble phosphates, unusually high intestinal alkalinity, and low vitamin D intake (in children), the amount and proportion of phosphorus eliminated in the urine decreases (increases in feces). Conversely, on a low calcium, moderately high phosphorus intake, about 75 per cent of the total excretion is urinary. The parathyroid hormone increases renal excretion of phosphate by diminishing its reabsorption in the tubules (p. 731). The "renal threshold" for phosphate excretion is about 2 mg. P/100 ml. plasma, excretion falling to a minimum at lower concentrations.

The phosphate ion appears in the urine in two forms, viz., $H_2PO_4^-$ and $HPO_4^=$. The ratio, $BH_2PO_4:B_2HPO_4$, varies with and largely determines the pH of the urine, since these substances constitute the major buffer system in that fluid. Relatively insoluble phosphates tend to form in alkaline urine, and are often important components of urinary calculi. The turbidity which develops in urine on standing (ammoniacal fermentation) is contributed to largely by precipitation of phosphates, including $MgNH_4PO_4$ ("triple phosphate"), insoluble at alkaline reactions.

Chloride

In normal subjects on an average diet (8 to 15 gm. NaCl intake), the quantity of chloride in the urine is second only to urea, among the solid constituents, approximating the intake (5 to 9 gm. chloride ion; 110 to 255 mEq.). The normal "renal threshold" for chloride is about 340 mg./100 ml. plasma; in normal subjects, as the plasma chloride concentration descends to this level, urinary excretion of chloride decreases (renal tubular reabsorption, p. 724). This is influenced by the level of adrenal cortical function (p. 710).

If the chloride intake is changed suddenly, some time may be required for the re-establishment of equilibrium between intake and output. For example, the sudden addition of a large amount of salt is usually followed by elimination of the excess within 48 hours. However, if the previous intake has been unusually low, the elimination of the increment may be delayed several days.

In conditions in which elimination of chloride through other channels is increased, e.g., excessive perspiration, diarrhea, vomiting, the urine chloride decreases correspondingly.

Sodium, Potassium

The kidney is the chief regulator of excretion, consequently of the body equilibrium of sodium and potassium, the chief cations of extracellular and intracellular fluids, respectively. Operation of these excretory mechanisms therefore plays an important role in the maintenance of water and acid-base equilibrium (pp. 309, 316). The daily urinary output of these elements by normal adults approximates their intake. Under usual dietary conditions, normal adults excrete in the urine about 3 to 5 gm. (130 to 215 mEq.) sodium and 2 to 4 gm. (50 to 100 mEq.) potassium daily (Na:K ratio about 5:3). During periods of fasting or inadequate protein intake, excessive tissue protein catabolism, with liberation of intracellular fluid components, results in an increase in urinary potassium and a change in the Na:K ratio.

Adrenal cortical hormones, especially aldosterone, increase reabsorption of sodium and excretion of potassium (p. 709). Potassium enters the urine from the plasma by glomerular filtration and also by active tubular secretion, the latter mechanism apparently competing with that for urine acidification. Details of this process are considered elsewhere (p. 318). The amount of potassium in the urine is therefore influenced by the requirement for urine acidification, increasing when this requirement is low (e.g., alkaline ash diet; alkalosis) and decreasing when it is high (highly acid ash diet; acidosis).

Abnormal loss, through extrarenal channels, of sodium (excessive sweating, diarrhea, etc.) or of potassium (diarrhea) results in decreased urinary excretion of these elements.

Calcium, Magnesium

Under usual dietary conditions in normal subjects, urinary excretion accounts for about 15 to 30 per cent of the total calcium and about 20 to 50 per cent of the total magnesium elimination, the remainder being excreted in the feces. At low or moderate levels of calcium intake (0.1 to 0.5 gm. daily), about 30 to 50 per cent is eliminated in the urine, whereas at high levels of intake (1.0 gm.) about 10 to 25 per cent is so eliminated. The dependence of the urinary excretion of these elements on their absorption from the intestine, and the factors involved (vitamin D, phosphate, etc.), are considered elsewhere (pp. 165, 638).

The "renal threshold" for excretion of calcium lies between 6.5 and 8.0 mg. per 100 ml. plasma, little being eliminated at lower plasma calcium concentrations. The influence of the parathyroid hormone in increasing urinary calcium is secondary to its action in increasing mobilization of calcium from the bones into the bloodstream (p. 730). The effect of vitamin D in increasing urine calcium is a consequence of its enhancement of absorption of calcium from the intestine (p. 163).

Carbohydrates (p. 441)

Normal urine may contain reducing substances ($<$1.5 gm./24 hours), up to 40 per cent of which are fermentable; concentrations over 0.25 per cent (Benedict's test) should be regarded as probably abnormal. A portion of this is glucose, the remainder being derived chiefly from the diet (galactose from lactose of milk; pentose from fruits; caramelized sugar and dextrins; proteins; products of intestinal bacterial action).

Glucose may appear in the urine in small amounts during normal pregnancy, particularly in the later months. Lactose is excreted frequently during lactation. Pentose (L-arabinose) may appear in the urine of normal subjects after ingestion of large quantities of foods rich in pentose, e.g., cherries, grapes, plums, prunes (alimentary pentosuria). There is a chronic, familial type of pentosuria, in which xylulose is excreted independently of the nature of the diet. Galactose and fructose rarely appear in the urine of entirely normal subjects except after administration of supertolerance doses of these sugars. Glycosuria may occur as an isolated abnormality or in association with others as a result of genetically determined single or multiple defects of renal tubular reabsorptive (transport) mechanisms (renal glycosuria, p. 446).

Miscellaneous

The urine of normal subjects may contain protein in amounts too small to be detected except by very sensitive procedures (100 mg. daily). It includes minute amounts of mucoproteins derived from the lower urinary tract and, mainly, serum albumin. The latter is present in the glomerular filtrate in a concentration of about 10 mg./100 ml. On this basis, about 18 gm. of protein enter the tubules daily, of which all but 100 mg. undergoes reabsorption. Pathological proteinuria may occur as a result of: (a) increased glomerular permeability (as in glomerulonephritis, congestive heart failure); (b) renal tubular damage, with defective reabsorption of serum albumin (nephrosis); (c) disease of the lower urinary tract (cystitis); (d) abnormal protein in the blood plasma (multiple myeloma).

The 24-hour urine may contain minute quantities of iron ($<$0.3 mg.), arsenic ($<$0.5 mg.), copper ($<$0.1 mg.), zinc ($<$0.6 mg.), iodine ($<$0.07 mg.), and trace amounts of cobalt, nickel, fluorine, silicon, and lead.

A number of the water-soluble vitamins and their metabolites are excreted in the urine, usually in proportion to their intake. The quantities eliminated in the urine under controlled conditions have been employed as a basis for clinical evaluation of the state of vitamin nutrition, and are considered in the discussion of the individual vitamins (q.v.).

Certain hormones or their metabolites are excreted in the urine, e.g., gonadotropins, estrogens, androgens, pregnanediol, adrenocortical hormones, catecholamines. Determination of the quantities eliminated is employed in the clinical evaluation of the state of functional activity of the respective endocrine glands (q.v.).

Normal urine contains only minute amounts of lipids. Rarely, fat may appear in the urine after ingestion of unusually large amounts of fat, e.g., cod liver oil ("alimentary lipuria").

BIBLIOGRAPHY

Annual Review of Physiology.

Berliner, R. W.: Renal excretion of water, sodium chloride, potassium, calcium and magnesium, Am. J. Med. *9*:541, 1950.

Berliner, R. W.: Relationship between acidification of the urine and potassium metabolism, Am. J. Med. *11*:274, 1951.

Bland, J. H. (ed.): Clinical Metabolism of Body Water and Electrolytes, Philadelphia, W. B. Saunders Company, 1963.

Cantarow, A., and Trumper, M.: Clinical Biochemistry, ed. 5, Philadelphia, W. B. Saunders Company, 1962, p. 373.

Lotspeich, W. D.: Metabolic Aspects of Renal Function, Springfield, Ill., Charles C Thomas, 1959.

Mudge, G. H., and Taggart, J. V. (eds.): Symposium on renal physiology, Am. J. Med. *24*:659, 1958.

Pitts, R. F.: Physiology of the Kidney and Body Fluids, Chicago, Year Book Medical Publishers, 1963.

Schmidt-Nielsen, B.: Urea excretion in mammals, Physiol. Rev. *38*:139, 1958.

Smith, H. W.: The Kidney: Structure and Function in Health and Disease, New York, Oxford University Press, 1951.

Smith, H. W.: Principles of Renal Physiology, New York, Oxford University Press, 1956.

Welt, L. G.: Water balance in health and disease, in Duncan, G. G. (ed.): Diseases of Metabolism, ed. 5, Philadelphia, W. B. Saunders Company, 1964, p. 449.

White, A. G.: Clinical Disturbances of Renal Function, Philadephia, W. B. Saunders Company, 1961.

INDEX